MILLER'S

ANTIQUES PRICE GUIDE

1989
(Volume X)

Compiled and Edited by

Judith and Martin Miller

MILLERS PUBLICATIONS

A printed tinplate two-seater open-tourer by Hess, flywheel driven, finished in two tone green, interior red with driver in yellow, passenger missing, 6¼in (16cm).
£420-460 *P*

MILLER'S ANTIQUES PRICE GUIDE 1989

Compiled, edited and designed by
M.J.M. Publishing Projects for
Millers Publications Limited
The Mitchell Beazley Group
Sissinghurst Court, Sissinghurst
Cranbrook, Kent TN17 2JA
Telephone: (0580) 713890

British Library Cataloguing in Publication Data
Millers antiques price guide – 1989 –
1. Antiques – Auction prices – Lists –
Serials
I. Millers guide
338.4'37451

ISBN 0-905879-49-X

While every care has been exercised in the compilation of this guide, neither the authors or publishers accept any liability for any financial or other loss incurred by reliance placed on the information contained in *Miller's Antiques Price Guide*

Typeset by Ardek Photosetters, St Leonards-on-Sea
Colour Originated by Spectrum Reproductions, Colchester
Printed and bound in England by William Clowes Ltd
Beccles and London

Front cover illustrations:
Top left: A Sheraton-style painted satinware Carlton House desk, £6,500 *(Bonhams)*
Top right: A Royal Worcester vase and domed cover by John Stanton, £1,800 *(Bonhams)*
Bottom left: Two Jumeaux dolls, both with jointed bodies, c1885-96, *l.*, £4,750, *r.* £3,000 *(Lilian Middleton)*
Bottom right: A large Wemyss ware pig, very rare, painted with national emblems of 4 home countries, £3,000 *(Rogers de Rin)*

ANTIQUE SHIPPERS IN BRITAIN

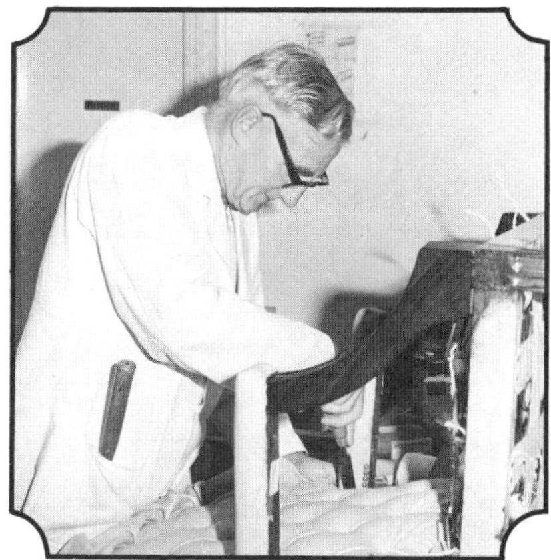

Member of L.A.P.A.D.A. Guild of Master Craftsmen

The Old Mint House

HIGH STREET, PEVENSEY
NEAR EASTBOURNE, EAST SUSSEX BN24 5LF

The Largest Antique Centre in the South of England

(Tel: (0323) 762337) (After hours (0323) 761251)

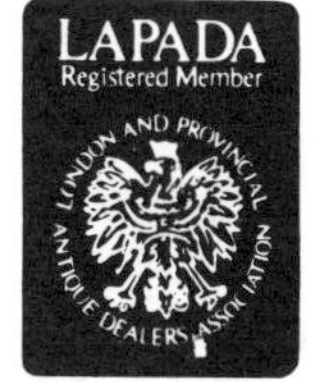

Couriers welcome

London trains met by appointment

Business hours:
Monday thru to Saturday 9.00 hrs to 17.30 hrs
(or otherwise by appointment)

The Old Mint House Antiques, established on its present site since 1901, with 28 showrooms containing the largest selection of Victorian and Antique furniture, Porcelain, Clocks and Metalware to be found on the South coast of England.

Rapidly changing stock but always 20,000 items available.
New consignments arriving daily.

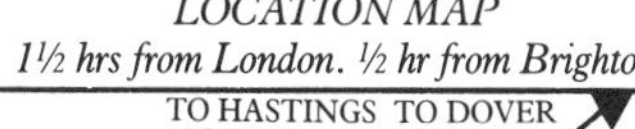

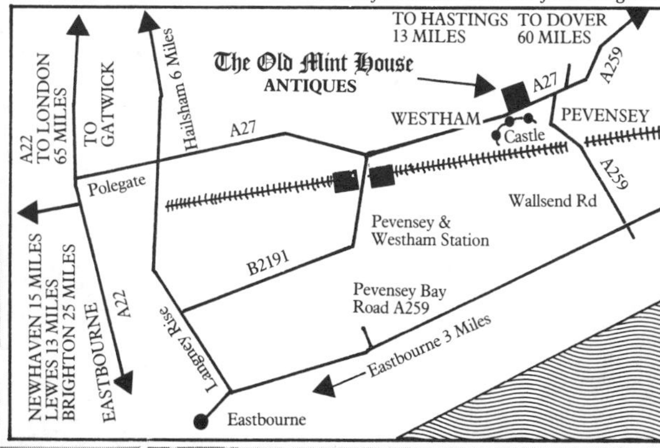

Also our shipping and export division situated at

45 TURKEY ROAD, BEXHILL, E. SUSSEX. Tel: (0424) 216056

which specialises in Victorian and Pre-War shipping goods for the larger trade buyer who wishes to find most of his requirements at one location

This 20,000 sq. ft. purpose built warehouse contains on two levels a huge selection of goods at the absolute lowest open trade prices

Video (all systems) available for the larger buyer

Hubbard Antiques

10,000 sq. ft. of fine 18th, 19th and 20th century furniture, accessories and decorative items specialising in library and dining furniture in fine showrooms.

IPSWICH

16 ST. MARGARETS GREEN
IPSWICH, SUFFOLK. (0473) 226033

The Debenham Gallery

Patricia Staines

Fine Paintings · Antique Furniture
Objects D'Arte · Oriental Rugs · Pianos

Bought and Sold

Fine Art Restorations · Relining · Cleaning
Traditional and Modern Framing · Carved
Frames · Commissions · Valuations

1 High Street, Debenham
Suffolk IP14 6QL

Telephone: Debenham (0728) 860707
Home: Helmingham (0473 39) 419

45,000 sq. ft. of Victorian and Georgian furniture, carved oak and shipping goods also stocked. Container and export facilities

Acknowledgements

The publishers would like to acknowledge the great assistance given by our consultant editors:

POTTERY:	**Jonathan Horne,** *66b and c Kensington Church Street, London W8.*
	Ron Beech, *Victorian Staffordshire Figures and Pot Lids, 150 Portland Road, Hove, East Sussex.*
PORCELAIN:	**Christopher Spencer:** *Greystones, 29 Mostyn Road, Merton Park, London SW19.*
	Nicholas Long, *Studio Antiques, Bourton-on-the-Water, Glos.*
WORCESTER:	**Henry Sandon,** *11 Perrywood Close, Worcester.*
GOSS & CRESTED WARE:	**Nicholas Pine,** *Goss & Crested China Ltd, 62 Murray Road, Horndean, Hants.*
FURNITURE:	**John Bly,** *50 High Street, Tring, Herts.*
	Richard Davidson, *Richard Davidson Antiques, Lombard Street, Petworth, Sussex.*
OAK:	**Victor Chinnery,** *Bennetts, Oare, Nr Marlborough, Wilts.*
LONGCASE CLOCKS:	**Brian Loomes,** *Calfhaugh, Pateley Bridge, N Yorks.*
GLASS:	**Wing Cdr R G Thomas,** *Somervale Antiques, 6 Radstock Road, Midsomer Norton, Bath, Avon.*
ART NOUVEAU & ART DECO:	**Eric Knowles,** *Bonhams, Montpelier Galleries, Montpelier Street, Knightsbridge, London SW7.*
LALIQUE:	**Russell Varney,** *Bonhams, Montpelier Galleries, Montpelier Street, Knightsbridge, London SW7.*
CARPETS & TEXTILES:	**Robert Bailey,** *1 Roll Gardens, Gants Hill, Essex.*
TOYS:	**Stuart Cropper,** *Grays Mews, 1-7 Davies Mews, London W1.*
ARMS & ARMOUR:	**Roy Butler,** *Wallis & Wallis, West Street Auction Galleries, Lewes, Sussex.*
PINE FURNITURE:	**Ann Lingard,** *Rope Walk Antiques, Rye, Sussex.*
JEWELLERY:	**Valerie Howkins,** *Peter Howkins, 39-40 and 135 King Street, Great Yarmouth, Norfolk.*
FISHING:	**Jamie Maxtone Graham,** *Lyne Haugh, Lyne Station, Peebles, Scotland.*

Key to Illustrations

Each illustration and descriptive caption is accompanied by a letter-code. By reference to the following list of Auctioneers (denoted by *) and Dealers (•), the source of any item may be immediately determined. In no way does this constitute or imply a contract or binding offer on the part of any of our contributors to supply or sell the goods illustrated, or similar articles, at the prices stated. Advertisers in this year's directory are denoted by †.

A	*	Aldridges of Bath Ltd, The Auction Galleries, 130-132 Walcot Street, Bath. Tel: (0225) 62830 & 62839
A&A	•	Arms and Armour, Stand 120, Grays Antique Market, 58 Davies Street, London, W1. Tel: 01-629 2851
AA	•	Art'Antica, Stand 16, Bond Street Antique Centre, 124 New Bond Street, London, W1
AAA	•	AAA, Stand 130, Grays Antique Market, 58 Davies Street, London, W1. Tel: 01-629 5130
AAn	•	Armand Antiques, Stand C17/18, Grays Mews, 1-7 Davies Mews, London, W1 Tel: 01-493 6692
ABA	•	Abacus, Stand 313, Grays Antique Market, 58 Davies Street, London, W1
AC	•	Angela Charlesworth, 99 Dodsworth Road, Barnsley, S Yorks. Tel: (0226) 282097 & 203688
ACT	•	Gallery of Antique Costume and Textiles, 2 Church Street, Marylebone, London, NW8. Tel: 01-723 9981
AD	•	Alan Douglas, Bartlett Street, Antique Market, Bath, Avon.
AF	•	Audrey Field, Alfies Antiques Market, Stand 806/7, 13 Church Street, London, NW8. Tel: 01-723 0449
AG	†*	Anderson & Garland, Marlborough House, Marlborough Crescent, Newcastle-upon-Tyne. Tel: 091-232 6278
AGr	*	Andrew Grant, St Marks House, St Marks Close, Worcester. Tel: (0905) 357547
AJ	†*	Arthur Johnson & Sons Ltd, Cattle Market, London Road, Nottingham. Tel: (0602) 869128
AL	†•	Ann Lingard, Ropewalk Antiques, Ropewalk, Rye, Sussex. Tel: (0797) 223486
AM	•	Alison Massey, Grays Mews, Stand J17/18, 1-7 Davies Street, London, W1. Tel: 01-493 1634
AnC	•	Antique Connoisseur, Grays Mews, 1-7 Davies Mews, London, W1. Tel: 01-629 2422
AO	•	Anthony Outred Antiques Ltd, Furniture Cave, 533 Kings Road, London, SW10. Tel: 01-352 8840
AP	•	Angela Page, 15 Cumberland Walk, Tunbridge Wells, Kent.
AR	•	Armada, Stand 122, Grays Antique Market, 58 Davies Street, London, W1. Tel: 01-499 1087
ARC	†•	Architectural Antiques, Savoy Showroom, New Road, South Molton, Devon. Tel: (076 95) 3342
AS	•	Arthur Seager Antiques Ltd, 25a Holland Street, Kensington, London, W8. Tel: 01-937 3262
ASA	†•	AS Antiques, 26 Broad Street, Pendleton, Salford 6, Lancs. Tel: 061-737 5938/ 061-736 6014
ASH	†•	Ashburton Marbles, London House, 6 West Street, Ashburton, Devon. Tel: (0364) 53189
AT	•	Andy Thornton, Architectural Antiques Ltd, Ainleys Industrial Estate, Elland, W Yorkshire. Tel: (0422) 75595

B * Boardman, Station Road Corner, Haverhill, Suffolk. Tel: (0440) 703784
Ba • Butchoff Antiques, 233 Westbourne Grove, London, W11. Tel: 01-221 8174
BA • Bratton Antiques, Market Place, Westbury, Wiltshire. Tel: (0373) 823021
Bea * Bearnes, Rainbow, Avenue Road, Torquay, Devon. Tel: (0803) 26277
BEL • Belmont Galleries Ltd, 533A Kings Road, London, SW10. Tel: 01-351 7388
BHA †• Beaubush House Antiques (Jane Winikus), 95 Sandgate High Street, Folkestone, Kent. Tel: (0303) 49099
BM †* Brown & Merry, 41 High Street, Tring, Herts. Tel: (044 282) 6446
Bon †* Bonhams, Montpelier Galleries, Montpelier Street, Knightsbridge, London, SW7. Tel: 01-584 9161
BOU • J H Bourdon-Smith, 24 Mason's Yard, Duke Street, St James's, London, SW1. Tel: 01-839 4714
BOW †* Michael J Bowman ASVA, 6 Haccombe House, Nr Netherton, Newton Abbot, Devon. Tel: (0626) 872890
BR * Bracketts, 27-29 High Street, Tunbridge Wells. Tel: (0892) 33733
Brd * Bridgfords, 1 Heyes Lane, Alderley Edge, Cheshire. Tel: (0625) 585347. (See also JRB.)
BRI • Britannia, Stand 103, Grays Antique Market, 58 Davies Street, London, W1. Tel: 01-629 6772
BS * Banks & Silvers, 66 Foregate Street, Worcester. Tel: (0905) 23456
Bur * Burlings, St Mary's Auction Rooms, Buxton Old Road, Disley, Cheshire. Tel: (06632) 4854
BWe * Biddle & Webb of Birmingham, Ladywood Middleway, Birmingham. Tel: 021-455 8042
C †* Christie, Manson & Woods Ltd, 8 King Street, St James's, London, SW1. Tel: 01-839 9060
CA • Crafers Antiques (Elizabeth Davies), The Hill, Wickham Market, Woodbridge, Suffolk. Tel: (0728) 747347
CAm * Christie's Amsterdam, Cornelis Schuytstraat 57 1071 JG, Amsterdam, Holland. Tel: (020) 64 20 11
CAN †• Cantabrian Antiques, 16 Park Street, Lynton, N Devon. Tel: (0598) 53282
CB †• Christine Bridge Antiques, 78 Castelnau, London, SW13. Tel: 01-741 5501
CBB †* Colliers, Bigwood & Bewlay, The Old School, Tiddington, Stratford-upon-Avon, Warks. Tel: (0789) 69415
CBD †* Cobbs, Burrows & Day, 39-41 Bank Street, Ashford, Kent. Tel: (0233) 24321
CBG †* Chesterton Bigwood, The Old School, Tiddington, Stratford-upon-Avon, Warks. Tel: (0789) 69415
CBS * C B Sheppard and Son, Auction Galleries, Chatsworth Street, Sutton-in-Ashfield, Notts. Tel: (0773) 872419
CCA • Combe Cottage Antiques, Castle Combe, Chippenham, Wilts. Tel: (0249) 782250
CCC †• The Crested China Co, The Station House, Driffield, East Yorkshire. Tel: (0377) 47042
CDC * Capes Dunn & Co, The Auction Galleries, 38 Charles Street, off Princess Street, Manchester. Tel: 061-273 6060
CEd * Christie's & Edmiston's Ltd, 164-166 Bath Street, Glasgow. Tel: 041-332 8134/7
CEK • Cekay, Stand 172, Grays Mews, 1-7 Davies Mews, London, W1
CER • Cerberus, Stand 372, Grays Antique Market, 58 Davies Street, London, W1. Tel: 01-493 9457
CG * Christie's (International) SA, 8 Place de la Taconnerie, 1204 Geneva, Switzerland. Tel: (022) 28 25 44
CH * Chancellors Hollingsworths, 31 High Street, Ascot, Berkshire. Tel: (0990) 27101
CHK * Christies Manson & Woods (Hong Kong) Ltd, 3607 Edinburgh Tower, 15 Queens Road, Central Hong Kong. Tel: (5) 215 396
CI • Circa Antiques, Stand K15, Grays Mews, 1-7 Davies Mews, London, W1. Tel: 01-629 1184
CJ • Carol & Jeffrey, Grays Antique Market, Stand 335/8, 58 Davies Street, London, W1.
CKK * Coles, Knapp & Kennedy, Tudor House, High Street, Ross-on-Wye, Herefordshire. Tel: (0989) 63553/4
CL • Carr Linford, 10-11 Walcot Buildings, London Road, Bath, Avon. Tel: (0225) 317516
CLA * Christies Los Angeles, 342 North Rodeo Drive, Beverley Hills, California, 90210. Tel: 213/275-5534
Clo †• Clover Antiques, 5-6 Soham Road, Fordham. Tel: (0638) 720 250
CM * Christie's (Monaco), SAM, Hans Nadelhoffer, Christine de Massy, Park Palace, 98000 Monte Carlo. Tel: 93 25 1933
CNY * Christie, Manson & Woods International Inc, 502 Park Avenue, New York NY 10022 USA. Tel: (212) 546 1000 (including Christie's East)
COB • Cobwebs (P A Boyd-Smith), 78 Northam Road, Southampton. Tel: (0703) 227458
COG †* County Group (formerly Butler Hatch Waterman), 102 High Street, Tenterden, Kent. Tel: (05806) 3233 (see also BHW)
CoH * Cooper Hirst, Goldlay House, Parkway, Chelmsford, Essex. Tel: (0245) 58141
CON • Continuum, Stand 124, Grays Antique Market, 58 Davies Street, London, W1.
COS • Cosy World, Stand 385, Grays Antique Market, 58 Davies Street, London, W1. Tel: 01-409 0269
CR * Christie's Roma, Piazza Navona, 114 Roma 00186. Tel: (06) 6564032
CRO • Stuart Cropper, L14/15 Grays Mews, 1-7 Davies Mews, London, W1. Tel: 01-499 6600
CRY * Chrystals Auctions, St James's Chambers, Athol Street, Douglas, Isle of Man. Tel: (0624) 73986
CS • Connie Speight, Stand 108, Grays Antique Market, 58 Davies Street, London, W1. Tel: 01-629 8624
CSK †* Christie's (South Kensington), 85 Old Brompton Road, London, SW7. Tel: 01-581 7611
CW * Cubitt & West, Fine Art Auction Galleries, Millmead, Guildford, Surrey. Tel: (0483) 504030
DA • Dee & Atkinson, The Exchange, Driffield, E Yorkshire. Tel: (0377) 43151
DB †• David Bridgewater, 14 Fountain Buildings, Lansdown Road, Bath, Avon. Tel: (0225) 69288/63652
DDM * Dickinson, Davy & Markham, New Saleroom, Elwes Street, Brigg, South Humberside. Tel: (0652) 53666
DDS †• Dorking Desk Shop, 41 West Street, Dorking, Surrey. Tel: (0306) 883327/880535
DEL • Marilyn Caron Delion, Stand 7 (Basement), Portobello Road, London, W11. Tel: (home) 01-937 3377
DJM • D J Mitchell, Glenwood Lodge, Temple Walk, Matlock Bath, Matlock, Derbyshire. Tel: (0629) 4253
DL †• Dunsdale Lodge Antiques, Brasted Road, Westerham, Kent. Tel: (0959) 62160
DLL †• Derek Loveland Fine Arts, 18-20 Prospect Place, Hastings, E Sussex. Tel: (0424) 441608
DM * Diamond, Mills & Co, 117 Hamilton Road, Felixstowe, Suffolk. Tel: (0394) 282281
DN * Drewett Neate, Donnington Priory, Donnington, Newbury, Berks. Tel: (0635) 31234
DR * Downer Ross, Charter House, 426 Avebury Boulevard, central Milton Keynes. Tel: (0908) 679900
DRA †• Derek Roberts Antiques, 24 & 25 Shipbourne Road, Tonbridge, Kent. Tel: (0732) 358986 or 351719
DSH †• Dacre, Son & Hartley, 1-5 The Grove, Ilkley, West Yorkshire. Tel: (0943) 600655

DWB • Dreweatts, Donnington Priory, Donnington, Newbury, Berks. Tel: (0635) 31234. See DN
EDR * Ernest R de Rome, 12 New John Street, Westgate, Bradford. Tel: (0274) 734116
EG * Elliott & Green, The Auction Sale Room, Emsworth Road, Lymington, Hants. Tel: (0590) 77225/6
EMA • Elias M Assad, Stand A16/17, Grays Mews, 1-7 Davies Mews, London, W1. Tel: 01-499 4778
ET • Eugene Tiernan, Stand H18, Grays Mews, 1-7 Davies Mews, London, W1. Tel: 01-629 3788
EWS †• E Watson & Sons, The Market, Burwash Road, Heathfield, Sussex. Tel: (043 52) 2132
FA • Frank Andrews, Unit 21, Portobello, 290 Westbourne Grove, London, W11. Tel: 01-881 0658
FF • Fritz Fryer, 12 Brookend Street, Ross-on-Wye, Herefordshire. Tel: (0989) 67416
FHF * Frank H Fellows, Bedford House, 88 Hagley Road, Edgbaston, Birmingham. Tel: 021-454 1261/1219
FR * Fryer's Auction Galleries, Terminus Road, Bexhill-on-Sea, Sussex. Tel: (0424) 212994
GAK G A Key, Aylsham Salerooms, off Palmers Lane, Aylsham, Norfolk. Tel: (0263) 733195
GAL Galerie 1900, 267 Camden High Street, London, NW1. Tel: 01-485 1001
G&CC†• Goss & Crested China Ltd, Nicholas J Pine, 62 Murray Road, Horndean, Hants. Tel: (0705) 597440
GC †* Geering & Colyer Auctioneers, 22-24 High Street, Tunbridge Wells, Kent. Tel: (0892) 25136
GeC †• Gerard Campbell, Maple House, Market Place, Lechlade-on-Thames, Glos. Tel: (0367) 52267
GH * Giles Haywood, The Auction House, St John's Road, Stourbridge, West Midlands. Tel: (0384) 370891
GKK • G K K Bonds Limited, PO Box 1, Kelvedon, Essex. Tel: (0376) 71138
GL The Gilded Lily, Stand 131, Grays Antique Market, 58 Davies Street, London, W1. Tel: 01-499 6260
GM * George Mealy & Sons, The Square, Castlecomer, Co Kilkenny, Ireland. Tel: (010 353 56) 41229
GOL • Golfiana, Stand B12, Grays Mews, 1-7 Davies Mews, London, W1. Tel: 01-408 1239
GOR • Ora Gordon, Stand J27, Grays Mews, 1-7 Davies Mews, London, W1. Tel: 01-499 1319
GRO • Gross and Baker, Stand H22, Grays Mews, 1-7 Davies Street, London, W1. Tel: 01-629 3788
GSP * Graves, Son & Pilcher, 71 Church Road, Hove, East Sussex. Tel: (0273) 735266
GW • George Weiner, 2 Market Street, The Lanes, Brighton, Sussex. Tel: (0273) 729948
H • Huntington Antiques, The Old Forge, Church Street, Stow-on-the-Wold, Glos. Tel: (0451) 30842
HA • Hadlow Antiques, No. 1, The Pantiles, Tunbridge Wells, Kent. Tel: (0892) 29858
HAB * Habsburg, Feldman SA, PO Box 125, 1213 Onex, Geneva, Switzerland. Tel: (022) 572530
HAG †• Hove Auction Galleries, 115 Church Road, Hove, E Sussex. Tel: (0273) 736207
HAR • Harris, Arthur, Stand B18/C19, Grays Mews, London, W1. Tel: 01-629 3644
HCH †* Hobbs & Chambers, 'At the Sign of the Bell', Market Place, Cirencester, Glos. Tel: (0285) 4736. Also: 15 Royal Crescent, Cheltenham, Glos. Tel: (0242) 513722
HOD †* Hoddell Pritchard Ltd, Six Ways, Clevedon. Tel: (0272) 876699
HP †* Hobbs Parker, Romney House, Ashford Market, Elwick Road, Ashford, Kent. Tel: (0233) 22222
HR * Hugo Ruef, Gabelsbergerstrasse 28, D8000 Munchen 2, W Germany. Tel: (089) 52 40 84-85
HSS †* Henry Spencer & Sons, 20 The Square, Retford, Notts. Tel: (0777) 708633
HyD * Hy Duke & Son, Dorchester Fine Art Salerooms, Weymouth Avenue, Dorset. Tel: (0305) 65080
IAT †• It's About Time, 863 London Road, Westcliff-on-Sea, Essex. Tel: (0702) 72574
IM * Ibbett Mosely, 125 High Street, Sevenoaks, Kent. Tel: (0732) 452246
JAD †• Jazzy Art Deco, 67 Camden Road, Camden Town, London, NW1. Tel: 01-267 3342/ 01-960 8988
JB • John Bly, 50 High Street, Tring, Herts. Tel: (044 282) 3030
JD †* Julian Dawson, Lewes Auction Rooms, 56 High Street, Lewes, East Sussex. Tel: (0273) 478221
JeB • Jean Brown, Furniture Cave, 533 Kings Road, London SW10. Tel: 01-352 1575
JeM • Jean Metcalf, 1st Floor, Furniture Cave, 533 Kings Road, SW10. Tel: 01-352 2046
JES †• Jess Miller, PO Box 1, Birnham, Dunkeld, Scotland. Tel: (03502) 522
JF †* John Francis, 19 King Street, Carmarthen. Tel: (0267) 233456/7
JG • Jill Gosling, 107 Grays Antique Market, 58 Davies Street, London, W1. Tel: 01-409 2012
JH * Jacobs & Hunt, Lavant Street, Petersfield, Hants. Tel: (0730) 62744
JHo †• Jonathan Horne (Antiques) Ltd, 66c Kensington Church Street, London, W8. Tel: 01-221 5658
JM • Jack Miles, Alfies Antique Market, Stand 253, 13-25 Church Street, London, NW8. Tel: 01-723 1513
JMG †• Jamie Maxtone Graham, Lyne Haugh, Lyne Station, Peebles, Scotland. Tel: (07214) 304
JRB * J R Bridgford & Sons, 1 Heyes Lane, Alderley Edge, Cheshire. Tel: (0625) 585347
JRP †* J R Parkinson & Son and Hamer Auctions, The Auction Rooms, Rochdale Road (Kershaw Street), Bury. Tel: 061-761 1612 & 761 7372
JTD * J T Davies & Sons Ltd, 7 Aberdeen Road, Croydon, Surrey. Tel: 01-681 3222
JUD • St Jude's Antiques, 107 Kensington Church Street, London, W8. Tel: 01-727 8737
JW †* John H Walter & Sons, No. 1, Mint Lane, Lincoln. Tel: (0522) 25454
KEY • Key Antiques, 11 Horse Fair, Chipping Norton, Oxon. Tel: (0608) 3777
L * Lawrence Fine Art of Crewkerne, South Street, Crewkerne, Somerset. Tel: (0460) 73041
Lan * Langlois, Westaway Rooms, Don Street, St Helier, Jersey, CI. Tel: (0534) 22441
LAM †• Penny Lampard, 28 High Street, Headcorn, Kent. Tel: (0622) 890682
LAY †* David Lay ASVA, Penzance Auction House, Alverton, Penzance, Cornwall. Tel: (0736) 61414
LAZ • Lazarell, Stand 325, Grays Antique Market, 58 Davies Street, London, W1.
LB • The Lace Basket, 1A East Cross, Tenterden, Kent. Tel: (05806) 3923
LBA * Lawrence Butler & Co, Butler House, 86 High Street, Hythe, Kent. Tel: (0303) 66022/3
LBP †* Lalonde Bros & Parham, 71 Oakfield Road, Bristol, Avon. Tel: (0272) 734052. (See also P(LBP)
LE †* Locke & England, The Auction Rooms, Walton House, 11 The Parade, Royal Leamington Spa. Tel: (0926) 27988
LG • Lynn Greenwold, 'Digbeth', Digbeth Street, Stow-on-the-Wold, Glos. Tel: (0451) 30398
LJ * Louis Johnson, Oswald House, 63 Bridge Street, Morpeth. Tel: (0670) 52210 & 513025
LM • Licht & Morrison, Stand 158, Grays Antique Market, 58 Davies Street, London, W1. Tel: 01-493 7497

LR • Leonard Russell, 21 King's Avenue, Newhaven, Sussex. Tel: (0273) 515153
LRG †* Lots Road Chelsea Auction Galleries, 71 Lots Road, London, SW10. Tel: 01-352 2349
LT †* Louis Taylors, Percy Street, Hanley, Stoke-on-Trent, Staffs. Tel: (0782) 260222
LW • Linda Wrigglesworth, Stand B17/A23, Grays Mews, 1-7 Davies Mews, London, W1. Tel: 01-408 0177
M * Morphets of Harrogate, 4-6 Albert Street, Harrogate, N Yorks. Tel: (0423) 502282
MA • Matthew Adams, A1 Rogers Antique Galleries, 65 Portobello Road, London, W11. Tel: 01-579 5560
MAC * Manton and Company, 140 Bromsgrove Street, Birmingham. Tel: 021-622 5002
MAI * Moore Allen & Innocent, 33 Castle Street, Cirencester, Glos. Tel: (0285) 61831/2862
MAN • F C Manser & Son Ltd, 53/54 Wyle Cop, Shrewsbury. Tel: (0743) 51120
MAY †* May & Son, 18 Bridge Street, Andover, Hampshire. Tel: (0264) 23417
MCA †• Millers of Chelsea Antiques Ltd, Netherbrook House, 86 Christchurch Road, Ringwood, Hampshire. Tel: (04254) 2062
McC †* McCartneys, 25 Corve Street, Ludlow, Shropshire. Tel: (0584) 2636
MD • Miles D'Agar Antiques, 533 Kings Road, London SW10. Tel: 01-352 6143
Mer • Mermaid Antiques, Stand 774/5, Alfies Antique Market, 13-25 Church Street, London, NW8. Tel: 01-723 6105
MET • Metropolis, 3 D'Arblay Street, Soho, London, W1. Tel: 01-494 2531
MG • Michael C German, 38B Kensington Church Street, London, W8. Tel: 01-937 2771
MGM †* Michael G Matthews, ASVA, ARVA, The Devon Fine Art Auction House, Dowell Street, Honiton, Devon. Tel: (0404) 41872 & 3137
MID * Midland Auctions, 14 Lowwood Road, Erdington, Birmingham. Tel: 021-373 0212
MJB * Michael J Bowman, 6 Haccombe House, Nr Netherton, Newton Abbot, Devon. Tel: (0626) 872890
MN †* Michael Newman, The Central Auction Rooms, Kinterbury House, St Andrew's Cross, Plymouth, Devon. Tel: (0752) 669298
MSM • MSM Antiques, The Furniture Cave, 533 Kings Road, London, SW10. Tel: 01-352 7305
MY • Mytton Antiques, Norton Cross Roads, Atcham, Nr Shrewsbury, Shropshire. Tel: (095 286) 229
N †* Neales of Nottingham, The Nottingham Salerooms, 192 Mansfield Road, Nottingham. Tel: (0602) 624141
Nam • V Namdar, Stand B22, Grays Mews, 1-7 Davies Mews, London, W1. Tel: 01-629 1183
Nes †* D M Nesbit & Company, 7 Clarendon Road, Southsea, Hants. Tel: (0705) 864321
NM • Nick Marchant, Bartlett Street Antique Market, Bath, Avon. Tel: (0225) 310457
NP • Nicholas Page, 15 Cumberland Walk, Tunbridge Wells, Kent.
NSF * Neal Sons & Fletcher, 26 Church Street, Woodbridge, Suffolk. Tel: (03943) 2263/4
NUB • Nubie Antiques, Stand H25, Grays Antique Market, 58 Davies Street, London, W1. Tel: 01-493 4843
O †* Olivers, 23/24 Market Hill, Sudbury, Suffolk. Tel: (0787) 72247
OB †• Oola Boola Antiques, 166 Tower Bridge Road, London, SE1. Tel: 01-403 0794 or 01-693 5050
OBA †• Old Bakery Antiques, St Davids Bridge, Cranbrook, Kent. Tel: (0580) 713103
OL * Outhwaite & Litherland, Kingsway Galleries, Fontenoy Street, Liverpool. Tel: 051-236 6561
ONS †* Onslow's, 14-16 Carroun Road, London, SW8. Tel: 01-793 0240
OSA • The Old School Antiques, Lt Col V and Mrs V O F Wildish, Dorney, Windsor, Berks. Tel: (06286) 3247
OSc †• Old School Antiques (P Rumble), Chittering, Cambridge. Tel: (0223) 861831
OT * Osmond Tricks, Regent Street Auction Rooms, Clifton, Bristol. Tel: (0272) 737201
P †* Phillips, Blenstock House, 7 Blenheim Street, New Bond Street, London, W1. Tel: 01-629 6602
PAC • Polegate Antique Centre, Station Road, Polegate, E Sussex. Tel: (032 12) 5277
PB * Phillips Inc Brooks, 39 Park End Street, Oxford. Tel: (0865) 723524
PBA †• Pryce & Brise, 79 Moore Park Road, Fulham, London, SW6. Tel: 01-736 1864
PC †* Peter Cheney, Western Road Auction Rooms, Western Road, Littlehampton, West Sussex. Tel: (0903) 722264 & 713418
PCA • Paul Cater Antiques, High Street, Moreton-in-Marsh, Gloucestershire. Tel: (0698) 51888
P(CW) †* Prudential Fine Art (Cubitt & West), Millmead, Guildford, Surrey. Tel: (0483) 504030
Pea †* Pearsons, now Prudential Fine Art Auctioneers (incorporating Pearsons), The Red House, Hyde Street, Winchester, Hampshire. Tel: (0962) 62515
P(EDH) †* Prudential Fine Art (Ekins), The Saleroom, The Market, St Ives, Cambs. Tel: (0480) 68144
PFo †* Phillips Folkestone, 11 Bayle Parade, Folkestone, Kent. Tel: (0303) 45555
PGA • Paul Gibbs Antiques, 25 Castle Street, Conwy, N Wales. Tel: (0492) 593429
PH †• Pennard House Antiques, Piccadilly, Bath, Avon. Tel: (074986) 266
Ph †• Phelps Ltd, 129-135 St Margaret's Road, Twickenham, Middx. Tel: 01-892 1778/7129
PHA †• Paul Hopwell Antiques, 30 High Street, West Haddon, Northamptonshire
PIN †• Pine Finds, The Old Cornmill, Bishop Monkton, Harrogate, N Yorks. Tel: (0765) 87159
PJ • Paul Johnston, Old Red Lion, Gedney, Spalding, Lincs. Tel: (0406) 362414
PL • P Lehman, Stand 664/5, Alfies Antiques Market, 13-25 Church Street, London, NW8. Tel: 01-723 0678
P(LBP) †* Prudential Fine Art (Lalonde Bros & Parham), 71 Oakfield Road, Bristol. Tel: (0272) 734052
PLJ * Philip Laney & Jolly, 12a Worcester Road, Malvern. Tel: (06845) 61169/63121-2
PO • Paul Orssich, Stands 2 & 3, Alfies Antique Market, 13-25 Church Street, London, W8. Tel: 01-723 0672
P(Pea) †* Prudential Fine Art (Pearsons), The Red House, Hyde Street, Winchester, Hants. Tel: (0926) 62515
P(PWC) * Prudential Fine Art (Parsons, Welch & Cowell), 49 London Road, Sevenoaks, Kent. Tel: (0732) 740310
PRe • Paul Reeves, 32b Kensington Church Street, London, W8. Tel: 01-937 1594
P(Re) †* Prudential Fine Art (Reeds Rains), Trinity House, 114 Northenden Road, Sale, Manchester. Tel: 061-962 9237
PSG • Patrick & Susan Gould, Stand L17, Grays Mews, 1-7 Davies Mews, London, W1. Tel: 01-408 0129 or 01-993 5879 (home)
PVH • Peter & Valerie Howkins (Peter Howkins), 39, 40 and 135 King Street, Gt Yarmouth, Norfolk. Tel: (0493) 844639
PW * Phillips West 2, 10 Salem Road, London, W2. Tel: 01-221 5303
P(WSW) * Prudential Fine Art (Wyatt & Son), 59 East Street, Chichester, West Sussex. Tel: (0243) 786581. Also at: Baffins Hall, Baffins Lane, Chichester, West Sussex. Tel: (0243) 787548
P(WP) * Prudential Fine Art (Ward & Partners), 16 High Street, Hythe, Kent. Tel: (0303) 67473/4
RA • Rogers of Alresford, Tom and Vasanti Rogers, 16 West Street, Alresford, Hampshire. Tel: (096 273) 2862

RBB †* Russell Baldwin & Bright Property, 38 South Street, Leominster, Hereford. Tel: (0568) 4123

RBE • Ron Beech, 150 Portland Road, Hove, Sussex. Tel: (0273) 724477

RdeR†• Rogers de Rin, 76 Hospital Road, Paradise Walk, London, SW3. Tel: 01-352 9007

Re * Reeds Rain (now Prudential Fine Arts Ltd), Trinity House, 114 Northenden Road, Sale, Cheshire. Tel: 061-962 9237

RG • Robert Grothier, Furniture Cave, 533 Kings Road, London, SW10. Tel: 01-352 2046

RID †* Riddetts of Bournemouth, 26 Richmond Hill, The Square, Bournemouth. Tel: (0202) 25686

RIP †• Ripley Antiques, 67 High Street, Ripley, Surrey. Tel: (0483) 224981

ROS * Rosebery Fine Art Ltd, 3 & 4 Hardwick Street, London, EC1. Tel: 01-837 3418

RP • Robert Pugh, 13 Walcot Buildings, London Road, Bath, Avon and 6 Goring Road, Llanelli, Dyfed. Tel: (0554) 772613

RW • R Wolkowinski, Grays Mews, Stand B15, 1-7 Davies Street, London, W1.

RYA †• Robert Young Antiques, 68 Battersea Bridge Road, London, SW11. Tel: 01-228 7847

SA • Sarah Antiques, Stand G21/H12, Grays Mews, 1-7 Davies Street, London, W1.

SAg * Sussex Auction Galleries, 59 Perrymount Road, Haywards Heath, Sussex. Tel: (0444) 414935

SAn †• Somerville Antiques, Killanley, Ballina, Co Mayo, Ireland. Tel: 096-36275

SB • Stanhope Bowry, Stand 104, Grays Antique Market, 58 Davies Street, London, W1. Tel: 01-629 6194

SBA †• South Bar Antiques, Digbeth Street, Stow-on-the-Wold, Gloucestershire. Tel: (0451) 30236

SD • Stuart Duggan, 1st Floor, Furniture Cave, 533 Kings Road, London, SW10. Tel: 01-352 2046

Sei • Seidler, C F, Stand 120, Grays Antique Market, London, W1. Tel: 01-629 7034

SG Stalker Gallery, 2975 W Maple Road, Troy, Michigan 48084, USA. Tel: (313) 288 3820

SH †• Shelagh Berryman, 15 Market Place, Wells, Somerset. Tel: (0749) 76203

SJV †* St John Vaughan (with John Hogbin), 53 High Street, Tenterden, Kent. Tel: (05806) 3200

SL * Simmons & Lawrence, 32 Bell Street, Henley-on-Thames, Oxon. Tel: (0491) 571111

Som †• Somervale Antiques, 6 Radstock Road, Midsomer Norton, Bath. Tel: (0761) 412686

SSD • Smith & Smith Designs, 58A Middle Street North, Driffield, E Yorkshire. Tel: (0377) 46321

ST †• Simon Tracy, 18 Church Street, London, NW8. Tel: 01-724 5890

Sto • Stockspring Antiques, 114 Kensington Church Street, London, W8. Tel: 01-727 7995

STY • Stylo, Room 301 (Ground Floor), Alfie's Antique Market, 13-25 Church Street, London, NW8. Tel: 01-724 0393

SUS • Susan Haines, Stand 376, Grays Antique Market, 58 Davies Street, London, W1.

SW †• Shirley Warren, 333b Limpsfield Road, Sanderstead, Surrey. Tel: 01-651 5180/ 01-657 1751

SWO †* Sworders – G E Sworder and Sons, 15 Northgate End, Bishops Stortford. Tel: (0279) 51388

TA • Talisman, Stand 362/4, Grays Antique Market, 58 Davies Street, London, W1. Tel: 01-409 2743

TAY * Taylors, Honiton Galleries, 205 High Street, Honiton, Devon. Tel: (0404) 2404/5

TC • Ted Coxhead, Stand 301, Alfie's Antique Market, 13-25 Church Street, London, NW8. Tel: 01-724 0393

TCW • The Clock Workshop, J M Yealland, 17 Prospect Street, Caversham, Reading. Tel: (0734) 470741

THA †• Tudor House Antiques, Bill Dickenson, 11 Tontine Hill, Ironbridge, Shropshire. Tel: (095 245) 3783

THG • Trevor Gilbert, Stand G10/11, Grays Mews, 1-7 Davies Mews, London, W1. Tel: 01-408 0028

TiB • Tibetan and Chinese Works of Art, Stand A14, Grays Mews, 1-7 Davies Mews, London, W1.

TK †• Timothy Kendrew Antiques, 5-8 George Hotel Mews, Stamford, Lincolnshire. Tel: (0780) 56072

TKN †* Tiffen King Nicholson, 12 Lowther Street, Carlisle, Cumbria. Tel: (0228) 25259

TM * Thos. Mawer & Son, The Lincoln Saleroom, 63 Monks Road, Lincoln. Tel: (0522) 24984

TRi • Trio, Stand L24, Grays Mews, 1-7 Davies Mews, London, W1. Tel: 01-629 1184

TRW • Tradewinds, Stand 148/9, Grays Antique Market, 58 Davies Street, London, W1 Tel: 01-629 5130

TS • The Thimble Society of London, Stand 134, Grays Antique Market, 58 Davies Street, London, W1

TUD • Tudor Antiques, 31 Cottle Road, Stockwood, Bristol 14. Tel: (0272) 48806

TVA • Teme Valley Antiques, 1 The Bull Ring, Ludlow, Shropshire. Tel: (0584) 4686

TW †* Thomas Watson & Son, Northumberland Street, Darlington, Co Durham. Tel: (0325) 462555 & 462559

UP †• Utopia Antiques Ltd, Holme Mills, Burton in Kendal, Carnforth, Lancashire. Tel: (0524) 781739

V †* Prudential Fine Art, Vidler & Co, Rye Auction Galleries, Cinque Ports Street, Rye, E Sussex. Tel: (0797) 222124

VEN †• Venners Antiques, 7 New Cavendish Street, London, W1 Tel: 01-935 0184

Vin • Vintage, Stand 371, Grays Antique Market, 58 Davies Street, London, W1. Tel: 01-493 9457

W • Woodstock, 1st Floor, Furniture Cave, 533 Kings Road, London, SW10. Tel: 01-352 2046

Wai • Wain Antiques, 45 Long Street, Tetbury, Gloucestershire. Tel: (0666) 52440

WAL †* Wallis & Wallis, West Street Auction Galleries, Lewes, Sussex. Tel: (0273) 480208

WAT * Watsons, 1 Market Street, Saffron Walden, Essex. Tel: (0799) 22058

WD * Weller & Dufty Ltd, 141 Bromsgrove Street, Birmingham. Tel: 021-692 1414/5

WHB * William H Brown, Westgate Hall, Westgate, Grantham, Lincs. Tel: (0476) 68861

WHL * W H Lane & Son, 64 Morrab Road, Penzance, Cornwall. Tel: (0736) 61447

WIL * Peter Wilson, Victoria Gallery, Market Street, Nantwich, Cheshire. Tel: (0270) 623878

Wor †* GA Property Services (Worsfolds), The Auction Galleries, 40 Station Road West, Canterbury, Kent. Tel: (0227) 763337

WP * Ward & Partners, 16 High Street, Hythe, Kent. Tel: (0303) 67473/4

WR * Walter & Randall, 7-13 New Road, Chatham, Kent. Tel: (0634) 41233

WRe • Walcot Reclamations, 108 Walcot Street, Bath, Avon. Tel: (0225) 66291

WRo • W Robinson, Stand K30/31, Grays Mews, 1-7 Davies Mews, London, W1. Tel: 01-408 0909

WSH †* Warners William H Brown, 16-18 Halford Street, Leicester. Tel: (0533) 519777

WSW * Wyatt & Son (with Whiteheads), 59 East Street, Chichester, West Sussex. Tel: (0243) 786581. Also at: Baffins Hall, Baffins Lane, Chichester, West Sussex Tel: (0243) 787548

WW * Woolley & Wallis, The Castle Auction Mart, Castle Street, Salisbury. Tel: (0722) 21711

YES • Yesterday, Stand H20/21, Grays Mews, 1-7 Davies Mews, London, W1. Tel: 01-629 3788

Colin MacLeod's
Antiques & Designer
Showroom

CONTENTS

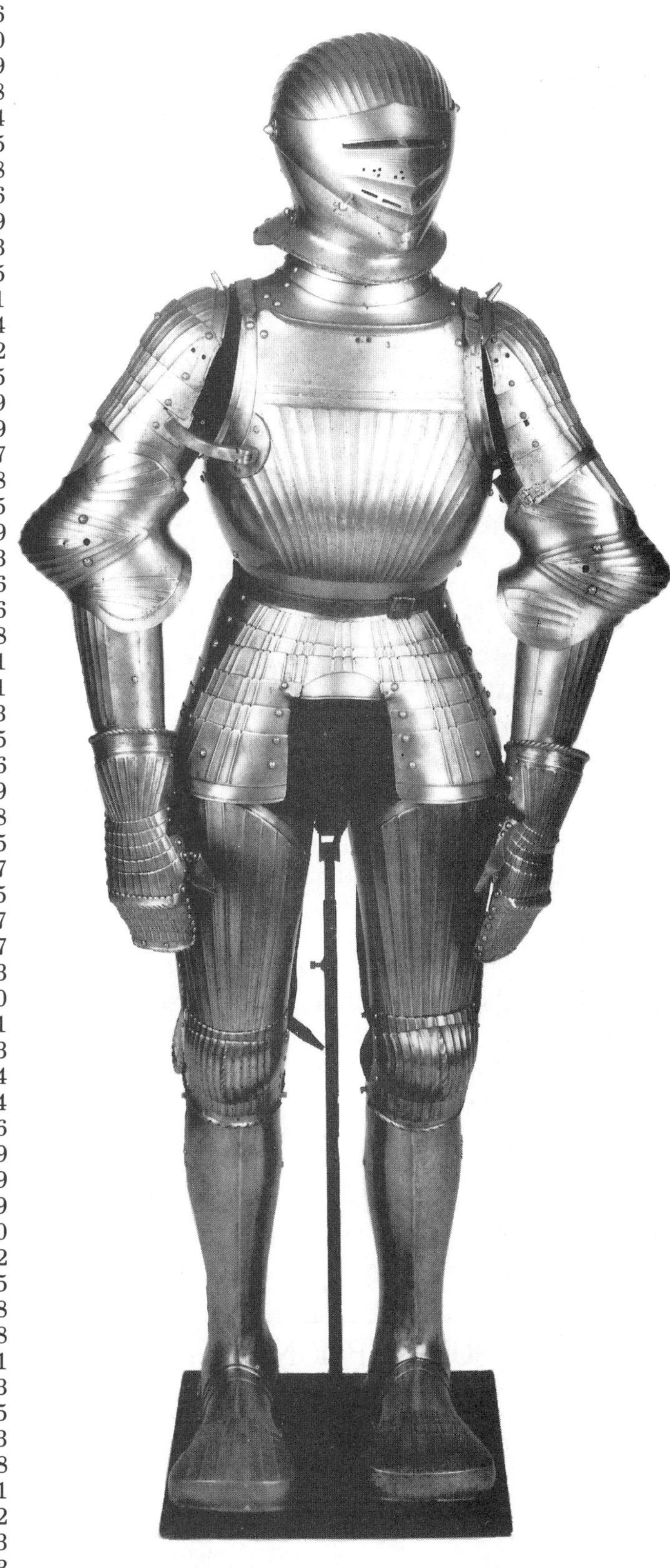

A composite "Maximilian" armour, comprising closed helmet with bellows visor and lifting peg, chin-piece, collar with spring peg hinges, which attach spaulders, both with assembly marks, one stamped with Nuremburg mark, sabatons with right toe fibreglass replacement, all elements fluted and enhanced with incised lines except greaves, main borders turned, early 16thC, approx. 66in (167.5cm).
£16,000-20,000 *CNY*

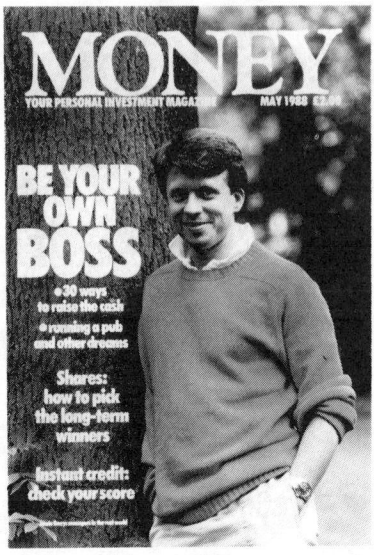

POTTERY

The market for pottery has continued along very much the same lines as last year. Occasional sales of well-known collections stimulate prices and these new levels remain stable or fall slightly over the next few years. The dearth of top class wares continues and selectivity amongst collectors ensures that only the best decorated amongst commoner wares arouse any real interest. If in good condition such pieces rise slightly above prevailing price levels.

Anything unusual has sold well. In particular, unusual examples of moulded white saltglaze have exceeded expectations. Coloured saltglaze in good condition remains popular but the market for run-of-the-mill pieces is less buoyant. The number of collectors of pottery appears to be growing. Even quite badly damaged pieces will find a ready market if they have decorative appeal or are unusual in some way.

This desire for pieces with decorative appeal extends into the market for 19th century pottery. It is hard to understand the chemistry by which a trend develops so widely in such a relatively short space of time. Within a year it appears that large numbers of collectors, in a variety of fields, have decided to display their pieces within room settings rather than in cabinets, and the resultant enthusiasm for ornamental pieces has been obvious.

Selective buying is evident but the market for large decorative pieces such as Mason's Ironstone vases or majolica garden seats is exceptionally buoyant. In this area of the market decorative appeal even outweighs considerations of attribution so that a pair of Minton's garden seats, whilst selling well at £8,250, were outshone in every way by a charming pair of unattributed seats modelled in the form of Egyptian slave girls which made £14,300.
General price levels for Wemyss ware continue to increase.
A pair of piglets fetched £7,700 last year whilst prices in the region of £3,000-£5,000 became the norm for adult pigs or rarities. Royal collecting interest has also stimulated demand.

Baskets

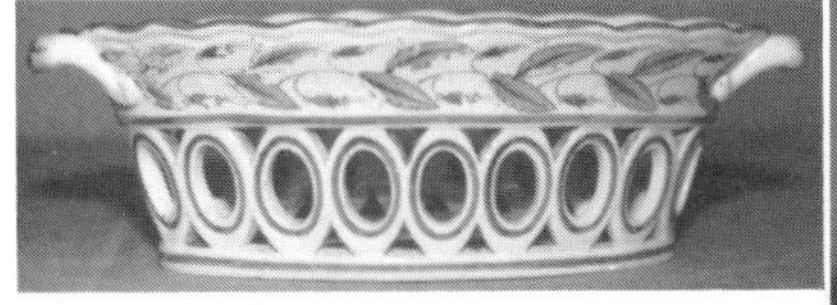

A Leeds creamware basket, handpainted with fuchsias in puce, blue and green, c1775, 3 by 9in (7.5 by 23cm).
£200-250 *CA*

A Rogers blue and white chestnut basket stand, Camel pattern, pierced, slight damage, impressed mark, c1815, 7 by 9in (18 by 23cm).
£35-40 *CA*

Bowls

A Bristol delft blue and white bowl, on a domed circular foot, slight rim chips, crack to base and slight restoration to foot, c1730, 10½in (26.5cm) diam.
£1,500-2,000 *C*

An English delft blue and white straining bowl, glaze chipped, mid-18thC, 8½in (21.5cm) diam.
£500-600 *Bea*

A Liverpool delft blue and white water bottle, small glaze imperfection, slight restoration, c1760, 9in (23cm).
£160-200 *CNY*

Miller's is a price GUIDE not a price LIST

Bottles

A Liverpool delft blue and white bottle, decorated with woman and child and a figure in a pavilion in a garden, c1760, 9in (23cm).
£700-900 *DEL*

A Wedgwood silver gilt mounted three-colour jasper scent bottle, the pale blue ground with 2 green medallions in white relief, mid-19thC, 3in (8cm).
£350-450 *C*

A Lambeth delft bowl, painted in blue, manganese, yellow and green with buildings in a continuous landscape, minor glaze chips, c1760, 10in (26cm) diam.
£350-400 *CNY*

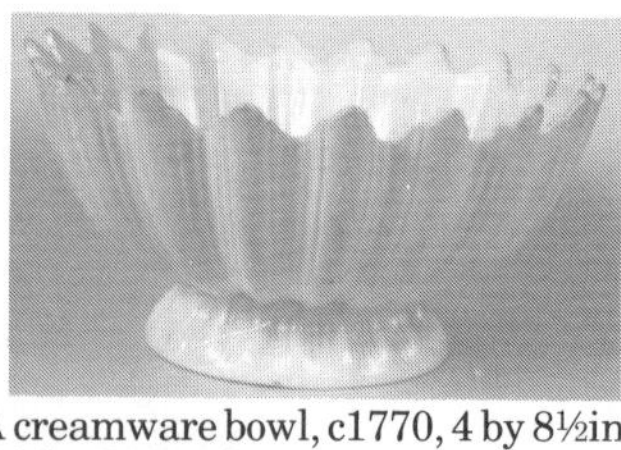

A creamware bowl, c1770, 4 by 8½in (10 by 21.5cm).
£400-450 *JHo*

A Wedgwood and Bentley black basalt encaustic decorated sugar bowl and cover, impressed lower case mark, c1775, 4½in (11.5cm) diam.
£2,000-2,500 *C*

A creamware bowl and cover, in mint condition, c1800, 8in (20.5cm).
£400-500 *BHA*

A Prattware coloured pottery bowl, possibly Liverpool, c1790, 11in (28cm) diam.
£950-1,050 *JHo*

An Adams blue and white jasper sugar bowl and cover, applied in white relief, the cover with swan finial, impressed mark, c1800, 6in (15cm) wide.
£600-700 *CNY*

CREAMWARE

- ★ a low fired earthenware glazed in a cream or butter colour with a porcelain effect
- ★ first produced in 1740
- ★ perfected by Josiah Wedgwood in the 1760s
- ★ named Queen's Ware by Wedgwood in honour of Queen Charlotte

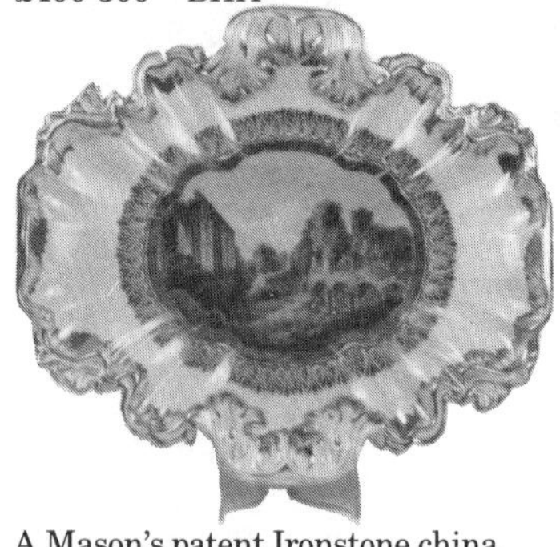

A Mason's patent Ironstone china dish, painted with Interior of the Hall of Kenilworth Castle, Warwickshire, impressed mark, c1820, 10½in (26.5cm) wide.
£400-500 *C*

A George Jones majolica strawberry dish, for cream and sugar, with a thrush between 2 nests, relief decoration of strawberry blossom, leaves and fruit, 1878, 11in (28cm) wide.
£500-550 *BRI*

A Sunderland lustre bowl, transfer printed with portrait of Sir Robert Peel, speech and mariners compass, splash lustre, c1840, 10in (25cm) diam.
£250-300 *LR*

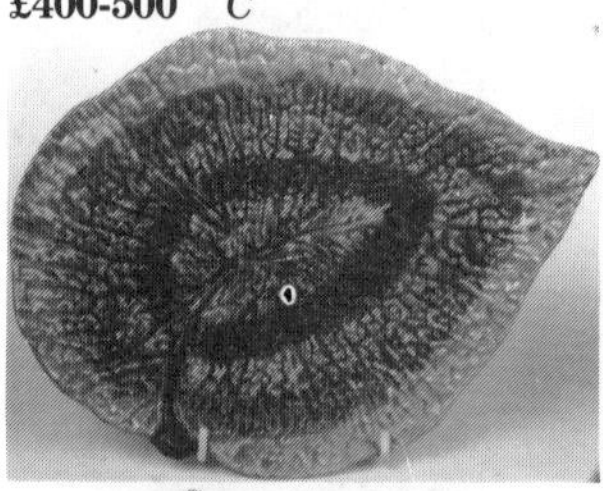

A Staffordshire majolica dish in the shape of a begonia leaf, c1885, 9½in (24cm).
£30-50 *BRI*

A George Jones majolica nut dish, with a squirrel holding a hazel nut, the dish decorated with hazel leaves and ferns in relief on a pink ground, 1886, 10in (25cm) wide.
£350-400 *BRI*

Busts

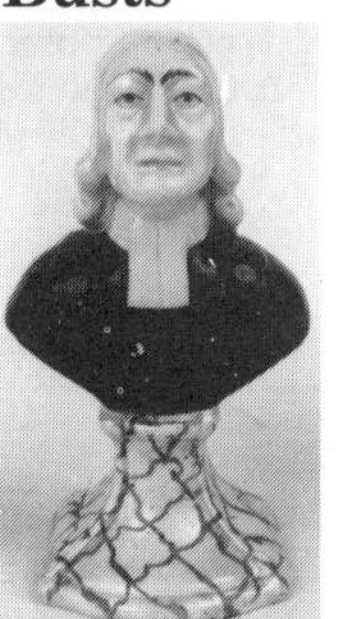

An Enoch Wood bust of Wesley, c1800, 4½in (11cm).
£220-275 *DL*

A Copeland parian bust of The Veiled Bride, marked, c1850, 14½in (37cm).
£1,000-1,200 *DL*

THE WOOD FAMILY
- ★ Ralph Wood Senior 1715-62
- ★ Ralph Wood Junior 1748-95
- ★ Aaron Wood (brother of R Wood Senior) 1717-85
- ★ Enoch Wood (son of A Wood) 1759-1840

An Enoch Wood bust of the Madonna, c1810, 16in (40.5cm).
£500-550 *DL*

A Staffordshire bust of Maria Foot Obadiah Sherratt type, wearing a yellow-edged pink dress, on a marbled blue socle and moulded four-footed base, some restoration to base and socle, c1816, 11½in (29cm).
£1,700-2,000 *C*

A Wedgwood black basalt library bust of Sir Francis Bacon, impressed marks to bust and socle, the socle with deleted 'made in England' marks, late 19th/20thC, 16in (40.5cm).
£450-550 *CNY*

A parian bust of Henry Wilson, after H F Libby, inscribed on the reverse 'H.F. Libby, Sculpt. Boston. Copyrighted', 'The Death of Slavery is the Life of the Nation', H Wilson, late 19thC, 13in (33cm).
£400-500 *C*

Henry Wilson (1812-75), the American politician, was an ardent anti-slavery advocate. He joined the American (Know Nothing) party in 1854 but soon withdrew because of its intolerance and failure to take a positive stand on the slavery issue. He was US Senator for Massachusetts (1855-73), one of the founders of the Republican party and Vice President of the United States (1873-75).

A parian bust of The Duke of Wellington, after the sculpture by Comte D'Orsay, wearing the collar and badge of the Order of the Golden Fleece, some damage, impressed marks and dated 1852, on an ebonised wood stand, 13in (33cm) overall.
£120-160 *C*

A Staffordshire pottery bust of The Duke of Wellington, forming a jug, decorated in colours and gilt, 7in (18cm).
£100-150 *P*

A Staffordshire pottery bust of The Duke of Wellington, forming a tobacco jar and cover, decorated in colours, chip to hat, 7½in (19cm).
£80-120 *P*

A Staffordshire bust of the virgin, wearing a yellow robe and a head scarf in crimson lined with blue, on a marbled socle and square base, 15in (38cm).
£80-120 *L*

Commemorative

A Staffordshire silver lustre commemorative jug, Molineux and Cribb, c1815, 5½in (14cm).
£370-400 *DL*

A commemorative jug of Princess Charlotte and Leopold, creamware with green enamel and purple lustre decoration, c1816, 6½in (16.5cm).
£200-250 *LR*

Make the Most of Miller's

In the commemorative section we have included both pottery and porcelain, as most dealers and collectors are more interested in the subject matter rather than the material.

A blue transfer printed plate inscribed 'Her Majesty Queen Caroline of England', c1821, 6½in (16.5cm) diam.
£200-250 *LR*

Three commemorative jugs, transfer printed and coloured, c1820-30.

l. Queen Charlotte, 5in (12.5cm).
£250-280

c. William IV and Adelaide, 6in (15cm).
£370-400

r. King George IV, 4in (10cm).
£370-400 *LR*

A commemorative plate, George IV visit to Edinburgh 1822, enamelled, lustred and titled, 8½in (21.5cm) diam.
£400-450 *LR*

A commemorative pottery jug of Viscount Clive of India obtaining his majority, November 5th, 1839.
£80-100 *THA*

A Staffordshire children's plate to commemorate the union of Queen Victoria and Prince Albert, with painted enamel decoration to the rim, c1840, 5in (12.5cm) diam.
£200-250 *BRI*

A mug with underglaze black transfer of the 14th Earl of Derby, decorated with enamelled blue circles, c1852, 3in (7.5cm).
£130-150 *BRI*

A Staffordshire mug printed in blue with a half-length portrait of Queen Victoria, 1837, 3½in (9cm).
£650-700 *BRI*

A porcelain underglaze transfer mug, with portrait and captions in black, February 4th, 1874, 3in (7.5cm).
£100-150 *BRI*

A footed porcelain mug with black transfer print, underglaze, c1852, 3½in (9cm).
£160-200 *BRI*

A porcelain mug with underglaze black transfer of the Wesleyan Methodist Chapel at Spilsby, Lincolnshire, c1890, 3½in (9cm).
£60-80 *BRI*

A mug with portrait of Robert Burns and Mrs Burns on the reverse, by C W McNay, Bo'Ness, Scotland, c1896, 3in (7.5cm).
£60-80 *BRI*

A Staffordshire commemorative mug, Wesley on one side, temple on other side and inside, c1891, 3in (7.5cm).
£70-100 *DL*

An earthenware mug with large portrait of Queen Victoria in a surround of national flowers, for the 1887 Jubilee, titled 'Queen of England – Empress of India', 3½in (9cm).
£100-140 *BRI*

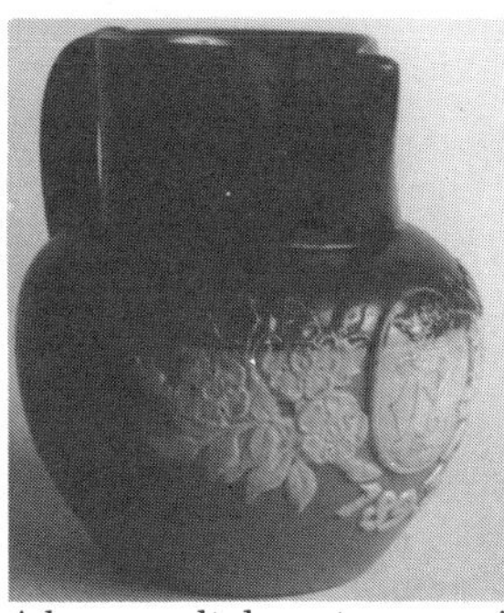

A brown saltglaze stoneware jug by Doulton to commemorate the wedding of George, Duke of York, and Princess May of Teck, 1893, 4in (10cm).
£160-200 *BRI*

A Copeland stoneware teapot, in buff with olive green glaze, decorated in white, the reverse with portrait of Queen Victoria with indented wording Diamond Jubilee 1897, 7½in (19cm).
£120-160 *BRI*

A Copeland three-handled loving cup, commemorating the end of the Boer War, brown outline with detailed hand colouring in enamels and gilding, titled on base 'Subscribers copy', 1900.
£450-500 *BRI*

A pottery mug with portrait of General Sir Redvers Buller, brown underglaze transfer with overglaze enamel clobbering, Boer War, c1900, 3½in (9cm).
£70-100 *BRI*

A Doulton glaze stoneware mug, commemorating the Trafalgar Centenary, portrait of Nelson and a rope twist border enclosing a depiction of the battle, 1905, 3in (7.5cm).
£140-200 *BRI*

A Doulton saltglaze stoneware jug, commemorating the centenary of Trafalgar, with relief portrait of Nelson and his famous signal, 'England expects every man will do his duty', 1905, 8½in (21.5cm).
£250-300 *BRI*

A mug commemorating the marriage of King George V and Queen Mary on July 6, 1893.
£40-70 *BRI*

A pottery mug commemorating the coming of age of Lewis Frederick Davis, Esq, Ferndale, 1912, 3in (7.5cm).
£40-70 *BRI*

A Staffordshire Toby jug, modelled as Thomas Woodrow Wilson, President of The United States, designed by Francis Carruthers Gould, in a limited edition of 500, c1917.
£400-450 *BRI*

A porcelain mug with portrait of the Rt Hon David Lloyd George, in 2 shades of brown, c1918, 3in (7.5cm).
£120-160 *BRI*

A Staffordshire Toby jug, modelled as Admiral Beatty, designed by Francis Carruthers Gould, in a limited edition of 350, c1918, 11in (28cm).
£350-400 *BRI*

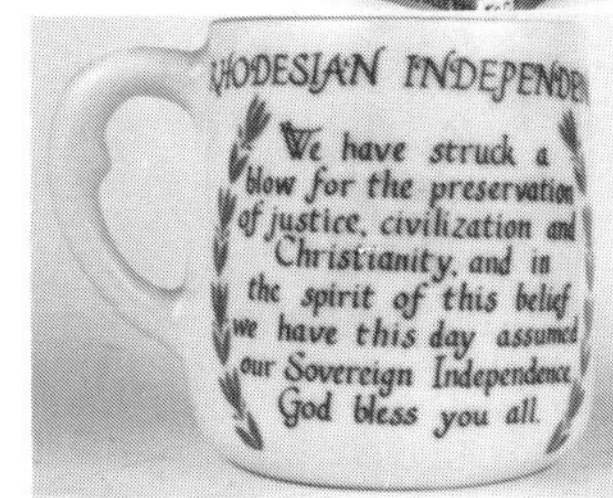

A pottery mug commemorating the Unilateral Declaration of Independence of Rhodesia, November 11th, 1965, with portrait of Ian Smith on the reverse.
£30-50 *BRI*

A commemorative jug of Admiral Sir David Beatty, at the German surrender, November 21st, 1918, 6in (15cm).
£120-150 *DL*

A pottery mug with portrait of George Washington, First President of The United States of America, celebrating the Bicentenary of Independence, 1976, 3½in (9cm).
£30-50 *BRI*

Cottages

A pottery 'organ' pastille burner, late 18thC, 6in (15cm).
£250-300 *McC*

A Staffordshire model of Stanfield Hall, c1850, 7in (18cm).
£180-240 *DL*

A Prattware money box in the form of Gothic cottage, sponged in blue, ochre, yellow and black, c1800, 5½in (14cm).
£550-600 *LR*

A Staffordshire flat-back house, c1855, 7in (18cm).
£160-180 *BA*

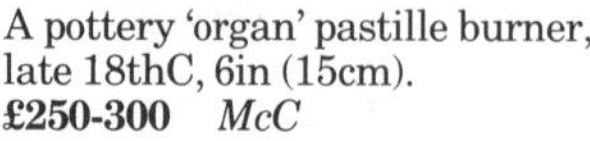

Cow Creamers

A Whieldon cow creamer, with unusual markings, c1770, 5in (12.5cm).
£1,700-2,000 *DL*

A Yorkshire cow group, coloured in blue, ochre, black and yellow, c1800, 5½in (14cm).
£1,200-1,400 *LR*

A cow creamer, probably North Country, sponged in purple and black, c1800, 5in (12.5cm).
£750-850 *LR*

Cups

A creamware cup and saucer, with green decoration, c1775, saucer 5in (12.5cm) diam.
£350-400 *JHo*

A Wedgwood and Bentley black basalt encaustic decorated cup and saucer, the borders painted in iron red and white, impressed lower case mark to saucer, c1775.
£800-1,000 *CNY*

A Staffordshire moulded white saltglaze coffee cup with ribbed loop handle, and a saucer, minor chip to saucer and hairline crack, c1775.
£600-700 *C*

A Nottingham stoneware loving cup, inscribed 'Made at Nottm. Novr. the 4th 1779 – Sarah Howels of Headwalton, Nottnsh', restored, 9½in (24cm).
£1,000-1,500 *N*

A Wedgwood green and white jasper teabowl and saucer, the dipped pale lime green ground moulded in white relief, impressed marks and 3, the saucer in lower case, c1790.
£650-700 *C*

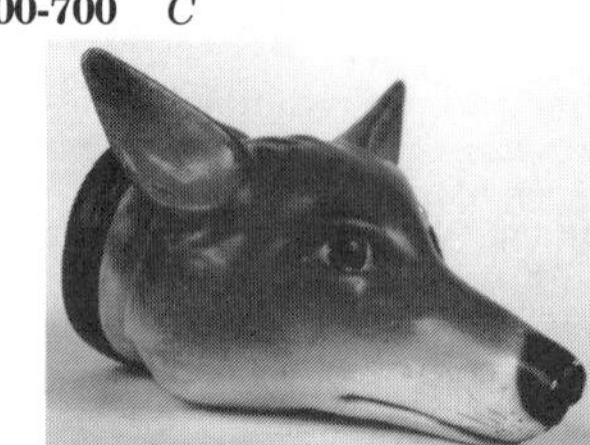

A pair of Staffordshire stirrup cups, c1820, 5in (12.5cm).
£1,500-2,000 *DL*

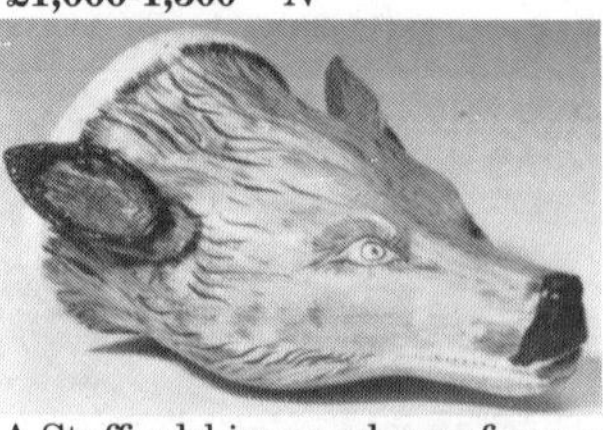

A Staffordshire pearlware fox mask stirrup cup, streaked in iron red and highlighted in black, one ear with slight chip, c1790, 5½in (13.5cm) long.
£1,000-1,500 *C*

A dog's head stirrup cup, marked Turner, c1800, 6½in (16cm) long.
£1,400-1,600 *DL*

Ewers

A pair of Wedgwood black basalt water and wine ewers, after designs by Flaxman, on spreading feet and square bases, impressed marks, late 19thC, 17½in (44cm).
£1,000-1,500 *CNY*

Figures – Animals

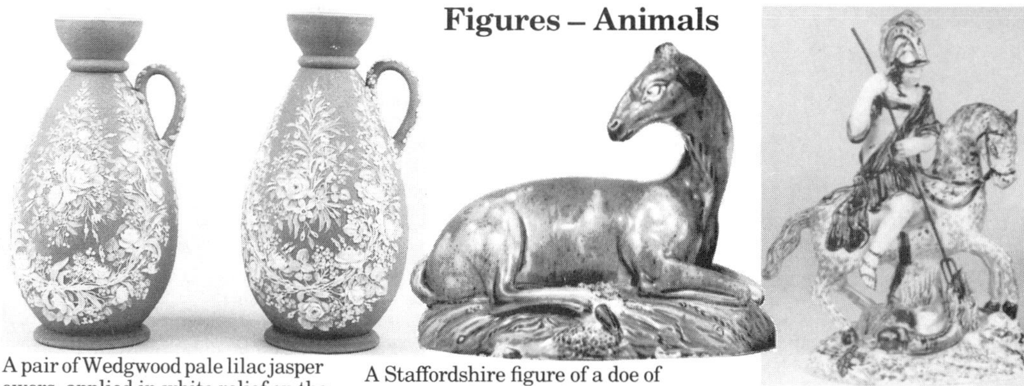

A pair of Wedgwood pale lilac jasper ewers, applied in white relief on the dipped ground, impressed marks and S, c1880, 8in (20cm).
£1,400-1,800 *CNY*

A Staffordshire figure of a doe of Ralph Wood type, with brown coat, on a green rockwork base, ears restored, chips to base, c1770, 6in (15.5cm) wide.
£700-800 *C*

A Staffordshire creamware group of St George and the Dragon of conventional Ralph Wood type, sponged and streaked in brown, the saddle cloth and dragon enriched in green, restoration to horse's ears and tail, c1780, 11½in (28.5cm).
£2,000-2,500 *C*

A Ralph Wood model of a lion, with deeply incised mane covered in a translucent olive green glaze, streaked in yellow on the shoulder, on a brown washed base, moulded with green foliage, part of tail lacking, slight chips to base, c1775, 12½in (31cm) wide.
£2,400-2,800 *C*

A Ralph Wood whistle in the form of a lion, c1780, 3in (7.5cm).
£500-550 *DL*

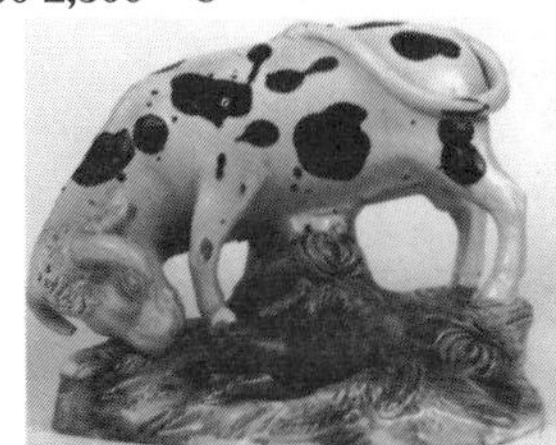

A Ralph Wood bull baiting group, c1780, 6in (15cm).
£2,000-2,500 *DL*

It is rare to have black spots, usually manganese.

A rare 'birds in tree' group, possibly from the Wood factory, underglazed decorated in green and yellow, c1785, 7½in (19cm).
£950-1,100 *LR*

A Mosbach figure of a dog, naturalistically painted in colours, tail missing, c1785, 4in (9.5cm).
£500-600 *C*

A Prattware cockerel, c1790, 4in (10cm).
£750-800 *DL*

A Prattware deer with bocage, c1790, 4in (10cm).
£550-600 *DL*

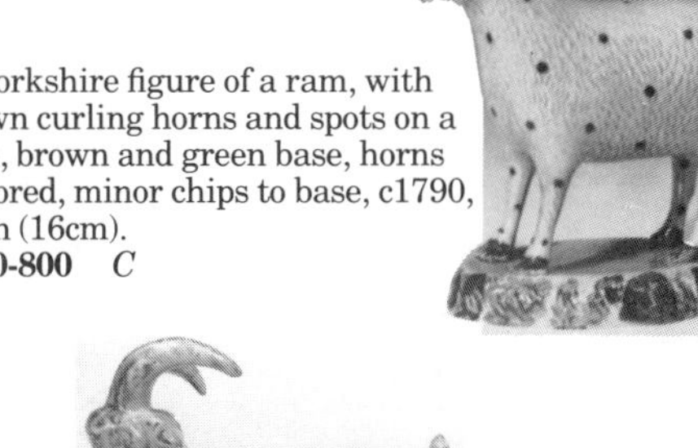

A Yorkshire figure of a ram, with brown curling horns and spots on a blue, brown and green base, horns restored, minor chips to base, c1790, 6½in (16cm).
£750-800 *C*

A creamware goat, c1800, 7in (18cm).
£1,000-1,500 *DL*

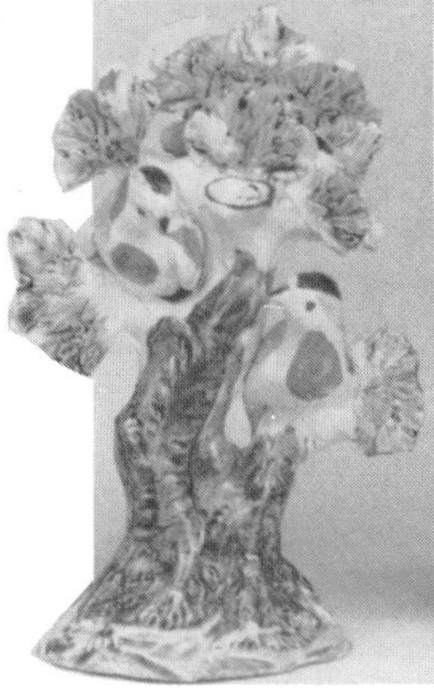

A pearlware 'birds in branches' group, in ochre, yellow and blue, probably Staffordshire, chips to tree and base, c1790, 7½in (19.5cm).
£650-700 *C*

A Staffordshire dog, with splashed brown markings and on yellow and blue cushion base, c1790, 3½in (8.5cm).
£130-160 *CSK*

A Yorkshire pottery ram, brown and ochre splashed on green base, c1800, 4½in (11.5cm).
£750-850 *LR*

A Staffordshire creamware recumbent stag, lightly sponged in green and ochre, on a green base, antlers and ears restored, c1800, 6in (15cm) wide.
£450-550 *C*

A Staffordshire pearlware figure of a recumbent stag, sponged in brown with green leaved tree, leaves and ears restored, antlers lacking, c1800, 8in (20.5cm).
£350-450 *C*

A Staffordshire pearlware figure of a cow, with brown patches, on a green and brown base applied with moss and coloured flowers, some restoration to horns and tail, c1800, 13in (32.5cm) wide.
£600-1,000 *C*

A Staffordshire pearlware figure of an eagle with brown plumage, pink sponged base, one wing with slight chip, minor flaking to enamel, c1810, 7½in (19.5cm).
£250-350 *C*

A Staffordshire creamware figure of a lion, with red coat and grey mane and paws, with yellow ball, on a shaped green base edged in red and pink, tail restored, c1810, 6½in (16cm).
£700-800 *C*

A Tittensor figure of a stallion with brown coat and yellow saddle, on an incised green base, tree damaged, ears chipped, impressed mark at back, c1815, 6½in (17cm).
£1,500-2,000 *C*

A Staffordshire pearlware figure of a cockerel, with multi-coloured plumage, tail restored, c1820, 10in (25cm).
£700-750 *C*

A pair of early Walton type dogs, c1820, 5½in (14cm).
£1,000-1,500 *LR*

A Walton type figure of a deer, with white spotted iron red hide with black muzzle and hooves, on moulded base with blue scrolls and enriched in green, ears restored, tree chipped, antlers lacking(?), c1820.
£250-350 *C*

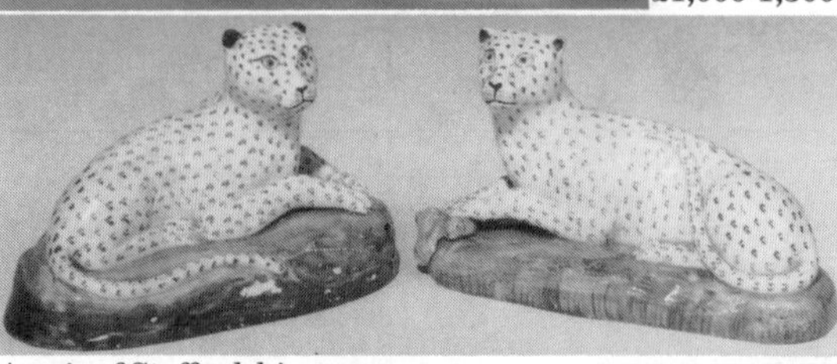

A pair of Staffordshire creamware leopards, with pale yellow coats and brown markings, one with a lump of meat, on green bases, ears chipped, one with some flaking to green enamel, c1820, 8½in (21cm) wide.
£5,000-6,000 *C*

In the Ceramics section if there is only one measurement it usually refers to the height of the piece

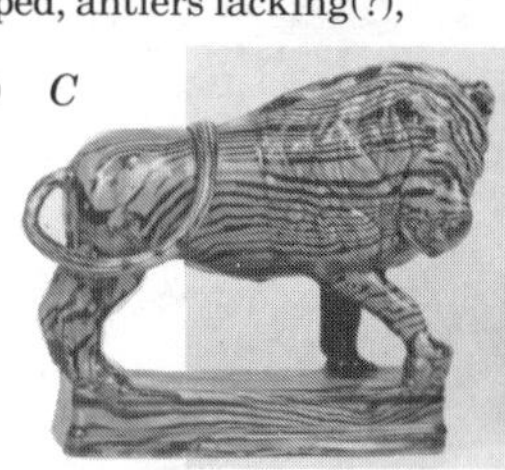

A slipware figure of a lion, his forepaw resting on a ball, with cream slip marbling beneath a treacle glaze, tail restored, early 18thC, 10in (25cm) long.
£300-400 *C*

An Obadiah Sherratt figure of a pointer with black markings, tail restored, c1825, 6in (15cm).
£250-350 *CSK*

A Staffordshire figure of a dog with black markings, entitled Rover, damage to bocage, c1840, 4½in (11cm).
£650-750 *CSK*

A pair of Staffordshire mares and foals, late 18thC, 11in (28cm).
£400-550 *BHA*

A pair of Staffordshire zebras, c1855, 6in (15cm).
£400-450 *DL*

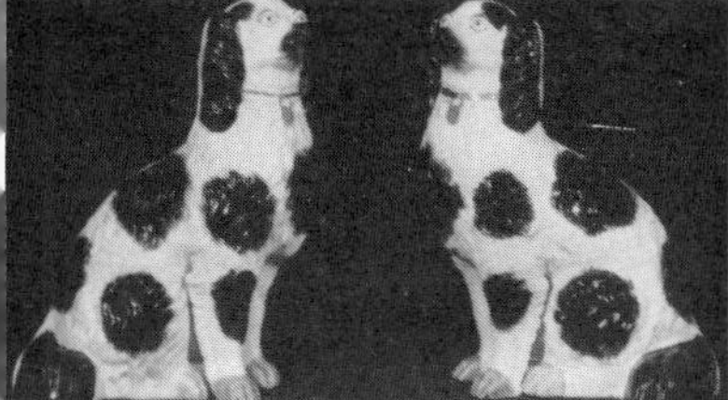

A Staffordshire miniature cow with bocage, marked salt, c1830, 2in (5cm) wide.
£225-300 *JUD*

A rare Staffordshire cat, in black and white on blue base, c1840, 6in (15cm).
£400-500 *BHA*

A Staffordshire pair of brightly coloured birds, c1850, 13in (33cm).
£750-800 *DL*

A pair of Staffordshire spaniels, with separate moulded forepaws, with gilt collars and black markings, both restored, c1860, 15½in (39cm).
£300-400 *CSK*

A pair of stoneware lions, c1830, 4in (10cm).
£70-100 *DEL*

A Staffordshire equestrian group of Obadiah Sherratt type, modelled as a gallant in opaque blue jacket and brown breeches, astride a sponged grey horse with a yellow saddle cloth and bridle, some restoration, c1830, 8½in (22cm).
£1,700-2,500 *C*

A large Staffordshire greyhound, c1845, 11in (28cm) long.
£450-500 *BA*

This model was produced over a long period. Examples vary enormously in quality and therefore price. The illustrated example is of good quality.

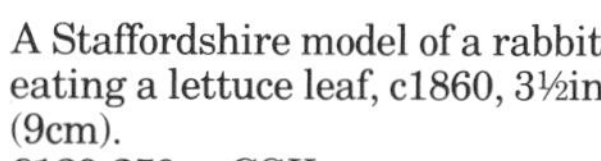
A Staffordshire model of a rabbit eating a lettuce leaf, c1860, 3½in (9cm).
£180-250 *CSK*

An early Staffordshire tiger, probably Portobello, Death of Lieutenant Monroe, c1875, 6½in (16.5cm).
£450-500 *DL*

A Staffordshire spaniel, c1860, 13in (33cm) wide.
£900-1,100 *BA*

A Wedgwood black basalt bulldog, with yellow glass eyes and wearing a copper collar, modelled by E W Light, impressed mark and C, c1915, 5in (12.5cm) long.
£170-200 *CNY*

A Staffordshire figure of a spaniel, with possibly the Princess Royal, 6½in (16.5cm).
£200-250 *BHA*

A figure of a *lion passant*, Staffordshire or perhaps Yorkshire, one paw resting on a ball, the body yellow with black spots and brown mane, 6in (15cm).
£3,000-3,500 *L*

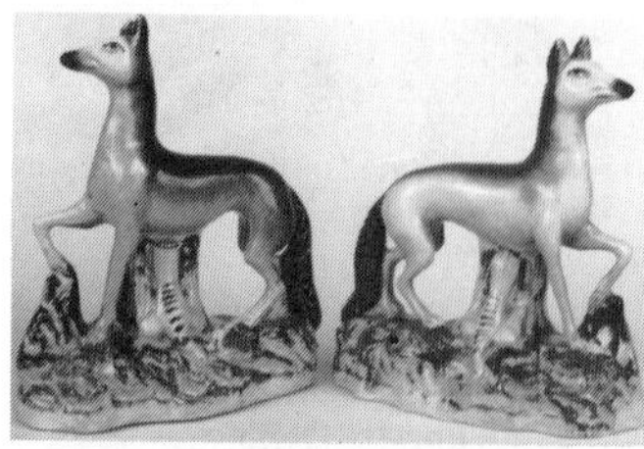

A rare pair of Staffordshire foxes, 6½in (16cm).
£400-550 *BHA*

A Wedgwood black basalt jackdaw, with black glass eyes, modelled by E W Light, impressed mark, tail restored, c1915, 7in (17.5cm) wide.
£40-60 *CNY*

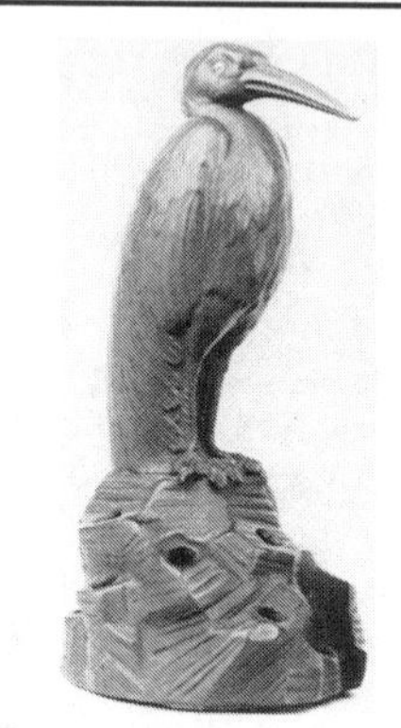

A Wedgwood black basalt egret, with yellow glass eyes, perched on pierced rockwork, modelled by E W Light, impressed mark at back, c1916, 8in (20cm).
£70-100 *CNY*

Ernest William Light was a celebrated modeller and sculptor in the Potteries who was later to become headmaster of Hanley School of Art. Wedgwood commissioned him to model this series of bird and animal figures between 1913 and 1919.

A Yorkshire ram group with attendant, typical dotted decoration in ochre, blue and black, 5in (12.5cm).
£900-1,100 *LR*

Miller's

Antiques Price Guide builds up year by year to form the most comprehensive photo-reference system available. The nine volumes already published contain over 80,000 completely different photographs

A Wedgwood black basalt cat, with later yellow glass eyes, modelled by E W Light, impressed mark and C, c1915, 4in (10cm) wide.
£170-200 *CNY*

A rare Staffordshire dismal hound, 4in (10cm).
£370-450 *BHA*

A pair of Staffordshire dogs with pheasants, 9in (23cm).
£400-450 *BHA*

Two Staffordshire Walton type models of deer with bocage, on grassy mound bases, 5½in (14cm).
£200-250 *HCH*

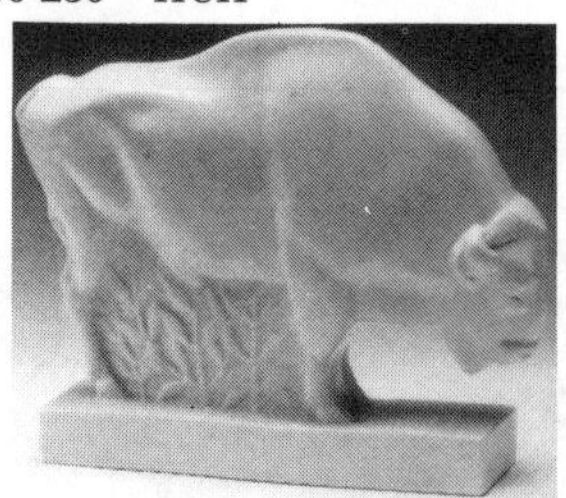

A Wedgwood white pottery model of a bison by John Skeaping, printed and impressed marks, 9in (23cm).
£150-250 *Bea*

Figures – People

A Ralph Wood group, St George and the Dragon, cream with brown trim, c1780, 11in (28cm).
£900-1,200 *DL*

A Ralph Wood figure of a gospeller, c1780, 9in (23cm).
£900-1,200 *DL*

A figure of a sailor in blue uniform and yellow striped waistcoat, on a marbled base, possibly Yorkshire, chip to hat, flag and base, c1780, 9½in (24.5cm).
£1,200-1,600 *C*

A Ralph Wood figure of a harvester in brown hat, grey waistcoat and green breeches, left hand and handle of scythe restored, impressed mark Ra. Wood Burslem, c1775, 8in (20cm).
£1,800-2,500 *C*

A Ralph Wood type figure, Venus coming out of the sea, c1790, 9in (23cm).
£350-400 *DL*

A Neale & Co figure of Apollo, impressed under base, c1785, 6in (15cm).
£400-450 *LR*

A Yorkshire figure of Liverpool Volunteer, in ochre and green, c1785, 5in (12.5cm).
£800-1,000 *LR*

A Ralph Wood figure of Sir Isaac Newton, in pale flowered clothes, on a marbled base, top of telescope lacking, impressed mark Ra. Wood Burslem 137, c1790, 12in (30.5cm).
£1,200-1,800 *C*

A rare pair of R Wood II rustic groups, c1795, 11in (28cm).
£1,800-2,200 *BA*

A Wood and Caldwell figure, c1800, 8½in (21.5cm).
£700-750 *BHA*

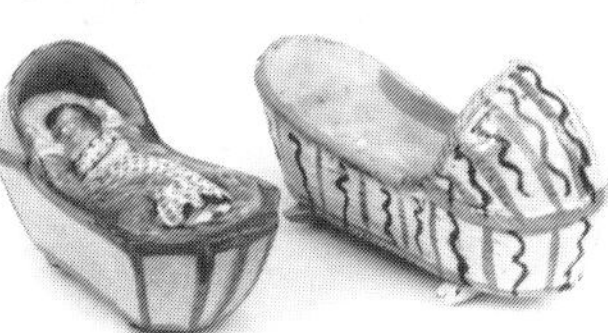

A pair of Staffordshire cradles, l. enamel, r. 'Pratt' decorated, c1800, 4½ and 5in (11 and 12.5cm).
£150-250 *BA*

An Enoch Wood group of quarrelling Cupids, from a famous bronze, c1800, 16½in (41.5cm).
£1,200-1,800 *DL*

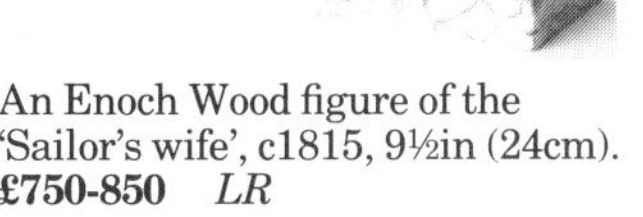

An Enoch Wood figure of the 'Sailor's wife', c1815, 9½in (24cm).
£750-850 *LR*

ENOCH WOOD OF BURSLEM

- ★ during the late 18thC and early 19thC one of the most productive factories
- ★ Enoch Wood commenced his apprenticeship in the early 1770s
- ★ went into business with his cousin Ralph Wood in 1784
- ★ a new firm Wood and Caldwell was established in 1790 changing to Enoch Wood & Sons in 1818
- ★ good figure models produced using overglaze colours
- ★ in-glaze colours used on earlier figures by Ralph Wood and Whieldon
- ★ blue-printed ware also produced, being exported to the USA in large quantities

A pair of Staffordshire musicians, after the Derby models, probably E Wood, with enamel finish, c1810, 6in (15cm).
£350-450 *LR*

A pair of figures of The Lovers and The Sailor and his Lass, with unusual blue bocage, c1815, 8½in (21.5cm).
£1,800-2,200 *DL*

A pair of Walton figures, Flight and Return from Egypt, enamel colours, marked, c1815, 6in (15cm).
£1,300-1,500 *LR*

A Staffordshire figure of a gentleman, in black top hat and tails, blue waistcoat and striped red trousers, base chipped and repaired, slight chipping to enamels, c1810, 9in (22.5cm).
£300-350 *C*

A Staffordshire group of Dandies, c1815, 7in (18cm).
£550-600 *DL*

A Staffordshire pottery group of The Dandies, in multi-coloured enamels, c1815, 8½in (21.5cm).
£500-700 *LR*

A Staffordshire tithe pig group, with a very rare figure of a clergyman, c1815, 10in (25cm).
£750-850 *DL*

A pair of enamel decorated figures of St Peter and St Paul, c1820, 10in (25cm).
£750-850 *LR*

A Staffordshire figure of Diana with dog, painted in enamel colours, c1815, 11in (28cm).
£350-450 *LR*

A Staffordshire figure, Tenderness, c1820, 6½in (16cm).
£500-550 *DL*

A Staffordshire group, Flight to Egypt, marked Walton, c1820, 7½in (19cm).
£750-800 *DL*

Three Staffordshire groups, marked Walton, c1820.
l. Reaper, 7½in (19cm).
£500-550

c. Songsters, 9in (23cm).
£700-800

r. Ewe and lamb, 6in (15cm).
£300-400 *BA*

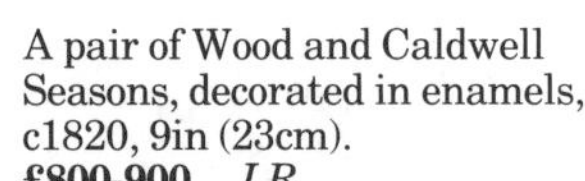

A pair of Wood and Caldwell Seasons, decorated in enamels, c1820, 9in (23cm).
£800-900 *LR*

An early Staffordshire group of Dandies, in mint condition, c1820, 8in (20cm).
£600-700 *DL*

A pair of John Dale Staffordshire figures of rural musicians, decorated in enamels, c1820, 4½in (11cm).
£750-850 *LR*

An Obadiah Sherratt figure entitled 'The Reading Maid', c1820, 11½in (29cm).
£450-550 *LR*

An Obadiah Sherratt group of Grecian and Daughter, some restoration, c1820, 10in (25cm).
£1,000-1,400 *LR*

A pair of Obadiah Sherratt figures, Elijah and the Widow, c1825, 11in (28cm).
£700-750 *DL*

A Staffordshire figure of a sheep shearer, c1855, 6in (15cm).
£100-120 *CA*

A Staffordshire figure of a shepherd, c1860, 12in (30cm).
£200-250 *BA*

A pair of Staffordshire cupids, by Ralph Wood, 7in (18cm).
£750-900 *BHA*

A set of 3 early Staffordshire pottery figures, 2 country men and one bare footed woman, all on bases with single iron red line to border, 6½in (16cm).
£200-250 *HCH*

A rare early Staffordshire figure of a girl in a chair, 3in (7.5cm).
£375-400 *BHA*

Staffordshire Figures

A Staffordshire pottery group of portrait figures, Victoria and child, and Albert, c1848, 7½in (19cm), (A,16,37) and (A,15,36).
£250-350 *DL*

STAFFORDSHIRE FIGURES c1835-95

★ can be made from either pottery or porcelain type body
★ 'Staffordshire Portrait Figures' by P D Gordon Pugh is the standard reference book and some collectors only buy examples appearing therein
★ unusual animals and theatrical figures very collectable
★ damage, wear, flaking all affect value as well as restoration
★ beware of fakes!

A pair of Staffordshire figures, Tam O'Shanter and Souter Johnny, c1840, 5in (12.5cm).
£180-200 *RBE*

Two Staffordshire groups, Before and After Marriage, c1840.
£250-280 *RBE*

A Staffordshire model of Shakespeare's house, c1850, 7½in (17cm), (H,7,22).
£180-200 *RBE*

A Staffordshire bird, c1845, 5½in (14cm).
£120-150 *RBE*

A Staffordshire quill holder, c1845.
£150-170 *RBE*

A Staffordshire figure of 'Omer Pacha', c1850, 10½in (27cm), (C,64,166).
£350-400 *DL*

A rare Staffordshire figure of James Blomfield Rush, in dark blue jacket, green waistcoat and pink trousers, named in gilt script on the oval base, minor restoration to the nose, c1850, 10in (25cm), (G,23,48).
£1,000-1,400 *CSK*

A Staffordshire hunting group spill vase, c1850.
£170-190 *RBE*

A Staffordshire figure of Admiral Napier, c1850, 9in (23cm), (C,42,101).
£200-250 *DL*

A rare Staffordshire figure of Marietta Alboni as Cinderella, in long blue dress, c1850, 9in (23cm), (E,20,43).
£550-650 *CSK*

A rare and unusual Staffordshire figure of the actor Menier in the part of Thelsitor from the play, *Porga*, with white turban, green sleeved jacket and stockings, named in French on the underside of the base and also inscribed with a part from one of the main songs, one finger restored, c1850, 10½in (26cm), (E,).
£350-450 *CSK*

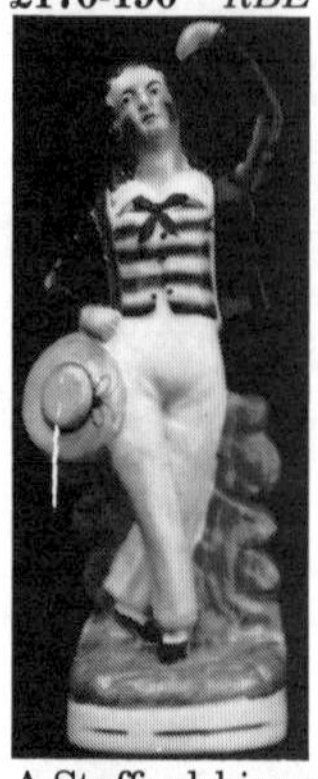

A Staffordshire sailor figure, T P Cooke as Ben Backstay, c1850, 8½in (21cm).
£60-100 *RBE*

A pair of dogs, c1850, 10in (25cm).
£350-400 *RBE*

A pair of red and white dogs, c1850, 12in (30cm).
£250-300 *RBE*

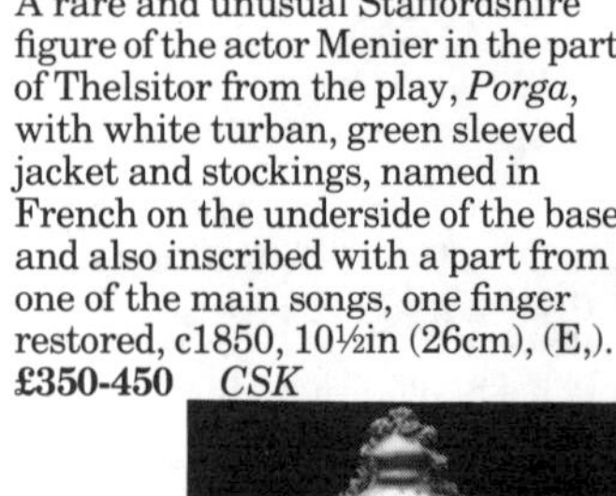

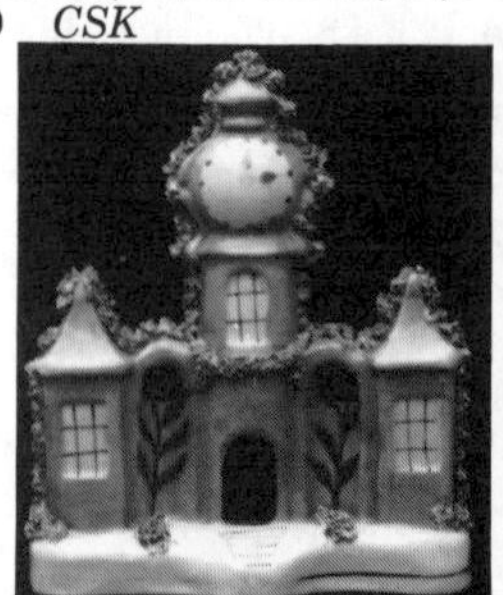

A Staffordshire castle, c1850.
£40-60 *RBE*

Make the Most of Miller's

CONDITION is absolutely vital when assessing the value of an antique. Damaged pieces on the whole appreciate much less than perfect examples. However a rare, desirable piece may command a high price even when damaged

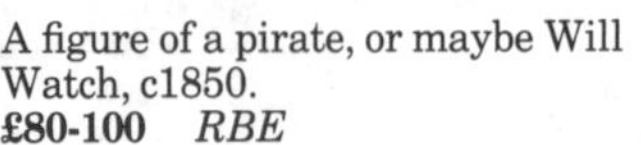

A figure of a pirate, or maybe Will Watch, c1850.
£80-100 *RBE*

A Staffordshire pastille burner, c1850, 8in (20cm).
£150-200 *RBE*

A rare Staffordshire group of Napoleon and Albert in dark blue military uniforms, named in gilt script on the rectangular base, c1854, 13½in (34cm), (C,78,227).
£300-400 *CSK*

A Staffordshire group of a lady and gentleman standing arm in arm, she in iron red and blue dress and he in dark blue and gilt military uniform, perhaps depicting Mrs Fitzwilliam in the part of Mrs Page from the *Merry Wives of Windsor*, 1855-70, 9in (23cm), (E,).
£150-250 *CSK*

A Staffordshire group of the Fortune Teller, c1850, 10in (25cm).
£120-180 *RBE*

A Staffordshire figure of a Crimean General, c1855, 9in (23cm), (C,59,155).
£400-450 *DL*

A Staffordshire figure of a sailor in dark blue jacket, named in raised gilt capitals 'Britains Glory', c1855, 11in (28cm), (C,69,186).
£40-60 *CSK*

A Staffordshire figure of a sailor, c1856, 6½in (16cm), (C,84,244).
£80-100 *RBE*

A pair of Staffordshire circus horses, c1855, 5½in (14cm).
£300-400 *RBE*

A Staffordshire figure of Benjamin Franklin with grey coat, floral waistcoat and brown breeches, holding a pink tricorn hat in his hand, c1860, 15½in (39cm), (B,21,68).
£70-100 *CSK*

A Staffordshire figure of a gentleman wearing a tam o'shanter, dark blue jacket and pink half cape, perhaps Prince Alfred, c1860, 12½in (31cm).
£100-150 *CSK*

A pair of Staffordshire figures of the Duke and Duchess of Cambridge, c1860, 14in (35cm), (C,59,157,158).
£550-600 *DL*

A Staffordshire group of Princess Alice with Prince Louis of Hesse, c1860, 14in (35cm), (A,70,218).
£175-195 *RBE*

A Staffordshire model of a hunter seated beside a dead tiger draped across the back of an elephant, c1870, 9in (23cm).
£250-300 *CSK*

A pair of Staffordshire Moody and Sankey figures, American, c1870, (D,5,9a,10a).
£300-350 *DL*

A pair of Staffordshire figures of the Prince and Princess of Wales, c1870, 12in (30cm), (A,65,200,201).
£450-550 *DL*

A Staffordshire flatback group, 'The Murder of Smith and Collier', 19thC, 13in (32cm), (G,27,54).
£200-250 *MN*

Two Staffordshire figures of Edward VII and Queen Alexandra, c1900, 13in (32cm), (A,85,242,3).
£150-180 *RBE*

A Staffordshire figure of Jumbo the elephant, painted in splashed brown glaze and named in raised capitals on the brown and green base, c1870, 11in (28cm).
£300-350 *CSK*

A Staffordshire figure of the King of Sardinia, glaze chip to base, 17in (42.5cm), (C,38,90).
£300-350 *RBE*

A model entitled 'The Wounded Soldier', 13in (32cm), (C,71,194).
£350-450 *RBE*

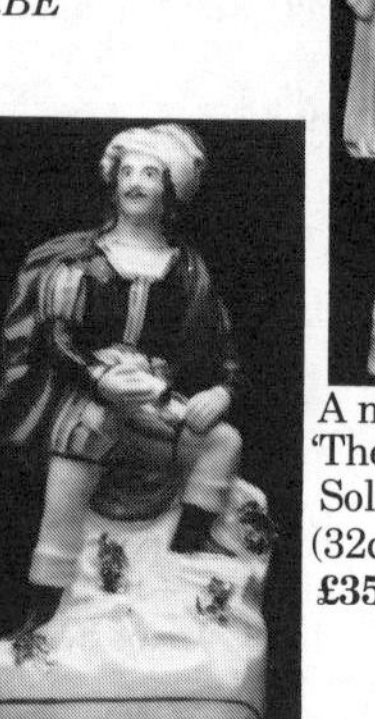

A Staffordshire model of a pirate played by Conrad, 6½in (16cm), (E,140,287a).
£80-100 *RBE*

Locate the source

The source of each illustration in Miller's can be found by checking the code letters below each caption with the list of contributors

A Staffordshire model of Palmers House, 8in (20cm), (G,18B,43).
£450-550 *RBE*

A pair of Staffordshire figures of Queen Victoria and Prince Albert, 8in (20cm), (A,27,71).
£200-250 *RBE*

A Staffordshire figure of Robert Evans, 11in (28cm), (D,24,49).
£550-650 *RBE*

A Staffordshire figure of St Winifred, 11in (28cm).
£150-200 *RBE*

Two Staffordshire apes, 3in (8cm).
£110-150 each *RBE*

A Staffordshire model of Potash Farm and Stanfield Hall, 8in (20cm), (G,20,44,46).
£550-650 each *RBE*

A colourful pair of Staffordshire pottery figures depicting the American evangelists Dwight Lyman Moody and Ira David Sankey, one damaged and one re-stuck, 14in (35.5cm), (D,5,9a,10a).
£170-250 *Bea*

A Staffordshire pottery portrait figure of Wellington, decorated in colours and gilt, hairline cracks, 13½in (34cm), (B,2,17).
£150-200 *P*

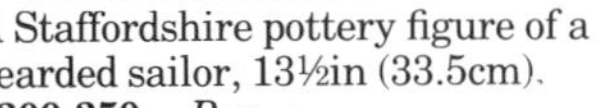

A Staffordshire pottery figure of a bearded sailor, 13½in (33.5cm).
£300-350 *Bea*

Flatware

A London delft blue and white Royalist portrait plate, painted with half-length portraits of William III and Queen Mary flanked by the initials WMR wearing coronation robes, within a turquoise line rim, slight glaze cracks and flaking to rim, c1690, 9in (22cm).
£1,500-2,000 *C*

A Staffordshire pottery group depicting the eccentric young women known as Alphington Ponies, identically dressed with yellow hats, orange check coats and green dresses, 4½in (11.5cm), (I,18,41).
£200-250 *Bea*

A London delftware moulded dish, c1710, 10in (25cm).
£800-1,200 *JHo*

An English delftware plate with a colourful design, c1730, 9in (23cm).
£600-800 *JHo*

A very rare London delftware plate depicting 2 birds cock-fighting, c1760, 8½in (21cm).
£3,000-4,000 *JHo*

A Whieldon type plate, with leaf decoration, c1765, 9in (23cm).
£800-900 *JHo*

An enamelled creamware plate, c1770, 10in (25cm).
£300-400 *JHo*

A Lambeth delftware blue and white dish, painted with Chinese stylised landscape, late 17thC, 14in (35cm).
£400-450 *DSH*

An English delftware manganese Wincanton plate, some chips, c1745, 9in (23cm).
£450-500 *JHo*

A saltglaze dish with enamel decoration, c1765, 6½in (16cm) wide.
£3,000-3,500 *JHo*

A Lambeth delft ballooning plate, with a green balloon in flight between blue trees, 2 pieces re-stuck to rim at 5-o'clock, rim chips, c1785, 9in (23cm).
£200-300 *C*

An English delftware farmyard plate, sponged in yellow, blue, red and manganese, restored, c1725.
£600-700 *LR*

A pair of London delft polychrome plates, c1750.
£270-300 *DEL*

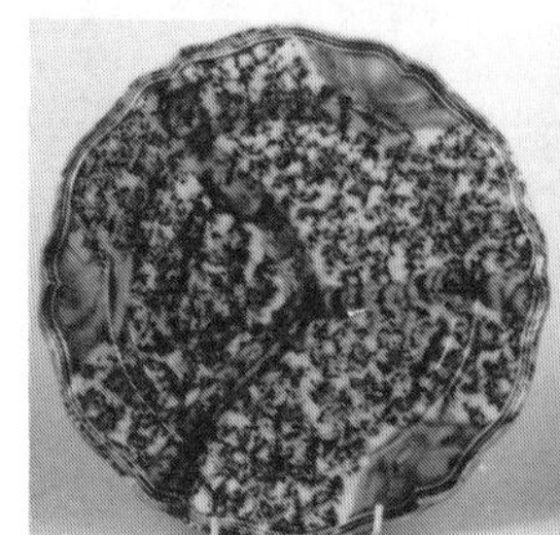

A Whieldon type plate, c1765, 10in (25cm).
£400-500 *JHo*

MAKE THE MOST OF MILLER'S

Every care has been taken to ensure the accuracy of descriptions and estimated valuations. Where an attribution is made within inverted commas (e.g. 'Chippendale') or is followed by the word 'style' (e.g. early Georgian style) it is intended to convey that, in the opinion of the publishers, the piece concerned is a later – though probably still antique – reproduction of the style so designated. Unless otherwise stated, any description which refers to 'a set', or 'a pair' includes a valuation for the entire set or the pair, even though the illustration may show only a single item

A Wedgwood creamware plate, c1775, 10in (25cm).
£350-450 *JHo*

A large Spode blue and white pottery meat dish with gravy well, printed with the Bridge of Lucano, early 19thC, 21in (52cm).
£250-300 *Bea*

An English transfer printed pottery plate by Pountney & Allies, St Vincent's Rocks, early 19thC, 10in (25cm).
£60-80 *DEL*

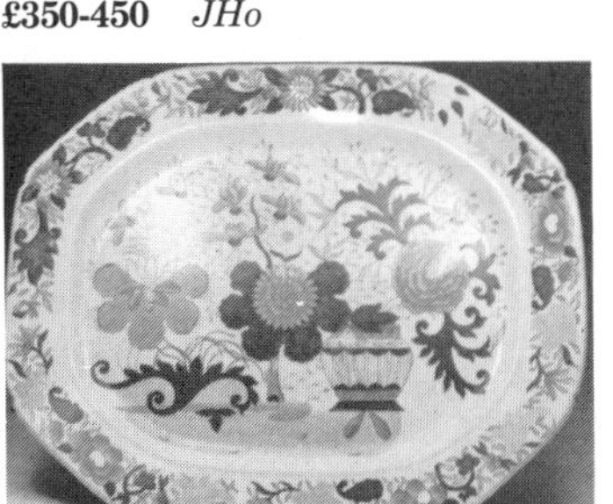

A Mason's Ironstone meat plate, decorated in blue and red, with printed and impressed marks, early 19thC, 21in (53cm).
£200-250 *MN*

A Wedgwood creamware armorial plate, c1800, 10in (25cm).
£140-170 *JUD*

A pair of creamware plates with flowers, c1805, 8in (20.5cm).
£900-1,200 *JG*

A Staffordshire meat dish, printed within border of garden flowers, the Views series, minor rim glaze chip, c1820, 21½in (54cm) wide.
£300-400 *CSK*

A Staffordshire earthenware Buffalo pattern blue printed plate, c1820, 10in (25cm).
£40-60 *TVA*

A pair of Mason's Ironstone plates, with impressed and printed marks, c1820, 8in (20cm).
£150-200 *JUD*

A Staffordshire meat dish, printed within a border of large tulips, c1820, 17in (43cm) wide.
£170-220 *CSK*

A Rogers meat draining dish, printed with a view of the Boston State House, impressed mark, c1820, 18in (46cm) wide.
£500-600 *CSK*

An Enoch Wood & Sons meat dish, with a rare print of hunting polar bears, crazed and stained, impressed mark, c1825, 16½in (42cm) wide.
£350-450 *CSK*

A Brameld Rockingham plate, c1830, 7in (18cm).
£200-250 *BHA*

A pair of Middlesbrough pottery plates, c1840, 6in (15cm).
£120-140 *THA*

A Staffordshire blue and white plate, c1820, 10in (25cm).
£50-70 *CA*

A rare Staffordshire meat dish, printed with the Durham Ox with his owner John Day, c1825, 22in (55cm) wide.
£700-1,000 *CSK*

A Brameld Rockingham plate, damaged, c1830, 7½in (19cm).
£50-150 *BHA*

A South Wales pottery dish, with damask border in shades of brown, W Chambers, c1839-54, 20in (50cm) wide.
£120-140 *THA*

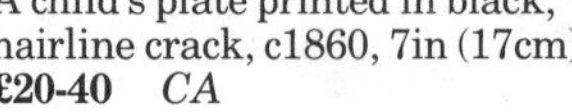

A child's plate printed in black, hairline crack, c1860, 7in (17cm).
£20-40 *CA*

A Rogers meat dish, printed with Britannia seated before the Horn of Plenty, minor glaze chip to rim, impressed mark, c1820, 21in (53cm) wide.
£150-250 *CSK*

A Mason's meat dish, printed with the Classical Landscape pattern, reverse with some crazing, c1830, 16in (40cm) wide.
£150-200 *CSK*

An English lustre saucer with the Print of Charity, c1840, 8in (20cm).
£40-70 *DEL*

A set of 20 Wedgwood plates with blue pattern taken from a painting by Claude, c1860.
£370-400 *THA*

Locate the source

The source of each illustration in Miller's can be found by checking the code letters below each caption with the list of contributors

A pair of pottery nursery plates, each printed in purple, one with the bust of King William IV, the other with Queen Adelaide, 7in (18cm).
£500-550 *Bea*

An English majolica dish, modelled with flowering strawberry vines, with separate cream jug, sugar bowl and spoon, 14½in (36cm) wide.
£400-500 *CSK*

A pottery nursery plate, the centre printed with portrait of the Princess Royal, 6in (15cm).
£100-150 *P*

A pair of pottery nursery plates, the centres printed in black with portraits and inscribed 'The Lily of England, Princess Royal' and 'The Swedish Nightingale, Jenny Lind', within moulded borders, 7in (17cm).
£120-160 *P*

A Staffordshire solid agateware saucer, 5in (13cm).
£650-750 *JHo*

A large Spode charger, decorated in blue and gilt, pattern number 3702, 20in (50cm).
£250-350 *DN*

A Castelli tazza, painted in the Grue workshop with the fall of Samson, extensively repaired, replacement foot, c1690, 11½in (29cm).
£600-1,000 *C*

A Liverpool delft dish, painted in polychrome in Chinese taste, 13½in (34.5cm).
£200-250 *L*

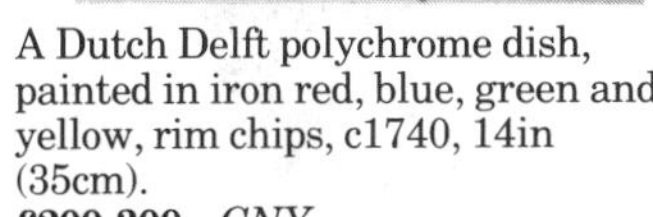

A Dutch Delft polychrome dish, painted in iron red, blue, green and yellow, rim chips, c1740, 14in (35cm).
£200-300 *CNY*

A Dutch Delft dish, painted in iron red, blue and green, chipped, early 18thC, 14in (35cm).
£250-350 *CNY*

A pair of Luneville dishes, painted in polychrome, with puce rims, slight glaze chips to rims, c1770, 13in (33cm).
£3,000-4,000 *C*

A Dutch Delft canted meat dish, brightly decorated in manganese, yellow and green, on a bright green ground, damaged, mid-18thC, 17½in (44cm).
£900-1,200 *DN*

A pair of Marseilles, Veuve Perrin, plates painted 'en camaieu vert', minute rim chips, manganese and brown VP monogram marks, c1765, 10in (25cm).
£400-600 *C*

A Low Countries blue and white majolica dish, painted with a portrait bust of a woman, the border with 3 blue lines, rim glaze chips, 17thC, 12½in (31cm).
£700-800 *C*

A Rouen plate painted in a 'famille verte' palette, rim chips, c1740, 10in (25cm).
£1,200-1,500 *C*

A slipware plate decorated in brown and green, on a yellow/cream ground, incised 1723, 11½in (29cm).
£250-350 *WW*

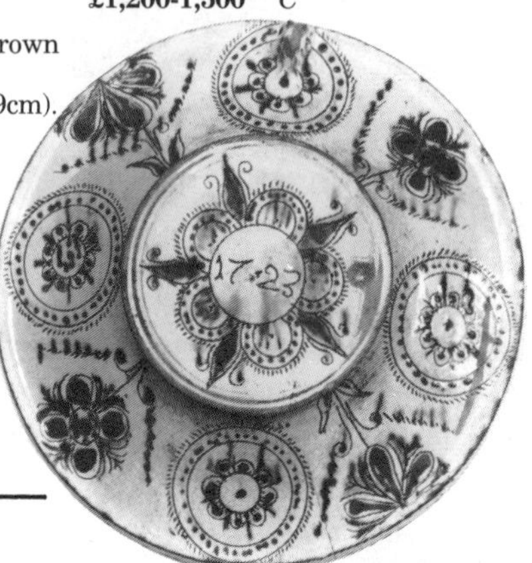

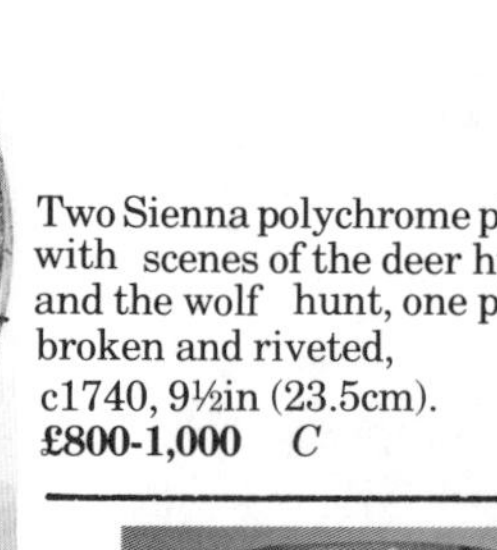

Two Sienna polychrome plates, with scenes of the deer hunt and the wolf hunt, one plate broken and riveted, c1740, 9½in (23.5cm).
£800-1,000 *C*

Jars

A London delft blue and white drug jar, rim chips and cracks at back, c1690, 7in (18cm).
£400-500 *C*

A London delft blue and white wet drug jar of 'man smoking pipe' type, named for Oxymel:Scill, cracked rim, handle, spout and foot chipped, c1680, 8in (20.5cm).
£2,000-3,000 *C*

A London delft drug jar, c1760, 3½in (8.5cm).
£500-600 *JHo*

A Wedgwood black basalt Capri-decorated pot pourri jar and cover, painted in colours and gilt, impressed and moustache marks, c1830, 13½in (35cm).
£700-800 *CNY*

A Dutch Delft drug jar and metal cover, hairline crack to neck, 11in (27cm).
£200-300 *CSK*

A Berrettino baluster blue and white wet drug jar, the contents named in Gothic script on a ribbon scroll above an oval pharmacy mark of 2 clasped hands, repaired, spout chip, Marchigian, c1580, 9½in (24cm).
£500-600 *C*

A Dutch Delft drug jar and metal cover, 10½in (26cm).
£250-350 *CSK*

A Deruta bottle for A Graminis, painted in blue, yellow, orange and copper-green, old repair to neck and body, c1530, 16in (40cm).
£5,000-6,000 *C*

A pair of Sicilian wet drug jars, with contents inscribed on yellow and green labels, the scroll handles with mask terminals and the pharmacy mark S beneath, one with repair to rim, chips, 17thC, 10in (25cm).
£1,000-1,500 *C*

Jugs

A Staffordshire saltglaze milk jug and cover, with aubergine crabstock handle and finial, on 3 mask and paw feet, cracks to rim, minor rim restoration, c1755, 6in (15.5cm).
£2,000-2,500 *C*

A Jackfield type pottery sparrow beak jug, c1760, 5in (12.5cm).
£100-120 *THA*

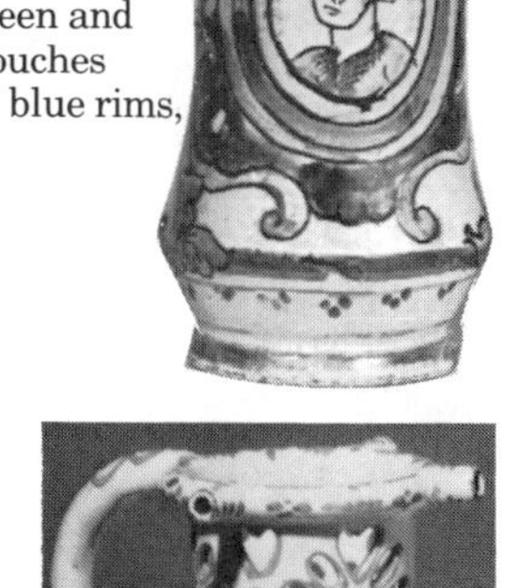

Three Sicilian waisted albarelli, painted in yellow, green and blue with scroll cartouches between blue bands, blue rims, small chips, 17thC, 9in (23cm).
£900-1,000 *C*

A creamware jug, painted in iron red and black and the inscription 'God Speed y Plough', and the inscription 'John & Mary Beckitt' beneath the handle, minute rim chips, c1770, 8in (20.5cm).
£750-850 *C*

A Leeds creamware dated baluster jug, with ear-shaped handle, painted in iron red with the inscription 'William Walker, 1777', minute rim chips and cracks, 8in (20cm).
£1,200-1,500 *C*

An English delft blue and white puzzle jug, the handle attached to the hollow rim with 3 short spouts above the cylindrical neck pierced with hearts and ovals, perhaps Liverpool, c1760, 7½in (19cm).
£1,500-2,000 *C*

Use the Index!

Because certain items might fit easily into any of a number of categories, the quickest and surest method of locating any entry is by reference to the index at the back of the book.
This has been fully cross-referenced for absolute simplicity

A pottery jug with polychrome decoration, possibly Liverpool, c1775, 2½in (6cm).
£100-120 *THA*

A pearlware jug, moulded with a female mask to the spout, inscribed 'A & T, 1779', chips to rim and body, 7in (18cm).
£200-300 *CSK*

A pearlware blue and white jug, inscribed 'Success to Trade', c1780, 7in (18cm).
£150-250 *CSK*

A Wedgwood green and white jasper cream jug, the dipped ground moulded in white relief with classical figures in medallions, impressed mark, c1800, 2½in (7cm).
£350-450 *C*

A Staffordshire lead glazed redware bear jug and cover, the loop handle applied with a monkey, removable head wearing a muzzle, his coat covered in frit chippings, some minor chipping, early 19thC, 11in (27.5cm).
£600-800 *C*

A Prattware military review jug, with underglazed colours and traces of original gilding, c1800, 6in (15cm).
£400-500 *LR*

A Prattware jug, Farewell and Return, c1790, 5½in (14cm).
£250-300 *DL*

A Prattware jug with serpent pattern handle, the body decorated with the Duke of York and the reverse with a figure holding 3 leopards, and initialled I.P., late 18thC, 7½in (19cm).
£200-300 *P[Re]*

STAFFORDSHIRE JUGS

- ★ made by many Staffordshire potteries
- ★ commenced manufacture c1825
- ★ very collectable, marked examples particularly, while value affected by damage and moulding quality
- ★ usually in 3 sizes and can be buff, pale blue, pale green, grey or white

A pearlware bear jug and cover, the black bear with mulberry muzzle and collar clutching Boney in his paws, perhaps Scottish, some damage, c1810, 11½in (28.5cm).
£400-600 *C*

A Staffordshire pearlware Fair Hebe jug, moulded as a youth and companion in bright blue and ochre clothes, impressed mark R.MA (?), c1800, 5in (12.5cm).
£600-1,000 *C*

A Wedgwood creamware jug, transfer printed in black with an allegory of the Peninsular Wars, chips to bottom rim, impressed mark, c1800.
£650-750 *C*

An Elsmore & Foster ale jug, the white ground decorated with typical transfers depicting The Great Cashmore Clown, 19thC, 14in (35.5cm).
£600-700 *WIL*

A silver lustre jug with a rural scene, c1820, 6½in (16cm).
£150-250 *DL*

A pair of Mason's Ironstone jugs printed and coloured in iron red, blue, green and gilt, with serpent handles, c1820, 8in (20.5cm).
£200-400 *CEd*

A Prattware jug with rose, thistle and shamrock design, c1829, 6½in (16cm).
£450-600 *BHA*

A puzzle jug, with coloured enamels and lustre decoration, c1835, 8in (20cm).
£350-450 *LR*

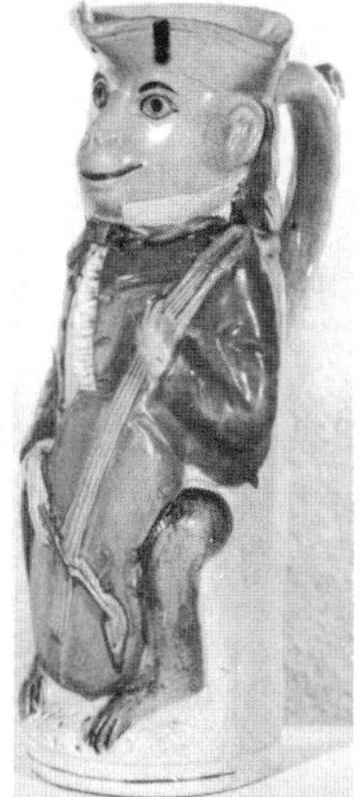

An unusual Staffordshire jug, in the form of a seated monkey in yellow tricorn hat and orange jacket playing a cello, c1860, 12in (30.5cm).
£120-180 *CSK*

A jug depicting The Oddfellows, multi-coloured transfer printed with arms and motto on reverse, lustre rim, c1835, 5½in (14cm).
£250-300 *LR*

A pearlware puzzle jug, the centre containing a white figure of a girl in Turkish dress, with ochre serpent handle with 3 spouts beneath a pierced blue neck, the body and foot boldly painted in Pratt colours with trailing flowers, some rim restorations, c1820, 11in (29cm).
£300-500 *C*

A Staffordshire majolica jug with ramshead mask and textured surface in lilac and green, c1870, 9in (23cm).
£50-100 *BRI*

A brown and saltglaze jug, with greyhound handle and moulded with stag and boar hunting scenes, made expressly for I D Bagster, c1830, 7in (18cm).
£120-150 *TVA*

On later 19thC wares, the greyhound does not look over the rim of the jug.

A Tyne lustre jug with coloured transfer prints, c1835, 7in (18cm).
£250-300 *LR*

A Minton majolica jug, moulded as a pineapple, c1869, 8½in (21cm).
£200-250 *BRI*

A majolica jug by Holdcroft, with fishes in low relief on a cobalt blue ground and bamboo handle, c1870, 8in (20cm).
£150-200 *BRI*

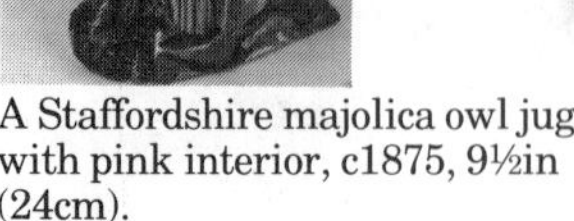

A Staffordshire majolica owl jug with pink interior, c1875, 9½in (24cm).
£150-200 *BRI*

A Carltonware pottery jug, with blue background with brown and yellow decoration, 14in (35.5cm).
£50-60 *THA*

A delft puzzle jug, perhaps Liverpool, painted in blue with a verse, 7in (18cm).
£750-800 *L*

A set of 10 Mason's Patent Ironstone graduated jugs, decorated in Chinese style in iron red and blue, with green and red lizard handles, 2 handles repaired, 3 not marked, 3 to 9½in (7.5 to 24cm).
£800-1,000 *WW*

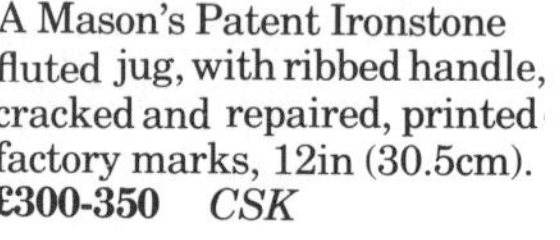

A Mason's Patent Ironstone fluted jug, with ribbed handle, cracked and repaired, printed factory marks, 12in (30.5cm).
£300-350 *CSK*

A white saltglaze cream jug, modelled in relief with pecten shells and formal flower sprays, on 3 shell and paw feet, 3in (7cm).
£400-500 *L*

A Mason's Patent Ironstone jug, decorated in the Chinese taste in bright colours, with dragon handle and lifting mask below the spout, printed mark in blue Mason's Patent Ironstone china and crown, 12½in (32cm).
£400-450 *L*

A Staffordshire jug, modelled in relief in pink and copper lustre and green with a hunting scene, *The Kill*, marked B in copper lustre, 5in (14.5cm).
£100-150 *L*

A Staffordshire jug, printed in puce with a fluted pink lustre ground, the neck with flowers in relief in colours, 5½in (13.5cm).
£100-150 *L*

A Wedgwood creamware jug, with botanical design, 4½in (11cm).
£200-250 *JUD*

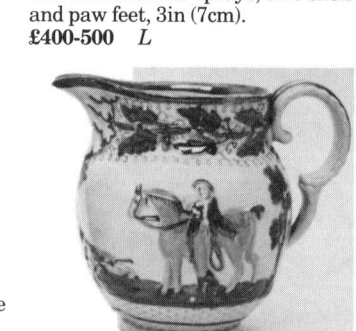

A Westerwald stoneware baluster jug, moulded all-over with relief rosettes on a blue ground, later metal cover, 12½in (32cm).
£400-500 *C*

WEDGWOOD BLUE PRINTED POTTERY

- ★ Wedgwood started by buying in printed wares from other factories, e.g. Minton
- ★ in 1805 Wedgwood produced its first blue and white printed pottery, using the Blue Bamboo pattern
- ★ from c1810 floral patterns introduced, with Chinese landscapes following on
- ★ impressed marks, normally Wedgwood plus numbers, letters or symbols appear on products

A Wedgwood milk jug of cauliflower design, 8in (20.5cm).
£700-800 *BHA*

A Savona blue and white fountain with loop over handle, mask head terminal, tapering spout and mask spout below, handle repaired, chips to feet and spout, blue crowned shield mark, c1700, 23in (59cm).
£4,000-5,000 *C*

Toby Jugs

A Staffordshire Toby jug of Ralph Wood type, in dark brown hat, pale brown coat, white waistcoat, pale yellow breeches and dark brown shoes, c1775, 10in (25cm).
£5,000-6,000 *C*

A rare and particularly well modelled example.

A Toby jug of Ralph Wood type, in mottled brown hat, pale green jacket, brown breeches and shoes, hand and base cracked, glaze chipping, c1770, 9½in (24cm).
£700-1,000 *C*

A Toby jug of Ralph Wood type, in brown hat, sponged brown jacket, yellow breeches and brown shoes, chips to jug, paint flaking, c1770, 9½in (24cm).
£1,000-1,500 *C*

A miniature Ralph Wood Toby jug, on unglazed base, c1780, 6½in (16.5cm).
£750-850 *DL*

A Staffordshire creamware Toby jug of Ralph Wood type, with translucent glazes, in dark brown hat, brown jacket, green waistcoat and yellow breeches, some restoration to hat, c1780, 10in (25cm).
£700-800 *C*

A Staffordshire Toby jug, with translucent glazed manganese hat, hair, breeches and shoes, in a mottled brown coat, chips and flaking to hat and jug, c1780, 10½in (26cm).
£500-800 *C*

A Staffordshire Toby jug of conventional type, with blue sponged edging, yellow waistcoat and blue shoes, chip to rim of hat, c1780, 10in (25cm).
£700-800 *C*

A Staffordshire 'Thin Man' Toby jug of Ralph Wood type, his tricorn hat and coat splashed in grey and with blue waistcoat, seated on a green framed chair, c1780, 9½in (23.5cm).
£5,500-6,500 *C*

Locate the source

The source of each illustration in Miller's can be found by checking the code letters below each caption with the list of contributors

A miniature Prattware Toby jug, damaged, c1790, 4in (10cm).
£160-200 *DL*

An early Staffordshire Toby jug, c1790, 9½in (24cm).
£890-900 *DL*

A Staffordshire Toby jug of conventional type, in mottled brown hat, sponged brown jacket, brown breeches and shoes, on a green base, hat rim restored, c1790, 10in (25cm).
£600-800 *C*

An Enoch Wood Toby jug, Dr Johnston, decorated in black and red enamels, c1790, 6½in (16cm).
£650-750 *LR*

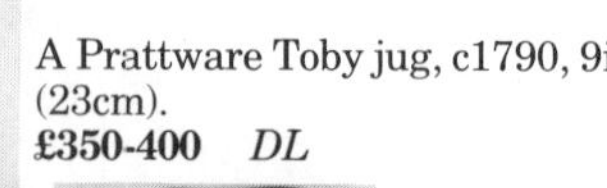

A Prattware Toby jug, c1790, 9in (23cm).
£350-400 *DL*

A Toby jug, possibly Yorkshire, Hearty Good Fellow, decorated in Pratt palette, c1790.
£1,300-1,600 *LR*

A pearlware Toby jug, possibly Yorkshire, painted in Pratt colours, in blue hat, ochre jacket, flowered waistcoat, green breeches and blue shoes, c1800, 9½in (23.5cm).
£500-700 *C*

A Staffordshire creamware Toby jug, in mottled brown coat, yellow waistcoat and splashed aubergine breeches holding a brown jug, restoration to hat, handle, jug and pipe, c1800, 10½in (25.5cm).
£400-500 *C*

An early Staffordshire sailor Toby jug, in enamel colours, c1800, 12in (30.5cm).
£900-1,200 *DL*

A Staffordshire planter Toby jug, in brown hat, ochre and yellow jacket and blue breeches, hat, hair and foot restored, c1800, 12½in (31cm).
£1,300-1,700 *C*

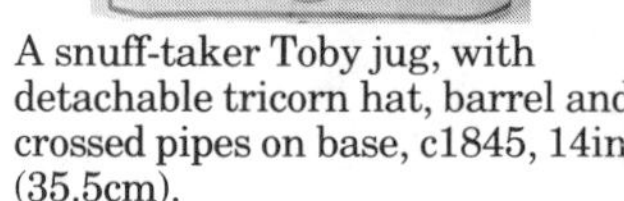

A snuff-taker Toby jug, with detachable tricorn hat, barrel and crossed pipes on base, c1845, 14in (35.5cm).
£350-400 *DL*

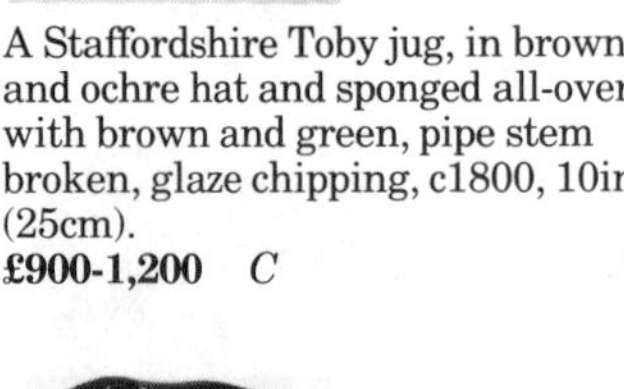

A Staffordshire Toby jug, in brown and ochre hat and sponged all-over with brown and green, pipe stem broken, glaze chipping, c1800, 10in (25cm).
£900-1,200 *C*

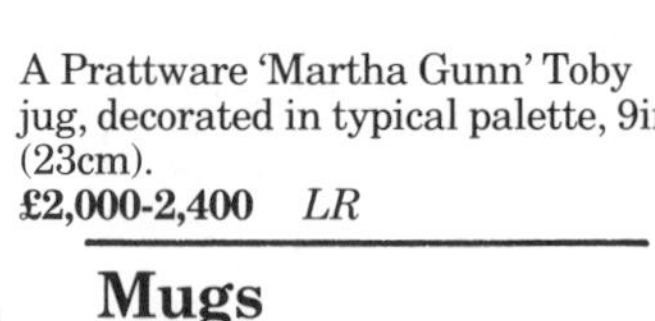

A Prattware 'Martha Gunn' Toby jug, decorated in typical palette, 9in (23cm).
£2,000-2,400 *LR*

A Yorkshire Toby jug, with impressed crown mark, 9½in (24cm).
£800-1,200 *DL*

A sailor Toby jug, with jug and beaker in his right hand, with blue decorated jacket and striped trousers, inscribed 'Dollers', 12in (30.5cm).
£1,000-1,500 *LT*

Mugs

A Bristol delft blue and white cylindrical mug, painted with an all over chequer pattern, minute glaze flaking to rim, c1730, 5in (12cm).
£800-1,200 *C*

A Liverpool tin-glazed stoneware cylindrical mug, painted in manganese with a tree with yellow-centred flowers and with grasses, crack at front, c1760, 2½in (6.5cm).
£1,500-2,500 *C*

A creamware mug, c1765, 4in (10cm).
£650-750 *JHo*

A creamware mug inscribed in black 'Rodney for ever', flanked by 4 coloured flower sprays, slight crack to rim and above handle, c1785, 5in (12.5cm).
£400-450 *C*

A transfer printed pottery mug, with unusual salmon pink ground, c1845, 4in (10cm).
£50-100 *DEL*

An early Staffordshire coloured print creamware mug with frog in it, c1815, 6in (15cm).
£450-500 *DL*

A John Aynsley black glazed cylindrical mug, inscribed with a verse proclaiming the virtue of good ale and the danger of credit, reserved within a cream painted cartouche, minor chip to rim, signed J. Aynsley, Lane End, late 18thC, 4½in (11cm).
£450-500 *Bea*

A Staffordshire majolica mug with relief decoration of a kingfisher above water lilies, c1882, 4½in (11cm).
£60-100 *BRI*

A Mettlach pewter-mounted beer mug, decorated after C Wurth, incised and painted in colours with an inscription on a ribbon cartouche on a pale blue ground, the cover with pewter mount and moulded mask thumbpiece, incised signature, impressed marks and numbers, c1910, 17in (42.5cm).
£600-700 *C*

A Sunderland lustre mug, printed on one side with the head and shoulders of 'Frederick King of Prussia' and on the other with a view of the iron bridge, slight chip under foot rim, early 19thC, 6in (15cm).
£200-300 *Bea*

Plaques

A large Prattware plaque of Bacchus and Venus in typical Pratt palette, c1800, 6in (15cm).
£500-600 *LR*

A Wedgwood black basalt plaque moulded in high relief and under-cut with Death of a Roman Warrior, cracked across and restored, impressed mark 4 times, c1800, 11 by 19½in (27 by 48.5cm).
£1,700-2,200 *C*

A Sunderland lustre plaque, with Adam Clarke, the Wesleyan minister, impressed Dixon & Co, c1815, 8 by 9in (20 by 22.5cm).
£90-120 *DL*

A Wedgwood & Bentley jasper medallion, the dipped slate blue ground moulded in high grey/blue relief with Andromache, impressed lower case mark, E. & F. and W, 3in (8cm).
£650-750 *C*

A Sunderland lustre plaque, with ships in full sail, c1825, 8½ by 9½in (21 by 24cm).
£90-120 *DL*

A Sunderland lustre plaque, 'May Peace & Plenty', impressed Dixon & Co.
£80-120 *DL*

A pearlware plaque of Queen Caroline moulded in high relief, wearing a blue dress with pink lustre collar within a pink lustre and iron red moulded frame pierced for hanging, slight corner chip, c1820, 5½ by 4½in (14 by 12cm).
£600-700 *C*

Pots

A Wedgwood and Bentley creamware large flower pot and stand, with bands of brown and black sponging, some glaze degradation and crack to stand, the stand with impressed upper case mark, c1775, the stand 10½in (27cm) diam.
£700-1,200 *C*

A Minton majolica cache pot, the sides decorated with panels of landscape and seascape by Rischgitz, 1878, 10in (25.5cm).
£600-700 *BRI*

A Wedgwood four-colour jasper dip flower pot, applied in white, impressed mark, and date code for 1882, 7in (17cm).
£650-750 *CNY*

An orange lustre plaque, with Adam Clarke, c1870, 7½ by 8½in (19 by 21cm).
£40-100 *DL*

A Wedgwood three-colour jasper jardinière, the dipped pale lilac ground with green flower heads beneath an anthemion border, the rim with green leaves, some minor chipping, impressed mark and z, 3½in (9cm), and a green ground stand similar, impressed mark, 6in (15.5cm) diam, c1790.
£700-1,200 *C*

A Wedgwood majolica cache pot, on brown basket-weave ground and rustic log feet, 1878, 7in (18cm).
£300-400 *BRI*

A Castle Hedingham, Essex, pottery two-handle pot, c1890, 8½in (21cm).
£80-90 *THA*

Make the most of Miller's

Miller's is completely different each year. Each edition contains completely NEW photographs. This is not an updated publication. We never repeat the same photograph

A Staffordshire green lustre plaque with Field Marshall Lord Roberts, c1900, 7½ by 8½in (19 by 21cm).
£40-60 *DL*

Two Wedgwood caneware flower bowls and pierced liners, the rims applied with a band of black trailing vine, on circular spreading feet, minor damage to one liner and foot, impressed marks and A, c1815, 8in and 7½in (20.5 and 18.5cm).
£350-450 *C*

A pair of Wedgwood three-colour jasper flower pots, in pale lavender and green with lion mask supports, impressed marks, c1880, 5in (13cm).
£600-700 *CNY*

Pot Lids

A small blue and white lid with scene depicting 3 uniformed men and a dog attacking a bear, within pearl dot and tear drop border.
£200-300 *P*

Great Exhibition (134).
£250-350 *RBE*

The Trysting Place (118).
£90-120 *RBE*

The Red Bull Inn (359).
£60-80 *RBE*

The Fishbarrow (58).
£50-60 *RBE*

Pretty Kettle of Fish (48).
£55-70 *RBE*

The Bear Pit (6).
£60-75 *RBE*

War (219).
£40-60 *RBE*

A reproduction commemorative pot lid, with silicone plastic coating, 3in (7.5cm) diam.
£worthless *THA*

An example of a fake.

Lady, Boy and Goat (316).
£70-90 *RBE*

Bear, Lion and Cock (19).
£90-110 *RBE*

The Begging Dog (270).
£50-70 *RBE*

POT LID PRICES

Pot Lids, during the past year, on the whole have all shown an increase in price, with a noticeable demand for the rarer lids. For lids to fetch the best prices they must have strong colours and the transfers placed to give a clear picture.

Bears at School (9) **£70-90**
The Ins, double line border (15) **£175-225**
Arctic Expedition (17) **£250-300**
Bear, Lion & Cock, white surround (19) **£75-95**
Bear, Lion & Cock, fancy border (19) **£90-110**
Pegwell Bay (Lobster Fishing) (25), fleur de lys border **£100-120**
Still Life – Game (35), print to edge **£80-90**
Still Life – Game (35), gold line **£120-140**
Landing the Fare (38) **£55-65**
Pretty Kettle Of Fish (48), 2nd ed. **£75-95**
Pretty Kettle Of Fish (48), 3rd ed. **£55-70**
Shell (52B) **£40-55**
Examining the Nets (53) **£45-60**
Sea Nymph & Trident, purple cloak (64) **£200-250**
Sea Nymph & Trident, blue cloak (64) **£150-200**
Paste Pot, The Fall Of Sebastobol (78) **£110-140**
Paste Pot, Meet Of The Foxhounds (81) **£75-100**
Paste Pot, Milking The Cow (86) **£110-130**
Paste Pot, Uncle Tom & Eva, set of three (91) **£450-650**
The Mirror (101) **£110-140**
Reflections In Mirror (104) **£350-400**
Floral Subjects, complete with pot (131/5) **£150-200**
Floral Subjects, complete with pot (131/19) **£150-170**
Jenny Lind (116), lid only **£2,000-2,200**
Dublin Exhibition (143) **£150-200**
Queen Victoria On Balcony **£250-275**
Robert Peel, with wheatear border (170) **£200-230**
Sandringham, seaweed border (181) **£100-120**
St Pauls (185) **£90-120**
Charing Cross (193) **£75-95**
The Battle Of The Nile (210) **£50-75**
The Redoubt (216) **£500-600**
The Volunteers (214) **£110-130**
Ning Po River, seaweed border (222) **£80-100**
Fair Sportswoman (250), complete **£100-120**
Six Dogs (264c) **£400-450**
The Begging Dog (270) **£50-75**
The Sea Eagle (289) **£80-100**
The Rivals (322) **£70-85**
Tam O'Shanter (347) **£90-110**
Little Red-ridinghood (358) **£60-80**
The Wild Deer (385), complete **£120-130**

Dr Johnson (175).
£40-50 *RBE*

Charing Cross (193).
£75-95 *RBE*

Pegwell Bay (Lobster Fishing) (24).
£60-80 *RBE*

Walmer Castle (45).
£40-60 *RBE*

The Rivals (322).
£70-85 *RBE*

Hamlet and His Father's Ghost (231).
£70-90 *RBE*

French Street Scene (312).
£55-70 *RBE*

Feeding the Chickens (267).
£50-70 *RBE*

Golden Horn (204).
£60-85 *RBE*

Strathfieldsay (187).
£130-160 *RBE*

Sauceboats

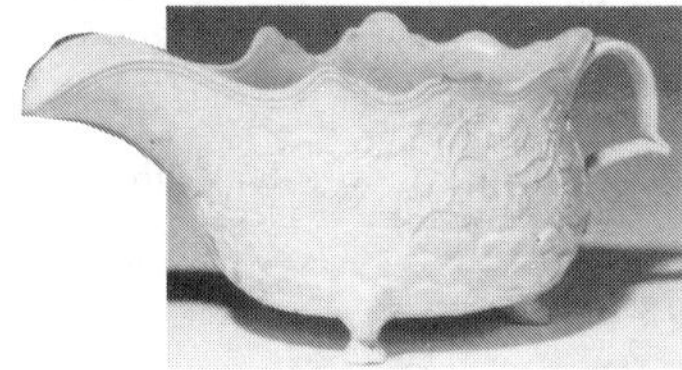
A Staffordshire saltglaze moulded sauceboat, on 3 mask and paw feet, chip and crack to rim and small crack to handle, c1755, 8in (21cm) long.
£250-350 *C*

A creamware sauceboat, c1765, 4in (10cm).
£400-450 *JHo*

A Wedgwood drabware sauceboat, c1820, 3½in (9cm).
£20-50 *CA*

Services

A Wedgwood solid pale blue and white jasper tête-à-tête, with white reliefs comprising: a cylindrical teapot, a cover and stand, a helmet shaped milk jug, 2 teacups and saucers, and a tray, some damage, impressed marks and 3, the tray with impressed mark and M, c1785, tray 13½in (35cm) wide.
£3,000-4,000 *C*

A creamware part tea service, painted with stylised iron red flower sprays beneath a band of entwined turquoise foliage and beaded rims, comprising: a teapot and cover, 5in (13cm) high, sugar bowl and cover, 4½in (11cm) high, a milk jug, 5½in (14cm) high, a cylindrical tea caddy, 3½in (8.5cm) high, and a slop bowl, 6in (15cm) diam, some damage, c1785.
£600-700 *C*

A Clews stone china part dinner service decorated in an Imari palette, comprising: a two-handled soup tureen, cover and stand, 3 vegetable dishes and covers, a square salad bowl, 2 oval two-handled sauce tureens, covers, stands and ladles, 2 sauceboats, an oblong carving dish, an oval pierced liner, 11 various serving dishes, 4 deep dishes, 2 small shell dishes, an oval hors-d'oeuvre dish with central carrying handle containing 3 shaped dishes, and 71 assorted plates, some damage, impressed Clews Stone China Warranted, enclosing a crown mark, c1830.
£6,000-7,000 *C*

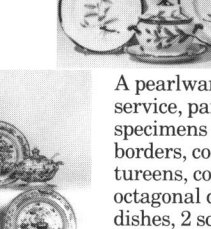

A pearlware botanical part dessert service, painted with named specimens within silver lustre borders, comprising: 2 oval sauce tureens, covers and stands, 3 octagonal dishes, 2 lozenge shaped dishes, 2 square dishes, 3 shell dishes, and 19 plates, each plant named in red script on the reverse, perhaps Swansea, some damage, c1805.
£6,500-7,500 *C*

A Staffordshire part moulded smearglaze service, comprising: 12 plates, 9in (23cm) and 6 dessert dishes, 11in (28cm) long, c1840.
£1,000-1,200 *JUD*

A Ridgway dessert service, decorated in iron red and green on a light green ground with brown edges, comprising: an oval footed centre dish, 3 leaf shape dishes and 11 plates.
£600-800 *L*

A Mason's Ironstone china part dinner service, comprising 24 pieces, with richly coloured chinoiserie decoration, late 19thC.
£800-1,200 *TW*

An ironstone china part dinner and dessert service, printed in colours, comprising 12 soup plates in 2 sizes, 14 meat plates in 2 sizes, 4 dessert dishes and 6 dessert plates, printed Royal Arms and Ironstone China mark.
£350-450 *L*

A Mason's Ironstone polychrome dinner service of Mughal pattern, comprising: tureen, cover and stand, 4 lidded entrée dishes, 2 lidded sauce tureens, 2 rectangular dishes, 3 stands, 11in (28cm), 5 stands, 9in (23cm), 73 assorted plates, 14 soup bowls, 3 large roast dishes, 6 large game dishes and a square bowl, standard printed crown mark.
£8,000-9,000 *M*

A Staffordshire pearlware dessert dish, printed in blue with classical figures in panels on a floral ground, 3 oval dessert dishes, and a pair of pierced oval baskets and stands of the same pattern, perhaps by Rogers.
£600-800 *L*

Miller's is a price Guide not a price List

The price ranges given reflect the average price a purchaser should pay for similar items. Condition, rarity of design or pattern, size, colour, provenance, restoration and many other factors must be taken into account when assessing values. When buying or selling, it must always be remembered that prices can be greatly affected by the condition of any piece. Unless otherwise stated, all goods shown in Miller's are of good merchantable quality, and the valuations given reflect this fact. Pieces offered for sale in exceptionally fine condition or in poor condition may reasonably be expected to be priced considerably higher or lower respectively than the estimates given herein

Tankards

A Staffordshire saltglaze stoneware tankard, with impressed 'AR' stamp, early 18thC, 5in (12.5cm).
£850-950 *JHo*

An agateware tankard, with grooved loop handle and spreading foot with striated brown and cream clays, slight chip to handle, c1745, 3in (8cm).
£800-1,200 *C*

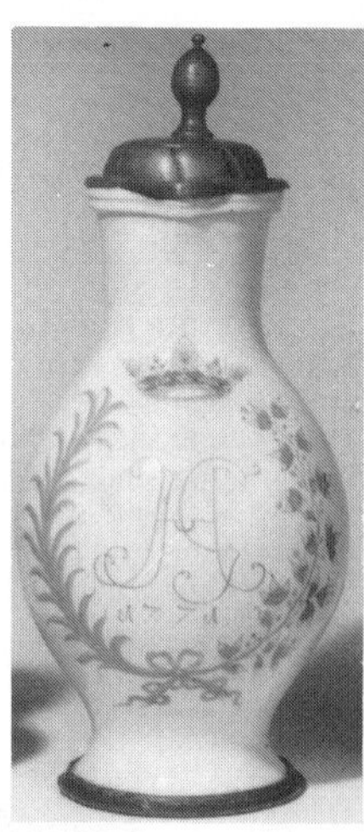

A Bayreuth, Pfeiffer, tankard, with contemporary hinged pewter cover and foot rim painted in colours, the crowned JGH monogram dated 1771, minor chip to handle and rim, puce O.B.P. marks of Pfeiffer and Oswald, 14in (35cm).
£1,500-2,000 *C*

A German faience cylindrical tankard painted in colours, with pewter mount and cover with ball thumb-piece, the cover engraved No. 10 and initials J.C.K., body cracks, dated 1759, 8½in (21.5cm).
£500-600 *CSK*

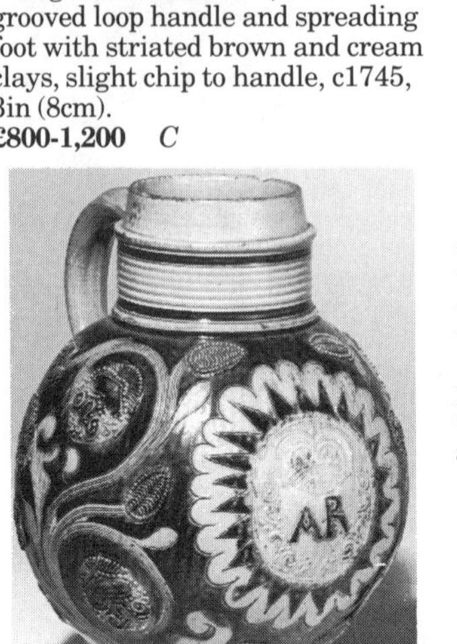

A Westerwald oviform tankard, painted in blue and manganese on grey body, crowned AR within roundel, reeded neck and foot, chips to neck, early 18thC, 9½in (24cm).
£300-400 *C*

A London delftware tankard with glass base, late 18thC, 5in (12.5cm).
£1,800-2,200 *JHo*

Tea Caddies

A creamware tea caddy of Wedgwood/Whieldon type, enriched in green and yellow on a moulded cell pattern ground, some minor restoration, c1760, 5½in (14cm) wide.
£1,500-2,000 *C*

A Wedgwood Whieldon type tea caddy, c1765, 5½in (14cm).
£450-550 *JHo*

An English delftware blue and white tea caddy, 4½in (11cm).
£850-950 *Jho*

Tea & Coffee Pots

A black glazed pottery teapot, 18thC.
£100-150 *P[Re]*

A saltglaze teapot, decorated in polychrome, c1745, 4½in (11cm).
£750-950 *LR*

A Staffordshire glazed redware moulded teapot and cover, glaze chip to rim above spout, c1745, 4in (10.5cm).
£2,500-3,500 *C*

A Staffordshire saltglaze teapot and cover, painted and gilt with trailing flowering branches and roses, spout restored, crack to base, c1750, 4½in (12cm) high.
£800-900 *C*

A Whieldon type teapot and cover, moulded with flowering plants covered in a brown, manganese, yellow and blue glaze, repair to tip of spout and chip to cover, c1750, 7½in (18cm) wide.
£250-350 *CNY*

A redware teapot, possibly Wedgwood, c1750, 7in (18cm).
£400-500 *BHA*

A Whieldon type teapot and cover, with green spout and scroll handle, the spout mounted with a silver tip, the cover with chain attachment, cover chipped, the spout slightly damaged beneath the mount, 4½in (11cm), with a similar dish, repaired and rim restorations, c1760, 6½in (16cm).
£800-1,200 *C*

A creamware coffee pot, with applied sprigging, c1765, 7½in (19cm).
£850-950 *JHo*

A creamware teapot, c1765, 6in (15cm).
£650-750 *JHo*

A Staffordshire saltglaze pecten shell moulded teapot and a cover, the spout moulded with a skeletal man, minute rim chips, c1755, 5in (13cm).
£1,000-1,500 *C*

A Whieldon teapot in blue, white and yellow, c1770, 3in (7.5cm).
£550-650 *DL*

A Staffordshire saltglaze teapot and cover, painted with panels of pink flowers on a dark green ground with black geometric designs, c1760, 6in (15cm) wide.
£700-800 *CSK*

A Staffordshire saltglaze teapot, c1765, 4½in (11cm).
£1,200-1,700 *JHo*

A Wedgwood creamware teapot and cover, with foliage moulded spout and handle painted in the atelier of David Rhodes, in purple and grey, minute chips to spout and staining to body, c1770, 5½in (13.5cm).
£2,500-3,500 *C*

Price

Prices vary from auction to auction – from dealer to dealer. The price paid in a dealer's shop will depend on:

1) what he paid for the item
2) what he thinks he can get for it
3) the extent of his knowledge
4) awareness of market trends

It is a mistake to think that you will automatically pay more in a specialist dealer's shop. He is more likely to know the 'right' price for a piece. A general dealer may undercharge but he could also overcharge

A Whieldon teapot, in typical mottled brown glaze, c1770, 5in (12.5cm).
£600-1,000 *DL*

A Wedgwood pale lilac and white jasper teapot and cover, the dipped ground moulded in white relief, chips to spout, impressed mark, c1790, 4in (10.5cm).
£600-800 *C*

A Staffordshire majolica teapot, c1878, 7½in (19cm).
£150-250 *BRI*

A Wedgwood pottery teapot, with widow figure on lid, burnt orange background, restored, 7in (18cm).
£100-150 *BHA*

A Holdcroft majolica teapot, modelled as a bird on its nest, on a separate stand of rustic logs, c1867, 7in (18cm).
£200-300 *BRI*

A Wedgwood creamware coffee pot and cover, transfer printed in iron red, minor chips to spout and inside cover, c1770, 10in (25cm).
£800-1,000 *C*

A creamware coffee pot, dated 1778, 9½in (24cm).
£750-850 *JHo*

A Wedgwood green and white jasper teapot and cover, slight rim chip, some staining, c1800, 3½in (9.5cm).
£350-450 *C*

A creamware teapot, William Greatbach, c1770, 6in (15cm).
£1,200-1,500 *JHo*

A Wedgwood creamware teapot and cover, transfer printed in black on both sides, chip to cover and spout, impressed lower case mark, c1780, 5½in (13.5cm).
£700-1,200 *C*

A Wedgwood blue and white jasper teapot and cover, in white relief with Domestic Employment, slight rim chip to cover, impressed mark and o, c1790, 4in (10.5cm).
£500-700 *C*

Tiles

A delft tile picture of 6 tiles, painted in colours, 18thC, 16 by 11in (40 by 27.5cm).
£350-450 *L*

A delft tile picture of 6 tiles, painted in manganese with touches of yellow, the ground in green, yellow and manganese, 18thC, 16 by 10½in (40 by 26.5cm).
£400-500 *L*

A delft tile picture consisting of 15 tiles, finely painted in colours, c1720, 26 by 16in (66 by 40cm).
£2,000-3,000 *L*

A London delftware blue and white tile, c1730, 5in (12.5cm) square.
£40-60 *JHo*

A Liverpool delftware religious tile, c1750, 5in (12.5cm) square. **£40-60** *JHo*

A set of 2 tiles by Craven Dunnill of Brossley, Shropshire, c1895, 6in (15cm) square.
£20-25 *THA*

A Liverpool blue and white tile, c1760, 5in (12.5cm) square.
£30-50 *JHo*

A Liverpool blue and white tile, c1760, 5in (12.5cm) square.
£30-60 *JHo*

A Liverpool blue and white tile, c1760, 5in (12.5cm) square.
£20-40 *JHo*

A Liverpool Sadler black printed tile depicting a dentist at work, c1765, 5in (12.5cm) square.
£100-140 *JHo*

A Lambeth blue and white tile, c1780, 5in (12.5cm) square.
£40-60 *JHo*

A very rare Prattware coloured tile, c1790, 5½in (13.5cm) square.
£320-370 *JHo*

A very rare Prattware coloured tile, c1790, 5in (12.5cm) square.
£300-340 *JHo*

Two Dutch Delft manganese tile pictures, depicting a cat and a dog, both with cracks and restoration, late 18thC, 15 by 10in (38 by 25cm), in black painted wood frames.
£350-450 *C*

A Victorian tile, 'Summer', depicting stag hunting, c1870, 6in (15cm) square.
£35-40 *TVA*

A Maws relief moulded tile with children, c1860, 6 by 6in (15 by 15cm).
£40-45 *TVA*

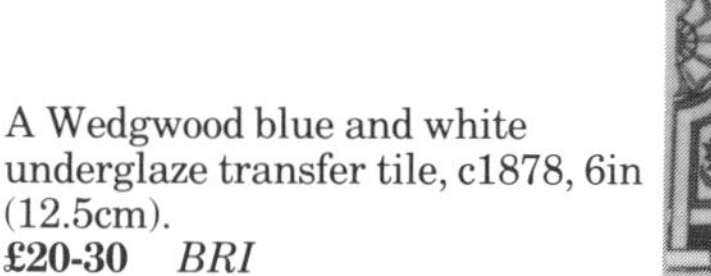

A Wedgwood blue and white underglaze transfer tile, c1878, 6in (12.5cm).
£20-30 *BRI*

A Minton blue and white tile designed by William Wise, 1879, 6in (15cm) square.
£40-60 *BRI*

A Minton tile, designed by William Wise, printed blue on white, 1879, 6in (15cm) square.
£30-50 *BRI*

A Minton tile, with underglaze printed design of poppy seed heads in ochre colours on pale grey ground, c1885, 6in (15cm) square.
£30-50 *BRI*

A solid clay tile, with painted design in 'Persian' style in shades of brilliant blue and green, with black and brown, impressed mark: William de Morgan, Merton Abbey, c1885, 6in (15cm).
£80-100 *BRI*

A Victorian pressed-dust tile, with relief design of flowers in yellow on green ground, c1890, 6in (15cm) square.
£10-20 *BRI*

A set of 5 English delft tiles, probably Liverpool, each painted in manganese enamel with Christ on the cross, some glaze chipping, 4 reduced in width, 5in (12.5cm).
£200-250 *Bea*

A pair of matching tiles depicting the martyrdom of Stephen, slight glaze chipping, one reduced in width.
£30-40 *Bea*

A Continental stove tile with blue decoration, 17thC, 7 by 8in (18 by 20cm).
£200-250 *JHo*

Tureens

A Wedgwood creamware sauce tureen, cover and pierced stand, painted in the manner of James Bakewell in purple monochrome, finial restored, c1770, the stand 10½in (26.5cm) wide.
£800-1,200 *C*

A pair of ironstone serving dishes with blue transfer printed decoration, with lions head finials, 19thC, 16in (40cm) wide.
£120-150 *P[CW]*

A Wedgwood majolica game dish with liner, marked, c1860, 6in (15cm).
£550-650 *DL*

A Derbyshire creamware tureen on stand, c1770, 7½in (18.5cm).
£1,000-1,500 *JHo*

A Wedgwood majolica sardine box, moulded as a roped crate floating on waves surrounded by rocks and seaweed, 1873, 8½in (21.5cm) wide.
£250-350 *BRI*

An English creamware vegetable dish and cover, painted in brown on both sides of the cover and base with an entwined monogram above the inscription 'Worlingworth Hall 1800' on a ribbon within brown line rims, c1800, 13in (33cm) wide.
£350-450 *C*

A George Jones majolica sardine box, with basket-weave base in blue and green, 1865, 7 by 8in (17.5 by 20cm).
£250-300 *BRI*

A Wedgwood pie dish of fine grained vitrified stoneware, c1790.
£250-350 *SBA*

These dishes were made from 1790 as substitutes for the pastry cases. Great pies of standing crust filled with meat or game appeared in every well-to-do household until banished by the Flour Tax levied during the Napoleonic Wars.

A Staffordshire majolica sardine box, with high relief fish handle and plant decoration, on brown ground, c1875, 7in (18cm) wide.
£150-250 *BRI*

A Wedgwood earthenware tureen by Eric Ravilious, with vignettes of train, motor car and snow scene, part of Travel series, 1936, 9½in (23.5cm) diam.
£100-150 *BRI*

A type of ware becoming increasingly interesting to collectors.

A Stilton cheese dish and cover in the style of Wedgwood, c1900, 12in (30cm).
£100-150 *LRG*

A Brameld Rockingham miniature pie dish, with green trim, 3½in (8.5cm) wide.
£200-250 *BHA*

A George Jones majolica game dish, cover and liner, the exterior moulded and painted against a light blue ground, liner and cover cracked, impressed marks, c1880, 13½in (34cm) long.
£750-900 *Bea*

Vases

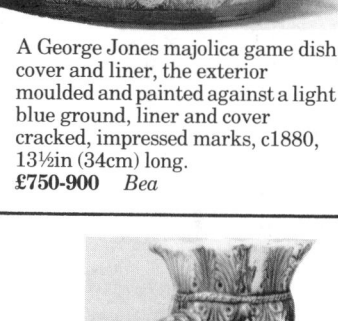

A Wedgwood and Bentley solid agate vase, on black basalt base, some restoration to handles and top rim, impressed lower case mark, c1775, 10in (25cm).
£2,000-3,000 *C*

A Staffordshire spill vase of Ralph Wood type, modelled as a youth in black hat, green jacket, flowered waistcoat and yellow breeches, some minor chipping, c1780, 9in (23cm).
£400-600 *C*

Did you know
MILLER'S Antiques Price Guide builds up year by year to form the most comprehensive photo-reference system available

A Staffordshire triple spill vase of Ralph Wood type, crook and sheep's ears restored, c1780, 11in (27cm).
£500-600 *C*

A Staffordshire creamware spill vase of Ralph Wood type, modelled as a gallant in translucent green glazed jacket and yellow breeches, on a green and brown rockwork base, slight chip to vase, c1780, 8in (20cm).
£400-500 *C*

A pair of Wedgwood blue and white jasper altar vases, the solid blue jasper grounds moulded in white relief, one vase with handle damaged and rim chip, the other with one handle lacking, impressed mark, c1785, 5½in (13.5cm).
£650-750 *C*

A Wedgwood blue jasper dip replica of the Portland vase, decorated in white, 19thC, 10½in (26cm).
£700-800 *Bea*

A Wedgwood black basalt encaustic-decorated vase, painted in grey and sepia, between bands of anthemion and iron red key pattern, repair to handles, rim and foot, impressed mark, c1800, 12in (30cm).
£600-1,000 *C*

An Obadiah Sherratt spill vase group with a boy and a girl in Turkish costume, the vase painted in splashed black, green and purple glazes, crack to vase, c1820, 7in (18cm).
£2,000-3,000 *CSK*

A Staffordshire spill vase in the form of a bull baiting group, c1820, 10½in (26cm).
£1,000-1,500 *DL*

A Wedgwood black basalt encaustic-decorated pot pourri vase, lid and pierced cover, painted in red and highlighted in white, minute chip to rim and lid, impressed and moustache and comma marks, c1820, 13½in (34cm) wide.
£1,000-1,500 *C*

A pair of Staffordshire spill vases, c1845, 5in (12.5cm).
£250-350 *DL*

A Staffordshire spill vase musician group, the spirally moulded striped pink and white flared vase with salmon pink interior, on a shaped green mound base, some restoration to vase, base and extremities, c1830, 9in (22.5cm).
£1,500-2,000 *C*

An unusual Staffordshire spill vase modelled as a ram with applied fur, standing before a tree outlined in pink and green, minor damage to horns, c1845, 4½in (11cm).
£100-150 *CSK*

A Wedgwood three-colour jasper vase, the dipped blue ground with a lilac medallion of a sacrifice subject, the neck with 7 lilac portrait medallions and raised prunus blossom in white relief, slight chips to relief, impressed mark, c1880, 6in (15cm).
£450-550 *CNY*

A pair of Staffordshire spill vases in the form of hounds with hares, c1860, 7in (17.5cm).
£300-400 *DL*

A Staffordshire copper lustre vase with Chinese figures, 6½in (16cm).
£100-200 *DL*

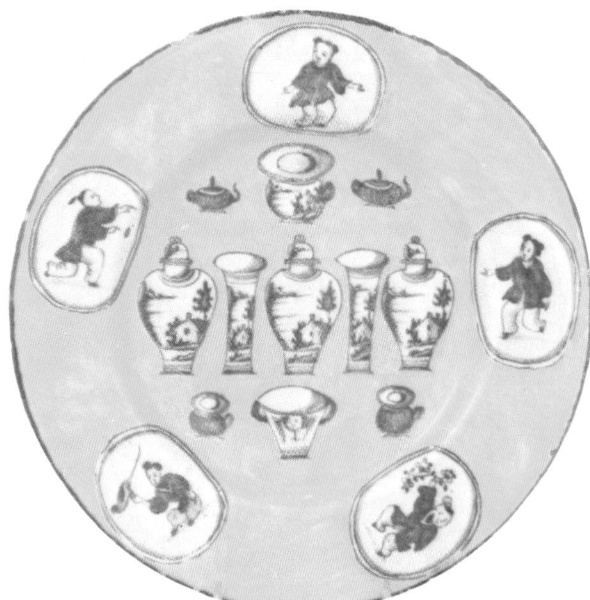

An English delft plate, the ground reserved on the rim with 5 roundels, each with Chinese figures, and centrally decorated with delft vases, 9in (23cm). **£6,000-8,000** *DN*

This is probably a retailer's sample plate, and similar Dutch examples are recorded.

A Bristol delftware charger, painted with a chinoiserie figure, with tin-glazed back, c1715, 13in (33cm). **£3,500-4,000** *JHo*

l. A Staffordshire slipware press moulded dish, by 'I.C', some areas with glaze lacking, c1680, 14in (35cm). **£6,000-8,000**

r. A Staffordshire slipware press moulded dish, by John Simpson, damage and repairs, c1680, 13½in (34cm). **£5,000-7,000** *C*

A saltglaze stoneware coffee pot decorated with enamels, possibly Staffordshire, c1755, 8in (20.5cm). **£8,000-10,000** *JHo*

A documentary Wrotham slipware tyg, by Nicholas Hubble, damage, 1656, 6½in (16.5cm). **£10,000-12,000** *C*

A Staffordshire creamware 'pebble dash' teapot and cover of Whieldon type, minor restoration, c1760, 5in (13cm). **£12,000-14,000** *C*

l. A blue and white delft dish, chips, mid-18thC. c. & r. Polychromed delft dishes, 13in (33cm). **£400-600 each** *Bea*

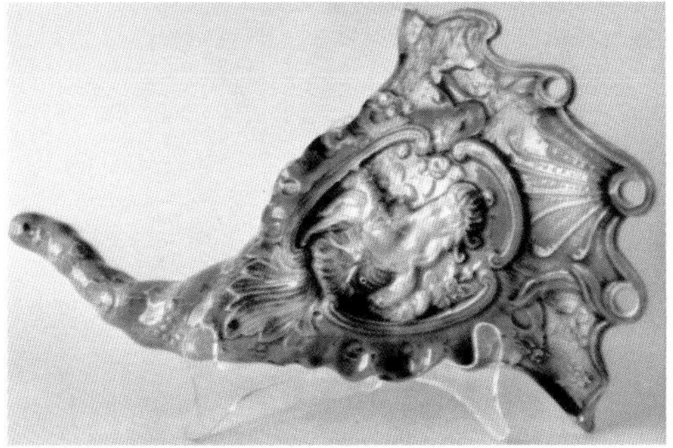

A Whieldon cornucopia wall pocket, depicting flora, translucent glazes, c1760, 11in (28cm).
£1,000-1,200 *LR*

A Staffordshire Whieldon school tea caddy and mask wall pocket, c1765, mask 10in (25.5cm) long, l. **£3,500-4,000** r. **£2,500-3,000** *JHo*

A pair of decorative grazing cows, on typical Obadiah Sherratt rainbow bases, c1820, 7in (18cm). **£1,000-1,200** *LR*

A Staffordshire saltglaze bear jug and cover, all covered in chippings, minor repairs and cracks, c1740, 9½in (24cm).
£7,000-9,000 *C*

A rare Obadiah Sherratt rural musical group including 12 sheep and a dog, enamel decorated, 9in (23cm) wide.
£2,800-3,500 *LR*

A Staffordshire saltglaze stoneware bear baiting jug and cover, slight damage, restored, 10in (25.5cm).
£5,500-7,500 *Bea*

A Toby jug with long face, in translucent coloured glazes, c1770, 10½in (26cm).
£2,000-2,500 *LR*

A Bristol delft polychrome dish, probably Limekiln Lane, minute rim chips, c1740.
£3,000-4,000 *C*

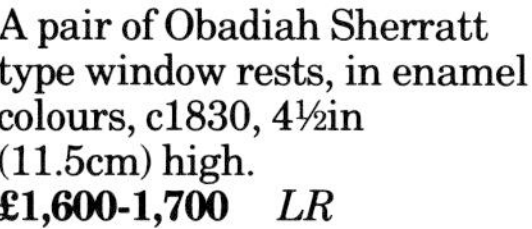

A pair of Obadiah Sherratt type window rests, in enamel colours, c1830, 4½in (11.5cm) high.
£1,600-1,700 *LR*

A massive Wedgwood black basalt encaustic decorated volute krater, minute chip to one handle, impressed and comma marks, c1800, 24in (61cm). **£12,000-14,000** *CNY*

An Urbino Istoriato dish, with the death of Achilles, painted by Nicola Pellipario, broken in many pieces and re-stuck, c1535, 10in (25.5cm). **£9,500-11,500** *C*

A Wedgwood black and white Jasper copy of The Portland vase by John Northwood, impressed and incised marks, c1878, 10in (25.5cm). **£16,000-18,000** *CNY*

An assembled Creil creamware part dinner service, comprising 92 pieces, each decorated with a black transfer reserve, mid-19thC. **£4,000-5,000** *CNY*

A Deruta dish, with a portrait medallion of a young woman in renaissance dress and cap, small chips to rim, c1500, 13in (33.5cm). **£12,000-14,000** *C*

An Italian Istoriato plate, painted with the Judgement of Paris, inscribed on the reverse, probably Urbino, c1544, 10½in (27cm). **£12,000-14,000** *C*

A Minton majolica stick stand, after a model by J. Henk, damage, marked, c1885. **£2,500-3,000** *Bea*

An Urbino Istoriato plate, painted with the Temptation of Adam, damage, c1560, 9in (23cm). **£4,000-6,000** *C*

A pair of Venetian vasi a palli, late 16thC, 13in (33cm). **£14,000-16,000** *C*

A Deruta lustre dish, with Hercules lifting the giant Antaeus, cracked, c1520, 16in (40.5cm). **£30,000-34,000** *C*

A Böttger teapot and cover, painted in 'Schwarzlot', enriched in gilding by Ignaz Preissler, in the Ming style, the handle with 'Laub-und-Bandelwerk', the shoulders and cover moulded with Chinese archaistic motifs, c1720, 6in (15cm). **£40,000-45,000** *C*

l. A German faience tankard, painted by a Nuremburg Hausmaler, with pewter cover, damage, the faience c1740, 10in (25.5cm). **£12,000-14,000**
c. A Crailsheinm faience tankard, cracked, c1750, almost contemporary pewter cover. **£1,100-1,300**
r. A German faience tankard, cracked, c1740, probably Erfurt. **£1,200-1,400** *C*

A Berlin two-handled campana vase in the neo-classical taste, blue sceptre and dash mark and impressed 4 to inside of foot, c1805, 17½in (45cm). **£10,000-14,000** *C*

A Böttger stoneware tankard and cover, with contemporary 18thC silver acorn thumbpiece, incised 'mock-seal' mark to the base of the handle, chips to footrim, c1715, 8½in (21.5cm). **£21,000-23,000** *C*

Two Sicilian vases, small chips to feet and rims, probably Sciacca, c1650, 9½in (24cm). **£3,000-4,000** *C*

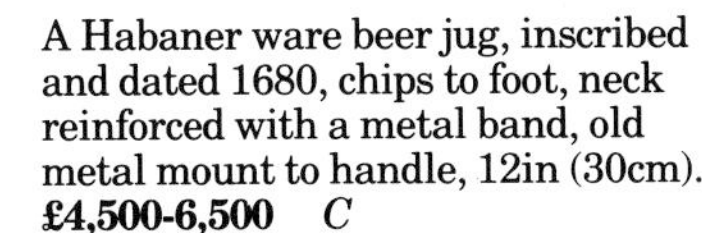

A Habaner ware beer jug, inscribed and dated 1680, chips to foot, neck reinforced with a metal band, old metal mount to handle, 12in (30cm). **£4,500-6,500** *C*

An unrecorded Capodimonte, Carlo III, group of 3 figures, modelled by Guiseppe Gricci, probably representing a doctor and youthful assistant attending to a patient, the doctor's left arm missing, chipped, c1750, 6in (15cm).
£20,000-25,000 *C*

A Champion's Bristol plate, with flat rim, 'X' mark in blue and '22' mark in red, 7in (18cm) diam. **£350-400** *LBP*

A Champion's Bristol sauceboat, with shaped iron red enamelled rim and lea capped scroll handle, the body enamelled, blue enamelled cross mark and numeral '11', 6½in (16.5cm).
£450-550 *LBP*

A Champion's Bristol ovoid tea jar, with gilt line and dentil neck borders and foot, unmarked, 5½in (14cm).
£300-350 *LBP*

A Bristol rustic figure, allegorical of Winter, from a group of The Seasons, depicted as a boy skater, impressed mark 'To', 11in (28cm). **£1,000-1,200** *LBP*

A Champion's Bristol tankard with groove moulded plain loop handle and enamelled rim, decorated with floral sprays, blue enamelled cross mark and numeral '17' to base 3in (7.5cm). **£450-550** *LBP*

A Champion's Bristol oval dessert dish, the sides moulded with 4 broad 'pleats', blue enamelled cross mark and numeral '1', 11½in (28cm) wide.
£800-1,000 *LBP*

A Champion's Bristol shallow dish, with gilt dentil rim, enamelled with floral festoons pendant from a gilt line, and centred with scattered sprigs, enamelled blue cross and numeral '5' mark, 8in (20cm). **£500-600** *LBP*

A Champion's Bristol double lipped cream jug, with entwined loop handle, unmarked, 4in (10cm).
£800-900 *LBP*

A Champion's Bristol baluster shaped jug, blue enamelled cross mark and numeral '1', 8in (20.5cm).
£450-500 *LBP*

A Champion's Bristol butter boat, Cookworthy mould, with relief moulded flowers, fruit and leaves, unmarked, 4in (10cm) long. **£350-450** *LBP*

A pair of Champion's Bristol plates, decorated in the Double Ribband pattern, one with blue enamelled cross mark, 9in (23cm).
£400-500 *LBP*

A Champion's Bristol coffee pot and domed cover, underglaze blue crossed swords and cross mark, 7½in (18cm).
£400-500 *LBP*

A Champion's Bristol dessert dish, in the Double Ribband pattern, blue enamelled cross and gilded numeral '6' mark, 7in (18cm) square.
£400-500 *LBP*

A Champion's Bristol écuelle, stand and cover, with gilded and moulded husk decoration, and gilt dentil rims, gilded cross mark and numeral '3', the stand 6½in (16.5cm) diam. **£300-350** *LBP*

A Champion's Bristol dessert dish, with fluted raised ogee sides and petal shaped gilt dentil rim, enamelled blue cross mark and numeral '5', 11in (28cm) wide. **£700-800** *LBP*

A Derby, Robt. Bloor & Co., part dessert service, comprising 43 pieces, crown, crossed batons and D marks in red, damage, c1815. **£5,000-7,000** *C*

Two Frankenthal groups by J. F. Luck, firing cracks, chips and restoration, crowned CT marks, c1765, 6½in (17cm).
top: **£6,000-7,000**
bottom: **£8,000-9,000** *C*

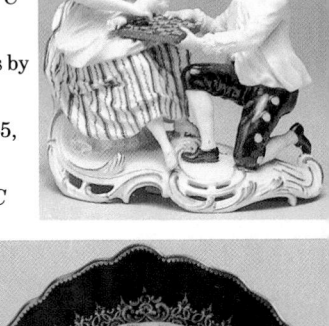

A Höchst group by J. P. Melchior, underglaze blue wheel mark, c1770, 9in (23cm). **£5,000-6,000** *C*

A Derby dish, painted in the manner of Jefferyes Hamet O'Neale, firing crack, Derby mark in puce, c1785, 9½in (24cm).
£2,000-2,500 *DDM*

A Chantilly bordalou, decorated in Kakiemon enamels, with twig handle, 18thC.
£4,500-5,000 *WW*

A Caughley kidney-shaped dish, painted in underglaze blue. **£220-250** *OSA*

A pair of Derby campana vases, painted with figures among ruins in wooded landscapes, 'On The River Dove, Derbyshire', and 'A View of Scotland', iron red crown, crossed batons and D marks, c1815, 13in (33cm). **£7,000-9,000** *CNY*

A pair of Fürstenberg white portrait busts, by J. C. Rombrich, probably of Herr Schrader von Schliestedt and his wife, parts of his cuirass and her lace coiffe missing, chip to her nose, c1758, 6in (15cm). **£6,500-7,500** *C*

A Meissen group of Mezzetin and Columbine, modelled by J. J. Kändler, her head re-stuck, chips to tree, blue crossed swords mark on base, c1740, 7in (18cm). **£4,000-6,000** *C*

A Meissen coffee cup and saucer, from the Swan Service, modelled by J. G. Ehder for Count Bruhl, bearing the arms of Heinrich, Graf von Bruhl and his wife Anna von Kolowrat-Krakowska, handle restored, blue crossed swords mark to both pieces, c1741. **£11,000-13,000** *C*

A pair of Louis XVI ormolu mounted Meissen figures, modelled by J. F. Eberlein, restorations, the porcelain c1750, 16½in (42cm). **£5,500-6,500** *C*

A Böttger porcelain Hausmalerei teabowl and saucer, painted by the Breslau Hausmaler Ignaz Preissler in Eisenrot and Schwarzlot, c1720. **£13,000-15,000** *CG*

A Meissen figure of a girl pancake seller, blue crossed swords mark to rear of base, c1750, 7½in (19.5cm). **£2,500-3,000** *C*

A Ludwigsburg group of dancers, modelled by Franz Anton Bustelli, dressed for the Masque, minor chips, blue crowned crossed C mark and incised UM3 to base, c1760, 6½in (16cm). **£13,000-15,000** *C*

A Meissen ormolu mounted ornament, from the Cris de Paris series, modelled by J. J. Kändler and P. Reinicke, c1756, 7½in (19cm) wide.
£6,000-7,000 *C*

Meissen figures of The Courtesan, by J. J. Kändler and P. J. Reinicke, and The Marquis, from the Cris de Paris, repairs, blue crossed swords marks, c1755, 5½in (14cm). l. **£2,000-2,500** r. **£2,500-3,000** *C*

A Meissen tankard, painted by Johann Gregor Höroldt, c1728, 4in (10.5cm).
£18,000-20,000 *C*

A Meissen group of lovers, modelled by Eberlein, repairs, blue crossed swords mark, c1745, 5½in (14.5cm).
£1,500-2,000 *C*

A Meissen silver mounted tankard, painted by J. E. Stadler, c1728, with contemporary Augsburg silver cover, by Hans Jacob Wild II, with the thaler of 1695, 7in (18cm). **£17,000-20,000** *C*

A Meissen Marcolini tête-à-tête, chips to 2 covers, crossed swords and star mark to all pieces, various impressed numerals and gilder's mark S, c1795. **£6,000-7,000** *C*

A Meissen deckelpokal and cover, repairs, blue crossed swords marks and gilder's 2. to both pieces, c1730, 8in (20cm).
£4,000-5,000 *C*

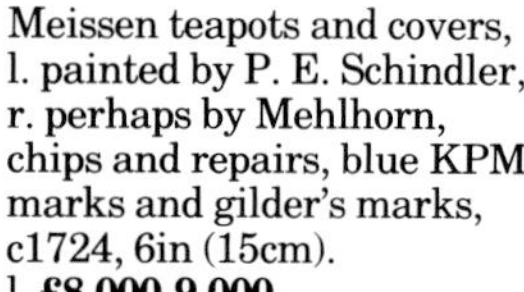

Meissen teapots and covers, l. painted by P. E. Schindler, r. perhaps by Mehlhorn, chips and repairs, blue KPM marks and gilder's marks, c1724, 6in (15cm).
l. **£8,000-9,000**
r. **£5,000-6,000** *C*

An ormolu and Sèvres porcelain encrier with 2 troughs, sander and inkwell, 11in (28cm) wide. **£3,000-4,000** *C*

A pair of hard paste porcelain pot pourri vases in the St. Cloud style, with silvered mounts, with pseudo incised mark for St. Cloud, Trou, 10½in (26.5cm). **£4,000-5,000** *C*

A Vienna tray, painted by Joseph Nigg, signed on the marble ledge, inscribed on the reverse, c1834, 16½in (41.5cm). **£14,000-16,000** *C*

A pair of Sèvres pattern Napoleonic vases and covers, painted by J. Pascault, both covers restored, imitation M Imple de Sèvres marks, late 19thC, 60in (152.5cm). **£25,000-30,000** *C*

A Vienna, Du Paquier, baroque moulded sauceboat, painted in the Imari style with flowers, c1740, 9½in (24.5cm) wide. **£5,500-6,000** *C*

A garniture of 5 Spode vases, each painted with an Oriental design in enamel colours and gold, pattern No. 967, early 19thC, central vase 6½in (16.5cm). **£4,500-5,000** *Bea*

A pair of Directoire ormolu and Vincennes ewers, the porcelain with blue interlaced L mark and twin dots, c1753, 8½in (21.5cm). **£2,500-3,000** *C*

Vienna, Du Paquier, beakers, teabowl and saucers. l. **£12,000-14,000** c. **£2,000-3,000** r. **£3,000-4,000** *C*

A First Period Worcester teacup and saucer, painted on a blue scale ground, with exotic birds, insects and flowers. **£400-500** *WW*

A pair of Worcester, Flight & Barr, armorial ice pails and covers, painted with a baronet's arms within a Garter Motto, liners missing, some rubbing, script mark, c1802, 11in (28cm). **£5,500-6,500** *CNY*

A Worcester plate from the Duke of Gloucester Service, the underside with fruit sprays, gold crescent mark, c1775, 9in (22.5cm). **£15,000-17,000** *C*

A pair of Flight, Barr & Barr ice pails and covers, each with slight chip below rim, early 19thC, 9in (22.5cm). **£3,000-3,500** *Bea*

A Worcester blue scale vase and cover, painted with exotic birds and scattered butterflies, blue square seal mark, c1770, 13in (33cm) high. **£6,000-7,000** *C*

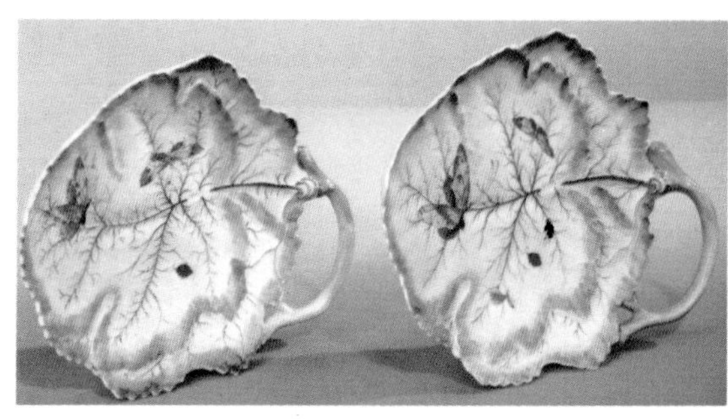

A pair of First Period Worcester leaf dishes, moulded with overlapping vine leaves, painted with butterflies and insects, hair crack, 18thC, 8in (20cm). **£950-1,050** *WW*

A Meissen clock case and stand, repairs, some damage, blue crossed swords mark and Pressnummer 25 to stand, c1745, 20in (50cm) high. **£5,500-6,500** *C*

A pair of Worcester blue scale ground chestnut baskets, pierced covers and stands, damage, blue seal mark, c1770, stands 11in (28cm). **£7,500-8,500** *CNY*

A Royal Worcester porcelain plaque, with painting of a sow and piglets around a water pump and tree in a farmyard, signed H. Davis, fully marked and with date code for 1924, 9 by 6in (23 by 15cm), in gilt frame. **£7,000-9,000** *DSH*

A Barr, Flight & Barr porcelain tureen and stand, the cover with applied 'pearls' and gilded with classical border, the tureen with painted panel attributed to Thomas Baxter, each piece impressed BFB below crown, the cover and stand with script mark, c1810, 7½in (19cm) wide overall. **£5,000-6,000** *DSH*

A Würzburg coffee pot and domed cover, painted with 2 large landscapes, neck, spout and cover restored, impressed CGW mark, c1775, 9½in (24cm) high. **£15,000-17,000** *C*

A painted grey pottery jar and cover, of bronze form, with animal head masks to each side, crack, minor damage to one handle, Han Dynasty, 26½in (67cm) high. **£7,000-8,000** *C*

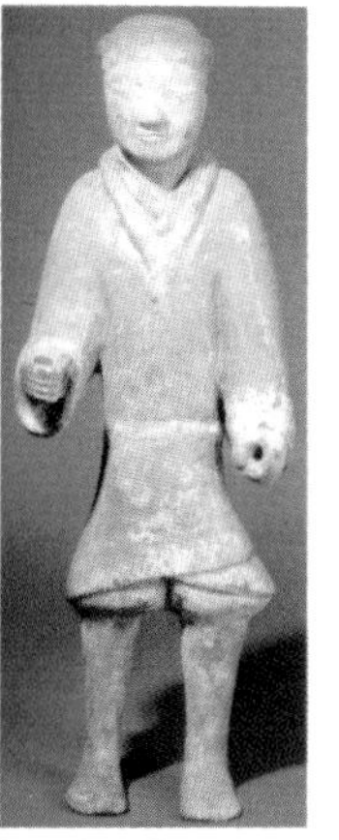

l. A painted grey pottery figure of a soldier, left hand pierced for sword attachments, restorations, Han Dynasty, 20in (50cm). **£30,000-40,000**

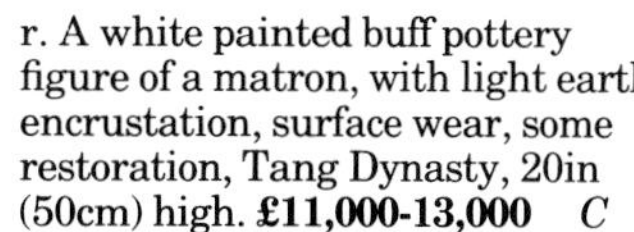

r. A white painted buff pottery figure of a matron, with light earth encrustation, surface wear, some restoration, Tang Dynasty, 20in (50cm) high. **£11,000-13,000** *C*

A pair of buff pottery figures of Bactrian camels, with raised heads and jaws agape, the necks and humps well modelled with tufted hair, the backs with simple oval saddle cloths, some traces of red pigment remaining, some restoration, Tang Dynasty, 30in (76cm) high. **£35,000-40,000** *C*

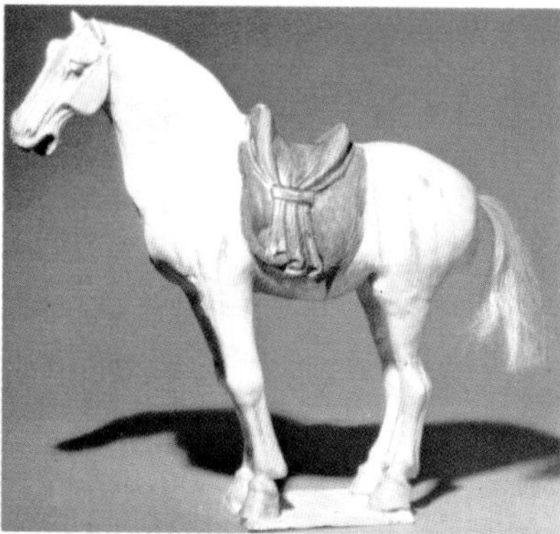

A Sancai buff pottery figure of a horse, the well-modelled body and head under a straw glaze, the saddle cloth under a deep green glaze splashing on the haunches, some restoration, Tang Dynasty, 18½in (46.5cm) high, tall wood stand. **£22,000-25,000** *C*

A Jun Yao tripod censer, with short neck and everted rim, the crackled lavender glaze liberally splashed with purple to the exterior and rim above the pale stoneware short feet, Song Dynasty, 3in (7.5cm) diam.
£18,000-20,000 *C*

A Dingyao bowl, carved and incised on the exterior with 2 lotus heads and scrolling foliage, under an ivory white glaze, pooling in tears above the deeply cut foot, the rim left in the biscuit, Northern Song Dynasty, 6½in (16.5cm) diam. **£7,000-9,000** *C*

A Yuan blue and white broad jar, guan, painted in soft cobalt with 4 fish swimming amongst water plants, comprising 3 carp and a pike perch, above a band of classic scrolls and lappets of circlets on the lower part, the shallowly-cut broad foot unglazed, horizontal crack to shoulder, minute rim chips, c1350, 13in (33cm) diam.
£170,000+ *C*

A Yuan blue and white broad baluster jar, guan, painted with an arching peony scroll, the neck with a band of formalised breaking waves, the shallow broad foot unglazed, minor chip to inside rim, c1350, 9in (23cm) high.
£65,000+ *C*

A Ming blue and white saucer dish, painted at the centre of the interior with 3 cloud scrolls, the exterior with 2 five-clawed dragons in pursuit of a flaming pearl, foot flakes from the biscuit, surface scratches on the interior, encircled Zhengde six character mark and of the period, 8½in (22cm) diam, fitted box.
£7,000-8,000 *C*

A Yaozhou celadon bowl, the centre freely carved with lotus blossom and downturned leaf with combed veins on a ground of foliate scrolls, the flaring unglazed foot fired brown, all under a transparent olive green glaze, Northern Song Dynasty, 7½in (18.5cm) diam, fitted box. **£9,000-11,000** *C*

A Ming blue and white dish, the reverse with 2 birds in flight, minor fritting, Wanli, 18½in (46.5cm). **£5,000-6,000** *C*

A Ming blue and white box and cover, painted with dragons chasing flaming pearls, minor cracks, cover restored, Wanli six-character mark and of the period, 12in (30.5cm) wide. **£6,000-8,000** *C*

A Ming blue and white jar, encircled Jiajing 6-character mark and of the period, 5in (12cm). **£10,000-12,000** *C*

A late Ming dish, painted in the centre with 2 herons, the sides with fish, frogs and crustacea, Tianqi/Chongzheng, 8in (20cm), fitted box. **£7,000-8,000** *C*

A late Ming blue and white saucer dish, encircled Wanli six-character mark and of the period, 7in (18cm), fitted box. **£6,000-8,000** *C*

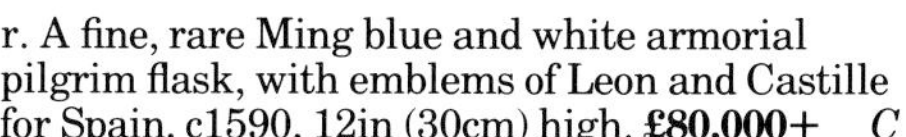

l. A fine, rare blue and white Magnolia vase, Kangxi, 18in (46cm) high. **£14,000-16,000**

r. A fine, rare Ming blue and white armorial pilgrim flask, with emblems of Leon and Castille for Spain, c1590, 12in (30cm) high. **£80,000+** *C*

A Transitional blue and white brush pot, painted with military scene, incised rim, c1640, 8in (20cm) high. **£3,000-4,000** *C*

A Ming tilemaker's pottery figure of a seated Warrior Immortal, edges restored, 16th/17thC, 25in (63cm) high, wood stand. **£7,000-8,000** *C*

An Imperial 'famille verte' coral red ground bowl, with everted rim and plain white interior, painted with exotic flowers, underglaze blue Kangxi 'yuzhi' mark within a double square and of the period, 4½in (11cm) diam. **£19,000-21,000** *C*

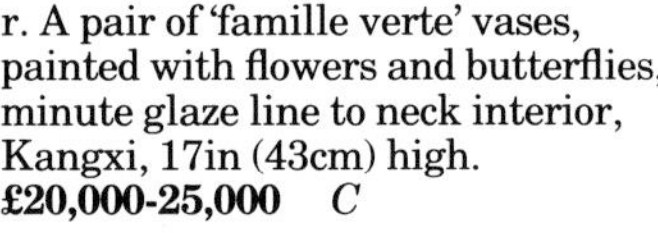

l. A blue and white vase, painted with a hunting scene, observed by dignitaries, Kangxi, 19in (48cm) high. **£5,500-6,500**

r. A pair of 'famille verte' vases, painted with flowers and butterflies, minute glaze line to neck interior, Kangxi, 17in (43cm) high. **£20,000-25,000** *C*

A pair of Transitional Wucai sleeve vases, vividly painted with dragons, one cracked, small rim chips, mid-17thC, 17in (43cm) high. **£6,000-8,000** *C*

A 'famille verte' Month cup, rim chip, Kangxi six-character mark and of the period, 2½in diam. **£3,000-3,500** *C*

A 'famille verte' rouleau vase, slight enamel flaking, Kangxi, 17in (43.5cm) high. **£3,500-4,500** *C*

A 'famille verte' scroll weight, the top with high relief prunus spray, the sides painted with flowers on a seeded green ground, edges rubbed, Kangxi, 14in (36cm). **£5,500-6,500** *C*

A pair of Doucai wine cups, delicately painted, one with glaze imperfection to interior, encircled Kangxi six-character marks and of the period, 2½in (6cm) diam, wood stand. **£25,000-27,000** *C*

A pair of 'famille rose' Laughing Twins, Hehe Erxian, neck crack, minor chips and fritting, Yongzheng, 12in (31cm) high. **£7,000-9,000** *C*

A Dehua blanc-de-chine group of 4 Europeans, minor damage to extremities, Kangxi, 6½in (16cm) wide. **£4,000-5,000** *C*

An underglaze copper red and white bowl, encircled Kangxi six-character mark and of the period, 6in (15cm) diam. **£11,000-13,000** *C*

A sang-de-boeuf pear-shaped vase, encircled Yongzheng six-character mark and of the period, 11in (28.5cm) high. **£8,000-10,000** *C*

A 'famille verte' flat-backed wall cistern, cover and oval basin, boldly painted with fish and crabs, restored, Kangxi, 18in (45cm) high. **£4,000-6,000** *C*

A massive blue and white tapering cylindrical vase, painted with panels of figures, neck crack, some fritting, Kangxi, 37in (94cm) high. **£4,500-5,500** *C*

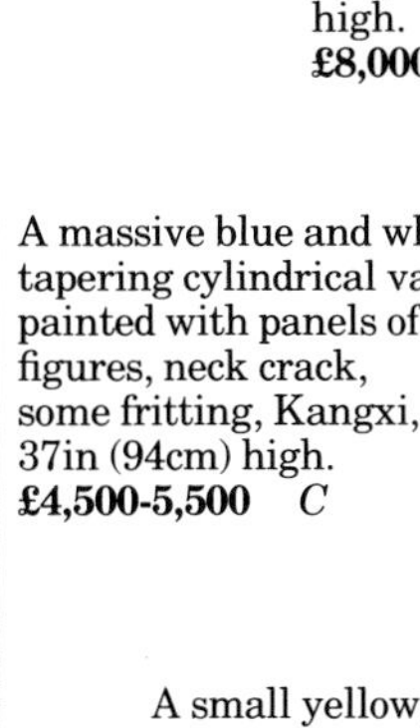

A small yellow, green and aubergine glazed saucer dish, incised and painted with dragons contesting a flaming pearl, encircled Kangxi six-character mark and of the period, 4½in (11cm) diam. **£4,000-5,000** *C*

A 'rose-verte' dish, painted in strong colours with figures in a walled garden, below scroll landscape panels on a green ground with peony and magnolia sprays, rim restored, Yongzheng, 21½in (55cm) diam. **£10,000-12,000** *C*

A 'famille rose' hunting punchbowl, painted with hunting scene on the interior, the exterior with unusual scene of a royal tiger hunt, some cracks, late Qianlong, 16in (41cm) diam. **£9,000-10,000** *C*

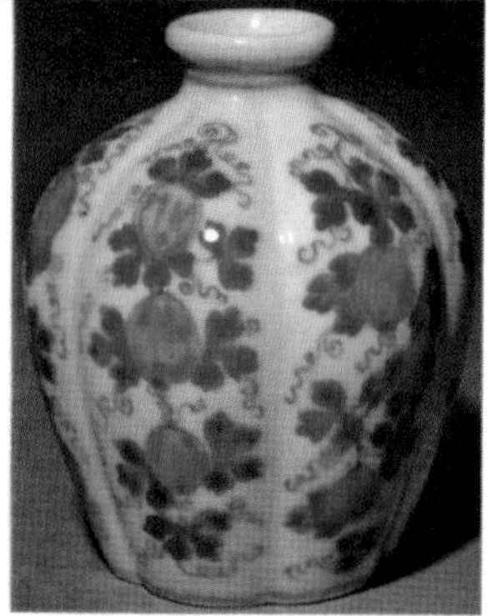

A blue and white jar, each lobe painted with gourds, Yongzheng six-character mark and of the period, 3½in (9cm) high. **£5,000-6,000** *C*

A Louis XVI ormolu-mounted Chinese 'famille rose' pot pourri vase, the porcelain Yongzheng, 5½in (14cm) high. **£4,000-5,000** *C*

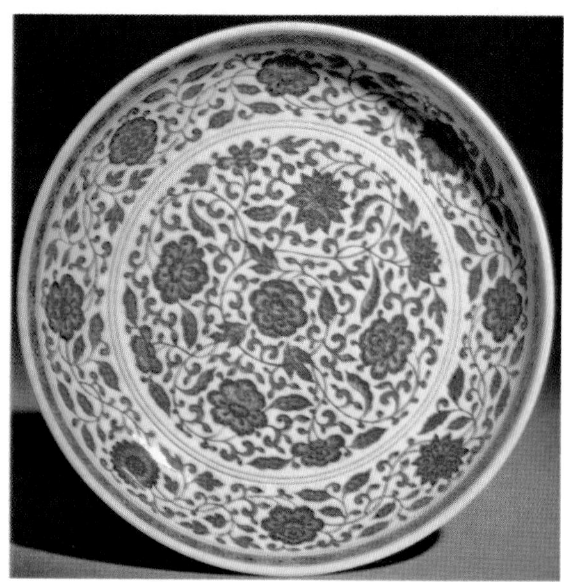

A blue and white yellow-ground saucer dish, painted at the centre with flowers on leafy stems, the exterior similarly painted, glazing flaw, Yongzheng six-character mark and of the period, 8½in (21cm). **£21,000-23,000** *C*

A garniture of 5 blue and white vases and 3 covers, each decorated with a peach-shaped panel of a pavilion, one cover odd, some restoration, early 18thC, vases 17½in (44cm) high, beakers 15in (38cm) high. **£4,000-6,000** *C*

An export armorial neo-classical punchbowl, painted after a European engraving in the manner of Bartolozzi, the interior with coat of arms, some damage and rubbing, c1790, 22in (55cm) diam. **£8,000-10,000** *C*

A Chinese Imari armorial shaving bowl, painted in underglaze blue, iron red and gilt at the centre, two rim chips restored, c1720, 11in (28cm). **£3,000-3,500** *C*

A pair of green dragon jars and covers, painted with dragons, in pursuit of flaming pearls, below bands of Buddhist emblems within ruyi heads and scrolls, rim chip, Qianlong six-character seal marks and of the period, 8in (20cm). **£6,000-8,000** *C*

A Doucai saucer dish, with 8 Buddhist emblems, Qianlong seal mark and of the period, 20½in (52cm) diam. **£11,000-13,000** *C*

A pair of 'famille rose' neo-classical urns and covers, in the style of Marieberg faience, one restored, one cover chipped, gilding rubbed, Qianlong, c1770, 16in (40cm) high. **£5,500-6,500** *C*

A pair of 'famille rose' Mandarin palette vases and covers, with iron red seated lion finials, repaired, Qianlong, 20in (49cm). **£8,000-9,000** *C*

A pair of 'famille rose' turquoise ground vases and covers, painted on both sides with figures, minor restorations, Qianlong, 18in (45cm) high. **£8,000-10,000** *C*

A 'famille rose' 'Pronk' plate, painted with The Doctor's Visit, slight wear, 9in (23cm). **£4,000-5,000** *C*

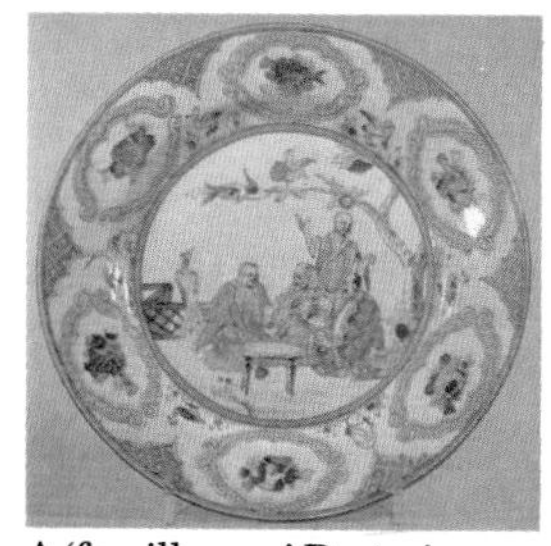

A 'famille rose' Doctor's Visit plate, Cornelis Pronk style, c1735, 9in (23cm). **£9,500-10,500** *C*

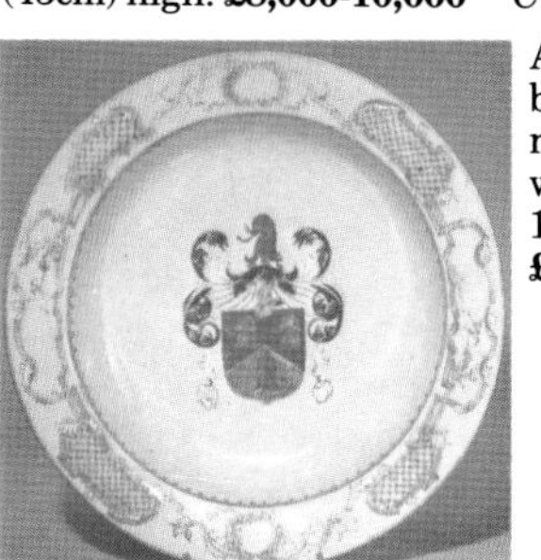

A pair of export armorial basins, enamelled in colours, minute rim chips, one border with large haircrack, c1745, 15in (38cm). **£6,000-7,000** *C*

An unrecorded documentary export shipping bowl, inscribed Elizabeth Cook 1747 and William Hillyard 1747, enamel restored, c1747, 10in (25cm). **£8,000-10,000** *C*

A set of 8 'famille rose' figures of Daoist Immortals, holding their appropriate attributes, one head re-stuck, extremities chipped, c1800, all about 8½in (21.5cm) high. **£4,500-5,500** *C*

A pair of celadon ground and gilt candlesticks, rim chipped, Qianlong seal mark and of the period, 11in. **£3,500-4,000** *C*

A pair of 'famille rose' armorial dishes, centres with European style landscapes, possibly Fort St. George, India, damage, c1745. **£4,500-5,500** *Bon*

A pair of blue and white garden seats, with 2 sides centrally pierced with interlocking cash on a band of scrolling lotus, c1800, 19in (48cm) high. **£4,000-5,000** *C*

A pair of export models of hawks, the wings and tails carefully detailed with sepia simulated feather markings, some restoration, Qianlong, 11in (28cm). **£19,000-21,000** *C*

A set of 4 'famille rose' erotic panels, each elaborately painted with a pair of lovers in a pavilion, a terrace, a garden and a chamber, mid-Qing Dynasty, 8 by 5in (20 by 12.5cm), wood frames. **£6,000-7,000** *C*

A 'famille rose' turquoise ground vase, painted with iron red bats in flight, repairs, Qianlong seal mark, 27in (68cm). **£12,000-14,000** *C*

A pair of export glazed models of cockerels, painted with iron red bodies, head extremities restored, 18th/early 19thC, 11in (27.5cm) high. **£4,000-5,000** *C*

A pair of 'famille rose' 'tobacco leaf' tureens and covers, with flowerhead handles and pomegranate finials, painted with overlapping coloured leaves scattered with flowersprays and peony, one spare cover, one tureen with handles missing, chipped, Qianlong, 12in (31cm) wide. **£5,500-6,500** *C*

Twenty-four blue and white plates, painted with peony below flowering pomegranate branch, within a band of trellis pattern, c1750, 9in (23cm) diam. **£4,000-5,000** *C*

A pair of 'famille rose' millefleurs vases, reserved with large oval landscape panels, each with figures in boats and on a promontory in a wooded river landscape, on brightly enamelled gilt and floral ground, 19thC, 28in (71cm) high.
£5,000-6,000 *C*

The Lord Mayor of London punchbowl, a 'famille rose' bowl for the English market, enamelled with views taken from prints of 18thC City of London, cracks stabilised, one area overpainted, c1805, 16in (40cm) diam.
£28,000-32,000 *C*

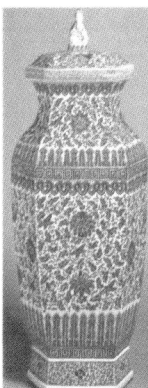

A blue and white vase and cover, with seated lady Immortal finial, boldly painted with lotus in leafy meanders, finial restored, 19thC, 40in (101cm) high. **£4,000-5,000** *C*

A pair of 'famille rose' yellow ground fish bowls, moulded and brightly painted in relief on the mustard yellow ground with vases of flowers, stands of scholars' utensils, archaistic vessels and scattered flowers, the interiors with swimming carp amongst water weeds, 19thC, 20in (51cm) diam.
£9,000-11,000 *C*

Twelve blue and white chocolate cups and saucers, painted with chrysanthemum, bamboo and daisy issuing around a jagged outcrop of rockwork, with elaborate loop handle of European inspiration, c1750, the cups 2½in (7cm), the saucers 5in (13cm) diam.
£3,000-4,000 *C*

Provenance: Nanking Cargo sale, 1986.

A pair of 'famille rose' celadon ground bottle vases and domed covers, with peach finials, the bodies decorated in bright enamels, trailed white slip and gilding with flying bats, wispy cloud scrolls, floral roundels and Buddhist emblems, beneath spearheads at the rims, one cover and rim restored, early 19thC, 35½in (90cm) high. **£7,000-8,000** *C*

A pair of 'famille verte' figures of seated Buddhistic lions on detachable bases, with green bodies and bushy tails, one with a pierced ball beneath its forepaw, the other with a cub, the bases pierced with kidney-shaped apertures, restorations, 19thC, 20in (50cm) high. **£4,000-5,000** *C*

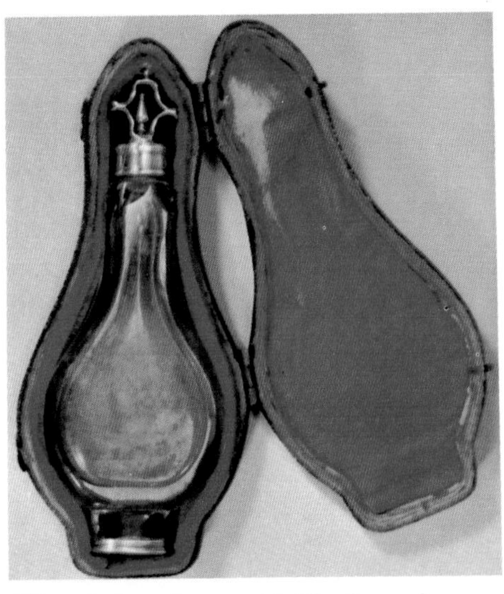

A French clear glass scent bottle of pear shape, with silver gilt mounts, engraved 'E & B', c1780. 3½in (9.5cm), in a fitted black shagreen case.
£450-500 *Som*

A red scent bottle, with white enamel decoration, gilt metal mount with finger ring and chain, c1880, 3in (8cm) long.
£70-90 *Som*

A red cut 'opera glass' scent with embossed silver gilt mounts and picture frame inside, c1880, 5½in (13.5cm).
£200-250 *Som*

A glass beaker, with gilt flower sprays and insects, attributed to Michael Edkins, c1780, 4½in (11.5cm). **£1,100-1,300** *Som*

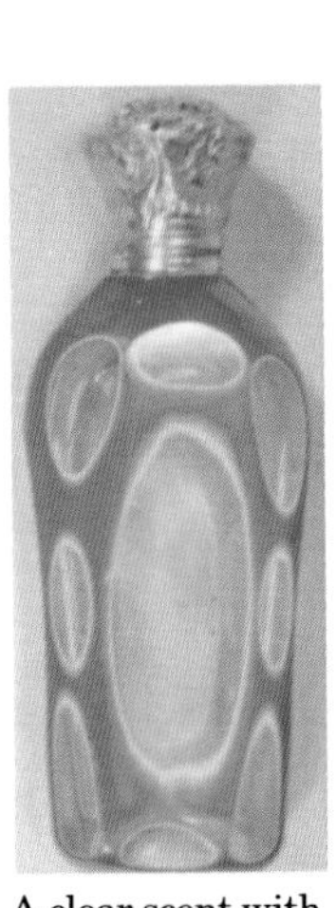

A clear scent with pink on white overlay, cut with printies, c1850, 3in (8cm).
£75-85 *Som*

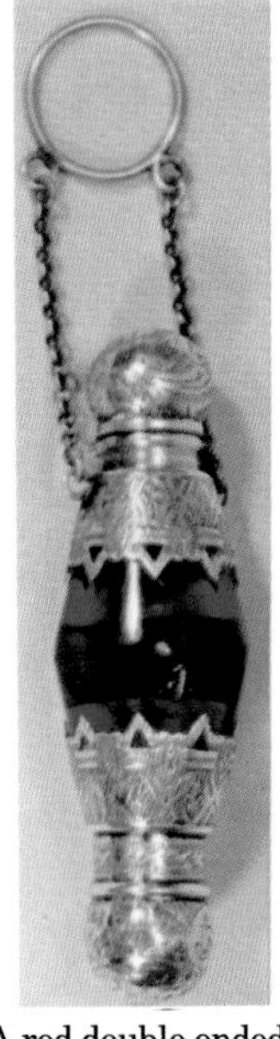

A red double ended scent with chased silver gilt mounts, c1880, 3in (8cm).
£200-250 *Som*

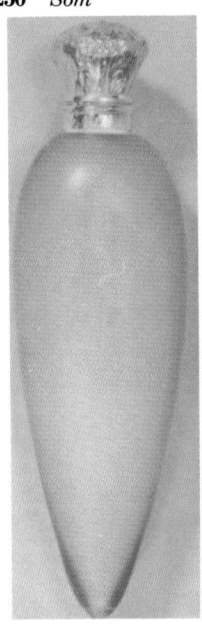

A blue satin scent, with embossed silver mount, c1880, 5in (12.5cm).
£180-220 *Som*

A French scent bottle with black bead cover, with fleur-de-lys and 'Vive le Roi' in white beads, silver mount, c1780, 2in (5cm). **£200-250** *Som*

Three clear glass scent bottles, c1815:—
l. Oval with diamond cutting, silver mount, 4in (10cm).
c. Rectangular with prism and diamond cutting, silver mount, 5in (13cm).
r. Round with diamond cutting, gold mount, 3in (8cm) diam. **£70-90 each** *Som*

A blue scent bottle with facet cut body, gilt floral decoration, c1800, 5in (13cm). **£350-400** *Som*

A pair of blue cruet bottles of urn shape, with gilt inscriptions 'Soy' and 'Anchovy' in gilt roundels, c1800, 4½in (11.5cm) high. **£260-300** *Som*

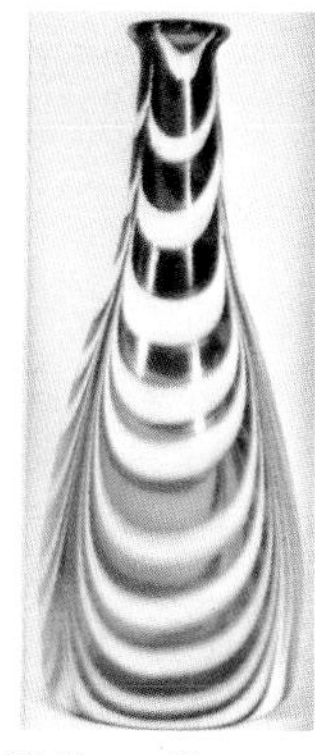

A Nailsea olive green bottle of tapered form, with white looped decoration, c1810, 9½in (23.5cm). **£200-240** *Som*

A set of 3 green spirit bottles, with canted corners and cut shoulders, pouring lips and cut ball stoppers, with gilt inscriptions, c1800, 6in (15cm). **£800-900** *Som*

Two blue overlay scent bottles:
l. Diamond cut with embossed silver gilt mount, c1860, 3½in (8.5cm). **£150-170**
r. Fan cut with plain silver mount, c1860, 4in (10cm). **£150-170** *Som*

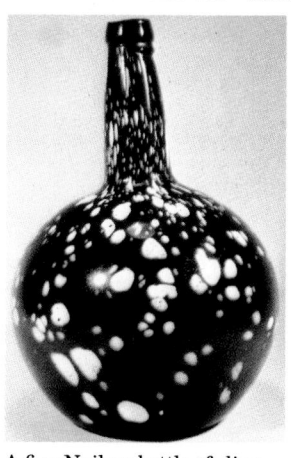

A pale green crown glass flagon, of Nailsea type, c1840, 10in (25cm). **£220-260** *Som*

A set of 3 spirit bottles, embossed silver mounts with hallmark Birmingham 1839, in a silver plated stand, bottles 13in. **£450-550** *Som*

A pair of spirit bottles, hallmark Birmingham 1839, 13in. **£340-380** *Som*

A fine Nailsea bottle of olive green tint, with white splashes, c1800, 10½in (27.5cm) high. **£400-450** *Som*

A pair of green wrythen moulded spirit bottles, of slightly different tints, with cork and metal stoppers, c1840, 12in (29cm). **£370-420**

A rare green shouldered decanter, with scale cut base and double band of looped stars and printies, facet cut neck and cut spire stopper, c1770, 10in (25cm). **£850-950** *Som*

A green mallet shaped decanter, with 3 plain neck rings, bevelled lozenge stopper, c1790, 7½in (19cm). **£200-250** *Som*

A Nailsea crown glass cream pan, of light green tint, with folded rim, c1810, 4½in (11cm) high, 8½in (22cm) diam. **£80-120** *Som*

A pair of ormolu and blue cut glass vases, with twin handles, foliate socles and square bases, one cracked, Swedish or Russian, late 18thC, 9½in (24cm) high. **£3,500-4,000** *C*

A pair of giltmetal and Bohemian glass candlesticks, the shaped storm shades painted with lions and trailing foliage, the square bases on winged lion feet, mid-19thC, 15in (38cm) high. **£5,000-6,000** *C*

A pair of English blue leaf dishes, with gilt decoration, one repaired, c1860, 4in (10cm) and 4½in (11cm) diam. **£70-90** *Som*

A set of 4 Venetian paintings on glass, after Pietro Longhi, depicting The Lady's Awakening, The Meeting of the Procurator and his Wife, The Declamation and The Dancing Lesson, mid-18thC, 20 by 16½in (51 by 42cm), in giltwood frames. **£19,000-21,000** *C*

A North Country blue sugar basin and cream jug the basin with hollow stem, folded foot, c1800, jug 3½in (9.5cm) high, basin 4in (10cm) high. **£250-280** *Som*

A North Country amethyst cream jug with faint wrythen decoration and folded rim, c1780, 4in (9.5cm) high. **£150-170** *Som*

A Wedgwood vase and cover, modelled in relief in white and gilt on a glazed blue ground, gilt satyr mask and loop handles, impressed mark and code for 1882, 9½in (23.5cm).
£200-300 *L*

A delft guglet, perhaps Dublin, painted in blue, 9½in (24cm).
£200-300 *L*

A Dutch Delft blue and white garniture, painted within moulded panels, some damage, blue mark of 'De Porceleyne Klaeuw', 19thC, 9½ to 14in (24 to 35cm).
£500-800 *CAm*

An Italian maiolica albarello, painted with a saint in an oval panel, reserved on a brown ground, hair cracks, chips, c1600, 11in (28cm).
£1,000-1,500 *C*

A Castelli campana vase, painted and enriched with gilding, probably painted by Liborio Grue, restored, c1740, 16½in (41.5cm).
£1,200-2,000 *C*

A Mettlach stoneware vase incised and painted, late 19thC, 13in (32.5cm).
£150-200 *Bea*

A Palermo vase painted in yellow and green on a blue ground between yellow bands, manganese lines and yellow bands to the neck and foot, chips, 17thC, 10in (25cm).
£600-800 *C*

Wemyss Ware

A Wemyss basket painted by Karl Nekola, c1900.
£450-550 *RdeR*

A Wemyss ware curtain tray used for advertising purposes, c1880, 10in (25cm) wide.
£300-400 *RdeR*

A Sciacca vase painted with a portrait of a bishop, reserved on a band of trophies and between bands of foliage in green, blue and yellow, chip to neck, 17thC, 10½in (26cm).
£1,000-1,500 *C*

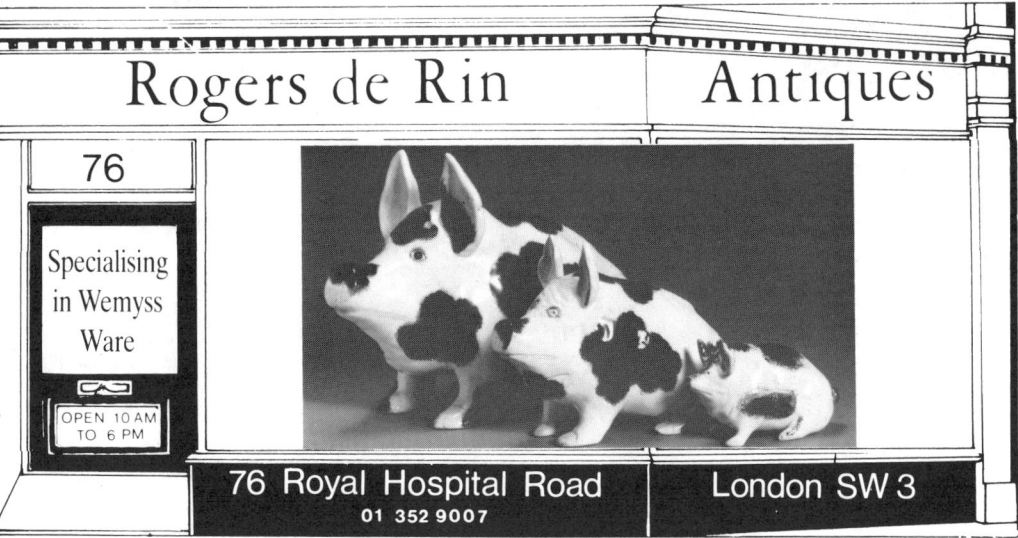

A Wemyss plate decorated with cockerels, c1880, 8½in (21.5cm) diam.
£100-150 *RdeR*

A Wemyss Ware basket, painted with dog roses and turquoise borders and handle, c1920, 16in (40.5cm) wide.
£200-300 *TW*

A pair of black and white Wemyss cats, Bovey Tracey, painted by Joseph Nekola, c1930, 12½in (31.5cm).
£1,500-2,000 *RdeR*

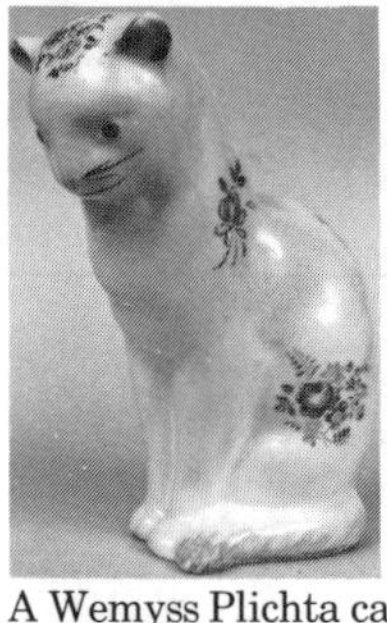

A Wemyss Plichta cat, 1930-47, 6in (15cm).
£50-100 *RdeR*

A Wemyss pig, modelled in a squatting position, its coat with large black splashes, pink ears and snout, impressed mark, 6½in (16.5cm) long.
£500-600 *CSK*

A Wemyss mug, painted with a black cockerel and 5 hens on grass below a red line rim, rim chips to foot rim, impressed Wemyss, 6in (15cm).
£250-300 *CEd*

A rare Wemyss tabby cat
£4,500-5,500 *McC*

A Wemyss vase, painted on a multi-coloured ground with thorny foliage, signed Crail, Wemyss, 213, 8in (20cm).
£150-250 *CEd*

A Wemyss spirally moulded bowl, painted with pink cabbage roses, painted mark, 8½in (21.5cm) diam.
£150-250 *CSK*

A Wemyss dog bowl, painted with apples, 6½in (16.5cm) diam.
£100-150 *RdeR*

A Wemyss plaque, inscribed on the reverse 'Wemyss, T. Goode & Co., London', and impressed Wemyss, 7½in (19cm) diam.
£100-150 *HCH*

A Wemyss sailor's jug, undecorated, 11in (28cm).
£200-250 *RdeR*

A Wemyss teapot with plum design, 4½in (11.5cm).
£350-400 *SBA*

A Wemyss tray with roses, 10in (25cm) wide.
£100-150 *RdeR*

A Wemyss plaque, inscribed Wemyss on the reverse and having Thomas Goode's retailing mark, 7½in (19cm) diam.
£100-150 *HCH*

A Wemyss three-handled tyg, restoration, 9½in (24cm) diam.
£450-500 *SBA*

A Wemyss vase, with rose and bud design, 8in (20.5cm).
£170-220 *SBA*

A Wemyss vase, with plum design, 8in (20.5cm).
£150-300 *SBA*

A Wemyss coombe pot with yellow irises, 7½in (19cm).
£250-300 *RdeR*

A Wemyss bulb bowl with cherries, 8in (20.5cm) diam.
£80-100 *RdeR*

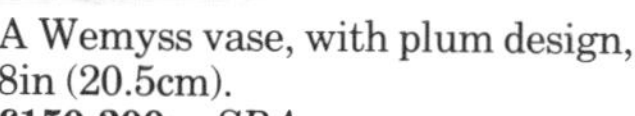

A Wemyss three-handled loving cup, decorated with plums, 7½in (19cm).
£250-300 *RdeR*

A Wemyss mug with tulips, 5½in (14cm).
£200-250 *RdeR*

A rare Wemyss peacock mug, 5½in (14cm).
£500-600 *RdeR*

A Wemyss strawberry quaich, 7½in (19cm) diam.
£150-200 *RdeR*

A Wemyss plate, decorated with red gooseberries, 5½in (14cm) diam.
£150-200 *RdeR*

A Wemyss plate, decorated with oranges, 7in (18cm) diam.
£75-100 *RdeR*

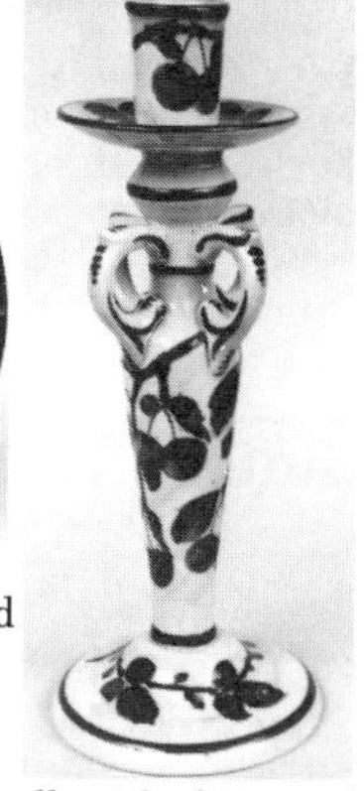

A Wemyss candlestick, decorated with cherries, 9½in (24cm).
£100-150 *RdeR*

WEMYSS WARE
c1883-1930

★ Robert Methven Heron introduced a group of continental artists into his Fife pottery in the 1880s. The very characteristic nature of Wemyss derives from their influence although roses, apples and cherries had been stiffly painted before
★ most of the artists returned home but Karel Nekola remained. Wemyss was always wanted by the rich and the ware was well supported by Scottish Lairds
★ Wemyss was fired at low temperatures to produce a biscuit body which would absorb the delicate brush strokes. Then it was dipped in a soft lead glaze and fired again at a low temperature. This accounts for the fragility of Wemyss and the relative rarity of exceptional quality pieces
★ Nekola trained James Sharp, David Grinton, John Brown, Hugh and Christina McKinnon and they were later joined by Nekola's sons Carl and Joseph
★ Karel Nekola tended to paint the large important pieces and also the commemorative pieces from Queen Victoria's Jubilee in 1897 until the Coronation of George V in 1911. He died in 1915
★ Edwin Sandiland became chief decorator in 1916. The change in public taste after the First World War, with the introduction of the Art Deco movement, saw a move away from the traditional Wemyss designs. Various new designs were tried but by the time Edwin Sandiland died in 1928, the end was in sight. The Fife Pottery closed in 1930
★ early pieces particularly with red border
★ unusual subject matters – nasturtiums, gorse, pink flamingoes
★ beware unmarked pieces – usually these were rejects or copies from another factory
★ the Bovey Tracy pottery in Devon bought the rights and moulds of the Fife pottery and gave employment to Joseph Nekola, who continued the familiar decorations to a high standard until his death in 1952. Royal Doulton subsequently acquired the rights
★ for more information buy the book *Wemyss Ware, A Decorative Scottish Pottery*, presented by Victoria de Rin and David Macmillan, written by Professor Peter Davis and Robert Rankine, published by the Scottish Academic Press

MINTON MAJOLICA

Throughout ceramic history, but particularly in the 18th and 19th centuries, there have been numerous examples of rediscoveries or reintroductions of types of body or techniques of decoration.

Minton majolica is an example of the reintroduction of an earlier type of ware following a period of intense experimentation to replicate and improve upon it. In 1848 Joseph Leon Francois Arnoux was appointed Art Director at Minton. His primary task was to introduce new products and to promote them in such a way that the reputation of the factory was enhanced and new markets created.

Arnoux sought to exploit the fashion for classical design and the growing interest in bright colour evident in paintings and architecture of the period. He turned for inspiration to the work of Bernard Palissy, whose naturalistic, brightly coloured maiolica wares had been popular in the 16th century.

Arnoux recreated Palissy's brightly coloured glazes but avoided the easily damaged delft-type body used by Palissy, employing instead a high-fired durable body akin to stoneware.

The body was given a coating of opaque white glaze which provided a surface for overpainting in brightly coloured opaque glazes. Later, transparent coloured glazes were also used over relief moulding. The new ware was specially promoted at the 1851 Great Exhibition in London where it was well received. These early wares included wine coolers, jardinières, flower pots and stands, all decorated in the majolica style.

Minton cleverly exploited the market over the next 40 years by introducing models in response to the dictates of fashion. Rival firms, notably Wedgwood and George Jones, were quick to copy the new product; like Minton their work, which is also of high quality, is usually impressed with factory marks. Some lesser factories also cashed in on Minton's innovation. Some of the work of these lesser factories is less impressive as the body is not always as highly fired as it should be.

Interest from the USA in the late 1970s and early 80s stimulated the price of majolica. For a time everything, whether marked or unmarked, perfect or damaged, found a ready market. By the mid 1980s damage or the lack of a factory mark severely limited interest and this trend still continues. Most saleable are wares with a strong decorative impact, regardless of factory. Of marked pieces Minton remains the market leader with some favour shown towards George Jones, Wedgwood and marked pieces from lesser factories.

Minton Majolica

A Minton majolica dish painted by Leon Arnoux after a design by Alfred Stevens, with Ceres in blue on an ochre ground within a wide border of manganese and white on a blue ground, the reverse with stylised radiating foliage, signed L.A....x, and Minton 1859, 17in (43.5cm).
£4,500-5,500 *C*

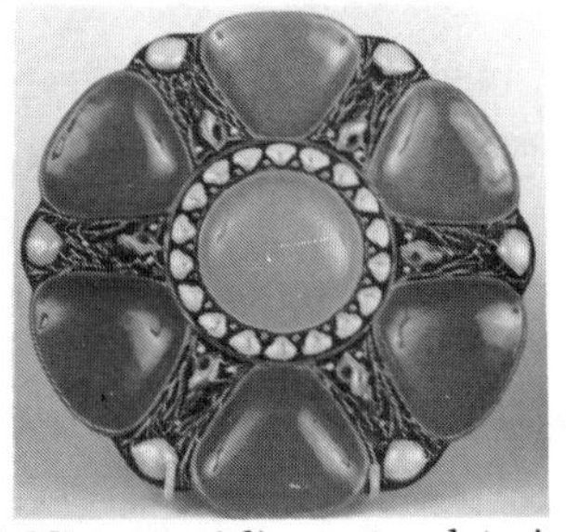

A Minton majolica oyster plate, in pink with relief decoration of shells and seaweed, 1878, 9in (23cm).
£70-100 *BRI*

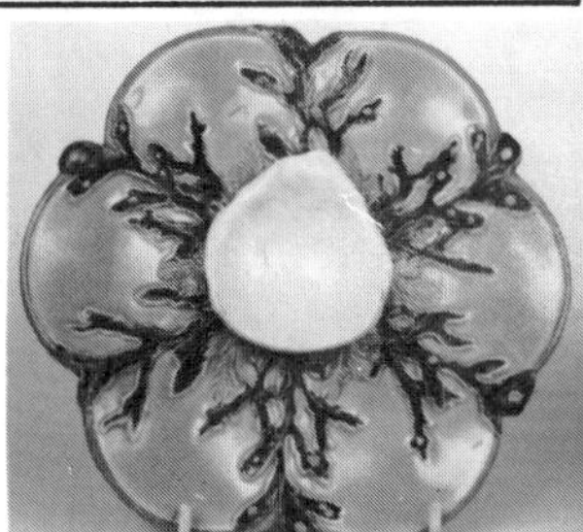

A Minton majolica oyster plate, with turquoise blue ground and relief decoration of seaweed, 1880 8in (20cm).
£70-100 *BRI*

A pair of Minton majolica table-centre dishes, 1877, 15in (38cm).
£650-750 *BRI*

A Minton majolica pierced tazza supported by 3 sparsely clad cherubs, impressed marks, dated cypher 1864, 10in (25cm).
£350-400 *CSK*

A Minton majolica centrepiece in the form of 3 cherubs supporting a basket, painted in typical enamel colours, impressed marks, c1870, 11½in (28.5cm).
£550-650 *Bea*

A Minton majolica game tureen and cover, moulded with pheasants on one side, the reverse with a hare, enriched in coloured glazes, the cover with recumbent hound finial, the interior covered entirely in a turquoise glaze, impressed marks, date code for 1867, 14in (36cm) long.
£1,000-1,500 *CNY*

A Minton majolica bowl covered in a bright blue glaze, impressed mark and date code for 1872, 12in (30cm).
£250-350 *Bea*

A Victorian Minton majolica comport, with dish supported by putto on naturalistic green and brown circular base, 14½in (36cm).
£150-200 *HCH*

A Minton majolica bowl, the base modelled as 3 doves, with a border of white flowerheads and green foliage joined by pink ribbon, with turquoise glazed interior, 2 chips to foot, hair crack to bowl, impressed marks, numerals and date code for 1874, 12½in (31.5cm).
£900-1,000 *C*

A Minton majolica vase, painted in typical enamel colours, one head re-stuck, impressed marks and date code for 1873, 16½in (41cm).
£500-700 *Bea*

A Minton majolica jug, modelled as a young girl with a fan and a purple cloak, impressed marks, 11in (28cm).
£350-450 *CSK*

A Minton majolica jug moulded and painted with mediaeval figures dancing, impressed mark and date code for 1871, 9½in (24cm).
£200-300 *Bea*

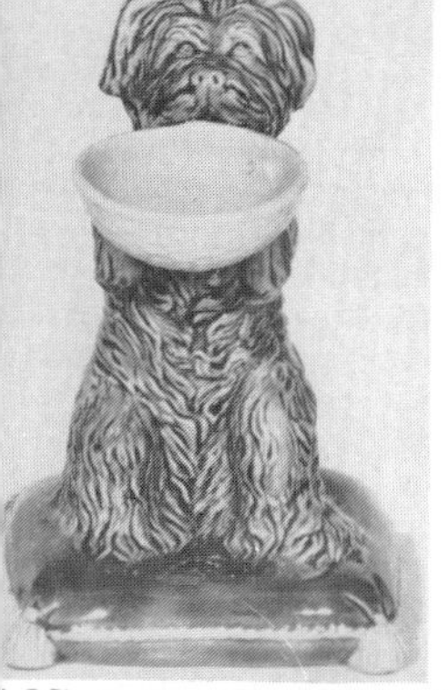

A Minton majolica salt modelled as a dog begging, on a pink cushion with orange tassels, impressed mark, 15in (38cm).
£400-500 *CSK*

A pair of Minton majolica tiles, decorated on a turquoise ground, impressed mark, year cypher, 8in (20cm).
£200-300 *WW*

A Minton majolica garden seat in the Oriental taste, the bright yellow ground moulded in low relief and decorated in a green glaze, impressed mark and date code for 1873, 20in (50cm).
£500-700 *C*

A Minton majolica figure, 8in (20cm).
£550-650 *BHA*

A Minton majolica model of a cockatoo, its plumage coloured in cream heightened in green and with yellow crest, impressed marks, 12½in (31cm).
£250-350 *CSK*

Miscellaneous

A London delft flower brick, c1730, 3½in (8.5cm).
£550-600 *JHo*

A Mason's Patent Ironstone foot bath, of fluted form and with twin mask handles, numerous cracks, printed marks, 20in (50cm) wide.
£400-600 *CSK*

A pair of Bristol delft blue and whit flower bricks, one with slight crack to rim, both with rim chips, c1740, 6in (15cm) wide.
£850-950 *C*

A Wedgwood blue and white foot bath, printed inside and out, large impressed mark, early 19thC, 20in (49cm) wide.
£1,200-1,500 *Bea*

A pair of delft blue and white flowe bricks, 18thC.
£550-650 *P[CW]*

A Staffordshire pottery pipe in the form of John Bull with small lion, decorated in enamel colours, c1815, 4in (10cm).
£800-900 *LR*

A foot bath printed with the Elephant pattern, probably Rogers, c1825, 18½in (46cm) wide.
£800-1,200 *CSK*

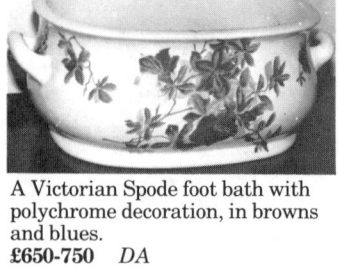

A Victorian Spode foot bath with polychrome decoration, in browns and blues.
£650-750 *DA*

A pearlware pipe modelled as a man, impressed with the name 'Jolly Pickman', in ochre collared and cuffed blue coat and ochre breeches, seated on a green baske and smoking a sponged blue and yellow pipe, perhaps Yorkshire, restoration to pipe and his hands, c1800, 6in (14.5cm).
£900-1,000 *C*

A pearlware pipe modelled as a man in a dark green hat, blue jacket, ochre waistcoat and striped trousers, the pipe bowl moulded with happy and sad faces, perhaps Yorkshire, minor stem restoration, c1800, 6in (15.5cm).
£900-1,000 *C*

A creamware pipe modelled as a lady, wearing blue and ochre sponged clothes, the pipe stem going through her body and the bowl modelled as a face, perhaps Yorkshire, pipe bowl restored, c1800, 7in (17cm).
£900-1,000 *C*

Did you know
MILLER'S Antiques Price Guide builds up year by year to form the most comprehensive photo-reference system available

A jardinière on a stand.
£900-1,200 *MGM*

A Jerome Massier Vallauris jardinière and stand, the lilac ground washed in cream and painted with iris in shades of green yellow and white, impressed mark 53in (134cm).
£1,000-2,000 *CSK*

A George Jones majolica cheese dome and stand, impressed marks, 12in (30cm).
£350-450 *DN*

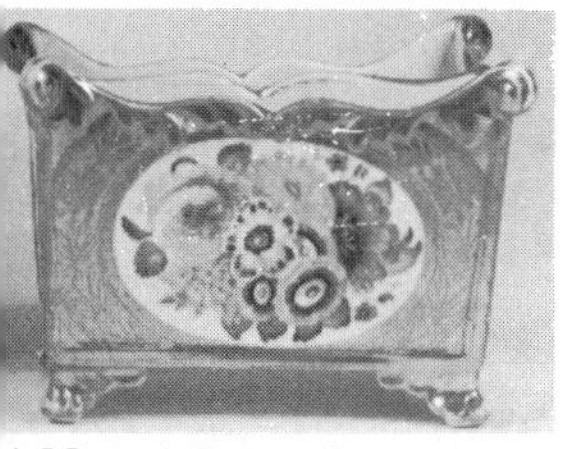

A Mason's Patent Ironstone china card rack, the grey/green ground reserved within oval gilt cartouches, the ends gilt between moulded gilt foliage borders and on 4 foliage feet, impressed marks, c1820, 5in (13cm) wide.
£300-400 *C*

An Alcora Holy water stoup painted in colours with a view of the Crucifixion, the cross inscribed with the Holy Monogram, glaze flakes, mid-18thC, 12in (30cm).
£400-500 *C*

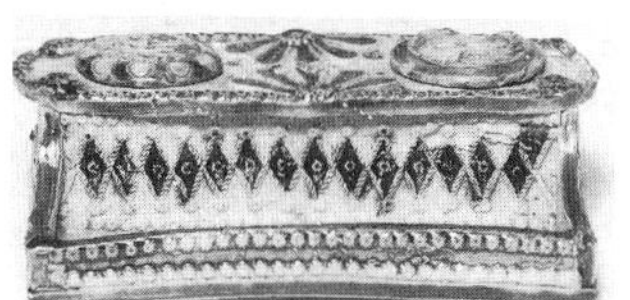

Three Westerwald saltglaze stoneware inkwells, with fitted sanders and inkpots decorated with manganese blue, one cracked, chips to liners, early 18thC, 5½in (14cm) wide.
£300-400 *C*

NEVERS FAIENCE

- ★ Nevers faience produced in various factories in the region
- ★ c1565 Italian potters came to the area and by 1600 had established a flourishing potting industry
- ★ early products resemble Italian faience
- ★ after c1625 Nevers bleu grounds became popular being produced throughout the 17thC in large quantities
- ★ decoration in the form of birds and flowersprays most common
- ★ although referred to as Bleu Persan these wares had no connection with Persian decoration

A Staffordshire pottery watch holder, of E Wood type, surmounted by a cockerel decorated in enamel colours, c1820, 8in (20cm).
£400-500 *LR*

A South Italian Holy water stoup painted in colours with Christ, the water bowl gadrooned and moulded with acanthus leaves, chipped, late 17thC, 13in (33cm), with a later gilt wood frame.
£900-1,200 *C*

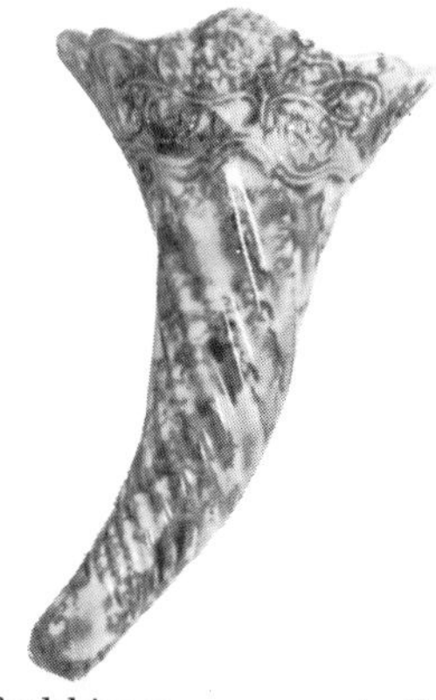

A Staffordshire creamware spirally moulded wall pocket of Whieldon type, splashed in brown, yellow, grey and green glazes, 2 minute rim chips, c1760, 8½in (21cm).
£500-700 *C*

A Staffordshire tipstaff moulded with the Royal Garter and the reverse with V.R., the lower part covered in a dark brown glaze, c1840, 11in (28cm).
£200-300 *CSK*

Miller's is a price Guide not a price List

The price ranges given reflect the average price a purchaser should pay for similar items. Condition, rarity of design or pattern, size, colour, provenance, restoration and many other factors must be taken into account when assessing values.
When buying or selling, it must always be remembered that prices can be greatly affected by the condition of any piece. Unless otherwise stated, all goods shown in Miller's are of good merchantable quality, and the valuations given reflect this fact.
Pieces offered for sale in exceptionally fine condition or in poor condition may reasonably be expected to be priced considerably higher or lower respectively than the estimates given herein

PORCELAIN

Influenced largely by the American market, wares with a strong decorative appeal are in great demand. Enthusiasm is running particularly high for 'botanical' wares, especially from the Chelsea and Bow factories. Other wares which would enhance the overall decoration of a room in 18th century style are equally popular.

Condition is of paramount importance in this area of the market. Wares in perfect condition command a premium but 'invisibly' repaired pieces also find a ready market through reputable dealers. As a result such dealers are often willing to buy damaged wares which can then be repaired. A customer should, of course, only buy from a dealer who can be trusted to make the degree of restoration clear.

19th Century Porcelain

The demand for quality continues unabated. Over the last year there has been a noticeable growth of interest in 19th century porcelain on behalf of buyers from the USA. Perfect condition, fine hand-painted decoration, size and shape are key factors affecting value.

Bearing these factors in mind, good quality ornamental vases of sufficient size to make a bold statement within a decorative scheme sell well, as do decorative services and centre pieces.

This interest in the decorative quality of 19th century wares does seem to have its negative side. In the American market decorative bone china saucers are in great demand as ash trays or for serving nuts. The cups which would normally accompany them are discarded, even left behind in the shop as not worth the trouble of carrying and certainly not suitable for nuts!

Baskets

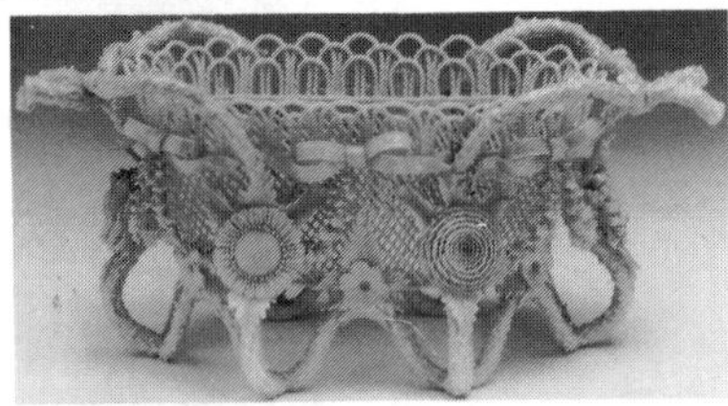

A Belleek opalescent basket, with triple strands applied with a ribbon and inscribed Belleek, Co. Fermanagh, one handle re-stuck, 12in (30cm) wide.
£1,500-2,500 *Bea*

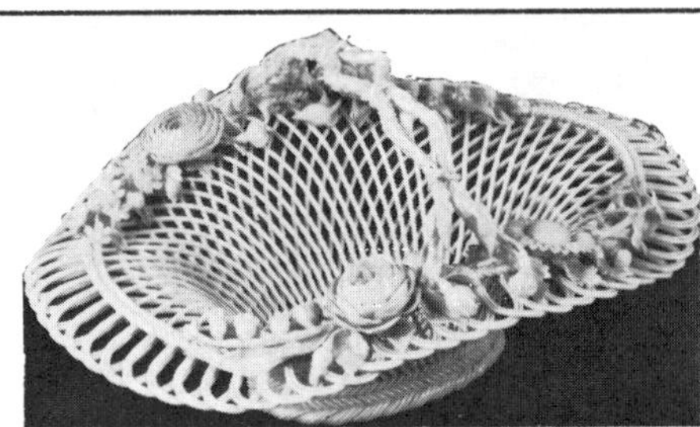

A First Period Belleek basket, impressed Belleek, Co. Fermanagh on a ribbon mark, 10½in (27cm) wide.
£300-500 *C*

A Coalbrookdale basket and pierced cover, the handle with mayflowers tied with a pink ribbon bow, 6½in (16cm).
£100-200 *L*

A Meissen basket, with green rope twist handles with coloured flower terminals, the exterior with blue flowerheads at the intersections, slight chips to terminals, blue crossed swords marks, c1880, 16½in (42cm) wide.
£700-900 *C*

A Rockingham primrose leaf moulded pot pourri basket, stand and cover, enriched in gilding, the cover with flower and foliage finial, cover repaired, the stand with puce griffin mark, c1835, 5½in (14cm).
£400-450 *C*

A pair of Spode Imari pattern pot pourri baskets and pierced covers, with gilt handles, painted beneath a white bead and gilt line rim, some slight rubbing to gilding, red marks and pattern No. 967, c1820, 5½in (14cm) wide.
£2,000-2,500 *C*

A Worcester quatrefoil basket, pierced cover and stand, one handle lacking to stand, some chipping to flowers, the cover incised 58, the base of the basket 13, c1760, the basket 8in (20cm) wide.
£1,000-1,200 *C*

A pair of Spode baskets, pattern No. 2600, marked, 8in (20cm) wide.
£150-200 *CB*

A Chamberlain's Worcester apple green ground basket, painted with a view of Derwent Water, script mark, c1820, 8½in (21.5cm) wide.
£350-450 *CEd*

A Chamberlain's Worcester blue ground basket with gilt carrying handle, painted with a view of Malvern, the underside with grey marbling, on 4 gilt paw feet, 2 feet chipped, script mark in iron red, c1830, 8in (20.5cm).
£400-500 *C*

A Chamberlain's Worcester miniature foliage moulded basket, the exterior enriched in puce, green and gilding, minor restoration to handle and slight crack to base, script mark in puce, c1840, 5in (12.5cm) wide.
£400-450 *C*

A Berlin ornithological basket, with blue sceptre mark and 3 incised lines and a 4, c1790, 11½in (29cm) wide.
£2,000-3,000 *C*

Bottles

A Worcester blue and white bottle and a basin, transfer printed with The Pine Cone and Foliage pattern, blue W marks, c1775, the bottle 8½in (22cm).
£900-1,200 *C*

Bowls

A Chelsea sunflower bowl and cover, enriched in yellow, with a green leaf finial, slight rim chips, cover repaired, finial restored, the cover with red anchor mark, c1756, 5in (13cm) wide.
£650-750 *C*

A Chelsea dish, c1760, 10½in (26.5cm) wide.
£250-350 *DEL*

A Derby miniature bowl and jug set, c1820, jug 1in (3cm).
£250-300 *BHA*

A Liverpool Herculaneum sugar bowl and cover, with fixed gilt ring handles, with a wide band of pink roses between gilt line rims, pattern No. 368 in gold, c1810, 5½in (14cm) wide.
£450-550 *C*

A lustre bat printed teabowl, c1810, 2½in (7cm) diam.
£25-35 *CA*

A Miles Mason sugar bowl and cover, with fixed gilt ring handle and moulded spire finial, painted in the 'famille verte' palette, with The Dragon in Compartments pattern between gilt lines, c1810-15, 6½in (16cm) wide.
£500-550 *C*

Miller's is a price Guide not a price List

The price ranges given reflect the average price a purchaser should pay for similar items. Condition, rarity of design or pattern, size, colour, pedigree, restoration and many other factors must be taken into account when assessing values

A Pinxton pale yellow ground sugar bowl and cover, with fixed gilt ring handles and finial, minor rubbing to gilding, script P No. 241 inside cover, c1795, 6in (15.5cm) wide.
£500-600 *C*

l. A First Period Worcester blue printed teabowl, Prunus Root pattern, slight damage, c1765, 2½in (6cm) diam.
£50-100

r. A First Period Worcester polychrome enamelled teabowl, c1750, 3in (7.5cm) diam.
£150-200 *CA*

A Ridgway bowl, Nutcracker and Siskin, 6½in (16.5cm) diam.
£240-300 *JG*

A Wedgwood Fairyland Lustre bowl, inscribed on base with printed urn mark and numbers Z4968, 11in (28cm) diam.
£1,000-1,500 *P[Re]*

A Worcester blue and white bowl, mid-18thC, 9in (23cm).
£200-300 *Bea*

A Worcester blue scale bowl of Lady Mary Wortley Montagu pattern, painted in the atelier of James Giles, enriched with gilt, some rubbing, blue square seal mark, c1770, 6½in (16.5cm) diam.
£600-700 *C*

A Worcester powder blue ground bowl, painted within gilt circular and fan shaped medallions, 6in (15cm) diam, and an unglazed waster of a similar bowl from the factory site, c1770.
£300-400 *C*

A Royal Worcester bowl, painted by Jas Stinton, signed, with shaded gilt borders, printed mark for 1916, 9in (23cm).
£500-600 *L*

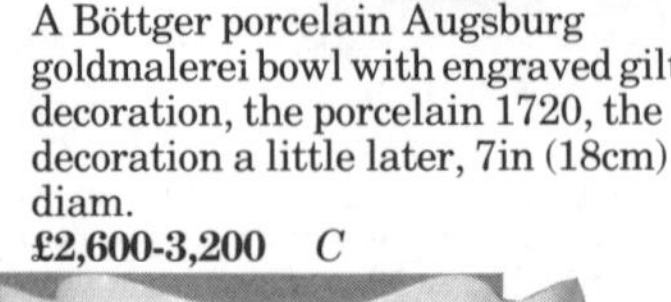

A Böttger porcelain Augsburg goldmalerei bowl with engraved gilt decoration, the porcelain 1720, the decoration a little later, 7in (18cm) diam.
£2,600-3,200 *C*

A Meissen purple ground sugar bowl and cover, with gilt and iron red bud finial, reserved on a purple ground, blue crossed swords mark and Pressnummer 80, painter's mark 5, to each piece, c1740, 4½in (11.5cm) diam.
£4,000-5,000 *C*

A Böttger porcelain bowl, the exterior with a band of Böttger lustre foliage edged in gilt, 2 minute rim chips, c1725, 7in (17.5cm) diam.
£7,000-8,000 *CG*

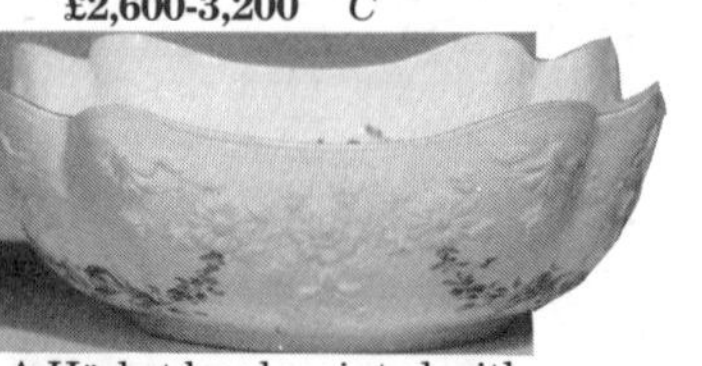

A Höchst bowl, painted with scattered flower sprays, with gilt rim, puce wheel mark and impressed IS, c1760, 8½in (21cm) square.
£500-600 *C*

A Meissen slop bowl, painted by Mehlhorn, with Böttger lustre gilt and iron red foliage surround, repaired, c1722, 7in (18cm) diam.
£2,700-3,200 *C*

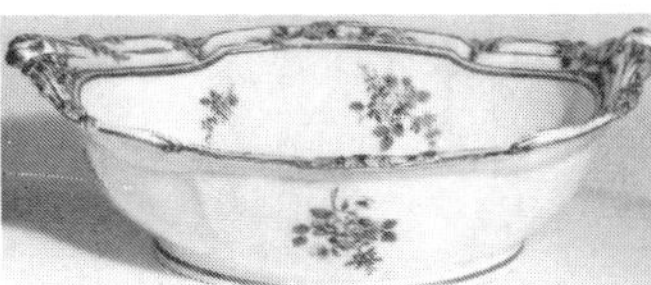

A Sèvres basin, painted in colours with gilt and blue lines, star crack in base, blue interlaced L marks enclosing date letter F for 1758, 12½in (31.5cm) wide.
£700-900 *C*

A Meissen chinoiserie bowl, the exterior painted in colours, the interior with an 'en camaieu rose' chinoiserie panel within gilt panelled and foliage rim, blue crossed swords mark, Pressnummer 8 and traces of gilder's mark 38, c1740, 6½in (17cm) diam.
£5,000-6,000 *C*

A Sèvres punch bowl, painted in colours between 'bleu celeste' and gilt bands, blue interlaced L marks enclosing the date letters for 1785, the painter's mark of Micaud, and the gilder's mark of Vincent, 13in (33cm) diam.
£5,000-6,000 *C*

A bowl by Samson of Paris, decorated within gilt scroll borders on a gold diaper ground, the inside with flowers and butterflies, 11½in (29cm) diam.
£250-350 *L*

A Vienna Du Paquier quatrefoil bowl, painted in Schwarzlot with continuous 'Laub-und-Bandelwerk', enriched with gilt, and 4 Schwarzlot lappets, gilt rims, c1735, 7in (18cm) diam.
£1,000-1,500 *C*

A Vienna Du Paquier bowl, the interior decorated, and with iron red rim, c1735, 7in (17.5cm) diam.
£2,500-3,000 *CG*

Boxes

A Meissen sugar box with gilt rim, cover missing, blue crossed swords mark, incised dreher's mark of 3 dots, gilder's number 30, c1730, 5in (13cm) wide.
£350-400 *CNY*

TYPES OF PORCELAIN

The distinction between hard and soft paste porcelain is:

- ★ **hard paste (or true porcelain)** – fired at a higher temperature than soft paste; feels cold to the touch; chip is flint or glass like; hard, glittery glaze
- ★ **soft paste (or artificial)** – file will cut easily into soft paste (not a test to be recommended!); chip is granular; warmer feeling to the touch; less stable in the kiln, figures in particular were difficult to fire; soft glaze – liable to crazing; the early soft paste was prone to discolouration

A Meissen silver mounted snuff box and cover, on green base, the interior and the cover with scattered 'deutsche Blumen', the silver mount chased with foliage, c1750, 2½in (6cm) wide.
£3,500-4,000 *CG*

A Spode box and cover, reserved on a blue ground gilt with scale pattern, pattern No. 1166, c1820, 3in (7cm) diam.
£800-1,000 *C*

A Mennecy silver mounted oval snuff box, modelled as a hen and chick, c1760, 2in (5cm) wide.
£2,500-3,000 *CG*

A Meissen snuff box and cover, the cover painted in the manner of Wagner with Plenty attended by cupids, with gilt metal mounts, minor chip to interior of cover, mid-18thC, 3in (7.5cm) wide.
£1,000-1,200 *C*

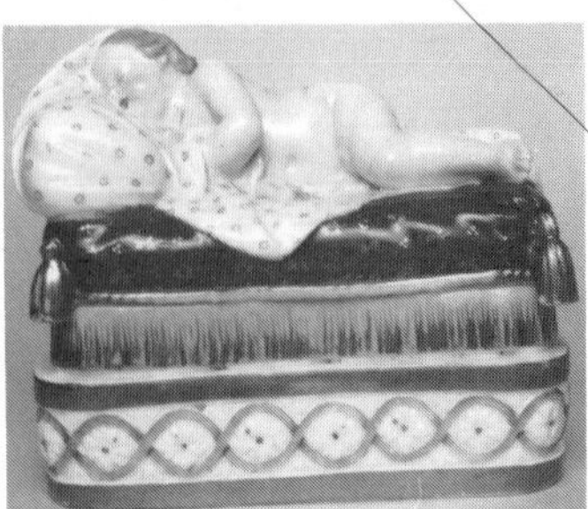

A Staffordshire porcelain box, modelled as a sleeping infant, c1840.
£225-300 *JUD*

Caddies

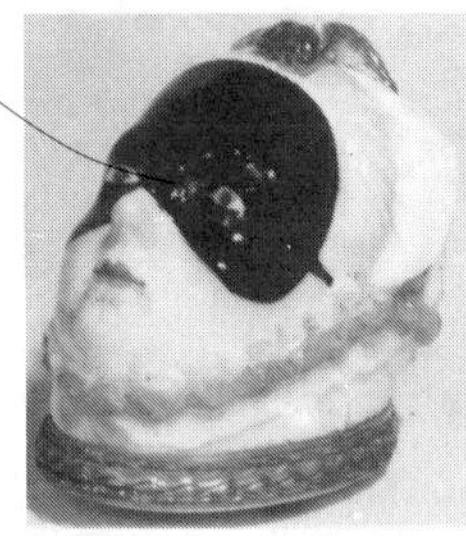

A Chelsea copper gilt mounted bonbonniere, with diamond chip eyes, the interior painted with scattered flowers, the enamel cover similarly painted, cracks to cover, c1755, 3in (8cm).
£800-1,200 *C*

A pair of inscribed Lowestoft tea caddies for Bohea tea and Green tea, Bohea with minute rim chip to circular aperture, painter's number 5, c1765, 5in (12cm).
£3,000-4,000 *C*

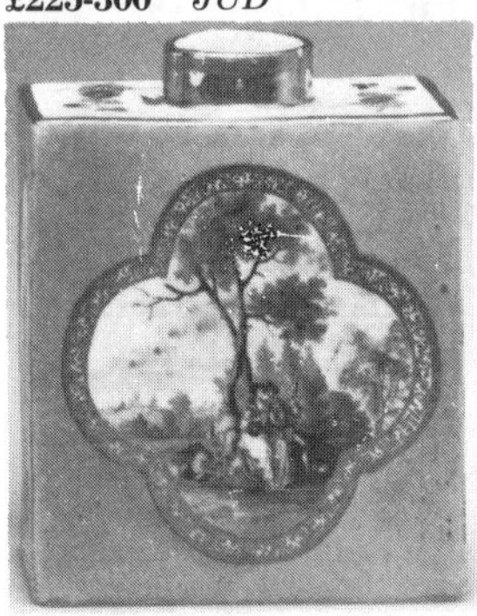

A Meissen tea caddy and cover with pine cone finial, cover repaired, blue crossed swords mark, c1750, 6in (14.5cm).
£1,000-1,500 *C*

A Meissen lime green tea caddy, blue crossed swords mark, c1740, 4in (10cm).
£1,500-2,000 *CG*

Candelabra

A set of 4 John Bevington two-branch candelabra, in the form of figures emblematic of the Seasons, in turquoise, puce and gilt, some damage, crossed swords and monogram mark in blue, 13½in (34cm).
£450-550 *DN*

A pair of Bow candlestick figures of a stag and doe, with mottled brown coats, brightly coloured foliate nozzles, the bases enriched in turquoise and blue, restoration to trees, antlers and doe's ears, crack to one nozzle, some minor chipping and restoration to extremities, c1765, 9½in (23.5cm).
£2,600-3,400 *C*

A pair of Bow candlestick figures of The New Dancers, enriched in underglaze blue and gold, she restored through waist, both with restoration to trees and nozzles, c1765, 11½in (29cm).
£1,200-1,500 *C*

A pair of Bow candle groups of Cupid with dog and bird, one restored, 9in (22.5cm).
£800-900 *BHA*

A pair of Coalport ormolu-mounted simulated bronze candlesticks, on pink lustre spreading bases and with gilt rims, rubbed, c1810, 11in (27cm).
£800-1,200 *C*

A pair of Chelsea fable candlesticks, modelled as The Dog and The Ass, the beast of burden carrying dead game in its panniers, and The Dog in the Manger barking at an ox, enriched in gilding, chips and restorations, repairs to nozzles, gold anchor marks at back, c1765, 13in (33cm).
£2,500-3,000 *C*

Use the Index!

Because certain items might fit easily into any of a number of categories, the quickest and surest method of locating any entry is by reference to the index at the back of the book.
This has been fully cross-referenced for absolute simplicity

A miniature Coalport candlestick, c1820, 2in (5cm).
£60-100 *DEL*

A miniature Coalport taper stick, c1820, 3in (7.5cm) diam.
£350-400 *JUD*

Two Derby candlestick groups, some damage, late 18thC, 9in (23.5cm).
£450-550 *Bea*

A pair of Derby candle groups with Continental sconces, c1770, 9½in (24cm).
£1,200-1,500 *BHA*

A pair of Derby porcelain candlestick figures, with green and gilded decoration, c1780, 9in (22.5cm).
£900-1,200 *DL*

A Liverpool Herculaneum griffin candlestick, the gilt beast on a painted plinth, some restoration to base, c1820, 7in (18.5cm).
£800-1,200 *C*

A pair of Derby candlestick groups, in the form of a gardener and his companion, some damage and restoration, 12in (30cm).
£550-650 *DN*

A pair of Bloor Derby figure candleholders, c1835, 11in (28cm).
£1,500-2,000 *BHA*

A pair of Meissen five-branch candelabra, modelled by J J Kändler from the Sulkowsky service, old damage and repairs to the branches and rear of one base, 1736, 24in (62cm).
£12,000-15,000 *C*

Centrepieces

A Derby blue and white centrepiece, surmounted by a kingfisher, minor damage, patch marks, c1768, 6½in (16.5cm).
£650-750 *CSK*

A Doccia white glazed centrepiece modelled as a bridge, fitted with 4 vases on pedestals with silver gilt flowering plants, the bridge 13in (33cm) wide, c1750, fitted with gilt wood supports simulating rippling water.
£600-800 *CNY*

A German porcelain floral encrusted tablecentre.
£250-300 *BWe*

A pair of Meissen candelabra, c1845, 12in (30.5cm).
£1,500-2,000 *BHA*

A pair of Bloor Derby vases of flowers, on a dark blue ground, on pierced white and gilt stands and 4 gilt paw feet, circular Bloor Derby mark and crowned Gothic D in red, 6½in (16.5cm).
£400-450 *L*

A pair of Meissen armorial candlesticks, modelled after silver originals, painted in colours with scattered 'Holzschnitt Blumen' enclosing the armorial device of Smith of Essex between gilt lines, one nozzle broken off and repaired, blue crossed swords marks and Pressnummer 46 to both pieces, c1745, 8½in (22.5cm).
£1,400-2,000 *C*

A Crown Derby bough pot, encrusted with flowers in a white and gilt panel on a rich blue ground, with pink rose handles, the cover composed of a mass of flowers, including irises, pansies and carnations, printed mark in red, crowned Gothic D, 7in (17cm).
£1,200-2,000 *L*

A colourful Meissen centrepiece, decorated with flowers and on either side with Chinese figures under a parasol, the interior painted with gold scrolling foliate designs, restored, inscribed B.195, 20in (53cm) wide.
£1,000-1,500 *Bea*

Clock Cases

A late Meissen clock case, modelled as a putto reading from an open book, cockerel's tail feathers re-stuck, 11in (28cm).
£2,000-2,500 *CSK*

A Sèvres pattern gilt bronze mounted centrepiece, painted on a blue ground, late 19thC, 11in (27.5cm).
£600-700 *C*

A large Meissen centrepiece group, painted in bright enamel colours, very slight damage, late 19thC, 14in (36cm).
£1,400-1,600 *Bea*

A late Meissen composite clock garniture, clock and one candlestick with chips to extremities, one candlestick with repairs, blue crossed swords and incised and impressed numerals, clock 12in (30.5cm).
£2,400-2,600 *CSK*

A Paris porcelain clock case, decorated in gold on a turquoise ground, complete with Paris clock movement, on wood stand under a glass dome, mid-19thC, 13in (33.5cm).
£400-500 *Bea*

A Paris, Jacob Petit, blue ground clockcase and stand, reserved on blue grounds, the movement by Hrr Marc à Paris, blue JP marks, c1835, 13in (34cm), with rectangular ebonized wood stand and glass dome.
£500-800 *C*

A Sèvres pattern gilt bronze mantel clock, the movement by Gasnier à Paris, Quai Voltaire, 17, c1875, 16in (41cm) wide.
£800-1,200 *C*

Cottages & Pastille Burners

A porcelain pastille burner, with sliding tray, probably Coalport, c1835, 5in (12.5cm).
£800-1,000 *DL*

An English porcelain cottage, c1835, 5in (12.5cm).
£350-450 *DL*

A Staffordshire white porcelain triple pastille burner, the roofs applied with coloured flowers and terminating in gilt finials, chips to flowers, finials re-stuck, hair crack to base, c1848.
£500-600 *C*

A Staffordshire pastille burner, minor chips to flowers, c1845, 6½in (16.5cm).
£500-600 *C*

A Staffordshire church, with detachable base, c1835, 4in (10cm).
£550-650 *DL*

A two-part porcelain pastille burner, with coloured flowers and gilding, c1830, 6in (15cm).
£400-500 *LR*

Miller's is a price Guide not a price List

The price ranges given reflect the average price a purchaser should pay for similar items. Condition, rarity of design or pattern, size, colour, provenance, restoration and many other factors must be taken into account when assessing values. When buying or selling, it must always be remembered that prices can be greatly affected by the condition of any piece. Unless otherwise stated, all goods shown in Miller's are of good merchantable quality, and the valuations given reflect this fact. Pieces offered for sale in exceptionally fine condition or in poor condition may reasonably be expected to be priced considerably higher or lower respectively than the estimates given herein

Cups

A Bow coffee cup, decorated with continuous chinoiserie scene of fishermen, c1770.
£200-250 *JG*

A miniature Bow trio, c1758.
£700-800 *VEN*

A Caughley polychrome teabowl and saucer, with Target pattern, c1780.
£110-120 *THA*

A rare Coalport John Rose faceted coffee can, c1800, 2½in (6cm).
£20-25 *TVA*

A Coalport egg cup, c1820, 2in (5cm).
£30-40 *JUD*

A Chelsea teabowl, with classical ruin decoration, raised anchor period, c1750, 3½in (9cm) diam.
£1,200-1,500 *VEN*

A Coalport trio, c1825.
£100-120 *JUD*

A Chelsea beaker painted with The Red Dragon pattern, the interior with scattered flowerheads, chip to foot rim, 2½in (7cm), and an octagonal saucer en suite, raised anchor mark, c1750.
£1,500-2,000 *C*

A Chelsea Derby cup and saucer, c1765, saucer 5in (12.5cm) diam.
£200-250 *BHA*

A Chelsea Derby cup and saucer, c1770, saucer 5in (12.5cm) diam.
£200-250 *BHA*

A Derby teacup and saucer, painted in monochrome, pattern No. 33, c1810.
£65-75 *TVA*

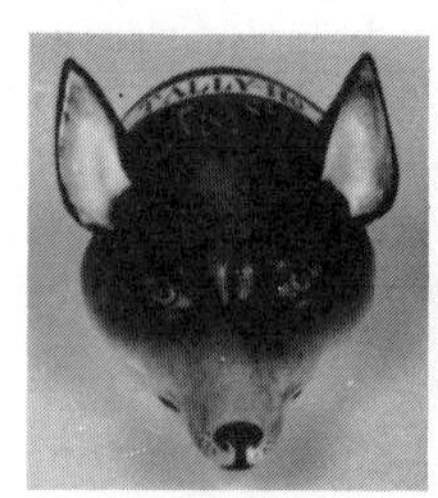

An English stirrup cup, probably Derby, with Tally Ho on the collar, c1835, 3in (7.5cm).
£450-500 *DL*

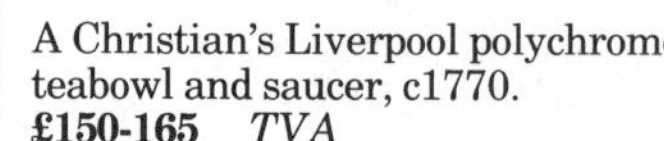

A Christian's Liverpool polychrome teabowl and saucer, c1770.
£150-165 *TVA*

A Minton cup and saucer with Sèvres mark, pattern No. 90, 2in (5cm).
£120-150 *JUD*

A New Hall teabowl, cup and saucer, 'en grisaille', pattern No. 171, c1790, cup 2½in (6cm).
£60-100 *DEL*

A Pennington's Liverpool coffee cup, c1775, 2½in (6cm).
£90-120 *DEL*

A Pinxton teacup and saucer, with pink and gilt swags with iron red tendrils and gilt line rims, cup cracked, the saucer with impressed], c1795.
£420-450 *C*

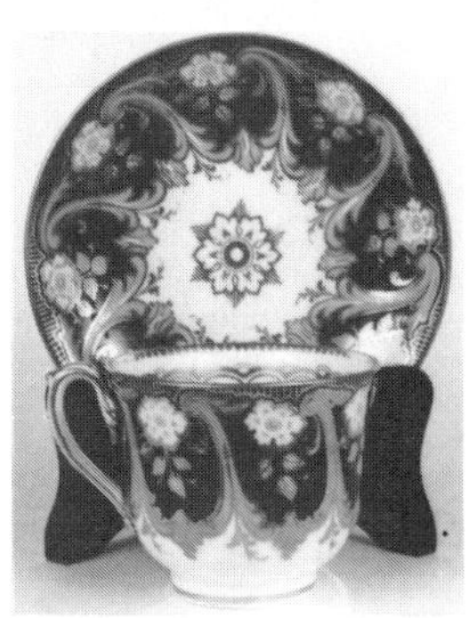

A Ridgway cup and saucer, pattern No. 5/3647, c1850.
£60-70 *TVA*

A Spode coffee can, c1820, 2½in (6cm).
£40-60 *JUD*

A Staffordshire stirrup cup, c1835, 5in (12.5cm).
£650-700 *DL*

A Worcester Flight & Barr teabowl and saucer, scratch B mark, c1790, saucer 5½in (13cm) diam.
£50-70 *TVA*

NEWHALL

- ★ Newhall was the second Staffordshire pottery to successfully make porcelain, Longton Hall being the first (although Neale may have been making porcelain)
- ★ the usual date for the commencement of the factory is 1782, however then it was known as Hollins, Warburton & Company
- ★ they used the Cookworthy method of making a class of porcelain known as hybrid hard-paste
- ★ porcelain is a greyish colour to transmitted light and is seldom crazed
- ★ Duvivier, who had worked at Derby and Worcester, also painted at New Hall from 1782-90 – because of the rarity of attributable pieces one wonders if some of his work at New Hall has been wrongly attributed to another factory
- ★ very few pre-1790 wares had a pattern number
- ★ around 1812 a new bone-china body was introduced and the factory was by this time known as New Hall
- ★ after 1820 the bone-china wares seemed to lose some quality and the factory closed in 1835
- ★ New Hall, above all other 18thC English factories, has seen what can only be called an explosion in price in recent years. This has probably been caused by the disparaging attitude of many porcelain dealers to the more ordinary Newhall wares in the past and hence their underpricing

A Wedgwood Fairyland Lustre melba cup, decorated with a version of the Leapfrogging Elves design under a sky studded with stars, pattern No. Z4968, 4in (10cm) diam.
£250-300 *Bea*

A Staffordshire teacup and saucer, by Charles Bourne, in colours and flaming orbs in iron red, mark in red C.B. and pattern No. 320.
£60-120 *L*

A Copeland Spode London teacup and saucer, pattern No. 2693, c1855.
£80-100 *TVA*

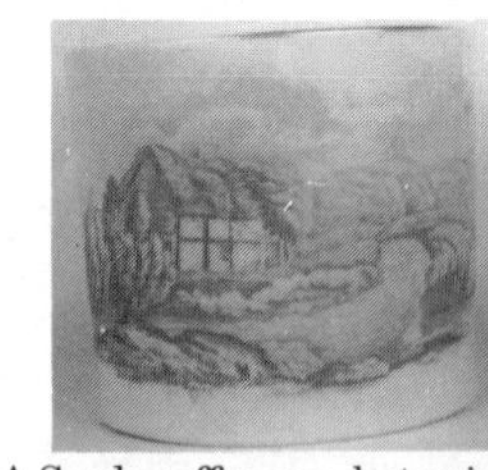

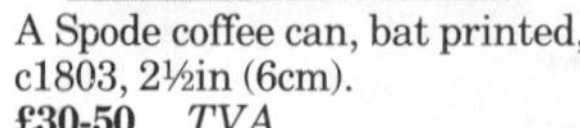

A Spode coffee can, bat printed, c1803, 2½in (6cm).
£30-50 *TVA*

A Chamberlain's Worcester egg cup in yellow and gilt, pattern No. 151, c1800.
£250-300 *JUD*

A Flight, Barr & Barr teacup and saucer, impressed mark, c1820.
£60-80 *TVA*

A Worcester Flight & Barr beaker, the wide top border painted in sepia, the lower part yellow with narrow gilt borders, inscribed in brown Flight & Barr, Worc. Manufacturers to their Majesties, a crown above, 4in (9.5cm).
£2,500-3,000 *L*

A Worcester three-piece by Giles, with rare twisted handles, saucer 5in (12.5cm) diam.
£400-500 *BHA*

A Worcester three-piece set comprising:
l. A thunderbolt teabowl and saucer, c1770, saucer 5in (12cm) diam.

r. A saucer dish decorated with iron red sunbursts, c1775, 7in (18cm) diam.
£400-450 *DEL*

l. A First Period Worcester coffee cup, hand painted in puce, green and gold, c1775, 2½in (6cm).
£60-80

r. A Pennington's Liverpool coffee cup, hand painted in pink and green, c1775.
£50-70 *CA*

WORCESTER PORCELAIN DATES

1751-1783	First Period
1751-1774	Dr Wall Period
1776-1793	Davis/Flight or Middle Period
1783-1793	Flight Period
1793-1807	Flight and Barr Period
1807-1813	Barr, Flight and Barr
1813-1840	Flight, Barr and Barr
1840-1852	Chamberlain and Company
1852-1862	Kerr and Binns (W H Kerr & Company)
1862	Royal Worcester Porcelain Company

A Worcester blue and white coffee cup and saucer, c1780.
£120-130 *THA*

A First Period Worcester cup and saucer, decorated with exotic birds in reserves on a scale blue ground.
£450-470 *OSA*

A Worcester cup and saucer, in the Kakiemon palette, with the Brocade pattern, saucer 4in (10cm) diam.
£400-450 *DEL*

A Worcester teabowl and saucer, printed in blue within a blue line border, disguised numeral 7 mark, c1780.
£70-120 *DN*

A hand painted cup and saucer, with dark blue borders and polychrome flowers, c1830.
£30-60 *CA*

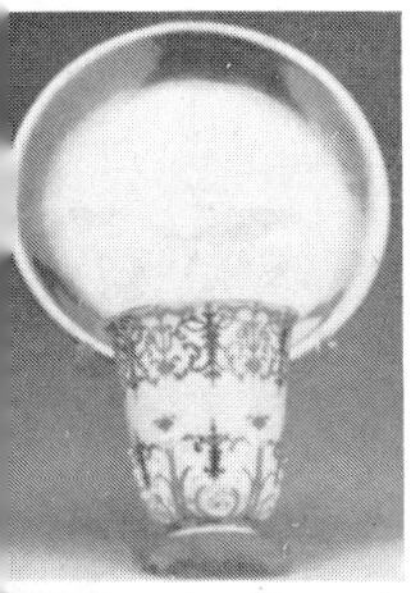

A Böttger beaker and saucer, moulded with bands of stiff leaves and gilt with symmetrical foliage with solid gilt interior, c1720.
£1,400-1,800 *CG*

A Meissen teabowl and saucer, the interior of both pieces with gilt 'Laub-und-Bandelwerk' borders, the interior of the teabowl with Schwarzlot indianische Blumen, blue crossed swords marks and the gilder's mark v., c1730.
£1,500-2,000 *C*

A Berlin teacup and saucer, painted with pink floral garlands within shaped pink borders gilt with foliage, blue sceptre marks, c1780.
£1,500-2,000 *CG*

A pair of Höchst cups and saucers, painted in the neo-classical taste 'en grisaille' within gilt surrounds, one saucer with chip and small crack, blue wheel marks and incised PI and IE marks, c1785.
£600-700 *C*

A pair of Meissen celadon fond cups and saucers, reserved on gilt and turquoise grounds, the handles with iron red dots, blue crossed swords marks, c1738.
£6,000-6,500 *CG*

A Meissen teabowl and saucer, with a spray of 'purpurmalerei' flowers to the well of the teabowl, c1735.
£900-1,200 *C*

A Berlin cup and saucer, the cup dated 1813 in foliage, the saucer with a map of Leipzig and inscribed 'Volkerschlacht bei Leipzig am 18 u 19 Oct', blue sceptre marks.
£1,500-2,000 *CG*

A Doccia teacup, coffee cup and saucer, moulded with mythological figures and monuments in landscapes, gilt rims, c1750.
£1,000-1,500 *C*

A Meissen beaker and saucer, painted with harbour landscapes, blue crossed swords marks and gilder's marks 8 to each piece, c1730.
£8,000-9,000 *C*

Make the most of Miller's

Miller's is completely different each year. Each edition contains completely NEW photographs. This is not an updated publication. We never repeat the same photograph

A Meissen dead leaf ground teabowl and saucer, painted with sprays of 'indianische Blumen' in the Kakiemon palette, blue crossed swords marks and impressed dreher's marks, c1738.
£2,000-2,500 *CG*

A pair of Meissen Hausmalerei teacups and saucers, painted by F F Meyer von Pressnitz, the cups with brightly coloured birds and flowers, the interiors gilt with 'Laub-und-Bandelwerk', blue crossed swords marks, c1740.
£3,000-4,000 *C*

A Meissen teacup and saucer, painted with scenes, gilt rims, crossed swords mark to both pieces, and Pressnummern 64 and 66, c1750.
£350-450 *C*

KAKIEMON

- ★ the Kakiemon family worked at the Japanese Arita factory towards the end of 17thC
- ★ their patterns are executed in a distinctive palette in iron red, pale yellow, turquoise and green
- ★ the Meissen factory copied from the Japanese originals and became fashionable in Europe

A Meissen chinoiserie teabowl and saucer, painted with Chinese figures, blue crossed swords marks, gilder's marks 38 to each piece, c1740.
£1,800-2,500 *C*

A Meissen green ground quatrefoil teacup and saucer, with 'ombrierte' gilt cartouches, saucer broken and re-stuck, crossed swords marks to base, c1740.
£700-800 *C*

A Meissen teacup and saucer, painted in colours with gilt rims, blue underglaze crossed swords marks and Pressnummern 64 and 66, c1750.
£350-450 *C*

A Meissen chinoiserie cup and saucer with gilt scrolled handle, the reverse of the saucer with scattered 'indianische Blumen', blue crossed swords marks, the cup with Pressnummer 24, gilder's numbers 38 to each piece, c1740.
£1,800-2,200 *C*

A Meissen armorial teacup and saucer, painted with a monogram flanked by military trophies and surmounted by the Imperial crown and with gilt trellis and lambrequin borders, blue crossed swords marks and Pressnummer 24 to each piece, c1740.
£2,000-2,500 *CG*

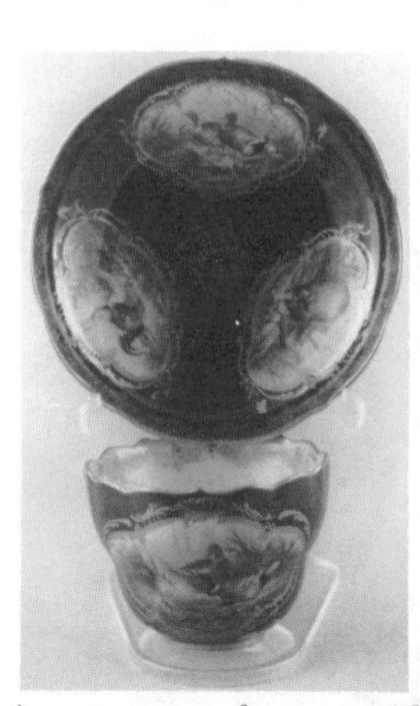

A Meissen teacup and saucer, with shaped rim and entwined handle, decorated on a blue ground, mark in blue, 19thC.
£400-500 *DN*

A Nyon teabowl and saucer, painted in colours with gilt dentil borders, blue fish marks, c1785.
£600-800 *CG*

A Nyon cup and saucer, painted in colours, minor chip to foot of cup, blue fish marks, c1785.
£1,200-1,500 *CG*

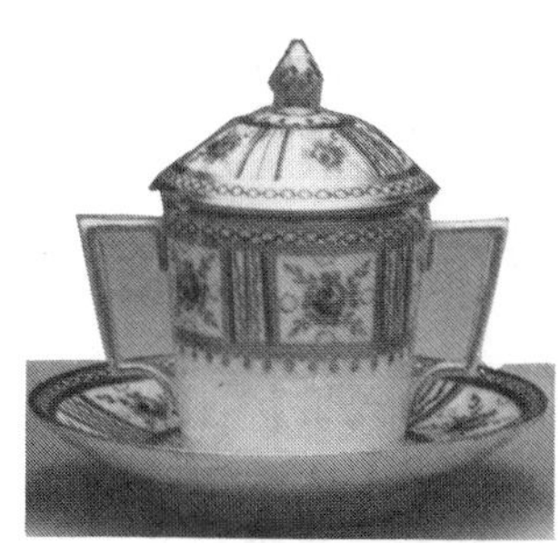

A Nyon trembleuse cup, cover and saucer, with gilt pine cone finial, painted with panels of roses divided by puce, green and gilt lines within borders of iron red chain pattern, blue fish marks, c1790.
£1,000-1,500 *CG*

A Paris cup and saucer, with floral painting in shades of brown and gilt, c1820, cup 3in (7.5cm).
£250-350 *BHA*

A Sèvres green ground cup and deep saucer, painted with garlands of pink roses in white reserves on a green ground heightened with gilding, interlaced L marks and date letter V for 1774, and painter's mark B.g.
£300-400 *C*

A Sèvres green ground cup and saucer, with gilt dentil rims, interlaced L marks, date letters D for 1756 and R for 1770, decorators' marks L B and E.
£550-650 *C*

A Sèvres cup and saucer, painted between shaped pale blue 'oeil-de-perdrix' and gilt seeded bands with gilt dentil rims, blue interlaced L marks enclosing the date letter Q for 1759, and with painter's mark of Thévenet père, incised marks.
£1,000-2,000 *C*

A Sèvres 'bleu nouveau' coffee cup and saucer, the panels reserved on 'bleu nouveau' ground with gilt, blue interlaced L marks enclosing the date letter N 1766 and painter's mark of Morin, incised marks.
£1,000-1,500 *C*

A Sèvres reeded cup and fluted saucer, painted in colours with a composite band of blue and yellow, alternating with green and yellow shells between brown and gilt bands with a blue line and gilt dash border and dentil rim, small chip to rim of cup, the saucer with interlaced L marks, date letter for 1768, and painter's mark of Thévenet père.
£400-450 *C*

A Paris, Jacob Petit, cup, cover and trembleuse stand, the sides encrusted with coloured bouquets, the cover with pink rose finial, chips to flowers, blue JP marks, c1840, the stand 6½in (16.5cm) diam.
£350-450 *C*

A Sèvres premier Empire coffee cup and saucer, painted with a broad band of gilt and silver chinoiseries on a black ground, various incised marks and red stencilled 'M.Imp. le de Sevres' marks to both pieces, c1808.
£1,200-1,500 *C*

A Vienna Du Paquier beaker, rim chips, perhaps decorated outside the factory, c1730.
£200-300 *CG*

A Vienna chocolate cup and square galleried tray, painted in green and black, within green and gilt beaded borders, blue beehive marks, the tray with crowned mark, the cup impressed 3, c1770, the tray 6½in (17cm) square.
£2,500-3,500 *C*

A Vincennes teabowl and saucer, with gilt rims, minor rim chips, the teabowl with blue interlaced L marks enclosing a dot, c1752.
£750-850 *C*

Ewers

A Coalport ewer, hand painted, unsigned, c1910, 7in (18cm).
£200-220 *THA*

A pair of Sèvres style ormolu mounted decorative faux ewers, with turquoise ground base, on acanthus moulded foot set on rounded plinth, 13in (33cm).
£750-1,000 *CNY*

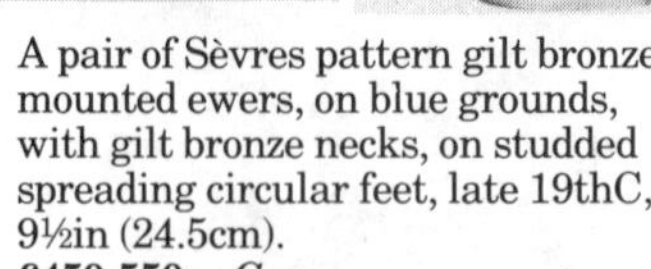

A pair of Sèvres pattern gilt bronze mounted ewers, on blue grounds, with gilt bronze necks, on studded spreading circular feet, late 19thC, 9½in (24.5cm).
£450-550 *C*

A Royal Worcester ewer with foliate moulded handle, pedestal foot and moulded shoulder, in muted enamels and gold, inscribed under the base January 4th 1980, 10½in (27cm).
£300-350 *Bea*

Figures – Animals

A Samuel Alcock dog, impressed numeral 311, c1835.
£235-300 *JUD*

A Bow white model of birds in branches, some restoration, c1755, 7in (18cm).
£250-300 *VEN*

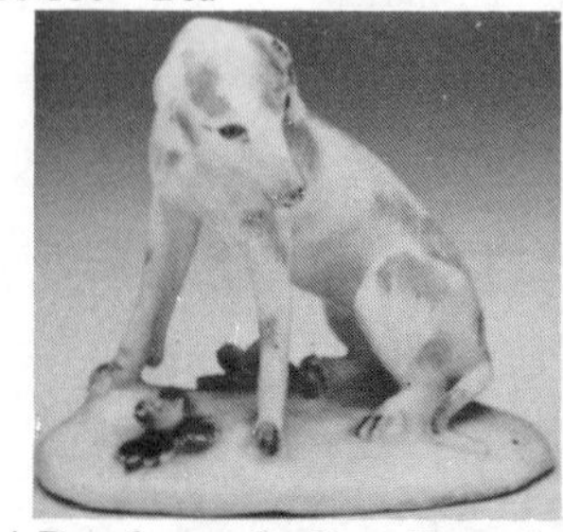

A Bow figure of a dismal hound, with light brown markings, base with applied flowers, 3in (8cm).
£2,000-3,000 *L*

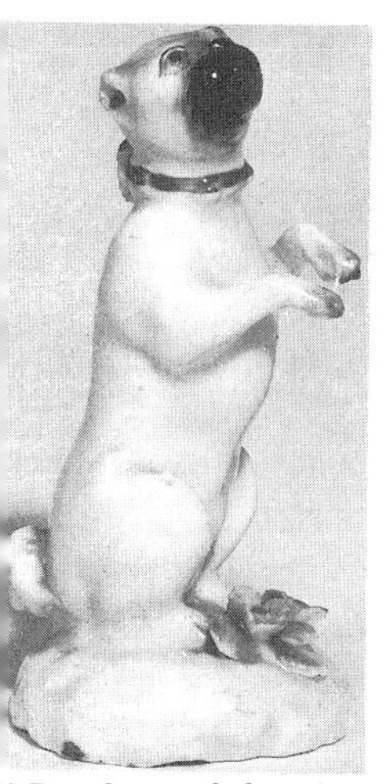

A Bow figure of a begging pug bitch, wearing a pink collar tied with a rosette, base applied with 2 coloured flowers, minute chip above left eye, c1758, 3½in (8.5cm).
£2,000-3,000 *C*

A Bow group of a hen and cockerel, with brown, puce and purple feather markings, restoration to hen's neck and through the base, c1760, 4½in (11cm).
£4,000-5,000 *C*

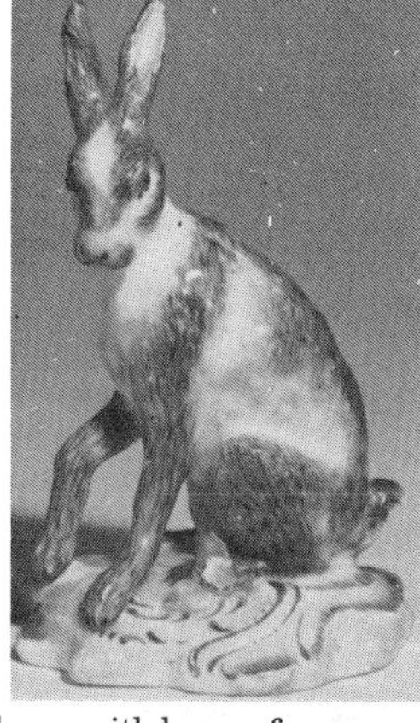

A Bow hare, with brown fur markings, the base enriched in green and applied with a flower, restored through top of front legs and re-stuck to base, ears restored, c1760, 5½in (14.5cm).
£2,500-3,500 *C*

A Bow bird group, well coloured, some restoration, c1760, 6½in (16.5cm).
£1,200-1,300 *BHA*

A Chelsea sheep, with brown markings, mound enriched in green, ears restored, red anchor mark, c1755, 3in (8cm) wide.
£700-1,000 *C*

A Derby dry edge figure of a boar, perhaps painted in the workshop of William Duesbury, tusks and one ear restored, Andrew Planché's period, c1753, 4½in (11.5cm).
£3,000-3,500 *C*

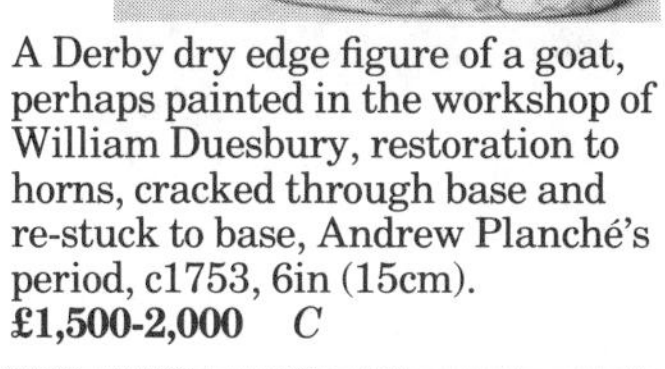

An English group of 3 pug dogs at play, chip to base, one tail and 2 legs repaired, c1850, 7in (18cm) wide.
£100-200 *CSK*

A Derby dry edge figure of a goat, perhaps painted in the workshop of William Duesbury, restoration to horns, cracked through base and re-stuck to base, Andrew Planché's period, c1753, 6in (15cm).
£1,500-2,000 *C*

A Derby figure of a leopard, with puce marked pale yellow coat, on a base applied with coloured flowers, tip of tail lacking, right forepaw and ear repaired, Wm Duesbury & Co, c1765, 3½in (9cm) wide.
£800-900 *C*

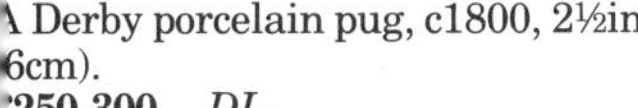

A Derby porcelain pug, c1800, 2½in (6cm).
£250-300 *DL*

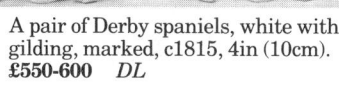

A pair of Derby spaniels, white with gilding, marked, c1815, 4in (10cm).
£550-600 *DL*

A pair of Bloor Derby models of peacocks, painted in gilt and blue enamel, chips to flowers, head feathers and beak of one, red painted marks and No. 8, 6½in (16.5cm).
£1,000-1,500 *CEd*

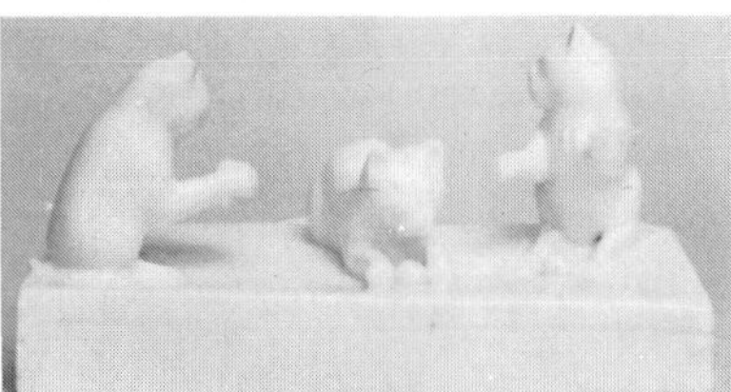
A Derby King Street cat group, c1870, 4in (10cm) wide.
£200-275 *BHA*

An English group of a recumbent cat with kittens playing at the side, painted in black and yellow and on pink rectangular and gilt lined base, perhaps Derby, minor restoration, c1825, 4½in (11.5cm).
£500-600 *CSK*

A Longton Hall white figure of a turkey of so-called 'Snowman' type, the stump perhaps originally surmounted by a nozzle, some minor chipping, c1750, 7½in (18.5cm).
£1,700-2,200 *C*

A Staffordshire porcelain Lloyd Shelton type eagle, unmarked, c1840, 7½in (19cm).
£300-350 *DL*

A Staffordshire porcelain dalmatian, c1840, 3in (7.5cm).
£175-250 *DL*

A Staffordshire porcelain swan, c1840, 3½in (9cm).
£200-250 *DL*

A pair of Staffordshire porcelain figures of dogs, with black and tan markings on a white ground, with gilt borders, 3½in (9.5cm).
£250-350 *L*

A Royal Worcester equestrian group, modelled by Doris Linder, 'Prince's Grace & Foal', No. 288 of a limited edition, 9½in (24cm), complete with a fitted wood stand and certificate.
£500-600 *Bea*

A Royal Worcester model of the racehorse Nijinsky, by Doris Linder, No. 193 of a limited edition, 11in (28cm), complete with fitted wood stand and certificate.
£500-600 *Bea*

A Höchst white figure of a dog, chips to ears, crack through hind legs, blue wheel mark to base, c1765, 4½in (12cm).
£250-400 *C*

A Meissen figure of a peacock, restoration to neck, minor frits to base, blue crossed swords mark, c1728, 7in (18cm).
£3,000-4,000 *C*

A Meissen miniature figure of a bear, with brown fur markings on mound base with foliage, ears restored, blue crossed swords mark at back, c1745, 3in (8cm).
£2,000-2,500 *C*

A Meissen white figure of a carthorse, modelled by P Reinicke, minor repairs, blue crossed swords mark at side, c1750, 8in (20cm) long.
£550-650 *C*

A Meissen figure of a swan, modelled by J J Kändler, on waterweed mound base, blue crossed swords mark at back, c1750, 4½in (11.5cm).
£5,000-6,000 *C*

A pair of porcelain Bolognese hounds in the Meissen style, seated on breccia marble plinths with gilt bun feet, 6½in (16.5cm) wide.
£2,500-3,500 *C*

A pair of Meissen canaries, in mint condition, c1850, 4½in (11cm).
£500-600 *BHA*

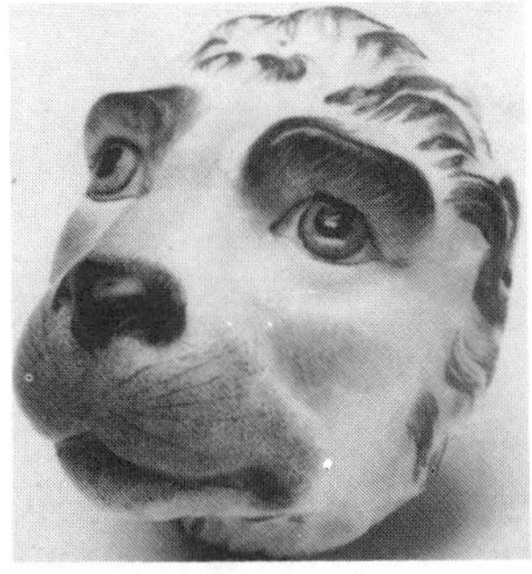

A Meissen bonbonniere base, moulded in the form of a lion's head and painted in naturalistic colours, the interior painted gold, cover missing.
£150-200 *Bea*

A Meissen finely modelled figure of a Bolognese terrier dog, in tones of white and brown, late 19thC, 9in (23cm).
£1,000-1,500 *GC*

A late Meissen group of a cockerel, hens and chicks, cockerel with damaged comb, chips to tail feathers, blue crossed swords, incised and impressed numerals, 8in (20.5cm).
£1,000-1,500 *CSK*

A pair of Minton porcelain poodles, c1845, 5in (12cm) wide.
£450-500 *DL*

Figures – People

A Belleek parian figure entitled 'The Prisoner of Love', after the model by Giovanni Fontana, named on the base, tassel at corner of drapery on base lacking, incised Giovanni Fontana Sc. at the back of the base, black printed Belleek, Co. Fermanagh, Ireland marks, second period, 25½in (65cm).
£5,000-6,000 *C*

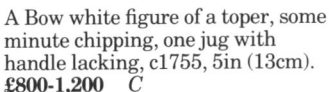

A Bow white figure of a toper, some minute chipping, one jug with handle lacking, c1755, 5in (13cm).
£800-1,200 *C*

A Bow white figure of Urania, by the Muses modeller, left hand and dividers lacking, chip to veil, c1752, 6½in (16cm).
£800-1,200 *C*

A Bow white figure of a sphinx said to represent the actress Peg Woffington, some minute chipping to headdress and tassels at back, c1750, 5in (12cm).
£1,500-2,000 *C*

A Bow white figure of Smell from a set of the Senses, slight chip to hem and tree, c1752, 5in (13cm).
£800-1,000 *C*

A Bow figure of a gallant, in pink lined blue frock coat, flowered waistcoat, pale yellow breeches and black shoes, with a black tricorn hat, left hand a replacement, flaking to enamel on coat, F mark in black, c1756, 6½in (16cm).
£800-1,200 *C*

A Bow white figure of Air, in flowing dress, c1758, 8½in (21cm).
£700-900 *C*

A Bow figure of a fish vendor, after the Meissen model in pink lined pale blue bodice and pink and flowered skirt, holding a white apron, on a green base, slight chips to fingers, tub, one fish lacking and chips to base, c1758, 6½in (16cm).
£1,200-1,700 *C*

A Bow figure of a lady in Turkish dress, after the Meissen model by J F Eberlein, in pale brown headdress, pale yellow flowered dress and pink skirt, crack to wrist, chips to tree and dress, one finger lacking, c1758, 6½in (17cm).
£1,000-1,500 *C*

An unmatched pair of Bow porcelain figures, of a shepherd and a shepherdess, c1760, 11½in (29cm).
£2,200-2,700 *DL*

A pair of Bow porcelain figures of the Seasons, Autumn and Winter, in mint condition, c1760, 7in (18cm).
£1,000-1,500 *DL*

A Bow figure of Pedrolino, with gilt edged pale yellow jacket, flowered culottes and black shoes and hat, some restoration to arms and jacket, c1765, 6in (15cm).
£650-750 *C*

A pair of Bow figures of a seated monk and nun, he in lime-green-lined blue cloak, plum coloured hood and scapular and pale pink tunic edged in gold, reading a red bound breviary, she in plum coloured pink lined veil and scapular and lime-green-lined blue habit, holding a gilt rosary, anchor and dagger marks in iron red, c1765, 5in (14cm).
£1,800-2,000 *C*

A Bow figure of a lady in red hat, pink jacket, striped and flowered dress and yellow underskirt, flowers chipped, fingers restored, c1765, 6in (15cm).
£650-750 *C*

A Bow sweetmeat figure, modelled as a new dancer in blue and pink hat, green bodice, iron red lined flowered apron and striped and patterned yellow dress, restoration to hat, hands, right arm and tree, c1765, 6½in (16cm).
£250-350 *C*

A large pair of Bow porcelain figures, a shepherd and shepherdess, c1765, 12in (30.5cm).
£1,200-1,500 *DL*

A pair of Bow Seasons figures, Autumn and Winter, c1765, 6½in (16.5cm).
£1,200-1,500 *DL*

A pair of Bow porcelain figures, from a set of the Elements, some damage, painted anchor and dagger marks, late 18thC, 10½in (26cm).
£500-700 *Bea*

A Bow figure of a Shepherdess, decorated in coloured enamels, anchor and dagger mark on base, 10in (25cm).

£650-750 *VEN*

A Bristol figure of Air, with flowing orange and yellow lined pink and gilt flowered dress, repairs to wings, raised right arm, foot and dress, chips, Richard Champion's Factory, c1775, 10½in (26.5cm).
£300-400 *C*

A Chelsea figure of a dancing peasant in black hat, pale aubergine jacket, white shirt and grey breeches, slight chips to hat, flowers and scarf, restoration to left shoulder and hand and edge of jacket, hand lacking, red anchor mark, c1755.
£1,200-1,500 *C*

A Chelsea group of a fisherman and companion, she wearing a green bodice, red skirt and white apron, he in pink jacket, white shirt and yellow breeches, restoration to her raised left hand and fish, handle of net and her back, gold anchor mark, c1765, 6½in (16cm).
£1,500-2,000 *C*

A Derby figure of a flautist, in turquoise lined white jacket, flowered waistcoat and yellow flowered breeches, some minute chipping, Wm Duesbury & Co, c1758, 6in (15.5cm).
£1,000-1,700 *C*

A Derby dry edge white figure of Minerva, 2 fingers chipped, Andrew Planché's period, c1753, 6½in (16.5cm).
£1,500-2,000 *C*

CHELSEA FIGURES

- ★ 1745-49 – Triangle period – figures extremely rare
- ★ 1749-52 – Raised anchor period – figures rare and many left in the white
- ★ 1753-57 – Red anchor period – the finest figures were made well proportioned and exquisitely enamelled with colours used sparingly
- ★ often direct copies of Meissen but due to soft porcelain appear 'softer', lacking brilliant whiteness and brittleness of the German counterparts
- ★ little gilding appears until c1759
- ★ 1758-70 – Gold anchor period – thicker glaze, and less restrained gilding in early wares following Sevres influence
- ★ figures often backed by heavy bocages and heavy scroll bases

A Derby figure of a gallant, in pale yellow hat, flowered jacket and turquoise breeches, the base enriched in puce, green and yellow, slight chips to hat, left hand restored, minor chipping, Wm Duesbury & Co, c1760, 5in (13cm).
£700-800 *C*

A pair of Derby figures of Juno and Jupiter, in pink and yellow flowered clothes, lightly enriched in gilding, Juno with restoration to peacock and left hand, both with minor chipping, Wm Duesbury & Co, c1765, 10½in (25.5cm).
£1,500-2,500 *C*

A Derby figure of General Conway, draped in a puce cloak, on a scroll moulded base enriched in gilding, slight damage to shield and cannon, Wm Duesbury & Co, c1770, 12½in (32cm).
£600-700 *C*

Two Derby figures of John Wilkes and General Conway, Wilkes in gilt edged white clothes and pink cloak, Conway in white cuirass, turquoise jacket and pink cloak, some minor restorations, Conway with restorations to base and back, Wm Duesbury & Co, c1765.
£1,200-1,500 *C*

A Derby figure of a singer, in turquoise lined pink cloak, iron red flowered jacket and yellow breeches, on a green rockwork base applied with flowers, some minute chipping, Wm Duesbury & Co, c1775, 8½in (21cm).
£400-500 *C*

A pair of Derby figures of a sailor and his lass, wearing pale striped and flowered clothes, he with restoration to arms, she to hat and right arm, trees chipped, Wm Duesbury & Co, c1765, 9½in (24cm).
£1,200-1,500 *C*

A pair of Derby porcelain figures of a Welsh tailor and his wife, c1800, 10in (25.5cm).
£1,500-2,000 *DL*

Large pairs are much rarer than small pairs which tend to be about 6in (15cm) high.

A Derby figure of a singer, in iron red lined black cape, pale yellow flowered jacket and pale yellow breeches, head re-stuck, some chipping, Wm Duesbury & Co, c1775, 8in (20.5cm).
£400-500 *C*

A pair of small Derby porcelain figures of a Welsh tailor and his wife, c1800, 6in (15cm).
£550-650 *DL*

A pair of Derby figures of Shakespeare and Milton, edged in gilding, incised No. 297 and 305, Robert Bloor & Co., c1820, 10½in (25.5cm).
£400-500 *C*

Make the most of Miller's

When a large specialist well-publicised collection comes on the market, it tends to increase prices. Immediately after this, prices can fall slightly due to the main buyers having large stocks and the market being 'flooded'. This is usually temporary and does not affect very high quality items

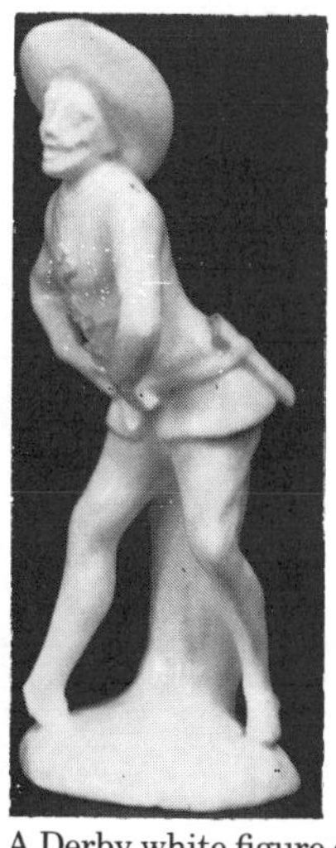

A pair of Derby figures of Autumn and Winter after the original model by Pierre Stephan, 9 and 8½in (23 and 21.5cm).
£500-600 *CSK*

A Derby white figure of Harlequin after the Meissen model, hat and foot chipped, sword lacking, Robert Bloor & Co, c1815, 5½in (14cm).
£600-700 *C*

A pair of Plymouth bocage figures of a gardener and his companion, some damage, late 18thC, 10½in (25.5cm).
£550-650 *Bea*

A Rockingham white biscuit bust of William IV, c1830, 6½in (17cm).
£400-500 *C*

A Rockingham biscuit figure of a paysanne du Mongfall en Tirol, hat, fingers and handle of basket restored, incised No. 15 and impressed marks, c1830, 7½in (19cm).
£600-700 *C*

A Staffordshire porcelain figure of a girl with a doll, c1835, 6in (15cm).
£300-400 *DL*

A Staffordshire porcelain figure of Dr Syntax, Landing at Calais, c1835, 5in (12.5cm).
£200-250 *DL*

A large Royal Worcester parian model 'The Bather Surprised', after an original model by Sir Thomas Brock, draped in pale green, some damage, impressed marks, late 19thC, 26in (66cm).
£700-800 *Bea*

A pair of Royal Worcester figures of children carrying baskets, after models by James Hadley, impressed and printed marks for 1883, 8½in (22cm).
£700-800 *DN*

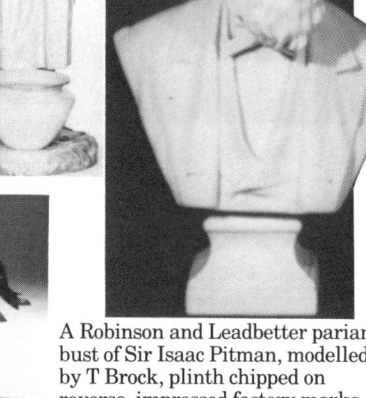

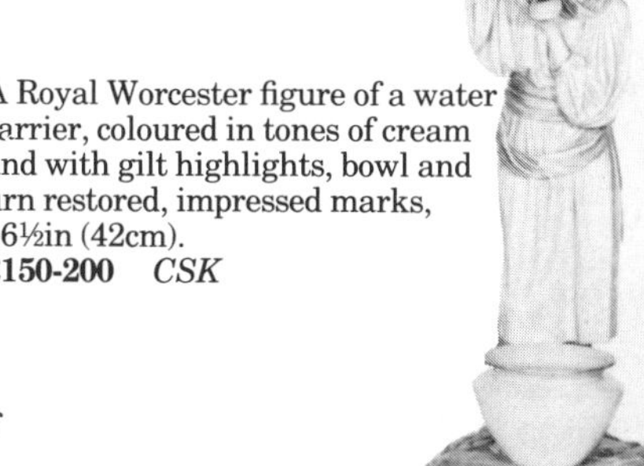

A Royal Worcester figure of a water carrier, coloured in tones of cream and with gilt highlights, bowl and urn restored, impressed marks, 16½in (42cm).
£150-200 *CSK*

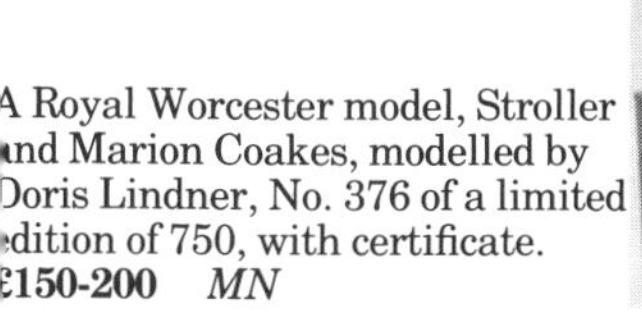

A Royal Worcester model, Stroller and Marion Coakes, modelled by Doris Lindner, No. 376 of a limited edition of 750, with certificate.
£150-200 *MN*

A Robinson and Leadbetter parian bust of Sir Isaac Pitman, modelled by T Brock, plinth chipped on reverse, impressed factory marks, impressed sculptor's name and dated 1887, 2½in (6cm).
£140-170 *CSK*

A pair of Berlin figures, painted in bright enamel colours, some damage, sceptre mark, 7in (18cm).
£400-500 *Bea*

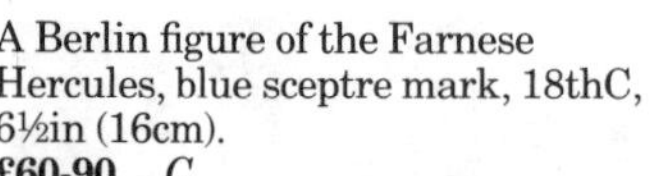

A Berlin figure of the Farnese Hercules, blue sceptre mark, 18thC, 6½in (16cm).
£60-90 *C*

A pair of Berlin figures from a set of the Months, one inscribed 'Marts', with a sign for Aries attached to the tree stump base, the other inscribed 'Februari', with the sign of Pisces, minor chips, blue sceptre marks, c1785, 4½in (11cm).
£500-600 *C*

A Berlin Wegely figure of Cupid, in disguise as a lawyer, restoration to hands and cape, blue mark at back, various impressed marks, c1755, 4½in (11cm).
£1,000-1,200 *C*

A pair of Berlin figures, decorated predominantly in blue, K.P.M. mark, late 19thC, 14½in (37.5cm).
£700-800 *Bea*

A French figure of a seated Chinaman, in Kakiemon colours, cover of globe missing, painted Chantille mark, 19thC, 10½in (26cm).
£300-350 *Bea*

A Capodimonte Carlo III figure of a man, modelled by Guiseppe Gricci, extensive repair to his head and right arm, c1750, 9½in (24cm).
£2,000-3,000 *C*

Apparently unrecorded in the literature of Capodimonte.

A pair of Dresden white figures of a gallant and his companion, some minor chipping, mock blue crossed swords marks, c1900, 18½in (46.5cm).
£1,200-1,400 *C*

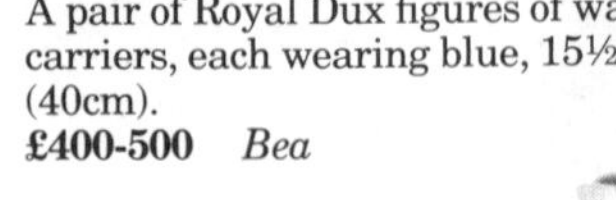

A pair of Royal Dux figures of water carriers, each wearing blue, 15½in (40cm).
£400-500 *Bea*

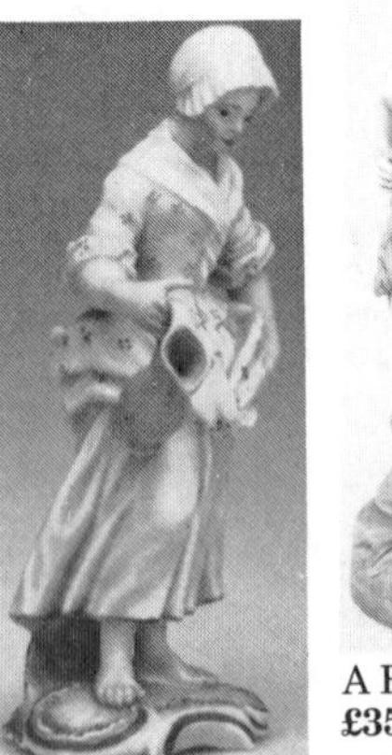

A Royal Dux group, 28½in (72cm).
£350-450 *P[Re]*

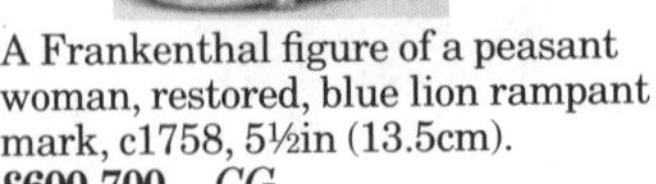

A Frankenthal figure of a peasant woman, restored, blue lion rampant mark, c1758, 5½in (13.5cm).
£600-700 *CG*

A Fürstenberg figure of a boy allegorical of Winter, wearing a brown ermine-lined cap and a lilac ermine-lined coat, some gilding, left hand and foot repaired, incised script B L and impressed 3 to base, c1780, 4½in (11.5cm).
£500-600 *C*

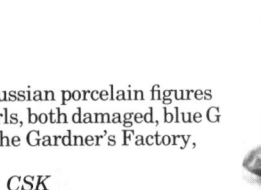

A pair of Russian porcelain figures of young girls, both damaged, blue G marks for the Gardner's Factory, 8in (20cm).
£300-350 *CSK*

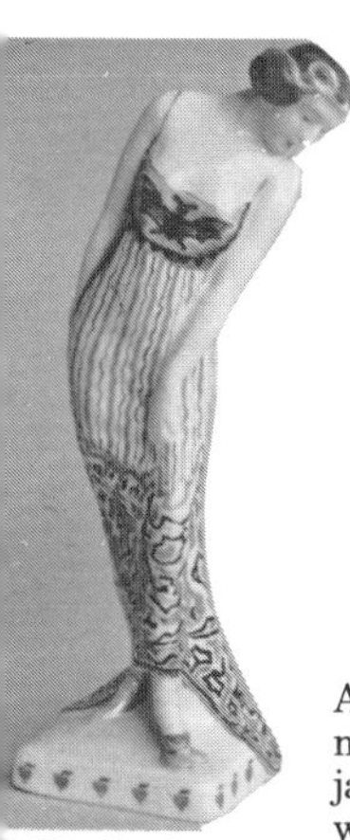

A Heubach porcelain figure of lady of mystic origin.
£350-400 *MGM*

A pair of Höchst figures of musicians, he in a pale orange jacket, pink trousers, a black hat with white feathers, she in a yellow dress, white pinafore, pink hat and bodice, restoration to his hand, the end of her mandolin, blue wheel marks to bases, c1765, 6½in (16.5cm).
£4,000-4,500 *C*

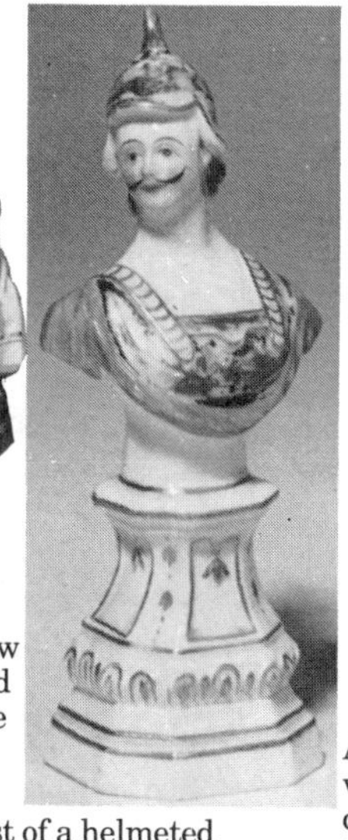

A Höchst bust of a helmeted warrior, painted in colours, enriched with gilding, red wheel mark to base and painter's mark C, c1755, 4½in (11cm).
£350-400 *C*

A Höchst figure of Harlequin, wearing a multi-coloured suit and a conical hat, his head restored, chip to hat, one of the goat's horns missing, the bagpipe broken, red enamel wheel and painter's c and incised $\frac{I}{K}$ marks to base, c1755, 6½in (16cm).
£4,000-5,000 *C*

A Höchst figure of a Chinaman, modelled by der Meister des Türkischen Kaisers, his coat with yellow border with scattered flowers over a green robe, chips to sleeves and tips of shoes, piece of base re-stuck, c1755, 4in (9.5cm).
£700-800 *C*

A Höchst figure of a dancing girl, modelled by Johann Peter Melchior, wearing a blue and iron red laced bodice, with gilt edged white skirt and yellow underskirt, thumb and forefinger of right hand missing, blue crowned wheel mark, c1775, 5½in (13.5cm).
£550-600 *C*

A pair of Kloster Veilsdorf figures of a sultan and sultana, after the Meissen model, his right hand, sword hilt and right boot restored, restoration to her hat, the sultan with incised G on the base, c1775, 7½in (19cm).
£3,000-3,500 *CG*

A Höchst figure of a lady, modelled by Johann Peter Melchior, her left hand missing and chips to base, blue crowned wheel mark, c1770, 7in (18cm).
£800-900 *C*

A Ludwigsburg figure of an apple seller, by Pierre François Lejeune, blue crowned interlaced C mark, and painter's mark L, c1770, 5in (12.5cm).
£1,200-1,600 *C*

A Limbach figure of a lady emblematic of Winter, with puce topcoat and puce flowered white skirt with orange hem, c1775, 6in (15cm).
£2,000-2,500 *C*

A Ludwigsburg figure of a lady with a muff, modelled by Pierre François Lejeune, in puce, orange, white and blue, chip to cape, blue crowned double C mark, and incised IC3 to base, c1760, 5in (12.5cm).
£900-1,000 *C*

A Meissen figure of Harlequin with a jug, modelled by J J Kändler, dressed in yellow and red chequered trousers and a multi-coloured harlequin's jacket, repairs to neck, both arms and other areas, c1737, on an ormolu base in the Louis XV style, 7in (17.5cm).
£2,500-3,500 *C*

A Ludwigsburg figure of a boy, wearing a black hat, green coat over a red vest, and carrying a blue bag, interlaced C mark to rear of base, c1775, 4½in (11cm).
£600-700 *C*

A Meissen crinoline figure known as The Countess Kosel, modelled by J J Kändler, with puce and green under-skirt, hair cracks, minor chips, blue crossed swords mark, c1745, 11in (28cm).
£2,000-3,000 *C*

A Meissen crinoline group of The Gout Sufferer, Der Gichtkranke, modelled by J J Kändler, sometimes called Augustus the Strong, and Gräfin Orgielska, he in white dressing gown and shirt, black breeches and yellow slippers, her dress reserved with 'indianische Blumen' on a grey ground, some restorations, a firing crack in the base, blue crossed swords mark under the base, c1742, 7½in (19.5cm) wide.
£7,000-8,000 *C*

Gräfin Orgielska was not, as might have been supposed, one of Augustus' many mistresses but his favourite illegitimate daughter.

A Meissen figure of Pulchinella, from the Commedia dell'Arte modelled by J J Kändler, repair to his right foot, left arm and sword, blue crossed swords mark at the back of base, c1740, 5½in (14cm).
£2,000-3,000 *C*

A Meissen figure of a huntsman, modelled by J E Eberlein, in black tricorn hat, green jacket and black boots, minor chips to extremities, c1745, 7in (17.5cm).
£1,500-2,500 *C*

A Meissen figure of a shepherd flautist, in yellow hat and puce tunic with yellow lining and shoes, restorations, blue crossed swords mark, c1750, 6½in (16cm).
£400-600 *C*

A Meissen figure of a woman, in white cloth cap, green-lined puce jacket, lilac apron and green-hemmed white skirt, some repair, tassel replaced, blue crossed swords mark, c1745, 6½in (16cm).
£2,000-2,500 *C*

A Meissen figure of a Turkish woman, modelled by P Reinicke, dressed in a white coat and headdress, puce pantaloons and yellow shoes, some repairs, trace of blue crossed swords mark to base, c1745, 6½in (17cm).
£700-800 *C*

A Meissen figure of an equestrian drummer, in black hat, yellow lined puce jacket with black boots and purple saddle cloth, chips to drumsticks, the horse's ears and extremities, blue crossed swords mark at back, c1750, 8in (20cm).
£2,500-3,500 *C*

A Meissen group of a shepherd and shepherdess, decorated in colours, extensively restored, c1745, 5½in (14cm) wide.
£1,400-1,600 *CG*

A pair of Meissen figures of children, ɔn high domed silver bases repoussé with swags and stiff leaves, minor ːhips, the porcelain c1750, the silver mounts Fribourg and probably ɔearing the maker's mark of Gotthard Leberecht Krumbholz, 1749-93, 6in (15cm).
£1,000-1,500 *C*

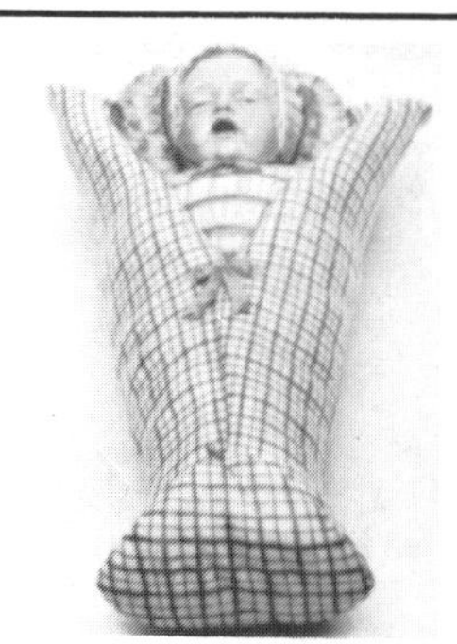
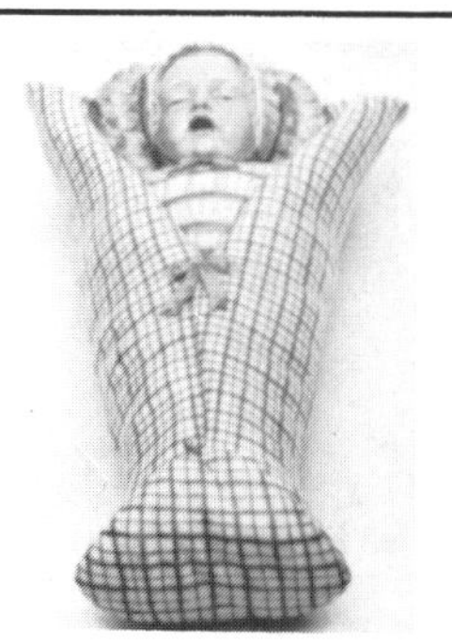

A Meissen figure of a sleeping child, the gown with floral ornament and 4 bands of blue and gilt and wrapped in a chequered cloth tied with a ribbon bow and fastened at the end with a gilt pin, crossed swords mark in underglaze blue, incised marks and impressed number 122, 16½in (42cm).
£1,600-2,200 *L*

The original was modelled by Kändler in 1741. These figures were given as New Year gifts in Saxony and were modelled after the figure of the Holy Child in the church of Santa Maria in Aracoeli in Rome.

A Meissen figure of Columbine, modelled by J J Kändler, in puce, yellow, white and gilt 'indianische Blumen', yellow shoes, repair to hat and left hand, chips to leaves, blue crossed swords mark to rear of base, c1750, 5½in (13.5cm).
£800-1,000 *C*

A Meissen equestrian group of a portsman, in black, yellow and rown, restorations, blue crossed words mark on base, c1750, 11in 27.5cm).
1,000-1,500 *C*

A Meissen figure of a tailor, from the series of Craftsmen, modelled by J J Kändler, in black, red and white, head restuck, hat and collar repaired, blue crossed swords mark at back of base, c1753, 9½in (23.5cm).
£2,000-2,500 *C*

A Meissen figure of a youth, holding a rooster and a long walking stick, in white, blue, yellow, pale puce and green, repair to hat, cane and right foot, traces of blue crossed swords mark to the rococo scroll moulded base, c1755, 6in (15cm).
£400-500 *C*

A Meissen figure of a coquille seller, modelled by P. Reinicke and J. J. Kändler, repair to his hat, right arm and basket, blue crossed swords mark and Pressnummer 21 to base, c1755, 6in (15cm).
£1,500-2,000 *C*

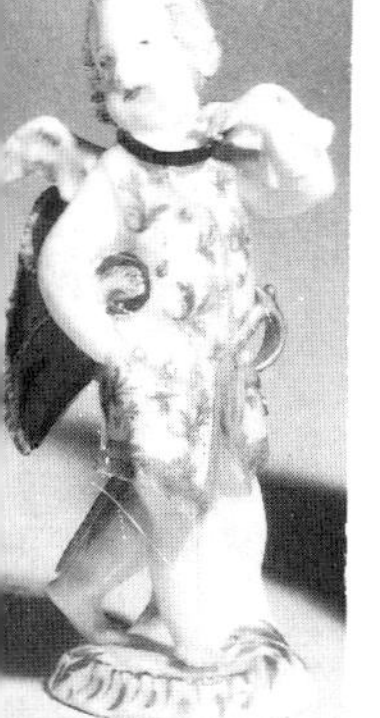

Meissen figure of Cupid as a ɔldier, repairs to one wing, sword, nd catagan, blue crossed swords ıark at back, c1755, 3½in (9.5cm).
300-400 *C*

pair of Meissen figures of a hepherd and a shepherdess, in pale uce, yellow and green, with ndianische Blumen', some estoration, faint blue crossed words marks on bases, c1755, 5½in 4.5cm).
1,500-2,000 *C*

A Meissen figure of a cellist, in white jacket with 'indianische Blumen', blue breeches, yellow shoes, extensive restoration, c1755, 4½in (11.5cm).
£700-1,000 *C*

A Meissen figure of Le Marquis from the 'Cris de Paris' series, in puce, yellow and manganese, the left hand restuck, traces of blue crossed swords mark on base and Pressnummer 36, c1756, 5in (13cm).
£2,000-3,000 *C*

A Meissen figure of a shepherdess, in puce bodice and striped skirt on gilt rococo scroll base, minor repair to her little finger and the sheep's ear, blue crossed swords and dot mark and Ritznummer 2723 at back, c1770, 6½in (16cm).
£500-700 *C*

A Meissen Marcolini Kindergruppe, modelled by Michel-Victor Acier, the brightly coloured figures of children set on a rococo scroll base, damage to several extremities, blue crossed swords and star mark to the base, c1775, 7½in (19cm).
£900-1,000 *C*

Two Meissen figures of children dressed as Harlequin and Columbine, in white, puce, yellow and red, restoration, he with Pressnummer 24, she with blue crossed swords and dot mark at back and incised G, c1760, 4½in (12cm).
£900-1,200 *CG*

A Meissen figure of Cupid as a Harlequin, dressed in puce and yellow chevron Harlequin's jacket, white and turquoise trousers and a pale green conical hat, hat chipped, end of slap-stick missing, c1765, 4½in (12cm).
£1,000-1,300 *C*

A Meissen figure of a violinist, in black, turquoise, gold, green and puce, repair to violin, hat, left hand, left leg restuck, blue crossed swords and dot mark at back, incised 2 to base, c1770, 8½in (22cm).
£550-650 *C*

A Meissen crinoline group, after an original by Kändler, he wearing blue, with a snuff box, she wearing a black dress, decorated with flowers, 19thC, 8½in (22cm).
£400-450 *Bea*

A Meissen equestrian figure of a sportsman in green, black and brown, some restoration, blue crossed swords mark on base, c1760, 5½in (14.5cm) wide.
£1,000-1,500 *C*

A Meissen figure of Alexander The Great, emblematic of Greece from a set of the Four Monarchies, modelled by J J Kändler, in puce, gilt, yellow and blue, right arm restuck, minor chips and repairs to his plumage and fingers, blue crossed swords mark, c1767, 9in (22.5cm).
£700-900 *C*

A Meissen Marcolini figure of a vestal, the priestess draped in puce, gilt and blue, the eternal flame burning in a bowl on the neo-classical plinth at her side, blue crossed swords and star mark to base, c1780, 11½in (29cm).
£350-450 *C*

A pair of Meissen dancing children, in green, white and yellow, impressed numerals 24 to base, 4½in (12cm).
£2,000-2,500 *C*

Meissen Marcolini group of a ancing putto and companion, raped in puce and yellow veils and arrying garlands of flowers, one ing missing from putto, blue ossed swords and star mark to ase, c1810, 4½in (11cm).
200-250 *C*

A Meissen porcelain figure of a girl, painted in bright enamel colours and gold, set on a circular base with pierced foliate sides, late 19thC, 5in (13cm).
£400-450 *Bea*

A Meissen figure of a bishop kneeling beside the Virgin Mary, in purple, orange, blue and gilt, hairline crack to base, damage to extremities, blue crossed swords mark.
£600-700 *CSK*

Meissen group of a young ood-cutter and companion, blue ossed swords, incised and mpressed, 5½in (14cm).
500-600 *CSK*

A Meissen sedan group, on ebonised wood plinth, supporting figures with chipped feathers in hat, 9½in (24cm) wide.
£400-500 *CSK*

A Meissen figure of a lady, painted with Indian flowers, with pale pink skirt and green bodice lined in yellow, head damaged, 5in (13cm).
£300-400 *CSK*

late Meissen group of 2 gentlemen nd a lady, chips to extremities, blue ossed swords and incised and mpressed numerals, 8in (20.5cm).
900-1,000 *CSK*

A Samson figure of 'Bier-la-la' after the Höchst original, wearing striped pink coat, tattered breeches and wig, blue wheel mark, 11in (28cm).
£100-150 *CSK*

A late Meissen figure of a lady, wearing lace trimmed bonnet, yellow jacket lined in fur and lilac robe, some damage, blue crossed swords and incised and impressed numerals, 8in (20.5cm).
£450-550 *CSK*

Miller's is a price GUIDE not a price LIST

A French biscuit group emblematic of America, late 18th/early 19thC, 11½in (29cm).
£500-600 *C*

A pair of Samson Commedia dell'Arte figures, on elaborate gilt metal scrolling bases, 11in (28cm).
£600-800 *CSK*

A pair of French porcelain figures of a gallant and his lady, dancing in bright 18thC costume, slight damage, late 19thC, 13in (33cm).
£350-450 *Bea*

A pair of Continental coloured bisque figures of an 18thC courtier and his companion, wearing elaborate costumes.
£400-500 *CSK*

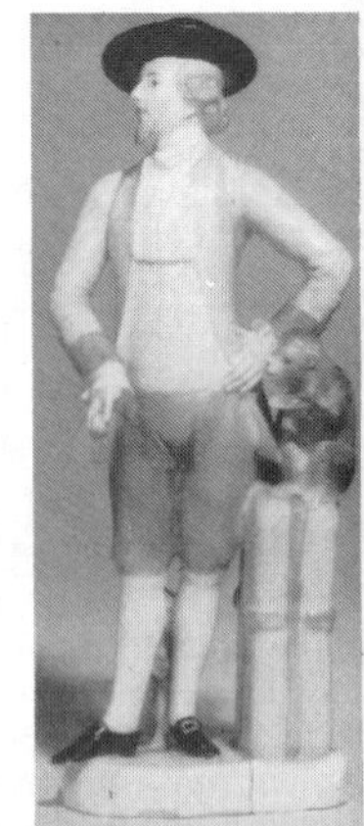

A Vienna figure of a man, painted in black, puce, yellow, green and blue, restoration to his hat, right hand and monkey's paw, blue beehive mark, impressed 3H and painter's mark 20, c1770, 7½in (19cm).
£550-650 *C*

Flatware

A Bow blue and white dish with twig handle, the centre painted within a blue rim, slight glaze damage, mid-18thC, 9in (22cm).
£250-300 *Bea*

A parianware group of 2 American Civil War soldiers, 20in (51cm).
£550-650 *Wor*

A French biscuit group emblematic of Plenty, minor repairs, 18thC, 13½in (34cm).
£500-800 *C*

Two Bow blue and white pickle dishes, 3 and 4½in (7.5 and 11.5cm).
£300-350 each *BHA*

A pair of Bow triple shell sweetmeat stands, boldly painted with pink and brown, both with impressed T on the base, 7in (18cm).
£1,800-2,500 *L*

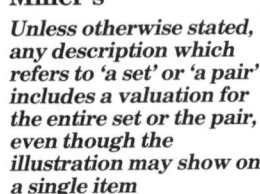

A miniature Caughley plate, hand painted with the Island pattern in underglaze blue, c1775, 4.4cm.
£140-155 *TVA*

A Caughley blue and white asparagus server, c1780.
£70-100 *THA*

Make the most of Miller's

Unless otherwise stated, any description which refers to 'a set' or 'a pair' includes a valuation for the entire set or the pair, even though the illustration may show only a single item

A Caughley fluted bread and butter plate, transfer printed with the Temple pattern, c1780, 7½in (19cm).
£100-120 *TVA*

A Caughley kidney-shaped dish, c1780, 11in (28cm) wide.
£110-130 *THA*

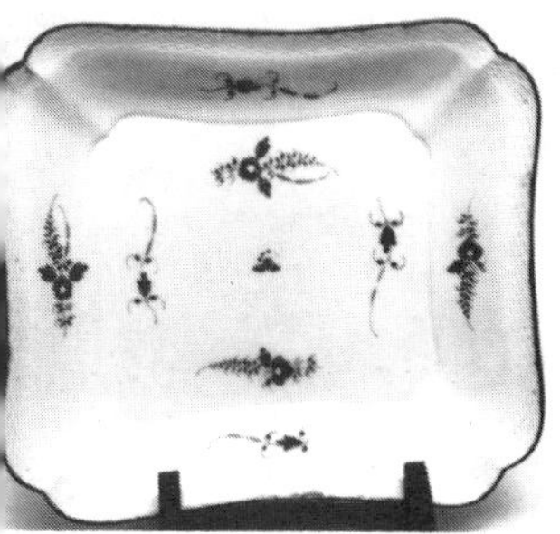

. Caughley blue and white dish, 1780, 10in (25cm) wide.
170-190 *THA*

Chelsea soup plate in the akiemon style, with The Hob in ıe Well pattern, within a border of on red and turquoise, some ımage, c1752, 8½in (21cm).
,300-1,700 *C*

Chelsea plate, painted in the akiemon palette, with the Hob in ıe Well pattern, red anchor mark, ½in (24cm).
700-800 *PB*

pair of Caughley plates om The Donegal Service, ainted at Chamberlain's ctory, c1793, 8½in 1cm).
,200-1,700 *C*

PORCELAIN – HAND-PAINTED/PRINTED

- ★ it is vital to the study of porcelain to know the difference between hand-painted and printed patterns. Easy and quick identification comes with constantly looking at comparative pieces. However, a few points:
- ★ a printed pattern follows an etched or engraved copper plate
- ★ a painted pattern is done by brush stroke and hence has a fluidity that is impossible with a print
- ★ a brush is much less precise than an engraving – hence the hatch marks evident on a print
- ★ brush work is most obvious where there is shading of colour

A Caughley blue and white plate, with pine cone pattern, c1785, 6½in (16.5cm).
£150-160 *THA*

Six Chelsea plates, the centres painted with scattered fruit, with gilt 'feuille-de-choux' wells, some minor rubbing to gilding, 3 with gold anchor marks, c1760, 8½in (22cm).
£3,000-4,000 *C*

A pair of Chelsea dishes, one with slight rubbing tc gilding, gold anchor marks, c1760, 10½in (27cm).
£1,200-1,500 *C*

An early Coalport armorial plate, c1805, 9in (23cm).
£100-120 *TVA*

A Coalport plate, c1820, 9in (23cm).
£80-100 *JUD*

A pair of Coalport shell-moulded plates, with hand painted yacht design on mother-of-pearl and gilded ground, c1880, 9½in (24cm).
£150-200 *TVA*

A pair of Coalport dessert dishes, painted in the manner of Thomas Baxter, with gold painted foot rim, marked 899 in gold, c1810, 11in (28cm) wide.
£1,200-1,500 *DSH*

A Coalport dessert plate from the service presented by Queen Victoria to the Emperor of Russia in 1845, with gold gadrooned shaped edge, rich dark cobalt border, 6 panels edged in gold with pale lemon ground bearing Imperial Russian orders, the white centre panel painted with Russian-Polish crowned two-headed eagle, marked on reverse with Royal Coat of Arms, surrounded by A.B. & R.P. Daniell Manufacturers to Her Majesty and The Royal Family, 120 New Bond St. and 18 Wigmore St., London, 10in (25.5cm).
£2,000-3,000 *DSH*

A pair of Coalport dessert dishes, hand painted in polychrome, c1820, 10½in (26.5cm) high.
£200-250 *CA*

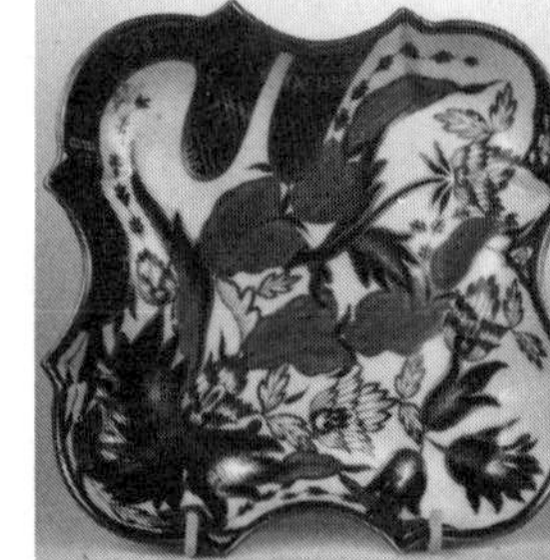
A Coalport finger and thumb pattern dish, c1825, 7in (18cm).
£500-600 *JG*

A Coalport plate with scale blue ground, a copy of Dr Wall Worcester version, c1885, 9in (23cm).
£120-140 *TVA*

A Coalport dinner plate, painted by Percy Simpson, with a named view of the River Severn near Shrewsbury, c1909, 10½in (26.5cm).
£160-180 *THA*

Two matching Coalport lobed dishes, with a rare combination of fruit and flowers, painting attributed to Thomas Brentnall, impressed 2 mark.
£650-750 *TVA*

A Copeland and Garrett meat draining dish, printed with figures leading out dogs, printed mark, named on the reverse, c1835, 19in (48cm) wide.
£450-500 *CSK*

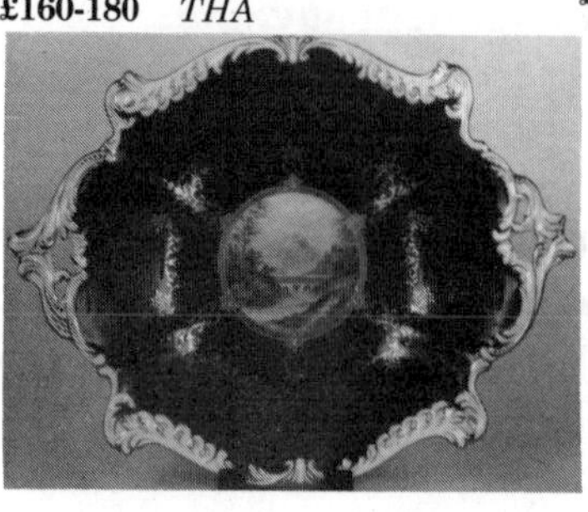
A pair of Coalport two-handled dishes, with named scenes of Ben Lomond and Hawthorden, on a royal blue ground, c1910, 11½in (29cm) wide.
£500-550 *TVA*

A Davenport blue and white plate, printed with a profile bust portrait of George III as an emperor, c1820, 7in (18cm).
£200-250 *CSK*

Copeland and Garrett meat dish, rinted with Shooting a Leopard, 1835, 20½in (52cm) wide.
ʼ500-550 *CSK*

A Derby armorial plate with a leopard, red mark, c1805, 9in (23cm).
£200-250 *JUD*

A Derby plate with salmon ground, red mark, c1810, 10in (25cm).
£200-250 *JUD*

hree Bloor Derby dishes, painted nd gilt with the Shrewsbury crest, 6th Earl, on dark green grounds, rinted mark, c1825, 8½in (21.5cm) ʼide.
450-500 *CSK*

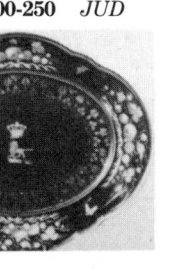

A Doccia blue and white charger painted with an oriental pattern, c1755, 12½in (31.5cm).
£200-250 *CNY*

A Doccia blue and white platter with Stampino floral decoration, c1745, 12in (31.5cm) wide.
£450-500 *CNY*

A pair of Doccia shell-shaped dishes, painted in an Imari palette, c1755, 12in (30.5cm).
£650-700 *CNY*

Doccia shell-shaped dish ecorated with flowers, painted in olours, c1760, 10in (25.5cm) wide.
250-300 *CNY*

An initialled Doccia dinner plate, decorated in blue and gold, c1780, 9½in (24cm).
£120-160 *CNY*

A pair of Doccia dishes with floral decoration, painted in colours, c1770, 9in (23cm).
£180-240 *CNY*

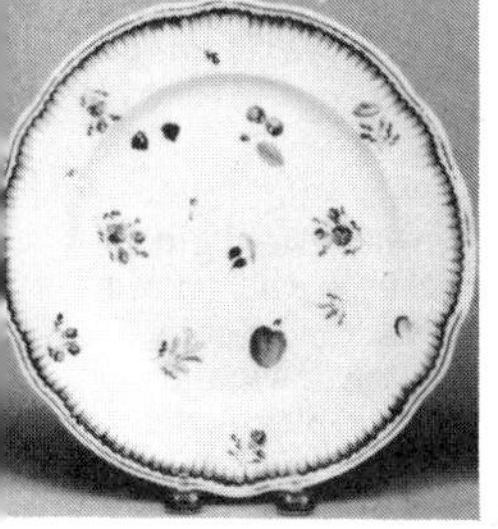

A Doccia plate decorated with fruit and flowers, enclosed by blue 'feuille-de-choux' borders in the Sèvres style below a gold band, c1780, 9½in (24cm).
£40-80 *CNY*

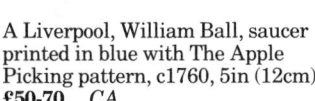

A Liverpool, William Ball, saucer printed in blue with The Apple Picking pattern, c1760, 5in (12cm).
£50-70 *CA*

A Limoges plate, by Haviland & Co, signed A. Nicol, c1910, 9½in (24cm).
£100-140 *TVA*

A Longton Hall leaf dish, painted in the manner of the Trembly Rose painter, c1755, 11in (27.5cm).
£900-1,000 *C*

A Longton Hall strawberry leaf-moulded plate, painted within a naturally moulded and coloured border of trailing strawberries and leaves with purple tendrils, slight rim chips, c1755, 9in (23cm).
£2,000-2,500 *C*

A Longton Hall dish with twig handle, painted in bright enamel colours, the rim painted with a dark red line, small chip to rim, mid-18thC, 8½in (21.5cm).
£800-1,000 *Bea*

A Longton Hall leaf dish with green rope twist handle, painted in the manner of the Trembly Rose painter, within a lobed chocolate line rim, slight rim chips, c1755, 9in (23cm) wide.
£400-450 *C*

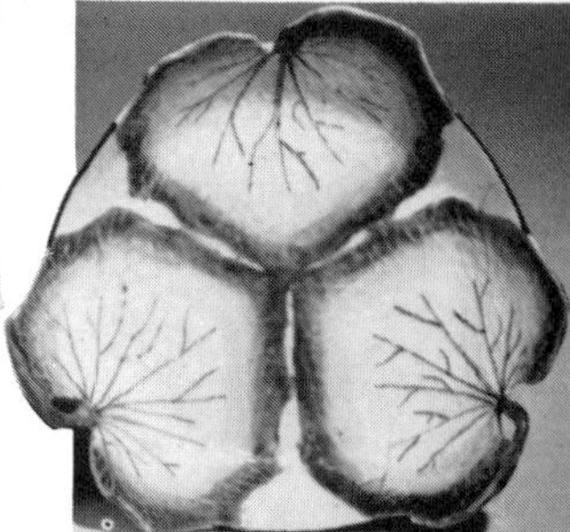

A Longton Hall dish, moulded and naturally coloured with 3 cucumber leaves with puce veins and edged in green and yellow, cracks to rim, c1755, 6in (15cm).
£700-800 *C*

A Meissen saucer, painted with merchants on a quayside with sailing vessels, blue crossed swords mark and gilder's mark 8, c1730.
£2,000-3,000 *C*

A Meissen armorial plate from the Sulkowski Service, modelled by J J Kändler, blue crossed swords mark and impressed Dreher's mark, c1737, 9in (23cm).
£2,800-3,000 *CG*

A Meissen blue and white barbed plate with brown rim, painted with 8 panels of chinoiserie figures and garden scenes, the reverse with continuous flowering foliage to the rim, blue crossed swords mark at the foot of the tree, and Pressnummer 20, c1740.
£2,000-2,500 *C*

A Meissen chinoiserie saucer, painted with iron red and gilt, the reverse with 3 sprays of 'indianische Blumen', blue crossed swords mark and gilder's mark 58, Pressnummer 2, c1740.
£700-800 *C*

A Berlin plate with raised gilt chinoiserie figures, with iron red border and gilt lines, rim chip repair, blue sceptre mark and Pressnummer 15, c1805, 9½in (24.5cm).
£1,500-2,000 *CG*

A Minton plate, hand painted and signed, A. Boullemier, c1870, 9in (23cm).
£225-250 *TVA*

A pair of Mintons yellow ground cabinet plates, painted within gilt dentil rims, impressed marks and pattern No. G1276, 1874 and 1881, 9½in (24cm).
£500-600 *C*

A Mintons plate, the centre painted 'en camaieu rose' within a gilt key-pattern band, on the turquoise ground, impressed and printed marks and date code for 1874, 9½in (24cm).
£450-550 *C*

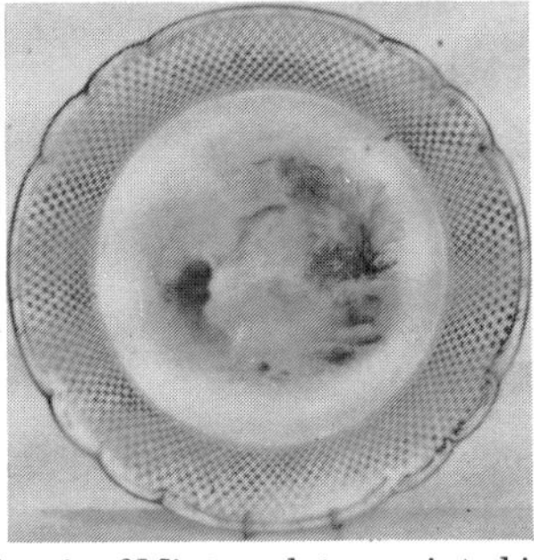

A pair of Minton plates, painted in colours, artist's initials A.H.W. within printed gilt diaper borders, impressed factory marks and printed New York retailer's mark, 9in (23cm).
£200-300 *CSK*

A pair of Mintons dessert plates, painted in white enamel on turquoise enamel ground, one signed Leroy, impressed Mintons and clay mark for 1877, stamped A.B. Daniell & Son, 46 Wigmore St., London, 9½in (24cm).
£1,300-1,500 *DSH*

MINTON

- ★ factory site bought in 1793 by Thomas Minton at Stoke on Trent
- ★ Minton had worked at Caughley and Spode
- ★ factory first produced earthenware, started to make porcelain c1798
- ★ factory mainly famous for its bone china
- ★ early patterns tend to be very similar to Newhall, Pinxton and Spode
- ★ early wares not marked but did often have a pattern number, sometimes with N. or No. in front
- ★ Minton palette is closest to Pinxton
- ★ much pre 1850 Minton is wrongly ascribed to other factories, particularly Rockingham, Coalport and Pinxton
- ★ the early figures are prone to damage – watch for restoration
- ★ very few heavily flower encrusted wares have escaped without damage
- ★ some beautiful ground colours with excellent gilding. Minton had particular success with a turquoise ground
- ★ as with most other factories, signed pieces are most desirable
- ★ artists of note include: G Hancock, J Bancroft, T Kirkby, T Allen, R Pilsbury, Jesse Smith and A Boullemier
- ★ note marks: MINTON became MINTONS from c1873

A set of 6 Minton dessert plates, produced for Thomas Goode & Co, decorated by Anton Boullemier after an original design by William Coleman, each on a pale green ground within gold rims, one with crazed glaze, impressed and printed marks, 9½in (24cm).
£800-1,000 *Bea*

Did you know

MILLER'S Antiques Price Guide builds up year by year to form the most comprehensive photo-reference system available

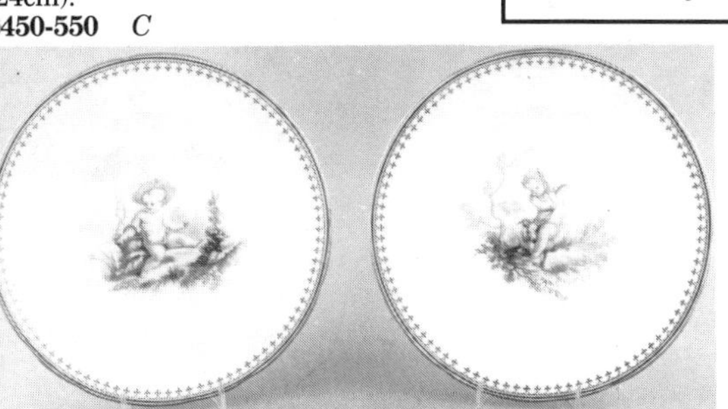

A Minton dessert service, printed in puce 'camaieu', within a gilt spearhead border, comprising 12 plates, 3 damaged, and 4 low stands, 3 damaged, impressed marks for 1865.
£350-450 *DN*

A Mintons plate, painted with a spray of pink roses and forget-me-nots, impressed mark Mintons and year mark for 1878, and printed mark from William Mortlock, 18 Regent St. London Mintons China, 9in (23cm).
£150-200 *L*

A Mintons plate, with a gilt key pattern rim, impressed mark Mintons and year mark for 1879, printed mark Mintons Bailey Banks & Biddle Philadelphia, 9½in (24.5cm).
£100-150 *L*

A Minton dessert plate with pierced gilded border, slight restoration to rim, signed L. Solon, c1880, 9in (23cm).
£300-500 *DSH*

A pair of Mintons plates, painted with Sunrise on the Danube and Cottage near Kie, impressed Mintons and year mark for 1880, 8½in (22.5cm).
£150-200 *L*

A set of 4 Nymphenburg plates, impressed mark, late 18thC, 9½in (24.5cm).
£750-850 *Bea*

A Pinxton saucer dish, slight rubbing, c1795, 7½in (19.5cm).
£150-250 *C*

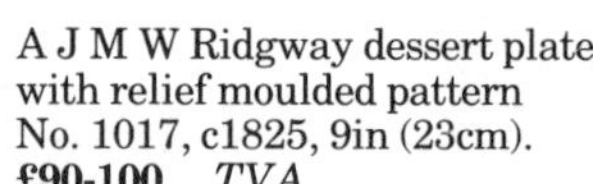

A J M W Ridgway dessert plate, with relief moulded pattern No. 1017, c1825, 9in (23cm).
£90-100 *TVA*

A Sèvres 'rose pompadour' tray, with pierced scroll border, reserved on a pink ground, enriched with gilding, minor damage to rim, blue interlaced L marks enclosing date letter E For 1759, and painter's mark of Noël and incised square, 5½in (14.5cm).
£4,000-4,500 *C*

A Sèvres 'bleu celeste' tray, with pierced scroll border, painted on a turquoise ground, enriched with gilding, one border flowerhead restored, traces of blue interlaced L mark, incised A, c1757, 5½in (14.5cm).
£900-1,200 *C*

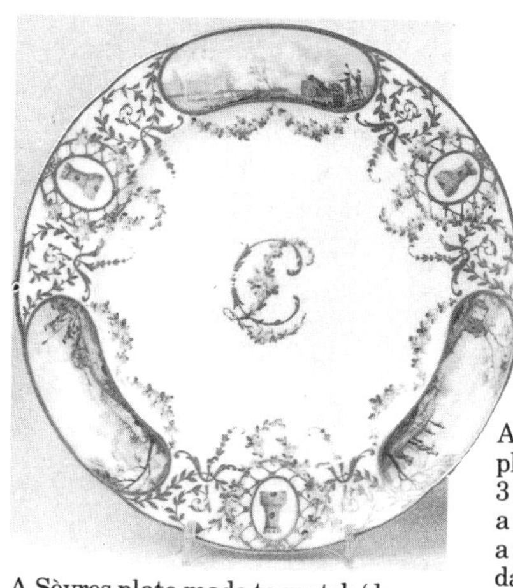

A Sèvres plate made to match 'des Asturies' service, painted with a gilt and floral monogram of CL for Charles IV of Spain and his consort Louise of Parma, blue interlaced L marks enclosing the date letter for 1759, and later painter's mark of Vieillard, 9½in (24cm).
£1,000-2,000 *C*

A matched set of 10 Sèvres dessert plates, the rim painted with 3 sprays within a gold cartouche on a green ground, 9½in (24.5cm), and a matching bowl, 8in (20.5cm), some damage, printed marks and date code for 1770.
£850-950 *Bea*

A Swansea lobed plate, c1805, 9in (23cm).
£100-150 *JG*

A Sèvres style dish, set on a gilt metal stand with foliate handles, reserved on a gold decorated deep blue band, late 19thC, 17in (43cm).
£400-500 *Bea*

A pair of Worcester leaf dishes with green stalk handles, raised puce veins and edged in green, one with 2 slight rim chips, c1760.
£2,500-3,000 *C*

A pair of Strasbourg hexafoil plates, painted in colours, rim chips, mid-18thC, 9½in (24cm).
£500-600 *C*

A Swansea crested dish with gilt twig handles, with motto 'Y DDUW BOR DIOLCH', c1819, 11in (28cm) wide.
£1,000-1,500 *DSH*

A pair of Swansea botanical plates, painted by William Weston Young, with Myosotis rupicola and Menziesia caerulea named on the reverses, perhaps some retouching to the enamels, c1820, 8½in (21.5cm).
£600-700 *C*

A Worcester blue and white pickle leaf, moulded underside and painted with flowers, rim chip, workman's mark, c1760.
£150-200 *TW*

A First Period Worcester blue and white butter shell, painted with The Two Peony Rock Bird pattern in underglazed blue, painter's mark in underglaze blue, c1760, 5in (12.5cm).
£450-550 *N*

A Worcester blue and white butter boat, with moulded feet and painted floral spray, crescent mark, c1760.
£200-250 *TW*

A set of 7 Worcester plates, in mint condition, open crescent mark, c1775, 8in (20.5cm).
£1,900-2,000 *BHA*

A First Period Worcester dish, in black, turquoise, gilt and deep blue, open crescent in underglaze blue, 10½in (26.5cm).
£700-1,000 *MN*

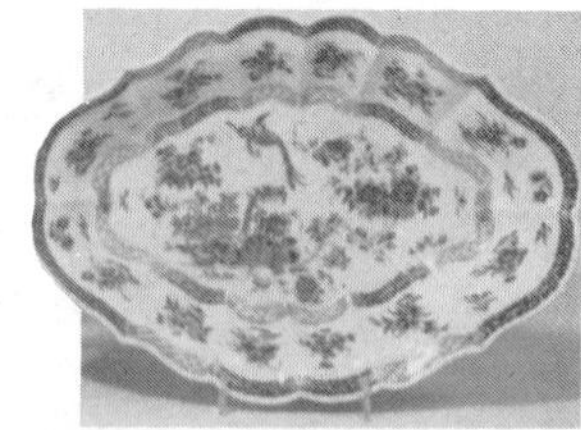

A Worcester fluted dish, painted in the Kakiemon palette, within a border for flower sprays divided by bands of iron red scrolls and gilt diaper pattern, c1770, 10½in (27cm).
£1,000-1,500 *C*

A set of 32 Worcester, Flight, Barr & Barr, plates and soup plates, c1815, 10in (25.5cm).
£5,600-6,200 *LG*

A pair of Worcester Imari pattern leaf dishes, painted with The Kempthorne pattern, one with minute rim chip, the other repaired, blue square seal marks, c1770, 10½in (26.5cm).
£600-800 *C*

A Chamberlain's Worcester dish, with gilt dentil rim, script mark, c1800, 10½in (26cm).
£1,600-2,000 *C*

A Grainger's Worcester comport, c1820, 5½in (14cm).
£160-180 *THA*

A Worcester, Flight, Barr & Barr, dessert plate with gilded edge, apple green border and central panel painted on a white ground, painting attributed to Smith, impressed FBB mark under crown, printed circular factory mark with Royal coat of arms and fleur-de-lys, c1815, 8in (20cm).
£750-1,000 *DSH*

A pair of Chamberlain's Worcester dessert plates, brightly painted within a band of gold leaves, reserves on a green ground, impressed marks, mid-19thC, 9in (23cm).
£250-350 *Bea*

A Grainger's Worcester fine painted plate, printed and impressed marks, c1875, 9½in (24cm).
£180-200 *TVA*

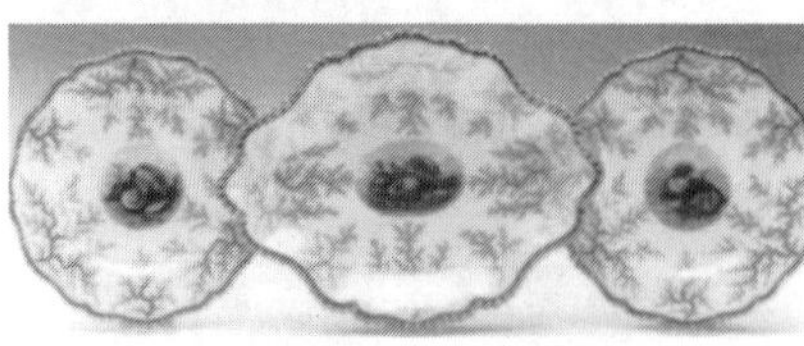

c. A Worcester, Flight, Barr & Barr, dessert dish, brightly painted within a gold gadroon rim, impressed marks, c1825, 12½in (31cm) wide.
£900-1,000
l. and r. A matching pair of dessert plates, printed on the reverse Royal Porcelain Works, Flight, Barr & Barr, Worcester & Coventry Street, London.
£1,000-1,200 *Bea*

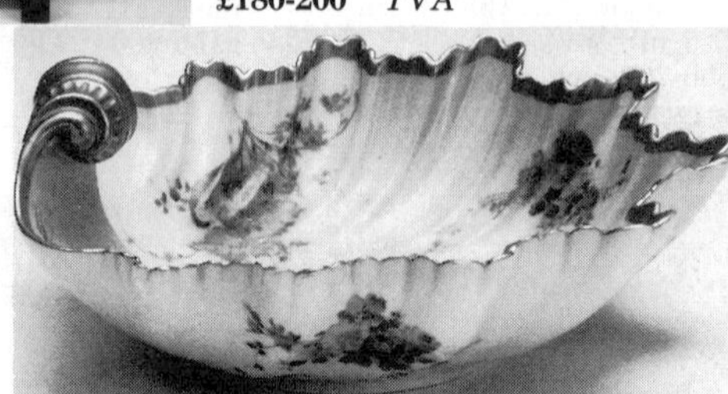

A Royal Worcester dish, boldly painted within a gold rim on an apricot and ivory ground, shape No. 1275, printed mark and date code for 1906, 9in (23cm).
£250-350 *Bea*

A Royal Worcester plate, signed Walter Sedgley, c1928, 8½in (21.5cm).
£200-225 *TVA*

A Worcester, Flight, Barr & Barr, dessert plate with gold gadrooned edge, underglaze blue ground and white jewelling, painting attributed to Henry Stinton, marked in red with crown and Royal Porcelain Works, Flight, Barr & Barr, Worcester and Coventry St., London, c1825, 10in (25.5cm).
£2,600-3,000 *DSH*

CHAMBERLAINS
c1780s-1852

* ★ Robert Chamberlain and his son left the main Worcester factory in 1783
* ★ initially they decorated porcelain on a free-lance basis, mainly for Thomas Turner of Caughley
* ★ Chamberlain started producing his own porcelain in the early 1790s
* ★ the early body of Chamberlain was hard-paste, very similar to Newhall
* ★ pattern numbers were sometimes used after 1794. Pattern No. 100 was reached by 1797; 400 by 1807; 610 by 1812; 790 by 1817; 1,000 by 1822
* ★ in 1807 the Prince of Wales allowed the mark 'Porcelain manufacturers to his Royal Highness the Prince of Wales' to be used
* ★ 'Regent China' was introduced in 1811
* ★ best period for Chamberlains 1810-1830
* ★ in the early 1840s bone china was introduced and the firm merged with Flight, Barr and Barr in 1852

A Royal Worcester tooled gilt plate, signed by Christopher Bowen, c1959, 11in (28cm).
£150-170 *TVA*

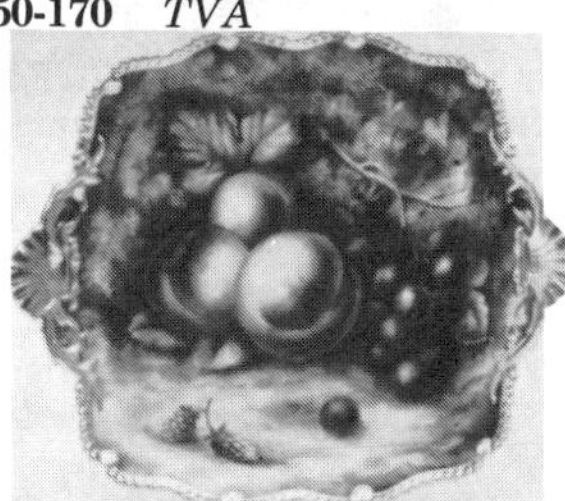
A Royal Worcester dessert dish, painted by H H Price, signed, with peaches, black grapes and loganberries, with similar gilt borders and handles, printed mark in black, 11½in (28.5cm).
£250-350 *L*

A Royal Worcester dessert dish, painted by H H Price, signed, with wavy gilt gadroon borders and shell and foliage handles, printed mark in black Royal Worcester Bone China made in England, 12½in (31cm).
£250-300 *L*

A First Period Worcester pickle dish, painted in underglaze blue with vines and flowers, with blue serrated edge, workman's mark a fylfot, 3½in (8.5cm).
£100-150 *L*

A Dr Syntax plate by Charles Ford, 'The Highwayman', c1871.
£100-150 *LG*

A Chamberlain's Worcester dish, brilliantly painted and gilded with Kylin or Dragons in Compartments pattern, orange scripted mark Chamberlain's Worcester 75, 12½in (30.5cm) wide.
£700-800 *DSH*

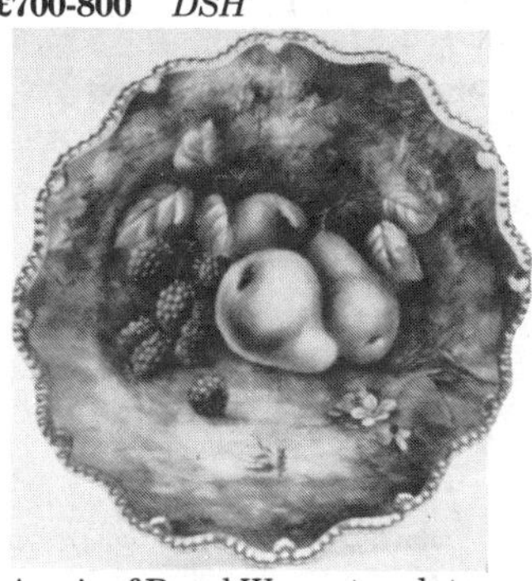
A pair of Royal Worcester plates, painted by H H Price, signed, with gilt borders, printed mark in black, 9in (22.5cm).
£250-300 *L*

A Chamberlain's Worcester dish, decorated in the Jaberwocky pattern in polychrome with turquoise borders, hair crack, pattern No. 1713, printed mark, 16½in (42cm) wide.
£250-300 *WW*

A Chamberlain's Worcester plate, the centre painted within a gilt cartouche and a border of gilt scrolling foliage, script mark in puce, c1800, 8½in (21.5cm).
£1,500-2,000 *C*

A Dr Syntax plate by Charles Ford, 'Doctor Syntax makes free of the cellar', signed, c1871, 9in (23cm).
£100-150 *LG*

A Dr Syntax plate by Charles Ford, 'Doctor Syntax and the Dairymaid', c1871.
£100-150 *LG*

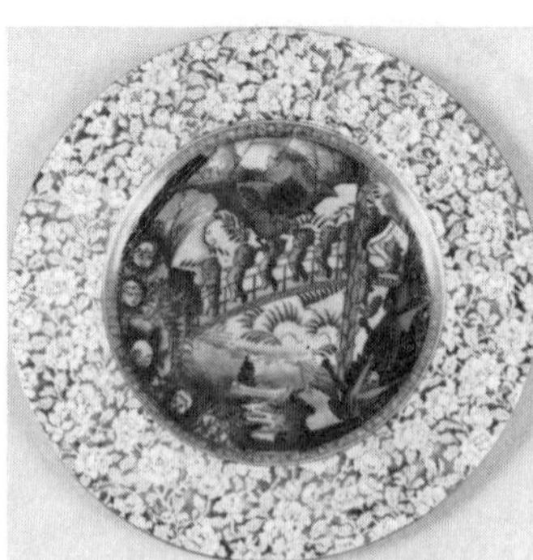

An important Fairyland Lustre plate, with coloured scene of imps walking over bridge in blue/grey floral border, 10½in (26.5cm).
£450-550 *JD*

A pair of English porcelain deep dishes, each painted with a coat of arms and the motto 'Praemium. Virtutus. Honor', probably made for the Cheere family, the deep blue border painted with a scrolling foliate design, early 19thC, 9½in (24.5cm).
£300-400 *Bea*

An English porcelain sample plate, the centre gilt with St George and the Dragon, the border with the emblems and arms of England, Scotland, Ireland and Wales, perhaps Minton, c1860, 9½in (23.5cm).
£150-200 *C*

A pair of Berlin ornithological deep plates, painted with bright colours, within green 'feuille de chou' and shaped gilt chain pattern borders with pink flowerheads, blue sceptre marks, c1790, 9½in (24cm).
£2,500-3,500 *C*

A set of 7 Nymphenburg plates, late 18thC, 9½in (24cm).
£1,000-1,500 *Bea*

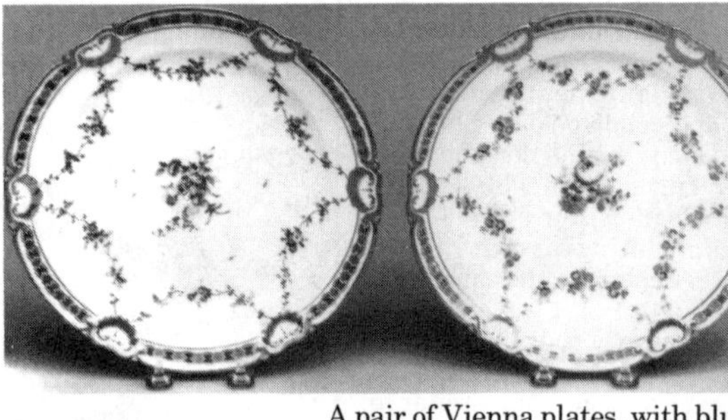

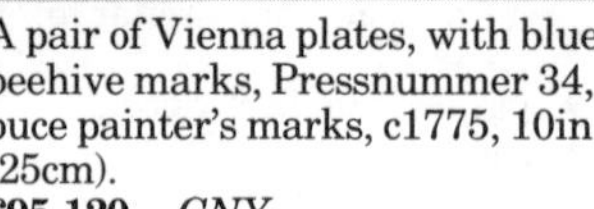

A pair of Vienna plates, with blue beehive marks, Pressnummer 34, puce painter's marks, c1775, 10in (25cm).
£95-120 *CNY*

Flasks

A rare Davenport blue and white moon flask with ring handles, with a profile bust portrait of George III, c1820, 6in (15cm).
£300-350 *CSK*

A Meissen pear shaped flask, decorated in Holland in the Oriental manner in green and red, the porcelain c1730, the decoration slightly later, 8½in (21cm).
£1,300-1,500 *CG*

Locate the source

The source of each illustration in Miller's can be found by checking the code letters below each caption with the list of contributors. In view of the undoubted differences in price structures from region to region, this information could be extremely valuable to everyone who buys and sells antiques

Ice Pails

A pair of Derby ice pails, covers and liners, painted in blue and gilt, with twisted scroll finials, one cover restored, puce crown cross batons and D mark, 10in (25.5cm).
£700-800 *CSK*

A pair of Coalport ice pails, covers and liners, the bodies painted in sepia and gilt on white grounds, some damage, replacement wooden pine cone finials, 13in (33cm).
£1,500-2,500 *CSK*

A Flight, Barr & Barr ice pail, cover and liner with pine cone finial and loop handles with ram mask terminals, on a ground of whorls and leaves in iron red, blue, green and gilt, on a low spreading foot to the square base, impressed marks, c1810, 14½in (36.5cm).
£6,000-7,000 *CSK*

Inkwells

A Samson desk set, applied with coloured porcelain flowers, cherub with small repair, 8in (20.5cm).
£300-400 *CSK*

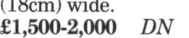

A Royal Worcester pen and inkstand, printed mark and date code for 1899, 10½in (26cm) wide.
£250-350 *Bea*

A Worcester, Flight & Barr, inkstand, centrally painted on a blue ground, finely gilded, 2 covers restored, incised B mark, c1800, 7in (18cm) wide.
£1,500-2,000 *DN*

A rare moulded Chamberlain's Worcester inkwell, c1820, 1½in (4cm).
£200-275 *TVA*

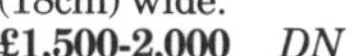

A Chamberlain's Worcester inkstand, in yellow on a matt blue base, heavily enriched in gilding, putto restored, script mark in gold, c1820, 5½in (14cm).
£450-550 *C*

A very rare Stevenson & Hancock Derby jewelled inkwell, painted mark, c1880, 4in (10cm).
£500-550 *TVA*

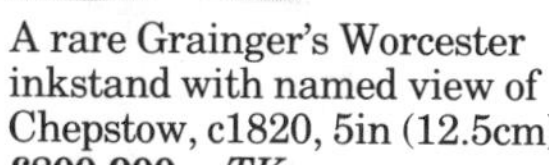

A rare Grainger's Worcester inkstand with named view of Chepstow, c1820, 5in (12.5cm).
£800-900 *TK*

Jardinières

A pair of Meissen jardinières, with 'Alt-ozier' borders, painted in colours with 'deutsche Blumen', one restored, blue crossed swords marks, c1745, 12in (31cm).
£800-1,000 *CG*

A Royal Worcester 'Hadley style' jardinière, with gilded rim and foot, signed W. E. Jarman, pattern No. 276, green mark, 1907, 8in (20.5cm) diam.
£1,200-1,500 *GH*

Jars

A Royal Worcester pot pourri jar, painted by Reginald Harry Austin, printed mark and date code for 1911, 7½in (18.5cm).
£500-600 *Bea*

A Mintons jardinière with brilliant turquoise enamel and gilded decoration, painting attributed to Antonin Boullemier, slight crack to rim, marked on base with gold crown and globe, also impressed Mintons and clay mark for 1875, 14in (35.5cm) wide.
£1,500-2,500 *DSH*

A Royal Worcester jardinière with pierced rim, boldly painted by Albert Shuck, shape No. H295, printed mark and date code for 1919, 9in (22.5cm).
£450-550 *Bea*

A pair of German pot pourri jars and covers, each brightly painted, slight damage, 15½in (39cm).
£1,500-2,000 *Bea*

A garniture of 5 Chelsea Derby covered jars, applied overall with green and gold flowerheads and branches with red berries, some damage, late 18thC.
£1,000-1,200 *Bea*

A pair of Sèvres Louis XVI style gilt-bronze mounted cobalt ground and gilt jars and covers, 21in (53cm).
£1,000-1,500 *CNY*

A pair of ormolu-mounted octagonal baluster jars, gilt and painted in iron red and underglaze blue in the Imari style, fitted for electricity, some damage, 13in (32cm).
£1,200-1,600 *CNY*

A pair of French porcelain jars and covers, potted and painted in the Chinese manner, in bright enamel colours and gold, slight damage, 14½in (37cm).
£400-500 *Bea*

A Wedgwood Fairyland Lustre black ground jar and cover, outline printed in gold and coloured, the ground gilt with a spider's web, printed Portland Vase mark and pattern No. Z4968i, c1925, 3½in (8.5cm).
£1,500-2,000 *C*

Jugs

A Caughley milk jug, transfer printed with the Fishermen pattern in underglaze blue, c1785.
£260-300 *TVA*

A Böttger gold Chinese milk jug and later domed cover, gilt in the Seuter workshop, reserved on a solid gold ground, chip to spout, the porcelain c1725, 7in (18cm).
£800-900 *C*

A Sèvres jar, cover and stand, painted within a decorated blue and gold rim, minor damage to one handle of the stand, painted mark with date code for 1780, stand 7in (17cm) wide.
£500-700 *Bea*

A Coalport spirally-mounted jug, painted with the monogram JEG, blue line rim, c1800, 9in (22.5cm).
£300-400 *C*

A pair of Coalport jugs, the bodies painted in colours, with the motto 'VIRTUTI NIHIL OBSTAT ET ARMIS', flanked by gilt foliage sprays between gilt line rims, one neck with slight restoration, some rubbing to gilding, c1800, 8in (20cm).
£1,000-1,200 *C*

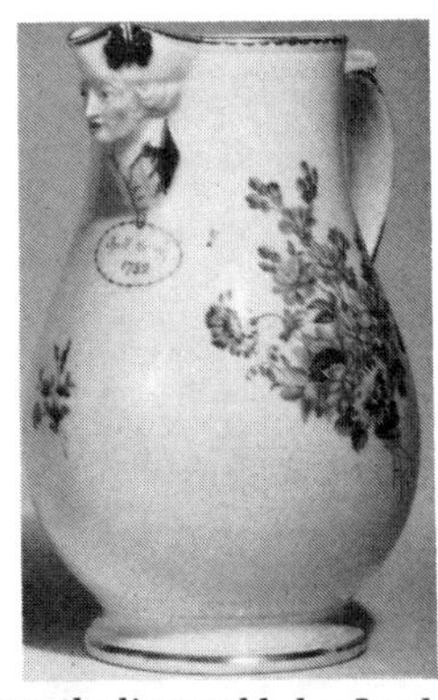

A Derby jug, the lip moulded as Lord Rodney with gilt inscription 'April the 12th 1782', repair to foot, crown, crossed batons and D marks in puce, Wm. Duesbury & Co, c1782, 9in (22cm).
£450-550 *C*

A Liverpool jug, painted in a dry palette within elaborate gilt diaper pattern borders, blue crossed L's and dot marks, Richard Chaffer's phosphatic porcelain, c1755, the painting perhaps West Pans and the gilding perhaps Worcester, 9in (23cm).
£800-1,200 *C*

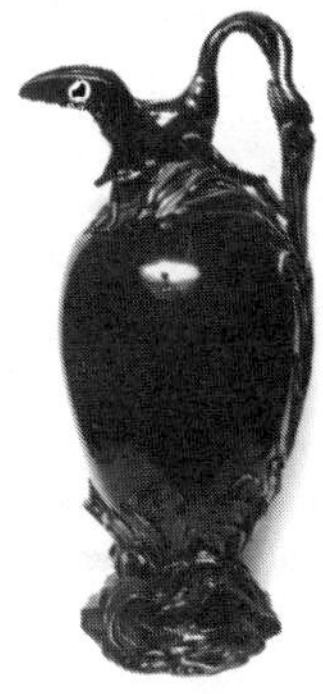

A Coalport porcelain blue ground water jug, some damage, c1860, 19½in (49cm).
£60-80 *THA*

A Pennington's Liverpool porcelain jug, with overglaze painting, c1700, 4in (10cm).
£140-160 *DEL*

A Liverpool blue and white jug, the pinched lip with a pierced strainer, attributed to William Ball's factory, part of lip lacking, chips and cracks to rims, c1760, 13in (32cm).,
£3,000-4,000 *C*

A Belleek cauldron creamer, c1895, 3in (7.5cm).
£25-30 *TVA*

A Miles Mason milk jug, bat-printed in grey with Moses in the Bulrushes between gilt line and foliage rims, impressed mark and 0, c1810, 4½in (11.5cm).
£120-170 *C*

A Minton jug with loop handle, pattern No. 248, c1805, 6½in (16.5cm) wide.
£200-300 *C*

A Meissen inverted baluster jug, modelled after a silver original, small chip to rim, blue crossed swords mark, c1755, 7½in (19cm).
£500-600 *C*

A Plymouth blue and white jug, minute chips to foot, blue 24 mark, c1770, 6½in (16.5cm).
£1,200-1,600 *C*

A Miles Mason jug, bat-printed in grey between gilt line rims, minute chip to lip, c1810, 8½in (21cm).
£250-350 *C*

A Meissen jug with hinged cover and contemporary silver-gilt mount, slight restoration to spout and cover, blue crossed swords mark, the mount with the décharge of Julien Berthe, fermier-général 1750-56, the porcelain c1740, 7½in (18.5cm).
£3,000-3,500 *CG*

A Rockingham jug, unmarked, 4½in (11cm).
£500-550 *BHA*

LIVERPOOL

- ★ porcelain from all Liverpool factories is eagerly collected
- ★ **Richard Chaffers & Co** 1754-65 – produced first a bone ash and later a soapstone porcelain, mainly blue and white, good painting, with some polychrome wares of high quality
- ★ **Samuel Gilbody** c1754-61 – rarest of Liverpool porcelains, soft glaze colours which tend to sink into glaze, very difficult to correctly attribute wares
- ★ **William Ball** 1755-69 – blue and white slightly more common from this factory, decoration very Bow-like, glaze can be confused with Longton Hall, but frequently has a greenish-blue appearance
- ★ **William Reid & Co** 1756-61 – mainly quite crude blue and white, often sanded, chinoiserie based decoration, sometimes resembling contemporary style on Liverpool delftware
- ★ **Philip Christian & Co** 1765-76 – greyish tone to underglaze blue, some fine painting, flatware is rare, but bowls were something of a speciality
- ★ **Seth Pennington** 1770-99 – many copies of Christian's wares, standard not as high as earlier factories, mainly blue and white
- ★ **Wolfe & Co** 1795-1800 – polychrome wares with chinoiserie decoration, blue and white extremely rare

A Sèvres cream jug with branch handle, painted with flowers, on 3 branch feet, with gilt dentil rim, blue interlaced L marks enclosing the date letter O for 1767 and painter's mark, 3½in (8.5cm).
£400-500 *C*

A Worcester blue and white feather moulded cream jug, with workman's mark, c1760.
£300-350 *TW*

A Chamberlain's Worcester blue ground jug, the neck with the monogram GR in gold within a gilt oak leaf cartouche, minor restoration to lip and foot, script mark, c1815, 7in (18cm).
£600-700 *C*

Chamberlain's Worcester eaf-moulded jug, painted in sepia vith a view of Worcester, some ninor rubbing and slight staining, cript mark, c1795, 5½in (13.5cm).
400-500 *C*

A Royal Worcester flat-back jug, shape No. 1094, painted by Henry William Shepherd, initialled, c1899.
£100-120 *TVA*

A pair of Royal Worcester claret jugs, shape No. 1047, c1910, 8in (20cm).
£550-600 *TVA*

Meissen yellow ground milk jug nd cover with pine cone finial, ninor repair to edge of cover, blue rossed swords mark and painter's ark 7. to each piece, c1740, 4½in 1.5cm).
,000-1,500 *CG*

A Pinxton Japan-pattern milk jug, painted with an elaborate Imari pattern, c1800, 6in (15.5cm) wide.
£400-500 *C*

A Sèvres helmet-shaped jug, foot rim re-gilded, blue interlaced L mark with the date letter G for 1759, and painter's mark of Aloncle, 5½in (14cm).
£700-800 *C*

A Royal Worcester miniature Toby ug, shape No. 2831, c1931.
70-75 *TVA*

pair of Italian white ewers, with nimal mask spouts and loop andles, silver gilt covers, some amage, the covers marked, c1770, in (16cm).
650-750 *CNY*

A cream jug, c1800, 4in (10cm).
£70-100 *DEL*

Mugs

A Bow blue and white cylindrical mug, c1758, 2in (5.5cm).
£600-700 *C*

A pair of Chantilly Kakiemon mugs, with manganese branch handles and leafy terminals, iron red hunting horn marks, c1740, 2½in (6.5cm).
£5,500-6,000 *CG*

A miniature Copeland Spode mug, c1900, 2in (5cm).
£40-60 *THA*

A Lowestoft blue and white mug, the interior rim with blue loop pattern, painter's numeral 5, c1765, 4in (9.5cm).
£4,500-5,500 *C*

A Sèvres coffee can, with rare chinoiserie painting, crowned red mark, c1778, 2in (5cm).
£300-400 *BHA*

A Chelsea tea plant beaker, enriched in colours beneath a chocolate line rim, rim chips, c1745, 3in (7.5cm).
£1,500-2,500 *C*

A Coalport mug, c1810, 3in (7.5cm).
£200-250 *JUD*

A miniature Royal Crown Derby mug, c1902, 1½in (3.5cm).
£60-80 *THA*

A Rockingham mug, the loop handle with gilt hoof terminal, painted between gilt line rims, some minor staining, puce griffin mark and Cl 2 in red, c1835, 4in (10cm).
£700-800 *C*

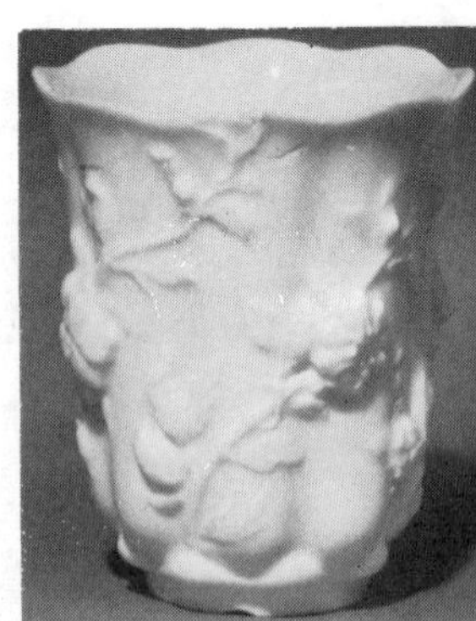
A Chelsea white tea plant beaker slight rim chip and repair, c1745, 3in (7.5cm).
£1,200-1,600 *C*

A Coalport two-handled mug, dated 1877, 4in (10cm).
£100-120 *THA*

l. A Derby Imari style coffee can c1800, 2½in (6in).
£50-70
r. Spode monochrome coffee can, c1800, 2½in (6cm).
£50-70 *CA*

A miniature Royal Crown Derby mug, c1909, 1½in (3.5cm).
£60-80 *THA*

A Staffordshire porcelain lilac and gilt moulded mug, 19thC, 3in (7.5cm).
£25-40 *DEL*

\ Worcester mug, transfer printed ı black by Robert Hancock with 'he King of Prussia, signed :. H. Worcester with the rebus of an nchor and the date 1757, 3½in)cm).
800-900 *C*

. Worcester blue and white ell-shaped mug, in mint condition, in (15cm).
400-550 *BHA*

'laques

\ Coalport plaque, painted by ames Rouse, small scratch to his ight eyebrow, signed J. Rouse, 856, green plush frame, 12 by 4½in (30.5 by 36.5cm).
1,300-1,600 *C*

Derby documentary plaque, ainted by Sampson Hancock, gned and dated on the reverse, ampson Hancock, May 31, 1865, by 8½in (15.5 by 21.5cm), giltwood 'ame.
450-650 *C*

A Worcester mug, transfer printed in black by Robert Hancock with Parrot Pecking at Fruit, signed R. Hancock fecit on the lower branch, c1760, 4½in (12cm).
£4,000-5,000 *C*

A Worcester blue and white mug, 4in (10cm).
£400-600 *BHA*

A William Fishley, Holland, pottery slipware tyg, c1920, 7in (18cm).
£50-70 *THA*

A Coalport documentary plaque, painted and signed by John Randall F.G.S., Coalport, Nov. 1870, 13½ by 9½in (34.5 by 24.5cm).
£1,000-1,200 *C*

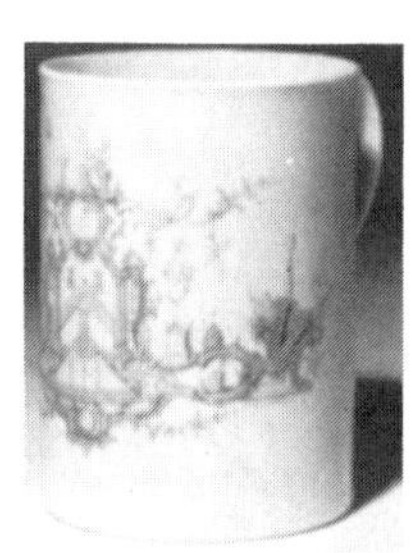

A Worcester mug, transfer printed in grey-green by John Sadler, with a masonic coat of arms after Jeremiah Evans, signed Sadler, Enl. Liverl., c1765, 4½in (12cm).
£1,500-2,000 *C*

A Worcester mug, in Kakiemon style, c1765, 5in (12.5cm).
£800-900 *BHA*

An English porcelain mug, painted with a spaniel chasing a pheasant, on claret ground, probably Coalport, c1830, 5½in (14cm).
£800-900 *TK*

A Derby plaque by T Tatler, painted on a shaded buff and brown ground, signed T. Tatler 1830, 11½ by 10in (29 by 25cm), framed.
£3,500-4,500 *L*

A Chamberlain's Worcester plaque, painted in sepia with a view of Worcester, script mark, c1795, 7in (18cm) wide.
£450-650 *C*

A pair of Rockingham documentary plaques, painted by W W Bailey, with Sunset, view on the Welsh coast and The Clyde, from Erskine Ferry, some very minor flaking to enamels, signed and inscribed in red on the reverses, c1835, 4½ by 5½in (11 by 14cm).
£2,000-3,000 *C*

An English porcelain plaque, inscribed on reverse, 'painted by W. Corden', and dated February 4th, 1823, 6 by 5in (15 by 12.5cm).
£350-450 *CSK*

A Flight, Barr & Barr plaque, painted by Samuel Astles, impressed mark FBB, crowned and incised number 22, 10½ by 8½in (26.5 by 21cm), in gilt frame.
£6,500-7,500 *L*

An early Victorian portrait miniature of Major General T S Nicolls.
£150-170 *TVA*

A Flight, Barr & Barr plaque, painted by Samuel Astles, with classical statuary in the background, 21½ by 16½in (55 by 42.5cm) frame.
£22,000-25,000 *L*

The plaque was exhibited at the Royal Academy in 1827. After the mezzotint by Richard Earlom, from the original painting by Jan Van Huysum in the Houghton Collection, sold by Lord Orford, son of Sir Robert Walpole, to the Empress Catherine of Russia.

A Berlin hand painted plaque, c1870, 8 by 6in (20.5 by 15cm).
£350-400 *CA*

An Austrian plaque, reserved on an intricate gold decorated iron red ground, the border on a deep blue ground, inscribed on the reverse, 'Die Toilette der Esther', 12½in (31.5cm).
£800-900 *Bea*

A Berlin plaque, painted after Murillo, impressed sceptre and KPM marks, c1875, 11 by 8½in (28 by 22.5cm), carved gilt-wood frame.
£2,000-3,000 *C*

A Berlin named plaque of Princess Louise, hand painted, signed Knoniller, impressed mark, KPM and sceptre, c1880.
£1,600-1,800 *TVA*

A Berlin plaque, painted by S A D Fordyce after Van Dyck, with the three eldest children of Charles I, signed and dated 1882, impressed sceptre and KPM marks, gilt metal frame, 9 by 11in (22.5 by 28cm).
£1,800-2,200 *C*

A Berlin plaque, painted after A Kauffmann with a vestal virgin, in a white dress, impressed KPM, sceptre, F and 5 marks, late 19thC, 10½in (27cm).
£1,600-2,000 *C*

A Berlin plaque, painted after Raphael with the Madonna di San Sisto, impressed KPM marks, late 19thC, 12½ by 10in (32 by 25.5cm).
£1,000-1,500 *C*

A pair of Berlin plaques, impressed KPM marks, sceptre and H/G marks, late 19thC, carved giltwood frames, 9½ by 5½in (23.5cm by 14.5cm).
£1,800-2,200 *C*

A Berlin plaque, painted with a young servant girl in a pink dress and white apron, impressed marks, late 19thC, 9½ by 6½in (24 by 16cm), with a gilded carved wood frame.
£1,700-2,200 *Bea*

A Berlin plaque, impressed KPM mark, 13in (33cm).
£2,100-2,600 *CSK*

A Berlin plaque, painted by Carl Muller, impressed marks, 10 by 8in (25.5 by 20.5cm).
£1,500-2,000 *CSK*

A German plaque painted by Louis Renders after David Neal, with Mary Queen of Scots' first encounter with Rizzio, inscribed on the reverse 'premiere rencontre de Marie Stuart avec Rizzio d'apres le tableau de David Neal/8 juin, 1887', small patch of flaked paint, signed, 11½ by 8½in (29 by 21.5cm), gilt metal frame.
£700-900 *C*

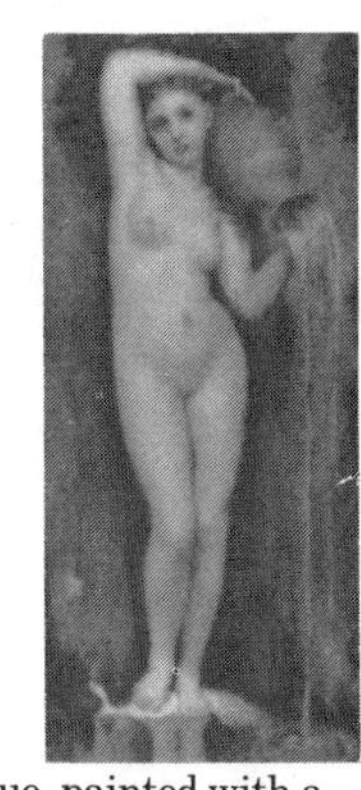

A German plaque, painted with a nude young woman, after a painting by Ingres entitled The Spring, late 19thC, 8 by 4in (20 by 10cm).
£900-1,000 *Bea*

A German plaque, painted with a portrait of a young girl in a white robe, 7½in (19cm), wood frame.
£600-800 *CSK*

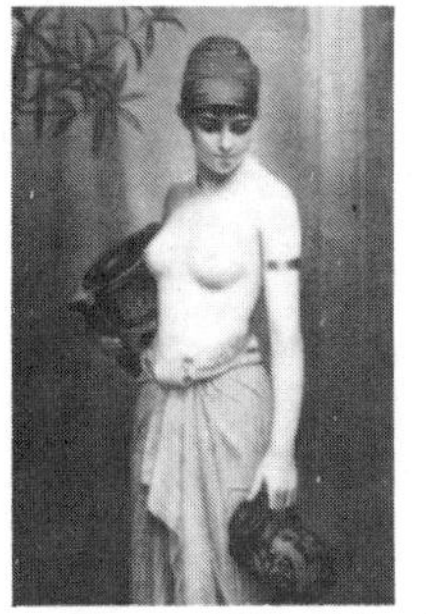

A German plaque, 5½in (14cm), with wood frame.
£1,000-1,200 *CSK*

A Vienna plaque, painted with Cleopatra and Anthony, in red, gold, pink and blue, the back with shield mark in underglaze blue and inscribed Kleopatra, 13½in (34cm), in wood and velvet frame.
£450-550 *L*

Pots

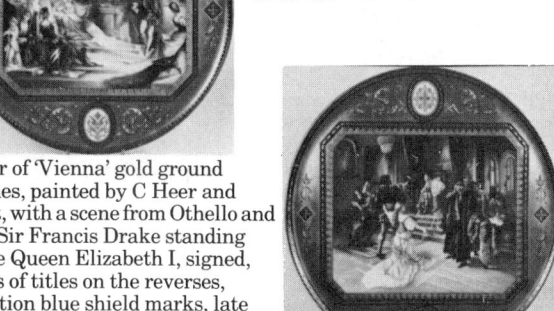

A Coalport yellow ground bough pot and pierced cover, perhaps painted in the studio of Thomas Baxter, slight chipping to cover, c1805, 11½in (28.5cm) wide.
£1,400-1,800 *C*

A pair of 'Vienna' gold ground plaques, painted by C Heer and E Lat, with a scene from Othello and with Sir Francis Drake standing before Queen Elizabeth I, signed, traces of titles on the reverses, imitation blue shield marks, late 19thC, 19½in (49cm) diam.
£3,200-3,600 *C*

A Coalport chocolate pot, painted in reds, blues and greens, heavily gilded, c1800, 6in (15cm).
£100-120 *THA*

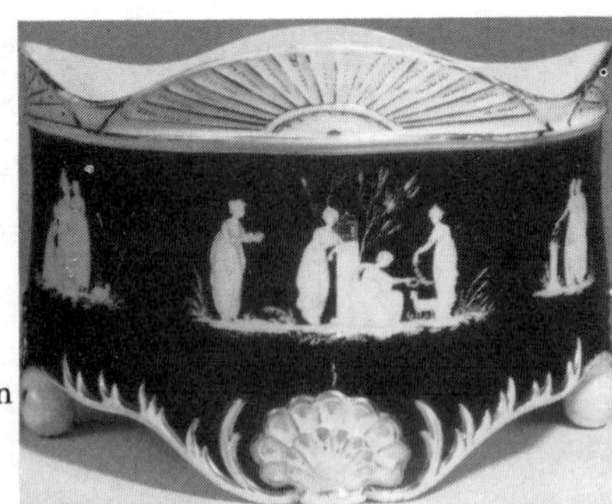

A Coalport bough pot, the chocolate brown ground incised and stencilled and heightened in brown, c1810, 12½in (31cm) wide.
£250-450 *C*

A Royal Crown Derby rouge pot, with Old Derby Witches pattern, c1921, 2in (5cm) diam.
£75-85 *TVA*

A pair of Derby iron red ground D-shaped bough pots and one pierced cover, with gilt rams' mask handles, crown, crossed batons and D marks in iron red, Duesbury & Kean, c1800, 10in (25cm) wide.
£2,500-3,500 *C*

A pair of Liverpool Herculaneum flower pots and 2 stands, with gilt mask handles, c1815, 6½in (17cm) wide.
£1,000-1,200 *C*

A Spode bough pot, with gilt 'feuille-de-choux' cartouche, and bronzed winged cherubs, slight cracks to edges and one foot, c1820, 12in (30.5cm) wide.
£300-400 *C*

A Miles Mason bough pot and cover, bat-printed with Cupid and Psyche, within elaborate gilt cartouches divided by moulded blue and gilt pillars with Ionic capitals between gilt line rims, the cover with blue and gilt gadroons, minute chips to rim, cover chipped and cracked, finial lacking, c1810, 11in (28cm).
£800-1,200 *C*

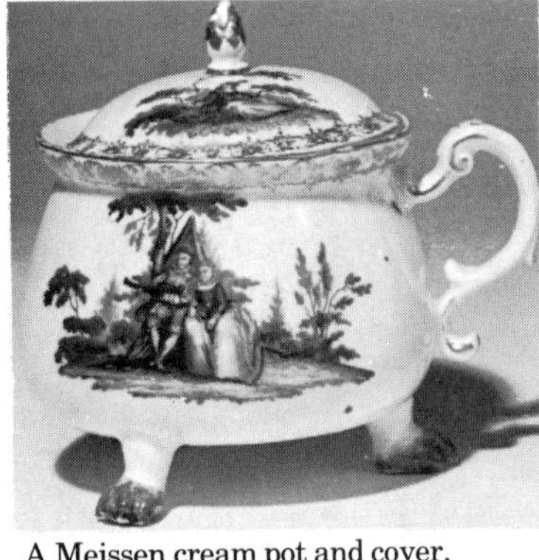

A Meissen cream pot and cover, painted in colours with 'Watteaumalerei' scenes of figures from the Commedia dell'Arte, blue crossed swords mark to base, c1745, 4½in (11cm).
£1,200-1,500 *C*

A Meissen pomade pot and cover, painted in colours with 'Holzschnittblumen' in the manner of Gottfried Klinger, gilt rims, handle restored, faint crossed swords mark to base, c1745, 6in (15cm).
£1,800-2,400 *C*

A Chamberlain's Worcester salmon pink ground bough pot and pierced cover, painted with Venus Attired by the Graces, slight restoration to finial, script mark in gold, the base inscribed, c1800, 7½in (18.5cm).
£2,200-2,500 *C*

A Worcester, Flight & Barr, salmon pink ground jam pot, cover and fixed stand, painted in colours within gilt cartouches, the rim of the stand gilt with key pattern, finial restuck, incised B mark, c1800, 4½in (12cm).
£1,000-1,200 *C*

Miller's is a price Guide not a price List

The price ranges given reflect the average price a purchaser should pay for similar items. Condition, rarity of design or pattern, size, colour, pedigree, restoration and many other factors must be taken into account when assessing values

Ạ Chamberlain's Worcester bough ɔot and pierced cover, bat-printed in ›lack, feet restored, the base nscribed with the views in gold, :1815, 8in (20.5cm).
:1,500-1,700 *C*

Ạ Royal Worcester pot pourri and :over, signed Kitty Blake, shape ·I.291, c1938.
:450-500 *TVA*

ɩn English porcelain bough pot, ›ainted with View of Okehampton :astle, Devonshire, named on the ›ase, c1805, 7½in (19cm) wide.
:500-600 *C*

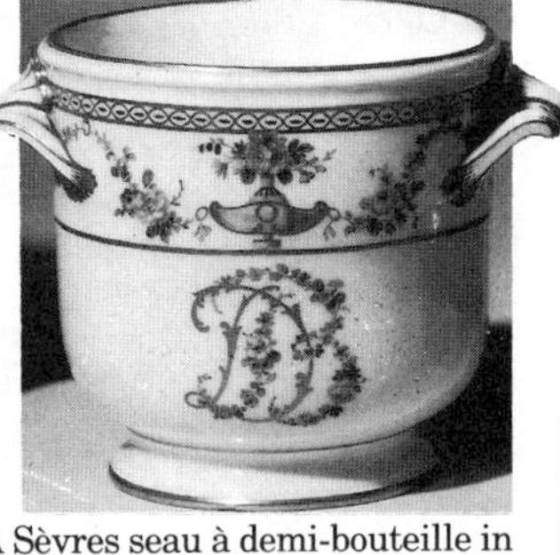

ɩ Sèvres seau à demi-bouteille in :olours from the Duchesse du Barry ervice, bearing the entwined ›nitials D and B in gilt, blue ›nterlaced L marks, date letters for .771, and decorator's mark LB for .e Bel junior, 5in (13cm).
:6,000-7,000 *C*

A Vienna pot with lid, c1840, 6½in (16.5cm).
£300-400 *BHA*

An unusual Grainger's Worcester pot pourri, with named view of Malvern Church, c1820.
£500-700 *TK*

A Chamberlain's Worcester blue ground incense or violet pot and pierced domed cover, minute chipping, script Regent China mark, c1820, 4½in (11.5cm) on wood stand.
£600-1,000 *C*

An English porcelain bough pot and pierced cover, painted in brown monochrome, in the manner of William Billingsley, with Berry Hill, Nottinghamshire, named on the base, cover damaged, c1810, 9½in (24cm).
£1,500-2,000 *C*

A Royal Worcester pot pourri and cover, hand painted on a blushed ivory ground, heightened with gilding, slight chip to knop, printed puce mark on base and date code for 1899, 13in (33cm).
£800-1,000 *OL*

A Worcester spittoon, printed in blue with the Zig-Zag Fence pattern, hatched crescent mark, 4in (10cm).
£400-500 *DN*

A Sèvres seau à bouteille, painted in blue and gilt between blue line and gilt leaf bands, blue interlaced L marks enclosing the date letter D for 1756, and with painter's mark of Rosset, 9in (23cm) wide.
£1,000-1,200 *C*

Two Sèvres seaux à bouteille, painted within blue and gilt 'feuille-de-choux' and blue line and gilt dash rims, one with small hair crack in rim, blue interlaced L marks enclosing the date letters II for 1786 and OO for 1792, and with painter's marks of Tardy and Tandart, 10½in (26cm) wide.
£1,200-1,600 *C*

Sauceboats

A Bow blue and white sauceboat, on 3 mask and paw feet, with a drab glaze, slight lip chips and some firing cracks to rim and handle, c1750, 9in (22cm) wide.
£700-900 *C*

A Caughley sauceboat, with the Fisherman pattern, c1780, 3in (7.5cm).
£190-200 *THA*

A pair of Buen Retiro cache pots with shell and satyr's mask handles, minor chips and restorations to both handles, blue fleur-de-lys marks and incised interlaced C on both pieces, c1770, 10in (25.5cm) wide.
£3,200-3,500 *C*

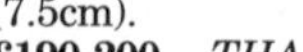

A Liverpool blue and white moulded sauceboat, attributed to William Ball's factory, c1758, 5½in (14.5cm) wide.
£2,500-3,000 *C*

A pair of Derby sauceboats in mint condition, c1765, 5in (12cm).
£900-1,000 *BHA*

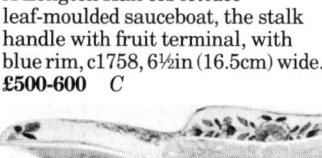

A Longton Hall cos lettuce leaf-moulded sauceboat, the stalk handle with fruit terminal, with blue rim, c1758, 6½in (16.5cm) wide.
£500-600 *C*

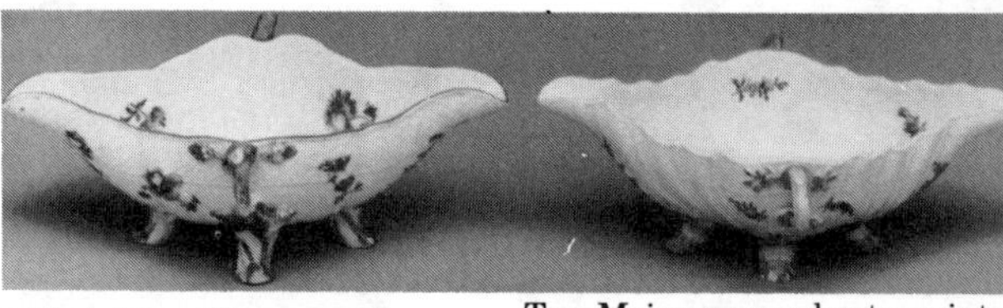

Two Meissen sauceboats, painted with 'deutsche Blumen' beneath 'ozier' bands, blue crossed swords mark, c1750, 9in (23.5cm) wide.
£200-250 *CNY*

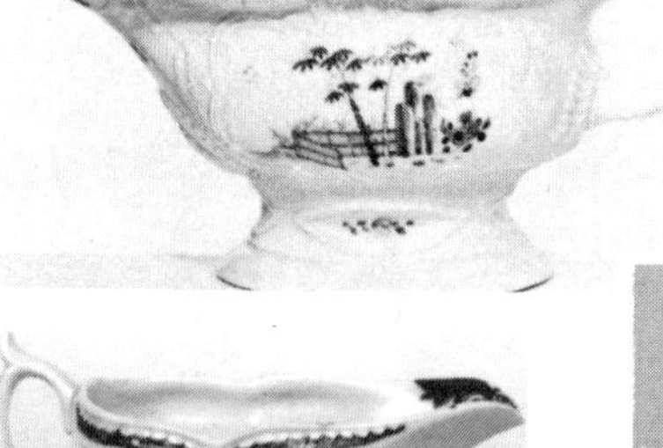

A large Worcester blue and white sauceboat, painter's mark, c1754, 9½in (24cm) wide.
£900-1,000 *CSK*

A Worcester blue and white silver shaped sauceboat, c1755, 7½in (19cm) wide.
£800-1,000 *CSK*

A small Worcester sauceboat, hand painted with the rare Little Fisherman pattern, 2 small chips to rim, c1765.
£300-350 *TVA*

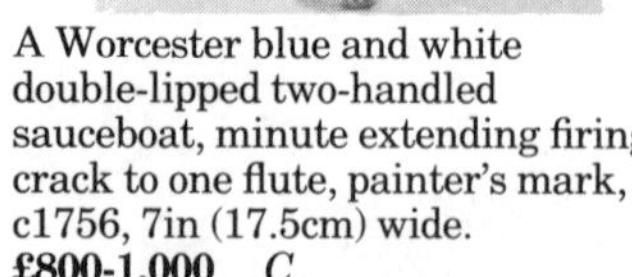

A Worcester blue and white double-lipped two-handled sauceboat, minute extending firing crack to one flute, painter's mark, c1756, 7in (17.5cm) wide.
£800-1,000 *C*

A pair of Worcester blue and white sauceboats, with scroll handles, one with minute chip to foot and rim, blue crescent marks, c1770, 7½in (18.5cm) wide.
£400-500 *C*

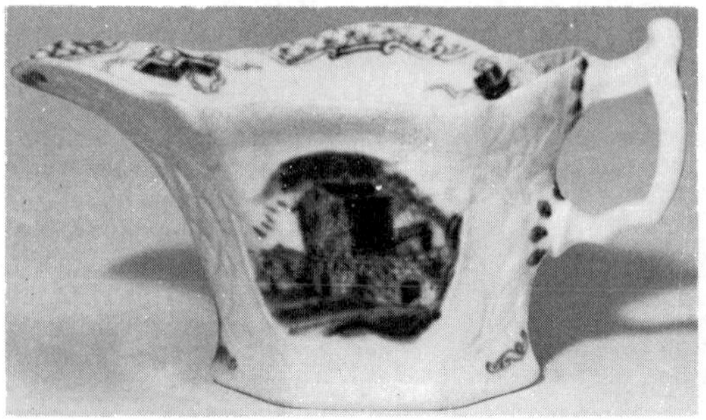

An English porcelain blue and white creamboat, perhaps Reid's Factory, Liverpool, c1755, or Newcastle-under-Lyme, c1750, 5½in (14cm) wide.
£2,000-2,500 *C*

Scent Bottles

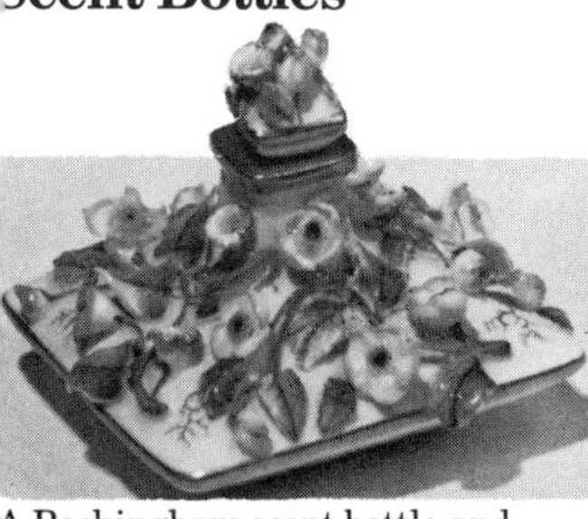

A Rockingham scent bottle and stopper, encrusted with coloured flowers between gilt line rims, slight chipping to flowers, crack to one side, puce griffin mark and C1 2 in red, c1835, 3in (8cm) square.
£450-550 *C*

Services

A Coalport Imari pattern part dessert service, painted in iron red and underglaze blue, enriched in gilding, comprising: 2 sauce tureens, covers and stands, a centre dish, 11 dishes and 30 plates, some damage, c1810.
£2,000-2,500 *C*

An English part tea service, probably by John Rose & Co, Coalport, in enamel colours and gold, comprising 27 pieces, pattern No. 299, early 19thC.
£300-350 *Bea*

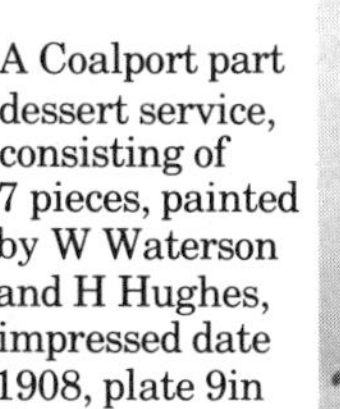

A Coalport part dessert service, consisting of 7 pieces, painted by W Waterson and H Hughes, impressed date 1908, plate 9in (22.5cm).
£1,000-1,200 *TVA*

A Coalport blue ground part dessert service, comprising: an ice pail, cover and liner, 2 sauce tureens, covers and stands, a centre dish on 4 feet, 10 dishes, 18 plates, some damage, c1810.
£5,000-6,000 *C*

A Copeland 51-piece part dinner service, painted with a Japan pattern in iron red, green, blue and gilt, comprising: 37 plates, 8 dishes, 3 tureens and covers on stands, c1875.
£2,000-3,000 *PB*

An H & R Daniel blue ground part tea service, painted in yellow and gilt, comprising: a teapot, a sugar bowl and cover, a milk jug, a slop basin, 8 teacups and saucers, pattern No. 3859, some damage, c1825.
£500-600 *C*

A tea and coffee service by H & R Daniel, comprising: teapot stand, bowl, 2 cake plates, 19 cups and 11 saucers, pattern No. 4367, c1827.
£1,700-2,200 *L*

A Derby coral red ground part tea and coffee service, comprising: a teapot and cover, a sugar bowl, a milk jug, a slop basin, 2 saucer dishes, 22 cups, 11 saucers, crown, crossed batons and D marks and pattern No. 745 in iron red, Duesbury & Kean, c1805.
£2,500-3,500 *C*

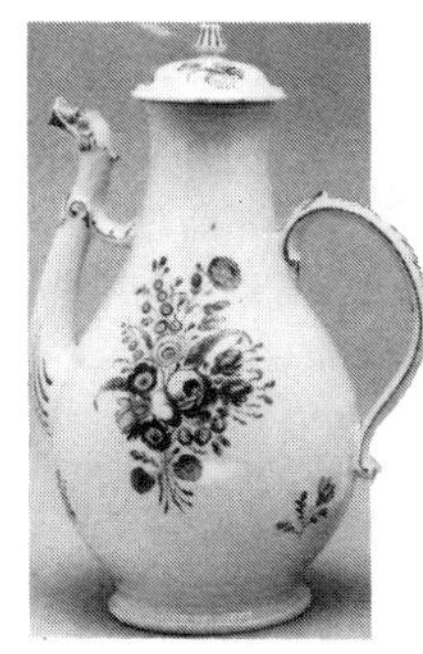

A Doccia coffee service, comprising: a coffee pot and cover, a sugar bowl and cover, 12 coffee cups and saucers, with repairs and imperfections, c1780.
£1,200-1,500 *CNY*

Price

Prices vary from auction to auction – from dealer to dealer. The price paid in a dealer's shop will depend on:

1) what he paid for the item
2) what he thinks he can get for it
3) the extent of his knowledge
4) awareness of market trends

It is a mistake to think that you will automatically pay more in a specialist dealer's shop. He is more likely to know the 'right' price for a piece. A general dealer may undercharge but he could also overcharge

A Minton sugar bowl and cover, in underglaze blue within gilt line rims, 5½in (14.5cm) diam, a cream jug, 3½in (9.5cm) high, and a trio, pattern No. 127, gilding rubbed, c1805.
£450-550 *C*

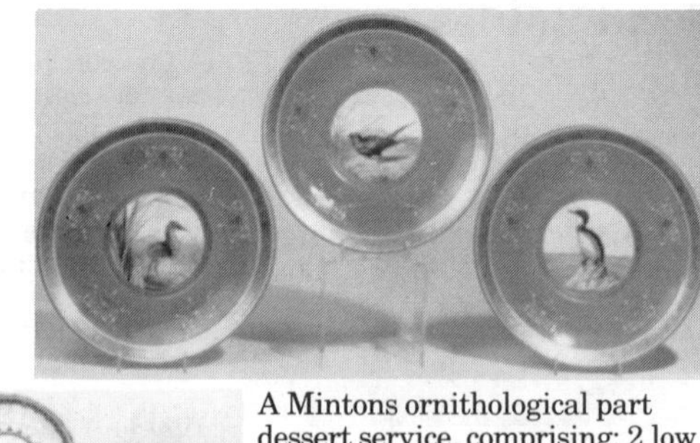

A Mintons ornithological part dessert service, comprising: 2 low stands, one slightly crazed, and 4 plates, pattern No. G3090, impressed marks and date code for 1882, puce printed retailer's mark for F & C Osler, 100 Oxford St, London.
£1,200-1,500 *C*

A Newhall part tea and coffee service, comprising: a teapot and cover, a milk jug, a slop basin, 15 cups and 7 saucers, some damage, c1785.
£700-1,000 *C*

A Spode tea service, decorated in colours and gold and underglaze blue with Imari pattern, comprising: teapot, sugar basin and milk jug, 6 cups and saucers, printed mark Spode in underglaze blue and pattern number 2638 in red.
£500-600 *L*

A Spode stone china dinner service, in pink, blue and green, comprising 9 dishes, 2 drainers, 2 vegetable dishes and covers and 41 plates, 19thC.
£1,000-1,500 *P[Pea]*

A Spode dessert service, painted in pink and green within brown edged rims, comprising: a centre dish, 2 pierced baskets and one stand, 4 dishes and 7 plates, impressed mark Spode and painted pattern number 2432.
£1,500-2,000 *L*

A Staffordshire porcelain part tea service, comprising: a teapot and cover, 2 saucer dishes, a slop bowl, a milk jug, a sugar bowl, 14 cups and 11 saucers, perhaps Neale, some damage, c1790.
£700-900 *CSK*

A Staffordshire porcelain dessert service, comprising: a centre dish, 8 stands and 18 plates, some damage, pattern no. 6/6140 in red, 19thC.
£700-1,000 *DN*

A Swansea tea and coffee service, painted in pink and gilt, comprising: a bowl, 21 cups and 11 saucers, and 3 Coalport plates and a breakfast cup and saucer, of a matching pattern.
£1,000-1,200 *L*

A Worcester part tea and coffee service, comprising: a coffee pot and cover, a milk jug and cover, a teapot, cover and stand, a sugar bowl and cover, a spoon tray, a saucer dish, 7 cups and 3 saucers, some damage, blue square seal marks, c1765, the teapot and sugar bowl painted by a different hand.
£4,500-5,500 *C*

\ Worcester part tea and coffee ervice, painted in bright 'dry' blue namel, comprising: a teapot and over, a sugar basin and cover, a slop asin, 2 saucer dishes, 7½in 18.5cm), 8 cups and 6 saucers, some lamage, painted crossed swords and numeral mark, late 18thC.
:1,600-2,200 *Bea*

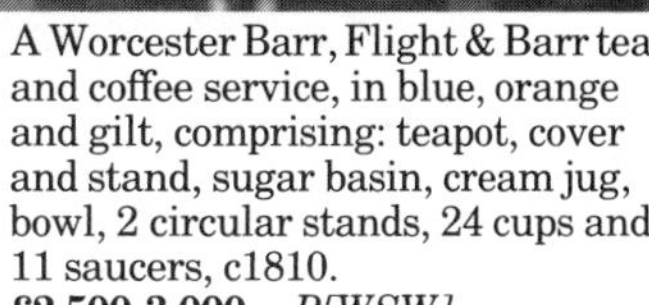

A Worcester Barr, Flight & Barr tea and coffee service, in blue, orange and gilt, comprising: teapot, cover and stand, sugar basin, cream jug, bowl, 2 circular stands, 24 cups and 11 saucers, c1810.
£2,500-3,000 *P[WSW]*

A Royal Worcester tête-à-tête service, comprising: a tray, 2 cups and saucers, cream jug, sugar bowl and cover, teapot and cover, some damage, impressed marks, date code for 1868.
£1,000-1,200 *CEd*

\ Royal Worcester dessert service, brightly painted with flowers and gold and green rim, comprising: 2 oval dishes, 2 square dishes and 12 plates, printed mark and date code for 1910.
:800-1,000 *Bea*

A Royal Worcester dessert service, painted on an apricot and ivory ground, comprising: 3 pairs of shaped dishes and 11 plates, printed mark and date code for 1903.
£700-900 *Bea*

A Barr Worcester part tea and coffee service, comprising: a teapot, cover and stand, cream jug, sucrier, slop bowl, 15 cups 10 saucers, 2 saucer dishes, some damage, incised B and impressed crown marks.
£700-900 *DN*

\ Berlin part service, comprising: n oval platter and 8 plates, painted n colours, all with blue sceptre narks and red printers KPM narks, impressed numerals and gilders mark, late 19th/early 20thC, plate 10in (25cm).
900-1,200 *CAm*

A Worcester tea and coffee service, painted in underglaze blue, and gilt, comprising: coffee pot and cover, teapot, cover and stand, sugar basin and cover, milk jug, bowl, 2 saucer dishes, 12 tea bowls, 8 coffee cups and 12 saucers, open crescent mark.
£1,500-2,000 *L*

An unusual part dessert service, in gilt on a yellow 'marbled' ground, comprising: a tureen and cover, 3 dishes and 3 plates, probably Coalport, some damage, c1810.
:300-350 *DN*

A Berlin solitaire, comprising: a coffee pot and cover, a teapot and cover, a milk jug and cover, a sugar bowl and cover, a cup and saucer, some damage, blue sceptre marks, c1785.
£7,000-7,500 *CG*

A Dresden dessert service, by Wolfson, painted in red, blue and gold, comprising: 2 compotiers, 4 dishes and 16 plates, D mark crowned in underglaze blue.
£2,000-2,500 *L*

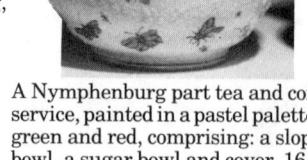

A Gotha coffee pot and cover, milk jug and cover, sugar basin and cover, and a coffee cup and saucer, the cup and saucer marked in underglaze blue R.g. for Rotberg, the proprietor, 1783-1805.
£450-550 *L*

A Meissen travelling tea service, comprising: a teapot and cover, an ogival teapot stand, a tea caddy and cover, a slop bowl and 12 cups and saucers, some repairs, blue crossed swords and dot marks and various Pressnummern, c1770, in contemporary green silk lined tooled leather case with brass lock and drop handles.
£7,500-8,500 *C*

A Nymphenburg part tea and coffee service, painted in a pastel palette of green and red, comprising: a slop bowl, a sugar bowl and cover, 16 cups, 19 saucers, some damage, impressed Bavarian shield marks, c1760.
£4,000-5,000 *C*

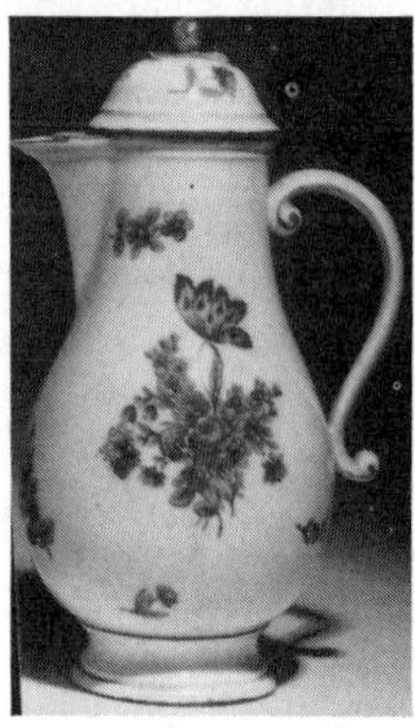

A Nymphenburg part tea and coffee service, painted in green and black with iron red borders, comprising: a coffee pot and cover, a teapot and cover, a sugar box and cover, 8 cups and saucers, some damage, impressed Bavarian shield marks, c1765.
£1,600-2,000 *C*

A Paris, Restoration, purple ground tea service, the teapot and hot water pot with animal mouth spouts, comprising: a teapot and cover, a hot water pot and cover, a sugar bowl and cover, a bowl and 12 cups and saucers, c1820.
£3,000-4,000 *C*

A Sèvres mocha set, comprising: 5 small cups with scroll handles, a stand with moulded 'feuille-de-choux' painted with bands of flowers 'en camaïeu rose' and with gilt rims, small chip to rim of stand, blue interlaced L marks enclosing the date letter G for 1759 and painter's mark of Catrice, the stand incised M.ai CU.
£500-800 *C*

A Sèvres part dessert service, painted in blue and manganese, comprising: 4 shaped plateaux bouret, 4 saucer dishes, 11 plates, some damage, interlaced L marks enclosing various date letters, 1783-90, various painter's marks.
£1,500-2,000 *C*

A Sèvres gilt and white part tea and coffee service, comprising: 2 sugar bowls and covers, a pair of oviform jugs, a bowl, 16 cups and 14 saucers, some damage, printed fleur-de-lys marks, interlaced L's and various date codes for 1824-26.
£1,000-1,500 *C*

A Sèvres pattern armorial royal blue ground coffee service, comprising: a coffee pot and cover, a hot milk jug and cover, a two-handled sugar bowl and cover, 8 coffee cans and saucers, some damage, imitation Sèvres marks in iron red, c1900.
£800-1,000 *C*

. Tournai blue and white part
ınner service, painted with La
ͻnda pattern, comprising:
 tureens and covers, a double
ᵖpped sauceboat with cover, a
ʷo-handled écuelle and cover,
 mustard pots and covers, 15 dishes
ı various sizes, 15 soup and dinner
ˡates in various sizes, some
amage, some pieces with Tournai
ˡue crossed swords marks and
arious marks, late 18thC.
1,200-1,500 *CAm*

. Meissen yellow ground sugar
ͻwl and cover, minor repairs to
ͻwer on finial, blue crossed swords
ᵃark, Pressnummer 10 and
ainter's mark 7, to each piece,
1740, 5in (12.5cm).
1,300-1,500 *CG*

Sucriers

A Coalport sucrier, c1810, 5½in (13.5cm).
£200-250 *JUD*

A Chamberlain's Worcester crested sugar bowl and cover, from the Admiral Yeo service, in Imari colours, c1815, 7½in (19cm) wide.
£1,000-1,200 *C*

 Meissen baluster sugar caster
ᵑd cover, finial chipped, rim
ᵉpair, blue crossed swords mark
1750, 6½in (16.5cm).
250-300 *CNY*

Tankards

 Grainger's Worcester tankard,
ᵃarked in orange script with panel
ᵗle and Grainger, Lee & Co.,
ʷorcester, c1815, 5in (12.5cm).
1,500-2,000 *DSH*

A Venice, Cozzi, part dinner service, painted in the Imari palette with Oriental river landscapes within borders of flowers, comprising: 5 oval dishes, a saucer dish and 19 plates, c1760.
£4,000-5,000 *C*

Price

Prices vary from auction to auction – from dealer to dealer. The price paid in a dealer's shop will depend on:
1) what he paid for the item
2) what he thinks he can get for it
3) the extent of his knowledge
4) awareness of market trends
It is a mistake to think that you will automatically pay more in a specialist dealer's shop. He is more likely to know the 'right' price for a piece. A general dealer may undercharge but he could also overcharge

Tea & Coffee Pots

A Bristol teapot and cover with moulded spout and grooved loop handle, blue X11 mark, Richard Champion's factory, c1775, 5½in (13.5cm).
£750-1,000 *C*

BRISTOL c1749-52

- ★ first porcelain to be produced was the soft-paste produced by Benjamin Lund from 1749-52
- ★ these porcelains are very rare but examples sometimes show the relief moulded marks 'Bristol' or 'Bristoll'
- ★ mostly underglaze blue ware with chinoiserie decoration
- ★ the glaze was tight fitting although it had a tendency to pool and bubble
- ★ the blue often looks watery where it has run in the firing
- ★ in 1752 Bristol moulds were sold to Worcester
- ★ it is extremely difficult to differentiate late Lund's Bristol from early Worcester

BRISTOL c1770-81

- ★ William Cookworthy transferred his Plymouth factory to Bristol in 1770
- ★ the body had a tendency to slight tears and firing cracks
- ★ early wares extremely difficult to differentiate from Plymouth – both show same firing imperfections, such as smoky ivory glaze and wreathing in the body
- ★ Champion took over the works in 1773
- ★ towards mid and late 1770s the dominant decorative style was neo-classical with particular reliance on delicate swags and scattered flowers
- ★ later pieces showed little imperfections in enamel and potting
- ★ later Bristol colours are sharp and gilding is of excellent quality

A Bristol teapot and cover, brightly decorated in coloured enamels, knop chipped, 6in (15cm).
£400-450 *DN*

A miniature Caughley teapot and cover, hand painted, slight chip inside cover, c1775, 3½in (8.5cm).
£500-550 *TVA*

A Caughley barrel shaped teapot, with the Temple pattern, c1780, 6in (15cm).
£150-180 *THA*

A Derby teapot, c1750, 6in (15cm).
£450-550 *BHA*

A Derby teapot and cover, edged in gilding, body cracked, Wm Duesbury & Co, c1770, 5½in (14cm).
£600-650 *C*

A Doccia coffee pot and cover, with purple landscape decoration, the rims gilt, one engaging tooth inside cover missing, c1780, 6in (15cm).
£250-300 *CNY*

A Mettlach pewter mounted 'castle stein, the reverse with an inscription on a panel beneath the handle and suspending a red seal, impressed marks and numbers, dat code for 1898, 16in (40cm).
£1,200-1,600 *C*

A Caughley polychrome teapot, c1780, 5½in (13.5cm).
£300-350 *THA*

A Chelsea fable teapot, painted in the manner of Jefferyes Hammet O'Neale with the fable of The Fox and The Goat in the Well, the reverse with 2 pieces restuck, c175 4in (10.5cm), the cover a late 18th enamelled tin replacement painted with flower sprays.
£1,700-2,200 *C*

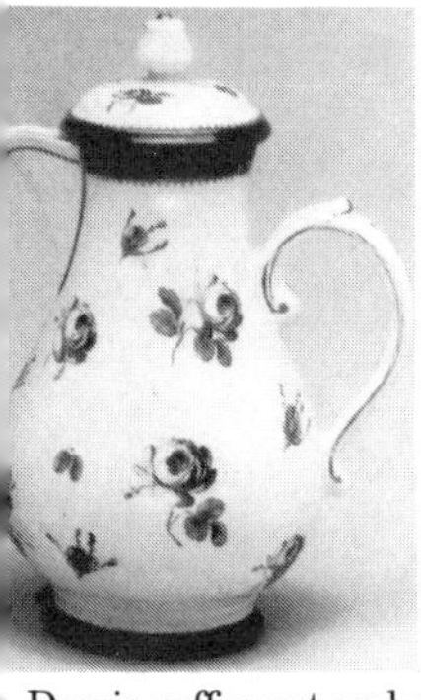

A Doccia coffee pot and cover, painted in dark pink, green and gilt, c1785, 6in (15cm).
£170-200 *CNY*

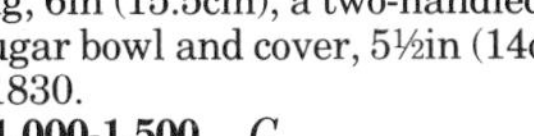

A Rockingham baluster teapot and cover, painted beneath a gilt dentil rim, 7in (17.5cm), a baluster milk jug, 6in (15.5cm), a two-handled sugar bowl and cover, 5½in (14cm), c1830.
£1,000-1,500 *C*

A Worcester teapot and cover with flower finial, decorated in 'famille rose' colours, 18thC, 6in (15cm).
£120-150 *HCH*

LOWESTOFT
- ★ Lowestoft factory commenced by 1758, after earlier trials
- ★ ceased production in 1799 and factory closed in 1802
- ★ Early Period c1757-61 Middle Period c1761-70 Late Period c1770-99
- ★ soft paste porcelain using bone ash
- ★ from 1757 to 1766 only blue and white painted wares produced
- ★ decoration of early wares is well detailed and less stylised than post 1765
- ★ unusual shapes very collectable
- ★ no factory mark, but many pieces pre-1775 numbered inside footrim or on base if no footrim
- ★ numbers are usually 1-11, letters of the alphabet also used
- ★ damage tends to stain brown

A Longton Hall cabbage leaf moulded teapot and cover, crack to base and one side, part of handle terminal missing, c1755, 4½in (11cm).
£12,500-13,500 *C*

A Plymouth yellow ground coffee pot and cover, painted in purple, crack to rim and top of handle, chips to spout and cover, c1770, 10in (25cm).
£400-450 *C*

A Royal Worcester white porcelain teapot and cover, probably decorated by George Owen, the handle, spout and cover applied with pale blue beads, impressed mark, c1890, 5in (12cm).
£3,000-3,500 *Bea*

A Böttger porcelain Goldchinesen Hausmalerei inverted baluster coffee pot, the handle, spout, knop and rims gilt all over, c1725, with contemporary silver-gilt footrim, 8½in (21cm).
£1,500-2,000 *C*

A Lowestoft teapot with Curtis-type decoration, c1782.
£400-450 *OSA*

A miniature Spode teapot and cover, with gilt mons on a blue ground gilt with scale pattern, chip ground to foot rim, red mark and pattern No. 1166, c1820, 2in (5cm).
£450-500 *C*

A Berlin coffee pot and cover, painted in red with scenes after Watteau, blue sceptre mark and Pressnummer 3, c1785, 9in (23cm).
£2,300-2,500 *CG*

A Böttger porcelain Hausmalerei coffee pot and domed cover, by Johann Philipp Dannhöfer, enriched with gilding, spout, rim and foot chipped, finial lacking, the porcelain c1725, the decoration slightly later, 7½in (19.5cm).
£3,500-4,000 *C*

A Böttger white porcelain teapot and cover, minor chips to rim, c1720, 6½in (16.5cm) wide.
£7,500-8,000 *CG*

A Meissen gold Chinese teapot and cover, shaped panels on solid gold ground, chips to spout and rims, c1725, 5½in (13.5cm) wide.
£600-700 *C*

A Meissen yellow ground coffee pot painted 'en camaïeu rose', reserved on a yellow ground, minor chip to the underside of cover, blue crossed swords mark and incised cross, c1740, 7½in (18.5cm).
£2,000-2,500 *CG*

A Meissen gold Chinese teapot and cover, gilt at Augsburg by Bartolomaüs Seuter, with silver-gilt chain attachment, minor chips to foot rim, one chip to rim, interior of cover chipped, c1725, 6½in (16.5cm) wide.
£6,000-7,000 *C*

A Meissen cylindrical chocolate pot and cover, with turned wood gilt metal mounted handle, chip to cover, c1745, 5in (13.5cm).
£480-520 *CNY*

A Meissen spirally moulded baluster coffee pot and cover and a hot milk jug, repair to lip of jug, blue crossed swords marks, c1750, coffee pot 9½in (24cm).
£300-400 *CNY*

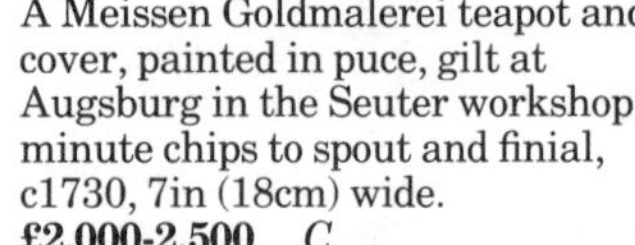

A Meissen Goldmalerei teapot and cover, painted in puce, gilt at Augsburg in the Seuter workshop, minute chips to spout and finial, c1730, 7in (18cm) wide.
£2,000-2,500 *C*

A Meissen baluster coffee pot and domed cover, picked out in colours and gilt and painted in sepia, hairline crack, rim chip repair, blue crossed swords mark, mid-18thC, 9in (23cm).
£300-400 *CNY*

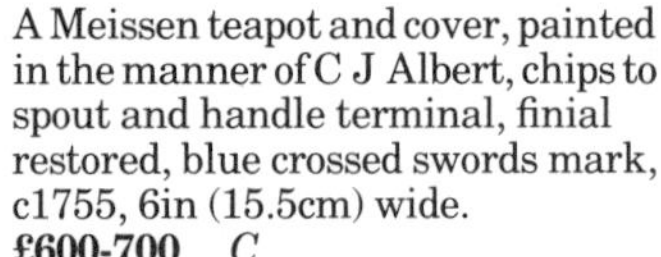

A Meissen teapot and cover, painted in the manner of C J Albert, chips to spout and handle terminal, finial restored, blue crossed swords mark, c1755, 6in (15.5cm) wide.
£600-700 *C*

A Weesp lilac ground teapot and cover, painted with Italian Comedy figures, the handle and spout with blue foliage scrolls, minor chip to rim of cover, c1760, 6in (15.5cm) wide.
£7,000-8,000 *CG*

A Meissen Marcolini chocolate pot, with gilt fittings, c1763, 7in (17.5cm).
£750-900 *BHA*

'ureens & Butter 'ubs

Coalport armorial tureen from the ·llection of the Duke of Cambridge, ith brown and gilt decoration, .800, 9in (22.5cm) wide.
100-120 *THA*

pair of Worcester partridge reens and covers, modelled in ack and brown, slight crack to one m, both covers repaired, c1760, 7in 8cm) wide.
,700-2,200 *C*

A Doccia ecuelle, cover and stand, probably painted by G B Fanciullacci, c1780, 9in (23.5cm) diam.
£300-350 *CNY*

A Worcester partridge tureen and cover, naturally modelled and coloured, the cover repaired and an area of restoration at the front, c1765, 6in (15cm) wide.
£800-1,000 *C*

A Chamberlain's Worcester pale blue ground armorial two-handled soup tureen, cover and stand, the cover with script mark, c1815, the stand 12in (31cm) diam.
£1,700-2,200 *C*

A Meissen coffee pot and cover, with shaped blue bands edged with gilt, finial re-stuck, blue crossed swords and dot mark, c1770, 10½in (27cm).
£300-350 *CNY*

A pair of Barr, Flight & Barr sauce tureens and covers, the covers with impressed BFB under crown, the bases with scripted panel titles and factory mark, c1805, 7in (17cm).
£5,000-6,000 *DSH*

A blue and white Goldfinch pattern sauce tureen, cover and stand, c1820, 6½in (16cm).
£150-200 *CA*

Berlin ecuelle and cover, painted colours, within gilt dentil rims, ip to rim of cover, blue sceptre ark, c1780, 7½in (19cm) wide.
,500-2,000 *C*

A Ludwigsburg tureen and cover, painted with flowers, chips to interior of rim and repair to finial, blue interlaced crowned C's mark and impressed A,2 and 20, c1770, 10in (25.5cm) wide.
£1,000-1,500 *C*

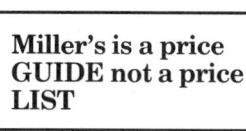

Miller's is a price GUIDE not a price LIST

A Frankenthal ornithological tureen and cover, painted with bright colours within puce scale borders, the base cracked, blue lion rampant mark, c1758, 8in (19.5cm) wide.
£1,500-2,000 *C*

A Meissen tureen and cover, painted in colours with the 'Koreanische Löwe' pattern, crack to body of tureen and old rivet, blue crossed swords mark to base, c1735, 12in (30cm).
£1,000-1,500 *C*

A Meissen ecuelle, cover and stand, painted in colours, each piece with the cypher 'PP1' surmounted by the Imperial crown on an escutcheon draped with flags and trophies, the cover repaired, blue crossed swords mark to the ecuelle and Pressnummer 6, c1745, the stand 7in (18cm) diam.
£1,800-2,200 *C*

A Meissen quatrefoil tureen, cover and stand painted in colours with 'Watteaumalerei' vignettes, gilt rims to all pieces, repair to knop, blue crossed swords marks and Pressnummern to base, c1750, the stand 11½in (28.5cm) wide.
£5,500-6,000 *C*

A Meissen Marcolini tureen and cover, naturalistically painted in yellow, red, green and grey, repairs, blue crossed swords marks and various incised marks to base, c1770, 11in (28cm) wide.
£650-750 *CAm*

A pair of Meissen tureens and covers, moulded with 'Neuebrandenstein', painted in colours, piece restuck to one cover, chips to handles, blue crossed swords marks, c1750, 11in (28cm) wide.
£2,000-2,500 *C*

A Meissen soup tureen, cover and stand, with cut lemon finial, painted with bouquets of 'deutsche Blumen', blue crossed swords marks, Pressnummern, c1750, the stand 17in (43cm) wide.
£1,500-2,000 *CNY*

A Meissen two-handled tureen stand, moulded with pierced scrolls, edged in puce and gilt, blue crossed swords and dot mark, c1770, 17in (44cm) wide.
£900-1,200 *CNY*

A Meissen tureen and cover, with cut lemon finial, painted with bouquets of 'deutsche Blumen', bas repaired, blue crossed swords mark c1750, 13½in (34cm) wide.
£150-200 *CNY*

A Meissen tureen and cover, with cut lemon finial, painted with bouquets of 'deutsche Blumen' within 'ozier' bands, minor chips to handles, blue crossed swords mark, c1750, 12in (30.5cm) wide.
£500-600 *CNY*

A Sèvres two-handled ecuelle, cove and stand, painted in colours on a blue and gilt 'oeil-de-perdrix' ground, chip to handle of stand, blue interlaced L marks, date letter for 1775, and blue decorator's mark for Thévenet, 10in (25.5cm) wide.
£1,000-1,500 *C*

Vases

A Belleek white porcelain vase, slight damage, first version printed mark in brick red, 8in (20.5cm).
£150-200 *Bea*

A Belleek spill vase, with black marks, c1895, 12½in (31.5cm).
£1,000-1,200 *TVA*

A pair of Bow vases and covers, painted in the 'famille rose' palette one body cracked and restored, c1750, 7½in (19.5cm).
£2,000-2,500 *C*

A Chelsea blue ground vase, painted in blue and gilt, some minor rubbing, gold anchor mark, c1760, 13in (33cm).
£1,200-1,500 *C*

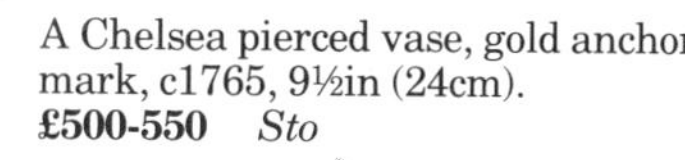

A Chelsea pierced vase, gold anchor mark, c1765, 9½in (24cm).
£500-550 *Sto*

A Coalbrookdale type flower encrusted vase, cover and detachable base, hairline cracks, 27½in (70cm).
£1,200-1,500 *CSK*

A Coalport brown ground beaker vase, painted in the manner of Thomas Baxter, some minute flaking to ground colour, c1810, 5in (13cm).
£300-400 *C*

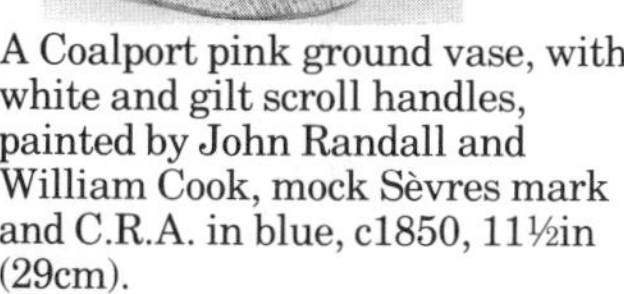

A Coalport pink ground vase, with white and gilt scroll handles, painted by John Randall and William Cook, mock Sèvres mark and C.R.A. in blue, c1850, 11½in (29cm).
£550-600 *C*

A pair of Coalport vases, c1850, 15½in (38cm).
£700-800 *THA*

A pair of Coalport vases of Chelsea shape, painted on a turquoise and puce scale pattern ground, gilt borders and handles, 10in (25cm).
£1,300-1,600 *L*

A Coalport turquoise ground vase and cover, painted by John Randall and William Cook, enriched in gilding, small rim chip, gilt ampersand mark, c1865, 18½in (47.5cm).
£700-800 *C*

A pair of Davenport vases, c1860, 14in (35.5cm).
£250-270 *THA*

A Crown Derby Porcelain Co vase, with matt cream and pale green glaze highlighted in gilt, shape 553, pattern 2582, dated cypher for 1885, marked Bailey, Banks and Biddle, Philadelphia, 9in (23cm).
£400-500 *WHB*

A set of 3 Derby flower vases with named views, 18thC.
£3,000-4,000 *Wor*

Make the Most of Miller's

Every care has been taken to ensure the accuracy of descriptions and estimated valuations. Price ranges in this book reflect what one should expect to pay for a similar example. When selling one can obviously expect a figure below. This will fluctuate according to a dealer's stock, saleability at a particular time, etc. It is always advisable to approach a reputable specialist dealer or an auction house which has specialist sales

A garniture of Spode vases, pattern No. 967, c1820.
£2,500-3,000 *JG*

A pair of Crown Derby Porcelain Co vases, painted in enamel colours and gold on a pale pink ground, c1885, 6½in (17cm).
£500-550 *Bea*

A matched pair of Derby beaker shape vases, painted on a dark blue ground with gilt, on 3 paw feet, 5in (12.5cm).
£550-650 *L*

A Liverpool Herculaneum buff ground vase, slight rubbing, printed mark in puce, c1815, 4in (9.5cm).
£600-700 *C*

A Minton pale turquoise ground 'munster pot pourri' vase and cover, some damage, the cover with blue crossed swords mark, c1830, 10½in (26cm).
£400-500 *C*

A pair of Minton pink ground campana vases, painted on shaded pink and yellow grounds, c1820, 6½in (17cm).
£1,700-2,200 *C*

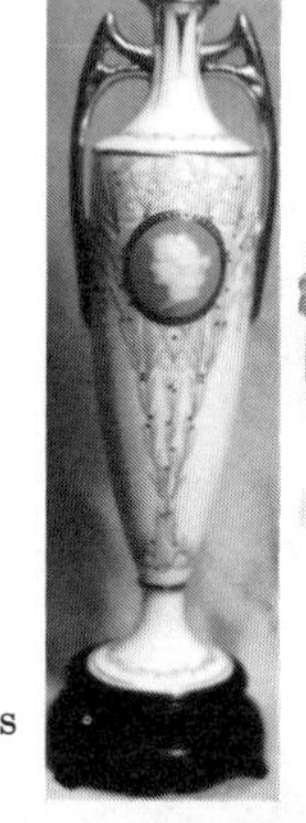

A pair of Minton pâté-sur-pâté vases by A Birks, c1890.
£500-600 *Wai*

A pair of Minton vases, c1880.
£480-550 *GOR*

A Pinxton yellow ground vase and 2 covers, painted 'en grisaille' in the manner of William Billingsley and highlighted in yellow, one cover repaired, c1797, one cover later, 10½in (27cm).
£1,700-2,200 *C*

A Wedgwood Fairyland Lustre vase, decorated on a pale blue and mauve ground, 9in (23cm).
£400-500 *HCH*

A Ridgway & Sons vase, on a bronzed foot, one handle damaged, impressed Ridgway & Sons and inscribed Brunswick, No. 326 in red, c1810, 7in (18cm).
£250-350 *C*

A pair of Spode vases, the base marked Spode 2575, c1815, 5in (12.5cm).
£1,600-2,000 *DSH*

A Rockingham blue ground vase and cover, painted in blue and edged in gilding, the cover with gilt seated monkey finial, c1828, 19in (48cm).
£1,100-1,500 *C* ▶

A Rockingham vase, c1830, 8in (20cm).
£750-900 *BHA*

RIDGWAY

- ★ one of the most important factories manufacturing English bone china
- ★ most of the early Ridgway porcelain from 1808-30 is unmarked; some, however, do have pattern numbers which are fractional, as did Coalport, with which it is often confused
- ★ the quality of the early porcelain is excellent, brilliant white and with no crazing in the glaze
- ★ there were many skilled flower painters employed at the Cauldon Place works including George Hancock, Thomas Brentnall, Joseph Bancroft
- ★ the development of the Ridgway factory is as follows:
  John Ridgway & Company, 1830-55
  Bates, Brown-Westhead & Moore, 1859-61
  Brown-Westhead, Moore & Company, 1862-1905
  Cauldon Ltd, 1906-20
  Cauldon Potteries Ltd, 1920-62

ᐧ Rockingham garniture, some ɩamage, all with puce griffin marks, 1835, 6½in (17cm) and 8½in 21cm).
2,500-3,500 *C*

A Rockingham vase, with painted sea shell motif, slight repair, puce mark, 4½in (11cm).
£450-500 *BHA*

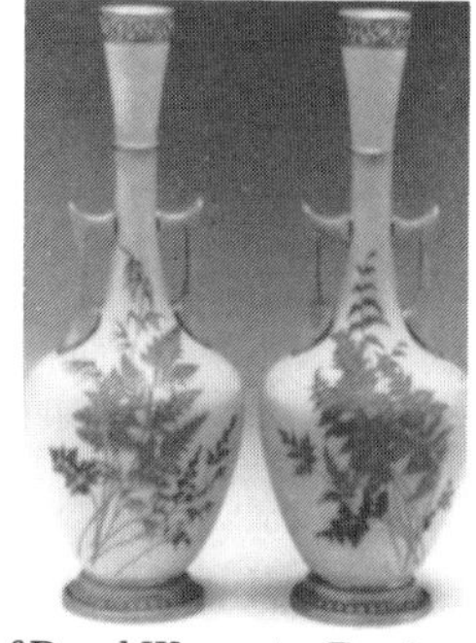

A pair of Royal Worcester Persian style vases, decorated in gold on an ivory ground, printed mark and date code for 1890, 12½in (32cm).
£500-600 *Bea*

ᐧ Ridgway & Sons Imari pattern ase and cover, some rubbing, mpressed Ridgway & Sons and 4, 1810, 8½in (21cm).
250-300 *C*

A Spode 'New French Jar' shaped vase, the base marked Spode 711, c1820, 9in (23cm).
£2,000-2,500 *DSH*

A Chamberlain's Worcester salmon pink ground vase, cover and finial stopper, with gilt ram's mask handles, minute rim chip to inside, script mark in gold and incised 27, c1800, 14in (35.5cm).
£2,000-2,500 *C*

A Worcester blue ground vase, painted by Jefferyes Hamet O'Neale, cracked through and restored beneath the cartouches, blue square seal mark, c1770, 13½in (34cm). ▶
£2,500-3,500 *C*

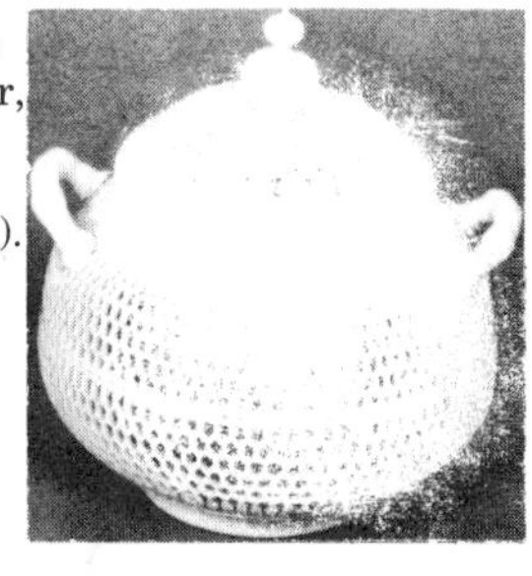

A Worcester, George Owen, vase and cover, repair to finial, gilt mark, date code for 1894, 5in (12.5cm).
£1,200-1,500 *CEd*

A Royal Worcester vase in Art Nouveau style, shape No. 2472, c1891, 9½in (24cm). ▶
£150-200 *TVA*

◀ A Royal Worcester pilgrim flask vase in Persian style, impressed and printed marks and date code for 1876, 13½in (34cm).
£800-1,000 *CSK*

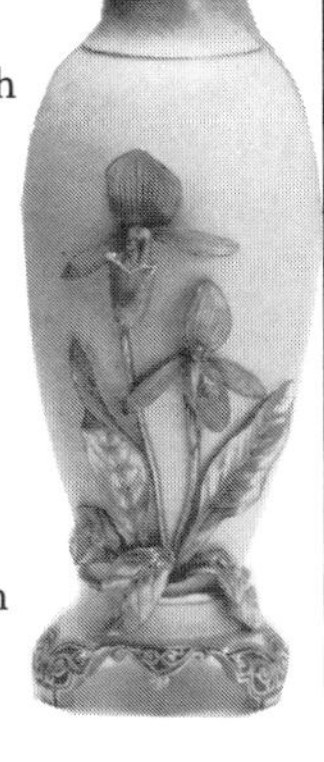

A Royal Worcester vase, applied and moulded in high relief, printed mark and date code for 1883, 11½in (29cm).
£400-500 *Bea*

A Minton vase, interior stained, gilt worn, one handle with cracked terminal, the interior with monogram J.W, 7in (18cm).
£300-400 *CSK*

ROCKINGHAM

- ★ works had for a long time produced pottery
- ★ porcelain factory opened c1826 and closed in 1842
- ★ potters of the Brameld family
- ★ bone china appears softer than contemporaries
- ★ of a smoky ivory/oatmeal colour
- ★ glaze had a tendency to irregular fine crazing
- ★ factory known for rococo style of decoration, frequently with excellent quality flower painting
- ★ tended to use green, grey and puce
- ★ large number of erroneous attributions made to the Rockingham factory, especially pieces actually made at Minton and Coalport

A Worcester, Flight, Barr & Barr, simulated shagreen ground vase, painted with flowers, inscribed 'Thy long lost Edwin from Goldsmith' on the base, restoration to one handle and part of rim, script mark, c1825, 8in (20cm).
£500-600 *C*

A pair of English vases and covers, perhaps Royal Worcester, one with restorations to handles, finial restuck and hair cracks, the other with hair cracks to base, c1870, 15in (37.5cm).
£400-500 *C*

A Royal Worcester garniture, with hand painted mask handles, initialled, shape No. 1716, c1895, 8 to 10in (20 to 25.5cm).
£1,000-1,500 *TVA*

WORCESTER PATTERNS

- ★ early period wares mainly confined to chinoiserie decoration
- ★ in the late First Period polychrome wares
- ★ most valuable standard type of decoration is birds, particularly if painted by James Giles
- ★ this is followed by English flowers
- ★ then Continental flowers
- ★ and finally the rather stylised Oriental flowers
- ★ it cannot be stressed strongly enough with Worcester that any rim rubbing or wear will greatly reduce the value, often by as much as half

A Grainger's Worcester vase, printed mark and date code for 1899, 13½in (34.5cm).
£400-450 *Bea*

A pair of Grainger's Worcester Persian style vases, painted in muted enamel colours and gold on an ivory ground, printed mark and date code for 1897, 12½in (31cm).
£450-550 *Bea*

A Royal Worcester vase and cover, with griffin handles, boldly painted on an apricot and cream ground, cover damaged and slight chip, printed mark and date code for 1898, 15in (38.5cm).
£300-350 *Bea*

A Royal Worcester moon flask, boldly painted with flowers on an ivory ground, printed mark, late 19thC, 15in (38cm).
£800-1,000 *Bea*

A Hadley's Worcester 'faience' vase, painted in sepia, slight glaze damage, c1898, 9in (22.5cm).
£200-250 *Bea*

Locate the source

The source of each illustration in Miller's can be found by checking the code letters below each caption with the list of contributors

A Royal Worcester vase with dragon handles, the body painted by John Stinton, signed, printed mark, shape No. G953, date code for 1905, 7in (18cm).
£700-800 *N*

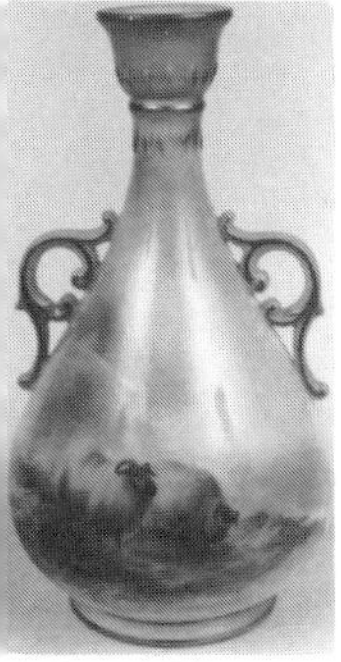

A Royal Worcester two-handled vase, signed by Harry Davis, shape No. G995, c1912, 6in (15cm).
£650-750 *TVA*

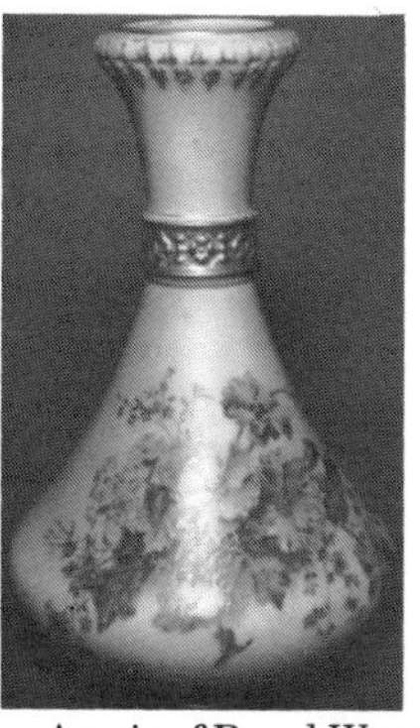

A pair of Royal Worcester vases, painted on peach grounds, date code for 1914, 10½in (26cm).
£400-500 *P[Re]*

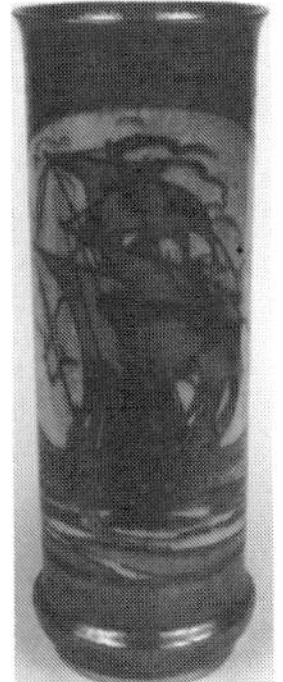

A Royal Worcester Crownware lustre vase, with galleon, shape No. CW281, c1926, 9½in (24cm).
£130-160 *TVA*

A vase and cover, painted by Barker, c1930, 9in (23cm).
£700-900 *CSK*

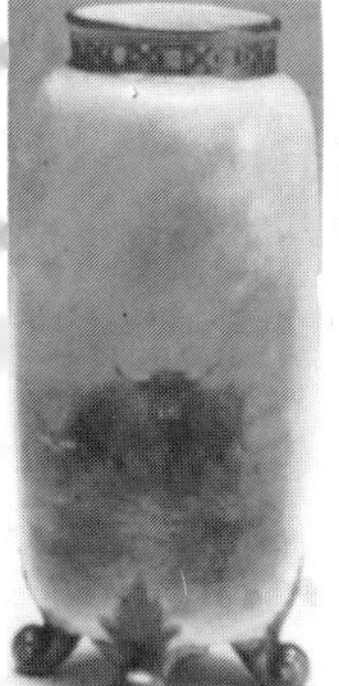

A Royal Worcester porcelain vase, signed Sedgley, 12in (30.5cm).
£500-600 *DSH*

A Royal Worcester vase, painted by Harry Stinton, shape No. G42, printed mark and date code for 1931, 6in (14.5cm).
£500-600 *Bea*

A Flight, Barr & Barr vase, the blue ground heightened in gilt, handles missing, impressed and painted factory marks with London retailers mark, 7in (18cm).
£700-800 *CSK*

A pair of English porcelain vases, with gilt dentil rims, one neck with hairlines, 5½in (14cm).
£150-200 *CSK*

An English porcelain vase, perhaps Spode, painted in pink, with gilt panels on an apple green ground and with white beaded borders, c1815, 6in (15cm).
£250-350 *CSK*

A Böttger white vase and cover, modelled by Johann Jacob Irminger, minor chips to roses, c1715, 6in (15cm).
£7,000-8,000 *C*

A Dresden vase, gilt worn, blue A.R. marks, 7in (18cm).
£200-250 *CSK*

A pair of Berlin pot pourri vases and covers, sceptre marks, c1880, 13in (34cm).
£1,700-2,000 *C*

A pair of Dresden spill vase groups, 15in (38cm).
£1,500-2,000 *CSK*

A pair of Berlin vases and covers, sceptre mark in underglaze blue, 19thC, 19in (48cm).
£1,700-2,000 *L*

A pair of Meissen pot pourri vases and pierced covers, some chips and repairs to foliage, one with traces of blue crossed swords mark, c1745, 7½in (28.5cm).
£2,500-3,000 *C*

A pair of Paris royal blue ground vases, painted after Teniers, on richly gilt square bases, c1820, 14½in (37cm).
£2,500-3,000 *C*

A pair of Paris vases, modelled as figures of a boy and a girl, painted in colours and enriched in gilding, minor chips to flowers, blue JP marks, c1850, 8½in (22cm).
£350-400 *C*

A Meissen vase, the 'Frauenkopf' handles with iron red and puce headdress, painted by F F Meyer von Pressnitz, chip to underside of base, the porcelain c1725, 5in (13cm).
£1,500-2,000 *C*

A pair of Meissen Marcolini presentation vases and covers, each painted with floral monograms for JP and MCP, one cover damaged and crack to one handle, blue crossed swords and star marks, c1810, 11in (28cm).
£600-800 *CEd*

A Paris neo-Renaissance pot pourri vase and cover, finial repaired, blue JP marks, c1840, 8½in (21.5cm).
£150-200 *C*

A Viennese vase and cover.
£150-200 *MGM*

A Frankfurt blue and white baluster vase, painted in the Ming manner, hair cracks, rim chips, c1690, 15½in (40cm).
£1,500-2,000 *C*

A massive Paris blue ground 'Medici' vase, richly painted, body and one handle with restorations, chips to underside of rim, c1820, 21½in (54.5cm).
£2,000-3,000 *C*

A pair of Paris pink ground vases, blue JP marks, c1840, 7in (18cm).
£700-900 *C*

A Sèvres pattern gilt metal mounted turquoise ground vase, damage to one handle, c1865, 27½in (70cm).
£2,200-2,600 *C*

A Paris Sèvres vase, with turquoise ground, interlaced L's mark, 19thC, 12in (30.5cm).
£600-700 *WW*

A massive Sèvres pattern green ground Napoleonic vase and cover, decorated by Desprez, richly gilt and silvered with crowned initial 'N', on a square ormolu base, cover restored, imitation M. Imple de Sèvres marks, late 19thC, 54in (138cm).
£5,700-6,000 *C*

A pair of Sèvres pattern green ground vases and covers, with white and gilt caryatid handles, the covers gilt with white and gilt knob finials, one vase with chip to rim, one cover riveted, both finials restuck, imitation interlaced L marks, late 19thC, 16½in (42cm).
£1,500-2,000 *C*

Miscellaneous

A Berlin butter curl, chip to end of curl, c1780, 7in (17cm) long.
£700-900 *C*

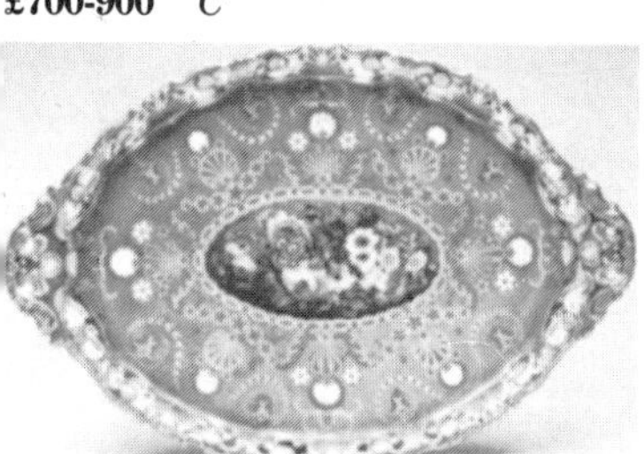

A Chamberlain's Worcester tray, painted in white and gold on a matt blue ground, script mark in red Chamberlain's Worcester, 155 New Bond Street, London, 17in (43cm).
£1,500-2,000 *L*

A Doccia triple salt with centre figure, shell restored, c1750, 7in (18cm).
£150-200 *CNY*

A Ridgway teapot stand, painted with a sandpiper, c1815, 6½ by 8in (16 by 20cm).
£250-300 *JG*

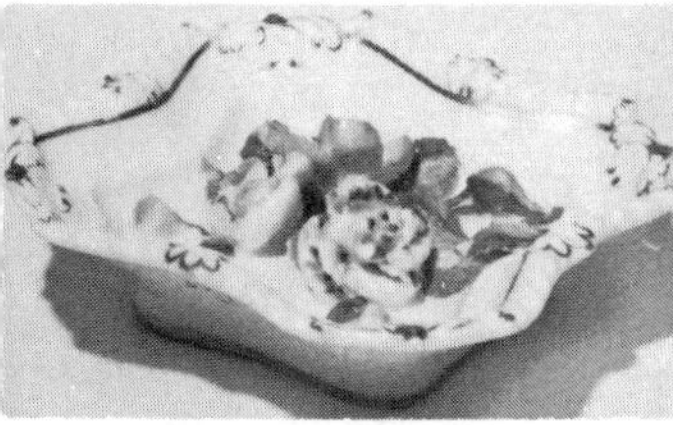

A Rockingham miniature tray, minute chipping to flowers, puce griffin mark and C1 2 in red, c1835, 4in (9.5cm) wide.
£400-500 *C*

A Coalport mantel ornament, painted in sepia and gilt, slight rim chips and cracks, c1810, 11½in (29cm) wide.
£1,200-1,500 *C*

A Schrezheim cane handle, modelled as the head and shoulders of a young woman with her hair 'en chignon' with a pink ribbon, small chips to one shoulder, impressed box twig at front, c1765, 3in (8cm).
£5,000-5,500 *CG*

A Caughley patty pan, decorated with the Fisherman pattern in underglaze blue, S mark, c1780, 4in (10cm) diam.
£250-300 *TVA*

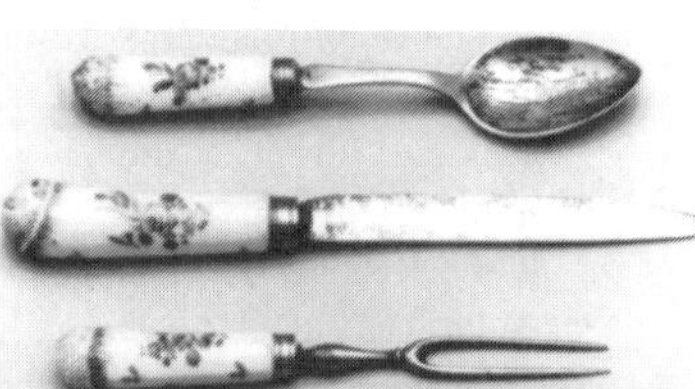

A Doccia porcelain handled knife, fork and spoon set, with silver and metal blades, c1770.
£100-150 *CNY*

A Flight, Barr & Barr porcelain pin tray, signed Flight, Barr & Barr, Worcester, and Coventry Street, London.
£70-100 *DEL*

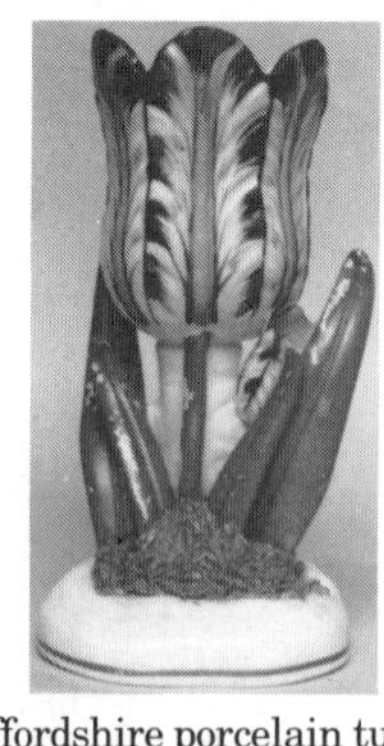

A Staffordshire porcelain tulip, c1840, 6in (15cm).
£400-450 *JUD*

A pair of Sèvres pattern gilt bronze mounted lamps, fitted for electricity, c1875, 26in (65cm) high overall.
£2,500-3,500 *C*

A Mennecy white pot pourri and cover, some damage to the flowers, incised D.V. mark to base of basket, c1760, 4in (10cm) wide.
£400-500 *C*

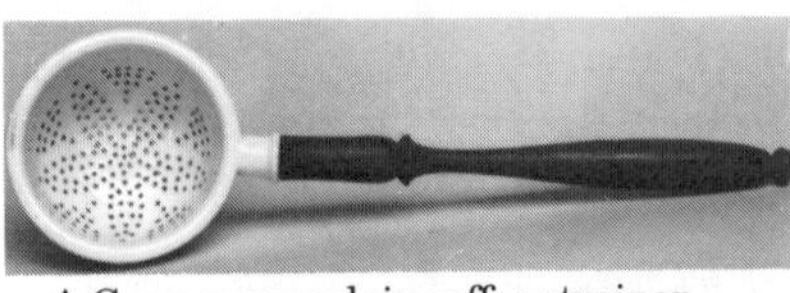

A German porcelain coffee strainer, with boxwood handle, 9in (23cm) long.
£200-250 *BHA*

A Sitzendorf chariot and cherub, wing missing, c1865, 10in (25cm).
£80-100 *CA*

A pair of Berlin porcelain hand painted eggs, ormolu mounted on alabaster stands, silk lined, c1840, 6½in (16cm).
£650-700 *CA*

A Copeland Spode bidet printed with the Tower pattern, printed mark, c1850, 19in (47cm) wide.
£250-350 *CSK*

A Vienna, Du Paquier, bourdalou, painted in 'Schwarzlot', extensively repaired, c1730, 9in (22cm) long.
£550-650 *CG*

A European lithophane of an eagle, probably German, c1880, 5½in (14cm) square.
£80-100 *TVA*

W H GOSS CHINA

Investors in Goss china have continued to watch the value of their collections grow. As the stock market gyrates uncertainly, Goss collectors have slept soundly in their beds, oblivious to it all.

The attraction of Goss porcelain is its quality. Of the 3 periods of manufacture, the 1st period (1858-87) is now 'antique'. This period encompasses parian busts, statuettes and ornamental ware. The 2nd period (1881-1934) concentrated on the popular heraldic Roman and Saxon urns and ewers and coloured cottages, with the 3rd period (1930-39) featuring coloured pottery and Doulton style ladies.

Collecting Goss is made easier as almost every piece has a factory mark, with the exception of the earliest prototype pieces. Each artefact or named model has its name printed on the base, so identifying the shape is simple.

Mentions on the *Antiques Roadshow* and Anglia TV *Bygones* on the subject have fuelled interest among collectors, as has the new book *William Henry Goss, The Story of the Staffordshire Family of Potters who Invented Heraldic Porcelain* by Lynda and Nicholas Pine (Milestone Publications), which is a biography of the family and the story of Goss china. Revealed within are the many facets to W H Goss's personality and the reasons why some of his own family hated him and his workforce loved him.

Isle of Man Ballafletcher cup
£28 *G&CC*

White Barnet Stone.
£85 *G&CC*

Cat and Fiddle Inn at Buxton.
£170 *G&CC*

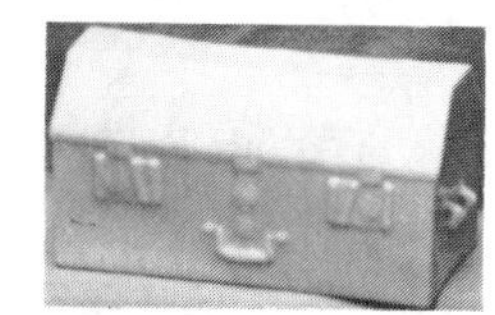

Queen Phillipa's record chest.
£27 *G&CC*

Rye Cannonball on plinth, matching arms.
£130 *G&CC*

A selection of domestic wares.
£4-20 *G&CC*

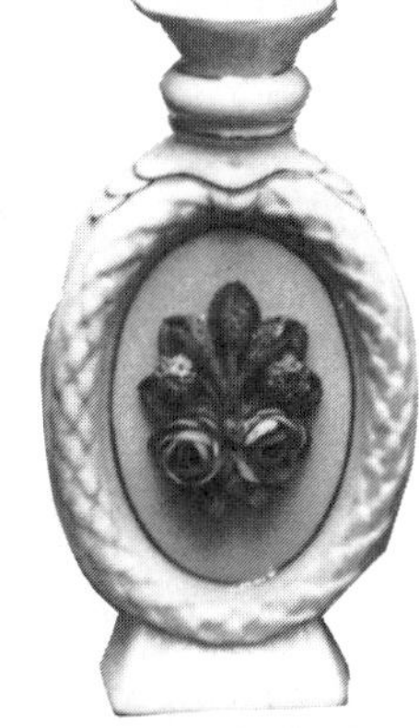

Brown Cornish style.
£70 *G&CC*

Early First Period vase with floral decoration in relief.
£85 *G&CC*

The range of National and International League models, 1901-32.
£35-750 *G&CC*

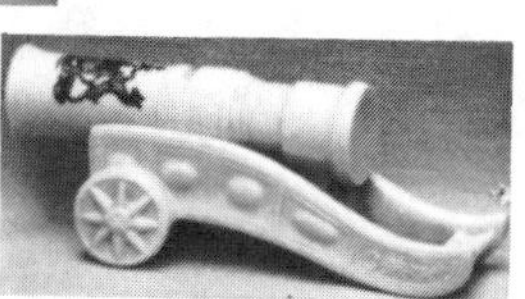

Mons Meg, Edinburgh Castle.
£35 *G&CC*

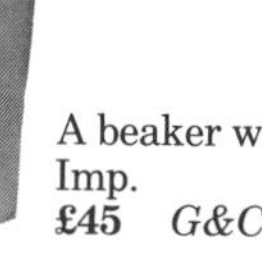

A beaker with outpressed Lincoln Imp.
£45 *G&CC*

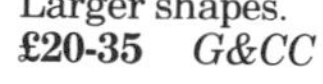

Larger shapes.
£20-35 *G&CC*

A parian bust of Sir Walter Scott.
£45 *G&CC*

Lincoln Imp for wall hanging.
£30 *G&CC*

A plaque for Goss cabinet, Goss arms.
£75 *G&CC*

A Maltese carafe.
£17 *G&CC*

A miniature forget-me-not beaker.
£15 *G&CC*

An Aylesbury duck with Aylesbury arms.
£225 *G&CC*

St Tudno's font, Llandudno.
£40 *G&CC*

Third Period Scottish wares.
£7-30 *G&CC*

Rufus Stone in New Forest.
£12 *G&CC*

A large Lanlawren urn, Penzance crest.
£25 *G&CC*

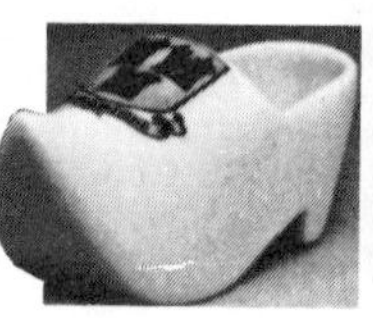

A Dutch sabot.
£17 *G&CC*

A Brixworth cup.
£5.50 *G&CC*

A selection of medium priced artefacts.
£12 each *G&CC*

A Kendal jug.
£6 *G&CC*

Two sizes of wall pocket.
£5-7 *G&CC*

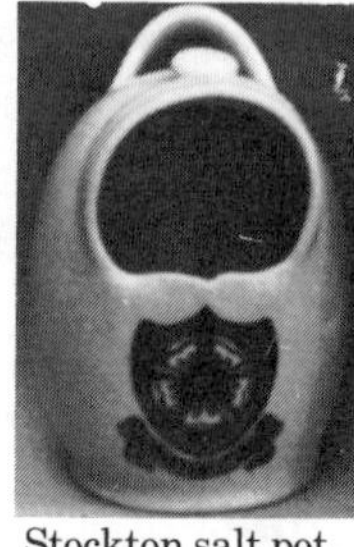

Stockton salt pot.
£6.50 *G&CC*

Lady Gwenda.
£155 *G&CC*

A Bournemouth pine cone.
£10 *G&CC*

A Strawberry preserve pot.
£58 *G&CC*

A Russian shrapnel shell.
£16 *G&CC*

A colourful section.
£15-110 *G&CC*

A Flags of the Allies plate.
£35 *G&CC*

An Agents change tray.
£220 *G&CC*

Brown parian crosses.
£80-1,300 *G&CC*

Thomas Hardy's birthplace, Dorchester.
£325 *G&CC*

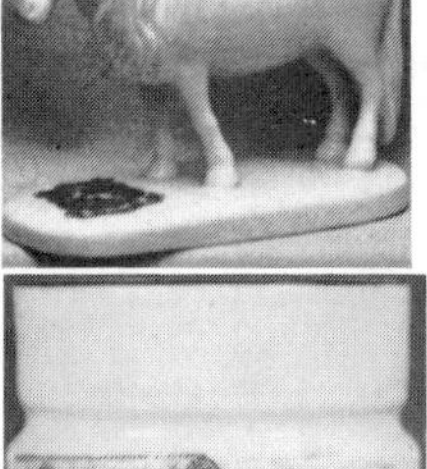

A Shetland pony.
£130 *G&CC*

Leek urn with black transfer 'Crystal Palace'.
£30 *G&CC*

Brown London stone at Staines.
£150 *G&CC*

A parian bust of Queen Victoria.
£95 *G&CC*

A Waterlooville bottle with same arms.
£25 *G&CC*

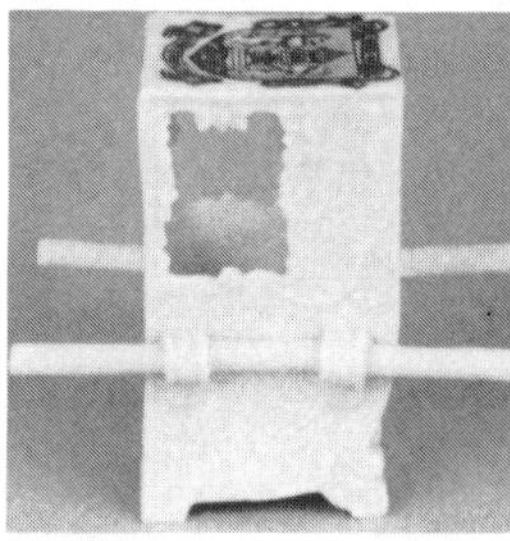
A Goss Boulogne sedan chair.
£45 *CCC*

Goss Stratford-on-Avon sanctuary mug, knocker in relief.
£240 *CCC*

Three military badges by Goss:
c. Candlestick.

l. and r. Highland milk crogans.
£60 each *CCC*

Goss Welsh lady candle-snuffer, coloured.
£60 *CCC*

Goss cottage pottery mug, handpainted.
£22 *CCC*

Goss globe vase with transfer of primroses.
£20 *CCC*

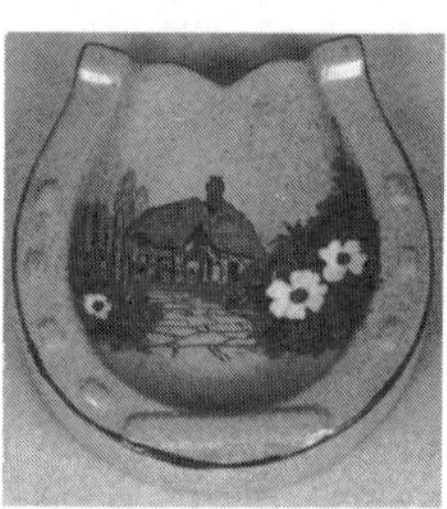
Goss horseshoe, handpainted with cottage scene.
£25 *CCC*

Goss Royal Commemoratives 1887 Garter Star, taper milk jug.
£70

1910 Death of Edward VII on urn.
£45 *CCC*

Goss battleship badge of HMS Superb, on bronze pot.
£50 *CCC*

Goss Hereford terracotta kettle.
£25 *CCC*

Christchurch Priory Norman Tower in grey.
£75 *G&CC*

GOSS & CRESTED CHINA

- ★ prices given are for pieces in perfect condition. Any chips, cracks or faded crests halve the value of a piece
- ★ firing flaws can be safely ignored, unless major, as can most manufacturing faults. The porcelain shrank up to 10% during firing, and this also accounts for minor variations in size of similar items

RESTED CHINA

he craze for Goss swept ritain in the 1890s. The mall porcelain models earing coats-of-arms were ollected mainly by the orking classes enjoying the ew found freedom of holidays estowed on them by nlightened employers. Other ot banks' within the taffordshire potteries soon aught on, and at a time when here was a depression in their ndustry, some 300 potteries ere churning out crested ouvenir ware, with the erman competition in hot ursuit.

here Goss concentrated on uality and strict reproduction f ancient artefacts, cottages, usts, crosses and fonts, the ther potteries including rcadian, Willow Art, arlton, Shelley, etc., caught he imagination of the public ith comic novelty shapes and raditional and national ouvenirs.

t was the outbreak of war in 914 which stopped the craze t its height, when the country uddenly had more serious hings to think about than rested china. The nanufacturers attempted to ppeal to the patriotic with heir replicas of guns, tanks, soldiers, aeroplanes, etc., and these sold well both during and after the war. But by the late 1930s trade was virtually at a standstill and production ceased.

The quality of the different makes varies and the standards of perfection applied to Goss to determine value cannot be applied to crested china generally, as most pieces tend to have firing flaws, inaccuracies of proportion and rubbed gilding. Yet there is something irresistible and appealing about these delightful porcelain mementoes of a bygone era.

In the last 15 years those previously unwanted miniatures have proved irresistible again and the prices are rising. For a full listing of all shapes produced and detailed information on every factory, see *The Price Guide to Crested China* by Nicholas Pine (Milestone Publications) and *Crested China* by Sandy Andrews (Milestone). Items similar to those illustrated on these pages are obtainable through the Goss & Crested China monthly catalogue, available from 62 Murray Road, Horndean, Hants PO8 9JL.

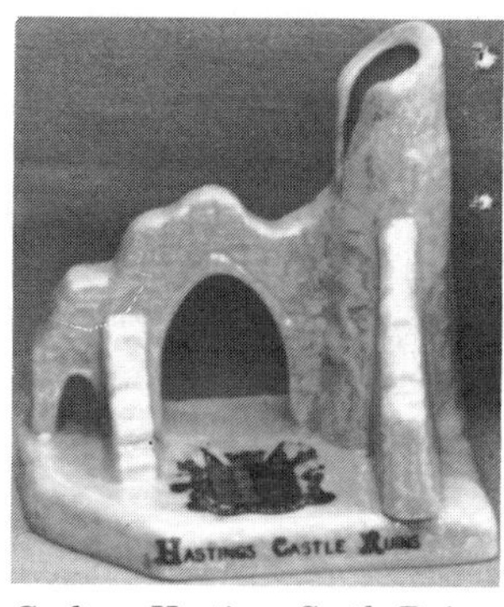

Carlton, Hastings Castle Ruins.
£20 *G&CC*

Carlton Stick Telephone.
£15 *G&CC*

Devonia Art Citadel Gateway.
£22 *G&CC*

ity of London landmarks.
5-30 *G&CC*

Corona Grandfather clock, **£10,** and Carlton weighing scales, **£25**
G&CC

Arcadian Shetland Pony.
£19 *G&CC*

rcadian dish with bird transfer.
10 *G&CC*

Early Willow 'vine' jug.
£10 *G&CC*

GOSS AND CRESTED WARE

Damage considerably affects the value of porcelain. Haircracks, chips and faded crests can halve the values recorded here. Full prices can only be obtained for perfection. Minor firing flaws can be ignored. Goss china shrank up to 10% in the firing processes so manufacturing flaws and minor differences in size are common

Carlton HMS Australia, **£55** and Savoy submarine EI.
£30 *G&CC*

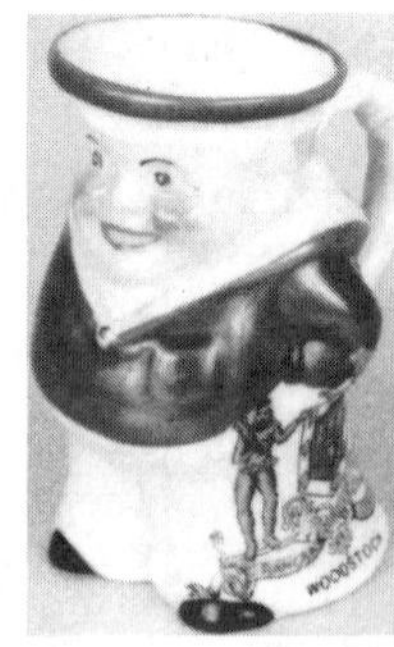

Arcadian coloured sailor Toby jug
£60 *CCC*

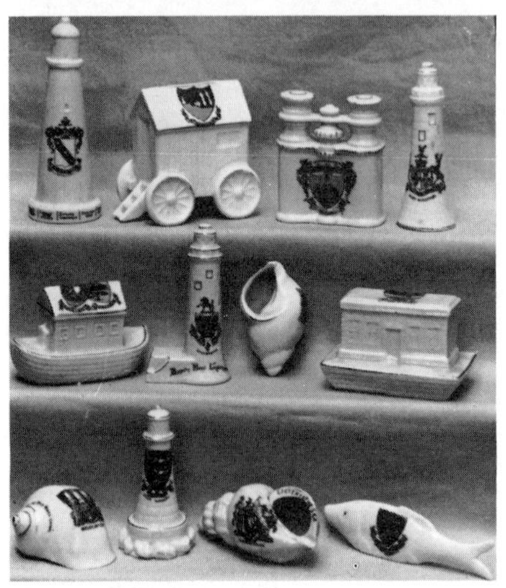

A selection of seaside shapes.
£3-20 *G&CC*

German butterfly.
£15 *CCC*

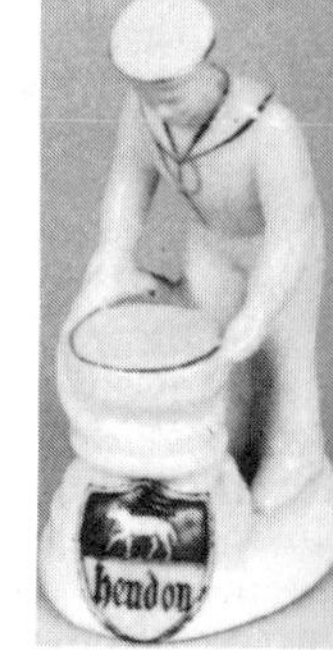

Arcadian sailor winding capstan
£80 *CCC*

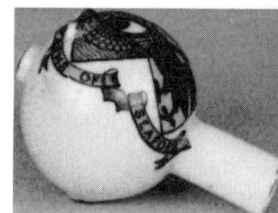

Arcadian plum pudding bomb
£80 *CCC*

Savoy Clara Cluck candle-snuffer.
£18 *CCC*

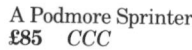

A Shelley Boxer.
£125

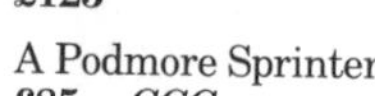

A Podmore Sprinter.
£85 *CCC*

Arcadian birds:
l. Warbler on tree stump.
£35
r. Fantail Dove.
£22 *CCC*

Shelley howitzer.
£32 *G&CC*

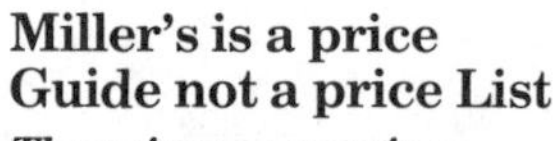

Miller's is a price Guide not a price List

The price ranges given reflect the average price a purchaser should pay for similar items. Condition, rarity of design or pattern, size, colour, provenance, restoration and many other factors must be taken into account when assessing values.
When buying or selling, it must always be remembered that prices can be greatly affected by the condition of any piece. Unless otherwise stated, all goods shown in Miller's are of good merchantable quality, and the valuations given reflect this fact. Pieces offered for sale in exceptionally fine condition or in poor condition may reasonably be expected to be priced considerably higher or lower respectively than the estimates given herein

Clocks.
£8-18 *G&CC*
Still clocking up good value!

Willow Art 'Box of Chocolates'.
£28 *G&CC*

Willow Art 'Jesus' vase.
£8 *G&CC*

Arcadian House.
£7 *G&CC*

Shelley Anti-Zeppelin candlestick.
£37 *G&CC*

Savoy trench mortar gun and Arcadian revolver.
£40 and £30 *G&CC*

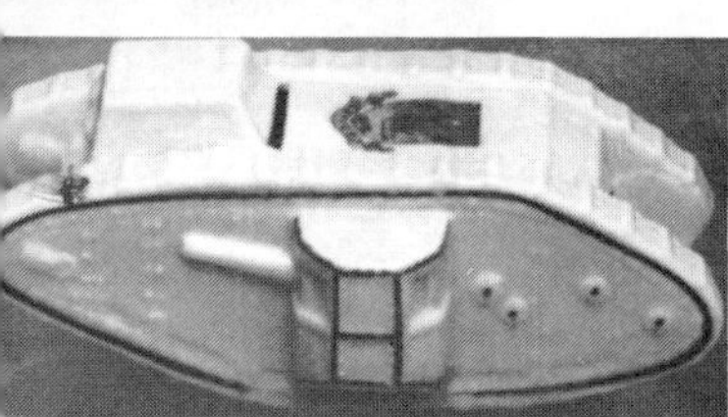

Shelley tank bank.
£40 *G&CC*

arlton, Martello Tower.
30 *G&CC*

Arcadian sailor 'H.M.S Dreadnought'.
£27 *G&CC*

Arcadian Russian cossack.
£145 *G&CC*

Arcadian chess King.
£20 *G&CC*

Anvils.
£4-7 *G&CC*

Arcadian lucky black cat on horseshoe.
£30 *G&CC*

Two Carlton dogs.
£11 and £8 *G&CC*

Miniature home/nostalgic shapes.
£4 each *G&CC*

A Carlton York Cathedral, Wes
Front.
£25 *G&CC*

Edwardian Boy and Girl pepper an
salt, unmarked.
£12 each *G&CC*

A German yellow/brown lustre Banbury Cross.
£8 *G&CC*

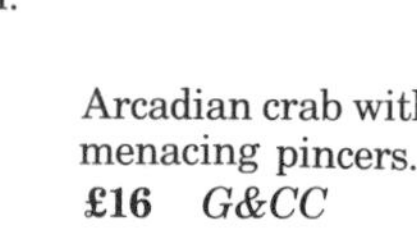

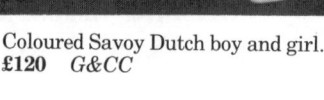

Coloured Savoy Dutch boy and girl.
£120 *G&CC*

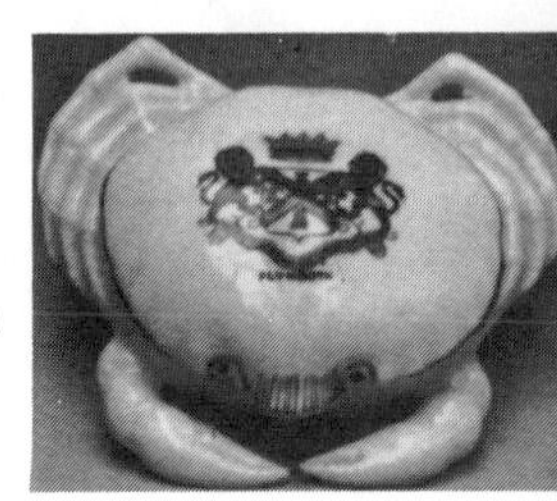

Arcadian crab with menacing pincers.
£16 *G&CC*

Willow Art Burns chair at Dumfries, corner seat version.
£10 *G&CC*

Willow Art Peeping Tom, bust.
£16 *G&CC*

An unmarked bust of General Booth.
£85 *G&CC*

Willow Art Truck of black coal.
£16 *G&CC*

Willow Art Melton Mowbray pie.
£15 *G&CC*

Arcadian, The Berkswell Stocks.
£18 *G&CC*

Grafton Horn lantern.
£6.50 *G&CC*

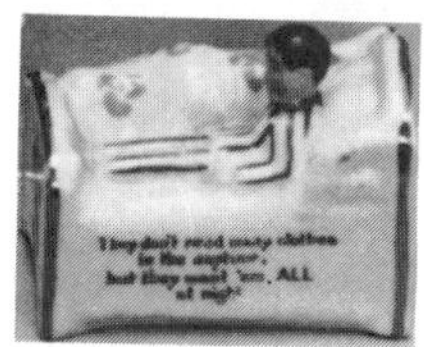

Arcadian Couple in Bed, lady with all the bedclothes.
£50 *G&CC*

Swan china royalty jug.
£14 *G&CC*

Birds of a feather.
£5+ *G&CC*

rcadian miners lamp.
4 *G&CC*

German made windmill.
) *G&CC*

Comical figures and shapes.
£15-40 *G&CC*

> **Price**
>
> ***Prices vary from auction to auction – from dealer to dealer. The price paid in a dealer's shop will depend on:***
> ***1) what he paid for the item***
> ***2) what he thinks he can get for it***
> ***3) the extent of his knowledge***
> ***4) awareness of market trends***
> ***It is a mistake to think that you will automatically pay more in a specialist dealer's shop. He is more likely to know the 'right' price for a piece. A general dealer may undercharge but he could also overcharge***

ORIENTAL POTTERY & PORCELAIN

Bottles

A late Ming blue and white 'kraak porselein' bottle, frit chip and firing crack to rim, Wanli, 11in (28cm).
£700-900 *C*

A pair of black ground bottle vases, one with hairline crack to neck, Qing Dynasty, 17½in (45cm).
£2,200-2,500 *C*

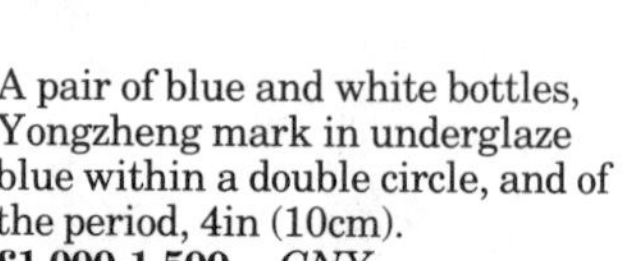

A pair of blue and white bottles, Yongzheng mark in underglaze blue within a double circle, and of the period, 4in (10cm).
£1,000-1,500 *CNY*

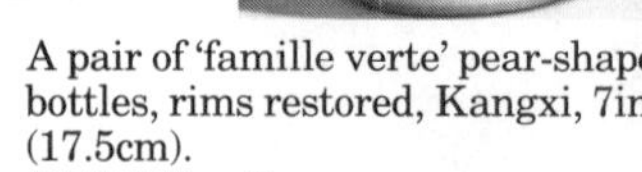

A pair of 'famille verte' pear-shaped bottles, rims restored, Kangxi, 7in (17.5cm).
£450-550 *C*

A 'famille rose' bottle, with underglaze blue garlic neck, painted with figures at leisure, Qianlong, 10in (25cm), lamp mount.
£400-500 *CSK*

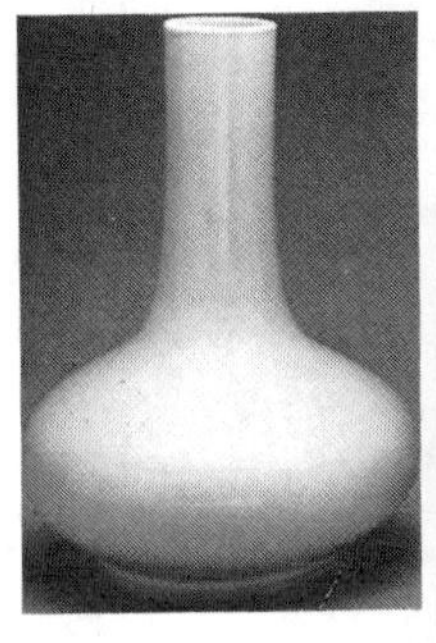

A celadon glazed bottle, Qianlong seal mark in underglaze blue and of the period, 11in (28cm).
£1,000-1,500 *CNY*

A blue and white pilgrim bottle, painted in violet blue tones, rim crack, 17thC, 10½in (26.5cm).
£3,500-4,000 *C*

A large 'famille rose' bottle, painted in blue enamel on a yellow ground, blue enamelled Qianlong mark, 21½in (55cm), wood stand.
£1,700-2,200 *C*

A pair of Arita apothecary bottles with silver mounted rim, painted in underglaze blue with song birds perched on trailing flowering and fruiting branches, late 17thC, 7in (18cm).
£1,200-1,500 *CAm*

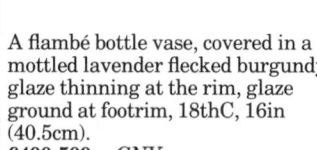

A flambé bottle vase, covered in a mottled lavender flecked burgundy glaze thinning at the rim, glaze ground at footrim, 18thC, 16in (40.5cm).
£400-500 *CNY*

A pair of 'Empress Dowager' 'famille jaune' bottle vases, with a yellow ground, turquoise interior, the underside with inscription of praise: Eternal Prosperity and Enduring Spring, c1900, 12½in (31.5cm).
£850-950 *CNY*

A pair of Chinese Imari bottles and covers, covers restored, early 18thC, 10in (25.5cm).
£1,500-2,000 *C*

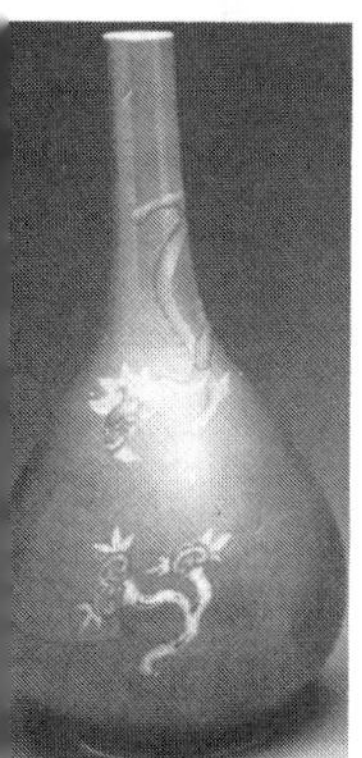

A pair of iron red painted powder blue ground bottle vases, enriched with gilt, the base with concentric circles in underglaze blue, 19thC, 16½in (42cm).
£750-1,000 *CNY*

Bowls

ı green and straw glazed water pot, he interior splashed in a straw ;laze, the mouth and exterior overed with a finely crackled leaf ;reen glaze stopping irregularly hort of the foot, Tang Dynasty, 5in 13cm) wide.
.2,500-3,000 *C*

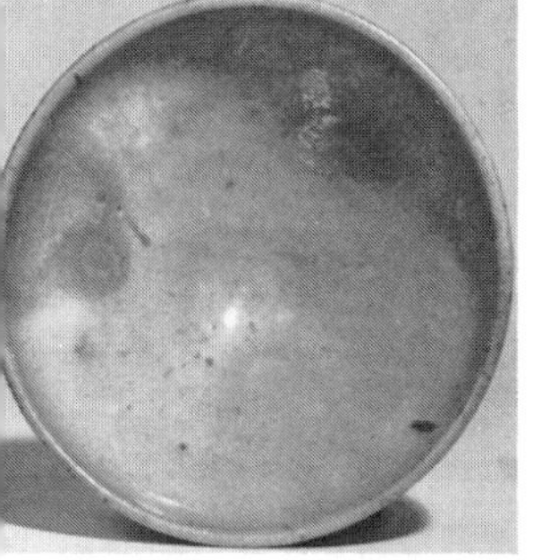

ı Junyao bowl, with a pale lavender laze with a purple splash to the ıterior thinning to a celadon at the im, Song/Yuan Dynasty, 7½in 19.5cm).
1,500-2,000 *C*

. large Ming blue and white saucer ish, Jiajing six-character mark in a ine below the rim exterior and of he period, 19½in (49cm) diam.
5,000-6,000 *C*

Two Longquan celadon bowls, covered in a pale olive green glaze oxidised in places, cracks, Yuan Dynasty, 5in (12cm) diam.
£500-800 *C*

An Annamese blue and white stem dish, 15thC, 12in (30.5cm) diam.
£1,700-2,200 *C*

A rare pair of blue and white 'kraak porselein' bowls, one repaired, chips, Wanli, 14in (35.5cm) diam.
£2,000-2,500 *C*

A Ming red dragon saucer dish, with a five-clawed dragon in underglaze blue, slightly warped, red enamels retouched, encircled Jiajing six-character mark and of the period, 7½in (18.5cm) diam, fitted box.
£1,500-2,000 *C*

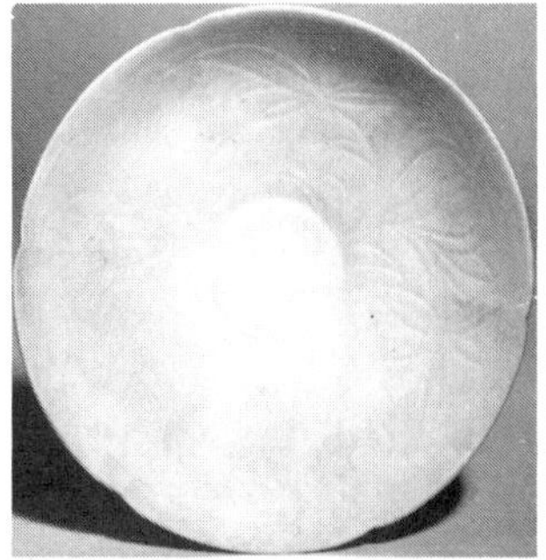

A Dingyao bowl, freely carved, the ivory glaze pooling slightly irregularly in 'tears' on and around the vertical foot and covering the base, minor rim polish, Song Dynasty, 7½in (18.5cm) diam.
£4,000-5,000 *C*

A Yingqing bowl, with a fine transparent glaze of delicate blue tones pooling heavily around the foot, minute chip, Song Dynasty, 8in (20.5cm) diam, fitted box.
£4,000-5,000 *C*

A celadon tripod bulb bowl, with a crackled pale olive glaze, 14th/15thC, 12½in (32cm) diam.
£1,000-1,200 *C*

A large Ming celadon dish, incised under a pale olive green glaze with traces of gilt to rim, 14th/15thC, 15½in (40cm) diam.
£1,000-1,500 *C*

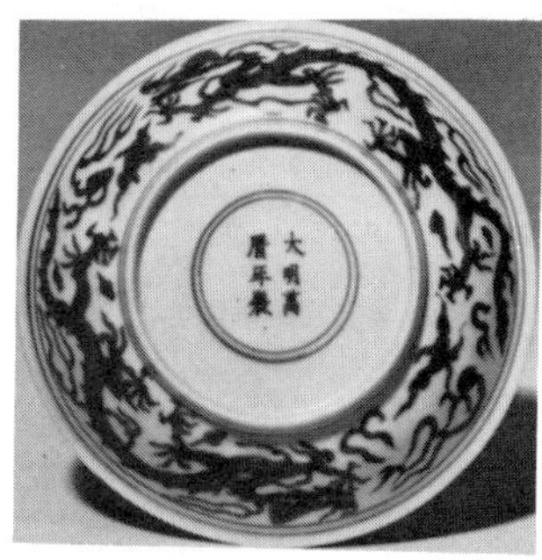

A late Ming blue and white saucer dish, hair crack, encircled Wanli six-character mark and of the period, 6½in (17cm).
£1,200-1,500 *C*

A Ming dated brown glazed saucer dish, with a thick white slip reserved on a brown glazed ground, Wanli dated mark to base and of the period, 8in (20.5cm) diam.
£1,500-2,000 *C*

A Chinese bowl with flared rim, the celadon glazed exterior incised with dense flowering peony, 9in (23cm) diam.
£350-450 *CSK*

A Kangxi blue and white bulb bowl, c1700, 5½in (14cm).
£900-1,000 *LG*

A Chinese blue and white bowl and cover, with metal handles and finial, Kangxi, 8in (20cm).
£500-600 *CSK*

CHINESE PORCELAIN – VALUE POINTS

- ★ about 80% of the marks that appear on Chinese porcelain are retrospective
- ★ if a piece bears a correct, as opposed to a retrospective, reign mark then its value compared to an unmarked but comparable specimen would probably be of the magnitude of 3 to 4 times more
- ★ a piece of a known date but bearing the mark of an earlier reign would be adversely affected and could possibly fetch less than an unmarked piece of the same vintage
- ★ as a rule condition will adversely affect a readily available type of ware more than a very rare or early type
- ★ original covers or lids can raise the price considerably – especially if the vessel appears more complete with it. Hence a baluster vase, for example, would be less affected than a wine ewer

A large Ming blue and white bowl, fritted, cracked, encircled mark 'fu gui jia qi' (fine vessel for the rich and honourable), late 16thC, 15in (38.5cm) diam, fitted box.
£1,500-2,000 *C*

A Japanese Imari bowl, painted in typical palette, late 17thC, 14in (36cm) diam.
£2,500-3,000 *Bon*

A 'famille verte' bowl and cover, handles missing, restored, Kangxi, 5½in (13.5cm) diam, wood stand.
£800-900 *C*

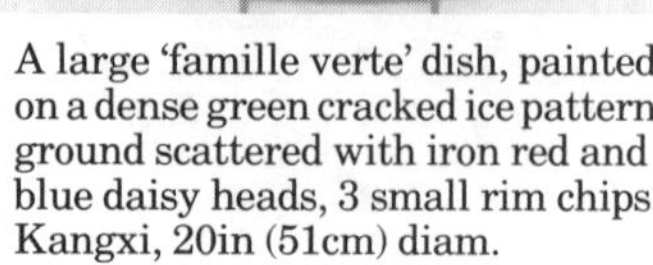

A large 'famille verte' dish, painted on a dense green cracked ice pattern ground scattered with iron red and blue daisy heads, 3 small rim chips, Kangxi, 20in (51cm) diam.
£5,500-6,500 *C*

An aubergine and green glazed bowl with white interior, the exterior painted on a dark green ground, cracked, encircled Kangxi six-character mark and of the period, 4in (10cm) diam.
£600-700 *C*

A Chinese 'famille verte' fish bowl, painted in Kangxi style on a seeded ground, 17in (43cm) diam.
£550-600 *CNY*

A pair of 'famille verte' dishes, enamelled within an iron red diapered border, one with minor rim restoration, Kangxi, 7in (18cm) square.
£400-600 *CNY*

A pair of 'famille verte' biscuit bowls with white interiors, both cracked, encircled Kangxi six-character marks and of the period, 5½in (15cm) diam.
£2,000-3,000 *C*

A pair of 'verte' Imari bowls, early 18thC, 6½in (16.5cm) diam.
£1,000-1,500 *C*

A Doucai bowl, painted in enamels with the eight Daoist Immortals, small rim chip, encircled four-character mark, 18thC, 7½in (18.5cm) diam.
£1,500-2,000 *C*

A blue and white bowl, the interior partially unglazed, 18th/19thC, 17½in (44.5cm) diam.
£700-800 *C*

An export mythological subject bowl, the exterior painted with a panel scene depicting 'The Judgement of Paris', within gilt and iron red borders, Qianlong, 10½in (25.5cm) diam.
£1,000-1,500 *CNY*

A blue and white phoenix bowl, Kangxi six-character mark and of the period, 8in (20.5cm) diam, wood stand.
£2,000-2,500 *C*

An aubergine ground Brinjal bowl incised and painted in green, yellow and cream enamels, square seal mark, Kangxi, 4½in (11cm) diam.
£1,800-2,200 *C*

A blue and white bowl, painted in the Ming style, Qianlong, 8½in (21.5cm) wide.
£900-1,200 *C*

A Chinese 'famille rose' bowl, restored, Qianlong, c1770, 10in (25.5cm).
£250-350 *WW*

A massive Canton 'famille rose' punch bowl, enamelled in the interior, restored, c1830, 20½in (52.5cm) diam.
£3,000-4,000 *C*

A Canton bowl, reserved in gold on a decorated celadon ground, the rim painted on a gold ground, 19thC, 18½in (47.5cm) diam.
£2,000-2,500 *Bea*

A gilt metal mounted Chinese Imari bowl, the porcelain 18thC, the mounts and cover later, 9½in (24cm) wide.
£1,000-1,500 *C*

A blue and white and underglaze copper red bowl, minute rim chips, 18thC, 8½in (21.5cm) diam.
£600-700 *C*

A blue and white bowl, Qianlong, c1770, 10½in (26cm) diam.
£350-400 *LG*

A Chinese blue and white basket and stand, c1800, 9in (23cm) diam.
£600-700 *CSK*

A Canton 'famille rose' basin, enamelled in the Mandarin palette, heightened in gilt, 19thC, 18½in (47cm) diam.
£1,000-2,000 *CNY*

JAPANESE ART PERIODS

- ★ ***Prehistory and Protohistory***
  c7000 BC Jomon culture; first recorded pottery with simple design
  c300 BC Yayoi culture; bronzes and more sophisticated pottery
  1st to 4thC AD Haniwa culture; bronzes and distinctive red pottery
  AD 220; first influence from Korea
- ★ ***Asuka Period*** – 552-645
- ★ ***Hahuko Period*** – 672-85
- ★ ***Nara Period*** – 710-94
- ★ ***Heian Period*** – 794-1185
- ★ ***Kamakura Period*** – 1185-1333
- ★ ***Muromachi (Ahikaga) Period*** – 1338-1573
- ★ ***Momoyama Period*** – 1573-1615
  1598: immigrant Korean potters begin kilns at Kyushu, producing the first glazed pottery
- ★ ***Edo (Tokugawa) Period*** – 1615-1867
  1616: first porcelain made by Ninsei (1596-1666)
  1661-73: great age of porcelain; Arita, Nabeshima, Kutani and Kakiemon
  1716-36: popularity of lacquering and netsuke as art forms
- ★ ***Meiji Period*** – 1868-1912
  Strong influence of Western cultures developing and growing. Japanese art appears to decline in many respects. Much trading with the West

A blue and white censer, Kangxi, c1690, 6½in (16cm).
£2,500-3,000 *LG*

A Dehua blanc-de-chine censer, with a glaze of pale ivory tones, rim chip polished, seal mark to base, 17thC, 5½in (13.5cm) diam.
£450-500 *C*

A pair of 'famille rose' chargers, decorated with flowers and butterflies, 19thC, 14in (35.5cm) diam.
£350-400 *LRG*

A Japanese Satsuma bowl, by Yabu Meizan, signed, chipped, c1880, 9½in (24cm) diam.
£7,000-8,000 *N*

A 'famille jeune' fish tank, early 20thC.
£500-600 *SAg*

A pair of lime green glazed bowls, one cracked, Guangxu six-character marks and of the period, 6in (15cm).
£1,000-1,200 *C*

A large 'famille verte' fish bowl, enamelled in bright colours, the interior enamelled with iron red fish swimming amongst seaweed, late Qing Dynasty, 22in (56cm) diam.
£1,500-2,000 *CNY*

Censers

A Ming blue and white tripod censer, cracked, Wanli/Tianqi, 7in (18cm) diam.
£800-900 *CSK*

A Dehua blanc-de-chine two-handled censer and cover, with a fine glaze of ivory tone, minute chip to lug handle, 17thC, 7½in (19cm), wood stand.
£5,000-6,000 *C*

A Chinese blue and white censer, Kangxi, 9½in (24cm).
£450-500 *Bea*

Cups

A Longquan celadon stem cup, covered in an even olive green glaze stopping above the oxidised exposed footring, Yuan Dynasty, 3in (8cm) diam.
£450-550 *CNY*

An Imperial yellow wine cup with white interior, encircled Kangxi six-character mark and of the period, 3in (7cm) diam.
£3,500-4,500 *C*

A 'famille verte' erotic cup, painted with a couple engaged in amorous pursuits on a floor rug, rim cracks, Kangxi, 4in (10cm).
£700-800 *C*

A 'famille rose' European subject teabowl, depicting Water from the 4 Elements after a design by Albani, early Qianlong.
£700-800 *C*

A 'famille rose' mug, painted with an elaborate coat of arms above an inscription in black, 'Moses, Adams, boat builder Gravesend', restored, c1750, 5½in (14cm).
£450-500 *C*

A Chinese export ware mug, decorated in colours, with underglaze blue borders, 6in (15cm).
£2,000-2,500 *GC*

Ewers

A Chinese blue and white kendi, Wanli, 7½in (18.5cm).
£900-1,000 *Bea*

A Ming blue and white ewer, minor fritting, early 17thC, 7½in (19.5cm) diam.
£2,500-3,500 *C*

A 'famille noire' wine ewer, minor damage, Kangxi, 6½in (17cm) wide.
£350-450 *C*

A pair of 'famille verte' lobed globular ewers, one spout restored, pierced, Kangxi, 9in (22cm).
£4,000-5,000 *CSK*

A rare 'famille verte' ewer, modelled as a standing Buddhistic lion, decorated in iron red and green with a yellow character 'wang' (virtuous king) below an aubergine horn, chipped, spout damaged, Kangxi, 8in (21.5cm).
£1,600-2,000 *C*

A pair of Chinese Imari ewers and covers, painted with lotus and chrysanthemum clusters, one restored, early 18thC, 7½in (19cm).
£2,000-2,500 *C*

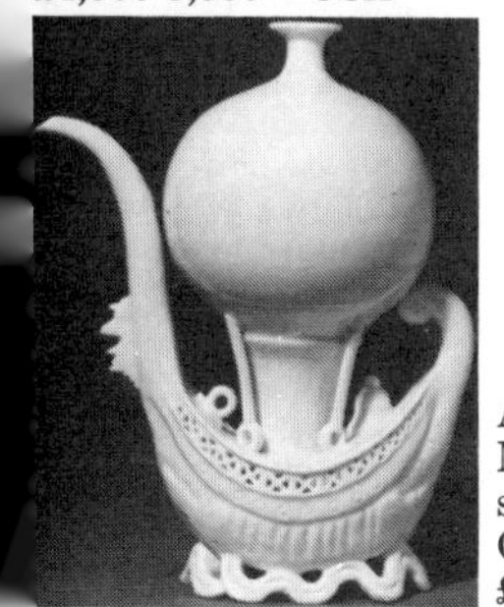

A rare Dehua blanc-de-chine Montgolfier balloon shaped ewer, supported on a pierced wave base, Qing Dynasty, 9½in (23.5cm).
£1,200-1,500 *C*

Did you know
MILLER'S Antiques Price Guide builds up year by year to form the most comprehensive photo-reference system available

Figures – Animals

A pair of red painted grey pottery horse heads, traces of white and ochre painted harnesses, some rubbing, one repaired, Han Dynasty, 5½in (14cm).
£700-900 *C*

A Sancai glazed buff pottery model of a caparisoned horse, glazed in ochre, pale straw and green, broken and restored, Tang Dynasty, 18½in (47cm), wood stand.
£10,000-15,000 *CNY*

A pair of painted red pottery earth spirits, some restoration, Tang Dynasty, 17½ and 18½in (44 and 47cm).
£3,000-3,500 *C*

A flambé glazed model of a parrot, in tones of pale lavender, purple and deep burgundy, 18th/19thC, 12in (30.5cm).
£600-800 *CNY*

A green glazed red pottery figure of a dog, restored, Han Dynasty, 11in (28.5cm) wide.
£1,000-1,500 *C*

A painted red pottery equestrian group, painted in white, black and red, right arm restored, Tang Dynasty, 14½in (36.5cm).
£3,500-4,000 *C*

A painted red pottery camel, traces of red, black, white and orange pigment, legs restored, Tang Dynasty, 18in (46cm).
£1,500-2,000 *C*

Make the Most of Miller's

CONDITION is absolutely vital when assessing the value of an antique. Damaged pieces on the whole appreciate much less than perfect examples. However a rare, desirable piece may command a high price even when damaged

A pair of painted grey pottery owls, painted with orange and white plumage and features, the heads pierced, Han Dynasty, 7in (18cm).
£700-1,000 *C*

A straw glazed Bactrian camel, traces of red pigment, the glaze degraded, some restoration, Sui/Tang Dynasty, 13in (33cm), wood stand.
£1,200-1,500 *C*

A buff pottery equestrian group, old repair and damage, early Tang Dynasty, 12in (30.5cm).
£2,000-3,000 *C*

A pair of Chinese pottery tilemaker's figures, Ming/Qing Dynasty, 14in (35.5cm).
£900-1,200 *CSK*

A pair of Fujian blanc-de-chine models of European figures seated on elephants, with rockwork bases, some restoration, firing crack, Kangxi, 12in (30cm).
£3,200-3,500 *C*

\ pair of white glazed cockerels, vith deep scarlet combs and eyes ıeighted in cobalt blue, one comb vith restoration, 19thC, 16in 40cm).
:3,000-3,500 *Bon*

A large export model of a white glazed goat, the horns, beard, eyes and short tail painted in a cobalt blue firing to an olive green, the base with impressed seal mark, late Qing Dynasty, 15in (38cm).
£2,500-3,000 *C*

A rare Sichuan red pottery figure of a dog, splashed with dots of pale buff glaze, damage to tail, Sichuan nine-character mark in relief within a recess roundel, late Qing Dynasty, 16in (40cm) wide.
£4,000-5,000 *C*

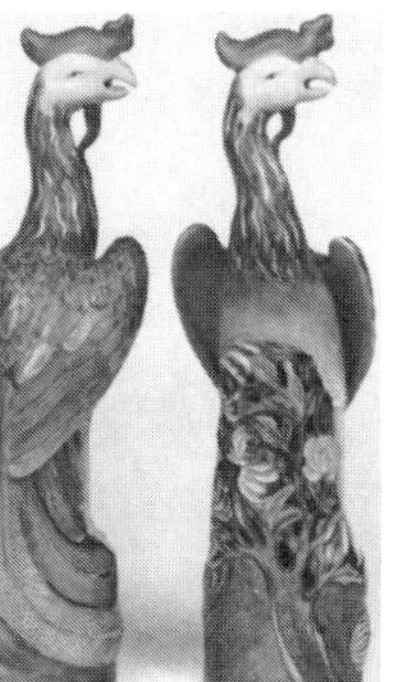

A pair of 'famille rose' models of phoenix, on pierced iron red rockwork painted with peony, the birds with multi-coloured feathers, impressed marks, 10in (25.5cm).
£350-550 *C*

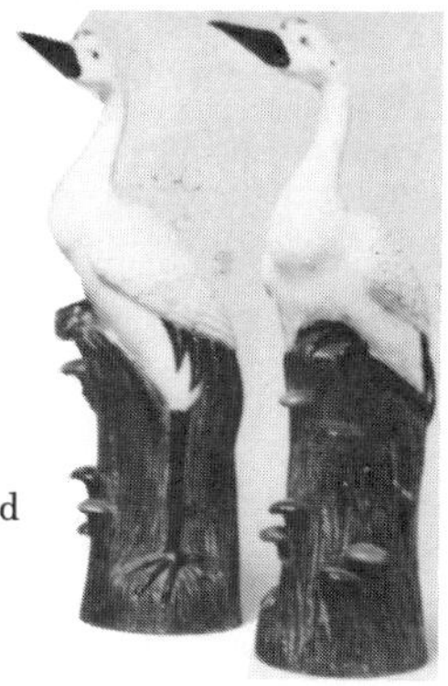

A pair of export figures of cranes, naturalistically moulded and coloured, one beak end chipped and short body crack, some damage, 19thC, 14in (35.5cm).
£2,500-3,500 *C*

Figures – People

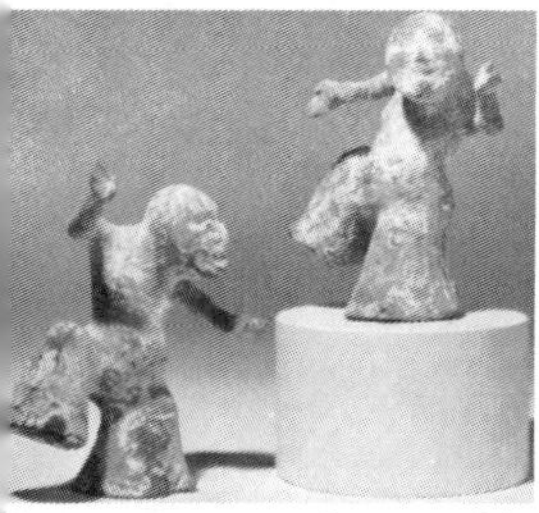

Two grey pottery figures of dancers, he grotesque heads with traces of ›igments, Han Dynasty, 5½in 14.5cm).
:3,500-4,000 *C*

A red pottery grotesque figure of a fat man, some restoration, Six Dynasties/Tang Dynasty, 14in (36cm).
£1,000-1,500 *C*

A pair of Cizhou painted figures of ladies, with a pale ivory slip and painted in dark brown, red and olive brown, Song Dynasty, 5in (12.5cm), fitted wood stands, fitted cloth box.
£450-550 *CNY*

A large Chinese pottery green, turquoise and ochre glazed figure of a seated Buddha, with detachable head, Ming Dynasty, 22½in (57cm).
£1,500-2,000 *CSK*

\ Qingbai figure of Avalokitesvara, ›overed in a thick greyish-white ;laze, where exposed, burnt orange n the firing, some restoration, Yuan)ynasty, 14in (35.5cm).
:2,500-3,500 *CNY*

\ late Ming blue and white figure of ;uanyin, damaged, Wanli, 16in 41cm).
:900-1,200 *C*

A Ming tilemaker's figure of Guandi, with detachable head, dressed in an elaborate armour, with turquoise and amber glazes, the hands unglazed, chips, 16th/17thC, 19½in (50cm).
£1,000-1,200 *C*

A tilemaker's equestrian figure, formed as a heavily armoured warrior, under green and yellow glazes, some restoration, Ming/Qing Dynasty, 15½in (39cm).
£800-1,000 *C*

A Dehua blanc-de-chine figure of Guanyin, holding a scroll in her left hand, impressed seal mark, virtue extends even to fishermen, Qing Dynasty, 6½in (17cm).
£1,200-1,500 *C*

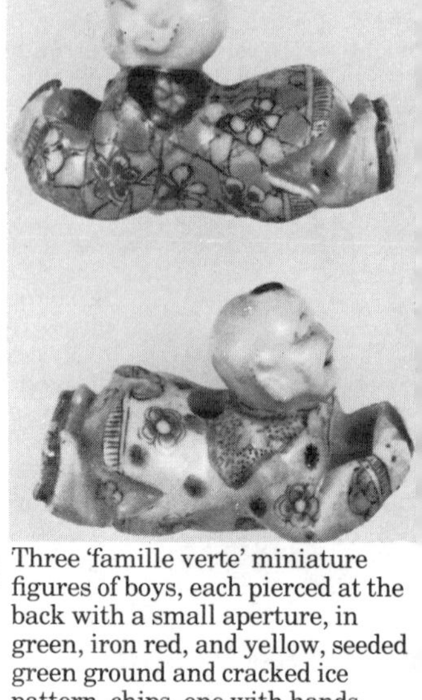

Three 'famille verte' miniature figures of boys, each pierced at the back with a small aperture, in green, iron red, and yellow, seeded green ground and cracked ice pattern, chips, one with hands restored, Kangxi, 2in (5cm) wide.
£1,500-2,000 *C*

A blanc-de-chine figure of Guanyin, under an ivory glaze, some chips, 17th/18thC, 9½in (24cm).
£700-900 *C*

A pair of Arita figures, painted in iron red, green enamel, gilt and black, glaze cracks, 2 feet damaged, late 17thC, 9in (23cm).
£2,000-2,500 *CSK*

A Dehua blanc-de-chine figure of Damo, standing with his arms crossed, small chips, early 18thC, 15in (38cm).
£3,500-4,000 *C*

A Satsuma figure of Kannon, signed at back, Seto Seizan with Shimazu mon, late 19thC, 15in (38cm).
£1,000-1,500 *CNY*

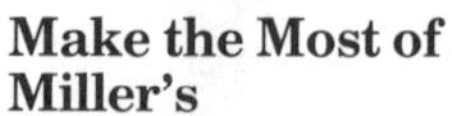

A pair of large soapstone figures, touched with red pigment and engraved with floral borders, damaged, 18thC, 11½in (29cm), wood stands.
£400-600 *C*

A pair of pottery tilemaker's figures, coiffed and dressed elaborately in ceremonial robes, glazed in turquoise, blue and brown, 13in (33cm).
£350-450 *CAm*

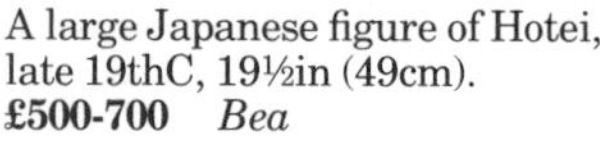

A large Japanese figure of Hotei, late 19thC, 19½in (49cm).
£500-700 *Bea*

Make the Most of Miller's

Every care has been taken to ensure the accuracy of descriptions and estimated valuations. Price ranges in this book reflect what one should expect to pay for a similar example. When selling one can obviously expect a figure below. This will fluctuate according to a dealer's stock, saleability at a particular time, etc. It is always advisable to approach a reputable specialist dealer or an auction house which has specialist sales

Flasks

A pair of triple neck moon flasks, enamelled in 'famille rose' with Shou Lao and Liu Hai, with his attendant three-legged toad, the rims edged in gilt, iron red seal marks for Qianlong, but 19thC, 4½in (12cm).
£300-400 *Bon*

A pair of large 'famille verte' moon flasks, with diaper grounds enriched with orange, green, and aubergine enamels, the shoulders with elaborate dragon handles, one neck restored, late Qing Dynasty, 18in (47cm).
£2,000-3,000 *C*

A Satsuma moon flask, enamelled in colours and gilt, the reverse reserved on a mottled glaze ground, signed underneath Dai Nihon Taizan tsukuru, late 19thC, 7½in (19cm).
£750-850 *CNY*

Flatware

An early Ming celadon dish carved with a quatrefoil panel, under a semi-translucent olive glaze, border crack, late 14th/15thC, 13in (32.5cm).
£700-900 *C*

A late Ming blue and white saucer dish, painted with scrolling pencilled lotus washed in a greyish-blue, Wanli six-character mark and of the period, 6in (15cm) diam, fitted box.
£1,500-2,000 *C*

A late Ming blue and white saucer dish with lobed floral rim, painted with a pair of deer by a river beneath pine, each moulded lobe with a floral spray, the exterior with emblems, minor fritting, Wanli, 8½in (22cm) diam.
£1,000-1,500 *C*

The moulded lobe developed into the so-called 'meisanda' style of decoration, featuring roundels instead of panels, which first appeared shortly after c1600 and was common among pieces of export blue and white porcelain recovered from the wreck of the 'Witte Leeuw', sunk in 1613.

A Ming blue and white dish, painted in pale blue and white, chipped, late 16thC, 16½in (42cm) diam.
£1,000-1,200 *C*

Two late Ming blue and white saucer dishes, fritted, Wanli, 8in (20cm) diam.
£900-1,100 *C*

A large Ming blue and white dish, centrally painted with 4 peony heads, minutely fritted, c1500, 20in (51cm) diam.
£1,500-2,000 *C*

A Ming blue and white 'kraak porselein' dish, minor fritting, Wanli, 19½in (50.5cm) diam, fitted box.
£2,700-3,200 *C*

A late Ming blue and white 'kraak porselein' dish, small rim chips, Wanli, 14in (36cm) diam.
£1,500-2,000 *C*

A blue and white foliate saucer dish, painted in inky blue tones, slight glaze nibbles to rim, Chenghua six-character mark, Kangxi, 6½in (16.5cm) diam.
£900-1,000 *C*

A large blue and white dish, minutely fritted, leaf mark, Kangxi, 20in (51cm) diam.
£8,500-9,500 *C*

A pair of 'famille verte' plates, reserved on floral green ground at the border, the plain white exteriors lightly incised with leafy sprays, one chipped and with original glaze imperfections, Kangxi, 9½in (25cm) diam.
£1,200-1,600 *C*

A Ming white glazed saucer dish, decorated in 'anhua' with a central peony, on a cruciform floral spray, chipped, encircled Jiajing six-character mark and of the period, 9in (22.5cm) diam.
£600-700 *C*

A pair of 'famille verte' dishes, boldly painted in strong enamels, one cracked, chipped, Kangxi, 14in (35.5cm) diam.
£2,700-3,000 *C*

A 'famille verte' dish, painted, with a green seeded floral border and gadrooned rim, Kangxi, 13in (33cm) diam.
£1,000-1,500 *C*

A 'famille verte' plate, painted within an elaborate green floral ground, Kangxi, 9in (23cm).
£2,500-3,000 *C*

A 'famille rose' green ground tea tray, the central reserve panel calligraphically inscribed in iron red and with a date corresponding to AD 1797, painted on a pale green ground, iron red Jiaqing six-character seal mark and of the period, 6½in (16cm) wide.
£1,000-1,500 *C*

A blue and white saucer dish, six-character mark 'Qiulin Langbai ziwan' (curio belonging to Qiulin Langbai), early Kangxi, 7in (17cm) diam.
£700-900 *C*

A 'famille verte' saucer dish, reserved on an iron red cell pattern ground at the well and underglaze blue leaves at the rim, the reverse with simple flower sprays, cracked and chipped, encircled lotus mark, Kangxi, 10½in (27cm) diam.
£900-1,200 *C*

A yellow glazed saucer dish, incised under the mustard yellow glaze with a pair of confronted phoenix, rim crack, encircled Kangxi six-character mark and of the period, 6in (15.5cm) diam.
£700-900 *C*

An 'egg and spinach' glazed plate, with a mottled glaze of yellow, green and aubergine, the footrim reserved in the biscuit, the base white glazed, crack, some rubbing, Kangxi, 8in (20cm) diam.
£500-700 *C*

A Chinese 'famille verte' plate, decorated in typical palette with a garden scene, the rim with flower and foliage border, Kangxi, c1725, 9in (23cm).
£450-500 *WW*

Six 'famille verte' plates, painted with an equestrian dignitary and a foot attendant, rim chips, restorations, Kangxi, 9in (22.5cm).
£1,800-2,500 *C*

Six 'famille verte' plates, painted with 5 lotus heads in iron red, yellow, black, blue and aubergine, below floral cell pattern borders, rim chips, one rim restored, Kangxi, 8½in (21cm).
£800-1,200 *C*

A pair of blue and white saucer dishes, boldly painted on a scale pattern ground, Kangxi, 15in (38cm) diam.
£800-1,000 *C*

A 'famille verte' saucer dish painted in vivid colours, border restorations, encircled Kangxi six-character mark and of the period, 9½in (24.8cm).
£2,000-3,000 *C*

A pair of blue and white saucer dishes, centrally painted below trellis ground floral panels at the compass points, one cracked, small rim chips, Kangxi, 14in (35cm) diam.
£800-1,200 *C*

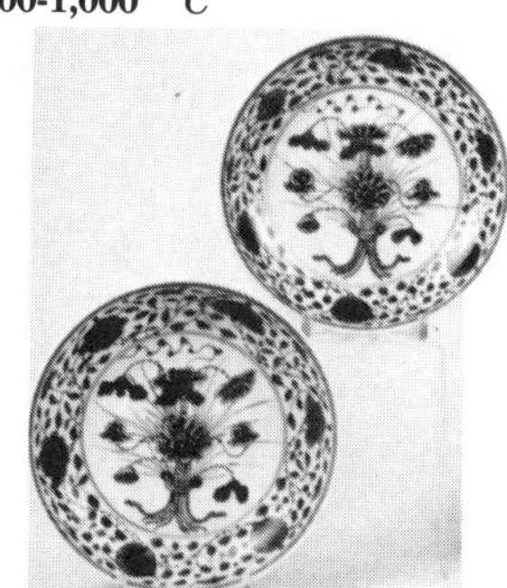

A pair of blue and white saucer dishes, painted in the Ming style, one small rim chip, encircled Yongzheng six-character marks and of the period, 7½in (19.5cm) diam, fitted box.
£1,000-1,500 *C*

A set of 6 'famille rose' soup plates, decorated with pink and green diaper, the exterior with iron red prunus sprigs, Yongzheng, 9in (23cm).
£2,500-3,500 *WW*

A blue and white dish, solidly potted and painted in the early Ming style, Yongzheng, 13in (33cm) diam.
£1,000-1,500 *C*

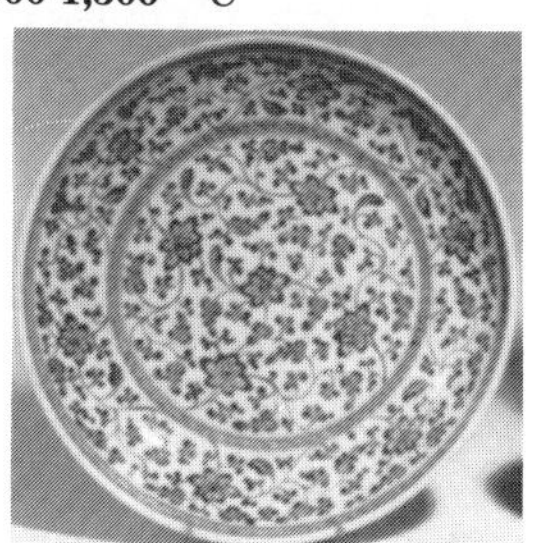

A 'famille rose' cockerel dish, Yongzheng, 14½in (37cm) diam.
£1,800-2,200 *C*

A pair of 'famille rose' saucer dishes, painted in iron red, shaded yellow, pink, white and green, one with 3 cracks, Yongzheng, 7½in (20cm) diam.
£1,000-1,200 *CAm*

A large 'famille rose' dish, painted after a design by Francesco Albani, within a gilt floral border, restored, Yongzheng, 16in (40cm).
£1,700-2,200 *C*

A large 'famille rose' deep saucer dish, painted with butterflies, insects and flowers, the rim gilt, encircled Yongzheng six-character mark and of the period, 21½in (54cm) diam.
£9,000-10,000 *C*

A large Chinese blue and white dee dish, rim chip, Qianlong, 19in (48cm) diam.
£450-550 *CSK*

A blue and white and underglaze copper red deep dish, Qianlong seal mark and of the period, 14in (37.5cm) diam.
£2,000-2,500 *C*

A 'famille rose' wavy rimmed plat outlined in gilt against reserves of iron whorls, Qianlong, 12½in (31.5cm).
£1,500-1,700 *Bon*

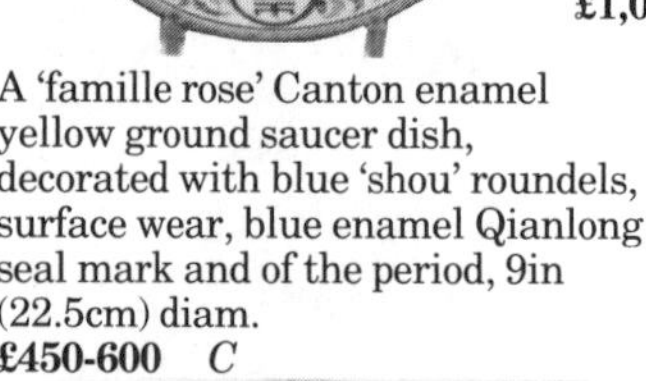

A Chinese meat dish, boldly painted in the Tobacco Leaf palette, the rim painted with a gold scrolling design on a brown band, Qianlong, 15in (38cm).
£1,000-1,500 *Bea*

A 'famille rose' Canton enamel yellow ground saucer dish, decorated with blue 'shou' roundels, surface wear, blue enamel Qianlong seal mark and of the period, 9in (22.5cm) diam.
£450-600 *C*

A large blue and white saucer dish, painted in the early Ming style, the deeply cut foot unglazed, Qianlong, 15½in (39cm) diam.
£2,000-2,500 *C*

A rare Cantonese enamel 'famille rose' quatrefoil dish, painted with 3 European figures in a wooded landscape, Qianlong, 11½in (29cm) wide.
£2,000-2,500 *CSK*

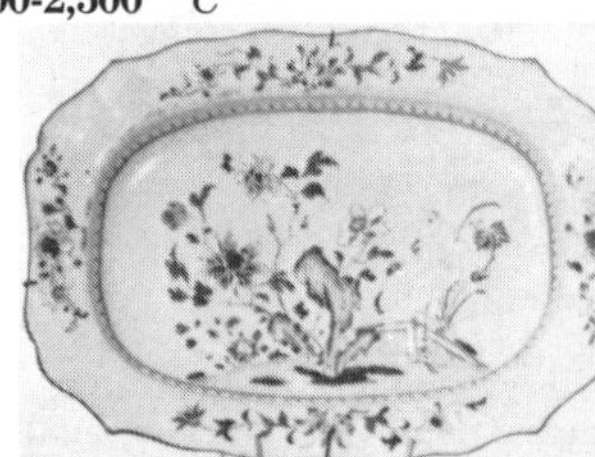

A pair of 'famille rose' meat dishes painted and gilt within a spearheac border, both cracked, Qianlong, 12½in (32cm).
£1,000-1,200 *CSK*

A pair of 'famille rose' 'Judgement of Paris' plates, painted in bright enamels with the 3 goddesses Juno, Minerva and Venus, one with rim chips restored, the other minute rim chips, Qianlong, 9in (22cm).
£800-1,000 *C*

A large 'famille rose' dish, painted in pink, blue, green and brown, small rim chip, Qianlong, 20in (49.5cm) diam.
£1,500-2,000 *C*

A pair of 'famille rose' armorial plates, painted with a small centra coat of arms and flower festoons at the border, one with minor chips, Qianlong, 9in (23cm).
£1,700-2,000 *C*

pair of Doucai saucer dishes, ainted in underglaze blue and aamelled in green, red, orange and ellow, one rim minutely chipped, ianlong seal marks and of the eriod, 9½in (24cm) diam.
2,500-3,000 *C*

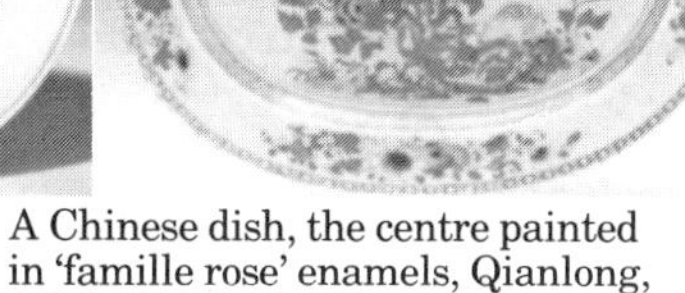

A Chinese dish, the centre painted in 'famille rose' enamels, Qianlong, 16½in (41.5cm) wide.
£1,000-1,500 *Bea*

A pair of 'famille rose' pseudo Tobacco Leaf plates, painted with flowerheads, chrysanthemum and leaves, Qianlong, 9in (23cm).
£1,500-1,700 *CSK*

pair of blue and white meat shes, Qianlong, c1760, 14in 5.5cm) wide.
00-1,000 *LG*

A blue and white shaped dish, Qianlong, c1780, 10in (25cm) diam.
£320-360 *LG*

A large blue and white saucer dish, minor rim chips, four-character mark 'yu tang jia qi' within a double circle, 17thC, 14in (35.5cm) diam.
£1,500-2,000 *C*

The mark reads 'fine vessel for jade hall'.

pair of 'famille rose' dishes, corated with the arms of the Duke Grafton, one chipped, Qianlong, in (25.5cm).
00-1,000 *DN*

Two blue and white European design plates in the Japanese style copying a Dutch Delft original, in the manner of Frederik van Frytom, the pattern traditionally known as Deshima Island, one chipped, the other fritted, one with imitation Japanese spur marks, late 17th/early 18thC, 7½in (19cm).
£700-800 *C*

blue and white European subject ate, painted after the Dutch raftsman Cornelius Pronk with the esign 'la dame au parasol', c1737, ½in (22cm).
4,500-5,500 *C*

Six dessert plates with pierced borders, painted in green and white on iron red bands, 5 with cracks, 2 chipped, late Qianlong/Jiaqing, 7½in (19cm).
£500-600 *C*

A pair of small Wucai dishes, painted in underglaze blue, green, iron red and mustard yellow enamels, minutely fritted, 17thC, 5½in (13.5cm) diam.
£900-1,000 *C*

Miller's is a price GUIDE not a price LIST

Garden Seats

A late Ming blue and white garden seat with lion mask handles, some restoration, Wanli, 15in (38cm).
£1,700-2,500 *C*

A Komai dish, richly decorated in takazogan and Komai numezogan, signed in a rectangular seal 'Kyoto ju Komai sei', 19in (48cm) diam.
£10,000-12,000 *CSK*

A Satsuma pottery plaque, decorated with shaped panels of figures dancing and feasting, 19thC 14in (35.5cm) diam.
£800-900 *HCH*

A pair of Guangdong stoneware barrel shaped garden seats, the mask handles and pierced sides covered in blue, green and cream glazes, 19thC, 20in (50cm).
£900-1,000 *C*

A Chinese blue glazed pierced garden seat, moulded in white relief, 19thC, 20in (50cm).
£600-800 *C*

A pair of 'famille rose' and 'famille verte' barrel shaped garden seats, decorated on a closely patterned gi ground, 19thC, 18½in (47cm).
£3,500-4,000 *GC*

A Canton 'famille rose' garden seat, painted with panels of figures and birds and pierced with double cash, between bands of moulded bosses on a ground of dense floral meander, late Qing Dynasty, 18½in (47cm).
£1,600-2,000 *C*

A Canton 'famille rose' garden sea decorated on a dense gilt floral ground, late Qing Dynasty, 18½in (47cm).
£1,600-1,800 *C*

Jardinières

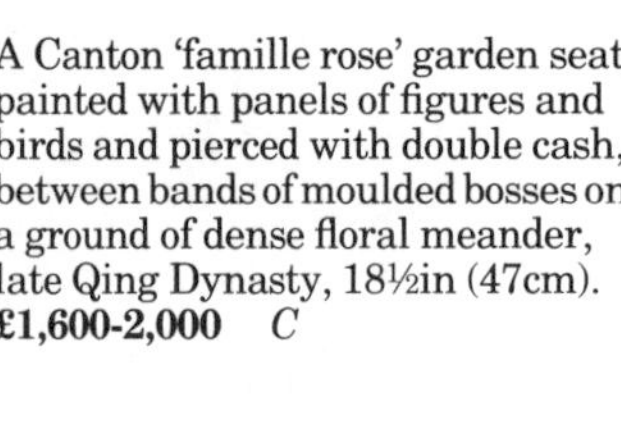

A Longquan celadon jardinière, the sides moulded with flowerheads, all covered in a rich green glaze thinning around the edges, cracked, Yuan/Ming Dynasty, 9½in (24cm) diam, wood stand, fitted box.
£600-900 *C*

A pair of Chinese 'famille rose' jardinières and stands, brightly decorated with alternate panels o inscriptions and Immortals, Daoguang seal marks and of the period, 9½in (24cm).
£900-1,200 *DN*

A Satsuma jardinière, Meiji period
£350-450 *Nam*

A massive blue and white jardinière, applied with 2 brown and gilt lion mask handles, rim chipped, 18thC, 25½in (64cm) diam, wood stand.
£3,500-4,500 *C*

Chinese blue and white porcelain •rdinière, decorated with panels of ndscape vignettes alternating ith peonies, lotus and rysanthemum, 18thC, 9in (23cm).
,500-2,000 *Bon*

A Canton jardinière and stand, with reserves on a gold decorated blue ground, the inside of the stand decorated with butterflies, fruit and flowers, stand repaired, jardinière 16in (41cm) diam.
£900-1,200 *Bea*

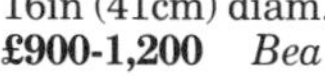

A pair of 'famille rose' jardinières, painted and enamelled in reserves with birds and flowering blossoms on floral grounds and pierced bases, one damaged, 10½in (26cm) diam.
£2,700-3,200 *P[Re]*

ars

green glazed jar, some storation, Han Dynasty, 7½in 9.8cm) diam.
,000-1,500 *C*

spotted Jizhou jar, covered with a ack glaze and grey spots, rising to wide neck and an everted lip, the se glazed, chips, Southern Song ynasty, 7½in (18.5cm).
,200-1,600 *C*

large Ming blue and white luster jar, 'guan', painted in illiant violet tones, the rim bound metal, cracks, Jiajing six-aracter mark and of the period, in (33cm).
,000-5,000 *C*

A glazed pottery baluster jar, in brown and blue chevrons, on an olive and straw streaky ground over a white slip, both slip and glaze stopping irregularly above the crisp recessed foot, some restoration, Tang Dynasty, 8in (20.5cm).
£3,000-3,500 *C*

A Transitional blue and white oviform jar, painted in inky blue tones with a continuous scene from Sanguo Yanyi (Romance of the Three Kingdoms), with 'anhua' bands, c1640, 12in (30cm).
£1,800-2,200 *C*

A Longquan celadon funerary jar and cover, with a widely crackled bluish green glaze, crack, finial damage, Southern Song Dynasty, 7in (18cm), stand, fitted box.
£2,000-2,500 *C*

A Ming blue and white jar and cover, c1650.
£700-1,000 *Wai*

A Ming white glazed jar, with an even milky white glaze, some wear, Jiajing six-character mark in a double square and of the period, 5in (12.5cm), fitted box.
£2,000-2,500 *C*

A Ming blue and white oviform jar, painted in bright tones, with dot lappets at the foot and cloud and pendant dot lappets at the shoulder, the tapering neck with stylised wave motifs, restored, Jiajing six-character mark and of the period, 9in (23cm).
£2,200-4,500 *C*

A Ming white glazed squat jar, lightly incised under the glaze with 2 phoenix, encircled Jiajing six-character mark and of the period, 4in (10.5cm).
£1,700-2,000 *C*

A Ming Wucai jar, painted with 8 boys at play, some surface fritting, base star crack and short neck crack, encircled Wanli six-character mark and of the period, 5in (12.5cm).
£7,500-8,500 *C*

A rare 'famille rose' armorial jar, painted in black, gilt and iron red feather scroll at the lowest point, foot restored, c1720, 8in (20.5cm).
£3,000-4,000 *C*

A pair of blue and white jars, painted in a bright blue, Kangxi, 8½in (22cm), wood covers and stands.
£2,500-3,000 *C*

A pair of blue and white square jars, with white metal mounted necks, edges fritted and chipped, body crack, Kangxi, 10½in (26.5cm).
£700-800 *C*

A pair of blue and white square tea jars and covers, painted within borders of trellis pattern divided by 'ruyi' lappets at the corners, chipped, one cover damaged, Kangxi, 11½in (29.5cm).
£5,000-6,000 *C*

A pair of 'famille verte' jars, painted in reserve with 2 vertical panels of 'bajixiang', drilled bases, one chipped, one cracked, Kangxi, 12½in (31cm), wood covers and stands.
£3,500-4,000 *C*

A Chinese blue and white baluster jar, painted with Buddhistic lions playing with brocade balls below a border of emblems, Kangxi, 12½in (31.5cm).
£1,000-1,500 *CSK*

Two blue and white baluster jars, freely painted, one neck with minor damage, Kangxi, 13in (33cm).
£1,000-1,500 *C*

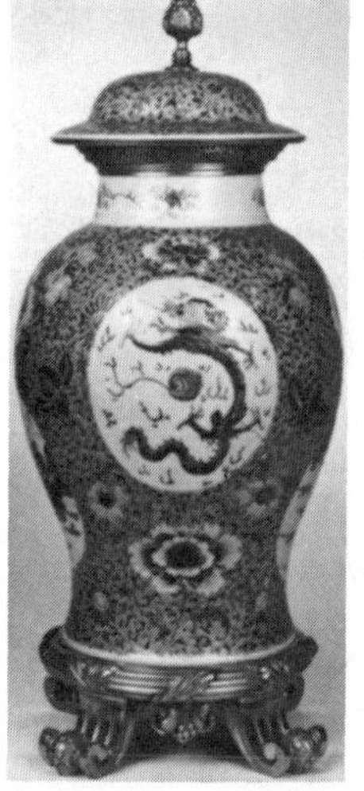

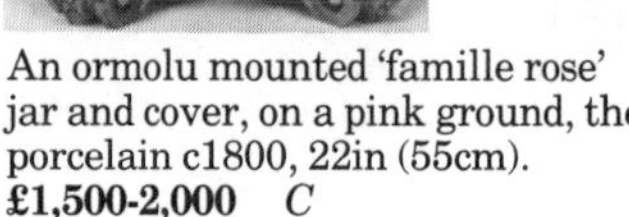

An ormolu mounted 'famille rose' jar and cover, on a pink ground, the porcelain c1800, 22in (55cm).
£1,500-2,000 *C*

A Transitional Wucai baluster jar and domed cover with knop finial, cover rim chip and finial restored, mid-17thC, 16in (40.5cm).
£2,500-3,000 *C*

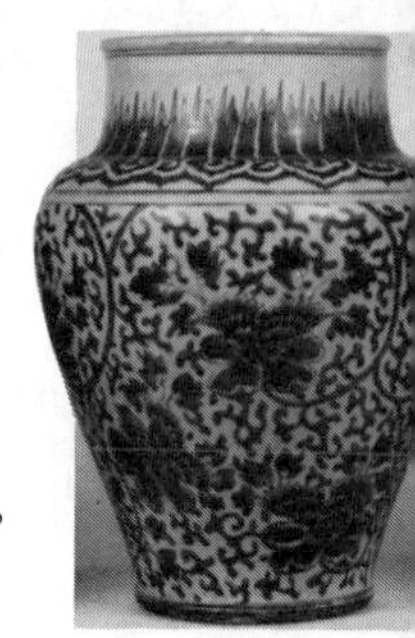

A large blue and white jar, fritted, mid-17thC, 18in (46cm).
£1,800-2,200 *C*

'ea & Coffee Pots & ervices

n export part tea service, painted extensive 'grisaille', iron red and lt, comprising: teapot and cover, eam jug and cover, spoon tray, teabowls and saucers, old damage, ongzheng/early Qianlong, and a apot, possibly decorated in olland, and 2 saucers, cracked, ianlong.
,000-1,500 *C*

A pair of 'famille rose' jars and covers, painted with phoenix, magpies, cranes and other birds, among trees and chrysanthemum issuing from rockwork, one damaged, 17in (43cm).
£500-700 *CSK*

A pair of Imari jars, painted on an inky blue ground, one cover damaged, early 18thC, 10½in (26cm).
£700-1,000 *Bea*

n export teapot and cover, painted each side 'en grisaille' and gilt, e cover with a peach finial within on red husk and simple green amel bands, chips to spout and ver, some enamel flaking, anlong, 9½in (23.5cm) wide.
00-600 *C*

A Chinese export miniature part tea service, painted in bright enamel colours, comprising: a teapot and cover, 2 teabowls, 2 cups and 8 saucers, slight glaze chipping, Qianlong.
£700-1,000 *Bea*

◀ A 'famille rose' teapot and cover, the cover with small knop finial enamelled in yellow, Qianlong, 4½in (12cm).
£250-300 *Bon*

Chinese export teapot and cover, ianlong, 5in (12.5cm).
200-300 *CSK*

A 'famille rose' teapot and cover, restoration to lower spout and body, c1760, 6in (15cm).
£2,000-2,500 *C* ▶

A Satsuma wine pot and cover, late 19thC, 4½in (12cm) wide.
£400-500 *Bea*

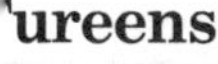

'ureens

A 'famille rose' and blue and white tureen and domed cover, cover chipped, Qianlong, 11½in (28.5cm) wide.
£4,500-5,000 *C*

IMARI PATTERNS

- ★ Imari named after port of shipment
- ★ decoration of Japanese porcelain often based on brocade patterns
- ★ made at Arita, Hizen Province, from early 18thC to early 19thC
- ★ Imari patterns copied and adapted by Derby, Worcester, Spode, Minton, Mason and others
- ★ patterns also made in China

A miniature partridge tureen and cover, moulded and painted in black and iron red with realistic feather markings, small chips, tail restored, Qianlong, 3in (8cm) wide.
£1,200-1,500 *C*

A Chinese white glazed tureen and cover, the base with rabbit's head handles, the cover with pierced crown finial, Qianlong, 12in (30cm).
£2,000-2,500 *Bon*

A blue and white soup tureen and cover, c1760, Qianlong, 10½in (26cm).
£1,600-2,200 *LG*

A pair of blue and white bombé tureens and covers, one painted in slightly darker tones than the other, one cover restored, late 18thC, 14½in (37cm) wide.
£2,000-2,500 *C*

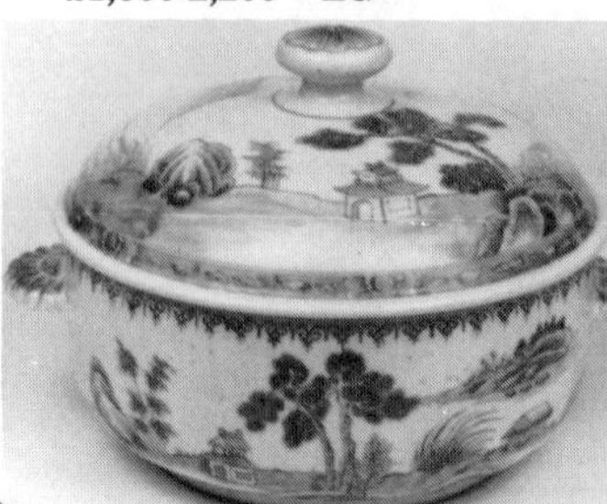

A blue and white tureen and cover frits to the handles, 18thC, 10½in (26cm) wide.
£800-1,000 *C*

A 'famille rose' tureen and cover, with iron red bud finial and pairs of lion mask handles suspending metal loops, late Qing Dynasty, 14½in (36.5cm) diam.
£2,000-2,500 *C*

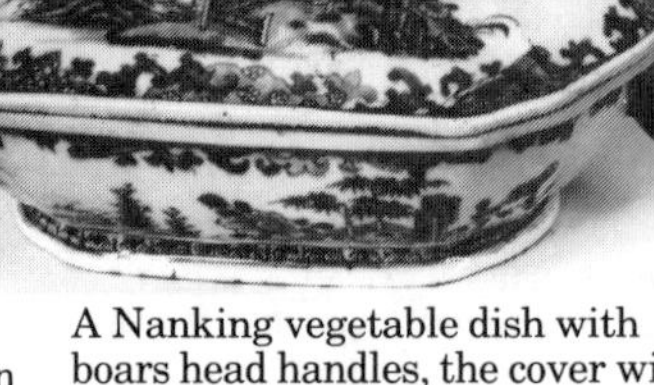

A Nanking vegetable dish with boars head handles, the cover wit fruit finial, Chien Lung, 14in (35.5cm) wide.
£900-1,100 *GC*

Vases

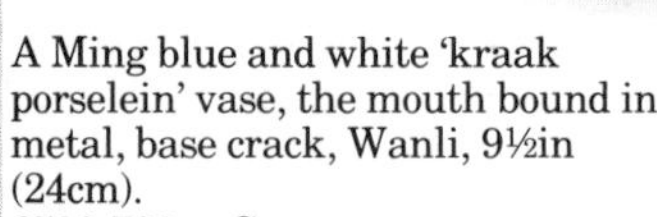

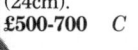

A Ming blue and white 'kraak porselein' vase, the mouth bound in metal, base crack, Wanli, 9½in (24cm).
£500-700 *C*

A Chinese blue and white double gourd vase, Wanli, 10½in (26cm).
£500-600 *Bea*

A pair of late Ming blue and white vases, meiping, minor fritting, Wanli/Tianqi, 10½in (27cm), wood stands, fitted boxes.
£2,500-3,000 *C*

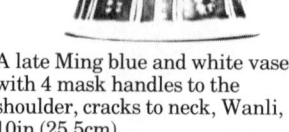

A late Ming blue and white vase with 4 mask handles to the shoulder, cracks to neck, Wanli, 10in (25.5cm).
£300-500 *CSK*

A Transitional blue and white bottle vase with garlic neck, c1640, 14in (35cm), wood stand, fitted box.
£2,700-3,200 *C*

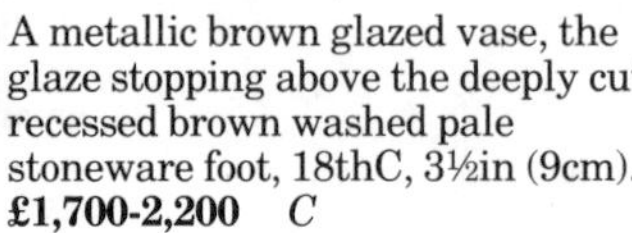

A metallic brown glazed vase, the glaze stopping above the deeply cut recessed brown washed pale stoneware foot, 18thC, 3½in (9cm).
£1,700-2,200 *C*

A Japanese Arita vase, decorated in blue, some damage, 17thC, 19in (48cm).
£1,000-1,200 *DN*

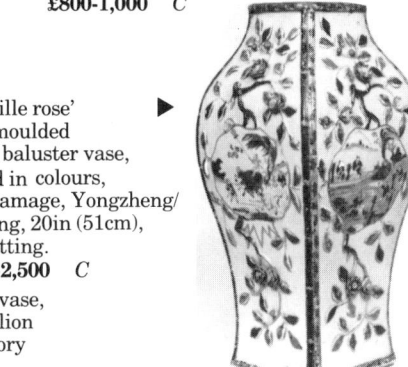

A blue and white vase, painted in grey-blue, rim probably polished, Kangxi, 10in (25cm), wood stand, fitted box.
£800-1,000 *C*

A blue and white celadon ground vase, meiping, lightly moulded and painted with 3 Immortals including 'Shoulao', minor glaze crack near luting line, Kangxi, 15½in (39cm).
£1,400-2,000 *C*

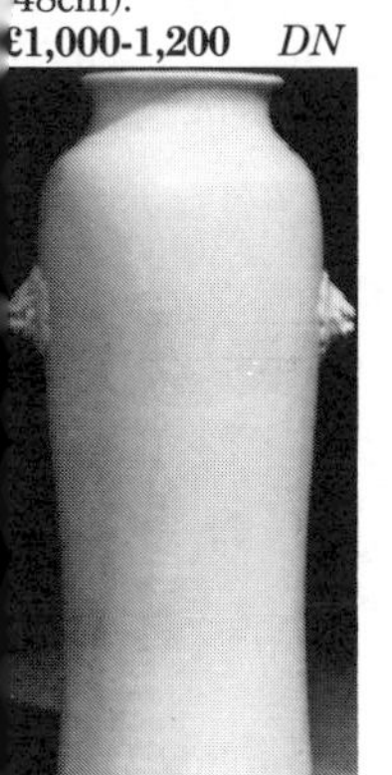

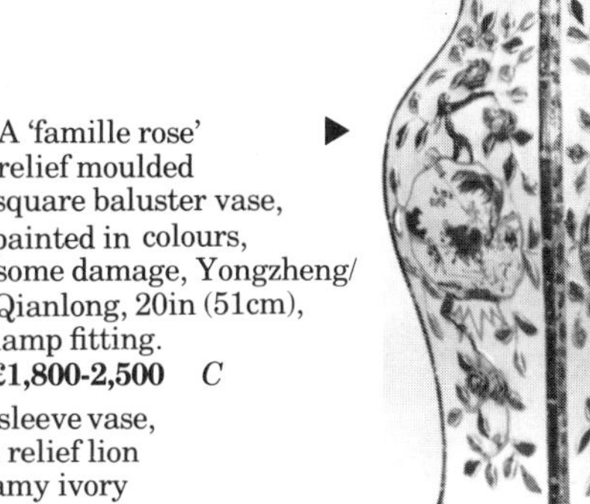

A 'famille rose' ▶ relief moulded square baluster vase, painted in colours, some damage, Yongzheng/Qianlong, 20in (51cm), lamp fitting.
£1,800-2,500 *C*

A Dehua blanc-de-chine sleeve vase, incised and applied with relief lion masks, under a pale creamy ivory glaze, the broad foot unglazed, Kangxi, 9½in (24.5cm).
£1,600-2,000 *C*

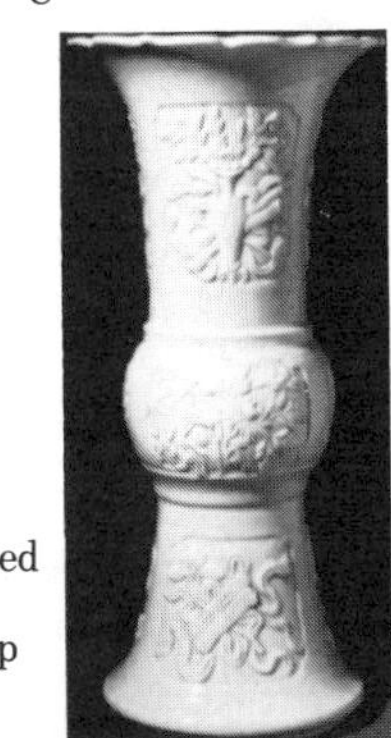

A Dehua blanc-de-chine gu-shaped beaker vase, 17th/18thC, 15½in (39.5cm), the interior with a lamp fitting.
£5,000-5,500 *C*

A large sang-de-boef ▶ hu-shaped vase, under a rich glaze firing white at the angles, c1800, 17in (43cm).
£1,000-1,500 *C*

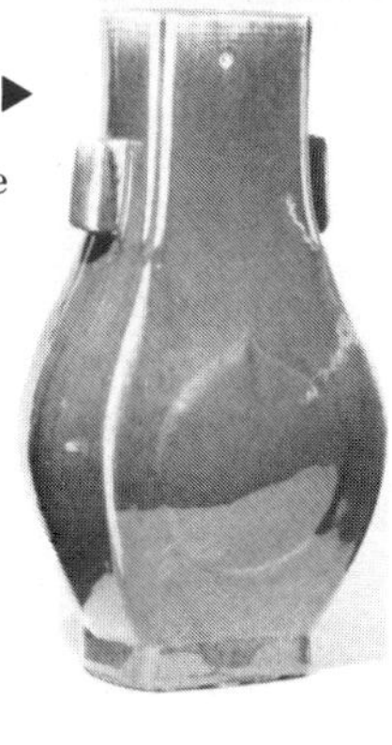

A pair of Imari vases and covers, painted with panels of flowering plants, the covers with 'shi-shi' knops, early 18thC, 10in (25cm).
£500-600 *L*

A Doucai vase, meiping, delicately pencilled in underglaze blue and enamelled in pale green, yellow, aubergine and coral red, repaired, 18thC, 14in (35.5cm).
£600-1,000 *C*

A tall bottle vase, by S Ichino, covered in a pale bluish white glaze with iron brown flecks, impressed Ichino character and St. Ives seals, Yingqing, 12½in (31.5cm).
£100-150 *C*

A Satsuma trumpet vase, enamelled in gossu blue, green and iron red and gilt, small rim flake, 19thC, 9in (23cm).
£350-400 *CNY*

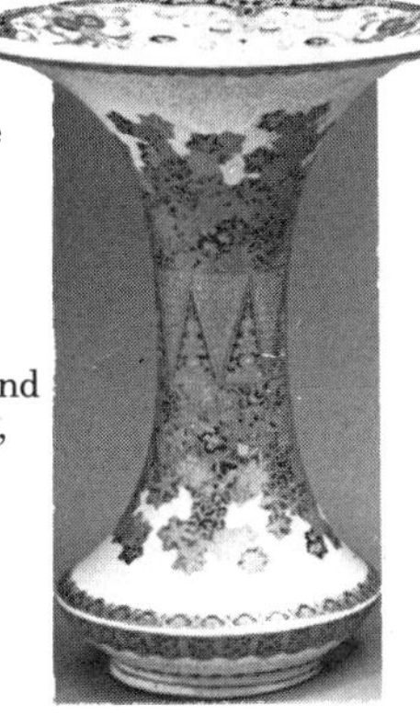

A large Canton 'famille rose' vase, with trumpet neck, cracked, early 19thC, 28in (71.5cm).
£1,200-1,500 *C*

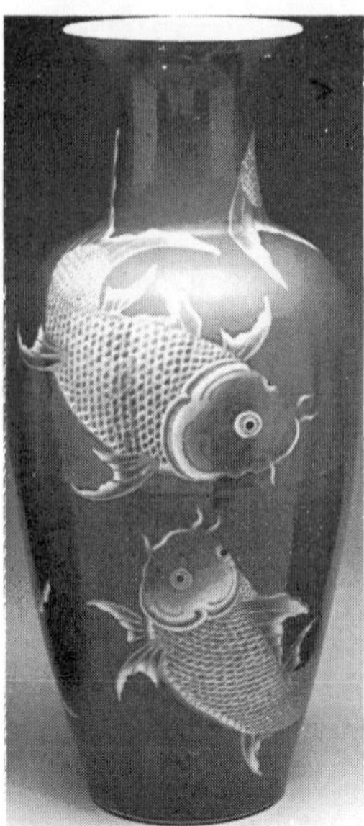

A baluster vase, in iron red painted on powder blue ground, 19thC, 17in (43cm).
£600-800 *CNY*

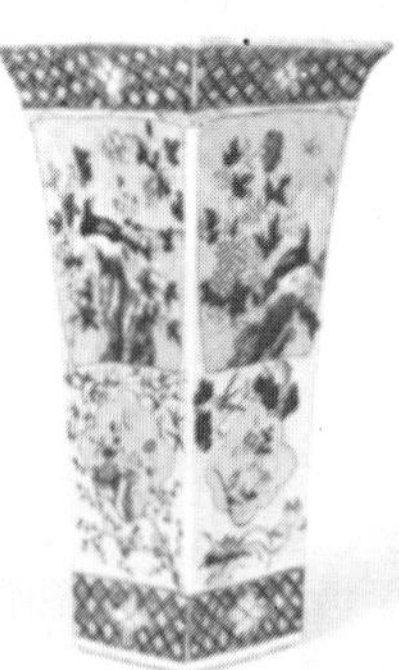

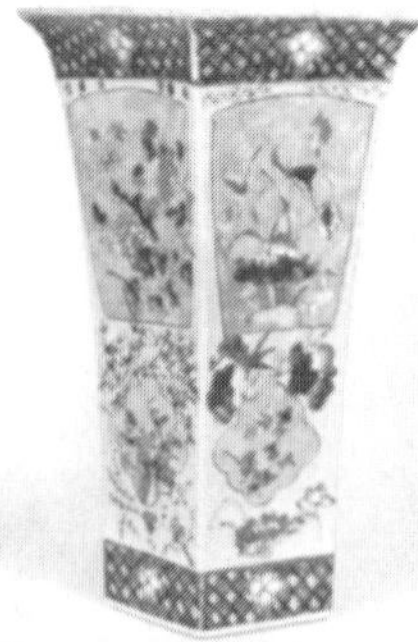

A pair of 'famille verte' yellow ground vases, painted on a mustard yellow ground, 19thC, 14in (35cm), wood stands.
£2,000-2,500 *C*

A cloisonné vase, decorated with birds and flowers on a blue ground, damaged, 19thC, 21in (53cm).
£1,600-1,800 *LRG*

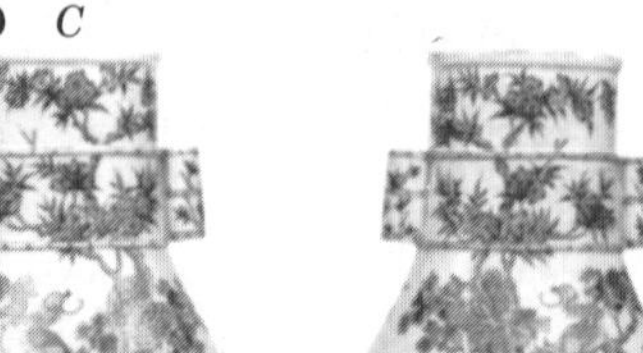

A pair of 'famille jaune' vases, with upright cylindrical handles, one restored, one chipped, 19thC, 15in (35cm), fitted for electricity.
£1,500-2,000 *C*

A Satsuma vase of faceted form, painted with alternate panels containing vases of flowers or blossom between a lappet foot and shoulder, 19thC, 9½in (24.5cm).
£3,000-4,000 *Bea*

A pair of Canton 'famille rose' vases, applied on the sides of the neck and shoulder with 6 relief dragons, 19thC, 22½in (57.5cm).
£3,000-4,000 *C*

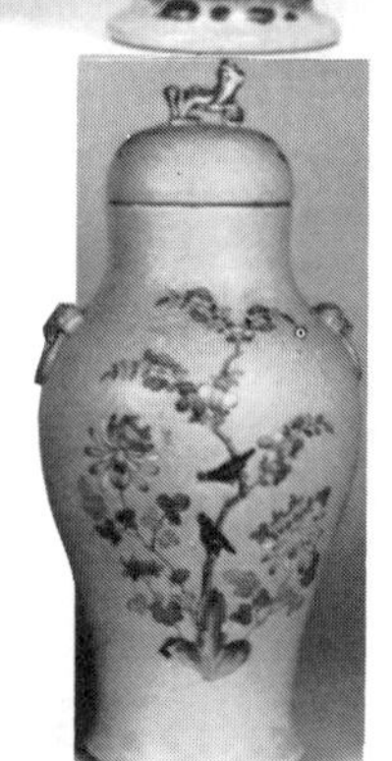

A pair of 'famille rose' pink ground baluster vases and domed covers, with crouching lion cub finials and blue enamel lion mask fixed ring handles, late Qing Dynasty, 19in (48.5cm).
£2,500-3,500 *C*

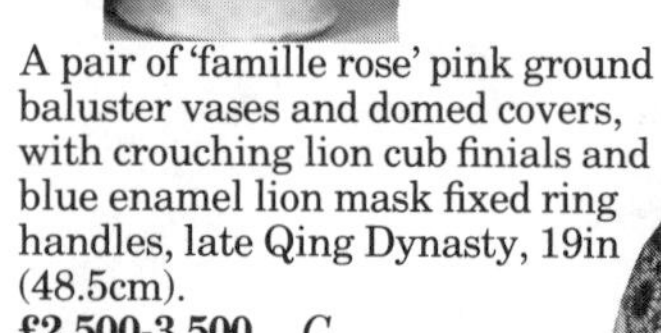

A robin's-egg glazed double gourd vase, standing on a slightly recessed base, the gilt rim with 3 circular apertures, Daoguang, 3½in (8cm).
£350-400 *C*

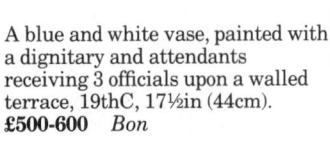

A 'famille rose' vase painted in blue, puce, yellow and gilt, star crack to base, iron red Jiaqing seal mark, 15in (38cm).
£1,500-2,000 *C*

A pair of 'famille verte' vases, one vase with hairline at rim, 19thC, 18in (45cm).
£600-700 *Bon*

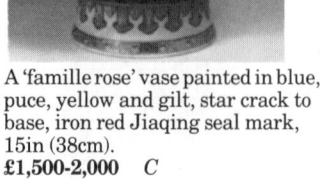

A blue and white vase, painted with a dignitary and attendants receiving 3 officials upon a walled terrace, 19thC, 17½in (44cm).
£500-600 *Bon*

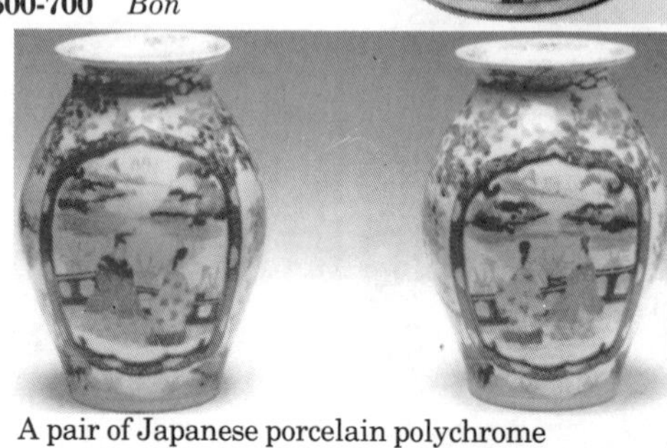

A pair of Japanese porcelain polychrome vases, late 19thC, 11in (28cm).
£300-400 *Bea*

A pair of Canton vases, brightly painted with panels, late 19thC, 15in (38cm).
£700-800 *Bea*

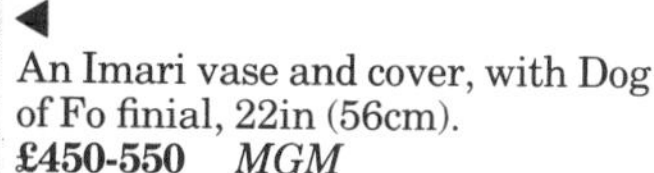

An Imari vase and cover, with Dog of Fo finial, 22in (56cm).
£450-550 *MGM*

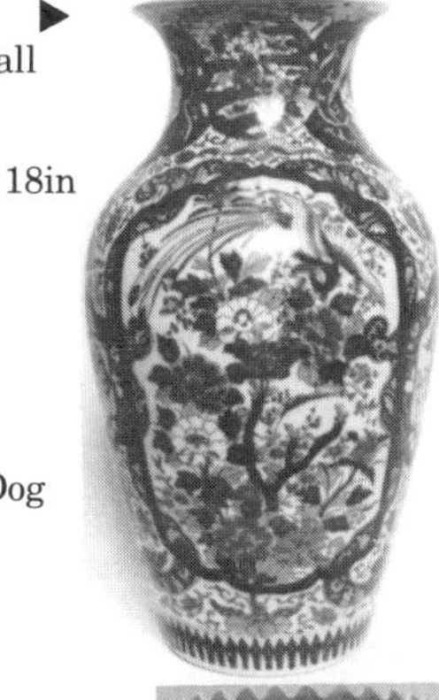

A pair of Imari vases, painted all over, gilded and enamelled in typical palette with birds of paradise, prunus and dragons, 18in (45.5cm).
£1,500-2,000 *P[Re]*

A blue Imari vase decorated with storks, 48in (122cm).
£700-750 *MGM*

A pair of Japanese slender cloisonné vases, decorated with hanging pendants of 'ho-o' below bands of stylised flowers and emblems, 9½in (24cm).
£350-450 *CSK*

A near matching pair of Japanese vases, 22in (57cm).
£600-800 *PWC*

A Chinese blue and white cinquefoil tulip vase, 9½in (24cm).
£550-650 *CSK*

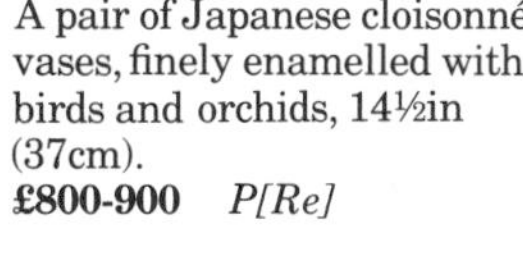

A pair of Japanese cloisonné vases, finely enamelled with birds and orchids, 14½in (37cm).
£800-900 *P[Re]*

A pair of Canton vases, reserved on a gold ground painted with flowers, foliage and moths, some damage, 23in (60cm), wood stands.
£3,500-4,000 *Bea*

A Chinese blue and white vase, brightly decorated with ducks and a kingfisher, and flowering plants, Transitional, 10in (25cm).
£1,500-2,000 *DN*

A pair of 'famille rose' vases, 18in (45.5cm).
£2,500-3,000 *CSK*

A pair of 'famille rose' vases, with grounds of pink, turquoise, blue, yellow and brown, 22½in (57cm).
£1,500-2,000 *CSK*

Miscellaneous

A blue and white and underglaze copper red box and cover, painted in a strong blue on a moulded panel, four-character hallmark to base, Qing Dynasty, 3½in (8cm) wide.
£2,500-3,000 *C*

The hallmark reads 'Xingtang Qingwan'.

A Canton 'famille rose' enamel plaque, inscribed with the letters 'PASDIA'(?), restored, early Qianlong, 7in (18cm).
£1,500-2,000 *C*

A 'famille verte' biscuit porcelain grotto, in aubergine, yellow and green and daubed in the 'egg and spinach' style around the perimeter of the exterior, slight damage and restoration, Kangxi, 7in (18cm).
£1,200-1,700 *CNY*

A pair of blue and white silver-shaped candlesticks, one stem restored, Qianlong, 7½in (19cm).
£2,000-2,500 *C*

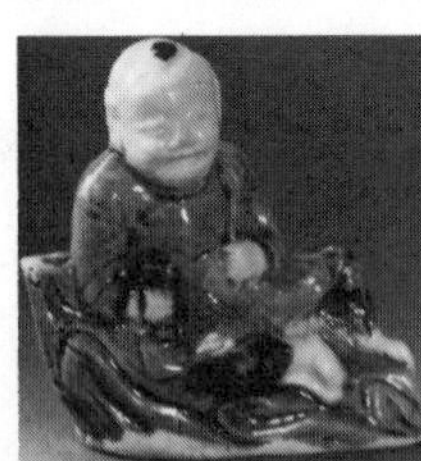

A 'famille verte' joss stick holder, Kangxi, c1720.
£200-300 *Wai*

An ormolu mounted Chinese 'famille rose' brush pot, painted in colours including puce, yellow, black and shades of blue, the porcelain Yongzheng, the mounts stamped E. F. Caldwell Co., Inc., New York, 7½in (19cm) diam.
£3,500-4,000 *CNY*

A 'famille rose' stupa reliquary, painted with lotus and Buddhistic lion masks on a deep blue ground, the base painted in iron red and gilt, the top mounted with an enamelled copper lotus supporting a lapis lazuli sphere, slightly chipped, mid Qing Dynasty, 12in (30cm).
£600-700 *C*

A Chinese blue and white violin shaped bidet, Qianlong, 22in (56cm) long.
£1,500-2,000 *CSK*

A 'famille rose' Meissen style stand, painted in shades of brown and iron red imitating bark, turquoise, green, yellow and pink, minor damage, c1775, 12in (30cm), mounted in pierced gilt-metal as a table lamp.
£750-850 *CNY*

A pair of Chinese blue and white candlesticks, painted with Buddhist emblems and mythological birds flying amongst clouds, some damage, 10in (25cm).
£300-500 *Bea*

A blue and white model of a well bucket, painted with wrythen panels of various diapering, blue four-character mark, 18½in (47cm).
£500-600 *L*

A pair of Chinese blue and white tea caddies and domed covers, 6in (15cm).
£550-600 *CSK*

A Cizhou pillow, modelled as a recumbent tiger, with bold deep brown stripes on a salmon brown ground, the head rest with an ivory white ground, minor chips, Jin Dynasty, 15in (38cm) wide.
£1,200-1,500 *C*

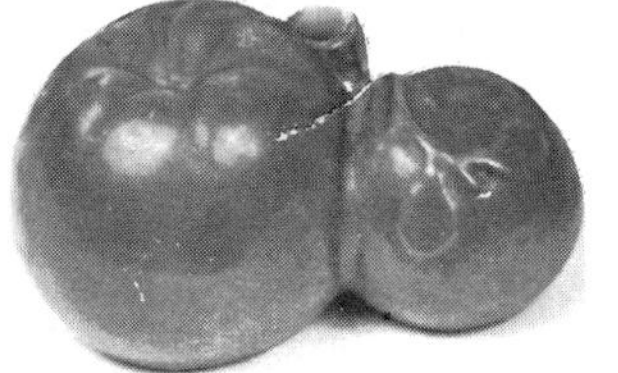

A pair of coral glazed water pots, in the form of conjoined tomatoes, Qing Dynasty, 4in (10cm) wide, wood stands.
£500-600 *C*

A dark olive glazed double gourd rosewater sprinkler, under an even shiny glaze thinning to a pale celadon at the rim of the neck and pooling between the gourds and at the base, traces of gilding remaining, minute rim glaze crack, 17th/18thC, 11in (28cm).
£800-1,000 *C*

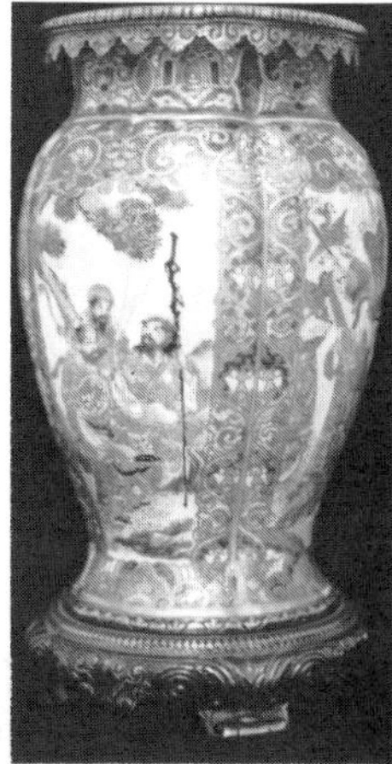

A Satsuma pottery gilt bronze mounted oil lamp base, finely enamelled and gilded, lacking oil lamp receiver, 12in (30.5cm).
£450-500 *P[Re]*

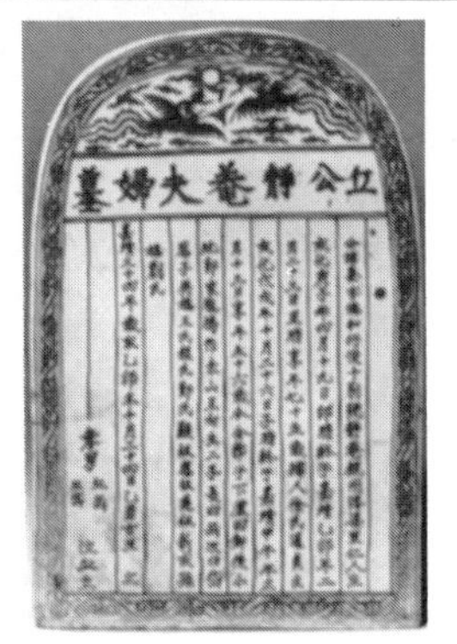

A rare Ming blue and white tablet, with arched top painted with a border of foliate scrolls, a pair of phoenix contesting a flaming pearl above a horizontal calligraphic band and 11 smaller vertical bands, firing crack, some glaze degradation to lower part, inscribed Jiajing 34th Year corresponding to AD 1555 and of the period, 13½in (34cm).
£3,000-3,500 *C*

A blue and white brush pot, painted in a rich blue with 2 rectangular panels, Kangxi, 5½in (13.5cm).
£1,000-1,500 *C*

A Cizhou white glazed oval pillow, the curving top incised to an ochre slip with a young boy holding a lotus spray, all under a finely crackled glaze over a white slip pooling at the edges, Song Dynasty, 8in (20cm) wide.
£1,200-1,800 *C*

A blue and white fan shaped water dropper, Yi Dynasty, 2½in (6cm) wide.
£350-500 *C*

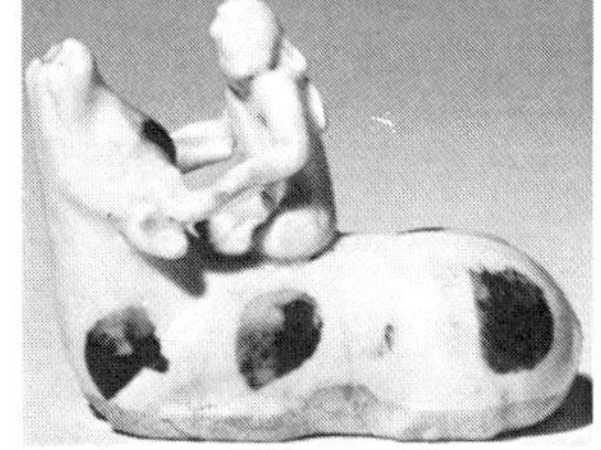

A white glazed water dropper, in the form of a young boy on the back of a seated buffalo, irregularly splashed with iron spots, Yuan Dynasty, 3½in (8.5cm) long, fitted box.
£800-1,000 *C*

A 'famille rose' candle holder, painted in pink, blue and green, with a long tailed bird, painted in green, salmon and blue enamel perched to one side, minor damage to extremities, Qianlong, 5½in (13.5cm) wide.
£2,000-2,500 *C*

A blue and white centrepiece, modelled after a Meissen original, fritting, cracked, restoration, Qianlong, 15in (38cm).
£900-1,200 *C*

A Chinese Imari chamber pot, handle frits, early 18thC, 8½in (22cm) wide.
£1,500-2,000 *C*

A blue and white wall cistern, early 19thC, 17in (43cm).
£1,200-1,500 *C*

An aubergine glazed hexagonal stand, the glaze pooling on the frieze recesses and at the apron, and stopping part way down the biscuit legs, some chips, 18thC, 9½in (24cm) wide.
£800-1,200 *C*

A robin's-egg glazed water pot, applied to one side with a brown glazed 'chilong' with unglazed feet, the base turquoise glazed, Daoguang, 2½in (6cm) wide.
£400-500 *C*

A Dehua incense burner, with glaze of creamy milk white colour, 17th/18thC, 4in (10cm) diam.
£450-550 *CNY*

A 'famille jaune' incense ball and cover, painted in green and iron red to the sides and base, the top with small aperture with cover, all suspended on a cord with 2 jade beads from an elaborately carved ivory stand, 18thC, 10in (25cm), including stand.
£4,000-5,000 *C*

A Cizhou figural form pillow, painted in café au lait and dark brown over a pale ivory slip, with brilliant glaze, 15½in (39cm) long.
£3,500-4,500 *CNY*

A 'famille jaune' cricket cage and stopper, with piercing between aubergine glazed mock wood borders, the ends with green glazed cell pattern, repaired, Kangxi, 7in (18cm).
£600-700 *C*

A 'famille verte' plaque, minor chips, Kangxi, 10½in (26cm) wide.
£2,000-3,000 *CNY*

A Ming blue and white drum shaped brush holder, painted in pale underglaze blue with a continuous band of meandering peony between key pattern borders, minor cracks, c1500, 4½in (11cm) diam.
£750-800 *CNY*

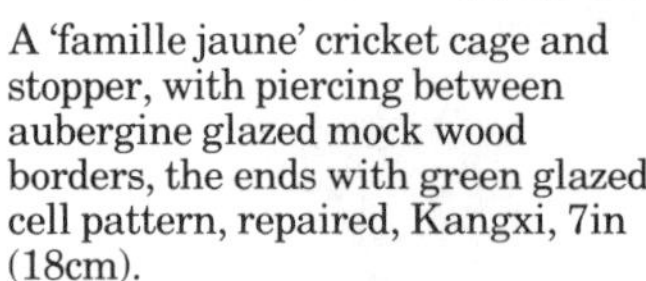

A 'famille verte' brush pot, painted in black enamel with a lengthy inscription of Su Tongpo's 'Ode to the Red Cliff' ending in an iron red seal, coloured blue, pale aubergine, yellow, iron red and green, Kangxi, 5½in (14cm), box.
£2,000-2,500 *CNY*

Make the most of Miller's

Unless otherwise stated, any description which refers to 'a set' or 'a pair' includes a valuation for the entire set or the pair, even though the illustration may show only a single item

A brush pot, Kangxi, 5in (12.5cm).
£650-750 *CNY*

Chinese dynasties and marks

Earlier Dynasties

Shang Yin, c.1532-1027 B.C.
Western Zhou (Chou) 1027-770 B.C.
Spring and Autumn Annals 770-480 B.C.
Warring States 484-221 B.C.
Qin (Ch'in) 221-206 B.C.
Western Han 206 BC-24 AD
Eastern Han 25-220
Three Kingdoms 221-265
Six Dynasties 265-589
Wei 386-557
Sui 589-617
Tang (T'ang) 618-906
Five Dynasties 907-960
Liao 907-1125
Sung 960-1280
Chin 1115-1260
Yüan 1280-1368

Ming Dynasty

Hongwu (Hung Wu)
1368-1398

永樂年製

Yongle (Yung Lo)
1403-1424

大明宣德年製

Xuande (Hsüan Té)
1426-1435

大明成化年製

成化年製

Chenghua (Ch'éng Hua)
1465-1487

大明弘治年製

Hongzhi
(Hung Chih)
1488-1505)

大明正德年製

Zhengde
(Chéng Té)
1506-1521

大明嘉靖年製

Jiajing
(Chia Ching)
1522-1566

大明隆慶年製

Longqing
(Lung Ching)
1567-1572

大明萬曆年製

Wanli (Wan Li)
1573-1620

大明天啟年製

Tianqi
(Tien Chi)
1621-1627

崇禎年製

Chongzhen
(Ch'ung Chêng)
1628-1644

Qing (Ch'ing) Dynasty

大清順治年製

Shunzhi
(Shun Chih)
1644-1661

大清康熙年製

Kangxi (K'ang Hsi)
1662-1722

大清雍正年製

Yongzheng (Yung Chêng)
1723-1735

大清乾隆年製

Qianlong (Ch'ien Lung)
1736-1795'

嘉慶年製

Jiaqing (Chia Ch'ing)
1796-1820

大清道光年製

Daoguang (Tao Kuang)
1821-1850

大清咸豐年製

Xianfeng (Hsien Féng)
1851-1861

大清同治年製

Tongzhi (T'ung Chih)
1862-1874

大清光緒年製

Guangxu (Kuang Hsu)
1875-1908

大清宣統年製

Xuantong
(Hsuan T'ung)
1909-1911

洪憲年製

Hongxian
(Hung Hsien)
1916

Glass prices have, for a change, moved up sharply in the last 18 months. Leading the field, as always, are the most sought-after glasses such as colour twists. Also in demand are the more unusual Beilbys, good 18th and 19th century engraved glass and glasses, early scents and good Stourbridge glass.

Most drinking glasses have appreciated more than usual although it would be unwise to quote any percentage as applying over the whole range increase. Nevertheless there are many exceptions and anomalies. The front runner, without doubt, is the humble decanter. In the late 1950s and early 1960s an ordinary Georgian decanter could be bought for 5 shillings (25p!); now such a piece sells for about £170 if in good condition and with the correct stopper. Taking account of inflation this still gives a percentage increase in real terms of around 750%! Can this be bettered in any other area? Yet who really wants to collect ordinary decanters? Unusual and finely engraved examples, yes! Plain, undecorated, no!

In practical terms, therefore, does the current obsession with price trends really matter? In the early 1960s there was nothing like the present interest in English glass, the number of both collectors and dealers was smaller and very few collectors ventured into the major salerooms. There was a plentiful supply of glass with little more than a notional price for 'run of the mill' items. Salerooms which then held glass sales about every two months in their open seasons, now have difficulty in managing two in a year.

It is generally agreed that the sale at Sotheby's in 1967-68 of the huge collection of the late Walter F Smith Jnr of New Jersey, USA, was a significant factor in the growth of interest in English glass. It took three separate sales to dispose of the 857 lots of English glass! How things have changed in the 20 years since then – or have they? More collectors, more dealers, more interest, therefore less to go round. And of course we now have printed estimates at sales, which both collectors and dealers tend to buy up to. Yet in spite of this, glass has not really 'taken off' and made the advances in price one might have expected. It is interesting, therefore, to speculate whether glass values will now appreciate faster than over the past 20 years. At a major London sale in November 1987 over 60% of the lots on offer went for a price in excess of the estimate – and in major salerooms estimates are usually realistic, but they have to exercise caution. Coloured glass, particularly 18th century wine glasses, 18th century scent bottles and drinking glasses did particularly well.

So where does this leave both collector and dealer? Any dealer or collector today accepts that when buying from either a specialist dealer's shop or a saleroom, there is often a strong case for paying over the 'norm' for above average and outstanding pieces. Over the years such pieces are likely to appreciate far more than 'run of the mill' examples. Conversely it would be foolish to pay more than the market price for mediocre examples, and the wise collector, unless he has particular gaps to fill in his collection, will save his money to buy one really good glass, rather than dissipate his funds on a number of ordinary pieces.

But what is the 'norm'? In the world of antiques, both dealer and collector are constantly having to exercise their judgement as to what is the 'norm' – a fair price – and in this respect detailed knowledge and experience is power. Such detailed knowledge is not of course usually available to the novice collector or inexperienced dealer. It is then that price guides can be especially helpful, in setting out the price realised over the past year for particular examples. Remember, however, that these prices may have taken account of restoration, damage, etc., which is not immediately obvious from the illustration. One should also differentiate between the source of the sale: dealer or saleroom.

It can therefore be said that, with the current scarcity of glass on the market, a specialist dealer will frequently pay a price above the 'norm', since, as a specialist, he must have stock on his shelves. The collector, to fill a gap or to obtain a particular sought-after piece, will pay to the limit of his ability. Both therefore operate irrespective of price trends.

Bottles

A green glass wine bottle, with seal inscribed 'Ino Eveligh 1736', some chipping, 7½in (19.5cm).
£600-700 *Bea*

A glass bottle with 'I. Gould' on the seal and date 1741, 9in (23cm).
£700-800 *JHo*

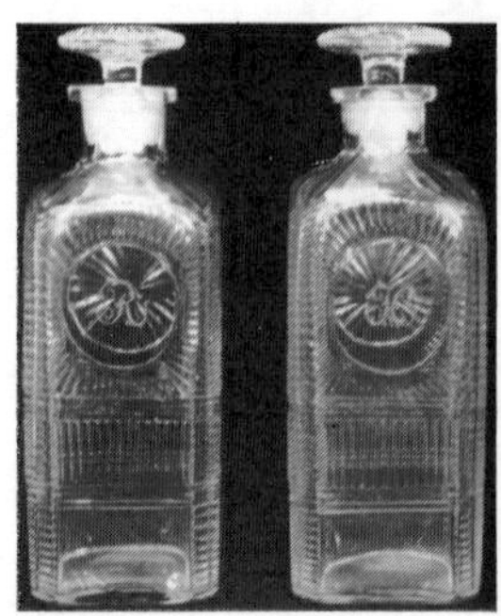

A pair of spirit bottles, with 'R' (rum) and 'H' (hollands) in medallions, cut mushroom stoppers, c1800, 8in (20.5cm).
£300-400 *Som*

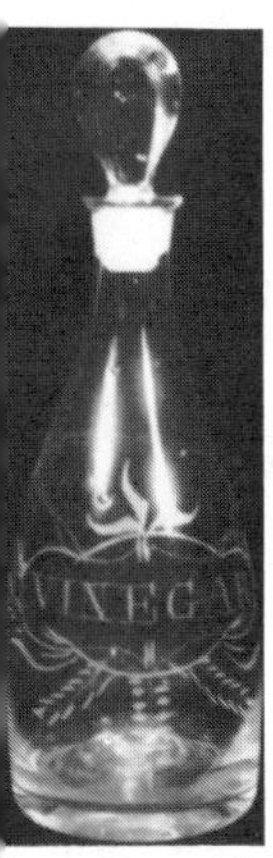

A condiment bottle, with plain lozenge stopper, c1780.
£70-100 *Som*

An English blue engraved port decanter, c1800, 9in (23cm).
£800-1,000 *PBA*

An amethyst onion shaped bottle decanter, c1830, 11in (28cm).
£200-250 *DEL*

An amethyst apothecary jar, c1840, 15in (38cm).
£300-400 *CB*

Three blue apothecary bottles, c1860, 9in (23cm).
£30-65 each *CB*

A pair of bottle green pharmacy jars, c1840, 12in (30.5cm).
£150-250 *CB*

Bowls

A Jacobite glass bowl, engraved with the words 'God Bless Prince Charles', 9in (23cm).
£500-550 *P[WSW]*

A bowl with applied blue rim, c1800, 6in (15cm) diam.
£50-75 *CB*

A cut glass turnover fruit bowl, damage, 18thC, 9in (23cm).
£450-500 *P[CW]*

A pair of 'Lynn' finger bowls and one stand, c1775, the bowls 4½in (12cm) diam.
£250-300 *C*

A well cut bowl with turnover rim, c1820, 13in (33cm) diam.
£750-1,000 *CB*

An Irish ovoid cut dish with prism cutting and serrated rim, fan cut handles, c1800, 9in (22.5cm) wide.
£150-200 *Som*

A sweetmeat bowl with facet knopped stem and egg-and-dart border, c1800, 6½in (16cm).
£250-300 *CB*

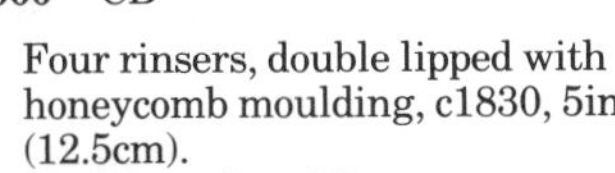

Four rinsers, double lipped with honeycomb moulding, c1830, 5in (12.5cm).
£25-45 each *CB*

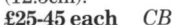

A pair of cut fruit bowls with strawberry and cross cut diamonds, and fan cut rims, c1830, 6½in (17cm).
£350-400 *Som*

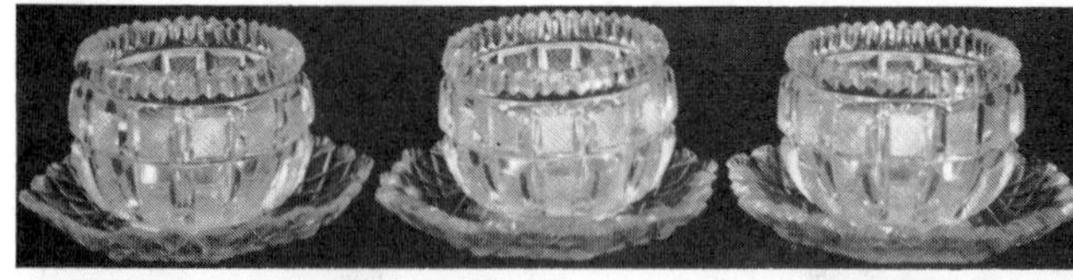

A set of 3 salts and stands, with panels of strawberry diamonds and prism cutting, c1830, 3in (7.5cm).
£150-200 *Som*

A fine cut covered bowl on pedestal base, c1840, 14in (35cm).
£400-500 *SW*

A set of 6 star-cut finger bowls, c1860, 2½in (6.5cm).
£150-180 *CB*

A set of 9 trailed glass bowls and under-dishes, c1880.
£300-500 *CB*

A Cork Glass Co engraved finger bowl, impressed mark to base, early 19thC, 5in (13cm) diam.
£650-750 *C*

Candelabra

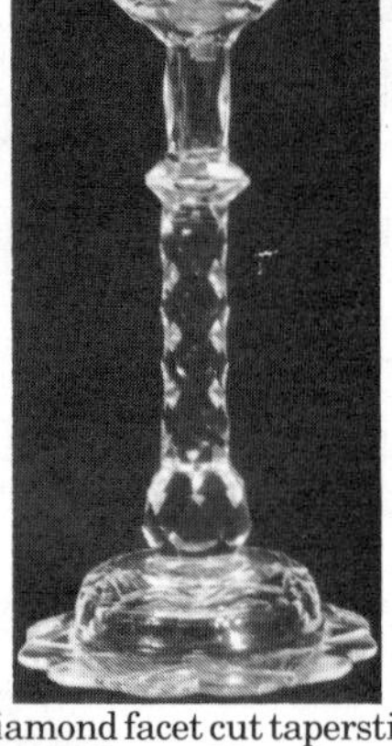

A diamond facet cut taperstick, with bladed collar and base knop, c1770, 6½in (16.5cm).
£400-500 *Som*

An Irish candlestick with hollow stem, on lemon squeezer base, c1800, 6½in (17cm).
£200-300 *Som*

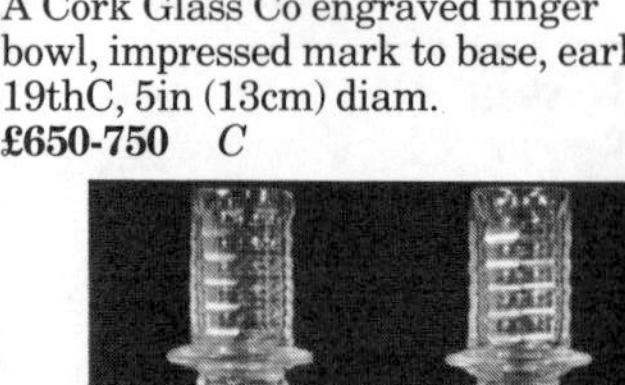

A pair of cut candlesticks with prism and flute cut sockets, diamond and ladder cut stems and step cut feet, c1810, 9in (22.5cm).
£600-650 *Som*

An opaque twist taper stick, c1765, 7½in (18.5cm).
£2,500-3,000 *C*

A pair of Regency bronze candle lustres in the shape of cranes, 9in (23cm).
£350-500 *CB*

A pair of glass candlesticks, with faceted stem and hexagonal knop, the nozzle with petal cut rim, early 19thC, 10in (25.5cm).
£550-650 *Bea*

A pair of Regency cut glass and ormolu candelabra, the nozzles on oblong trip tray, supported on twin scrolling gilt arms with grotesque eagle heads.
£2,600-3,000 *P*

A pair of Regency ormolu and cut glass three-light candelabra, the faceted shafts flanked by scrolling foliate branches, adapted and restored, 17½in (44.5cm).
£2,000-2,500 *C*

Chandeliers

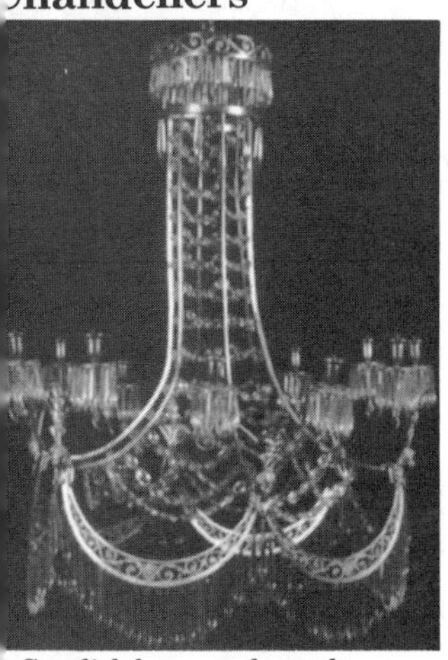

Swedish brass and cut glass twelve-light chandelier, 19thC, 27in (68.5cm) diam.
5,000-6,000 *C*

An Empire style gilt bronze and glass chandelier, suspended by beaded chains from an upper tier, hung with pendant drops, 19thC, 27in (69cm) diam.
£6,500-7,000 *P*

A George III cut glass six-light chandelier, part late 18thC, 38in (96cm) diam, fitted for electricity.
£5,000-5,500 *CNY*

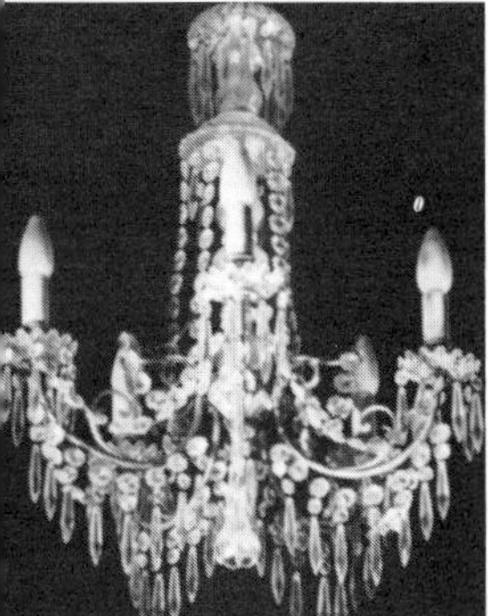

A pair of ormolu and cut glass five-light chandeliers, hung with 'coffin' drops and issuing swags, 34in (86cm) high.
£2,000-3,000 *C*

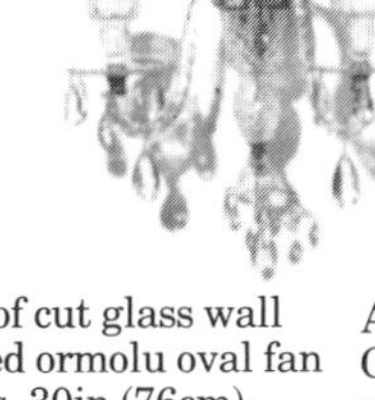

A harlequin pair of cut glass wall lights, with pierced ormolu oval fan shaped backplates, 30in (76cm) high.
£1,000-1,500 *C*

A cut glass waterfall chandelier of George III design, with twin silvered metal coronas pierced with anthemions and foliage, 75in (190.5cm), fitted for electricity.
£6,000-7,000 *C*

Decanters

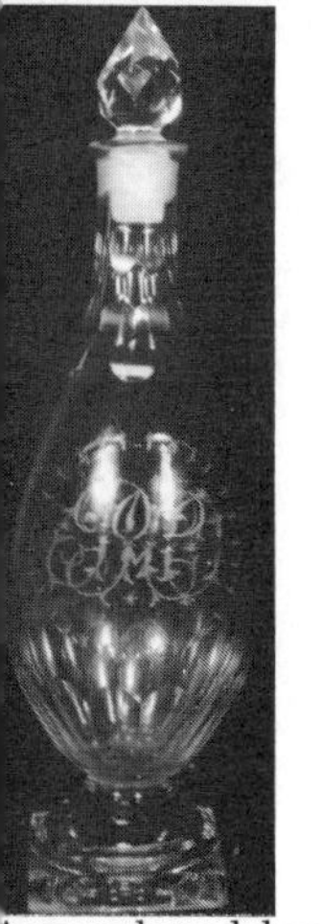

A 'Lynn' decanter of club shape with horizontally ribbed sides and kick-in base, c1775, 9½in (23.5cm).
£550-600 *C*

A pear shaped decanter with flute cutting, engraved with monogram 'P.I.C.O.', c1780, 11in (28cm).
£500-600 *Som*

A pair of blue gilded decanters with original stoppers, c1790, 7½in (19cm).
350-450 *CB*

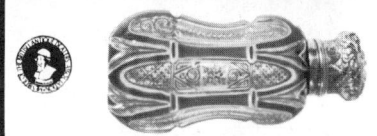

l. & r. A pair of blue decanters with lunar cut stoppers, c1800, 9½in (24cm).
£650-750
c. A smaller decanter with bevelled lozenge stopper, c1800, 8½in (21.5cm).
£250-350 *Som*

A pale green decanter with steeple shaped stopper, c1840, 14in (35.5cm).
£150-250 *TRW*

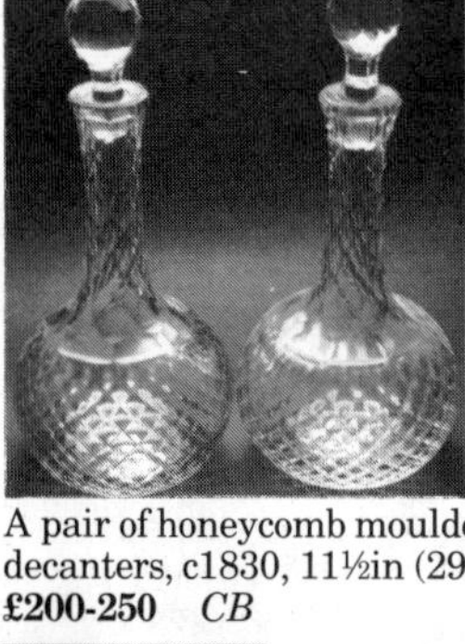

A pair of honeycomb moulded decanters, c1830, 11½in (29cm).
£200-250 *CB*

A swag cut decanter, c1820, 9½in (24cm).
£100-150 *CB*

A pair of English chrysoprase decanters, with original stoppers, c1840, 12in (30.5cm).
£400-500 *CB*

A decanter with 'A.M' monogram within a laurel leaf circle, c1780, 9½in (24cm).
£300-350 *Som*

Two ovoid shaped decanters:
l. Flute cut with lozenge stopper, c1810, 8½in (21.5cm).
£150-200
r. Plain with target stopper, engraved 'M', c1800, 9in (22cm).
£150-200 *Som*

Two decanters with cut mushroom stoppers, c1810, 8½in (22cm).
£150-200 each *Som*

A pair of Georgian decanters, c1820.
£450-550
A pair of papier mâché coasters, c1820.
£300-400 *CB*

l. & r. A pair of Irish decanters wit spiral neck rings and lozenge stoppers, c1790, 9½in (23.5cm).
£850-950
c. An unusual Irish barrel shaped decanter with alternate panels of cut diamonds and sunbursts, c181 8in (20cm).
£400-450
A papier mâché coaster with gilt decoration, c1810, 5in (12.8cm) diam.
£80-100 *Som*

A set of 3 Georgian green decanter 8½in (22cm).
£550-750 *CB*

A pair of decanters with 3 cut ne rings and target stoppers, c1815, 8½in (21.5cm).
£600-650 *Som*

A set of 3 Georgian decanters i blue, with stand, c1800, 9½in (24cm).
£600-700 *CB*

Three hobnail cut glass spirit decanters with facet stoppers, and plated tantalus with gadroon, shell and acanthus borders, c1880.
£500-600 *P[Pea]*

A pair of decanters, the bodies with arched panels and cut mushroom stoppers, c1830, 7½in (19cm).
£300-350 *Som*

A pair of cut ship's decanters with bull's eye stoppers, c1810.
£750-850 *SW*

A set of 3 cut spirit bottles, in silver plated stand, c1880, 13in (33cm) wide.
£400-450 *CB*

A Low Countries cut decanter bottle, c1780, 9½in (24cm).
£80-120 *CB*

A Regency rosewood decanter stand with 3 contemporary green glass bottles and 2 plated labels, 9½in (24cm).
£500-550 *DN*

A Nuremburg engraved serving bottle, c1700, 10in (25cm).
£900-1,000 *C*

A pair of cut glass decanters and stoppers, the waist engraved with cell pattern and scrolling, late 19th/early 20thC, 15½in (39cm), with silver plated labels.
£300-350 *CAm*

A Dutch double-handled decanter, engraved, gilt decorated and trailed, 10in (25.5cm).
£100-150 *CB*

Drinking Glasses

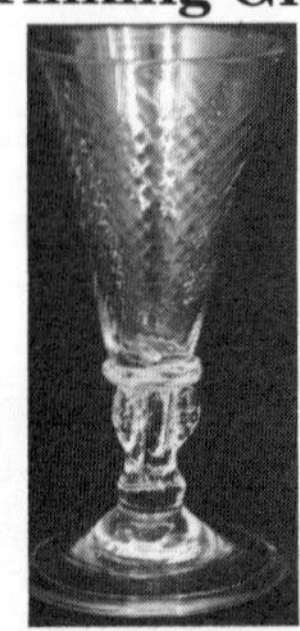

An early ale glass, the wrythen bowl set on a propellor stem and folded conical foot, c1700.
£850-950 *SW*

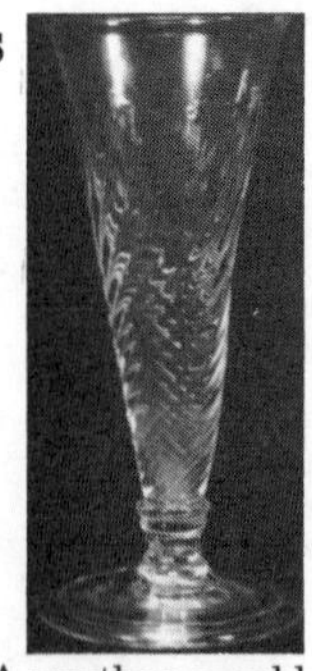

A wrythen moulded ale glass, the body on a short collared stem, c1690, 6in (15.3cm).
£350-400 *Som*

Three dwarf wrythen moulded ale glasses, on folded conical feet, c1745, 4½ to 5in (11.5 to 13cm).
£200-250 each *Som*

Two champagne flutes, c1800, 7½in (19cm).
£30-50 each *CB*

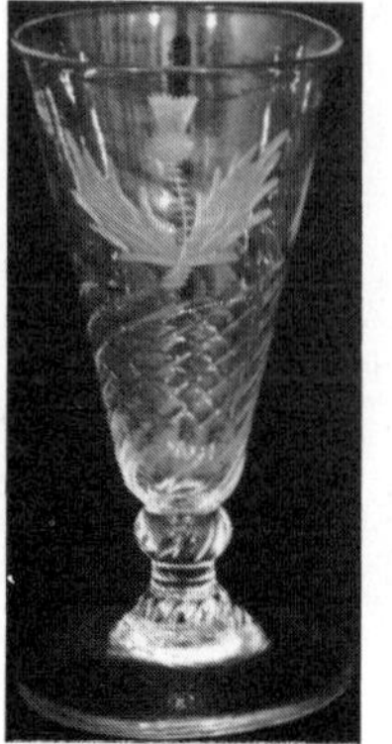

A wrythen ale glass, engraved with a thistle, c1740.
£60-70 *SW*

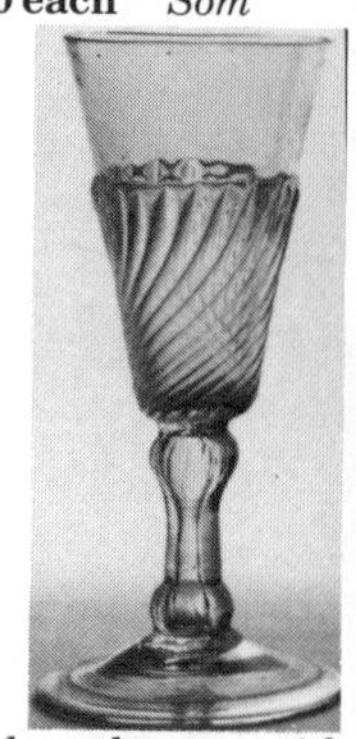

An ale glass, the stem with shoulder and basal knops enclosing an elongated tear, on a folded conical foot, c1730, 6in (15cm).
£400-500 *C*

A set of 6 dwarf ale glasses, moulded and engraved with hops and barley, c1810.
£300-350 *Som*

A set of 8 facet cut ale glasses, engraved with hops, 7½in (19cm).
£300-400 *CB*

A champagne glass on a Silesian stem and folded domed foot, c1750, 5½in (14.5cm).
£450-500 *Som*

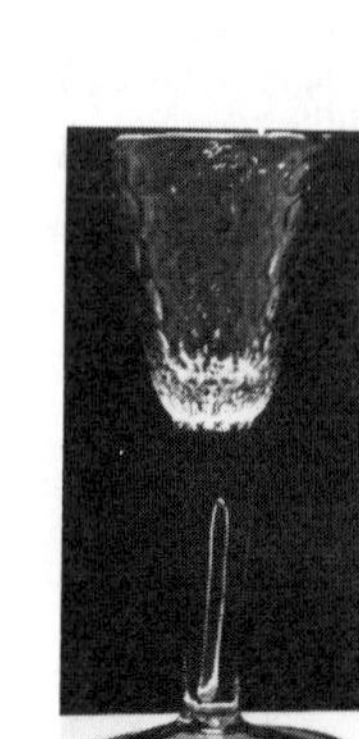

An ale glass, the engraved bowl on a stem with multiple spiral air-twist and 2 knops, plain conical foot, c1750, 7½in (18cm).
£450-500 *Som*

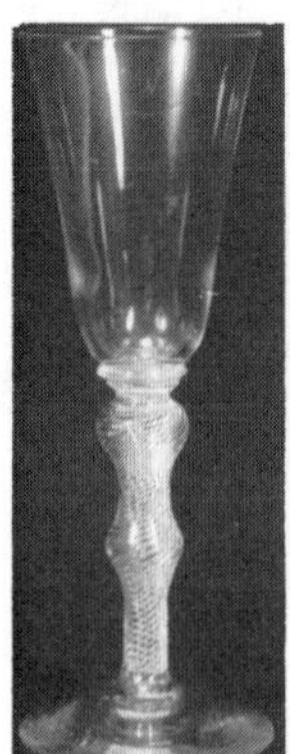

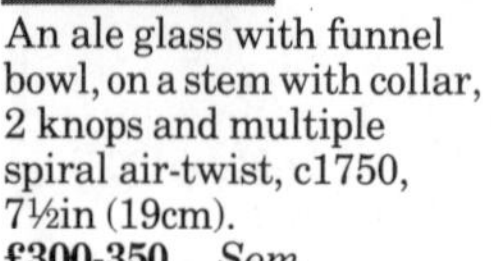

An ale glass with funnel bowl, on a stem with collar, 2 knops and multiple spiral air-twist, c1750, 7½in (19cm).
£300-350 *Som*

An unusual wine glass with honeycomb moulded bowl, on a plain stem with elongated tear and conical foot, c1745.
£450-500 *SW*

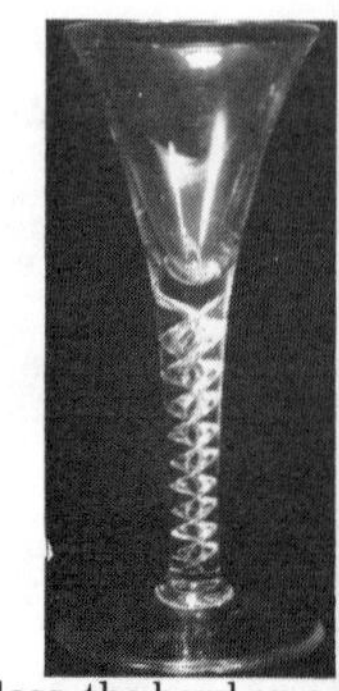

A wine glass, the bowl on a stem with mercury air-twist, on plain conical foot, c1750, 6½in (17cm).
£250-300 *Som*

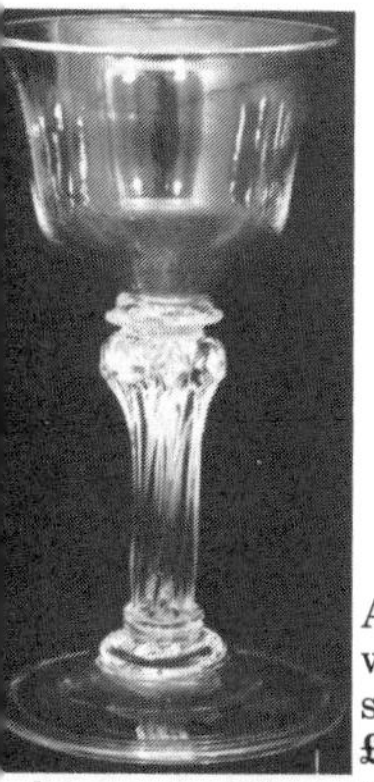

A pair of champagne flutes, with half-facet bowl and stem, 9½in (24cm).
£40-60 each *CB*

A wine glass with ogee bowl, plain stem on plain conical foot, c1750, 5½in (14.5cm).
£250-300 *Som*

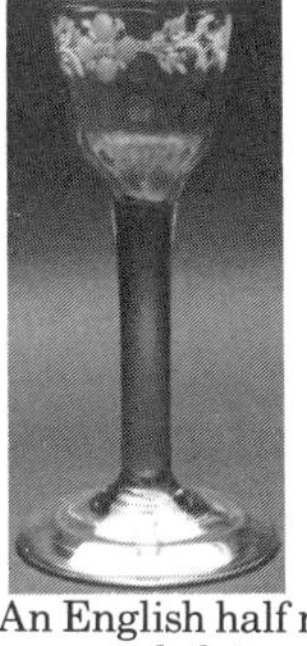

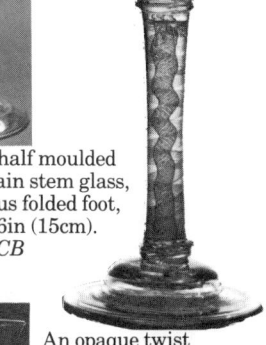

An English half moulded engraved plain stem glass, with generous folded foot, mid-18thC, 6in (15cm).
£150-200 *CB*

. champagne glass, the gee bowl with everted rim n a moulded stem and lded conical foot, c1745, ½in (18cm).
280-320 *SW*

An opaque twist champagne glass, the stem with a gauze core within a multi-ply spiral above a domed and folded foot, c1765, 7in (18cm).
£850-900 *C*

Four plain stemmed wine glasses, c1740.
£90-120 each *SW*

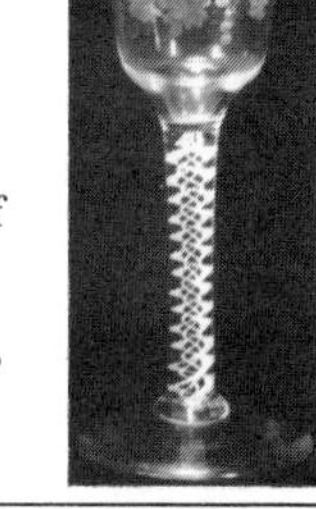

A wine glass with band of gilt fruiting vine and gilt rim, on a double series opaque twist stem, c1760, 7in (18cm).
£250-300 *Som*

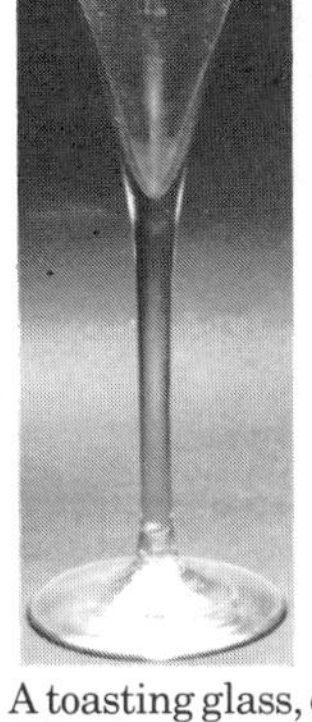

A toasting glass, c1780, 9in (23cm).
£150-200 *CB*

. gilt decorated emerald reen goblet, the stem nclosing an elongated ear and on a plain foot, 1765, 5½in (14cm).
1,000-1,200 *C*

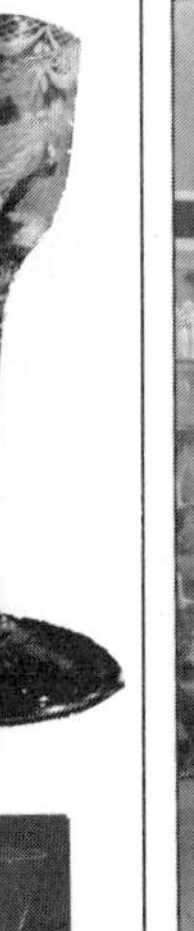

An ogee bowl plain stemmed wine glass, on conical folded foot, with etched body, 5in (13cm).
£60-70 *CSK*

. blue/green tint wine lass, the double ogee bowl upported on a plain stem nd foot, c1765, 6in (15cm).
800-900 *C*

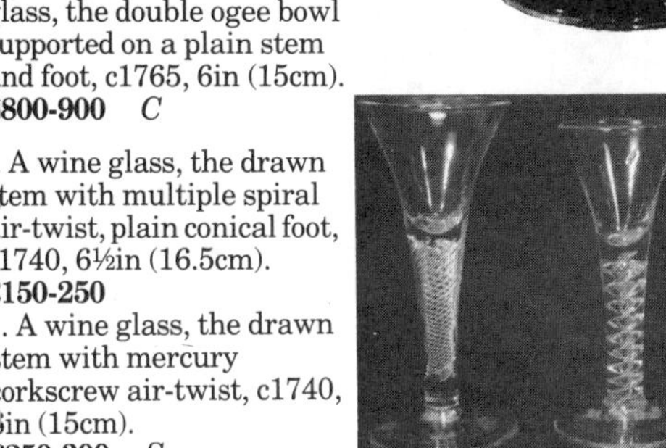

. A wine glass, the drawn tem with multiple spiral ir-twist, plain conical foot, 1740, 6½in (16.5cm).
150-250

. A wine glass, the drawn tem with mercury orkscrew air-twist, c1740, in (15cm).
250-300 *Som*

A baluster wine glass, with tear in base on a drop-knop above a true baluster stem and domed and folded foot, c1700.
£600-650 *SW*

A mercury-twist wine glass, the drawn bowl on a double spiral air-twist stem and conical foot, c1750.
£300-350 *SW*

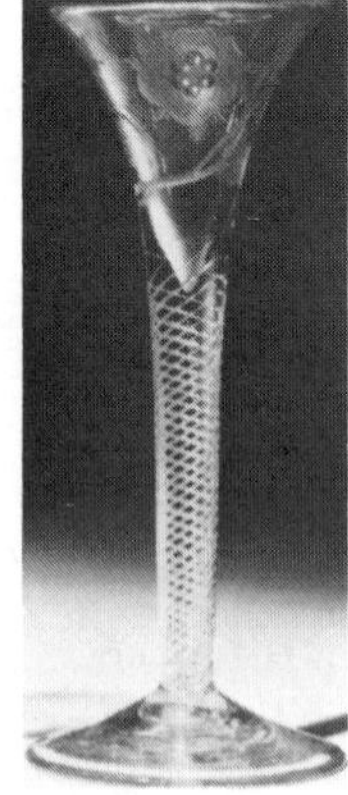

A Jacobite air-twist wine glass of drawn trumpet shape, engraved and inscribed with the motto 'Fiat', the stem filled with spiral threads above a conical foot, c1750, 6½in (17cm).
£850-900 *C*

A dark blue/green tint wine glass, the bucket shaped bowl lightly ribbed and drawn from a plain stem, on a plain foot, 18th/early 19thC, 6in (15cm).
£200-250 *C*

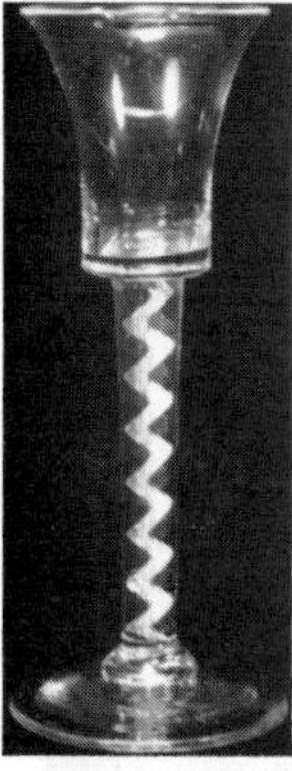

A wine glass with waisted bucket bowl, on plain conical foot, c1745, 6½in (16cm).
£250-300 *Som*

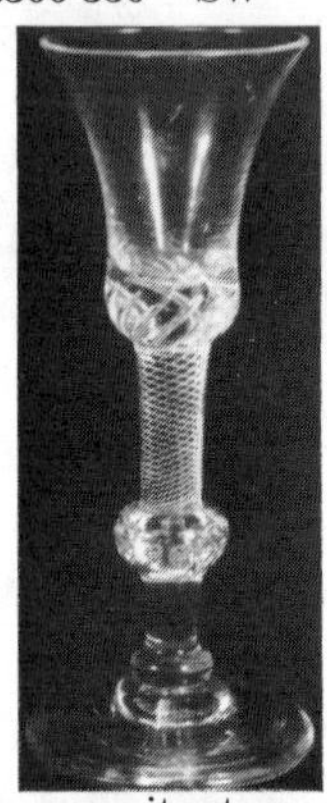

A composite stem wine glass, with bell bowl on a stem with multiple spiral air-twist, above a beaded air-knop, and plain section with base knop, c1750, 6½in (16.5cm).
£400-450 *Som*

A wine glass with bell bowl, on a shoulder knopped multiple spiral air-twist stem, and folded conical foot, c1750, 7in (18cm).
£150-250 *Som*

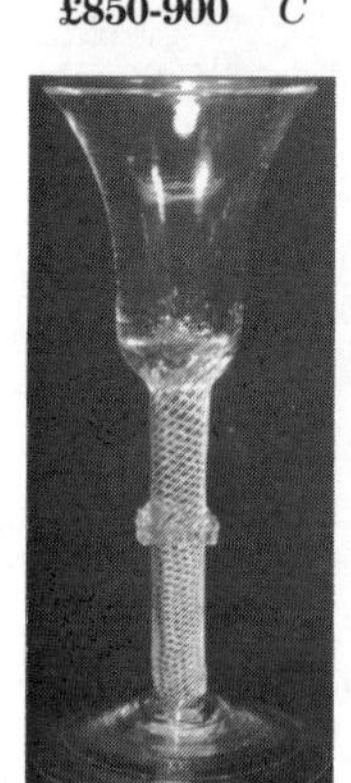

A wine glass, the stem with multiple spiral air-twist and vermicular collar, c1750, 6½in (16.5cm).
£400-450 *Som*

A dram glass, with engraved bowl, on a double series opaque twist stem and thickened plain foot, c1760.
£250-300 *SW*

A Newcastle engraved composite stemmed goblet, with 2 knops above a hexagonally moulded pedestal section and basal knop, on a folded conical foot, mid-18thC, 6½in (16.5cm).
£300-350 *C*

A set of 6 deep green drinking glasses, on swelling knopped stems, 5in (12cm).
£200-250 *CSK*

An engraved wine glass, on plain conical foot, c1750, 6½in (16cm).
£750-800 *Som*

A pair of goblets, the bowls decorated with a hunting scene, on knopped stem and circular foot, 6½in (17cm).
£120-160 *PB*

A façon-de-Venise engraved goblet, on a tapering hollow stem and plain foot, Liège or France, c1800, 5in (13cm).
£200-250 *C*

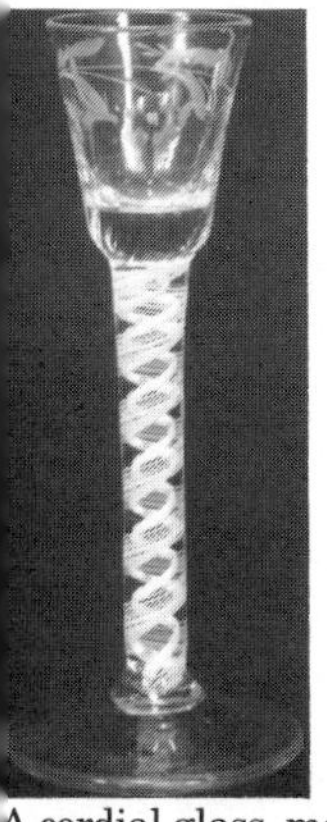

A cordial glass, moulded and engraved with flowers, on a stem with double series opaque twist, c1760, 6½in (16.5cm).
£400-450 *Som*

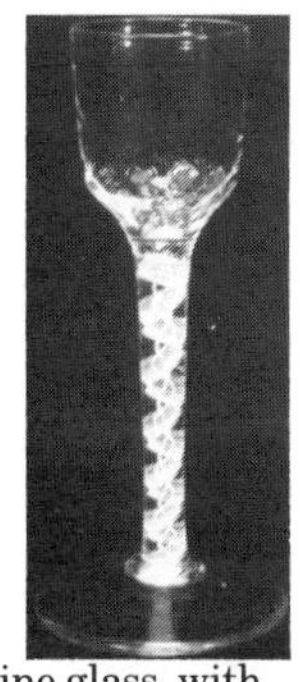

A wine glass, with honeycomb moulded bowl, c1760, 7in (17.5cm).
£250-300 *Som*

A pair of engraved wine glasses, with single series opaque white twists, on plain conical feet, c1760, 5½in (14cm).
£300-350 *Som*

A Beilby opaque twist wine glass, the ogee bowl enamelled in white, 2 tiny chips to footrim, c1765, 5½in (14.5cm).
£1,100-1,400 *C*

A pair of double twist stem drinking glasses.
£200-250 *MGM*

A half wrythen moulded ogee bowl wine glass, with double series air-twist stem on conical foot, 6in (15cm).
£70-90 *CSK*

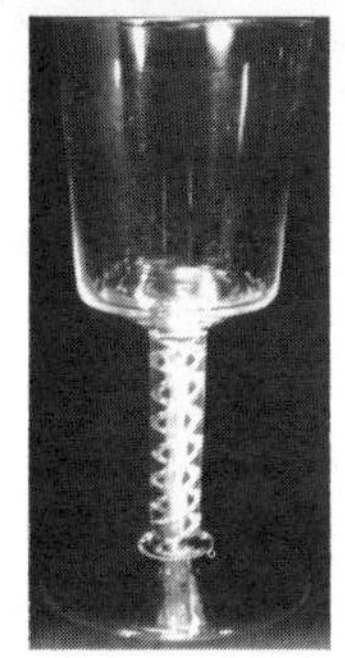

A goblet on a double series air-twist stem, c1745, 9in (23cm).
£450-500 *Som*

DRINKING GLASSES

Ordered in line with the E Barrington Haynes system (see Pelican Books *Glass* by E Barrington Haynes)

Group		
I	**Baluster Stems**	**1685-1725**
II	**Moulded Pedestal Stems**	**1715-1765**
III	**Balustroid Stems**	**1725-1755**
IV	**Light (Newcastle) Balusters**	**1735-1765**
V	**Composite Stems**	**1740-1770**
VI	**Plain Straight Stems**	**1740-1770**
VII	**Air Twist Stems**	**1740-1770**
VIII	**Hollow Stems**	**1750-1760**
IX	**Incised Twist Stems**	**1750-1765**
X	**Opaque Twist Stems**	**1750-1780**
XI	**Mixed and Colour Twist Stems**	**1755-1775**
XII	**Faceted Stems**	**1760-1800**
XIII	**Other glasses with short or rudimentary stems: Dwarf Ales; Jelly Glasses; Rummers; Georgian Ales, wines and drams; 18th-19thC**	

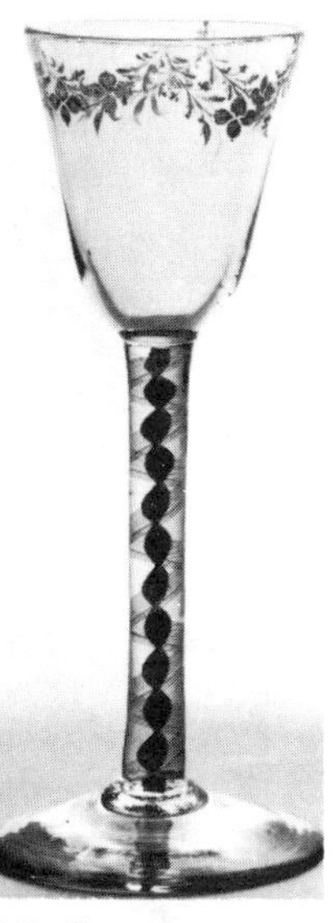

A Beilby opaque twist wine glass, the funnel bowl enamelled in white, the stem with an opaque corkscrew cork within a multi-ply spiral, on a conical foot, c1770, 6in (15.5cm).
£1,100-1,400 *C*

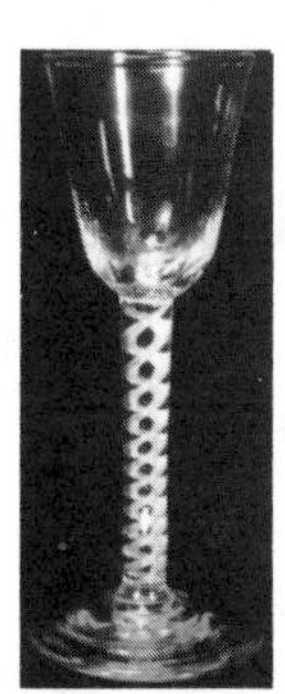

A wine glass with round funnel bowl moulded at the base, on a single series opaque twist stem, c1745, 6½in (17cm).
£250-300 *Som*

An incised twist wine glass, with bowl with honeycomb moulded base, on an incised twist stem, with domed plain foot, c1750, 6½in (16cm).
£350-400 *Som*

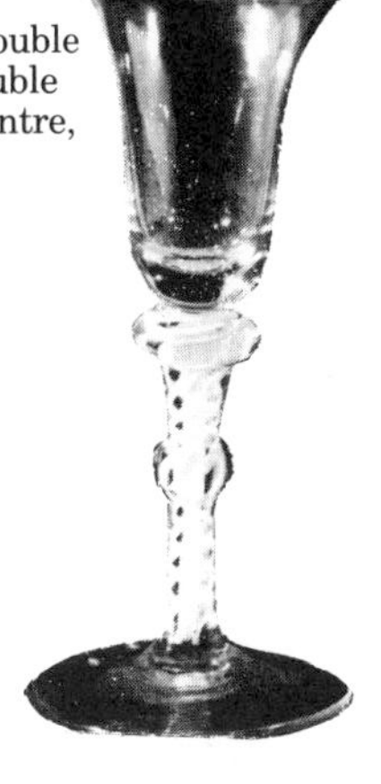

A drinking glass, on double knopped stem and double series opaque twist centre, 6½in (16.5cm).
£70-100 *CSK*

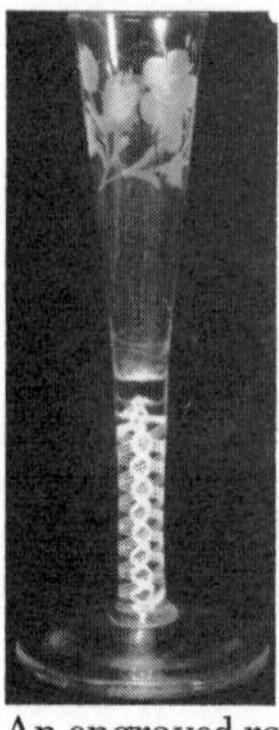

An engraved ratafia glass, with double series opaque twist stem, plain conical foot, c1760, 7in (17.5cm).
£450-500 *Som*

A large suite of table glass, engraved below a decorated gold band, comprising: 12 goblets with conical bowls, 8½in (22cm), and 67 matching glasses.
£1,500-1,700 *Bea*

A light green export wine glass, the stem with an inverted baluster knop and ball knops, c1760, 5½in (13.5cm).
£200-250 *Som*

A cut bowl goblet, c1820, 4½in (11.5cm).
£50-75 *CB*

l. and r. Three barrel shaped rummers with looped laurel leaf decoration, and cushion knop stems, c1820, 4½in (11.5cm).
£150-200

r. A similar rummer with double ogee bowl, c1820, 5in (12cm).
£50-100 *Som*

l. A balustroid wine glass, with engraved ogee bowl and ball knop, 5in (14cm).
£200-250

c. A balustroid wine glass, with hatched rose decoration, and ball knop, 6in (15cm).
£200-250

r. A balustroid wine glass with hatched loop decoration and swelling knop, 5½in (14.5cm).
£200-250 *Som*

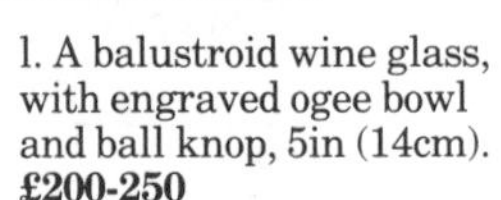

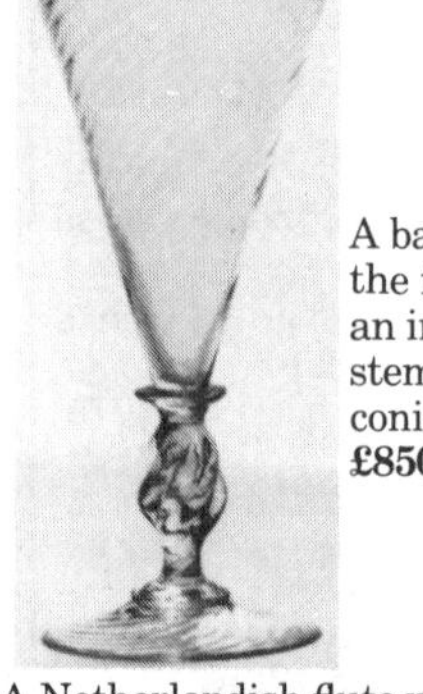

A Netherlandish flute with wrythen moulded funnel bowl, the stem with spiral pincered ornament above a wrythen moulded conical foot, 18thC, 6½in (16cm).
£300-350 *C*

A baluster goblet, the funnel bowl on an inverted baluster stem and folded conical foot, c1700.
£850-950 *SW*

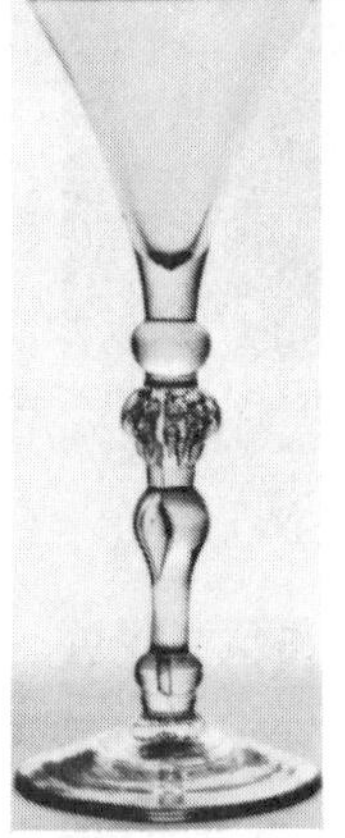

A light baluster wine glass with a trumpet shaped bowl, inverted baluster section enclosing a tear and basal knop, on a conical foot, c1750, 7½in (18.5cm).
£550-600 *C*

A wine glass, with trumpet bowl, on a stem with air-tear and ball knop, c1740, 5½in (13.5cm).
£300-350 *Som*

A heavy baluster wine glass, on a stem with inverted baluster and base ball knops, c1700, 5½in (14cm).
£800-850 *Som*

A heavy baluster wine glass, the bowl on a stem with cusp and base ball knops, c1710, 7in (18cm).
£700-750 *Som*

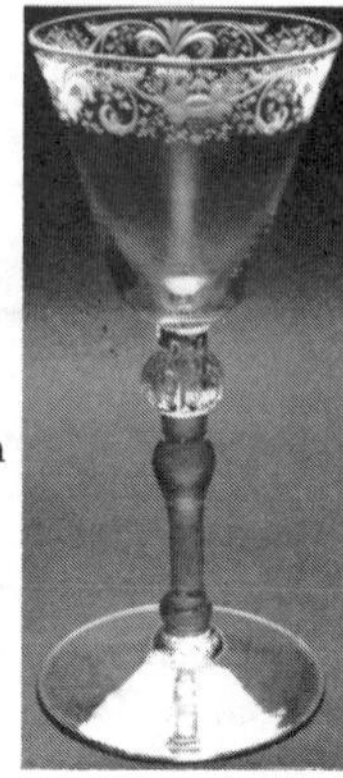

A Newcastle glass, Dutch engraved with leaf and fruit design, c1745, 8½in (21.5cm).
£600-800 *CB*

A two-knop baluster wine glass, with folded foot, c1740, 6in (15cm).
£180-220 *CB*

A Newcastle wine glass engraved with a band of baroque scrolling and parrots, c1750, 7½in (19cm).
£750-800 *Som*

A Central European enamelled 'Jagd' tumbler, the flared sides enamelled in colours with a standing sportsman holding a gun and blowing a horn and with hounds driving a hare into a diagonally placed net, an inscription above and beneath a band of iron red and yellow lines, perhaps late 18thC, 6½in (16.5cm).
£4,000-5,000 *C*

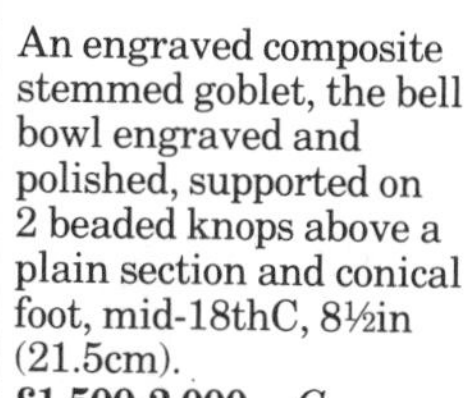

An engraved composite stemmed goblet, the bell bowl engraved and polished, supported on 2 beaded knops above a plain section and conical foot, mid-18thC, 8½in (21.5cm).
£1,500-2,000 *C*

A balustroid wine glass with trumpet bowl, on stem with straight solid section, c1750, 7in (17.5cm).
£350-400 *Som*

A gilt decorated blue tumbler, from the atelier of James Giles, with gilt rim, c1765, 4in (10.5cm).
£750-800 *C*

A set of 6 Georgian wines, with engraved bucket bowls and knopped stems, c1820, 4in (10cm).
£300-350 *Som*

A façon-de-Venise beaker, applied with 3 small lugs suspending loose rings beneath an everted rim, on a plain circular foot, German, 17thC, 3½in (8.5cm).
£600-800 *C*

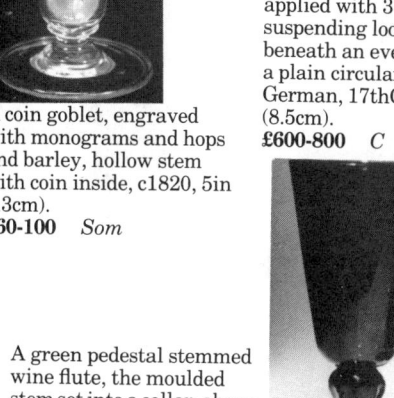

A coin goblet, engraved with monograms and hops and barley, hollow stem with coin inside, c1820, 5in (13cm).
£60-100 *Som*

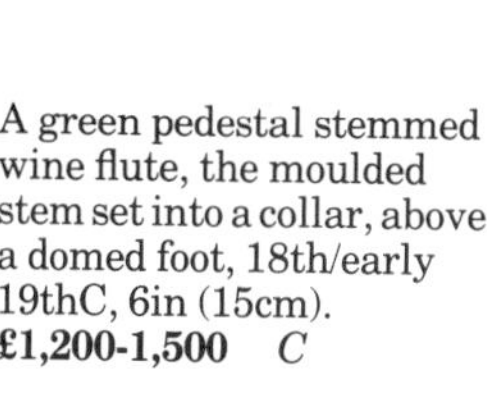

A green pedestal stemmed wine flute, the moulded stem set into a collar, above a domed foot, 18th/early 19thC, 6in (15cm).
£1,200-1,500 *C*

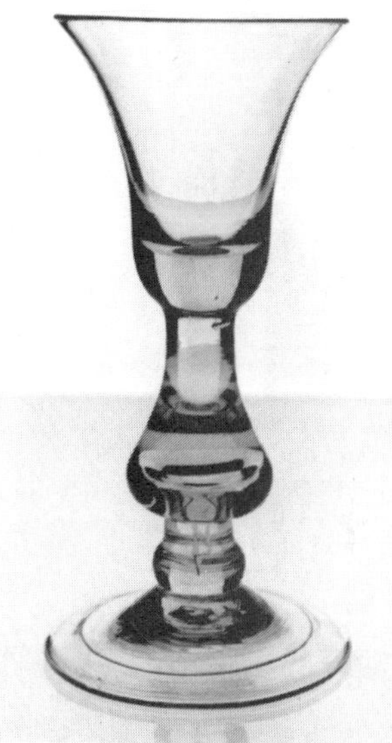

A Lynn tumbler, c1800, 2½in (6cm).
£80-100 *CB*

A tumbler engraved with Sunderland bridge and a ship beneath, inscribed 'Sunderland Bridge', with hops and barley decoration, c1810, 4in (10cm).
£250-300 *Som*

A Mary Gregory glass tumbler, c1880, 3½in (8.5cm).
£40-50 *CB*

A large Masonic goblet, engraved with Masonic emblems, initials and dated 1840, for the Scottish, Scoon & Perth No. 3. Lodge, 6½in (17cm).
£300-400 *Bea*

A Dutch goblet, engraved with a bird above a basket of flowers, set on a baluster stem and folded conical foot, 8½in (21.5cm).
£250-300 *Bea*

A Bavarian goblet, engraved on one side with a woman and a wolf in a landscape, reserved within an inscribed band, on a foliate engraved conical foot, 7in (18cm).
£350-400 *Bea*

A pair of Bohemian amber goblets, with numerous Rhineland scenes, 9in (23cm).
£1,000-1,500 *BHA*

A rummer, engraved with a barons coronet and the initials 'RDR', the reverse side with initials 'CR', capstan stem and plain foot, c1830, 5½in (13.5cm).
£200-250 *Som*

A Masonic rummer, engraved with 3 panels of Masonic symbols and monogram 'IHG', on a domed lemon squeezer foot, c1800, 5in (12.5cm).
£300-400 *Som*

An Absolon rummer with emerald green tint, the ovoid bowl decorated in gilt, heightened in black, inscribed above 'Success to......' the reverse inscribed 'A Trifle from Yarmouth', gilding rubbed, c1800, 5in (12cm).
£500-600 *C*

A set of 7 rummers, engraved with egg and tulip decoration, on domed lemon squeezer feet, c1800, 5½in (13cm).
£900-1,000 *Som*

l. A rummer, the ovoid bowl engraved with band of laurel leaves and bows, c1810, 4½in (11.5cm). £50-75

c. A rummer, engraved 'J.M.Lang', with capstan stem, c1800, 5½in (14cm). £120-160

r. An ovoid bowl rummer, c1810, 4½in (11.5cm). £70-100 *Som*

A well cut Georgian rummer, c1825, 5in (13cm). **£40-70** *CB*

A large bucket shaped Orange Lodge rummer, flute cut with Masonic symbols, on short knopped stem, c1825, 9in (22.5cm). **£200-300** *Som*

A Masonic rummer, engraved with various Masonic symbols and 'PSP' and 'CSK', the reverse with 'Joined Nov 25th, 1840, Lodge No. 5', Perth Lodge, with star cut foot, 6½in (17cm). **£500-600** *Som*

A Masonic rummer, engraved with symbols, dated 1848, 5½in (14cm). **£150-200** *CB*

A sweetmeat with honeycomb moulded bowl, on a stem with coarse incised twist, plain conical foot, c1750, 5½in (14cm). £550-600 *Som*

A German engraved colour-twist double bowl goblet, the 2 opposing bowls joined by a wrythen moulded section enclosing entwined dark blue and white thread, late 18thC, 9in (22.5cm). **£350-450** *C*

A sweetmeat, with double ogee bowl, on a stem with double series opaque twist, on domed and folded foot, c1760, 5½in (14.5cm). £500-600 *Som*

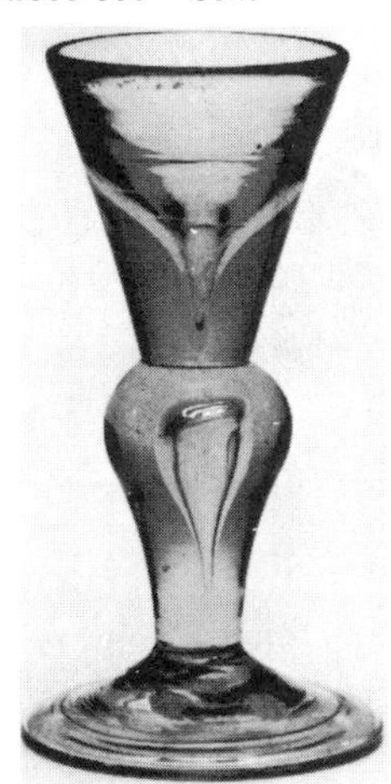

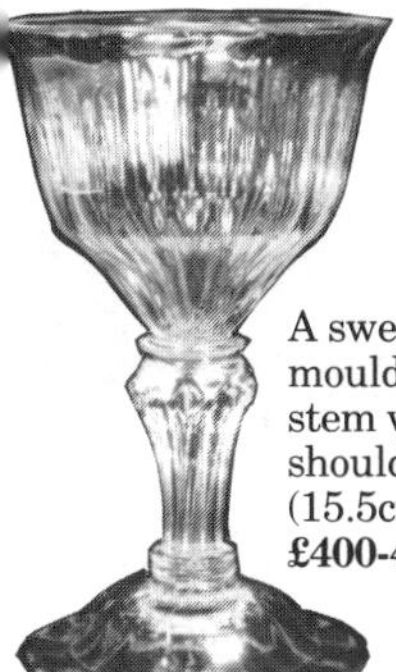

A baluster toastmaster's glass, set on an inverted baluster stem enclosing a tear above a folded conical foot, c1710, 4½in (12cm). **£350-450** *C*

A German Royal Armorial goblet and a cover, engraved with the motto and arms of England as borne by King George I, goblet slightly criselled, the glass perhaps Thuringia, the engraving Potsdam, c1725, 12½in (32cm). **£1,700-2,200** *C*

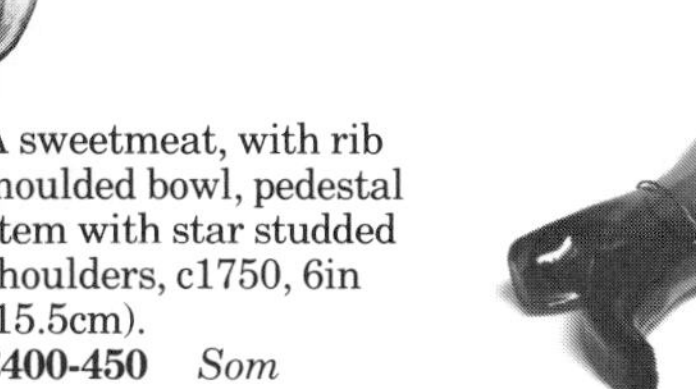

A sweetmeat, with rib moulded bowl, pedestal stem with star studded shoulders, c1750, 6in (15.5cm). **£400-450** *Som*

Flasks

A cranberry flask in a boot shape, c1870, 10½in (26cm) long. **£150-200** *CB*

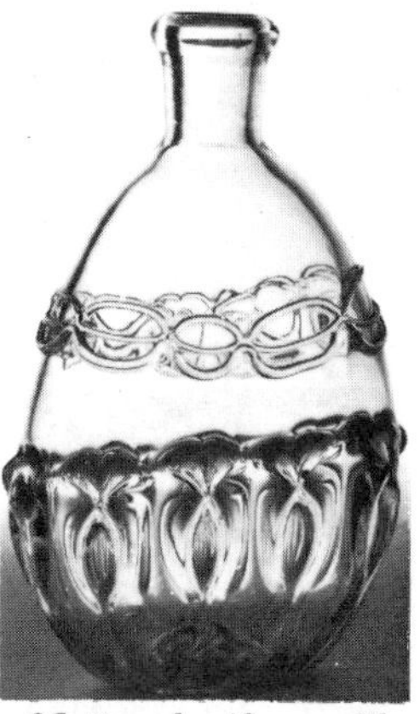

A flask of flattened oviform, with short neck and everted rim, minor chipping to trailing, c1695, 5½in (13.5cm). **£550-650** *C*

Jelly Glasses

A two-handled jelly glass, with gadrooned bowl and domed foot, c1760, 4in (10cm).
£100-150 *CB*

A jelly glass, with applied double loop handles, some damage to bowl, c1720.
£200-250 *Som*

A set of 5 bonnet glasses, with egg and tulip engraved decoration, c1800, 3½in (10cm).
£150-200 *Som*

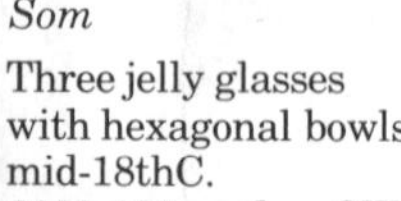

Three jelly glasses with hexagonal bowls, mid-18thC.
£130-180 each *SW*

A cut cream jug, with diamond and prismatic cutting and star cut base, c1820.
£250-300 *SW*

A jelly glass with thumb facets, and applied handle, c1880, 3½in (9cm).
£15-30 *CB*

A bonnet glass with scalloped foot, 3in (7.5cm).
£60-100 *CB*

A water jug, cut with vertical and horizontal prism, c1830, 8in (20.5cm).
£200-250 *Som*

Jugs

A water jug with flute, prism and diamond cutting, and cut strap handle, c1810, 7in (17.5cm).
£170-220 *Som*

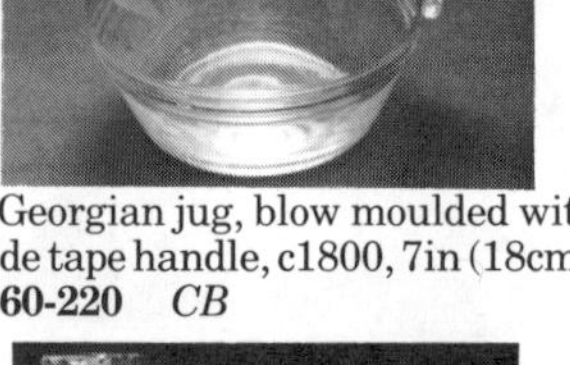

A Georgian jug, blow moulded with wide tape handle, c1800, 7in (18cm).
£160-220 *CB*

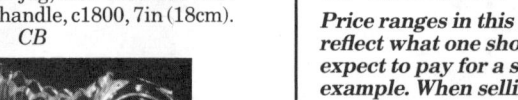

MAKE THE MOST OF MILLER'S

Price ranges in this book reflect what one should expect to pay for a similar example. When selling one can obviously expect a figure below. This will fluctuate according to a dealer's stock, saleability at a particular time, etc. It is always advisable to approach a reputable specialist dealer or an auction house which has specialist sales

A water jug, with diamond and prism cutting, and scalloped rim, c1825, 6½in (16cm).
£200-250 *Som*

A cream jug with prismatic, diamond and facet cutting, c1820.
£200-250 *SW*

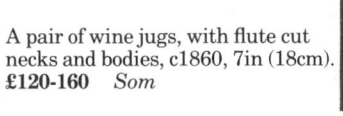

A pair of wine jugs, with flute cut necks and bodies, c1860, 7in (18cm).
£120-160 *Som*

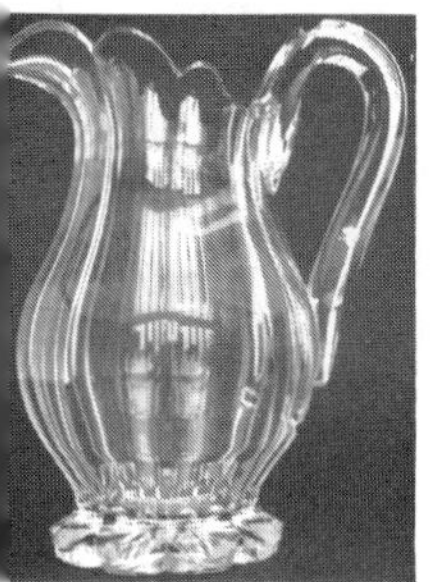

A jug, c1840, 8½in (21.5cm).
£150-200 *CB*

A ruby trailed glass ewer, with applied snake trim.
£150-200 *CB*

A Baccarat garlanded spray weight, on a star cut base, 2½in (6.5cm) diam.
£1,200-1,600 *C*

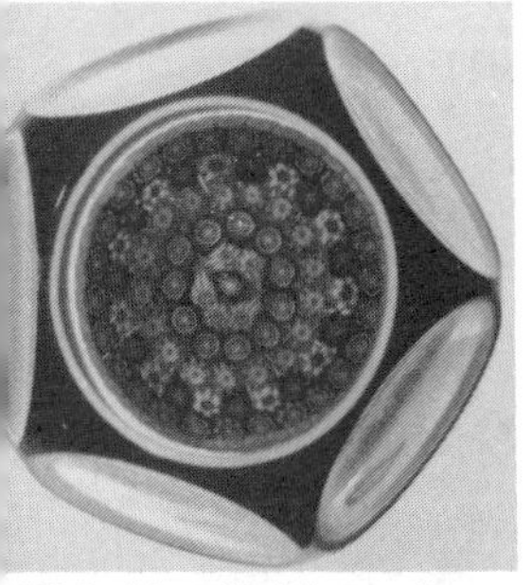

A Clichy blue double overlay concentric millefiori mushroom weight, in shades of green, purple, light blue, green and white, on a strawberry cut base, 3in (8cm) diam.
£1,200-1,700 *C*

A rare Clichy faceted red ground sulphide weight, set with a sulphide profile portrait of the young Queen Victoria, cut with a window, the sides with 5 printies alternating with flutes, 3in (7.5cm) diam.
£900-1,000 *C*

A Victorian jug and lid, engraved with floral decoration, c1870, 5½in (14cm).
£50-70 *Som*

Paperweights

A Baccarat dated scattered millefiori weight, with a cane inscribed 'B1848', 3in (7cm) diam.
£600-700 *C*

A Baccarat garlanded white double clematis weight, on a star cut base, 2½in (6.5cm) diam.
£600-800 *C*

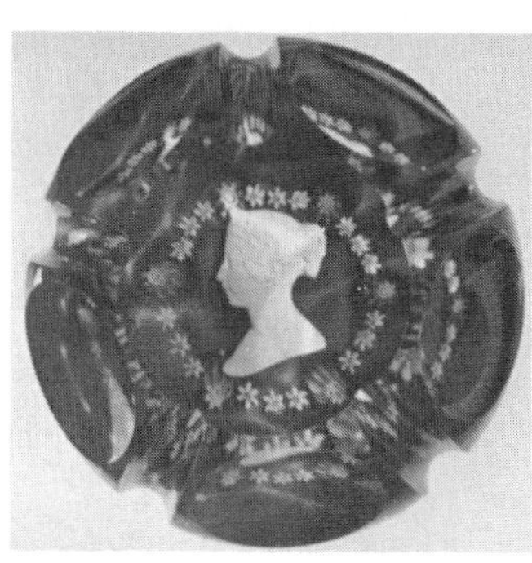

A Stourbridge lemonade set, consisting of jug and 2 goblets, engraved with convolvulus decoration, c1880, jug 13in (33cm).
£200-250 *Som*

An Apsley Pellatt sulphide and heavy cut glass jug, with cameo portrait of George IV wearing the collar of the Order of the Garter, very small chips to foot, 8in (20cm).
£5,000-6,000 *GC*

A Baccarat garlanded primrose weight, the flower set within a garland of alternate white and claret canes, on a star cut base, 2½in (6.5cm) diam.
£600-700 *C*

A Clichy blue and white swirl weight, the alternate royal blue and white staves radiating from a central pink, white and green cane, 3in (8cm) diam.
£800-900 *C*

A Clichy turquoise ground patterned millefiori weight, with a bright opaque turquoise ground, 3in (8cm) diam.
£600-700 *C*

A St Louis crown weight, the red and green twisted ribbon radiating from a salmon pink, green and white central cane, 2½in (6.5cm) diam.
£1,000-1,500 *C*

A St Louis faceted blue double clematis weight, the flower set on a cushion of spiral white latticinio thread, cut with 6 printies, 3in (8cm) diam.
£500-700 *C*

Scent Bottles

A pair of blue tapering scent bottles and stoppers, gilt in the atelier of James Giles, in a contemporary Birmingham gilt metal filigree case with hinged cover, one stopper repaired, c1760, the case 2in (5cm) high.
£1,000-1,200 *C*

A Clichy moss ground concentric millefiori weight, with a ground of moss canes, 2½in (5.5cm) diam.
£1,400-1,600 *C*

A St Louis faceted upright bouquet weight, the sides with all-over honeycomb facets, 3in (7.5cm) diam.
£1,000-1,500 *C*

A St Louis pink double clematis weight, the ten striped pink petals about a yellow centre, with a green leaf showing behind, 3in (7.5cm) diam.
£300-500 *C*

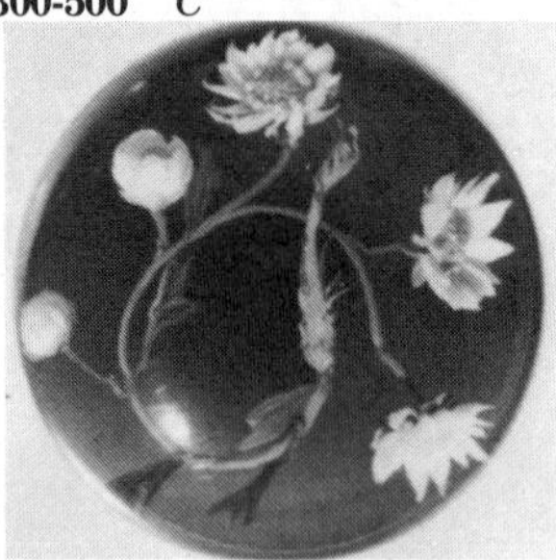

A Paul Stankard daisy spray weight, with a translucent ruby ground, etched 'Paul J. Stankard, B977 1983', 3in (7.5cm) diam.
£750-800 *C*

A Clichy patterned concentric millefiori weight, 2½in (6.5cm) diam.
£350-450 *C*

A St Louis pansy weight, on a star cut base, 2½in (6cm) diam.
£600-700 *C*

A St Louis faceted garlanded blue flower and bud weight, cut with a window and 5 printies, 3in (7.5cm) diam.
£500-800 *C*

A large English green glass dump triple flower in pot paperweight/door stop, c1870, 5in (13cm) high.
£50-80 *CB*

A paperweight with a single pansy with yellow and purple leaves, having a star cut base, 2½in (6cm) diam.
£300-350 *PB*

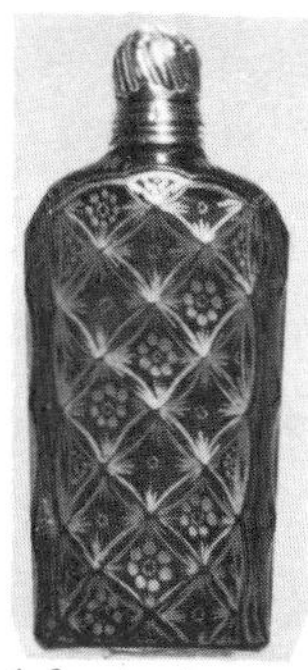

A facet cut green scent bottle, stopper and gold screw cover, gilt in the atelier of James Giles, c1765, 2½in (6cm) high.
£1,000-1,500 *C*

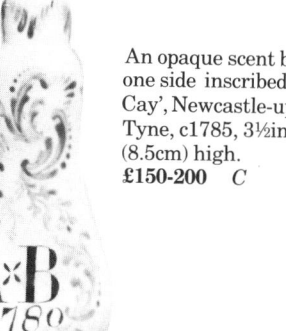

An opaque white scent bottle, of tear drop form with facet cut sides, gilt in the atelier of James Giles, the sides and neck enriched in gilding, minute chip to rim, later metal stopper, in a contemporary shagreen case, c1770, 3in (8cm) high.
£500-550 *C*

A dated opaque scent bottle, one side inscribed 'A B 1780' within blue and green foliage scrolls, with blue 'feuille-de-choux' rim, Newcastle-upon-Tyne, 3in (7.5cm) high.
£400-500 *C*

An opaque scent bottle, one side inscribed 'I E Cay', Newcastle-upon-Tyne, c1785, 3½in (8.5cm) high.
£150-200 *C*

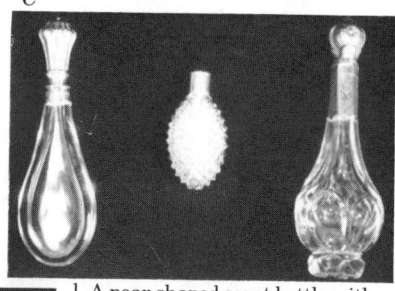

l. A pear shaped scent bottle with embossed silver gilt mount, c1830, 4½in (11.5cm).
£150-200
c. A diamond cut scent bottle with silver cap, c1840, 2in (5.5cm).
£50-75
r. A fluted moulded scent bottle, with chased hinged silver mount, c1830, 5in (12cm).
£70-100 *Som*

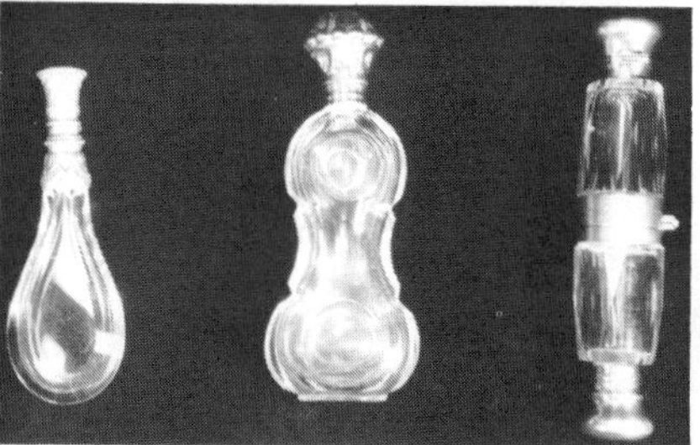

l. A clear glass scent bottle with an embossed gilt metal mount with bloodstone end, c1830, 4in (10.5cm).
£160-200
c. A moulded scent bottle with embossed gilt brass mount, c1850.
£140-170
r. A double ended facet cut scent bottle with plain silver gilt mounts, c1860, 5½in (13cm).
£100-150 *Som*

A pair of English dressing table bottles, c1840, 9in (23cm).
£80-130 *CB*

A cameo citrine ground silver mounted scent bottle, overlaid in opaque white, the silver mount to the neck with hinged ball cover, the silver with maker's mark JNM, London, 1884, 5½in (14.5cm) long.
£300-350 *C*

A commemorative cut glass perfume bottle, engraved 'Jubilee 1887', and a family crest on the reverse.
£200-250 *SW*

cameo silver gilt mounted scent ottle and screw cover, the urquoise body overlaid in pale blue, vith silver gilt mount and screw all cover, maker's mark of ampson Mordan, London, 1884, in (15cm) long.
200-250 *C*

A group of cut crystal boudoir items, comprising: a pair of Russian cut cologne bottles, a cruet, a cologne bottle with enamel stopper and printed oval of Marie Antoinette, and 5 other scent bottles, one with broken stopper.
£250-300 *CNY*

Tankards

A Milch glass cylindrical tankard, with applied looped handle, the body painted in colours, small hairline crack in the body, 5in (12.5cm) high.
£200-250 *CSK*

A garniture of 3 green and white layered glass vases, with cut lozenge shaped decoration, painted in gilt, mid-19thC, 10½ to 12in (26 to 30.5cm).
£700-750 *P[WSW]*

A pair of Shropshire glass vases after the antique, in black with enamelled colours, possibly Paris taking Helen to Troy, 10in (25.5cm).
£200-300 *ET*

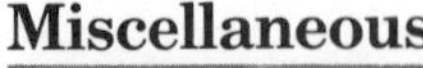

Miscellaneous

A cameo glass biscuit barrel, with plated mount and cover, the citrus coloured body decorated in pink and white, 6in (15.5cm) high.
£1,000-1,200 *Bea*

Vases

A selection of coloured Victorian bulb vases.
£30-50 *CB*

Note: shape, age and colour are important factors.

A French enamelled opaque glass vase, c1860, 7in (18cm).
£100-150 *CB*

A diamond cut glass table lamp and shade, 17in (43cm).
£250-300 *P[CW]*

A pair of Victorian vaseline glass bulb vases, 4in (10cm) high.
£80-100 *CB*

A vase, engraved with celery, c1870, 10in (25.5cm).
£60-80 *CB*

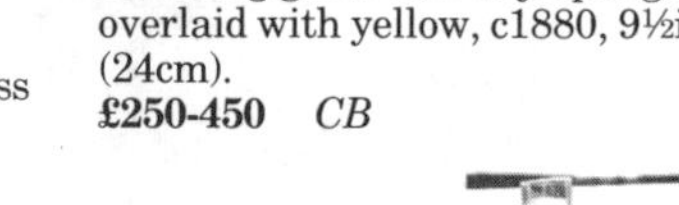

A Peking glass vase in jasper gree overlaid with yellow, c1880, 9½in (24cm).
£250-450 *CB*

A ruby glass oil lamp, c1820, 31in (79cm).
£450-600 *CB*

A hollow stem lacemaker's lamp, c1830, 7½in (19cm).
£180-250 *CB*

A French blue opaline oil lamp, c1880, 21in (53cm) high, converted to electricity.
£250-350 *CB*

TYPES OF GLASS

- ★ **Cased Glass:** Glass of one colour covered with one or more layers of different coloured glass. Decoration is engraved through the upper layer. First made in Bohemia in the early 19thC
- ★ **Cut-glass:** Fashionable during the late 18thC. Decorated with facets in the form of geometric patterns
- ★ **Engraved Glass:** Type of decoration done with the aid of a diamond point
- ★ **Etched Glass:** Hydrofluoric acid was used to decorate glass during 19thC
- ★ **Frosted Glass:** Glass with a matt, opaque outer surface
- ★ **Fruit Glass:** First made in Venice during the 18thC. Revived in the 19thC at Stourbridge. Usually arranged in a basket with glass leaves
- ★ **Lacy Glass:** Pressed glass with a stippled background. Manufactured in America by the Boston and Sandwich Glass Co
- ★ **Lime Glass:** Substitute for lead glass discovered in 1864 by William Leighton
- ★ **Lutz Glass:** Thin, transparent glass striped with coloured twists. Sometimes called 'candy stripe' glass. Introduced by Nicholas Lutz, a French glassworker
- ★ **'Mary Gregory' Glass:** Glass printed with figures of children c1870
- ★ **Vaseline Glass:** Decorative glass often known as yellow opaline. Best qualities are greenish-yellow. Produced end of 19thC

A square base salt with lemon squeezer foot, c1790, 3½in (8.5cm).
£30-50 *CB*

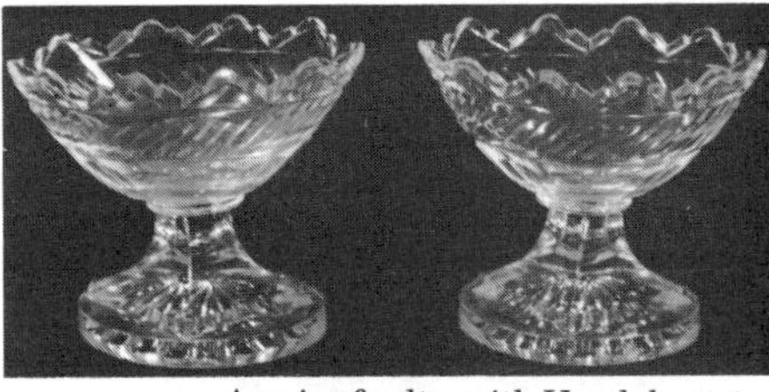

A pair of salts, with Vandyke cut rims, c1810, 3in (7.5cm).
£150-200 *Som*

A square base salt, with lemon squeezer foot, 3½in (8.5cm) high.
£30-60 *CB*

A selection of pairs of Victorian cranberry coloured salts.
£60-100 each pair *CB*

An amethyst cornucopia, with fold-over rim, 6½in (16.5cm) high.
£150-200 *CB*

A pair would be worth £450-550.

A pale green opaline glass hat, with applied white rim and gilt headband, 2in (5cm).
£80-100 *CB*

A pair of French turquoise opaline tazze with gilt decoration, c1830, 3in (7.5cm) high.
£300-500 *CB*

A pair of potichomania glass ornaments, decorated with various birds and butterflies on a blue and green background, 15½in (39cm) high.
£600-650 *CSK*

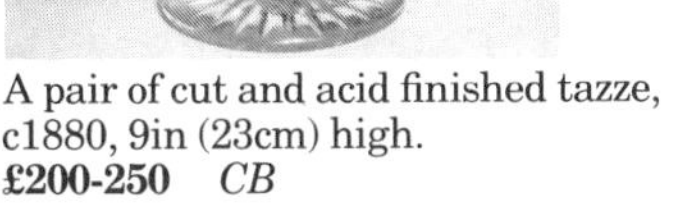

A pair of cut and acid finished tazze, c1880, 9in (23cm) high.
£200-250 *CB*

A small comport and cover, with flute, blaze and diamond cutting, c1810, 7in (18cm).
£200-250 *Som*

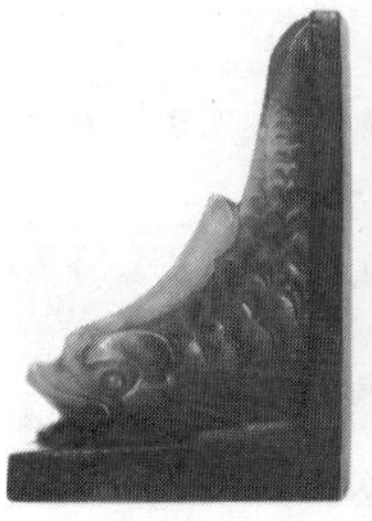
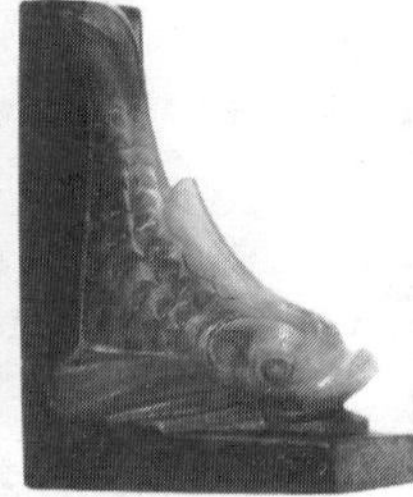

A pair of Nancy pâté-de-verre bookends, fashioned as dolphins, impressed 'Walter Nancy' and signed X Momillon.
£3,000-3,500 *LRG*

A butter dish, cover and under-dish, 7in (18cm) high.
£200-250 *CB*

An apothecary's cut glass globe sign, on blue painted wooden bas 24in (61cm) high.
£300-500 *CB*

A clear and black enamelled condiment bottle and stopper, the tapering cylindrical form moulded with bands of zig-zags, 5in (13cm).
£500-550 *Bon*

A clear and frosted cigarette box, 'Hirondelles', with canted corners, the cover moulded with a flock of swallows, the sides with a geometric design, 4in (10cm).
£300-350 *Bon*

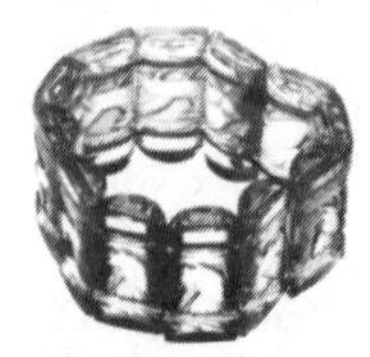

A clear, frosted and blue-stain glass bracelet formed as 12 segments.
£1,000-1,500 *Bon*

GLASS APPENDIX

Alabastron
A vessel for holding ointments used by the ancients. Named after Alabastron, a town in which there was a manufactory of small vessels.

Beilby, William (1740-1819) and Mary (1749-97)
Famous English glass enamellers from Newcastle upon Tyne. William started in Birmingham as a maker of enamel boxes, but was decorating glasses in Newcastle by 1762. Mary decorated glasses from 1767 onwards.

Bristol
First mention of glass manufacture in Bristol was made in 1696. During the 18thC Bristol became a famous glass making centre, noted for the coloured glass produced there. (A lot of coloured glass has been erroneously attributed to Bristol in the past.) The peak of the coloured glass making period was 1790-1820. The most popular colour was blue and amethyst; red was also used, as was green, especially after 1850.

Bute Glass
Named after the unpopular British Prime Minister Lord Bute who was forced to resign in 1763. He was commemorated with the Bute or Boot Glass.

Clutha Glass
Inspired by old Roman glass, designed by Christopher Dresser and made by James Couper and Son, Glasgow, who patented it in c1890. Reputedly named after the cloudy River Clyde, the metal is clouded, streaked and bubbled.

Cork Glass Company
Opened in 1783 by Hayes Burnett and Rowe. It survived until 1818 when it was succeeded by the Waterloo Glass Company which lasted until 1836.

Egermann, Frederick (1777-1864)
Bohemian glass decorator, invented Lithyalin in 1828; he also introduced yellow and red flashed glass in 1820 and 1840.

Hurdels Verk
18thC Scandinavian glass making factory. Used coloured as well as clear glass. Blue glass used quite extensively from 1780. Factory closed down in 1809.

'Kit Kat'
A type of drinking glass so called because of a painting by Sir Godfrey Kneller in the National Portrait Gallery showing members of the 'Kit Kat' Club using similar shaped vessels. The Kit Kat Club was a London Whig Literary Club, c1690-1720, which met for a time in the pie shop of Christopher Cat or Catling.

Lithyalin
Name for valuable coloured opaque glass invented by Egermann (1777-1864) of Blottendorf in 1828. It resembles a semi-precious stone in appearance and was much imitated in Bohemia and Silesia.

'Mary Gregory' Glass
Glass items decorated in white enamels with Victorian children at play by Hahn of Galonz in Bohemia from 1850 onwards. So called because an American, Mary Gregory, copied the designs on the Bohemian glass whilst working in Boston.

Millefiori
Ornamental glass made by fusing coloured canes together, used from 1840s in paperweights where the canes were enveloped in clear flint glass.

Nailsea
Glass factory established 1788 by John Robert Lucas. Used cheap non-lead glass to make bottles and crown window glass. Benefited in 1793 from the tax which burdened the makers of lead glass. Lucas later went into partnership with Edward Homer. Produced objects decorated with white enamel, probably obtained from Bristol. A great deal of coloured glass was supposed to have been made at Nailsea, but there is no evidence to support this. The Nailsea factory closed in the 1870s. A lot of Nailsea-type glass was made in other parts of the country and has been reproduced.

Opaline Glass
Semi-opaque ornamental glass used in Victorian times; could not be cut.

Printie
Small wheel ground circular hollow cut in glass, more heavily cut in Victorian times.

)AK & COUNTRY 'URNITURE

MONARCH CHRONOLOGY

Dates	Monarchs	Period
1558-1603	Elizabeth I	Elizabethan
1603-1625	James I	Jacobean
1625-1649	Charles I	Carolean
1649-1660	Commonwealth	Cromwellian
1660-1685	Charles II	Restoration
1685-1689	James II	Restoration
1689-1694	William & Mary	William & Mary
1694-1702	William III	William III
1702-1714	Anne	Queen Anne
1714-1727	George I	Early Georgian
1727-1760	George II	Georgian
1760-1812	George III	Late Georgian
1812-1820	George III	Regency
1820-1830	George IV	Late Regency
1830-1837	William IV	William IV
1837-1860	Victoria	Early Victorian
1860-1901	Victoria	Late Victorian
1901-1910	Edward VII	Edwardian

An oak bed with panelled headboard, on square legs with rollers, late 16thC, 52in (132cm) wide.
£2,500-3,500 *C*

Provenance:
Possibly made for the new grammar school at Thame, Oxon, opened in 1570 and associated with John Hamden. Edmund Waller the poet may have been responsible for the initials E.W. and date 1617. The carving 'Kipling' on the frame refers to one of John Kipling's sons, who was headmaster 1729-68. The school closed in 1877.

}eds

n oak tester bedstead, the ›adboard with arched panels ırved with scrolling foliage and ıilloches centred by the monogram D.AD, partly 17thC, with box ›ring and mattress, 59in (150cm) ide.
,500-2,000 *C*

An oak cradle with turned finials and moulded panelled hood, ends and sides, bearing the carved date 1739, 36in (91.5cm) long.
£500-600 *DSH*

A Continental oak single bed, 18thC.
£400-500 *TM*

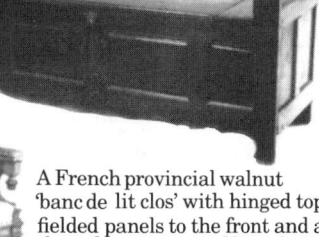

n early Victorian oak day bed in .e Gothic style, the seat covered in ɔse nailed green leather, on square ɔthic panelled legs with pierced ıgles, 77in (196cm) wide.
,500-3,000 *C*

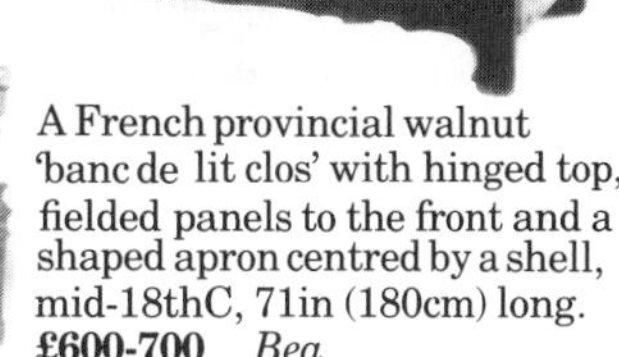

A French provincial walnut 'banc de lit clos' with hinged top, fielded panels to the front and a shaped apron centred by a shell, mid-18thC, 71in (180cm) long.
£600-700 *Bea*

BEDS

Beds have invariably been altered. The most common change being in length – we are simply much taller now. This is regarded as acceptable generally if the bed is to be used. Size can account for considerable differences in price – a good Charles II four poster of, say, 4ft 7in wide by 6ft long might well be less desirable than a less good bed measuring 5ft 6in wide and 7ft long. Most bed buyers *do* want to use their 'fantasy' furniture while retaining 20thC comfort

Bookcases

An oak book press of the Pepys model, with carved cornice and bun feet, 57in (145cm).
£4,500-5,500 *C*

The celebrated 12 bookcases commissioned by Samuel Pepys, Secretary to the Navy, in the late 1660s from 'Sympson the joyner' were bequeathed to Magdalene College, Cambridge. Pepys is credited with the invention of the free-standing case book-press. A similar press was commissioned by Charles Sergison of Cuckfield Park, Sussex.

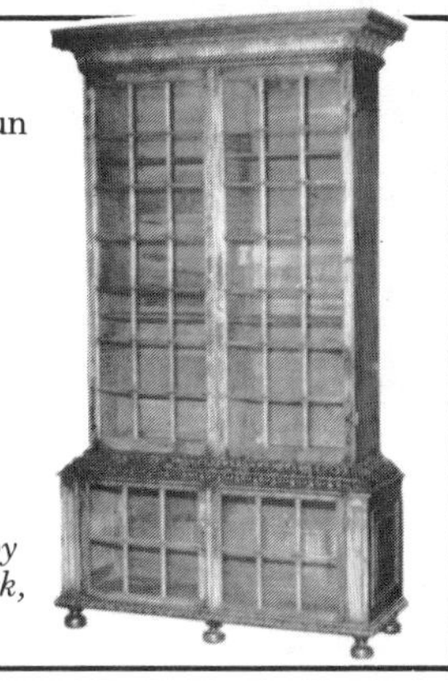

A Regency pollard oak bookcase, with channelled beaded angles and claw feet, 40½in (103cm).
£2,500-3,500 *C*

A carved oak breakfront bookcase, 62in (157cm).
£800-900 *CoH*

A late Victorian oak bookcase, with heavily carved decoration, the upper doors with coloured leaded light glazing, 89in (226cm) high.
£400-500 *MJB*

Bureaux

An oak bureau, 18thC.
£700-800 *HP*

An oak bureau, with graduated fitted interior with well, brass swan neck handles and bracket feet, some damage, 18thC, 30in (76m).
£1,500-2,500 *JD*

A William and Mary oak bureau with a fitted interior, on later bracket feet, bearing a rare contemporary trade label of John Gatehouse, 38½in (98cm).
£2,000-2,500 *P*

An oak kneehole desk, on reduced shaped bracket feet, early 18thC, 29½in (75cm).
£1,500-2,500 *Bea*

A George II walnut veneered bureau, inlaid with chevron lines, enclosing a stepped interior with a cupboard, pigeonholes, drawers and a well, 35½in (90cm).
£2,500-3,000 *Bea*

A mid-Georgian walnut bureau, inlaid with boxwood lines, the sloping flap enclosing a fitted interior, on later bracket feet, 34½in (86cm).
£4,500-5,500 *C*

A George III oak bureau cabinet, with moulded cornice above a pair of fielded panelled doors over a fall enclosing a fitted interior, on bracket feet, 38½in (98cm).
£2,000-2,500 *Bon*

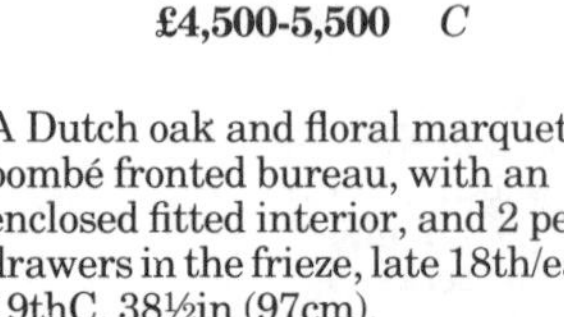

A Dutch oak and floral marquetry bombé fronted bureau, with an enclosed fitted interior, and 2 pen drawers in the frieze, late 18th/early 19thC, 38½in (97cm).
£3,000-4,000 *P*

n oak bureau, the hinged writing
ıll enclosing a fitted interior, on
racket feet, 36in (91.5cm).
850-950 *P[Pea]*

A German oak cylinder bureau bookcase, with fitted interior with an easel slide, waved apron and bracket feet, late 19thC, 47½in (120cm).
£1,500-2,000 *C*

An oak roll top pedestal desk, 50in (127cm).
£600-700 *CoH*

Cabinets

A George III oak bureau cabinet, the fall enclosing an interior of drawers, with 4 graduated long drawers below, 44in (111.5cm).
£1,200-1,700 *Bon*

A late Victorian pollard oak sideboard, with a central mirror door flanked by a pair of panelled cupboard doors, on plinth base, stamped Gillows & Co, 91in (231cm).
£600-900 *CSK*

An American oak 1874 Wootton Patent desk.
£5,000-6,000 *MGM*

A pair of Directoire fruitwood corner cabinets, with mottled black marble tops and 2 panelled doors, enclosing shelves, flanked by pilasters on plinth bases, 30½in (76cm).
£2,000-3,000 *C*

An American Dutch style bombé fronted walnut and oak glazed display cabinet, with brass handles, 72in (182.5cm).
£1,500-2,000 *GH*

An oak bureau cabinet, the sloping fall front enclosing a fitted interior, on bracket feet, 45in (114cm).
£3,000-3,500 *Bea*

Chairs

A pair of Charles II oak side chairs, on scrolled legs joined by pierced front stretchers carved with foliage and baluster H-shaped stretchers.
£1,500-2,000 *C*

A Charles II ebonised oak side chair, with padded seat, on baluster turned legs, joined by an H-stretcher on turned feet.
£400-600 *C*

A single oak chair with bobbin turned uprights, solid seat, turned front stretchers and 5 flat stretchers, feet renewed, late 17thC.
£150-250 *WIL*

A pair of Carolean decorated oak armchairs, the cane panel seats on scroll supports.
£600-900 *P*

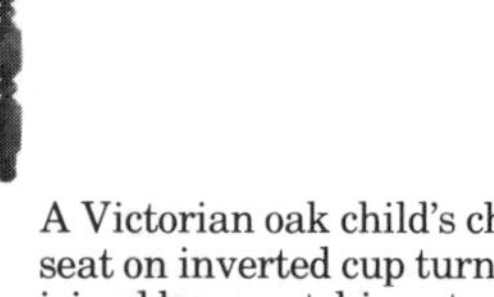

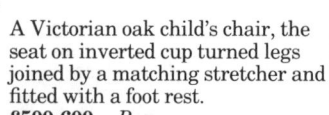

A Victorian oak child's chair, the seat on inverted cup turned legs joined by a matching stretcher and fitted with a foot rest.
£500-600 *Bon*

A set of 8 Charles II style oak dining chairs, including 2 armchairs, with leather panelled backs above matching seats on bobbin turned legs joined by barleytwist stretchers.
£750-850 *Bon*

A William and Mary American walnut elbow chair, the back with a dip crest for a periwig, the front turned block legs with a bulbous apron stretcher, front Spanish feet, plain H-stretchers, with a squab cushion, cane seat distressed.
£750-850 *WW*

A matched set of 9 late Georgian elm dining chairs, including 2 armchairs.
£3,000-3,500 *C*

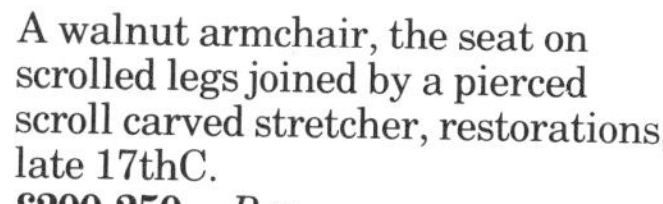

A walnut armchair, the seat on scrolled legs joined by a pierced scroll carved stretcher, restorations, late 17thC.
£200-250 *Bon*

A harlequin set of 3 Derbyshire dining chairs, the uprights centred by scrolls with later plank seats, one with padded seat, on block and baluster turned legs, joined by turned stretchers, basically late 17thC.
£700-1,000 *C*

A set of 14 oak dining chairs of 17thC design, including a pair of open armchairs, upholstered in simulated leather, with bobbin turned legs and front stretchers.
£1,000-1,500 *CSK*

An oak open armchair, with solid seat and shaped arm supports on column legs united by stretchers, 17thC.
£1,000-1,500 *P*

Two oak open armchairs, the ring turned backs filled with rails, the solid seats on conforming legs and stretchers, one with moulded arms and later seat, 17thC.
£1,500-2,000 *C*

A carved oak wainscot chair, 17thC.
£1,000-1,200 *PCA*

A pair of walnut open armchairs in 17thC style, with outscrolled arm supports and cane seats on scrolling legs, joined by H-shaped stretchers.
£600-800 *C*

A Chippendale oak chair, 18thC.
£200-250 *PCA*

A yew wood and elm Windsor armchair, with pierced fret carved vase splat and stick uprights, on turned splayed legs united by a crinoline stretcher, late 18thC.
£1,500-2,000 *P*

A set of 8 matched Macclesfield dining chairs with rush seats, early 19thC.
£3,000-4,000 *BM*

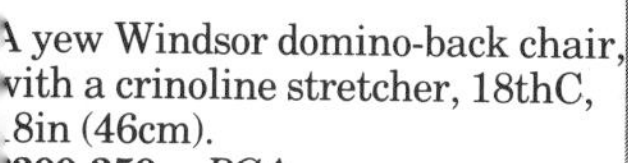

A yew Windsor domino-back chair, with a crinoline stretcher, 18thC, 18in (46cm).
£300-350 *PCA*

A set of 9 'Korenaarstoelen', comprising one armchair and 8 dining chairs, 18th/19thC.
£2,200-2,500 *CAm*

A matched set of 14 spindle back chairs, including 2 armchairs, on turned legs with pad and ball feet, late 18th/early 19thC.
£3,000-4,000 *Bea*

An oak wing armchair with solid wings, rope seat and velvet lined squab cushion, on square legs and conforming stretchers, early 19thC.
£1,000-1,500 *C*

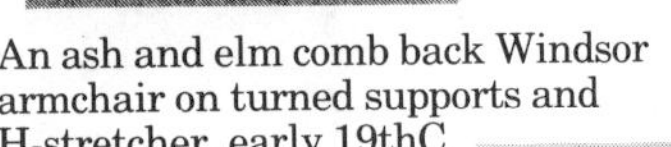

An ash and elm comb back Windsor armchair on turned supports and H-stretcher, early 19thC.
£250-300 *P[Re]*

A yew wood and elm Windsor elbow chair, with pierced vase splat and stick uprights, on turned splayed legs united by crinoline stretcher, early 19thC.
£1,000-1,500 *P*

A yew wood and elm Windsor armchair, with a spindle filled hoop back, early 19thC.
£950-1,200 *Bea*

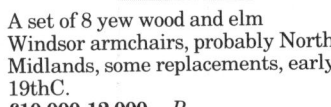

A set of 8 yew wood and elm Windsor armchairs, probably North Midlands, some replacements, early 19thC.
£10,000-12,000 *P*

A set of 6 Wigan ash and elm ladderback chairs, c1780.
£1,200-1,600 *P[EDH]*

A George III oak open armchair, inscribed 'This wood was part of Adm-De Winter's Fleet capturd. by Adml Duncan Octr 11 1797', c1800.
£2,700-3,200 *CNY*

A George III yew wood and elm Windsor armchair in the Gothic taste, the splayed seat on cabriole legs and pad feet joined by shaped stretchers.
£2,500-3,500 *C*

A pair of Jacobean oak elbow chairs, profusely carved with mythical beasts, 19thC.
£600-1,000 *LRG*

A George III oak corner chair, with cabriole front leg and pad foot.
£600-700 *BM*

A birch armchair, painted overall, with rush seat and bow front, mid-19thC.
£300-400 *WIL*

A George III beech and elm comb back Windsor armchair.
£900-1,200 *P[Re]*

A set of George III yew and elm Windsor armchairs, each with hoop back, pierced baluster shaped splat and saddle-seat, early 19thC.
£4,500-5,500 *CNY*

A pair of Gothic style oak dining chairs, on turned splayed legs, joined by a stretcher, 19thC.
£450-550 *CSK*

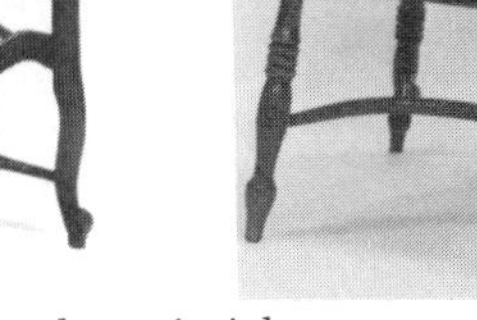

A hardwood Windsor stick back elbow chair with pierced splat, turned supports and crinoline stretcher, 19thC.
£250-350 *HCH*

A set of 6 French provincial farmhouse chairs, 19thC.
£750-1,000 *RIP*

A harlequin set of 8 oak, ash and fruitwood dining chairs, including 2 elbow chairs, on tapered legs and pad and ball feet, 19thC.
£2,500-3,000 *P*

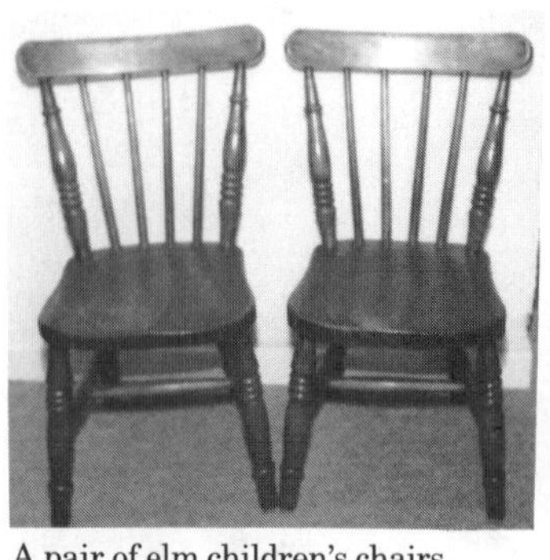

A pair of elm children's chairs, 19thC.
£150-200 *PCA*

An elm spindle back chair, 19thC.
£100-150 *PCA*

An elm Windsor wheel back elbow chair.
£200-250 *PCA*

A set of 4 carved oak chairs, 19thC.
£700-800 *PCA*

A set of 8 Victorian elm chairs, including 2 armchairs, on club legs joined with cross stretchers, and a set of 4 similar side chairs.
£3,500-4,000 *CSK*

A pair of oak bobbin turned elbow chairs, with vertical splats and finials, the solid seats on similar turned underframe.
£400-500 *P*

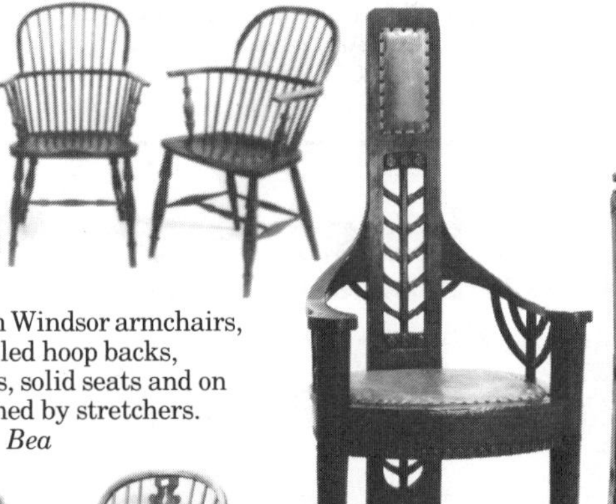

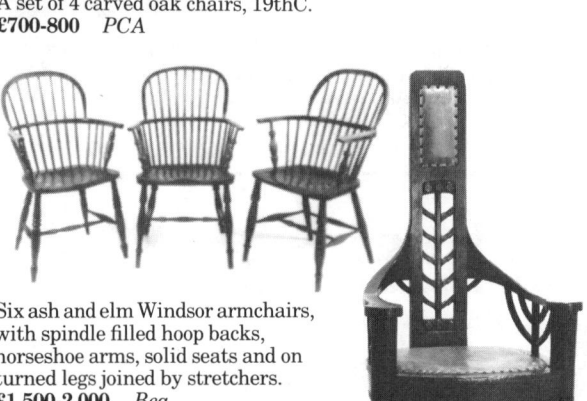

Six ash and elm Windsor armchairs, with spindle filled hoop backs, horseshoe arms, solid seats and on turned legs joined by stretchers.
£1,500-2,000 *Bea*

An oak framed chair, with carved narrow back and shaped arms.
£400-450 *LRG*

A pair of oak framed Ecclesiastical chairs.
£500-700 *LRG*

Two ash and elm Windsor chairs.
£250-300 each *SAg*

A pair of French provincial fruitwood fauteuils, upholstered in brown repp, on partly fluted turned tapering legs headed by rosettes.
£2,200-2,600 *C*

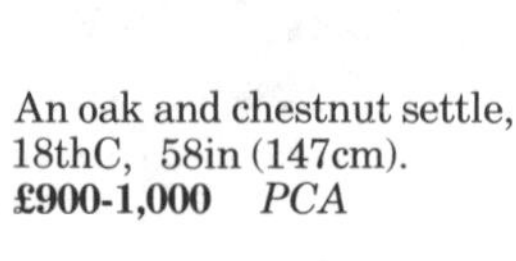

An oak and chestnut settle, 18thC, 58in (147cm).
£900-1,000 *PCA*

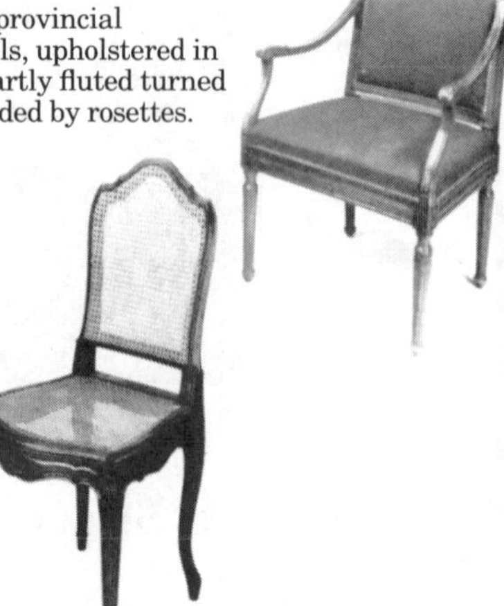

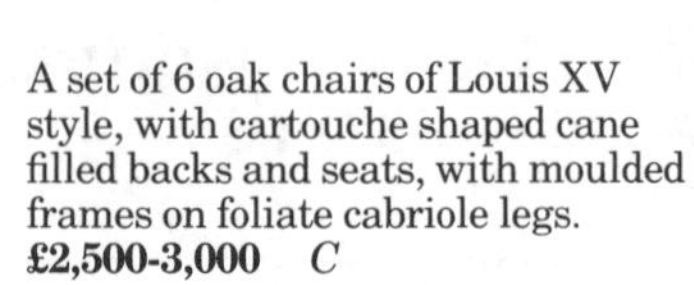

A set of 6 oak chairs of Louis XV style, with cartouche shaped cane filled backs and seats, with moulded frames on foliate cabriole legs.
£2,500-3,000 *C*

An oak settle, with panelled carved back and inscription 'John Hutchinson 1646 God is our strength', with hinged solid seat, 70in (178cm).
£1,500-2,000 *C*

An oak three-panel settle, 38in (97cm).
£600-700 *P[WP]*

An oak bench, the padded back and squab covered in tapestry, on turned legs and moulded stretchers, 57½in (146cm).
£700-1,000 *C*

Chests

An oak coffer, with later panelled top and frieze, on moulded square legs, late 16th/early 17thC, 104in (264cm).
£1,000-1,300 *C*

A James I carved oak coffer, the arcaded front with guilloche decoration, bearing the initials IP 1613, with contemporary iron lock, on block feet, probably South Lancashire or North Cheshire, 54in (137cm).
£2,000-2,500 *P*

A Cromwellian oak chest, inlaid with bone and mother-of-pearl, with one frieze drawer and dated 1651, 47in (120cm).
£4,000-4,500 *C*

An Italian carved walnut fronted cassone with hinged top, embellished in parcel gilt, on scroll supports, reconstructed, 17thC and later, 68in (174cm).
£900-1,200 *P*

An oak breakfront chest-on-chest in 17thC style, with stile feet, 42in (106.5cm).
£1,300-1,600 *Bea*

A James II oak chest, with yew wood moulded edge and frieze fitted with 2 fruitwood veneered drawers inlaid in ivory with the initials A R and dated 1687, on block feet, 41in (104cm).
£3,000-3,500 *P*

An Italian walnut cassone, with decorated front panel, basically late 17thC, 70in (178cm).
£1,500-2,000 *CSK*

An oak panelled coffer, 17thC, 49in (125cm).
£500-550 *PCA*

An oak chest, the frieze drawer with 3 dummy drawer fronts, with fielded panels and split mouldings, above 2 similar doors, enclosing 3 long drawers, 17thC, later brass handles, 45in (114cm).
£1,500-2,000 *DN*

An oak chest, with moulded cornice and one frieze drawer, above a fielded and panelled deep drawer, applied with twin split mouldings, the base with 3 enclosed drawers, mid-17thC, 45in (114cm).
£2,500-3,500 *C*

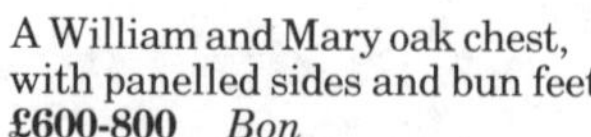

A William and Mary oak chest, with panelled sides and bun feet.
£600-800 *Bon*

An oak chest on stand, with original iron clasp and lock, 17thC, 37in (94cm).
£1,000-1,500 *HOD*

An oak and walnut chest, 17thC, with later bracket feet, 39in (99cm).
£800-1,000 *P*

A Flemish oak coffer, with plank top and fitted interior, the front inlaid with ivory and ebony, mid-17thC, 52½in (133cm).
£1,000-1,500 *C*

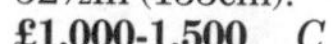

A William and Mary walnut, crossbanded and featherstrung chest in 2 parts, with oak panelled sides and later block feet, 38in (96cm).
£1,100-1,400 *P*

A yew wood chest with a moulded edge, late 17thC, on later bun feet, 35in (90cm).
£3,500-4,000 *P*

An oak chest with panelled top enclosing a fitted interior, on moulded feet, early 18thC, 55in (141cm).
£1,500-2,000 *C*

A walnut chest, with moulded top above 2 short and 4 long graduated and banded drawers, on bracket feet, 18thC, 42in (106.5cm).
£800-1,200 *CSK*

An oak mule chest, with hinged moulded top above an ogee arched fielded panel front, on a stand with 3 short drawers and a shaped apron, 18thC, 56in (142cm).
£700-1,000 *CSK*

An Anglo-Dutch elm, walnut and oak chest in 2 sections, with oak panel sides, on bun feet, late 17th/early 18thC, 51in (131cm).
£3,000-4,000 *P*

A South German walnut and oak crossbanded chest, with moulded overhanging top and carrying handles to the sides, on moulded base, 18thC, with later feet, 43in (110cm).
£2,000-2,500 *P*

A French provincial carved walnut serpentine commode, with moulded edge and arched fielded panel sides, shaped apron with neo-classical paterae and garland ornaments, on scroll feet, 18thC, 56in (142cm).
£2,500-3,000 *P*

An oak chest, one drawer initialled A.F in brass studs, ovolo carcase mouldings and on stile feet, late 17thC, 38in (96.5cm).
£1,100-1,500 *Bea*

An oak chest of drawers, 18thC, 33½in (85cm).
£800-1,000 *PCA*

A burr elm chest of drawers, with original handles, and fielded panels to sides, c1760, 36in (91.5cm).
£2,000-2,500 *SBA*

A Dutch oak chest, inlaid with marquetry, on later bracket feet, 18thC, 34in (86cm).
£2,500-3,000 *CSK*

A mid-Georgian Lancashire oak and mahogany banded chest, with hinged planked lid above a simulated drawer front and 3 drawers, with an undulating apron and ogee bracket feet, 56in (142cm).
£600-700 *CSK*

A French provincial oak commode, with panelled sides and shaped feet, mid-18thC, 47in (119cm).
£2,500-3,000 *C*

A George III crossbanded oak mule chest, with brass drop handles, on bracket feet, 49in (124.5cm).
£600-800 *HCH*

A Dutch oak kettle base commode, late 18thC, 34in (86cm).
£800-1,200 *Bon*

A George III miniature chest of drawers with original brass handles, 13in (33cm).
£300-500 *RYA*

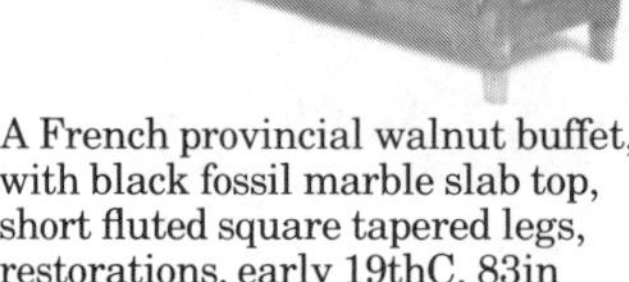
A French provincial walnut buffet, with black fossil marble slab top, short fluted square tapered legs, restorations, early 19thC, 83in (210cm).
£2,000-2,500 *Bon*

A French provincial oak chest of drawers, with original cast handles, early 19thC.
£2,000-2,500 *RIP*

A French provincial oak commode, on cabriole feet headed by foliate clasps, 51½in (130cm).
£3,500-4,000 *C*

An oak chest, on block feet, 38½in (98cm).
£2,000-2,500 *C*

A massive German oak, maple, rosewood and ebonised coffer, with inverted front, the hinged lid inset with 2 bird's eye maple panels enclosing a small hinged cupboard and 2 later trays, the architectural front and sides inlaid with foliate scrolls flanked and divided by pilasters, the sides with carrying handles, on bun feet, the frieze inlaid ANNO 1648, with grey steel hinges and lock, 78in (198cm).
£3,000-4,000 *C*

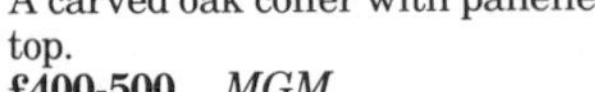
A carved oak coffer with panelled top.
£400-500 *MGM*

Cupboards

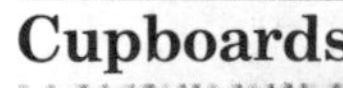

A James I oak joined press cupboard.
£3,000-6,000 *PHA*

A William and Mary oak cupboard, with original cornice dated 1694 and initialled I.H.A.
£4,000-6,000 *PHA*

A Jacobean oak cupboard with arcaded frieze, 49in (124.5cm).
£2,500-3,000 *GC*

William and Mary Lancashire
ak press cupboard with original
rass handles, dated 1699, 34in
6cm).
3,000-6,000 *PHA*

A German oak cupboard, the figures with inscriptions for Faith, Hope, Love and Justice, with bun feet, early 17thC, 51in (129.5cm).
£3,000-5,000 *C*

A small oak cupboard, with enclosed drawers, 32in (81cm).
£700-1,000 *P[WSW]*

An English oak enclosed fitted spice cupboard, dated 1696.
£1,500-2,000 *RYA*

A Flemish walnut cupboard with deep carved decoration, the door with engraved steel lock and key and enclosing 2 small drawers and 2 shelves, late 17thC, 39in (99cm).
£1,500-2,000 *P[WSW]*

n Italian carved walnut and
hequer inlaid credenza, on paw
eet, 17thC, 33in (83cm).
1,500-2,000 *P*

Lakeland livery cupboard,
ith good colour and
atination, c1750. ▶
2,000-3,500 *PHA*

A Queen Anne oak corner cupboard, c1715.
£600-1,000 *PHA*

◀

small George I N. Wales oak
idarn, with panelled doors and
awers, c1720.
3,500-6,000 *PHA*

An English oak cupboard base, c1710.
£4,500-5,000 *RYA*

A George III oak hanging corner cupboard.
£300-350 *BWe*

A small George I oak panelled tridarn, good colour and patination, c1725, 53in (135cm).
£6,000-7,000 *PHA*

A Georgian oak cupboard, with moulded cornice and a pair of cupboard doors above 3 false drawers, flanked by turned pilasters, with 2 short and 3 long drawers, on bracket feet, 55in (139.5cm).
£1,800-2,500 *C*

An oak corner cupboard with a drawer, 18thC, 30in (76cm).
£300-350 *PCA*

A George III oak press, the base fitted with 2 long drawers and 4 false drawers, on block supports, 72in (182.5cm).
£1,000-1,500 *CEd*

An oak tallboy, made for Amy Thomas on her 21st birthday in 1778.
£3,500-5,000 *PHA*

A Louis XVI provincial carved oak armoire, c1770, 67in (170cm).
£3,000-4,000 *N*

An oak wall cupboard, 18thC, 19½in (49cm).
£400-450 *PCA*

An oak corner cupboard, 18thC, 31½in (80cm).
£350-400 *PCA*

An elm bacon cupboard, with brass drop handle and iron 'H' shaped hinges, over a plain box seat with 2 rising panels, shaped arms and plain panelled base, 18thC, 49in (125cm).
£3,500-4,000 *HSS*

A French provincial oak armoire, 18thC.
£3,000-3,500 *RIP*

\ highly carved oak Dutch food upboard, made for the 1851 xhibition, 80in (203cm) high.
1,500-2,000 *P[Pea]*

An oak clothes press, on stile feet, 19thC, 53in (134.5cm).
£1,500-2,000 *Bea*

A Flemish rosewood and oak kas with ebony mouldings, fitted with a long drawer, on brown glazed earthenware bun feet, 18thC, 80in (204cm).
£3,000-4,000 *P*

\n oak standing corner cupboard vith shaped fielded panels, 41in 104cm).
3,000-4,000 *PJ*

A Welsh fitted spice cupboard in solid walnut,with carved heart decoration.
£2,000-2,500 *RYA*

An oak clothes press with 2 false drawers, 2 short drawers and on bracket feet, 49in (124.5cm).
£1,000-1,500 *Bea*

)ressers

\ N Wales oak tridarn, good colour ınd patination, c1710.
:4,500-6,000 *PHA*

An oak dresser, with brass drop handles and knobs, early 18thC, 65in (165cm).
£9,000-10,000 *DSH*

A carved oak court cupboard, with bun feet.
£1,500-2,000 *MGM*

\ Georgian oak and elm dresser, the ılate rack above 2 frieze drawers, haped and pierced apron and pot oard, 50in (127cm).
2,000-2,500 *LRG*

A Georgian Welsh oak dresser, with original iron hooks and later backing, probably from Carmarthen, S Wales, 67in (170cm).
£3,200-3,500 *L*

A George III oak canopy cupboard dresser, with spoon slots in shelf, c1760.
£6,000-8,000 *PHA*

A mid-Georgian oak dresser, inlaid with mahogany bands, adaptations, 75½in (192cm).
£2,600-3,000 *CSK*

A George III Shropshire inlaid oak dresser, some restoration, 72in (182.5cm).
£2,000-2,500 *N*

A George III oak cabriole legged dresser and rack, with cupboards crossbanded with mahogany, c1820.
£4,500-6,000 *PHA*

A George III oak dresser, with mahogany crossbanding and brass swan neck handles, on shaped bracket supports, 71in (180cm).
£3,000-3,500 *BWe*

A late Georgian oak dresser, the later plate rack with waved cornice, the front fitted with 3 drawers above a shaped apron, on square tapering legs, 72½in (183cm).
£1,200-1,500 *CSK*

A George III oak dresser, the shelf superstructure with a moulded cornice above a scroll fret frieze and flanked by panelled pilasters, 69in (175cm).
£3,200-3,500 *Bon*

An oak dresser, with bracket feet, 18thC and later, 57½in (145cm).
£3,000-4,000 *C*

A late Georgian oak dresser, the front fitted with 7 short drawers, each with a bone diamond escutcheon, with 2 arched panel doors, on bracket feet, 67in (170cm).
£4,000-5,000 *CSK*

A late Georgian oak dresser, with iron hooks, 55in (120cm).
£2,000-2,500 *PB*

An oak dresser, with plate rack beneath a dentil moulded cornice and pierced frieze and fitted with 2 arched panel doors, the base with 3 frieze drawers, banded in mahogany and chequered lines, on cabriole legs and pad feet, part 18thC, 78in (198cm).
£2,000-2,500 *CSK*

An oak dresser, the rack with an ogee moulded cornice above shelves the base with a moulded edge abov 5 short frieze drawers and fan brackets, on turned columns joined by a pot board, the base 18thC with a later rack, 69in (175cm).
£1,000-1,200 *Bon*

An oak dresser, with pierced shaped frieze, on cabriole supports and claw-and-ball feet, 18thC, 77½in (195.5cm).
£3,000-4,000 *P[Re]*

An oak dresser, inlaid with satinwood and boxwood, on turned tapering legs, parts 18thC, 74½in (189cm).
£1,500-2,000 *CSK*

An oak dresser, on cabriole legs and pointed pad feet, 18thC, the plate rack later, 76in (193cm).
£2,000-2,500 *CSK*

An oak dresser, 18thC.
£2,000-2,500 *LRG*

An oak dresser, with turned columns and a panelled pot board, restorations, mid-18thC, 75in (192cm).
£1,500-2,000 *Bon*

An elm dresser, fitted with a plate rack, on vase shaped supports, renovations, 18thC, 71in (180cm).
£2,500-3,000 *CSK*

A North Country oak and mahogany dresser, 19thC.
£2,500-3,000 *DWB*

An oak dresser, with spice drawers, all crossbanded in burr oak, mid-18thC, 74in (188cm).
£5,500-6,500 *PJ*

An oak dresser, with raised ogee arched panels and on ogee bracket feet, mid-18thC, 72in (182.5cm).
£6,000-7,000 *Bea*

A North Wales cupboard dresser, mid-18thC.
£5,000-7,000 *PHA*

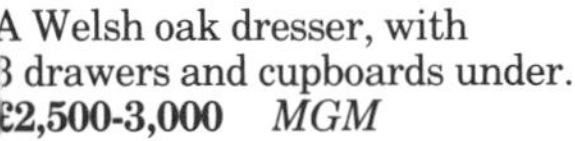

A Welsh oak dresser, with 3 drawers and cupboards under.
£2,500-3,000 *MGM*

An oak dresser, early 19thC, 70in (177.5cm).
£2,000-3,000 *Bea*

An oak dresser base, 18thC, 72in (182.5cm).
£3,000-4,000 *PJ*

An oak dresser base with 9 drawers, a pair of panelled doors to central cupboard, on ogee feet, 18thC.
£3,500-4,000 *MGM*

An oak dresser, with moulded cornice and 3 shelves, with 3 frieze drawers, on turned supports, joined by a pot rack, 54in (137cm).
£2,500-3,000 *CSK*

An early Georgian oak dresser, on ogee bracket feet, 73in (185cm).
£3,000-4,000 *CSK*

An oak three drawer dresser base, crossbanded in walnut, with backboard, shaped apron and cabriole legs at the front, oak lined, brass knobs and escutcheons, early 18thC, 70in (177.5cm).
£3,500-4,000 *WIL*

An oak dresser base, late 17thC, 77in (195.5cm).
£3,000-4,000 *DWB*

An oak low dresser, with brass drop handles and moulded edges, turned front supports, late 17thC, 68in (172.5cm).
£2,500-3,000 *HCH*

A George III oak dresser base, fitted with 3 frieze drawers above an undulating frieze, on square tapering legs, adaptations, 75in (190cm).
£2,000-2,500 *CSK*

A George II oak long dresser, with pierced undulating apron, on cabriole legs with hoof feet, 73in (185cm).
£3,000-4,000 *CSK*

An oak low dresser, with moulded top and 3 frieze drawers, on baluster legs, 18thC, legs partly replaced, 72in (183cm).
£1,700-2,000 *C*

An oak lowboy, 18thC, with later handles, 33in (84cm).
£500-550 *PCA*

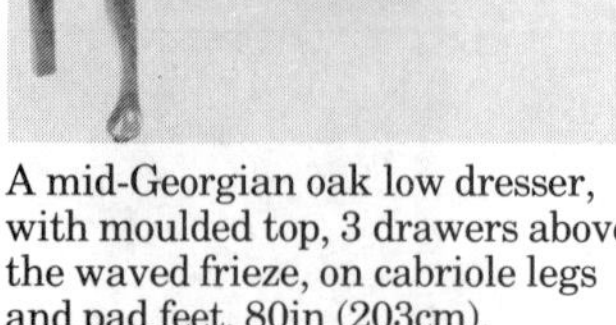

A mid-Georgian oak low dresser, with moulded top, 3 drawers above the waved frieze, on cabriole legs and pad feet, 80in (203cm).
£5,000-6,000 *C*

An oak low dresser, on baluster turned legs and block feet joined by a stretcher, 71in (180cm).
£2,000-2,500 *C*

A Glasgow style stained oak dresser, fitted with 4 drawers with metal bale handles, 72in (182.5cm).
£7,000-8,000 *CEd*

George III oak and mahogany anded low dresser, on square oulded legs with pierced wings, ₎in (177.5cm).
2,500-3,500 *CSK*

tools

oak stool, the seat with a oulded edge, on ring turned and luster supports united by etchers, and block feet, 17thC.
,800-2,200 *P*

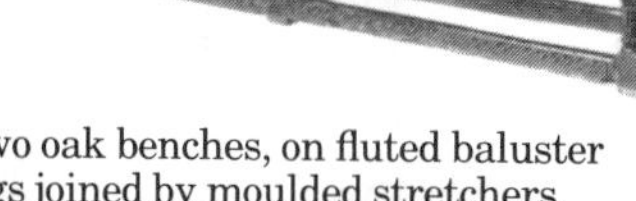

vo oak benches, on fluted baluster gs joined by moulded stretchers, 'thC, 71in (180cm).
,000-3,000 *C*

Regency pollard oak, oak and lly commode stool, by George llock, with hinged top, the nelled sides with beading, on rned feet, lacking one foot, 22in 5cm).
,000-2,500 *C*

An oak joint stool, c1640, 18in (46cm).
£1,800-2,200 *PJ*

An oak stool, the seat with a moulded edge, on turned tapered supports united by stretchers, with bun feet, 17thC.
£1,000-1,500 *P*

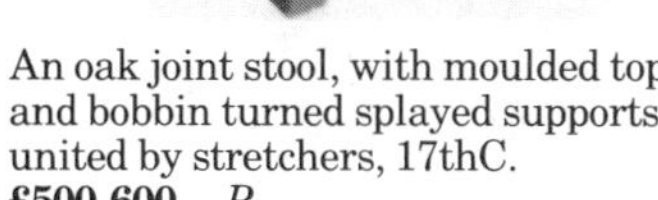

An oak joint stool, with moulded top and bobbin turned splayed supports united by stretchers, 17thC.
£500-600 *P*

An early Victorian oak stool in the Gothic style, with padded seat covered in close nailed green leather, the panelled frieze on square Gothic panelled legs with pierced angles, branded JHEH, 51in (129.5cm) long.
£5,500-6,000 *C*

An English oak joint stool, mid-17thC.
£1,000-1,500 *PHA*

An oak stool, the seat with a moulded edge, on turned columnar supports, united by stretchers, on block feet, 17thC.
£900-1,200 *P*

An English elm child's joint stool, c1680.
£2,000-2,500 *RYA*

Make the Most of Miller's

Every care has been taken to ensure the accuracy of descriptions and estimated valuations. Price ranges in this book reflect what one should expect to pay for a similar example. When selling one can obviously expect a figure below. This will fluctuate according to a dealer's stock, saleability at a particular time, etc. It is always advisable to approach a reputable specialist dealer or an auction house which has specialist sales

Tables

TURNED TABLE LEGS OF THE SEVENTEENTH CENTURY

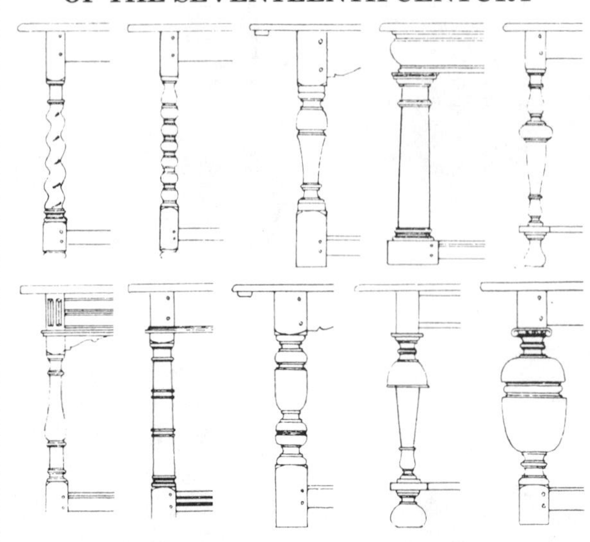

A Jacobean style oak draw leaf refectory dining table, with a carve fluted frieze, on bulbous legs joine with cross stretchers, 131in (332cr extended.
£2,500-3,000 *CSK*

An early 17thC style oak draw le refectory table, on massive onion turned end columns, 119in (302cr extended.
£600-700 *Bon*

A Jacobean style oak refectory dining table, 103in (262cm).
£2,000-3,000 *CSK*

An Italian walnut centre table, the coffered sides with masks on paw feet, minor restorations, Tuscan, early 17thC, 41½in (105cm).
£3,500-4,000 *C*

An oak bench, with stretchers and turned supports, early 17thC, 80in (203cm).
£1,500-2,000 *Wor*

An oak gateleg table, with oval twin-flap top on ring turned legs and moulded stretchers, with one frieze drawer, basically 17thC, 36½in (92cm).
£1,000-1,500 *C*

A Charles II oak side table with ripple moulded panelled frieze drawer, on bobbin turned legs an moulded stretchers, 31½in (76cm
£1,200-1,700 *C*

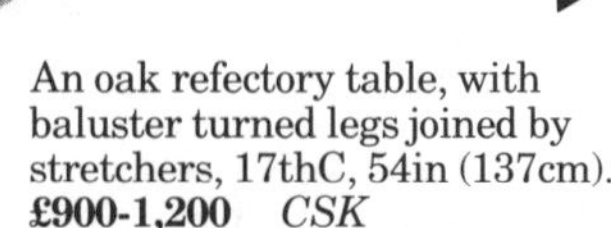

An oak refectory table, with baluster turned legs joined by stretchers, 17thC, 54in (137cm).
£900-1,200 *CSK*

A walnut table, on 4 columnar supports united by stretchers and block feet, 17thC, 49in (125cm).
£3,500-4,500 *P*

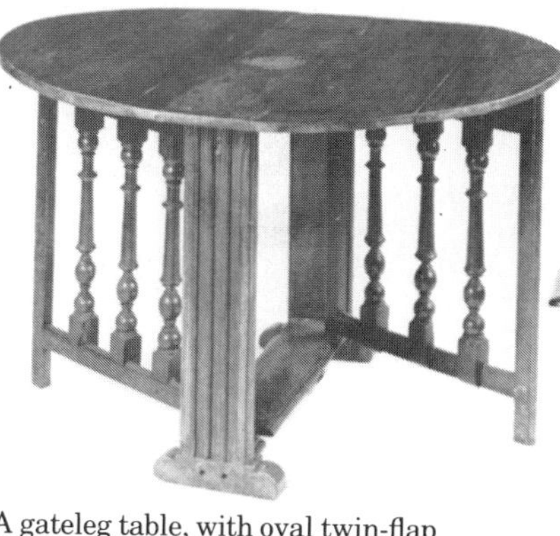

A gateleg table, with oval twin-flap top and moulded channelled trestle ends, basically 17thC, 46in (116.5cm).
£1,500-2,000 *C*

An oak side table, c1670, 33in (84cm).
£2,500-3,500 *PJ*

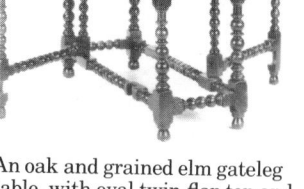

An oak and grained elm gateleg table, with oval twin-flap top and one frieze drawer, on baluster legs, minor restorations, mid-17thC, 68in (172cm).
£4,000-5,000 *C*

An oak refectory table with plank top, on ring turned legs and moulded stretchers, basically 17thC, 97½in (246cm).
£9,000-11,000 *C*

An oak gateleg table, with turned baluster legs, c1680, 34in (86cm).
£600-900 *PJ*

A Tuscan walnut refectory table, with solid top, on H-shaped baluster supports and plinth bases with foliate mouldings, the top 17thC, 105in (267cm).
£4,000-5,000 *P*

A William and Mary oak gateleg table, fitted with 2 later drawers.
£1,600-2,000 *P*

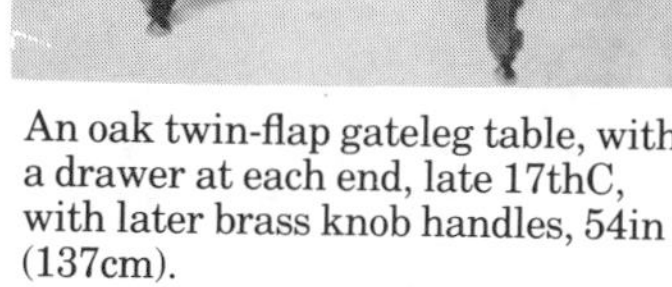

An oak twin-flap gateleg table, with a drawer at each end, late 17thC, with later brass knob handles, 54in (137cm).
£3,000-4,000 *WW*

An oak gateleg table, with single drawer with brass knob, baluster turned legs and moulded stretchers, late 17thC, 45½in (115cm).
£1,500-2,000 *DSH*

An oak gateleg dining table, the planked folding oval top above a frieze drawer on baluster underframe, late 17thC and later, 51½in (130cm).
£800-1,000 *CSK*

An oak side table, the top with moulded edge and frieze drawers, on turned legs united by stretchers, late 17th/early 18thC, 30½in (78cm).
£1,000-1,500 *P*

A French oak table, fitted with 2 inlaid drawers, late 17thC, 70in (178cm).
£1,500-2,000 *GC*

A burr yew wood side table, the top with a moulded edge and frieze drawer, on baluster turned legs united by stretchers, late 17th/early 18thC, 30in (76cm).
£3,000-3,500 *P*

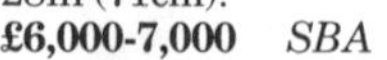

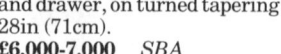

A Regency oak and holly side table by George Bullock, with banded top and drawer, on turned tapering legs, 28in (71cm).
£6,000-7,000 *SBA*
Provenance:
Great Tew Park, probably one of the 4 chamber tables, invoiced in 1817 at a cost of £3 each.

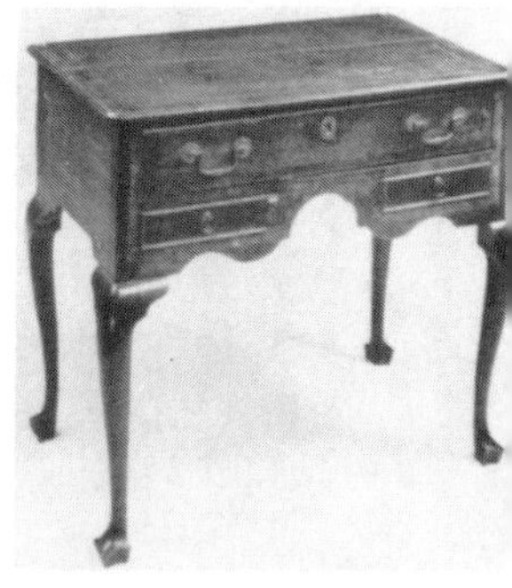

An early Georgian oak side table, on cabriole legs and trifid feet, 31in (79cm).
£1,000-1,500 *C*

An oak cricket table, 18thC, 28in (71cm) diam.
£400-500 *PJ*

An oak cricket table with shelf, 18thC, 20in (52cm).
£350-400 *PCA*

An early Georgian oak side table, with 5 drawers around a kneehole with pierced scrolling fretwork, on square tapering club legs and pad feet, 34in (86cm).
£2,500-3,000 *C*

An oak tripod table, 18thC, 18in (46cm).
£300-350 *PCA*

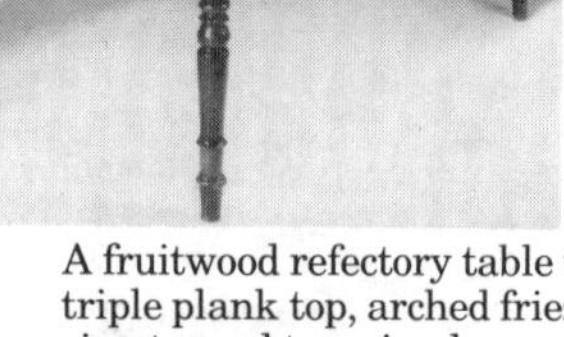

A fruitwood refectory table with triple plank top, arched frieze and ring turned tapering legs, early 19thC, 88½in (224cm).
£4,000-5,000 *C*

An early Victorian oak occasional table in the style of A W N Pugin, with parquetry top, on a spirally turned and foliate carved pedestal with arched brackets pierced with trefoils, on a quadripartite splayed base, 20in (51cm).
£950-1,200 *C*

A Victorian Gothic Revival oak extending dining table, on a central column and 4 leaf headed columnar supports, 57in (144.5cm), with 2 extra leaves.
£1,500-2,000 *Bea*

A mid-Victorian oak dining table, on ring turned baluster legs, with 6 large leaves and one small leaf, stamped Gillow and Company, Lancaster, 216in (548cm) extended.
£1,500-2,000 *CSK*

A William IV pollard oak card table, c1840, 29in (74cm) high.
£2,000-2,500 *SBA*

A pair of William IV pollard oak tea tables, with hinged D-shaped crossbanded tops, with foliate scroll and paw feet, one surface with veneer missing, 35in (90cm).
£6,000-7,000 *P*

\ pollard oak dining table, c1840, ·8in (122cm) diam.
:3,500-4,500 *SBA*

An oak refectory table.
£1,500-2,000 *CSK*

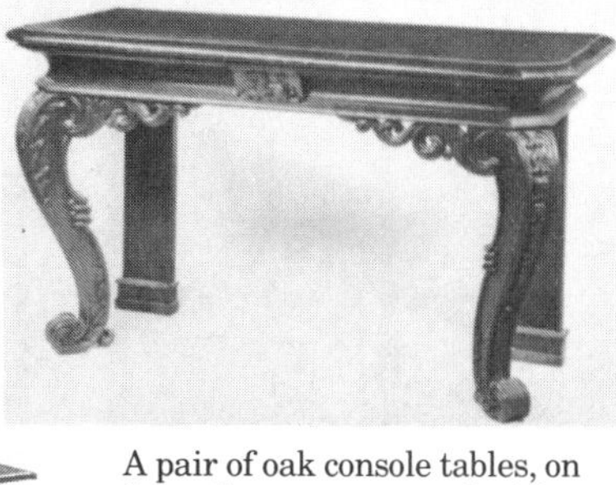

A pair of oak console tables, on S-scroll supports carved with acanthus and bellflowers, 19thC, 65in (165cm).
£900-1,200 *CSK*

\n oak gateleg table with twin-flap op, and baluster legs with onforming stretchers, 64in 162.5cm).
:2,000-2,500 *C*

An oak refectory table with plank top, on massive cup-and-cover legs carved with strapwork and flowerheads, joined by moulded stretchers, 110in (279cm).
£2,000-3,000 *C*

A Spanish walnut side table, with 3 frieze drawers with geometric carving on scrolling pierced trestle ends, 66½in (168cm).
£3,000-4,000 *C*

.n oak refectory table with plank op and plain frieze, on columnar ·gs joined by plain stretchers, 102in 258cm).
3,000-4,000 *C*

An oak refectory table with plank top, the moulded trestle ends pierced with trefoils joined by a pierced arcaded stretcher centred by a turned boss, 67in (170cm).
£2,500-3,500 *C*

An Italian walnut and fruitwood ·efectory table, the top inlaid with strapwork, on solid scrolling trestle ends with claw feet, joined by a shaped stretcher with a grotesque mask, 119in (302cm).
:15,000-16,000 *C*

A walnut, oak and ash refectory table, with solid top within a veneered frame, branded twice E.P., 108in (274cm).
£5,000-6,000 *C*

Miscellaneous

\ French walnut provincial nisericord, 18thC, 72in (182.5cm).
'850-1,000 *RIP*

An English oak delft rack, c1770.
£1,000-1,300 *PHA*

A pair of oak spiral carved columns, 50in (127cm) high.
£350-400 *DN*

A William and Mary carved oak table box, dated 1697.
£350-500 *PHA*

Beds

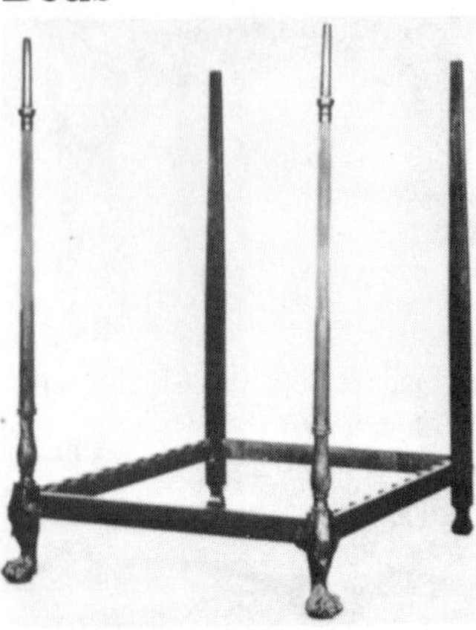

A George II Irish mahogany bedstead, with later tester, on carved hairy paw feet headed by applied scrolling knee brackets with square tapering headposts, restorations, 58in (143cm) wide.
£2,500-3,500 *CNY*

A Regency mahogany and brass campaign bed, with double arched tester and turned tapering posts with brass urn finials, with inscribed brass plaque 'Butler's Patent, Catherine St', 26in (66cm) wide.
£4,500-5,500 *C*

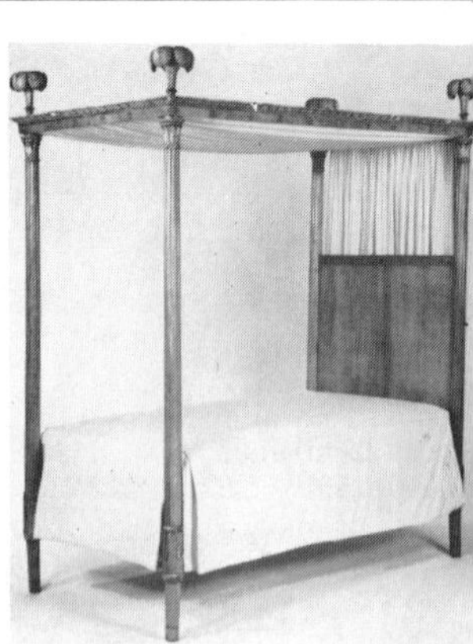

A Regency parcel gilt and fruitwood four-poster bed, with solid headboard, possibly later, box-spring and mattress, on tapering feet, with valance, 43½in (110cm) wide.
£4,000-5,000 *C*

A Regency ivory and green-painted beechwood day bed, upholstered in crimson damask on fluted sabre legs, 87in (221cm) wide.
£2,500-3,000 *C*

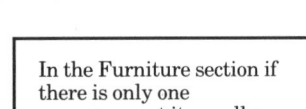

A George III mahogany day bed with scrolled padded ends, seat and squab, on square legs joined by moulded stretchers, 92in (234cm) wide.
£4,500-5,000 *C*

A Regency rosewood day bed, upholstered in red and white striped repp, on splayed legs and brass paw feet, 83in (211cm) long.
£1,500-2,000 *C*

A Regency mahogany day bed, on ribbed splayed legs and brass feet, upholstered in green repp with a squab, with pen inscription 'Ferguson Christie', 74½in (189cm) wide.
£6,000-7,000 *C*

A George III mahogany four-poster bed, with fluted ring turned baluster shaped foot and head posts, later tester, 62in (157cm) wide.
£2,000-3,000 *CNY*

In the Furniture section if there is only one measurement it usually refers to the width of the piece

Make the most of Miller's

Unless otherwise stated, any description which refers to 'a set' or 'a pair' includes a valuation for the entire set or the pair, even though the illustration may show only a single item

A four-poster bed in Chippendale style, with mahogany cluster columns, giltwood carved frieze, c1780.
£1,500-2,000 *RIP*

A George III painted cradle, with ogee arched hood and cane filled sides suspended from spreading uprights on splayed legs, later decorated with berried foliage, 41in (102cm) long.
£900-1,200 *C*

Victorian mahogany half tester ·d, with shaped footboard centred ith an oval panel.
00-1,200 *TM*

A mahogany four-poster bedstead, on block feet, with box-spring and mattress, labelled Heal & Son, Makers of Bedsteads and Bedding, London, W., 74in (188cm).
£4,000-5,000 *C*

A pair of walnut day beds, each upholstered in yellow damask, on pierced S-scroll supports applied with roundels, early 19thC, 84in (213cm).
£1,500-2,000 *CSK*

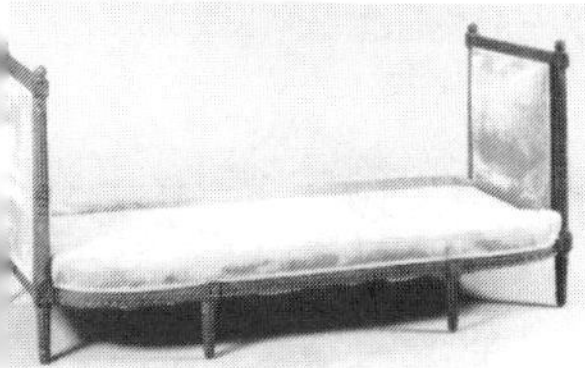

Louis XVI green painted 'lit alcove', with padded sides, the seat il carved with 'guilloche', pholstered in apricot velvet, storations, 74in (188cm) wide.
,100-2,500 *CNY*

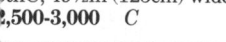

An Italian blue painted and parcel gilt four-poster double bedstead, the headboard with broken swan neck pediment centred by a caryatid above a panel of scrolling foliage and putti, the footboard similar, the posts with fluted urn-shaped finials and foliate capitals decorated with entrelacs, including side rails, 19thC, 71in (180cm) wide.
£1,500-2,000 *C*

A small mahogany four-poster bed with arched canopy, turned supports and solid headboard, with box-spring and mattress and hangings, 43in (109cm) wide.
£3,000-4,000 *C*

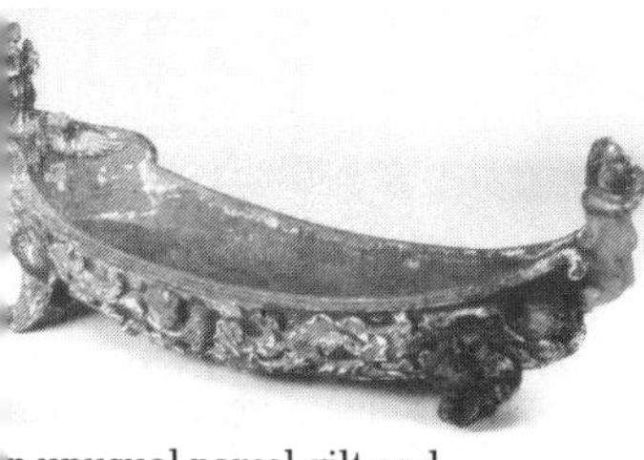

n unusual parcel gilt and lychrome hanging cradle of avette form, the prow carved with putto, the stern with the Virgin d Child, on scroll feet with bronze ndles, Spanish or Venetian, early thC, 49½in (125cm) wide.
,500-3,000 *C*

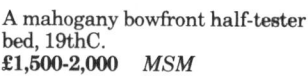

A mahogany bowfront half-tester bed, 19thC.
£1,500-2,000 *MSM*

onheur du Jour

Regency mahogany bonheur du r, with three-quarter gallery and small drawers with one frieze awer and ring turned tapering s, 19in (48cm).
,900-2,200 *C*

A Regency rosewood bonheur du jour with shelves and cupboards, with enclosed cedar-lined drawers, the frieze drawer with leather-lined easel, above a pair of cupboard doors on square tapering legs, 34½in (87cm).
£4,000-5,000 *C*

A decorated satinwood bonheur du jour, 19thC.
£2,000-3,000 *RIP*

A black lacquered bonheur du jour, 19thC.
£700-900 *P[CW]*

A Victorian figured walnut bonheur du jour, decorated with ormolu handles and mounts.
£2,000-2,500 *LRG*

An Edwardian satinwood bonheur du jour, crossbanded in rosewood, on 8 square tapered supports, 67in (170cm).
£3,500-4,000 *P[Pea]*

A scarlet boulle and ebonised bonheur du jour, inset with 'premier partie' panels and applied with gilt metal mounts, on cabriole legs mounted with sabots and caryatid headings, 33in (84cm).
£1,500-2,000 *CSK*

A Victorian walnut bonheur du jour, inlaid with satinwood scrolls and a border of coloured wood crossbanding and with ormolu embellishments, on cabriole legs, 42in (107cm).
£1,500-2,000 *M*

A late Victorian ormolu-mounted ebonised bonheur du jour, mounted with Sèvres style plaques, with partially leather-lined top, on square tapering cabriole legs with female mask-clasps reaching to foliate sabots, stamped Edwards & Roberts, Wardour St London, 43in (109cm).
£900-1,200 *C*

Make the Most of Miller's

In Miller's we do NOT just reprint saleroom estimates. We work from realised prices either from an auction room or a dealer. Our consultants then work out a realistic price range for a similar piece. This is to try to avoid repeating freak results – either low or high

A Victorian mahogany bonheur du jour, inlaid with urn satinwood ovals in boxwood line outlines, 29½in (75cm).
£1,300-1,600 *CSK*

A late Victorian satinwood bonheur du jour, the hinged top crossbanded with rosewood and fitted with an arched superstructure, enclosing 8 various sized drawers, the frieze fitted with a drawer, on square tapering legs, 34in (86cm).
£2,500-3,000 *C*

A satinwood bonheur du jour, the top crossbanded with rosewood with 2 frieze drawers on square tapering legs, 27½in (70cm).
£1,700-2,000 *C*

A satinwood veneered bonheur du jour with Maple & Co. trade label, with brass urn finials to the gallery, lift-over flap, front frieze drawer with ornate brass swan neck handles, the square tapering legs on casters, 28½in (72cm).
£1,500-2,000 *WW*

. tulipwood and marquetry
onheur du jour, with galleried
nottled black and red marble top,
ne base with leather-lined flap
nlaid with vases of flowers and
nstruments, with a drawer, on
apering legs, 26in (66cm).
1,800-2,200 *C*

A neo-classical style satinwood bonheur du jour, on turned tapering legs, 29in (74cm).
£2,500-3,000 *CSK*

Breakfront Bookcases

A George II style mahogany serpentine breakfront bookcase, on scrolling block feet, 83in (210.5cm).
£4,000-5,000 *CSK*

A George II style pinewood breakfront library bookcase, with fluted Vitruvian scroll carved panels, divided by pilasters with patera headings, on plinth base, 71in (180cm).
£6,000-6,500 *CSK*

Use the Index!

Because certain items might fit easily into any of a number of categories, the quickest and surest method of locating any entry is by reference to the index at the back of the book.
This has been fully cross-referenced for absolute simplicity.

A Regency mahogany bookcase, with figured panelled doors flanked by outset spirally reeded columns continuing to ring turned legs, the upper section possibly of different origin, 48in (121cm).
£900-1,200 *Bon*

A Regency mahogany breakfront library bookcase, on a plinth base, 105in (267cm).
£12,000-15,000 *P*

A mid-Georgian style elm and mahogany breakfront library bookcase, the arcaded dentilled moulded cornice above 4 glazed astragal doors and 4 panel cupboa doors applied with radial and shel mouldings, divided by reeded quadrant pilasters, on ogee bracke feet, 93in (236cm).
£2,000-2,500 *CSK*

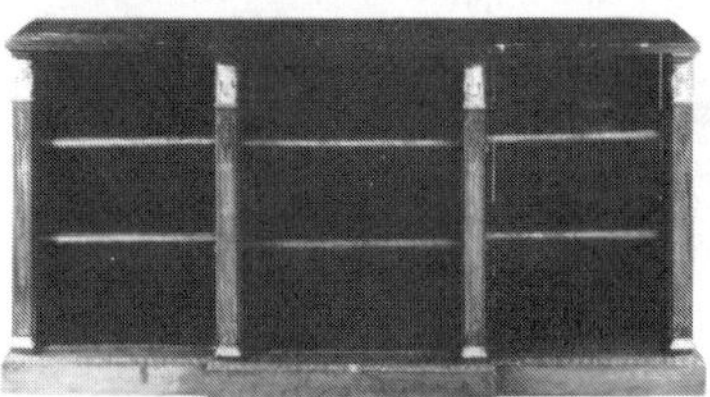

A Regency rosewood bookcase, brass inlaid and panel gilt with ebonised reeded edge, fitted with guilloche moulded gilt gesso shelves flanked by stiles with caryatid masks and cut brass inlay, on a plinth base.
£2,000-2,500 *P*

A George III mahogany bookcase chest, with 2 long and 2 short drawers, and 3 shallow frieze drawers on ogee bracket feet, 50in (127cm).
£700-800 *M*

A George III mahogany breakfron bookcase, the base with a pair of doors enclosing slides, flanked by 10 drawers, 100in (254cm).
£5,000-6,000 *C*

A George III mahogany breakfront bookcase, on a plinth base, 78in (198cm).
£4,000-4,500 *WW*

An early Victorian calamander bookcase, on a plinth base, 46in (117cm).
£2,000-2,500 *Bon*

A George III mahogany and band inlaid breakfront library bookcase, fitted with adjustable shelves enclosed by 2 pairs of barred glass doors, the base with folio trays enclosed by a pair of oval panelled doors flanked by 10 drawers with brass handles, 73in (185cm).
£5,000-6,000 *GC*

A mahogany breakfront bookcase, with fitted secretaire flanked by cupboards, 19thC.
£4,000-4,500 *MGM*

Victorian mahogany bookcase.
,000-1,500 *TW*

A late Victorian mahogany breakfront library bookcase, the top section with a pierced spindle baluster gallery, on graduated block feet, stamped Lamb, Manchester, 106in (269cm).
£2,000-3,000 *CSK*

An early Victorian carved mahogany library bookcase, the upper part with a moulded cornice enclosed by arched glazed panel doors between headed foliate brackets, the lower part enclosed by panel doors below, on a plinth base, 122in (310cm).
£4,000-5,000 *P*

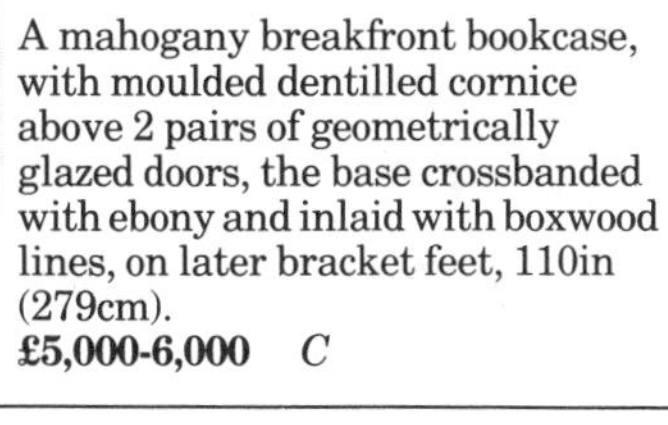

A mahogany breakfront bookcase, with moulded dentilled cornice above 2 pairs of geometrically glazed doors, the base crossbanded with ebony and inlaid with boxwood lines, on later bracket feet, 110in (279cm).
£5,000-6,000 *C*

ureau Bookcases

George III mahogany bureau okcase, the interior with 'Ich en' and bell husk decoration, ass swan neck handles, and ogee acket feet, 47in (119cm).
,000-6,000 *HOD*

An early Georgian crossbanded and feather inlaid walnut bureau bookcase, with fully fitted interior, brass handles and pierced escutcheons, on bracket feet, some damage, 43in (109cm).
£7,000-8,000 *GC*

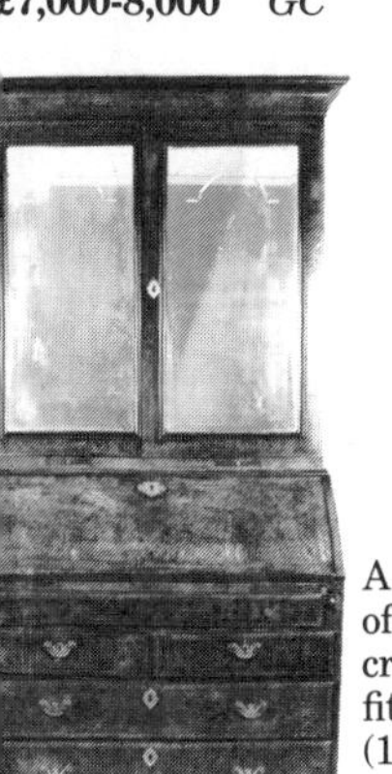

A George I walnut bureau bookcase, of faded colour, with feather crossbanding, the interior fully fitted, on bracket supports, 40in (101.5cm).
£5,500-6,500 *P[Pea]*

A George III mahogany bureau bookcase, the upper part with architectural dentil cornice, with fitted interior, the lower part with 4 long drawers, original brass handles, on bracket feet, 39in (99cm).
£4,500-5,500 *DN*

A Georgian mahogany bureau bookcase, with fitted interior, 6 drawers and bracket feet.
£3,000-4,000 *MGM*

A George I walnut bureau bookcase, the sunburst mirrored doors enclosing adjustable shelves, the fall front enclosing oak lined fitted interior, with brass drop handles and escutcheons, on bracket feet.
£4,500-5,500 *P[Wor]*

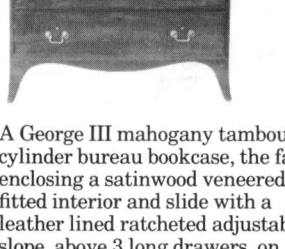

A George III mahogany tambour cylinder bureau bookcase, the fall enclosing a satinwood veneered fitted interior and slide with a leather lined ratcheted adjustable slope, above 3 long drawers, on swept bracket feet, 41in (104cm).
£8,000-9,000 *P*

A George III mahogany bureau bookcase with a swan neck pediment, the sloping front with fitted interior, on ogee bracket fee[t], 48in (122cm).
£4,500-5,500 *OL*

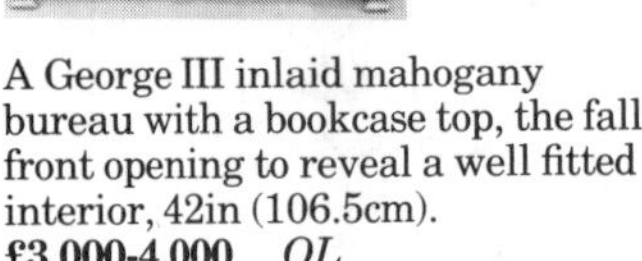

A George III inlaid mahogany bureau with a bookcase top, the fall front opening to reveal a well fitted interior, 42in (106.5cm).
£3,000-4,000 *OL*

A late Georgian mahogany bureau bookcase with broken scroll pediment, astragal glazed doors, on splay bracket feet, 44in (111.5cm).
£2,000-2,500 *JRB*

A mahogany bureau bookcase with fitted interior, dentil moulded cornice under a broken architectural pediment, some restoration, late 18thC, 84in (213cm) high.
£3,000-4,000 *BM*

A George III elm bureau bookcase, the upper section with moulded cornice above a pair of lozenge astragal glazed doors, the fall enclosing a fitted interior, 39in (99cm).
£3,500-4,500 *Bon*

A mahogany bureau bookcase, with a fitted interior enclosed by writing flap, 19thC, 38in (96cm).
£2,500-3,500 *P[Pea]*

A mahogany bureau bookcase, with moulded arcaded cornice above a panelled cupboard door, the crossbanded sloping flap enclosing a fitted interior, above 3 graduated long drawers, on bracket feet, 31in (79cm).
£2,000-3,000 *C*

A Chippendale carved mahogany bureau bookcase, the upper part with a dentil moulded swan neck pediment and cornice with rosette and pierced blind fret ornament, the sloping fall enclosing a fitted interior, on bracket feet, pediment damaged, 45in (115cm).
£7,500-8,500 *P*

An Edwardian mahogany bureau bookcase, inlaid with satinwood, 36in (91.5cm).
£2,000-3,000 *RIP*

)warf Bookcases

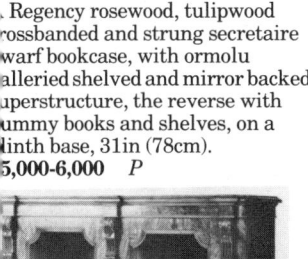

A George IV mahogany dwarf bookcase, with 4 tiers, joined by baluster columns with X-shaped spindles on a plinth base, 40in (101.5cm).
£1,600-2,000 *C*

A Regency mahogany bookcase, with waved top and sides, on bun feet, 36in (91.5cm).
£1,200-1,500 *C*

. Regency rosewood, tulipwood ·rossbanded and strung secretaire warf bookcase, with ormolu alleried shelved and mirror backed uperstructure, the reverse with ummy books and shelves, on a linth base, 31in (78cm).
5,000-6,000 *P*

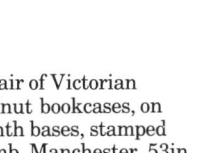

A pair of Victorian walnut bookcases, on plinth bases, stamped Lamb, Manchester, 53in (134cm).
£2,000-2,500 *Bon*

A mahogany dwarf bookcase, the top fitted with a two-tier three-quarter galleried superstructure on brass supports, with 2 brass grille panel doors, early 19thC, 36in (91.5cm).
£2,200-2,500 *CSK*

A burr walnut breakfront side cabinet bookcase, 19thC, 73in (185cm).
£1,500-2,000 *DN*

The reason so many side cabinets are being called bookcases is due to the ready market for the latter.

BOOKCASES

- ★ check that the glazing bars match the rest of the bookcase in quality, timber and age. Breakfront wardrobes of the mid to late 19thC can be turned into bookcases by removing the solid panels to the doors and glazing the frames
- ★ during the late 19thC many old glazed door cabinets were removed from their bureau or cupboard bases to have feet added and the tops fitted in to make 'Georgian' display or bookcases. This was not an 18thC form; the correct version was much taller and often had drawers to the frieze base. The low 'dwarf' bookcases without doors became popular during the late 18thC
- ★ the earliest form of adjustable shelf on the better quality bookcases was achieved by cutting rabbets into the sides of the cabinet into which the shelves could slide. Next came a toothed ladder at each side, the removable rungs forming the shelf rests. Finally, by the end of the 18thC, came movable pegs fitting into holes. Regency examples were often made of gilt metal or brass
- ★ check when a bookcase sits on a bureau or cupboard base that it is slightly smaller than the base, and it is preferable that the retaining moulding is fixed to the base not the top; also, it is unlikely that the top surface to such a base would have been veneered originally
- ★ a bureau made to take a bookcase on top will have a steeper angle to the fall front to create a greater depth to accommodate the case or cabinet

A rosewood dwarf cabinet, the top inlaid with brass paterae, above a pair of glazed and trellis filled recessed panelled doors, flanked by columns with chased ormolu capitals, on bun feet, 36in (91.5cm).
£3,000-4,000 *C*

A pair of William IV rosewood dwarf bookcases, with gilt scrolling foliate uprights, the lower ones headed by lion's masks, on moulded base and foliate bun feet, 37in (94cm).
£5,500-6,500 *C*

Library Bookcases

A Georgian carved mahogany breakfront library bookcase, with a swan neck pediment, and pierced trellis dentil cornice, 99in (250cm).
£20,000-22,000 *P*

A George III mahogany bookcase, with geometrically glazed cupboard doors, the base with oval panelled doors, 52in (132cm).
£8,000-10,000 *C*

A George III mahogany bookcase with moulded cornice, astragal glazed doors, a shaped apron below and on splayed bracket feet, 62in (157cm).
£2,200-2,500 *Bea*

A Victorian mahogany bookcase, the top section with a bolection moulded cornice, on plinth base, 75½in (192cm).
£2,000-2,500 *CSK*

A George III mahogany secretaire library bookcase, with moulded dentilled swan neck breakfront pediment above 2 glazed cupboard doors, the lower part with secretaire drawer and fitted interior, on moulded base, 67in (170cm).
£12,000-14,000 *CNY*

A late Georgian mahogany bookcase, inlaid with chequered boxwood lines, spandrels and roundels, the top with a broken pediment, on splayed bracket feet, 76in (193cm).
£3,000-4,000 *CSK*

A small Regency style ormolu mounted mahogany bookcase, on a plinth base, 36in (91.5cm).
£2,000-2,500 *C*

A pair of Regency mahogany bookcases with ebony stringing and later scrolled broken pediment, adapted, 52in (132cm).
£13,000-15,000 *C*

A Regency mahogany bookcase, with 2 panelled doors to the lower section, on bun feet, 37½in (95cm).
£3,500-4,500 *Bea*

A Regency rosewood library bookcase, with gilt metal grillwork applied with rosettes with green silk behind, enclosing a shelf, on moulded plinth, 43in (109cm).
£2,500-3,500 *CNY*

A carved mahogany bookcase, with interlaced blind fret decoration, on a plinth base, 19thC, 57in (146cm).
£3,000-4,000 *P*

A George IV mahogany breakfront library bookcase, on plinth base, 113in (287cm).
£4,500-5,500 *P[Re]*

late Regency mahogany pedestal ›okcase, the top with a banded ieze above open adjustable shelves ıd 2 long base drawers, between lt metal sphinx headed turned lasters, on plinth base, laptations, 30in (76cm).
ı00-700 *CSK*

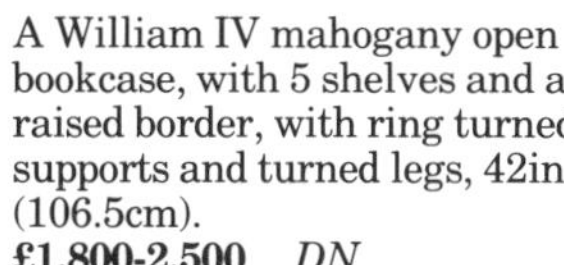

A William IV mahogany open bookcase, with 5 shelves and a raised border, with ring turned supports and turned legs, 42in (106.5cm).
£1,800-2,500 *DN*

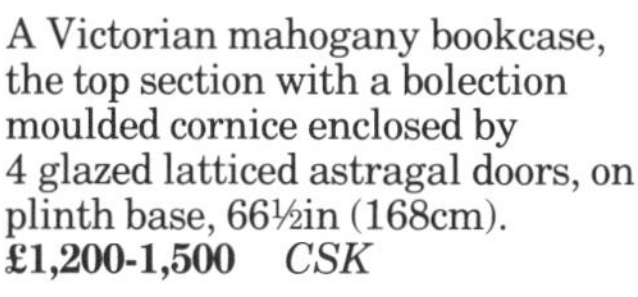

A Victorian mahogany bookcase, the top section with a bolection moulded cornice enclosed by 4 glazed latticed astragal doors, on plinth base, 66½in (168cm).
£1,200-1,500 *CSK*

A Victorian burr walnut breakfront open bookcase, 48in (122cm).
£1,000-1,500 *TW*

A George III style mahogany breakfront library bookcase, c1900, 74in (188cm).
£3,700-4,500 *N*

A mid-Victorian walnut bookcase, with moulded cornice above 3 glazed cupboard doors and 3 arched panelled doors, on plinth base, 89in (226cm).
£5,000-6,000 *C*

A Victorian mahogany bookcase, the moulded cornice above a pair of arched plain glazed doors, the base with a pair of arched panelled doors, on plinth base, 57in (145cm).
£1,500-2,000 *Bon*

A pair of ebonised and green painted bookcases, with fall flaps decorated with ribbon tied scrolling foliage, on square tapering legs, 30in (76cm).
£5,500-6,000 *C*

A bookcase, the sides painted with diamonds within wave borders, the 2 cupboard doors painted with animals leaving the Ark, beneath the inscription 'The rain is over and gone', 56in (142cm) high.
£600-1,000 *P[CW]*

A mahogany bookcase, with plinth base, 83in (211cm).
£2,500-3,000 *C*

An Edwardian satinwood banded mahogany revolving bookcase, 19½in (50cm).
£1,000-1,500 *P[CW]*

A Biedermeier satinbirch bookcase, the upper part with a moulded cornice and enclosed by a pair of ebonised arched astragal glazed doors, with a pair of panel doors below, on bracket feet, 51½in (131cm).
£600-700 *P*

A pair of George III mahogany bookcases, with moulded dentilled cornices and geometrically glazed doors enclosing shelves, on moulded plinths, 52in (132cm).
£8,500-9,500 *C*

A mahogany bookcase, with moulded arcaded cornice above 3 glazed cupboard doors and 3 panelled cupboard doors, lacking plinth base, 54½in (164cm).
£2,200-2,600 *C*

Secretaire Bookcases

A George III mahogany secretaire bookcase, applied with radial mouldings, 47½in (120cm).
£2,000-2,500 *CSK*

A George III mahogany secretaire cabinet, with moulded dentilled cornice above a pair of geometrically glazed cupboard doors, the baize lined secretaire drawer enclosing a fitted interior, on bracket feet, 48in (122cm).
£3,000-4,000 *C*

A George III mahogany secretaire bookcase, the base with a baize lined secretaire drawer above 3 graduated long drawers, on bracket feet, replacements, the top and base possibly associated, 43½in (110.5cm).
£3,000-3,500 *C*

A George III mahogany breakfront secretaire bookcase, now adapted into 3 separate bookcases, with fall front writing drawers and fitted interiors, the centre bookcase 51in (129cm) wide, the pair of bookcases each 32½in (82.5cm).
£6,000-8,000 *C*

A Regency mahogany secretaire bookcase, 41in (104cm).
£1,500-2,000 *Bon*

A Regency mahogany secretaire bookcase, c1820, 48in (122cm).
£1,500-2,000 *N*

A Regency mahogany secretaire bookcase, inlaid with ebony and applied with ormolu mounts, the lower section with a satinwood fitted interior above 2 panelled doors between pilasters headed by anthemions, on lion's paw feet, 50in (127cm).
£2,000-3,000 *CSK*

A late Regency mahogany secretaire bookcase, inlaid with satinwood, shells and boxwood lines in rosewood banded borders, 38½in (98cm).
£3,000-3,500 *CSK*

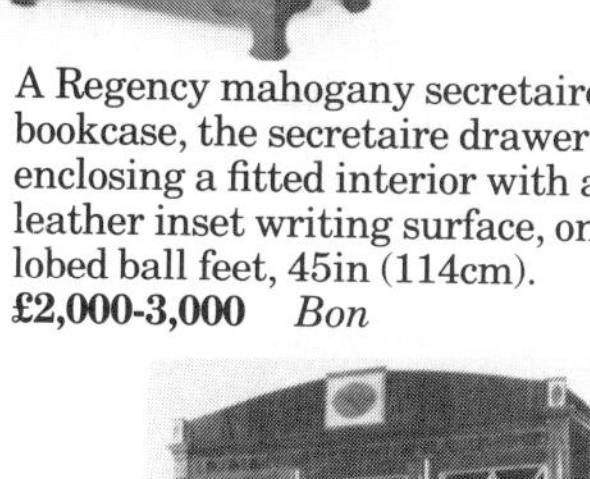

A Regency mahogany secretaire bookcase, the secretaire drawer enclosing a fitted interior with a leather inset writing surface, on lobed ball feet, 45in (114cm).
£2,000-3,000 *Bon*

A Regency mahogany secretaire bookcase, the fall front secretaire drawer revealing lidded document wells and baize covered writing part, 54in (137cm).
£5,500-7,500 *M*

A Regency mahogany and satinwood banded secretaire bookcase, the lower section with a secretaire drawer enclosing pigeonholes above 3 oval panelled cupboard doors, on outswept bracket feet, 69in (175cm).
£4,000-5,000 *Bon*

A Georgian mahogany satinwood banded and boxwood strung secretaire bookcase, with tooled leather-lined fall enclosing a fitted interior, on bracket feet, 45½in (115cm).
£3,000-3,500 *P*

A mahogany secretaire bookcase, the 2 doors with satinwood strung astragal glazing enclosing adjustable shelves, the secretaire drawer with pigeonholes and small drawers faced in maple, early 19thC, 51in (130cm).
£2,000-3,000 *P[PWC]*

An inlaid mahogany secretaire bookcase with key pattern cornice, on bracket feet, 19thC, 40in (101cm).
£2,500-3,000 *HCH*

A William IV carved mahogany lady's bookcase, in the manner of Richard Brown, the upper part enclosed by a pair of brass grille an glazed panel doors, 28½in (72cm).
£8,000-9,000 *P*

A William IV mahogany secretaire bookcase, 49in (125cm).
£1,500-2,000 *P[Pea]*

A mahogany secretaire bookcase, with 2 simulated drawers enclosin a writing slide and lidded compartments, the 2 panelled door applied with C-scrolls, foliage and flowers, on acanthus carved brack feet, 40½in (103cm).
£2,300-2,700 *Bea*

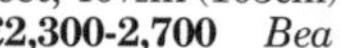

Buckets

A George III Irish mahogany peat bucket with brass bands, swing handle and liner, 14in (35.5cm) diam.
£600-650 *P[Pea]*

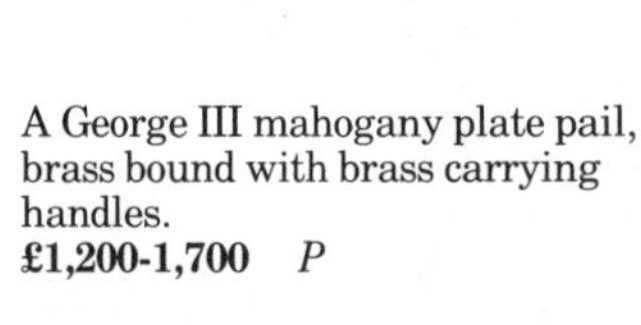

A George III mahogany plate pail, brass bound with brass carrying handles.
£1,200-1,700 *P*

Two George III brass mounted mahogany peat buckets, with brass swing handle and brass liner, 14 and 13in (36 and 33cm) wide.
£1,500-2,000 *P*

A Georgian brass bound mahogany plate bucket, with swing handle.
£1,000-1,500 *GC*

A Georgian mahogany caned plat bucket with brass liner and loop handle, 14in (35.5cm).
£2,500-3,000 *Wor*

A Georgian mahogany plate bucket, banded in brass, c1760.
£1,500-2,000 *RIP*

A Regency mahogany brass bound plate bucket, with carrying handle and tapering sides, 16½in (42cm) high.
£1,000-1,500 *C*

A Regency mahogany brass bound bucket, with tin liner and tapering body with a carrying handle, 12in (30.5cm).
£1,000-1,500 *C*

Bureaux

A walnut bureau, the crossbanded and herringbone banded fall enclosing a fitted interior, early 18thC with restoration, 36in (91.5cm).
£1,600-2,000 *Bon*

A walnut and herringbone banded bureau, the fall with fitted interior, on bun feet, early 18thC, 40in (101.5cm).
£4,000-5,000 *P[CW]*

A walnut, crossbanded and featherstrung bureau, the sloping fall enclosing a fitted interior with pigeonholes, the lower part with 2 short and 2 long drawers, on bracket feet, restored, early 18thC, 34½in (87cm).
£2,700-3,200 *P*

A George I walnut, crossbanded and featherbanded bureau, the fall enclosing a graduated interior with secret compartments, on bracket feet, 36in (91cm).
£2,500-3,500 *P*

A Dutch walnut and floral marquetry bombé printed bureau, the sloping fall enclosing a fitted interior, with a rocaille palmette spray in the apron, terminating in claw-and-ball feet, 18thC, 48in (123cm).
£6,000-7,000 *P*

A Dutch walnut and floral marquetry bombé bureau, with stepped fittings and well enclosed by a decorated fall, on carved paw feet, 18thC, 40in (101.5cm).
£5,000-6,000 *DN*

A George I walnut veneered bureau, inlaid with featherbanding, on bracket feet, re-polished, 31in (79cm).
£12,000-15,000 *Bea*

A walnut bureau, 18thC with later feet and interior, requiring restoration, 38in (96.5cm).
£1,300-1,700 *SAg*

A Georgian figured mahogany bureau, the fall front revealing a central cupboard with fitted interior, 40in (101.5cm).
£700-800 *JRB*

A mahogany bureau, with fitted interior, brass swan neck handles, and bracket feet, 30in (76cm).
£1,600-2,000 *JD*

A Georgian mahogany bureau, the fall front revealing a mahogany veneered interior, the drawers boxwood strung and inlaid with shell patera, 48in (122cm).
£1,000-1,500 *TM*

A George II burr yew-wood bureau, the sloping fall enclosing an oak fitted interior with secret compartments, on bracket feet, 34½in (88cm).
£6,000-7,000 *P*

A George I walnut bureau, inlaid with featherbanding, the sloping front enclosing a fitted interior, on later base and bracket feet, 39½in (100cm).
£3,500-4,500 *C*

A Georgian mahogany bureau, with fitted interior, on bracket feet.
£1,500-2,000 *MGM*

A Georgian mahogany bureau.
£800-1,200 *HP*

BUREAUX

Points to look for:

- ★ originality and condition
- ★ good colour and patination
- ★ good proportions
- ★ quality of construction
- ★ original handles and escutcheons
- ★ original feet
- ★ small size (3ft is about average)
- ★ stepped interior and a central cupboard
- ★ fitted 'well' with a slide
- ★ oak drawer linings
- ★ secret compartments

A George I walnut bureau, inlaid with chequered lines, the sloping front enclosing a fitted interior, on later bracket feet, 41½in (105cm).
£13,000-15,000 *C*

An early Georgian burr yew and burr walnut bureau, the crossbanded sloping front enclosing a fitted interior, on later bracket feet, possibly formerly with a well, 39in (99cm).
£3,500-4,500 *C*

A Georgian mahogany writing bureau with fitted interior, on bracket feet.
£500-600 *MGM*

A late George III mahogany bureau, the sloping front enclosing a fitted interior, on ogee supports, 44in (111.5cm).
£1,200-1,600 *P[Re]*

A George III mahogany cylinder tambour front bureau, the fall enclosing a satinwood veneered interior, with lozenge inlay and tambour shuttered enclosed compartments, with a green leather hinged slope, 40in (101cm).
£2,500-3,500 *P*

A George III mahogany bureau, the sloping flap enclosing a fitted interior above 4 long drawers, on partly replaced bracket feet, 36in (91.5cm).
£2,000-2,500 *C*

A late Georgian mahogany bureau, with crossbanded fall front enclosing pigeonholes and drawers, above 3 long and 2 short drawers, with brass handles and oval stamped backplates, 38in (96.5cm).
£500-600 *LBP*

A George III mahogany and satinwood banded tambour cylinder bureau, the top above a boxwood and ebony strung tambour fall enclosing a fitted interior, on later turned legs, 39½in (99cm).
£2,500-3,500 *Bon*

A George III mahogany bureau on stand, with three-quarter gallery, and sloping front enclosing a fitted interior, on square chamfered legs and shaped feet, 36in (91.5cm).
£2,000-2,500 *C*

A George III mahogany bureau, with a sloping fall front enclosing drawers and pigeonholes, on bracket feet, 37in (94cm).
£1,500-2,000 *Bea*

A George III mahogany bureau, the sloping fall front inlaid with a shell medallion and quadrant fans, 40½in (102cm).
£1,500-2,000 *Bea*

A Dutch mahogany bureau à cylindre, inlaid with marquetry in boxwood line borders, on fluted block and bracket feet, early 19thC, 45in (114cm).
£3,500-4,000 *CSK*

A Dutch walnut and floral marquetry bombé cylinder bureau, the inlaid fall enclosing a baize lined slide and fitted interior, on splayed bracket feet with gilt metal sabots, late 18th/early 19thC.
£4,000-5,000 *P*

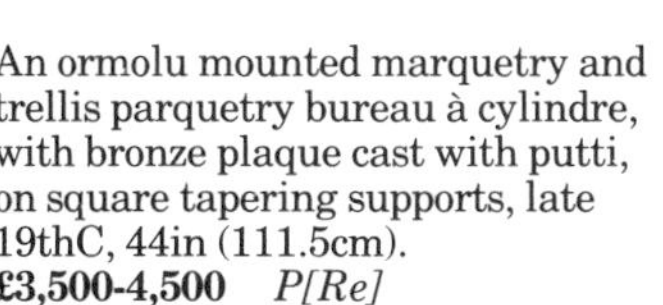

An ormolu mounted marquetry and trellis parquetry bureau à cylindre, with bronze plaque cast with putti, on square tapering supports, late 19thC, 44in (111.5cm).
£3,500-4,500 *P[Re]*

NOTES ON DUTCH MARQUETRY BUREAUX

- ★ beware badly split flaps and slides
- ★ marquetry on walnut fetches more than marquetry on mahogany, which in turn fetches more than marquetry on oak
- ★ cylinder bureaux as a general rule fetch less than fall front bureaux
- ★ always look out for marquetry which includes bone and/or mother-of-pearl
- ★ marquetry including birds and insects is slightly rarer than the usual floral marquetry

A Dutch mahogany bombé bureau, the fall flap enclosing a fitted interior, on large claw-and-ball feet, 19thC, 52in (132cm).
£2,500-3,500 *L*

A Dutch walnut and foliate marquetry bombé bureau, with fitted interior, 19thC, 50in (127cm).
£6,500-7,500 *CSK*

A French tulipwood bureau, banded in rosewood, with chased gilt metal mounts, on cabriole legs, late 19thC, 25in (63cm).
£1,400-2,000 *DN*

A Victorian figured walnut and gilt metal mounted bureau de dame, inlaid with boxwood lines and arabesques, the top with a mirrored superstructure, 32in (81cm).
£1,500-2,000 *CSK*

An early Victorian rosewood escritoire, 43½in (110cm).
£850-950 *DN*

An Edwardian inlaid lady's cylinder writing bureau, with fitted interior 2 drawers, and brass gallery to back.
£700-800 *MGM*

A French mahogany bureau de dame, applied with metal mounts, with three-quarter galleried marble top above 3 frieze drawers, between fluted uprights above a cylinder painted in the manner of Vernis Martin, enclosing a fitted interior, late 19thC, 31in (79cm).
£1,500-2,000 *CSK*

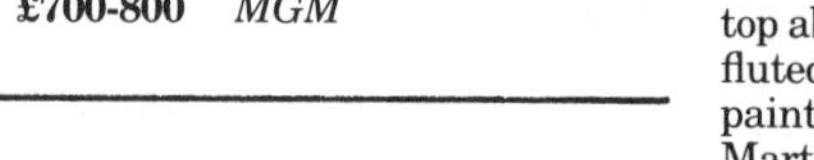

A late Victorian walnut cylinder bureau, with pierced gallery and frieze drawer, the cylinder enclosing fitted interior and pull-out writing slide, 30in (76cm).
£450-650 *LBP*

Bureau Cabinets

A walnut crossbanded and featherstrung bureau cabinet, on bracket feet, reveneered, early 18thC, 42½in (107cm).
£6,500-8,000 *P*

A walnut secretaire cabinet, early 18thC.
£13,000-15,000 *DN*

A George III mahogany bureau cabinet, on bracket feet, 38½in (98cm).
£2,500-3,500 *CSK*

A Dutch marquetry escritoire, the fall front enclosing an arcaded shelf, drawers and central cupboard, on turned feet, early 19thC, 40in (101cm).
£2,000-3,000 *GC*

A Georgian walnut bureau bookcase, inlaid with feather and crossbanding, with brass handles and pierced escutcheons, raised on bracket feet, 38in (96.5cm).
£1,500-2,000 *AG*

A George III mahogany secretaire cabinet, the arched dentilled cornice carved with a patera and bell-flower swag, the base with a fitted secretaire drawer, above 2 short and 2 graduated long drawers, on bracket feet, 51in (129.5cm).
£7,000-8,000 *C*

. Queen Anne bureau cabinet, on gee bracket feet, bearing the label Restored by Albert Bromley August 28 1917, Furniture restorer, Blackburn', 41in (104cm).
8,000-10,000 *Bon*

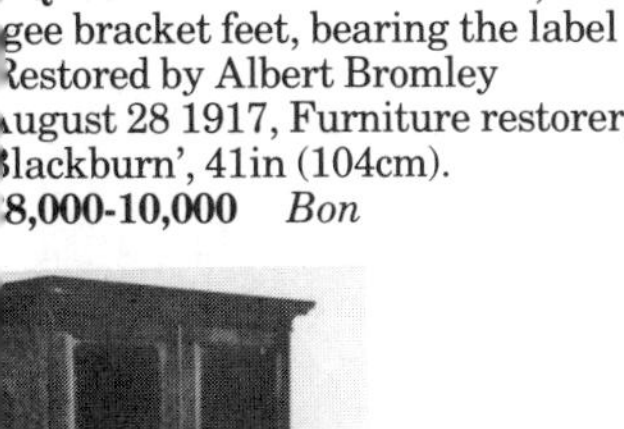

An Edwardian satinwood bookcase cabinet, crossbanded in rosewood, with oval figure panels after Angelica Kauffman, on apron stand, 32in (81cm).
£3,000-4,000 *P[Pea]*

A George III mahogany secretaire cabinet, with bowed cornice above a pair of Gothic glazed cupboard doors, the base with a fitted secretaire drawer, 43in (109cm).
£6,000-7,000 *C*

. walnut bureau cabinet with moulded cornice above a pair of bevelled glazed cupboard doors, enclosing a partly fitted interior with 2 candle slides, the sloping flap enclosing a fitted interior, 39½in (100cm).
4,500-5,500 *C*

An inlaid rosewood music cabinet, with upper gallery and door panels inlaid with urns, standing on square legs.
£500-600 *MGM*

A Dutch mahogany and fruitwood cabinet, with a stepped cornice above a long drawer enclosing secret drawers, a pair of panel doors enclosing a fitted interior, on bracket feet, 18thC, 47in (119cm).
£1,500-2,500 *AG*

A Dutch mahogany and gilt metal mounted secretaire à abattant, with 2 glazed panel doors above a fall front, enclosing an elm and ebony inlaid interior, early 19thC.
£1,500-2,000 *CSK*

A Dutch mahogany secretaire à abattant, inlaid with brass geometric lines, the top with a frieze drawer above a fall writing panel, enclosing a fitted interior, early 19thC, 40½in (102cm).
£2,000-3,000 *CSK*

A Dutch mahogany crossbanded and inlaid escritoire, with a friez drawer and fall with ebony lines broken outline and chequer stringing, on square tapered legs the interior converted, early 19t
£2,500-3,500 *P*

A French boulle cabinet, the lower doors decorated in red tortoiseshell and cut brass, the sides with conforming boulle panels, gilt brass bun feet, 38in (96.5cm).
£9,000-12,000 *PWC*

A late Empire mahogany secretaire à abattant with brass mounted outlines, with marble top above a fall writing panel with enclosed fitted interior, on tapering feet, 37½in (95cm).
£2,500-3,500 *CSK*

An Empire ormolu mounted secretaire à abattant, with mottl black marble top, the leather lin fall flap enclosing a fitted interio on shaped feet, 39in (99cm).
£2,500-3,500 *C*

A Louis XV tulipwood and kingwood secretaire à abattant, with later red marble top above a fall flap inlaid 'à quatre faces' enclosing a fitted interior, stamped L Boudin twice, JME 4 times, and J. Tuart once, 36in (91.5cm).
£2,500-3,500 *C*

A Scandinavian mahogany bureau cabinet, decorated with flutings and roundels, with geometric boxwood lines, on block feet, early 19thC, 45in (114cm).
£2,500-3,500 *CSK*

A German mahogany secretaire à abattant, the arched panelled fall enclosing a fitted interior, on a plinth base, late 19thC, 42in (106cm).
£3,000-4,000 *Bon*

An Italian walnut and marquetry secretaire cabinet, the fall flap inlaid with scrolling foliage, enclosing 15 various-sized drawers on later bracket feet, 41in (104cm)
£3,000-4,000 *C*

Cabinets on Stands

A Louis XVI kingwood, tulipwood and crossbanded escritoire, surmounted by a black slate top, the fall enclosing a fitted interior, with gilt metal ornament, on bracket feet, 32½in (83cm).
£2,000-3,000 *P*

A George III harewood cabinet, with shelves enclosed by 2 featherbanded doors, decorated with marquetry, 33in (84cm).
£1,500-2,000 *DN*

An Edwardian inlaid mahogany music cabinet, with 4 drawers and open shelf.
£400-600 *LRG*

A Charles II black painted cabinet-on-stand, the stand with a frieze drawer on spirally turned legs, joined by a platform base and bun feet, 41in (104cm).
£2,000-3,000 *C*

A Queen Anne japanned and gilt chinoiserie cabinet-on-stand, with brass keyplates, angles and hinges, carrying handles to the sides, the ebonised base on cabriole legs with pad feet, some restoration, the stand 18thC, 27in (68cm).
£2,000-2,500 *P*

A William and Mary marquetry and walnut cabinet-on-stand, 46in (116.5cm).
£17,000-20,000 *B*

A William and Mary walnut cabinet-on-stand.
£4,000-5,000 *DN*

A kingwood, parquetry and ormolu mounted cabinet, with three-quarter pierced gallery, on cabriole legs and sabots, joined by an undertier, 37in (94cm).
£1,800-2,200 *CSK*

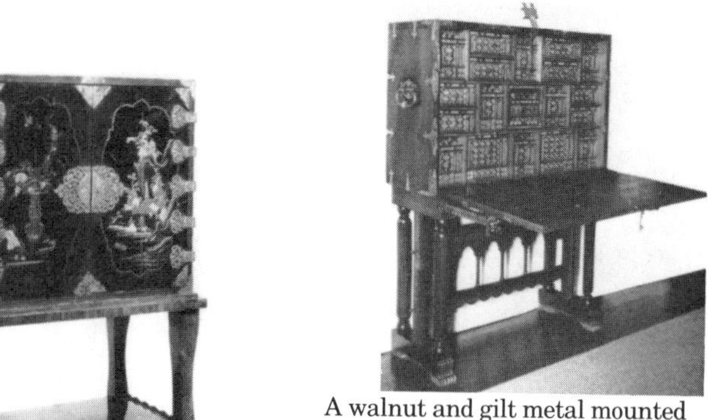

A rosewood, satinwood and japanned cabinet-on-stand, with engraved brass lockplates and hinges, the interior with 11 various sized drawers, the cabinet early 18thC, the stand early 19thC, 41in (104cm).
£2,000-2,500 *C*

A walnut and gilt metal mounted vargueno, applied with parcel gilt and inlaid in bone, with carrying handles to the sides, on bar and ribbed feet, 44in (112cm).
£3,000-4,000 *CSK*

A walnut escritoire, with quarter-veneered and herringbone banded fall, enclosing a mirrored interior, 45in (114cm).
£1,000-1,500 *Bon*

A Flemish ivory inlaid, ebony and tortoiseshell cabinet-on-stand, the central cupboard doors enclosing a mirrored interior, the cabinet 17thC, 40in (101.5cm).
£3,000-4,000 *C*

A Flemish rosewood, ebony and tortoiseshell cabinet-on-stand, 17thC, with later turned baluster supports and bun feet, joined by a rectangular undertier, 34in (86cm
£2,500-3,500 *CEd*

A Flemish walnut, tortoiseshell and ebonised cabinet-on-stand, inlaid with ivory and ebony strapwork, the later stand with spirally turned legs and H-shaped stretcher, 30in (76cm).
£1,700-2,000 *C*

A Flemish padouk, tortoiseshell, ebony and amboyna cabinet-on-stand, the stand with foliate cabriole legs and pad feet, 19thC, 33in (84cm).
£2,000-2,500 *C*

A Flemish tortoiseshell and ebonised cabinet-on-stand, the drawers with oval tortoiseshell panels applied with gilt metal foliate cast borders, the whole veneered in red stained tortoiseshel with ebonised borders, 52in (132cm
£10,000-15,000 *HSS*

A Flemish gilt metal mounted tortoiseshell and ebony cabinet-on-stand, with panelled cupboard doors enclosing later rosewood specimen drawers, the stand with a slide and panelled frieze on moulded legs headed by female caryatids, 55½in (140cm).
£7,000-8,000 *C*

A North Italian kingwood and fruitwood dressing cabinet-on-stand, with moulded cornice and inlaid with light lines, with central ratchet mirror glass, Lombardy or Piedmont, late 18thC, 43in (109cm).
£3,500-5,000 *CNY*

A German carved walnut and burr veneered serpentine cabinet-on-stand, the stand with a pierced undulating apron, on cabriole legs, united by an undertier and scroll feet, 19thC, 38in (98cm).
£1,500-2,000 *P*

A South German marquetry table cabinet-on-stand, the panel doors decorated with japanned chinoiserie, the base on square tapered legs united by an undertier, early 18thC, the stand later.
£3,000-3,500 *P*

A Spanish marquetry cabinet-on-stand, the pierced moulded cornice with gilt metal fretwork, the reverse painted with a bull and a ram with inscriptions, 19thC, 49in (124cm).
£4,500-5,500 *C*

;ollectors' Cabinets

17thC style Antwerp ebonised ırquetry coin cabinet, mid-19thC, ;in (63cm).
,000-8,000 *N*

A William IV mahogany table cabinet, with concealed frieze drawer, on carved bun feet, 19in (48cm).
£350-550 *P[Re]*

A South German walnut, ash and marquetry table cabinet, inlaid with chequered boxwood lines, fitted with a fall front, the sides fitted with carrying handles, late 18thC, 20in (51cm).
£1,300-1,600 *CSK*

n Italian ebonised and gilt metal ounted cabinet, with ripple ouldings and inlaid with lines, the awers mounted with verre ;lomisé panels, the central mpartment with 4 enclosed awers, carrying handles, 17thC, ;in (148cm).
,500-4,500 *P*

A William and Mary trinket cabinet, with star inlaid panels, fitted with drawers and enclosed by a single door, 9½in (24cm).
£900-1,200 *P[Pea]*

A pair of mahogany chart cabinets with walnut crossbanding, each with 36 slides, c1935, 28½in (72cm).
£2,500-3,500 *Ba*

Made for the Greenwich Maritime Museum.

)isplay Cabinets

William and Mary style burr alnut display cabinet-on-stand, on verted cup turned legs joined by a aved stretcher, on ball turned feet, ;in (160cm).
00-1,200 *Bon*

An early 18thC style walnut china cabinet, the stand with 3 featherbanded drawers above a shaped apron, on shell headed hipped cabriole legs and acanthus scroll feet.
£1,200-1,500 *CSK*

An 18thC style mahogany display cabinet, with acanthus carved waist moulding, 2 moulded doors and on acanthus carved cabriole legs with claw-and-ball feet, 52in (132cm).
£1,500-2,000 *Bea*

A George III mahogany corner display cabinet, outlined with boxwood stringing, the panelled doors veneered with ovals and on bracket feet, 45in (114cm).
£3,500-4,500 *Bea*

A Regency rosewood dwarf breakfront display cabinet, inlaid with boxwood lines.
£12,000-15,000 *CSK*

A George III mahogany display cabinet with later pierced arched pediment, the base with a geometrically glazed sloping front and silk lined interior, 40in (101.5cm).
£3,000-3,500 *CNY*

A pair of mahogany and brass mounted display cabinets, with pierced gallery above 2 glazed panel doors between reeded three-quarter column uprights, on toupie feet, late 19thC, 55½in (140cm).
£4,500-5,500 *CSK*

A rosewood display cabinet, inlaid in various woods and ivory in the Mannerist style, on square tapering legs, late 19thC, 72½in (186cm).
£3,000-4,000 *Bea*

A pair of William IV rosewood display cabinets, applied with bead and reel split mouldings, on later turned feet, 25½in (64.5cm).
£8,000-10,000 *C*

A Victorian walnut and marquet pier cabinet, the inlaid frieze ove shaped plain glazed door flanked gilt metal mounted and marquet inlaid pilasters, on a plinth base, 30½in (77.5cm).
£550-650 *Bon*

An Edwardian inlaid mahogany display cabinet.
£1,500-2,500 *TW*

An Edwardian mahogany and satinwood crossbanded display cabinet, on square tapering legs with a platform undertier, 49in (125.5cm).
£1,500-2,000 *AG*

An Edwardian satinwood displa cabinet, outlined with ebony stringing, the lower section with inlaid panelled doors, on square tapered legs and spade feet, 49ir (124.5cm).
£1,200-1,800 *Bon*

An Edwardian Sheraton design mahogany display cabinet, decorated with satinwood stringing and chequered crossbanding, on square tapering supports and spade feet, 45in (114cm).
£1,000-1,500 *BWe*

An Edwardian satinwood display cabinet with chinoiserie decoration.
£3,000-3,500 *MGM*

An Edwardian mahogany hanging corner display cabinet, with swan neck pediment and moulded cornice, 26in (66cm).
£400-500 *Bon*

A late Edwardian mahogany display cabinet, with brass gallery, mirror backs and fret applied glass doors, on French cabriole legs, 44in (111.5cm).
£1,000-1,400 *WIL*

An Edwardian inlaid mahogany display cabinet, with lift-up bijouterie compartment, on square tapering legs with spade feet, 27in (68.5cm).
£1,000-1,200 *JD*

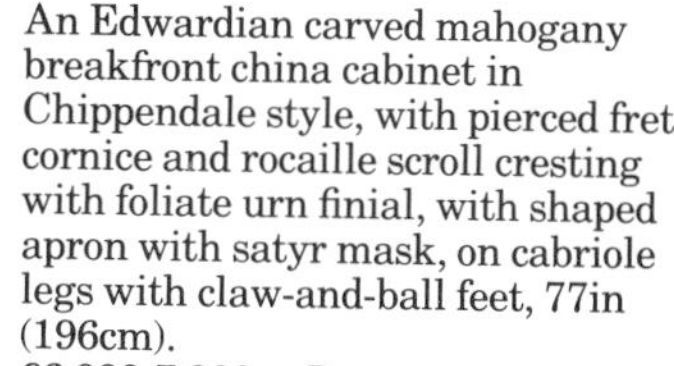

An Edwardian carved mahogany breakfront china cabinet in Chippendale style, with pierced fret cornice and rocaille scroll cresting with foliate urn finial, with shaped apron with satyr mask, on cabriole legs with claw-and-ball feet, 77in (196cm).
£6,000-7,000 *P*

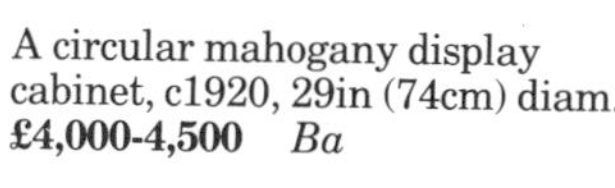

A circular mahogany display cabinet, c1920, 29in (74cm) diam.
£4,000-4,500 *Ba*

A walnut herringbone inlaid and crossbanded display cabinet, with carved brackets in the form of dragon heads, designed by W. F. Crittall and made by E. W. Beckwith, signed with initials and dated 1921, 45in (114cm).
£1,500-2,000 *P*

A Sheraton revival china cabinet, decorated with satinwood crossbanding and central inlaid portrait panel.
£2,500-3,000 *MGM*

A mahogany china display cabinet, with fabric back interior, on claw-and-ball feet, 59in (149.5cm).
£900-1,000 *WW*

A burr yew display cabinet, inlaid with boxwood lines and applied with gilt metal mounts, on turned tapering feet, 38in (96.5cm).
£1,500-2,000 *CSK*

An open display cabinet on chamfered legs, joined by stretchers, 53in (134.5cm).
£1,500-2,000 *Bea*

A Dutch marquetry display cabinet, with glazed cupboard doors with bead-and-reel border, the base with 3 drawers and chamfered waved angles, on claw-and-ball feet, 66in (167.5cm).
£6,500-7,500 *C*

A Dutch walnut and floral marquetry china cabinet, on ebonised bun feet, 19thC, 50in (126cm).
£5,500-6,000 *P*

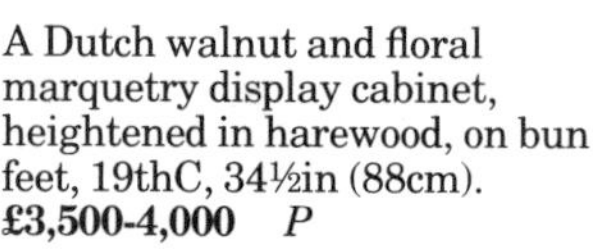

A Dutch walnut and floral marquetry display cabinet, heightened in harewood, on bun feet, 19thC, 34½in (88cm).
£3,500-4,000 *P*

A Dutch marquetry display cabinet, on a plinth base inlaid with foliage, 35in (89cm).
£1,000-1,500 *C*

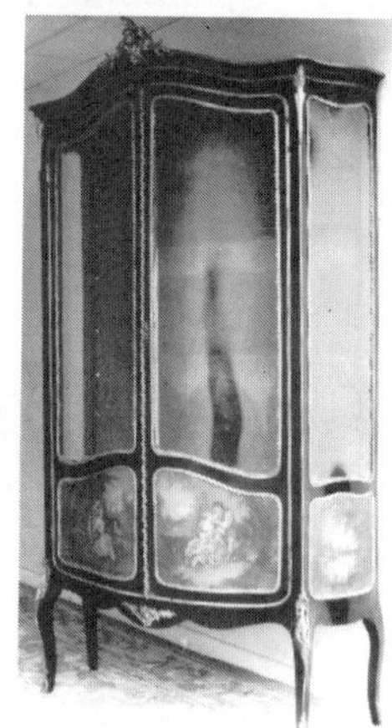

A French vitrine display cabinet, with serpentine front and figure panels after Watteau.
£900-1,200 *MGM*

An Italian hardwood display cabinet, inlaid with ivory in the Moorish style, on block supports, bearing the wax seal of Dogani di Milano, 19thC, 42in (106.5cm).
£2,600-3,000 *P[Pea]*

A Louis XV style kingwood display cabinet, applied with gilt brass mouldings, on cabriole legs, bearing Fontainbleu railway labels and an inventory number, 37½in (95cm).
£2,000-3,000 *Bea*

Side Cabinets

A Regency mahogany secretaire chiffonier, inlaid with geometric ebonised lines, the top with a shelved ledge back on turned supports, the frieze drawer with fitted interior, 34in (86cm).
£1,500-2,000 *CSK*

\ Regency mahogany side cabinet
vith crossbanded top, above 2 pairs
f panelled doors filled with
iltmetal flowerhead trellis and
leated peach silk, 63in (152cm).
:1,500-2,000 *C*

\ Regency rosewood side cabinet,
he panelled doors flanked by split
ilasters, 54in (137cm).
:1,500-2,000 *C*

A Regency rosewood side cabinet, with mirror panelled doors, 81in (205.5cm).
£2,000-3,000 *Bon*

A Regency brass inlaid rosewood side cabinet, the top with a pierced three-quarter gallery, the central door filled with brass trellis enclosing shelves and flanked by 2 panelled doors, 75in (190.5cm).
£3,000-4,000 *CNY*

A Regency brass inlaid rosewood side cabinet, with 2 stepped plinths above a pair of cupboard doors edged with giltmetal foliage and filled with trellis backed by pleated silk, 97in (246cm).
£5,000-6,000 *C*

A Regency mahogany breakfront side cabinet, the panelled doors with later gilt trellis and backed with green pleated silk, 63in (160cm).
£1,200-1,800 *C*

CREDENZAS

- ★ side cabinets are often known as credenzas
- ★ a credenza normally implies the more ornate pieces, in the French or Italian taste
- ★ some of these pieces display the over elaborate decoration and lack of craftsmanship which would decrease their desirability
- ★ serpentine shaped front and sides is always a good feature

A Regency mahogany breakfront side cabinet, brass mounted with Egyptian terms, on turned feet, 63in (160cm).
£6,000-7,000 *Bea*

A Regency mahogany chiffonier, on splayed bracket feet, 34in (86cm).
£900-1,500 *HOD*

A late Regency rosewood chiffonier, with a frieze drawer and a pair of recessed panelled doors filled with gilt trellis and backed with green silk, 40in (101.5cm).
£1,500-2,000 *C*

A Regency mahogany chiffonier, inlaid with ebonised lines, with 2 later open shelves on turned supports, the frieze with 2 fitted drawers, the panelled doors filled with giltmetal trellis, on giltmetal paw feet, 36in (91.5cm).
£2,000-3,000 *C*

A pair of Regency rosewood chiffoniers, with mirrored doors and brass galleries, 47in (119cm).
£4,000-5,000 *Wor*

A late Regency rosewood side cabinet, with ogee frieze, flanked by twin scroll supports headed by a lotus capital, 38in (96.5cm).
£4,000-5,000 *CNY*

A pair of late Regency mahogany chiffoniers, the mirrored backs with pierced three-quarter brass galleries on baluster column supports, above silk pleated brass grill panel doors, on plinth base, 19½in (49cm).
£3,500-4,500 *CSK*

A Regency gilt and simulated rosewood side cabinet, with crossbanded top, the panelled doc enclosing a later fitted interior, o plinth base, 51in (129.5cm).
£3,000-4,000 *C*

A Regency brass mounted rosew chiffonier, the top with pierced three-quarter gallery and colum supports, the door filled with plea yellow silk, on plinth base, 25½i (63.5cm).
£2,000-3,000 *C*

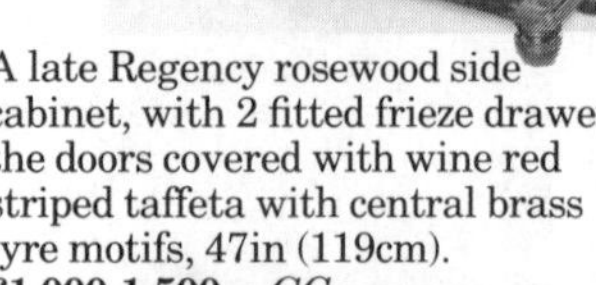

A late Regency rosewood side cabinet, with 2 fitted frieze drawe the doors covered with wine red striped taffeta with central brass lyre motifs, 47in (119cm).
£1,000-1,500 *GC*

A late Regency rosewood chiffonier, with brass inset geometric lines and mounted borders, the top crossbanded, adaptations, 44in (111.5cm).
£700-1,000 *CSK*

late Regency mahogany ıiffonier, inlaid with brass in ›aded banded borders, the mirror ıed back with S-scroll supports, ›ove 4 mirror panelled cupboard ›ors, divided by voluted pilasters, .in (205.5cm).
,000-4,000 *CSK*

A parcel gilt and rosewood side cabinet with later Verde Antico marble slab, adapted, early 19thC, 42½in (108cm).
£2,000-3,000 *C*

A late Regency rosewood chiffonier, the shelved back on scroll metal supports with a pierced three-quarter gallery, above 2 frieze drawers and 2 silk pleated panel doors, 38½in (98cm).
£1,600-2,000 *CSK*

Regency faded rosewood ıiffonier, the upper part with ıirrored back and giltmetal alleries to shelf, the gilded anelled doors with pleated silk, ıclosing shelves, 39in (99cm).
2,000-3,000 *CNY*

A boulle dwarf corner cabinet, brass inlaid into red tortoiseshell, with shaped marble top, 19thC, 30in (76cm).
£750-1,000 *LRG*

A pair of walnut cabinets, with marble tops and Sèvres plaques in the centre, Waring and Gillow, c1870, 25in (63.5cm).
£4,500-5,500 *Ba*

kingwood, rosewood crossbanded, molu mounted and inlaid ›akfront side cabinet, with a ırble top, the panel door with a ral spray and fruit, with rquetry panels to either side, ırble top broken, 19thC, 45in 5cm).
,000-3,000 *P*

A Victorian walnut and floral marquetry inlaid breakfront credenza, the lined interior enclosed by 3 glazed doors, with ormolu mounts, 67in (170cm).
£1,000-1,500 *GC*

An early Victorian mahogany chiffonier, with 2 short frieze drawers and brass lattice work doors, 60in (152cm) high.
£1,200-1,500 *AG*

A Victorian figured walnut side cabinet, inlaid with boxwood lines and applied with painted porcelain plaques in ebonised and giltmetal mounted borders, 57in (144.5cm).
£2,000-3,000 *CSK*

An early Victorian inlaid burr walnut side cabinet, 48in (122cm).
£750-1,000 *P[Re]*

A Victorian burr walnut and marquetry side cabinet, banded in amaranth and applied with ormolu mounts, the central panelled door with musical trophy, 72in (182.5cm).
£2,500-3,500 *CSK*

A Victorian walnut serpentine credenza, applied with giltmetal mounts, the crossbanded top above 2 panelled doors inlaid with floral marquetry, flanked by serpentine open shelves, 83in (210.5cm).
£1,500-2,000 *CSK*

A Victorian figured walnut and ormolu mounted side cabinet, inlaid with boxwood lines and arabesques and banded in rosewood, on plinth base and turned feet, 49in (124.5cm).
£1,400-1,800 *CSK*

A Victorian walnut and marquetry side cabinet, with gilt brass mounts and amboyna crossbanding, the panelled door with a harewood panel inlaid with an urn, strapwork drapery, flowers and foliage, 34in (86cm).
£1,200-1,500 *Bea*

A Victorian walnut pier cabinet, with a giltmetal banded plinth base, 33in (84cm).
£500-800 *Bon*

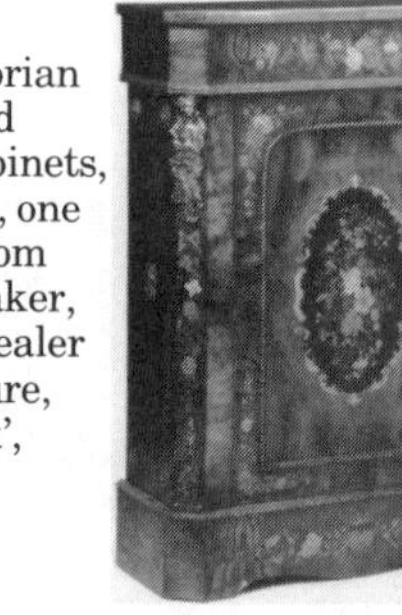

A pair of mid-Victorian figured walnut and marquetry side cabinets, inlaid with flowers, one bearing a label 'From W. Greenwood, Maker, Upholsterer and Dealer in Ancient Furniture, 24 Stonegate, York', 31½in (80cm).
£2,000-2,500 *C*

A Victorian burr walnut chiffonie inlaid with boxwood lines and amboyna bands, and applied with giltmetal mounts, labelled James Shoolbred & Company, Tottenha House, Tottenham Court Road, London, 48in (122cm).
£1,500-2,000 *CSK*

A Victorian figured walnut and purplewood banded side cabine inlaid with boxwood lines and arabesques and applied with giltmetal mounts, 50in (127cm
£1,200-1,500 *CSK*

A late Victorian shaped front walnut side cabinet, inlaid with marquetry and parquetry panels in boxwood lined borders and applied with giltmetal mounts, No. 16934, 72in (182.5cm).
£2,200-2,500 *CSK*

A pair of Victorian burr walnut side cabinets, inlaid with marquetry, boxwood lines and applied with giltmetal mounts, stamped Edwards and Roberts, 21 Wardour Street, 31½in (80cm).
£3,500-4,500 *CSK*

An Edwardian rosewood side cabinet, stamped Edwards an Roberts, 54in (137cm).
£600-900 *CSK*

A Dutch inlaid mahogany side cabinet, with crossbanded top, 46in (116.5cm).
£1,400-1,800 *Bea*

An Italian stained walnut and inlaid secretaire side cabinet, geometrically decorated 'a la certosina', the top fitted with short drawers and stationery compartments beneath a moulded pediment, the frieze fitted with a secretaire drawer, 19thC, 53in (134.5cm).
£2,000-3,000 *CSK*

A Dutch satinwood side cabinet, crossbanded and inlaid with barber-pole stringing, later painted with flowers and foliage, the frieze drawer above a tambour shutter and deep drawer, 24in (61cm).
£1,000-1,500 *Bea*

Canterburies

A Regency mahogany canterbury with central handle, on ring turned supports, the frieze with a drawer on turned legs, 21in (53cm).
£1,800-2,500 *C*

A late Regency rosewood canterbury, the frieze fitted with a drawer, on splayed legs, 24in (61cm).
£1,700-2,000 *C*

A Regency mahogany music canterbury, with one drawer, on slender turned supports, with brass feet and casters.
£1,300-1,500 *P[Pea]*

A George IV mahogany canterbury, on turned column with platform base.
£600-650 *TW*

A standing canterbury with spiral turned uprights, and shaped lower drawer, 19thC, 22in (56cm).
£400-600 *LRG*

A William IV rosewood canterbury, on turned moulded legs with casters, 22in (56cm).
£1,000-1,500 *CSK*

A mahogany canterbury, on turned supports and casters, 19thC, 21in (53cm).
£600-800 *HCH*

CANTERBURIES

- ★ name denotes a piece of movable equipment usually used for sheet music
- ★ first music canterburies appeared c1800
- ★ round tapered legs appeared in c1810
- ★ the canterbury shows quite well the stylistic development of the 19thC – from the quite straight, slender severe to the bulbous and heavily carved later examples
- ★ many Victorian examples with good carving fetch more than the earlier examples
- ★ elegance is one of the major criteria in this small expensive piece of furniture
- ★ note that some are made from the base of a whatnot or étagere but even more are modern reproductions

A mahogany canterbury, with ring turned uprights and slatted sides on turned tapering legs and brass feet, 18in (46cm).
£1,000-1,500 *C*

A Victorian walnut writing canterbury, the frieze drawer with an adjustable reading rest, the 4 divisions pierced and carved with scrolls, a concave fronted drawer below on bell shaped feet, 27in (68.5cm).
£1,500-2,000 *Bea*

An early Victorian rosewood canterbury, on turned tapering legs with brass casters, 20½in (52cm).
£1,000-1,500 *GC*

A rosewood canterbury, with X-shaped divisions centred by roundels with one frieze drawer and ring turned legs, 20in (51in).
£1,800-2,000 *C*

Chairs – Open Armchairs

A Charles II walnut farthingale chair, with spirally turned and square legs with stretchers, later blocks, minor restoration.
£700-1,000 *C*

A Charles II walnut open armchair, the moulded arms on baluster legs, joined by conforming stretchers, minor restoration.
£1,500-2,000 *C*

A walnut framed armchair, upholstered in crimson velvet, late 17thC.
£500-600 *P[Pea]*

A William and Mary walnut open armchair, the waved stretcher centred by a later urn, later blocks, minor restoration.
£1,000-1,500 *C*

A George II mahogany library armchair, re-railed.
£4,000-4,500 *CNY*

A Georgian mahogany open armchair of Gainsborough type, with square legs united by stretchers, parts replaced.
£1,000-1,500 *P*

A George II mahogany elbow chair with pierced vase splat, slip-in seat, on cabriole legs with trifid pad feet.
£1,200-1,500 *P*

ENGLISH CHAIRS

- ★ c1630 backs of chairs were like panelled sides from a coffer
- ★ early 17thC chairs very square and made of oak
- ★ in Charles II period principal wood walnut – such chairs tend to break as walnut splits easily and is relatively soft
- ★ chairs have carved top rails, often with a crown, the stretcher will then be similarly carved, the legs are either turned or plain and simple spirals – sometimes called barley sugar twists; the caning in the backs is usually rectangular – any chair with oval caning is highly desirable
- ★ by the end of the 17thC backs were covered in needlework, the cabriole leg made its appearance, now stretchers have subtle curves
- ★ the beginning of the 18thC – the Queen Anne spoon back chair – with upright shaped splat, plain cabriole front legs, pad feet
- ★ George I – carved knees and claw-and-ball feet, solid splats were walnut or veneered, often in burr-walnut
- ★ William Kent – introduced heavy carved mouldings – greatly influenced by Italian baroque
- ★ from this time on chairs became lighter in design through the work mainly of Chippendale and Hepplewhite
- ★ splats now pierced, legs square or tapered
- ★ the square legs were also much cheaper than the cabriole legs, so they appealed to the large and growing middle class
- ★ many of the designs came from France
- ★ Hepplewhite, in particular, developed the chair with tapered legs, no stretchers and very plain splats
- ★ during the 19thC the taste was once again for heavier more substantial furniture

A pair of George II style mahogany framed library armchairs, the serpentine seats on scrolled acanthus carved cabriole legs, with claw and ball feet, upholstered in floral gros point needlework.
£1,300-1,500 *Bon*

A George II style walnut open armchair.
£1,500-2,000 *Bea*

A mahogany open arm elbow chair, the shaped back with carved shell crest and foliate decorated paterae meeting entwined ribbon back splat, mid-18thC.
£16,000-18,000 *HOD*

A mahogany open armchair of George II style, the arm supports with lion mask terminals and padded drop-in seat.
£2,000-3,000 *C*

A George II style mahogany library armchair, upholstered in green damask, on hipped acanthus headed cabriole legs and claw and ball feet.
£1,600-2,000 *CSK*

George II style black and red cquer armchair, the bowed seat d the blind fret-carved seat rail on uare pierced strapwork legs and ock feet.
,800-2,000 *CNY*

A fruitwood framed elbow chair with pierced vase shaped splat and lift out padded seat. 18thC.
£1,300-1,500 *P[WSW]*

An early George III mahogany armchair.
£1,000-1,200 *Bon*

An early George III mahogany open armchair, on square chamfered legs joined by stretchers.
£1,300-1,500 *CSK*

A Georgian mahogany elbow chair in the French style.
£2,000-3,000 *McC*

A pair of George III carved mahogany elbow chairs, re-railed.
£1,200-1,500 *P*

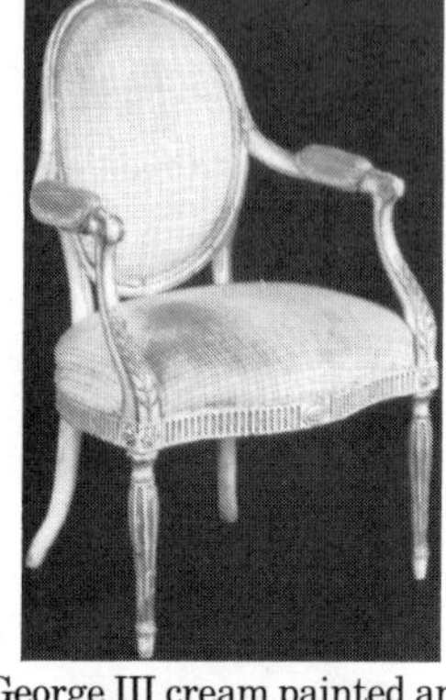

A George III cream painted and parcel gilt open armchair, with fluted seat rail and fluted tapering legs, later blocks.
£1,500-2,000 *C*

A pair of George III mahogany open armchairs, each with a bowed bar toprail above a railed back, with upholstered seats, on ring turned tapering legs, with 5 similar George III mahogany dining chairs.
£2,000-2,500 *CSK*

A George III carved mahogany frame elbow chair in the French Hepplewhite taste, on cabriole legs with fan mouldings.
£1,200-1,500 *P*

A George III carved mahogany elbow chair in the Chippendale taste, on square chamfered legs united by H-stretchers.
£600-1,000 *P*

A pair of George III mahogany open armchairs, with woolwork upholstered drop-in seats, and on tapering square legs joined by stretchers.
£850-1,000 *Bea*

A George III carved mahogany elbow chair, on square chamfered legs with block feet.
£3,000-3,500 *P*

A George III mahogany library armchair, the arched padded back and seat with gros point floral needlework upholstery, later blocks, partly re-railed.
£1,800-2,200 *C*

Miller's is a price Guide not a price List

The price ranges given reflect the average price a purchaser should pay for similar items. Condition, rarity of design or pattern, size, colour, pedigree, restoration and many other factors must be taken into account when assessing values.

A George III blue painted child's chair, with split cane filled bowed sloping back and stepped seat, on square tapering legs.
£1,300-1,800 *CNY*

A George III giltwood open armchair attributed to Thomas Chippendale, on turned tapering legs headed by stiff leaves with ribbed feet.
£2,000-2,500 *C*

A George III mahogany Gainsborough chair, repairs to back legs.
£1,000-1,500 *DN*

A George III giltwood framed open armchair, on stop fluted tapering legs with foliate feet, now with sprung seat.
£800-1,000 *Bea*

A George III white painted and parcel gilt open armchair, in the manner of Thomas Chippendale, on fluted turned tapering legs, later blocks, redecorated.
£7,000-8,000 *C*

A pair of George III black painted armchairs, with bow fronted split cane filled seats, on square tapering legs and spade feet, decorated with trailing foliage and flowerheads.
£3,000-3,500 *CNY*

A George III mahogany library chair, upholstered in blue floral needlework, the square channelled legs joined by pierced fret stretchers, reduced, later blocks and restorations.
£2,000-2,500 *C*

A Regency mahogany bergère with caned back, arms and seat on ring turned tapering legs, later casters.
£800-1,000 *C*

A pair of George III cream painted and parcel gilt armchairs, upholstered in orange cut velvet, redecorated.
£3,500-4,000 *CNY*

A George III carved mahogany elbow chair in the Hepplewhite taste, on chamfered legs united by H-stretchers.
£1,500-2,000 *P*

A George III mahogany library armchair, upholstered in red leather, on cabriole legs headed by foliage with paw feet, the rear feet slightly reduced.
£5,500-6,500 *C*

A George III Chippendale design mahogany framed Gainsborough chair, with serpentine seat and back upholstered in foliate patterned crimson satinised brocade.
£1,000-1,200 *LBP*

A Regency mahogany library bergère, with cane filled back, arms and seat with buttoned olive green leather cushions.
£1,200-1,500 *C*

A pair of mahogany open armchairs of George III design, each with a serpentine padded back, arm-rests and serpentine seat covered in light cream damask.
£3,500-4,500 *C*

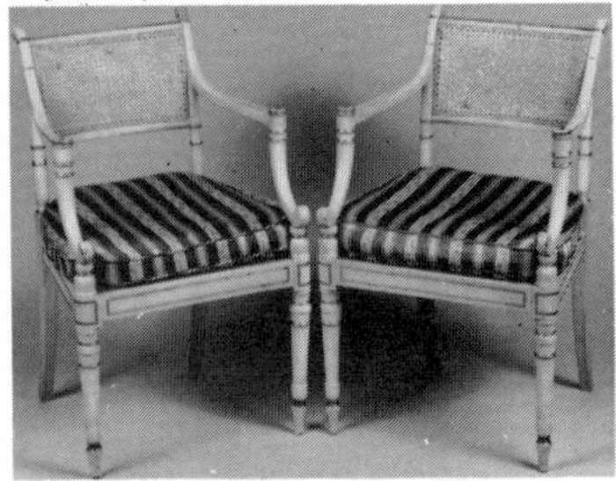

Four Regency white and gilt painted elbow chairs, with turned bamboo effect frames, cane seats and backs, with loose cushions in striped damask.
£7,000-7,500 *JD*

A pair of Regency blue painted and parcel gilt armchairs, stamped T. Gray, redecorated.
£12,000-13,000 *C*

A parcel gilt and white painted open armchair of Regency design.
£4,000-4,500 *C*

A pair of Regency rosewood and brass mounted elbow chairs.
£5,500-6,000 *DN*

A Regency ebonised and parcel gilt open armchair, the split caned seat on ring turned tapering legs with green damask covered squab, redecorated.
£1,500-2,000 *C*

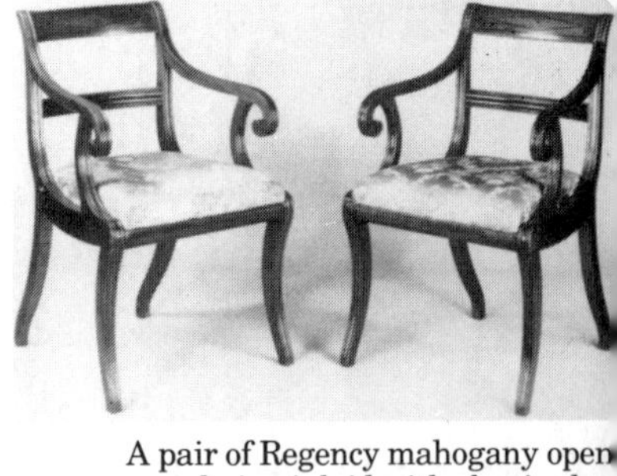

A pair of Regency mahogany open armchairs, inlaid with ebonised lines, with blue brocade covered drop-in seats, later front rails.
£2,500-3,000 *C*

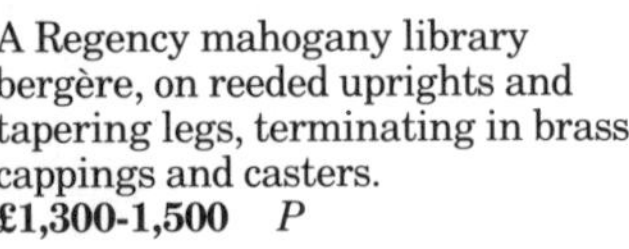

A Regency mahogany library bergère, on reeded uprights and tapering legs, terminating in brass cappings and casters.
£1,300-1,500 *P*

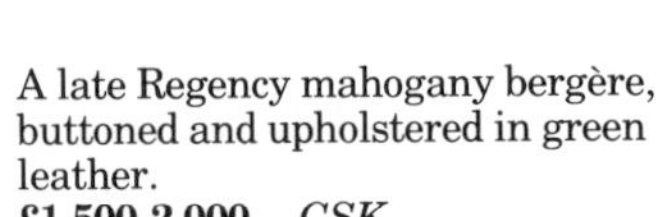

A late Regency mahogany bergère, buttoned and upholstered in green leather.
£1,500-2,000 *CSK*

. George IV mahogany library rmchair, with buttoned chamois overed squab.
2,000-2,500 *C*

A Victorian walnut three-piece drawing room suite, comprising a chaise longue, a gentleman's armchair and a lady's chair.
£1,200-1,800 *CSK*

A George IV mahogany library armchair, the yoke shaped back with cane filled centre carved with flowers, the cane filled seat with leather squab cushion.
£1,500-2,000 *C*

marquetry inlaid open armchair ith stuffover seat, 19thC.
400-500 *HCH*

A mahogany bergère chair, upholstered in leather, c1860.
£900-1,200 *Ba*

A William IV mahogany framed library armchair, with leatherette cushions, the cane back damaged.
£350-450 *LRG*

mid-Victorian ebonised oak open rmchair, with a label of J. Kendell Co., No. 53536, and the orkman's name Hill.
500-600 *C*

An early Victorian simulated rosewood open armchair.
£200-300 *LRG*

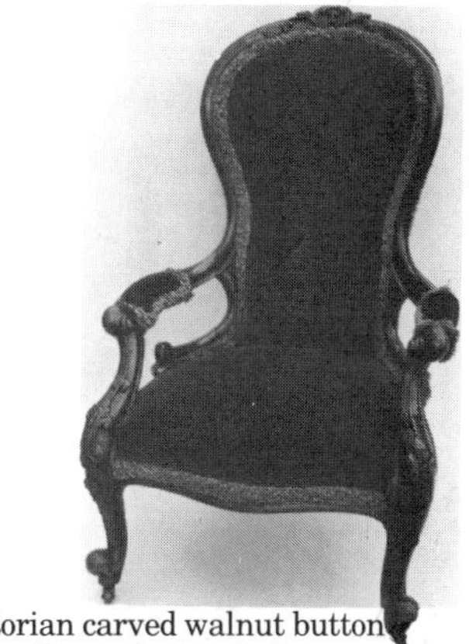

A Victorian carved walnut button back gentleman's armchair.
£600-800 *MGM*

An early Victorian walnut open armchair.
£400-500 *CSK*

A Victorian mahogany tub chair, upholstered in red leather.
£400-500 *CSK*

An Edwardian five-piece inlaid walnut salon suite, upholstered in blue dralon, on turned supports.
£650-750 *LRG*

A pair of Edwardian walnut tu[b] armchairs.
£200-500 *LRG*

A pair of Sheraton decorated elbow chairs.
£1,700-2,000 *P*

A late Victorian 8 piece mahogany drawing room suite, comprising 2 wing back armchairs, 4 side chairs and 2 nursing chairs.
£600-900 *CSK*

A pair of Edwardian mahogany elbow chairs, inlaid with ivory an[d] rosewood.
£500-600 *LRG*

A set of 6 black lacquered and parcel gilt chairs, of Sheraton design, with loose upholstered seat squabs, by Restall Brown and Clennall, Alfred Place, WC1.
£7,000-8,000 *CSK*

A Sheraton painted and gilt decorated elbow chair.
£600-800 *P*

A large mahogany open armchai[r] with serpentine toprail and interlaced splat, restorations.
£1,000-1,500 *C*

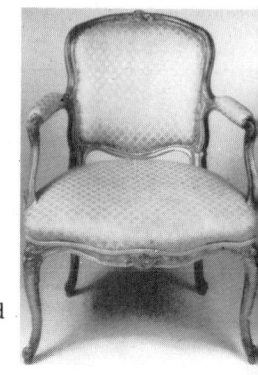

A Chippendale carved mahogany elbow chair, repairs to back.
£1,500-2,000 *P*

A Louis XV walnut fauteuil, with cartouche shaped padded back and bowed seat, and another similar, later cream painted.
£1,500-2,000 *C*

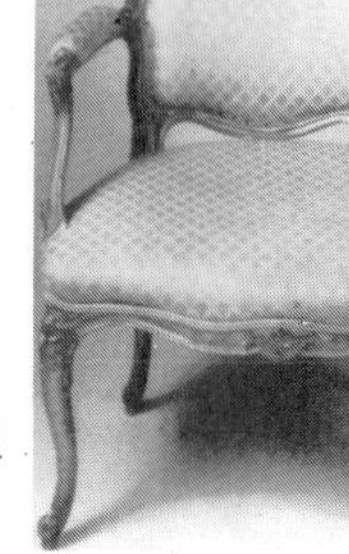

A matched pair of Louis XV fauteuils, with cartouche shaped padded backs and seats upholstered in salmon repp.
£1,500-2,000 *C*

A Charles I oak and fruitwood livery cupboard, the base with an arched door flanked by carved foliate panels, mid-17thC, 38½in (98cm). **£6,000-7,000** *C*

A Spanish walnut vargueno, the fitted interior with drawers and cupboards, 45in (114cm). **£4,000-5,000** *C*

A George I oak press cupboard, dated 1723, probably Welsh, 55in (140cm). **£4,000-5,000** *C*

A Charles II oak low dresser, with moulded rectangular top and 4 geometrically panelled drawers, on baluster turned legs with block feet, 88½in (225cm). **£9,500-10,000** *C*

An oak court cupboard, with convex frieze drawers, 17thC and later, 44½in (113cm) wide. **£4,000-5,000** *C*

A spice cupboard with secret drawer in lid, original inside drawers, Romayne head carved decoration on door, c1700, 15½in (39cm). **£1,600-1,800** *NP*

A rare Gothic oak cupboard, in original condition, late 15thC. **£30,000-50,000** *H*

Above. A Spanish walnut and red painted cabinet, late 16thC, 48in (122cm) wide. **£21,000-23,000** *C*
Left. An oak table, mid-18thC, 27in (68cm) wide. **£500-550** *AP*

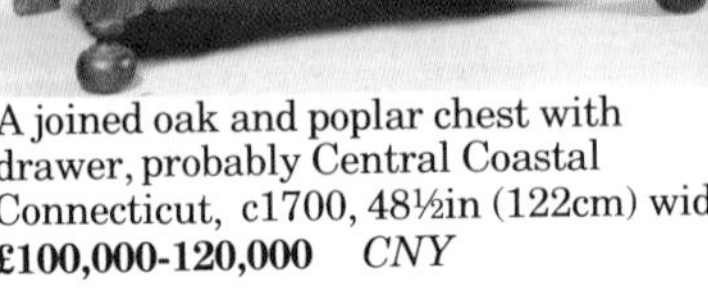

A joined oak and poplar chest with drawer, probably Central Coastal Connecticut, c1700, 48½in (122cm) wid

£100,000-120,000 *CNY*

A fine Elizabethan oak tester bed. **£25,000-40,000** *H*

A George III oak and fruitwood dresser, the plate rack with moulded canopy and pendant finials, 64½in (164cm) wide, c1775. **£14,000-16,000** *C*

An original pine lambing chair, with ash arms, c1780, 25in (63cm) wide. **£1,800-2,000** *AP*

A harlequin set of 14 oak dining chairs, including 2 armchairs. **£4,000-5,000** *C*

An original ash and elm three-legged spindle back chair, mid-18thC, 24in (61cm) wide. **£1,000-1,200** *AP*

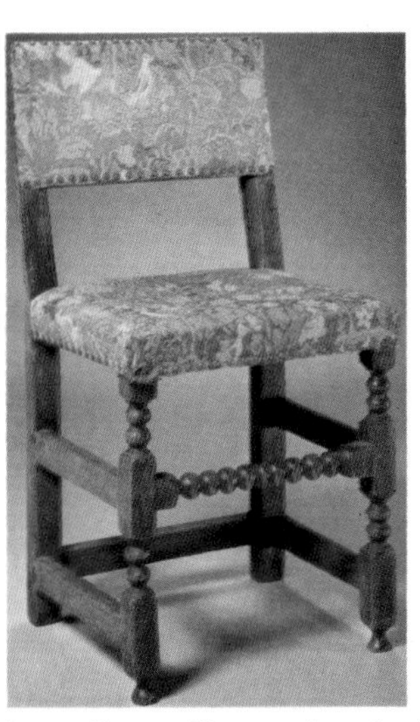

A rare Cromwellian maple and oak chair, Massachusetts, c1665, 34in (86cm) high, 18in (46cm) wide. **£5,000-7,000** *CNY*

A Charles II walnut armchair, with later scrolling X-stretcher. **£4,000-5,000** *C*

A pair of George I walnut chairs, inlaid with the coat of arms of the Suckling family, the needlework seats with the same arms, motto and date 1732, arms possibly later. **£22,000-25,000** *C*

A James I oak armchair, the toprail with inscription and initials IT, the carved back dated 1609, with later solid seat, Welsh. **£6,000-7,000** *C*

A Chippendale maple corner chair, on Marlborough legs, Rhode Island or Massachusetts, c1770, 32½in (82.5cm) high. **£2,000-3,000** *CNY*

A pair of Yorkshire yew wood Windsor armchairs, with arched spindle filled backs, bearing label. **£4,000-5,000** *C*

An original Queen Anne painted pine dresser, 60in (150cm) wide.
£6,000-7,000 *AP*

A Continental painted pine cupboard, mid-18thC, 29in (73cm) wide.
£800-900 *AP*

An original French painted pine food cupboard, mid-18thC, 30½in (76cm) wi
£900-1,000 *AP*

An East Anglian painted pine chest, in original condition, 18thC, 25in (63cm) wide. **£600-700** *AP*

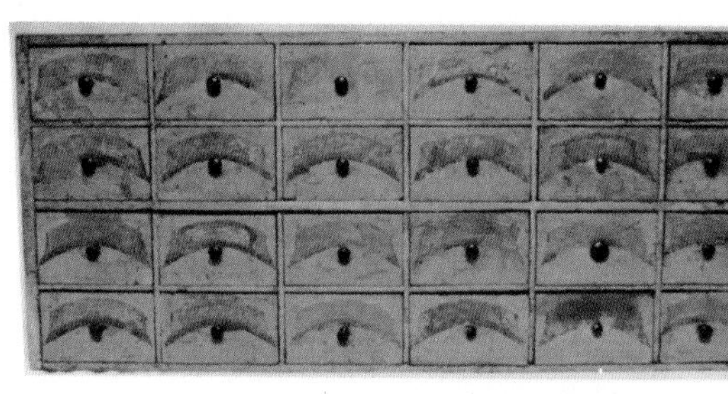

A painted pine flight of drawers, c183(44½in (112cm). **£400-450** *AP*

A pine spoon rack, c1850, 12in (30cm) wide.
£200-250 *AP*

A French painted pine hanging cupboard, containing a collection of children's plates, 18thC, 31in (78cm) wide.
£600-700 *AP*

A pine papered decorative box, c1740, 16in (40cm) wide.
£300-350 *AP*

Jeorge III mahogany breakfront bookcase, the se with a fitted secretaire drawer, flanked by raduated drawers and 2 panelled doors, 2½in (335cm) wide. **£180,000+** *C*

An early George III mahogany breakfront bookcase, the base with 3 frieze drawers above 4 panelled doors with applied roundels, 85½in (217cm) wide. **£80,000-100,000** *C*

fine Continental neo-classical patinated bronze d ormolu mounted mahogany bed, German or Austrian, rly 19thC, 71in (180cm) wide. **£50,000-60,000** *CNY*

A George III mahogany double breakfront library bookcase, adapted, 220in (559cm) wide. **£13,000-15,000** *C*

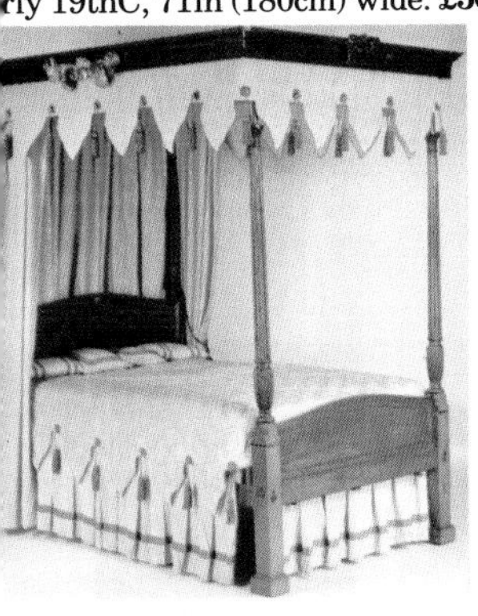

A mahogany four-poster bed, the blind fret carved canopy with giltwood foliate clasps and coronet at the end, 54½in (139cm) wide. **£3,000-5,000** *C*

An Empire ormolu-mounted mahogany bed, now with large casters, boxspring and mattress, 59½in (151cm) wide. **£22,000-24,000** *C*

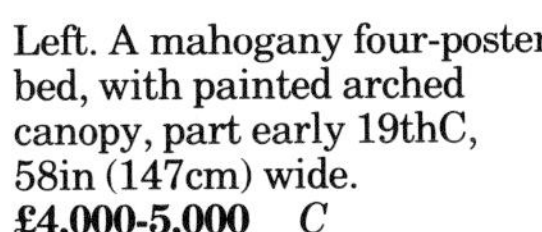

Left. A mahogany four-poster bed, with painted arched canopy, part early 19thC, 58in (147cm) wide. **£4,000-5,000** *C*

A pair of George II mahogany bookcases, minor variations, 69in (175cm) wide. **£40,000-50,000** *C*

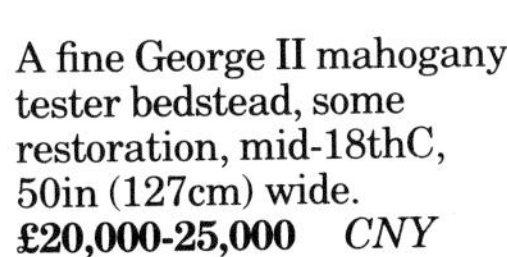

A fine George II mahogany tester bedstead, some restoration, mid-18thC, 50in (127cm) wide. **£20,000-25,000** *CNY*

A Regency mahogany bookcase in Gothic style, with central recessed section, slightly distressed, possibly adapted, 132in (336cm).
£14,000-16,000 *C*

A late George III mahogany library cabinet, with moulded broken dentilled pediment and cornice, above glazed doors with chinoiserie blind fret carved strapwork, c1800, 109in (276.5cm).
£11,000-13,000 *CNY*

A pair of mid-Victorian figured walnut open bookcases, by Morant, Boyd & Morant, 66in (167.5cm). **£4,000-6,000** *C*

A pair of Regency brass inlaid mahogany dwarf bookcases, the panelled sides with lion mask and ring handles, on tapering feet, 33½in (85cm).
£30,000-35,000 *C*

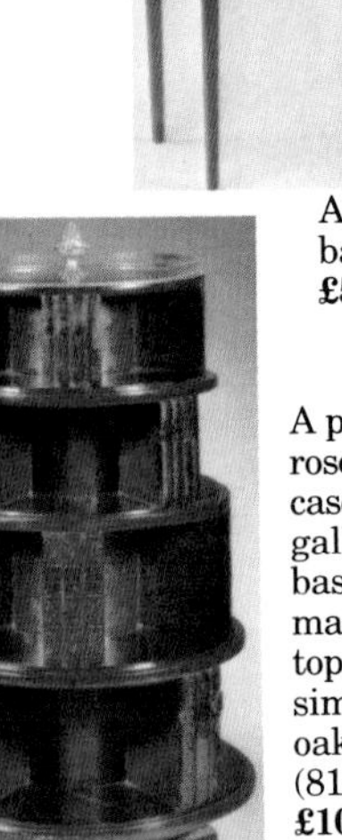

A pair of satinwood bonheur du jour, banded with amaranth, 26½in (67cm).
£5,000-6,000 *C*

A Regency rosewood revolving bookstand, with pierced brass gallery, 57in (144.5cm) high. **£25,000-30,000** *CNY*

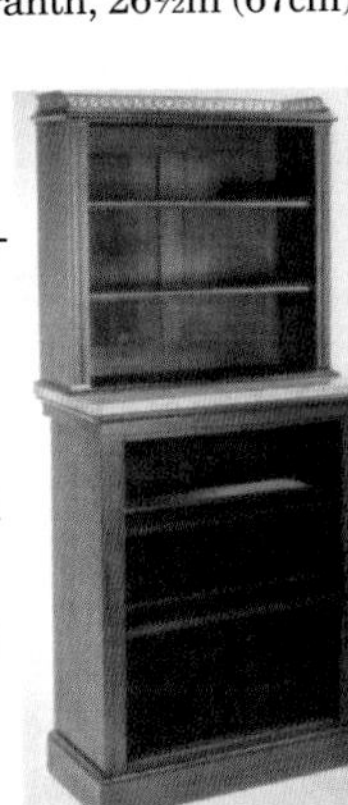

A pair of Regency rosewood open bookcases, with galleried tops, the bases with Siena marble tops, the tops with later simulated rosewood oak shelves, 32in (81cm).
£10,000-12,000 *C*

A Louis XV style amboyna and partridgewood bonheur du jour, applied with gilt brass foliate mouldings and inlaid with arabesques, the base with a frieze drawer with adjustable writing rest, on cabriole legs, 33in (84cm). **£4,000-5,000** *Bea*

A pair of Regency satinwood dwarf bookcases, with adjustable shelves and recessed turned tapering pilasters, on tapering feet, 36in (91.5cm). **£15,000-17,000** *C*

A George IV mahogany bookca[se] with 3 Gothic glazed doors, flanked and divided by foliate volutes, 66in (167.5cm). **£10,000-12,000** *C*

A George I walnut bureau, with crossbanded top, the sloping lid enclosing a fitted interior, on later bracket feet, 24in (61cm).
£11,000-13,000 *C*

A George II yew wood bureau, with pierced brass handles, on bracket feet, 37in (94cm).
£6,000-7,000 *P*

A Chippendale mahogany desk, the thumb moulded sloping front enclosing a blocked and fitted interior with 3 fan carved drawers, Salem, Massachusetts, c1755, 43½in (110cm) **£11,000-13,000** *CNY*

A mid-Georgian walnut bureau, inlaid with boxwood and ebonised stringing, on bracket feet, 2 replaced, 38½in (97cm). **£7,000-8,000** *C*

A George I walnut bureau, the feather-banded sloping lid enclosing a fitted interior, on later bracket feet, minor restorations, 39in (99cm).
£7,000-9,000 *CNY*

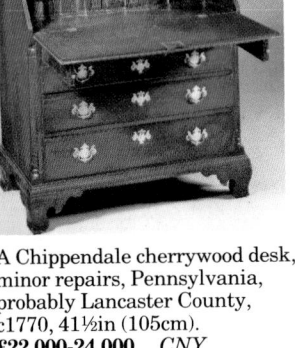

A Chippendale cherrywood desk, minor repairs, Pennsylvania, probably Lancaster County, c1770, 41½in (105cm).
£22,000-24,000 *CNY*

An early Georgian walnut bureau, banded with elm, on bracket feet, 36½in (92cm). **£6,000-8,000** *C*

A William and Mary stained burr elm kneehole bureau, in the manner of Coxed and Woster, crossbanded with walnut and inlaid with pewter lines, on later bun feet, 39½in (100cm).
£12,000-14,000 *C*

A George III flame mahogany veneered bureau, the sloping front enclosing a fitted interior with a Gothic blind fret decorated door, on ogee bracket feet, 39in (99cm).
£3,000-4,000 *WW*

An oyster veneered laburnum bureau, the sloping lid enclosing a fitted interior with a well and central door, on bun feet, 32in (81cm).
£5,000-6,000 *C*

A Chippendale carved figured maple desk, the interior drawers and prospect door in red cedar, repair to prospect door, Rhode Island, c1770, 38in (96cm).
£6,000-7,000 *CNY*

A laburnum bureau, the crossbanded sloping front enclosing fitted oak interior all inlaid with a chevron pattern, on bracket feet, 38in (96.5cm).
£4,000-5,000 *C*

A Queen Anne green japanned bureau cabinet, finely gilt with chinoiserie figures, birds and landscapes, 40in (102cm).
£50,000-55,000 *CNY*

A late George II mahogany bureau cabinet, the shaped mirrored doors with foliate carved gilt slips, the fall enclosing a fitted interior, 39in (99cm).
£4,000-5,000 *Bon*

A George I burr walnut bureau cabinet, with enclosed fitted interior and leather lined featherbanded sloping front, on reduced bracket feet, 42in (106.5cm). **£32,000-36,000** *C*

A Queen Anne walnut and featherstrung secretaire cabinet on chest, 41½in (105cm).
£11,000-15,000 *P*

A Queen Anne figured walnut secretaire, the fall flap enclosing fitted interior, on later bun feet, 43in (109cm). **£17,000-20,000** *C*

A George II parcel gilt mahogany and olive wood bureau bookcase, in the manner of William Kent, 40½in (102cm).
£75,000-95,000 *CNY*

A Queen Anne black and gold lacquer bureau cabinet, the mirrored doors enclosing a later partly fitted interior, partly re-decorated, 42in (106.5cm). **£40,000-50,000** *C*

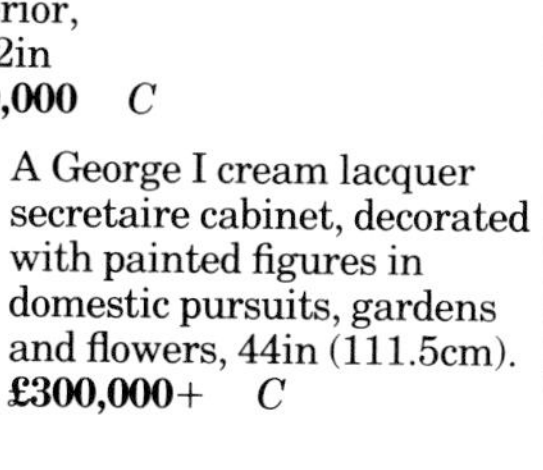

A George I cream lacquer secretaire cabinet, decorated with painted figures in domestic pursuits, gardens and flowers, 44in (111.5cm).
£300,000+ *C*

An Empire mahogany secretaire à abattant, with mottled black marble top, 38in (96.5cm).
£19,000-22,000 *C*

A pair of Regency mahogany library cabinets, with alterations, early 19thC, 44in (112cm). **£5,000-7,000** *CNY*

A Dutch walnut and floral marquetry bureau cabinet in 3 parts, c1800, 55in (139cm). **£12,000-14,000** *P*

A George III mahogany library cabinet, with moulded swan neck pediment pierced with spreading flutes, the lower part with crossbanded doors, late 18thC, 39in (99cm). **£4,000-5,000** *CNY*

A George III mahogany secretaire cabinet, 43in (109cm).
£12,000-14,000 *C*

A George III mahogany secretaire cabinet, inlaid with boxwood lines, 44½in (112cm). **£5,500-6,500** *C*

A giltmetal mounted bureau à cylindre in the Empire style, with enclosed drawers and leather lined writing surface, 51in (130cm).
£4,000-5,000 *C*

A Federal mahogany bookcase/writing desk, in 2 sections, minor repairs and veneer losses, Massachusetts, c1805, 41in (104cm). **£3,000-4,000** *CNY*

A Danish Empire mahogany and fruitwood bureau cabinet, on ebonised claw feet, 51in (129.5cm). **£5,000-6,000** *C*

A Charles II style shagreen cabinet on silvered stand, the cabinet and doors edged with ivory, and with strapwork hinges and lockplate, fitted interior with 2 glass bottomed drawers, 26in (66cm).
£6,000-8,000 *CNY*

An early Georgian red lacquer cabinet-on-stand, 40½in (103cm).
£6,000-8,000 *C*

A William and Mary oyster veneered walnut marquetry cabinet-on-stand, the spirally turned legs joined by a later shaped flat stretcher, and later ebonised bun feet, 51in (130cm).
£13,000-16,000 *C*

A Florentine parcel gilt and walnut bureau cabinet, by Luigi Frullini, 52in (132cm).
£11,000-13,000 *C*

An English oak and ormolu mounted neo-Gothic cabinet-on-stand, c1840, 27½in (70cm). **£2,500-3,000** *CNY*

An early Victorian display cabinet, 64in (162.5cm).
£4,000-5,000 *C*

A South German ebonised, walnut and marquetry cabinet-on-stand, late 17thC, 60in (152cm).
£10,000-12,000 *C*

A Biedermeier fruitwood secretaire à abattant, the fall front enclosing an architectural fitted interior, c1800, 44in (112cm). **£4,000-6,000** *C*

A Charles II black and gold lacquer cabinet-on-stand, the later silvered stand with gadrooned border, 41in (104cm). **£11,000-13,000** *C*

A George III mahogany cabinet-on-stand, the panelled doors with re-entrant corners, enclosing drawers, the stand with chamfered square legs headed by pierced brackets, 32in (81cm). **£4,000-5,000** *C*

A Louis XVI style ormolu mounted mahogany and parquetry vitrine, late 19thC. **£8,000-12,000** *CNY*

A Regency parcel gilt and rosewood side cabinet, the white marble top with concave sides and ribbed edge, above a pair of cupboard doors cross-banded with calamander and filled with brass trellis backed with pleated silk, 38½in (97cm). **£13,000-16,000** *C*

A Regency ormolu mounte rosewood and ebonised sid cabinet, 29in (74cm). **£22,000-24,000** *C*

A Portuguese Colonial ebony and hardwood cabinet, Goanese, 18thC, 32½in (82cm). **£19,000-23,000** *C*

A Regency rosewood and parcel gilt side cabinet in the Southill manner, with breakfront D-shaped front, regilded, 59½in (150cm). **£30,000-32,000** *C*

A pair of Italian rococ inlaid walnut corner cupboards, mid-18thC 26½in (67cm). **£12,000-15,000** *CN*

An Italian ebony and pietra dura cabinet-on-stand, the sides with cartouches centred by the Medici coat-of-arms, the later stand with cabriole legs, 47in (119cm). **£19,000-22,000** *C*

A pair of Regency ormolu mounted dwarf cabinets, with grey marble tops, later glazed panel door, 41½in (105cm). **£7,000-9,000** *C*

A pair of Régence ormolu mounted king wood and parquetry encoignure with 'arc en arbalette' tops, 29in (74cm). **£25,000-30,000** *C*

A pair of Regency brass and ebony inlaid side cabinets, with later tops, 29½in (75cm). **£10,000-12,000** *C*

A mid-Victorian figured walnut folio stand and cupboard, locks stamped J. Bramah, 124 Piccadilly, 43in (109cm). **£15,000-18,000** *C*

ı pair of George III mahogany library ırmchairs, covered in close nailed 'elvet, with sloping arm supports, n square legs joined by stretchers, ne re-railed. **£7,000-8,000** *C*

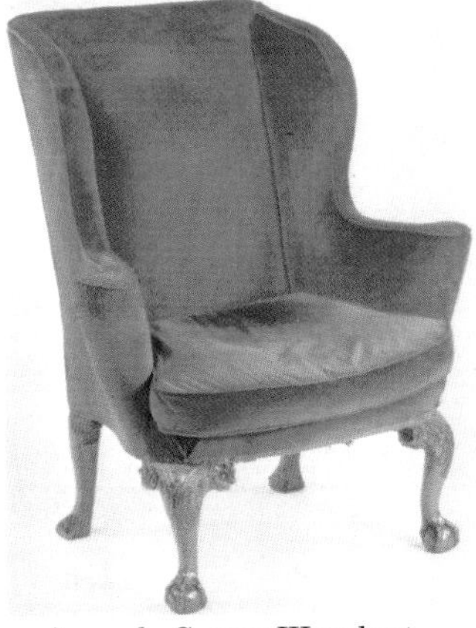

An early George III walnut wing armchair, the bowed seat with a squab cushion, with claw-and-ball feet.
£9,000-11,000 *C*

An early George III mahogany library armchair, some repairs.
£20,000-25,000 *CNY*

A pair of mahogany and ɔarcel gilt library arm- :hairs, the channelled arm supports and seat rails :arved with ribbon tied osettes, on cabriole legs ıeaded by scrolling foliage, with pad feet and foliate oes. **£25,000-30,000** *C*

A Regency mahogany bergère, the sides filled with split cane, the reeded frame with scroll arm supports.
£3,500-4,500 *C*

A pair of George II mahogany library armchairs, the drop-in seats covered with restored contemporary gros and petit point needlework, c1760.
£100,000-125,000 *CNY*

A George II mahogany library armchair, with cartouche shaped padded back and seat covered in cut velvet, extensively re-railed.
£9,500-11,500 *C*

A Regency ebonised bergère, with deep :urved toprail and upholstered back ınd seat covered in leather, the :ibbed scrolled arms on sabre legs ıeaded by anthemions.
£9,500-11,500 *C*

A set of 8 George III giltwood open armchairs, with moulded frames on fluted seat rails and tapering fluted legs headed by oval beaded paterae.
£30,000-35,000 *C*

Left. A Regency ebonised open armchair, decorated with gilt, later feet.
£2,500-3,500 *C*
Right. A Regency mahogany Windsor chair.
£3,000-4,000 *C*

A set of 10 George III painted ope armchairs, restorations.
£12,000-14,000 *C*

A pair of Regency bamboo bergères, in the Brighton Pavilion taste, early 19thC.
£3,000-4,000 *CNY*

A set of 6 George III black japanned open armchairs, later caned, re-decorated.
£4,000-5,000 *C*

A pair of George IV parcel gilt and cream painted bergères, in the style of Morel & Hughe previously blue painted. **£18,000-21,000** *C*

A George IV simulated rosewood bergère, stamped T. Bradley twice.
£6,000-8,000 *C*

A George III chair.
£2,000-3,000 *C*

A pair of Régence walnut fauteuils
£3,500-4,500 *CNY*

A set of 5 Regency painted and parcel gilt open armchairs, the caned seats with silk squab cushions, and another en suite, of later date.
£15,000-18,000 *C*

Left. A George IV simulated rosewood bergère.
£2,000-2,500 *C*
Right. A pair of Regency painted bergères, with bowed toprails centred by panels of frolicking putti and trellis splats. **£9,500-11,500** *C*

A set of 8 early Victorian rosewood open armchairs in George II style, profusely carved with shells and foliage, with eagle's claw-and-ball feet. **£11,000-13,000** *C*

A pair of Russian mahogany, parcel gilt and ebonised open fauteuils, early 19thC, redecorated, 26in (67cm). **£11,000-13,000** *C*

A Chippendale mahogany corner chair, Newport, Rhode Island, c1760. **£14,000-16,000** *CNY*

A set of 4 early George II mahogany side chairs, upholstered in part-18thC gros point, c1735. **£6,000-7,000** *CNY*

An Empire mahogany fauteuil, one back foot spliced. **£4,000-5,000** *C*

Two similar George IV rosewood and parcel gilt bergères, attributed to Morel and Seddon, one with cresting deficient, the other with later finials and lacking leg mouldings. **£9,000-11,000** *C*

A pair of early Victorian rosewood open armchairs, carved with flowerhead crestings and centres to the seat rails. **£8,000-10,000** *C*

A pair of Empire mahogany fauteuils, with slightly bowed panelled toprails carved with fruiting foliage, upholstered in damask, the foliate scrolling arms on dolphin supports, on ribbed cabriole legs headed by foliage and rosettes. **£18,000-20,000** *C*

A set of 11 George II walnut dining chairs, probably by Giles Grendey, restorations to front feet, c1740, and a side chair and an armchair of a later date. **£30,000-35,000** *CNY*

An early Victorian oak open armchair, attributed to A. W. N. Pugin, upholstered in contemporary foliate cut velvet. **£6,000-8,000** *C*

A giltwood suite of seat furniture of Louis XV style, comprising a canapé and a set of 4 fauteuils, labelled E.G. Gaze Meubles Anciens Dorures Rue Charles V, No. 8 Paris, late 19thC, the canapé 86in (219cm). **£9,500-11,500** *C*

A set of 9 Regency mahogany dining chairs including a pair of armchairs, and one of a later date.
£11,000-13,000 *C*

A set of 8 Regency rosewood and parcel gilt dining chairs, including 2 armchairs. **£21,000-23,000** *C*

A set of 12 George III carved mahogany dining chairs in the Hepplewhite taste.
£16,000-18,000 *P*

A set of 12 Regency simulated rosewood and parcel gilt dining chairs, variously stamped. **£19,000-23,000** *C*

A harlequin set of 11 mahogany dining chairs of Chippendale design, stamped Hindley & Wilkinson.
£10,000-12,000 *CSK*

A set of 4 George III mahogany dining chairs, including an open armchair, later blocks.
£6,000-7,000 *C*

A set of 12 early George III style mahogany dining chairs, the chamfered legs carved with Gothic panels and headed by C-scroll brackets.
£10,000-15,000 *CNY*

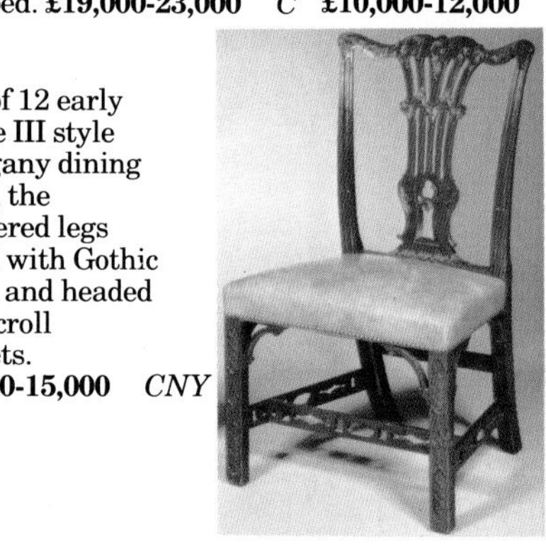

A set of 12 Regency mahogan dining chairs in the style of Gillows, including 2 armchairs. **£20,000-23,000** *C*

A set of 6 George III mahogany dining chairs, inlaid with boxwood lines.
£3,000-4,000 *C*

A set of 10 Regency painted and parcel gilt dining chairs, variously stamped.
£17,000-19,000 *C*

A set of 8 mahogany dining chairs, including a pair of armchairs.
£4,500-5,500 *C*

A set of 3 Russian neo-classical ormolu mounted Karelian birch side chairs, the crest panels mounted with ormolu martial trophies, c1820.
£3,500-4,500 *CNY*

A set of 12 Portuguese walnut dining chairs, including a pair of open armchairs, mid-18thC.
£9,000-11,000 *C*

A set of 21 George IV mahogany dining chairs, in the manner of Gillows, 7 stamped F.F.
£33,000-38,000 *C*

Left. A pair of George II painted hall chairs.
£6,000-7,000 *C* Right. A pair of Queen Anne walnut side chairs, c1750. **£10,000-12,000** *CNY*

A set of 8 George IV simulated rosewood dining chairs.
£5,500-6,500 *C*

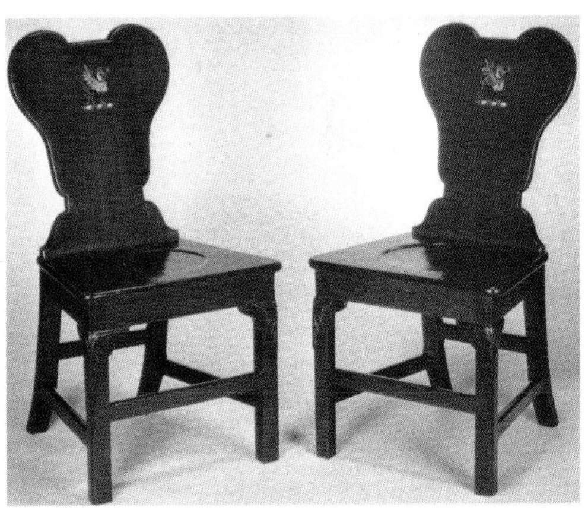
A set of 8 mid-Georgian mahogany hall chairs, the solid backs with the crest of a cockatrice.
£7,500-8,500 *C*

Above. A William & Mary scarlet and gold lacquer side chair, partly redecorated, c1700. **£1,500-2,000** *CNY*
Left. A set of 10 Louis XVI painted dining chairs, upholstered in red leather.
£18,000-20,000 *C*

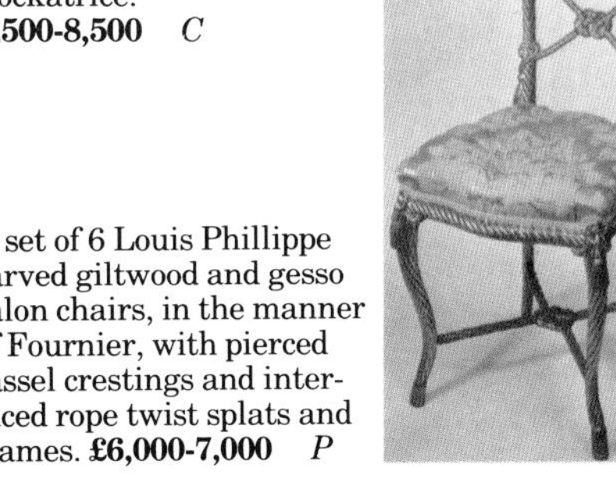
A set of 6 Louis Phillippe carved giltwood and gesso salon chairs, in the manner of Fournier, with pierced tassel crestings and interlaced rope twist splats and frames. **£6,000-7,000** *P*

A Queen Anne walnut bachelor's chest, the crossbanded folding top inlaid with pollard oak, bordered with herringbone lines, 31½in (80cm).
£40,000-45,000 *C*

A George III mahogany serpentine chest of drawers, fitted with a brushing slide, easel and compartments, c1760, 41½in (105cm). **£3,000-4,000** *CNY*

A Chippendale mahogany chest of drawers, on straight bracket feet, with patch to one side, Massachusetts, c1765, 36in (92cm). **£28,000-30,000** *CNY*

A William & Mary fruitwood chest, the top with geometric walnut crossbanding 31½in (80cm). **£11,000-14,000** *C*

An early Georgian walnut kneehole coffer, the hinged leather lined top enclosing a fitted interior, 35in (89cm). **£3,000-4,000** *C*

A Dutch lacquered and japanned bombé chest, with brass handles and escutcheons, 22in (56cm).
£4,000-5,000 *AG*

A George III mahogany chest, crossbanded with rosewood, fitted with a brushing slide, 37in (94cm).
£6,000-8,000 *C*

A George III mahogany bombé chest, with baize lined slide, easel and enclosed compartments, 49in (124.5cm).
£8,000-10,000 *CNY*

A Chippendale carved maple chest, attributed to the Dunlap family, New Hampshire, c1780. **£11,000-13,000** *CNY*

A Queen Anne walnut chest, with crossbanded top above a slide, on later bracket feet, 27in (68.5cm).
£13,000-15,000 *C*

A George I walnut bachelor's chest, the crossbanded top lined with velvet, enclosing a fitted interior, on later turned feet, 33in (84cm).
£9,000-11,000 *C*

A figured walnut chest, with featherbanded top, basically early 18thC, with later bun feet, 30in (76cm).
£6,500-7,500 *C*

A Queen Anne walnut bachelor's chest, the top crossbanded and the drawers inlaid with featherbanding, on later bracket feet and back, 32in (81cm).
£13,000-15,000 *C*

Régence bronze mounted kingwood commode, ıe bowfronted top inlaid with strapwork, the ·awers with Bacchic mask lockplates and foliate ındles, 51in (129.5cm). **£17,000-20,000** *C*

A George I figured walnut chest-on-stand, crossbanded with elm, 42in (106.5cm). **£8,500-9,500** *C*

A George I walnut tallboy, 42in (106cm). **£7,500-8,500** *C*

George III satinwood commode, banded with ahogany, the top edged with boxwood, the doors ith rosewood banded oval centres, 54in (137cm). **7,000-19,000** *C*

A George III ormolu mounted mahogany and marquetry commode, crossbanded with satinwood and rosewood, 55in (140cm). **£25,000-28,000** *C*

George III mahogany and marquetry commode, ıth rosewood banded top, the legs restored, ½in (123cm). **£12,000-14,000** *C*

A George III painted commode, 48in (122cm). **£16,000-18,000** *C*

Queen Anne walnut cabinet- -chest, fitted interior, later bracket feet, 44in)9cm). **£12,000-14,000** *C*

A Chippendale carved walnut chest-on-chest, restorations, Philadelphia, c1775, 45in (114cm). **£20,000-25,000** *CNY*

A George I burr walnut tallboy, the drawers inlaid with chevron pattern lines, 39½in (100cm). **£3,000-4,000** *CNY*

An Empire ormolu mounted bois citronnier and purpleheart commode, possibly Russian, 51in (127cm). **£30,000-35,000** *C*

A pair of North Italian lacquer bombé commode some redecoration, minor variations, mid-18thC 59in (150cm). **£35,000-40,000** *C*

A Louis XV lacquer bombé commode with marble top, 53in (134cm). **£42,000-44,000** *C*

A Régence ormolu mounted kingwood commode later mouldings, 51½in (130cm). **£7,000-9,000** *C*

A Régence ormolu mounted kingwood bombé commode, stamped Mondon, 52in (132cm). **£16,000-18,000** *C*

A Transitional tulipwood and purple heart commode, the marble top with three-quarter gallery, the drawers inlaid with harewood lines, back replaced, 52½in (133cm). **£7,000-9,000** *C*

A Louis XV kingwood and parquetry commode, by P. F. Quéniard, 32in (81.5cm). **£6,000-8,000** *C*

Pierre-François Quéniard, maître in 1767.

A Louis XV kingwood crossbanded and ormolu mounted bombé commode, by Pierre Roussel, with quarter veneered cartouche shaped panels with stringing 53in (135cm). **£9,000-12,000** *P*

A Louis XV ormolu mounted tulipwood and kingwood bombé commode, stamped D. Genty JME, partly remounted, 45in (114cm). **£8,000-10,000** *C*

A pair of Italian walnut, rosewood and marquetry commodes, with crossbanded tops, with fitted secretaire drawer, 40in (101.5cm). **£21,000-23,000** *C*

A pair of ormolu mounted première and contra partie boulle side cabinets, with foliate friezes and panelled doors, mid-19thC, 54½in (138cm). **£11,000-13,000** *C*

An early George III mahogany clothes press, 49in (124cm). **£5,000-6,000** *C*

A German Renaissance oak, marquetry cupboard, restorations, probably Cologne, late 16thC, 47in (119cm). **£5,500-6,500** *CNY*

An Italian rosewood, crossbanded and inlaid commode, the top with a central panel depicting Pan, the drawers veneered à traverse with Hippodamia struggling with Eurytus, restored, part 18thC, 50in. **£4,000-6,000** *P*

A Regency satinwood clothes press, with enclosed slides, 50½in (127cm). **£10,000-12,000** *C*

An Italian rococo Lacca Povera armoire, decorated with hand coloured engravings, mid-18thC, 49in (124cm). **£5,000-6,000** *CNY*

A Dutch brass mounted mahogany armoire, late 18thC, 74in (188cm). **£10,000-12,000** *C*

A pair of North Italian, Milanese, walnut and ivory bedside commodes, 2 feet replaced, late 18thC, 24in (61cm). **£11,000-13,000** *C*

A South German baroque walnut armoire, probably Bayern, early 18thC, 85in (216cm). **£9,000-11,000** *CNY*

An early George III mahogany partners' desk, with leather lined top, each kneehole with recessed panelled cupboard, 57in (145cm). **£7,500-8,500** *C*

A William III walnut and featherstrung kneehole bureau, the fall enclosing a graduated fitted interior, on later bun feet. **£9,000-11,000** *P*

A George III mahogany architect's desk, with enclosed pigeonholes and drawers, late 18thC, 55½in (140cm). **£2,000-3,000** *CNY*

A George II mahogany library pedestal desk, the kneehole surrounded by 13 drawers with 2 open shelves, the back also with 13 drawers, 60in (152cm). **£16,000-18,000** *C*

A George III faded mahogany architect's desk, the crossbanded easel top with removable bookrest, the figured frieze drawer with writing slide, central easel and compartments, 48in (122cm). **£4,500-5,500** *CNY*

A George III mahogany architect's desk, 6 drawers enclosed by panelled doors, 43½in (109cm). **£4,000-5,000** *CNY*

An Italian walnut kneehole desk, the moulded quartered top above a slide, the frieze with 3 drawers, 18th 42½in (107cm). **£7,000-8,000** *C*

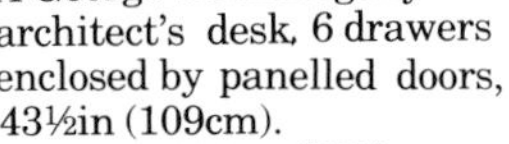

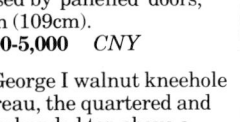

A George I walnut kneehole bureau, the quartered and crossbanded top above a frieze drawer, 30in (76cm). **£6,000-7,000** *C*

A George III kneehole gentleman's dressing chest, fitted with a baize lined slide and an adjustable mirror flanked by various compartments, on later ogee bracket feet, 41½in (105cm). **£2,000-3,000** *CNY*

A George I walnut kneehole desk, crossbanded and featherstrung, fitted with a long frieze drawer, arched apron and 6 short drawers, with central recessed cupboard, 30in (76cm). **£4,000-5,000** *P*

. George I walnut kneehole desk, with cross-
anded top and a moulded arched kneehole flanked
y pilasters and 9 drawers, 50in (127cm).
27,000-30,000 *C*

A Regency mahogany Carlton House desk,
hree-quarter brass gallery and brass
etter slot, the back inlaid with oval
anels, 61½in (156cm).
:132,000-140,000 *C*

n early George III lacquer kneehole desk, the
p decorated in raised gilt, 48in (122cm).
6,000-8,000 *C*

. George III satinwood Carlton
louse desk, crossbanded with
osewood, 42in (107cm).
26,000-30,000 *C*

An early Victorian oak and burr walnut partners' desk of Gothic style, the moulded top inset with leather, and 6 pedestal drawers to either side, 84in (213cm). **£5,000-6,000** *C*

A William IV walnut pedestal desk, with leather lined top and 2 frieze drawers with waved panelled front, 63½in (161cm).
£8,000-10,000 *C*

Above. A Regency satinwood Carlton House desk, 41½in (105cm).
£7,000-10,000 *C*

Left. A painted pine and maple desk, probably Connecticut, c1720, 34in (86cm). **£3,000-4,000** *CNY*

A mahogany library desk, the leather lined top with 4 easel flaps, late 19thC, 79in (200cm).
£3,500-4,500 *C*

A William IV mahogany pedestal desk, with frieze drawers, 52in (132cm).
£6,000-8,000 *C*

A Queen Anne giltwood overmantel, arched bevelled triple plates, in faceted bevelled surround. 35 by 62½in (89 by 158cm).
£30,000-35,000 *C*

A George II giltwood mirror, with later bevelled plate, the frame previously with candle branches, 51 by 31in (130 by 79cm). **£7,500-8,500** *C*

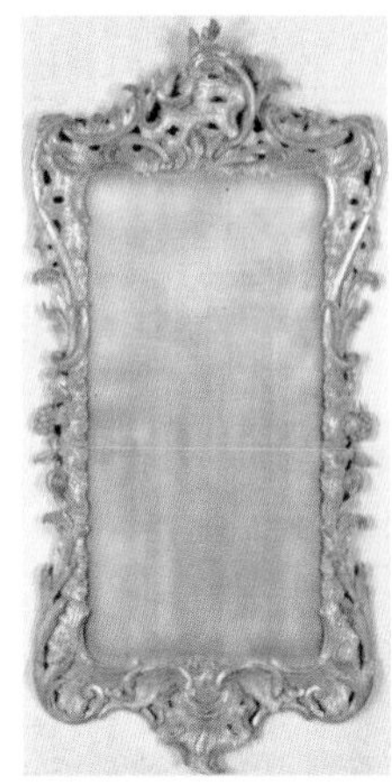

A George II giltwood mirror, mid-18thC, 53 by 25in (135 by 64cm).
£2,500-3,500 *CNY*

A William and Mary walnut and paper mirror, with bevelled plate and moulded slip, the divide glazed frame with panels of gilded and coloured rolled paper, the top one with a miniature of Christ and the Paschal Lamb, 31½ by 28½in (80 by 72cm). **£11,000-13,000** *C*

A George I giltwood mirror, early 18thC, 61 by 37in (155 by 94cm).
£6,000-8,000 *CNY*

A pair of early George II giltwood girandoles, with later candle arms, 44 by 2 (112 by 61cm).
£14,000-16,000 *CNY*

A George II giltwood pier glass, attributed to John Boson, 93 by 62in (236 by 157cm). **£42,000-45,000** *C*

A George I style giltwood mirror, with divided bevelled plate and 2 brass candle branches, 28in wide.
£4,000-6,000 *C*

A George I giltwood mirror, the bevelled plate bordered with egg-ar dart ornament, the pierced foliate cresting centred by channelled stra work, 38 by 25½in (97 by 63.5cm).
£14,000-16,000 *C*

A George III giltwood overmantel, with centre plate in ogee mirror-borders overlaid with scrolling foliage, restorations and re-gilded, 57½ by 82in (145 by 208cm). **£8,000-9,000** *C*

A George III silvered overmantel by Thomas Chippendale, restoration, 69½ by 91in (176 by 231cm). **£27,000-30,000** *C*

A George III giltwood overmantel, 88 by 71in (224 by 180cm). **£29,000-32,000** *C*

A George III giltwood mirror, mid-18thC, 52in (132cm) high. **£3,000-5,000** *CNY*

A George III giltwood mirror, with later plate, 60 by 31in (152 by 78.5cm). **£10,000-12,000** *C*

Left. A pair of George III giltwood mirrors, partially re-gilded, late 18thC, 79in (200cm) high. **£100,000-125,000** *CNY*
Right. A Queen Anne walnut mirror, 45½in (114cm) high. **£4,000-5,000** *C*

Left. A pair of Queen Anne gilt gesso girandoles, with 2 later scrolled brass candle branches and nozzles, 37in (94cm) high. **£33,000-35,000** *C*
Right. A pair of early George III giltwood mirrors, 90in (229cm) high. **£38,000-40,000** *C*

A pair of George III giltwood mirrors, with later plates, the surrounds carved with rushes and flowerheads, 43½ by 26½in (110 by 66cm).
£17,000-20,000 *C*

A Louis XVI giltwood trumeau, the frieze centred by a cartouche of putti painted en grisaille in the manner of P. Sauvage, with a strapwork and trailing foliage surround, possibly Italian, late 18thC, 58 by 38½in (147 by 96.5cm).
£8,500-9,500 *C*

A giltwood overmantel, with triple divided plate, inset with a painting of a harbour scene in the manner of van Diest, the frame carved with C scrolls and rockwork foliage, 59 by 63in (150 by 160cm).
£22,000-25,000 *C*

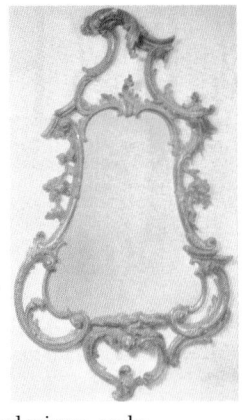

Left. A German gilt lead framed mirror, early 18thC, 51 by 29½in (129.5 by 75cm).
£14,000-16,000 *C*
Right. A Chippendale period carved giltwood mirror, 23in (60cm) wide.
£5,000-6,000 *P*

Left. A pair of Regency convex mirrors, early 19thC, 34 by 20in (86 by 51cm).
£3,000-4,000 *CNY*
Right. A George III giltwood mirror, with later plate, 64 by 34½in (162.5 by 87.5cm).
£7,000-9,000 *C*

Left. A Louis XV giltwood mirror, with arched crest above a divided plate within mirrored borders, carved throughout with flowering branches, C-scrolls and wave pattern, mid-18thC, 80in (203cm). **£3,500-4,500** *CNY*
Right. A pair of George III giltwood mirrors, 48 by 30in (122 by 76cm). **£32,000-35,000** *C*

Left. A Chippendale period carved giltwood mirror, with contemporary plate, 43½ by 21in (110 by 53cm). **£6,500-7,500** *P*
Right. A Regency convex giltwood mirror, the crest with a painted and parcel gilt seahorse standing on rockwork suspending chains from its mouth, 44in (112cm) high. **£5,000-6,000** *CNY*

Two Persian sunken panelled gilt and lacquered doors, minor damage, 19thC, 75in (190cm) high. **£1,500-2,500** *CNY*

A Dutch chinoiserie painted and gilt leather 6 leaf screen, mid-18thC, 95½in (242cm) high. **£4,500-5,500** *CNY*

A walnut and parcel gilt mirror, possibly Danish, mid-18thC, with later plate, 59in (150cm) high. **£5,000-6,000** *C*

An Empire ormolu mounted firescreen, the central column with 2 silk embroidered leaves, with moulded base, 46in (116.5cm) high. **£25,000-30,000** *C*

A Louis XVI giltwood and painted firescreen, stamped G. Jacob, late 18thC, 42½in (107cm) high. **£7,000-9,000** *CNY*

An early George III walnut polescreen, with needlework scene, 51in (129.5cm) high. **£2,500-3,000** *C*

A lacquer toilet mirror, the sloping lid enclosing a fitted interior, 18in (46cm). **£2,000-2,500** *C*

A brass mounted, mahogany and parcel gilt cheval mirror, probably German, late 18thC, with later plate, 77½in (196cm) high. **£3,000-4,000** *C*

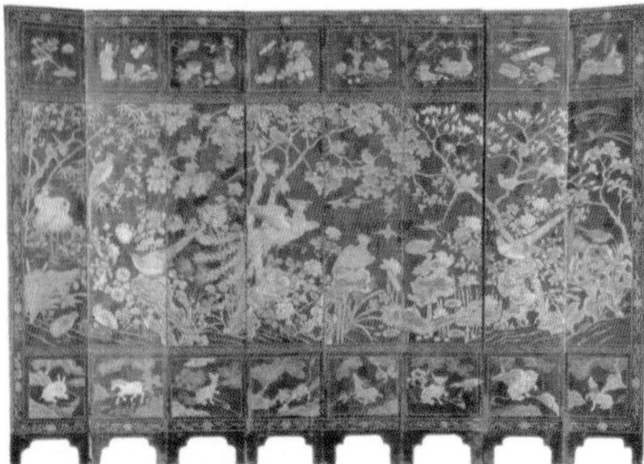
An 8 panel coromandel carved and incised screen, Qianlong, each panel 97 by 17in (246 by 43cm). **£7,000-9,000** *CNY*

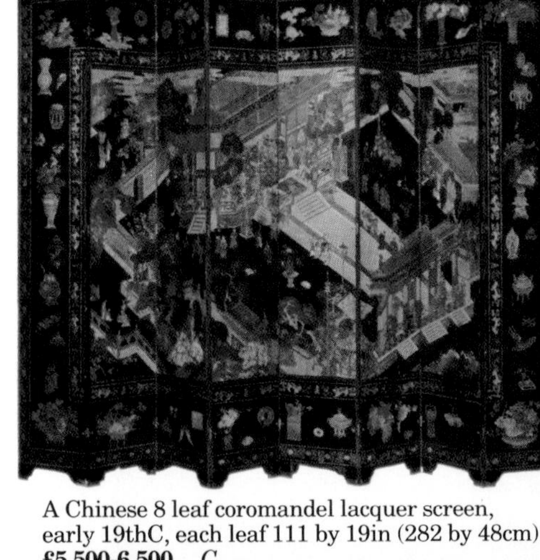
A Chinese 8 leaf coromandel lacquer screen, early 19thC, each leaf 111 by 19in (282 by 48cm). **£5,500-6,500** *C*

A Dutch 8 leaf painted and gilded leather screen, 18thC, each leaf 96½ by 22in (244 by 56cm). **£17,000-19,000** *C*

A Chinese 8 leaf lacquer and hardstone screen, with rosewood borders and glass panels, 19thC, 91in (231cm) high. **£11,000-13,000** *C*

A Regency 3 leaf painted screen, decorated with panels of chinoiserie landscapes, each panel 63½ by 24½in (161 by 62cm). **£8,500-9,500** *C*

A rare Chinese export 7 leaf armorial lacquer screen, c1802, each panel 84 by 20in (213 by 51cm). **£35,000-40,000** *CNY*

A French 6 leaf painted canvas screen, the painted canvas panels mid-18thC, 77in (195.5cm) high. **£4,500-5,500** *C*

A 6 leaf lacquer screen, 97in (246cm) high. **£17,000-20,000** *C*

George II mahogany sofa with padded back, arms ɪd seat upholstered in linen, with spliced aw-and-ball feet, frame possibly altered, 62in 57cm). **£10,000-12,000** *C*

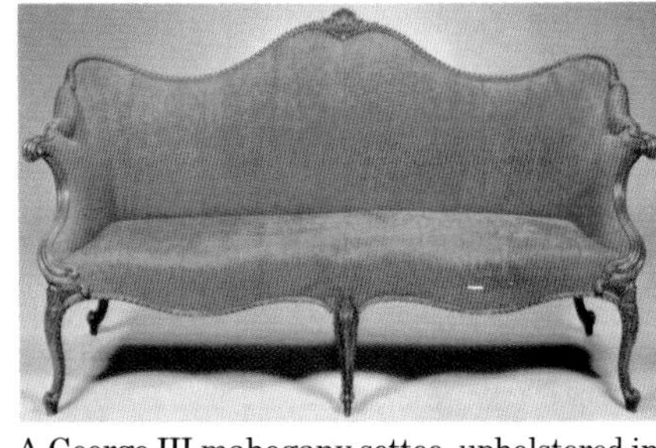

A George III mahogany settee, upholstered in 18thC moiré, 71in (180cm). **£25,000-30,000** *CNY*

Regency oak and parcel gilt sofa, attributed ɔ George Bullock, the seat rail inlaid in cut rass with silk covered wooden bobbin fringe, 1½in (156cm). **£66,000-70,000** *C*

A William and Mary style walnut sofa, with fragments of 17thC tapestry, 82in (208cm). **£6,000-8,000** *C*

. George III carved mahogany twin chairback ettee in the Gothic and Chinese Chippendale aste. **£8,500-9,500** *P*

A George II giltwood sofa, re-decorated, the frame adapted, 67in (170cm). **£2,500-3,500** *C*

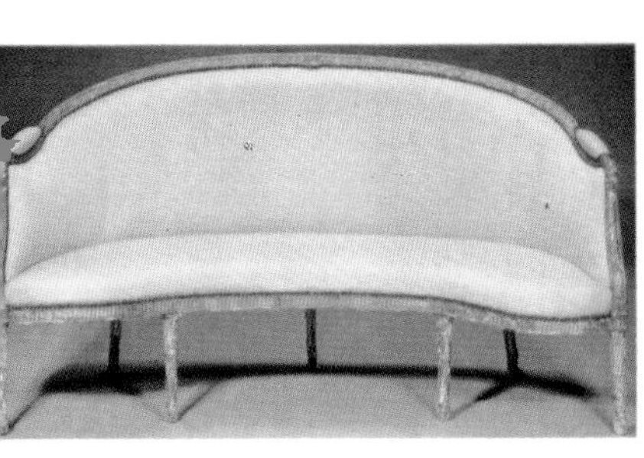

pair of George III giltwood settees, pholstered in silk, partly re-gilded, ate 18thC, 65½in (166cm). **10,000-12,000** *CNY*

An early George III giltwood sofa, in the manner of John Linnell, 89in (226cm). **£7,500-8,500** *C*

A George I walnut double chairback settee, upholstered in floral needlework, stamped IH twice, 62½in (158cm). **£12,000-14,000** *C*

CHILSTON PARK

Home of Miller's Antiques Price Guide

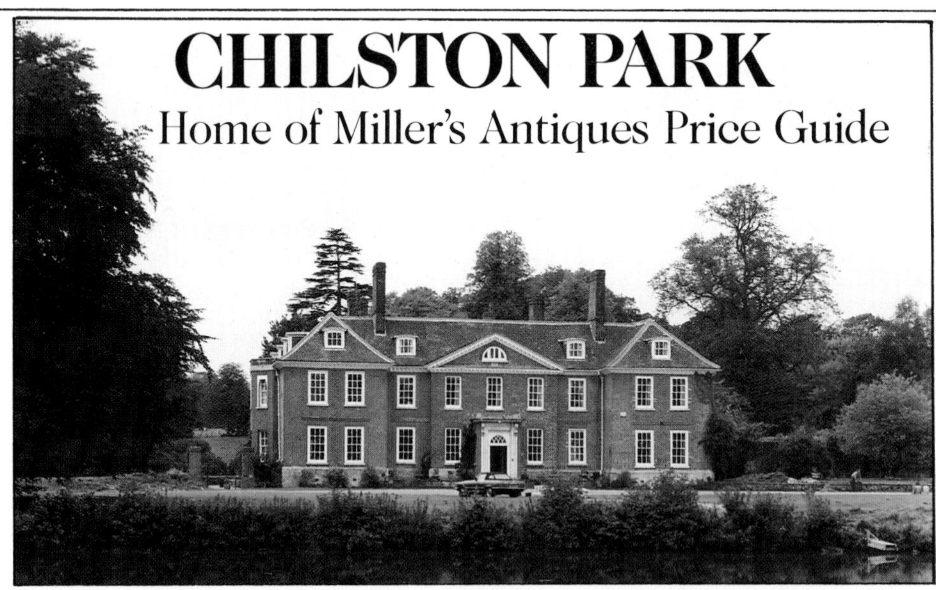

A traditional English country house set in 250 acres of rural Kent. Reflecting the style and elegance of a bygone era.

The private residence of publishers, Martin and Judith Miller, this 17th century antique show house has recently opened as a country house hotel and restaurant.

This stately home is filled with a treasure trove of antiques chosen by the Millers to complement and enhance the style and quality of life at Chilston.

To complete the picture, the staff at Chilston Park, from the butler, who heads the household, to the 'Boots' and maids, provide a level of service commensurate with the best stately home traditions.

Champagne Breaks. Why not stay at Chilston on one of our special 2 day breaks – only **£130 per person** fully inclusive

For details please write to Martin Miller
Chilston Park, Sandway, Maidstone ME17 2BE Tel Maidstone 859803

Toll free reservations USA: 800 448 8355 or any UTELL office world-wide

The Private Dining Room...
English cooking and fresh food are the main principles of Chilston's excellent Dining Room. Breakfast, for instance, might include porridge, kidneys, bacon, scrambled and coddled eggs, kippers, kedgeree and muffins. A baron of beef, roast saddle of lamb, game, hams...and a variety of proper puddings feature on the menu.

The Reception Hall...
Atmosphere, warmth and light flickering from chandeliers welcome you to Chilston. Gleaming wood, bright with the patina of age, sets off a gathering of family portraits...dogs doze in front of a blazing log fire...and your hosts wait to receive you.

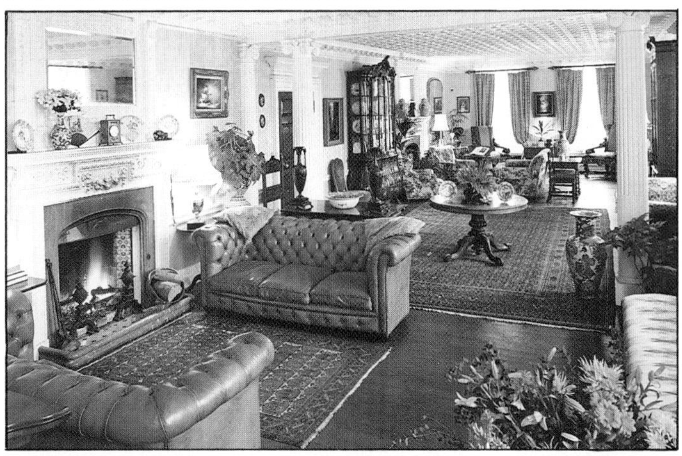

The Drawing Room...
With an emphasis placed upon comfort, the Drawing Room provides a quiet retreat. Somewhere to rest after a journey or a day's entertainment...to take tea in the afternoon or foregather with friends for a drink before dinner...and to relax completely at the end of the day.

The Bedrooms...
There are 25 bedrooms at Chilston, all of which have private bathrooms en suite. All are luxuriously appointed and delightfully furnished and guests are quite likely to find themselves in a four-poster bed. A special degree of personal comfort is provided by traditional hot-water bottles, complete with hand-knitted woollen covers.

A Russian parcel gilt and green painted sofa, with heavily carved back, arms and frieze, partly re-railed, mid-18thC, 74in (188cm). **£4,000-5,000** *C*

A pair of early Victorian rosewood sofas, the moulded shaped backs and bowed seats with buttoned upholstery, 96in (244cm). **£10,000-15,000** *C*

A Dutch painted hall bench, the arched back centred by a large shell framed by pierced trellis and flowerhead decoration, early 18thC, 72in (182.5cm). **£5,000-6,000** *C*

A Federal mahogany, flame birch and bird's eye maple veneered sofa, North Shore, Massachusetts, c1805, 78in (198cm). **£26,000-30,000** *CNY*

A classical mahogany sofa, with veneered front rail, New York, c1820, 80in (203cm). **£11,000-15,000** *CNY*

A Louis XV walnut canapé, stamped I. Avisse, 82½in (209cm). **£3,500-4,500** *C*

Jean Avisse, maître in 1745.

A Charles X mahogany canapé, bearing pencilled inscription Joseph Pillon, 66in (167.5cm). **£2,000-3,000** *C*

A Regency rosewood sofa, with padded back, arms and seat covered in floral patterned wool damask, replaced front rail, 81in (206cm). **£6,000-8,000** *C*

A classical mahogany sofa, re-upholstered in woven horsehair with brass nails, attributed to Duncan Phyfe, New York, c1815, 94in (236cm). **£10,000-15,000** *CNY*

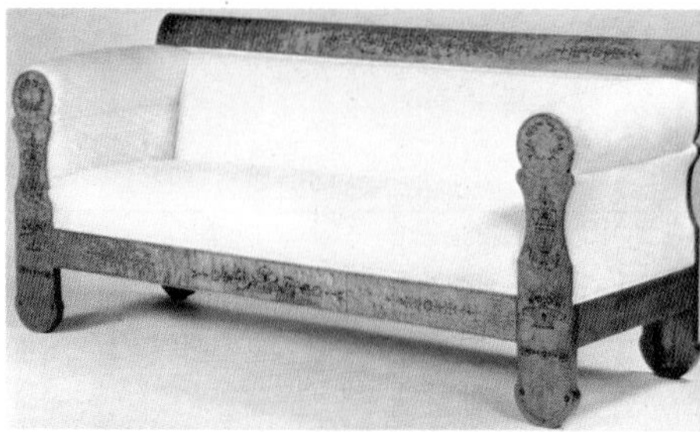

An Empire bird's eye maple sofa, the toprail inlaid with rosewood foliate arabesques, upholstered in calico, 76in (193cm). **£2,000-3,000** *C*

George III mahogany stool,
›in (48cm).
£,000-2,500 *C*

An Empire giltwood tabouret, stamped L. Ternisien A Paris, 25½in (64cm).
£7,000-9,000 *C*

Regency oak footstool, attributed to George
ullock, with ormolu borders and rosettes,
3½in (34cm) square. **£14,000-16,000** *C*

A pair of Regency oak and ebonised stools, attributed to George Bullock, 24½in (62cm).
£21,000-24,000 *C*

pair of giltwood stools of Régence design,
overed in 18thC tapestry woven with DVF
onogram, 32½in (82cm). **£9,000-11,000** *C*

pair of Charles X fruitwood
abourets, upholstered in silk,
arly 19thC, 21in (53cm).
4,000-6,000 *CNY*

A George IV parcel gilt and cream painted oak stool, probably designed by A. W. N. Pugin and made by Morel & Seddon, for Windsor Castle, redecorated, c1828, 17in (43cm) square.
£15,000-20,000 *CNY*

A set of 6 Federal mahogany side chairs and table, repairs, New York, c1825. **£13,000-15,000** *CNY*

A William and Mary walnut card table, with crossbanded folding suede lined top, 33½in (85cm). **£8,500-9,500** *C*

A George III mahogany reading table, with easel supported top, later brackets. **£3,000-4,000** *C*

A Regency rosewood breakfast table, the tip-up top with plain frieze, 54in (137cm) diam. **£4,000-5,000** *C*

A George I mahogany games table, with hinged triple flap top, 36in (91.5cm). **£11,000-15,000** *C*

A George I burr walnut card table, the crossbanded baize lined top with candle stands and counter wells, with frieze drawer, 2 feet spliced, 35in (89cm). **£15,000-20,000** *C*

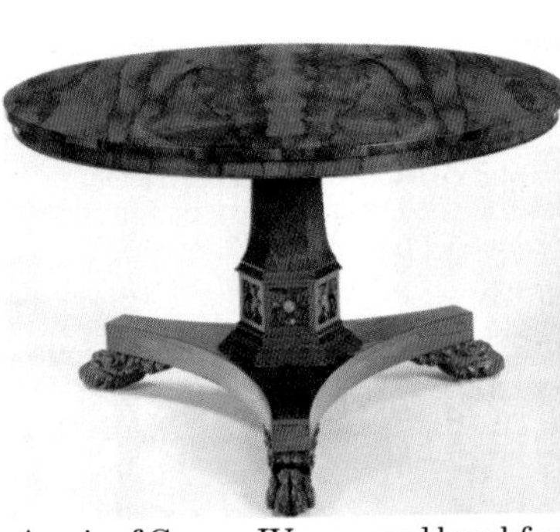

A pair of George IV rosewood breakfast tables, with tip-up tops and hexagonal shafts with quatrefoil panels centred by giltmetal rosettes, on carved paw feet, 47½in (120cm). **£9,000-11,000** *C*

A Federal mahogany breakfast table, repairs, New England, c1810, 46in (116.5cm). **£2,000-3,000** *CNY*

A George III satinwood games table, with baize lined top crossbanded in rosewood, 23½in (60cm). **£4,000-5,000** *C*

A George III mahogany architect's table, with easel top, the frieze with a drawer with divided interior and baize lined slide, scalloped edge and pierced angle brackets, 40in (100cm). **£5,000-6,000** *C*

A George III mahogany breakfast table, the tilt top crossbanded with satinwood and rosewood, late 18th/early 19thC, 54in (137cm) diam. **£7,000-10,000** *CNY*

A pair of Regency Anglo-Indian rosewood card tables, the tops opening to reveal baize lined surfaces, early 19thC, 36in (91.5cm). **£10,000-12,000** *CNY*

A George III mahogany library table, with leather lined top, 4 frieze drawers and 4 false drawers, on ring turned shaft with moulded splayed legs and brass paw feet, 47in (119cm). **£9,000-11,000** *C*

A George IV rosewood games table, the folding top enclosing an inlaid chess-board, with bone chess pieces, stamped BS&P Patent, 23in (58cm). **£2,000-3,000** *C*

A pair of George IV rosewood card tables, each with canted folding top with gadrooned edge, with ormolu shell feet, 36in (91.5cm). **£12,000-14,000** *C*

Left. A Regency rosewood games table, the cross-banded sliding top enclosing a leather backgammon board, 28in (71cm). **£4,500-5,500**
Right. A Chinese export lacquer games table, mid-19thC, 60in (152cm), open. **£3,000-4,000** *C*

A Louis XVI ormolu mounted mahogany trictrac table, with inset leather top reversing to a baize lined surface, the table with ebonised and inlaid back-gammon board, restorations, 45½in (115cm). **£2,500-3,500** *CNY*

A Sheraton period mahogany crossbanded and strung drum table, 23½in (60cm). **£5,000-7,000** *P*

A George IV mahogany and marquetry games table, the top inset with an ebony and ivory chessboard inlaid with flowerheads, c1825, 34½in (88cm). **£9,000-12,000** *CNY*

A Regency rosewood card table, with burr yew crossbanded baize lined top, early 19thC, 36in (91.5cm). **£3,500-5,000** *CNY*

A George III mahogany centre table, adapted, 28in (71cm). **£2,500-3,500** *C*

A Regency rosewood games table, attributed to Gillows, for bagatelle and troumadame, with a cue, rake and 9 balls, 60in (152cm). **£36,000-40,000** *C*

A Regency ormolu mounted rosewood centre table, 42in (106.5cm). **£9,000-11,000** *C*

A Regency rosewood and parcel gilt centre table, with moulded tip-up top, 53½in (135cm) diam. **£18,000-20,000** *C*

An early Victorian amboyna and marquetry centre table, in the style of E. H. Baldock, with inlaid top and crossbanded frieze, 54in (137cm). **£6,000-8,000** *C*

A tortoiseshell, walnut and parcel gilt centre table, the crossbanded top bordered with ivory, 33in (84cm). **£7,500-8,500** *C*

A Regency mahogany library table, with leather lined top and cedar lined drawers, 48½in (122cm). **£9,000-10,000** *C*

An ormolu mounted boulle centre table, with inset breccia marble top and coved frieze inlaid with strapwork, inscribed, early 19thC, 27in (69cm). **£5,000-6,000** *C*

A mahogany centre table, with moulded verde antico marble top with centred chessboard, c1830, 37in (94cm) diam. **£21,000-23,000** *C*

A William IV parcel gilt, oak veneered and crossbanded centre table, 51in (129.5cm). **£9,000-10,000** *Bea*

A pair of George IV mahogany centre tables, with later tops, 67in (170cm). **£17,000-20,000** *C*

A pink and grey veined marble table, with brass bound specimen marble top, on baluster support and plinth base, mid-19thC, 34in (86cm) diam. **£6,000-8,000** *C*

Above. An ormolu mounted mahogany centre table, stamped Jacob D. R. Meslee, 37in (94cm). **£4,000-6,000** *C*
Right. A mahogany veneer drum table, Baltimore, c1815, 20in (51cm).
£6,000-8,000 *CNY*

A Dutch oak centre table, in the manner of H. Vredeman de Vries, 17thC, the apron and top possibly later, 56in (142cm). **£3,500-4,500** *C*

An Irish mahogany centre table, with heavily carved frieze, on faceted cabriole legs and hairy paw feet, 73in (185cm).
£4,000-5,000 *C*

A walnut centre table, with moulded verde antico marble top, the concave frieze with moulded edge, on cabriole legs with pad feet, 51in (130cm).
£4,000-5,000 *C*

An Empire mahogany and parcel gilt gueridon with marble top, on bearded centaur monopodia supports and tripartite base, 34in (86cm).
£5,500-6,500 *C*

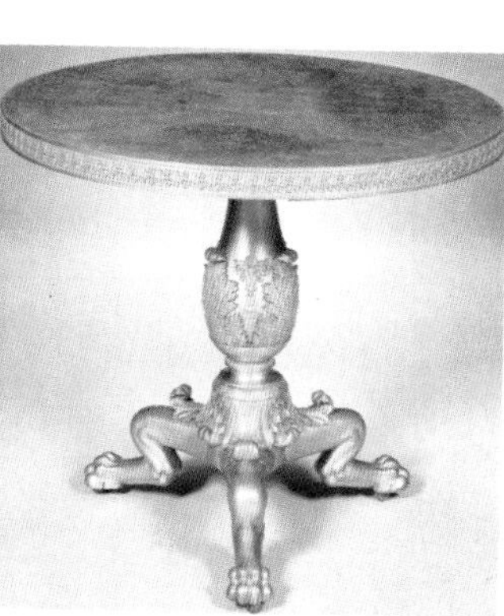

An Empire ormolu and porphyry gueridon, early 19thC, 36in (91.5cm).
£25,000-30,000 *CNY*

An early Victorian ebonised and parcel gilt centre table, with Italian scagliola painted top and ebonised rosewood moulding, 36in (91.5cm).
£8,000-10,000 *C*

An Empire mahogany gueridon, with specimen marble top, 30in (76cm).
£11,000-13,000 *C*

A figured mahogany veneer drum table, New York, c1810, 24in (61cm).
£6,000-8,000 *CNY*

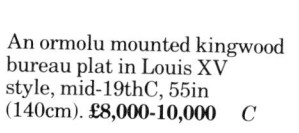

An ormolu mounted kingwood bureau plat in Louis XV style, mid-19thC, 55in (140cm). **£8,000-10,000** *C*

A late George III mahogany pedestal dining table, early 19thC, 130in (331cm).
£9,000-12,000 *CNY*

A Louis XV giltwood console table, mid-18thC, 52½in (133cm).
£5,000-8,000 *CNY*

An Italian neo-classical painted and parcel gilt console table, c1780, 52½in (133cm). **£5,000-7,000** *CNY*

A James I oak dining table, 165in (419cm).
£18,000-22,000 *C*

A George III mahogany dining table, with 2 extra end sections, 106in (269cm). **£17,000-20,000** *C*

A George III mahogany pedestal dining table, with 2 additional leaves, restorations, late 18thC, 152½in (387cm). **£8,000-10,000** *CNY*

A Swiss walnut refectory extending table, with initials IBR MCATM 1782, 84in (213cm).
£10,000-12,000 *C*

A pair of George II giltwood console tables, partly re-gilded, mid-18thC, 51in (129.5cm). **£6,000-8,000** *CNY*

A Regency mahogany dining table, in the manner of Gillows, 235in (597cm) including 7 extra leaves.
£17,000-20,000 *C*

A giltwood centre table, restored, early 18thC, 42in (107cm). **£7,000-10,000** *C*

A George II pine console table, with marble top and Greek key pattern frieze, 48½in (123cm).
£30,000-35,000 *C*

A Louis XV style coiffeuse, :1900, 59in (150cm). **£4,000-6,000** *CNY*

A George III satinwood, tulipwood crossbanded and marquetry dressing table in the French taste, 27in (69cm). **£3,500-4,500** *P*

A George III satinwood and marquetry Pembroke table, in the manner of John Cobb, 35in (89cm) wide, open. **£10,000-12,000** *C*

An early George III mahogany dressing table, crossbanded and inlaid, 24in (61cm). **£11,000-13,000** *C*

A Queen Anne walnut dressing table, Pennsylvania, c1750, 34in (86cm). **£22,000-25,000** *CNY*

A Charles X ormolu mounted amboyna dressing table, 32in (81cm). **£7,000-10,000** *C*

A Queen Anne cherrywood dressing table, Connecticut River Valley, c1750, 32in (81cm). **£46,000-50,000** *CNY*

A Federal inlaid mahogany Pembroke table, old break to one leg, New York, c1800, 39in (99cm) wide, open. **£4,000-6,000** *CNY*

A Transitional kingwood and tulipwood table, with hinged writing flap enclosing a fitted interior, 29in (74cm). **£11,000-13,000** *C*

A Queen Anne walnut dressing :able, Pennsylvania, c1745, 36in (91.5cm). **£10,000-12,000** *CNY*

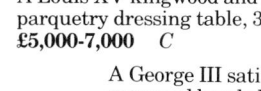

A Louis XV kingwood and tulipwood parquetry dressing table, 35in (89cm). **£5,000-7,000** *C*

A George III satinwood and rosewood banded bonheur du jour, in Sheraton style, 30in (76cm). **£5,000-6,000** *C*

A George IV oak writing table, early 19thC, 29in (74cm).
£6,000-8,000 *CNY*

A pair of mahogany pier tables, with marble tops, early 19thC, 19in (48cm).
£10,000-12,000 *C*

A Regency mahogany writing table, with later X-stretcher, 48in (122cm).
£26,000-30,000 *C*

A Regency mahogany and ormolu mounted library table, in the manner of McLean, the crossbanded top with Gothic arched brass gallery, 48in (122cm).
£12,000-15,000 *P*

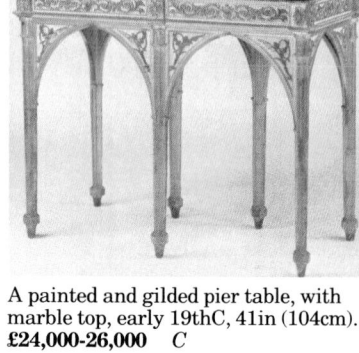

A painted and gilded pier table, with marble top, early 19thC, 41in (104cm).
£24,000-26,000 *C*

An Empire mahogany dressing table, the shelf with inset marble, 20in (51cm).
£2,500-3,500 *C*

A George III satinwood and marquetry pier table, 50in (127cm).
£7,500-8,500 *C*

A George III mahogany writing table, with leather lined top, additions, 47in (119cm). **£28,000-30,000** *C*

A Regency mahogany writing table, formerly with leather lined top, with 3 drawers each side, 58in (147cm).
£42,000-45,000 *C*

A George III mahogany writing table, with leather lined top and 3 frieze drawers, 43½in (110cm).
£5,000-6,000 *C*

A George III mahogany table, the top inlaid with a boxwood outline, one leg spliced, 60in (152cm).
£10,000-12,000 *C*

A George II mahogany side table, with marble top, 39½in (100cm). **£17,000-20,000** *C*

A George II giltwood side table, late 18thC, now with marble top and the back carved identical to the front, 66in (168cm). **£5,500-6,500** *CNY*

A pair of George II satinwood and marquetry side tables, late 18thC, 50in (127cm). **£27,000-30,000** *CNY*

A George I walnut side table, the quartered top cross-banded with burr walnut, 31in (79cm). **£9,000-11,000** *C*

A George I gilt gesso side table, with verde antico marble top, 36in (91.5cm). **£5,000-7,000** *C*

A George III sycamore, marquetry and gilt gesso side table, with satinwood inlaid top, 48in (122cm). **£7,000-9,000** *P*

An Empire ormolu mounted mahogany and bronze table à écrire, with gilt tooled leather lined top, 43in (109cm). **£16,000-20,000** *C*

Below. A Continental rococo walnut writing table, restorations, mid-18thC, 50in (127cm). **£5,000-6,000** *CNY*

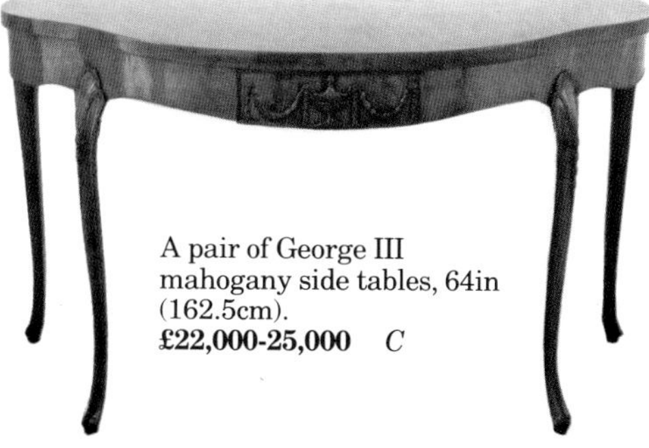

A pair of George III mahogany side tables, 64in (162.5cm). **£22,000-25,000** *C*

A pair of George III painted side tables, some re-decoration, 44in (112cm). **£21,000-23,000** *C*

An Empire mahogany pier table, 43in (109cm). **£7,500-8,500** *C*

A pair of Regency mahogany serving tables, with scrolling three-quarter galleries and D-shaped tops, 89in (226cm) wide. **£6,000-8,000** *C*

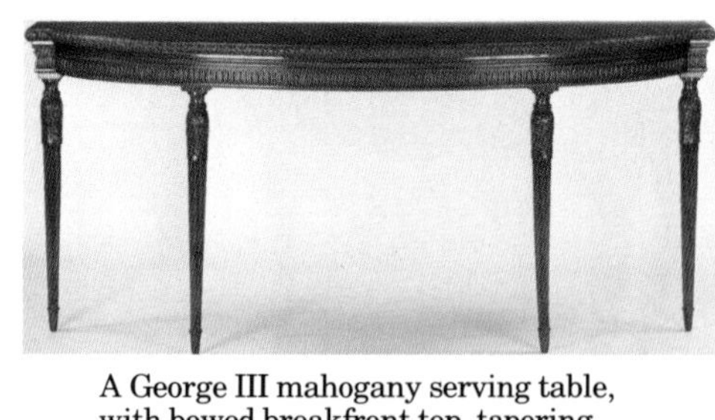

A George III mahogany serving table, with bowed breakfront top, tapering legs carved with acanthus, 82in (208cm) wide. **£18,000-20,000** *C*

A pair of Regency mahogany side tables comprising a card table and a tea table, 36in (91cm). **£7,000-9,000** *C*

A rosewood side table, with specimen marble top, three-quarter brass gallery, mirror-glazed back, 45½in (116cm) wide. **£5,000-7,000** *C*

A George III mahogany and satinwood banded sofa table, with boxwood and ebony lines. **£7,000-9,000** *P*

A Regency rosewood and carved giltwood serving table, the marble top with a gadrooned frieze, 93in (236cm) wide. **£6,000-8,000** *P*

A Régence walnut side table, with moulded serpentine top, 58½in (148cm) wide. **£20,000-22,000** *C*

A satinwood and marquetry demi-lune sideboard, 19thC, 58½in (148cm). **£6,000-8,000** *Bea*

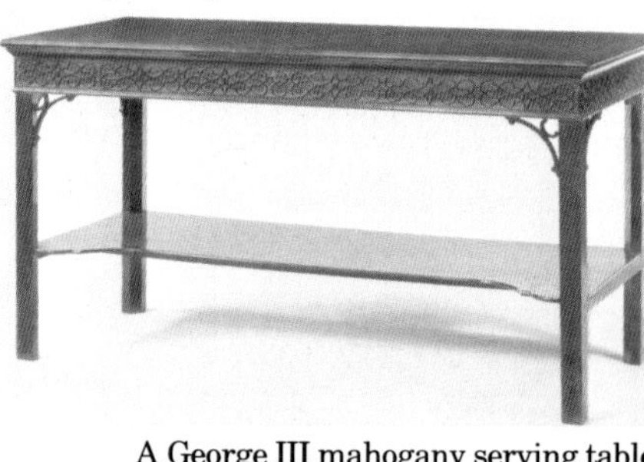

A George III mahogany serving table, with blind fret frieze, 71½in (182cm). **£4,000-6,000** *C*

A George III mahogany serving table, late 18thC, 73½in (187cm) wide. **£14,000-16,000** *CNY*

A Regency mahogany wine table, in the manner of Gillows, damaged, 54in (137cm). **£5,000-7,000** *P*

A Regency rosewood sofa table, with rounded crossbanded twin-flap top and 2 frieze drawers, 56½in (144cm) wide, open. **£4,000-6,000** *C*

A Regency rosewood sofa table, the twin-flap top crossbanded with yew-wood and zebrawood, 60in (152cm) wide, open. **£8,000-10,000** *C*

A Regency faded rosewood sofa table, with rossbanded twin-flap top above 2 frieze drawers and 2 false drawers, 60in (152cm) wide, open. **8,000-10,000** *C*

. Regency figured mahogany ofa table, the twin-flap top rossbanded with calamander ood, the frieze with 2 rawers and 2 false drawers, 0in (152cm) wide. **3,000-5,000** *CNY*

An early Victorian giltwood and composition side table, with serpentine moulded marble top, 81in (205cm) wide. **£4,000-6,000** *C*

A Regency brass-inlaid rosewood sofa table, the twin-flap top crossbanded with mahogany and inlaid with ebonised stringing with brass roundels, 60in (152cm). **£40,000-45,000** *C*

A Charles X rosewood sofa table, the top crossbanded and inlaid with trailing foliage and fleur-de-lys above 2 frieze drawers, 60in (152cm) wide, open. **£4,000-6,000** *C*

A George III mahogany tea table, the folding top edged with ebonised and boxwood stringing, 35in (89cm) wide. **£3,000-5,000** *C*

A George III satinwood and inlaid sofa table, the 2 frieze drawers with stringing, 62in (157cm). **£14,000-16,000** *P*

A pair of George IV figured maple tripod tables, the top inlaid with dark lines and the edge moulded with gadrooning, repaired, 18in (45cm) diam.
£4,000-7,000 *CNY*

A William IV japanned tray top tea table, 26in (67cm) wide. **£3,000-5,000** *CNY*

A late Federal bird's-eye maple work table, Mass., 16in. **£4,000-6,000** *CNY*

A Queen Anne walnut tray top tea table with candleslides, repaired, Massachusetts, c1750, 21in (53cm) wide. **£12,000-15,000** *CNY*

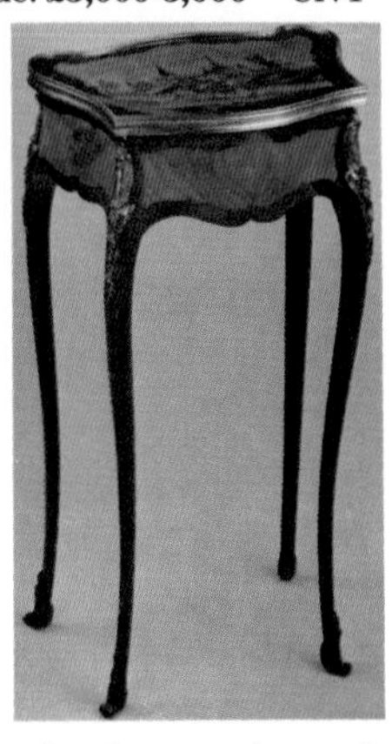

A kingwood and marquetry work table, the shaped top inlaid with a townscape, 14½in (37cm) wide. **£2,000-3,000** *C*

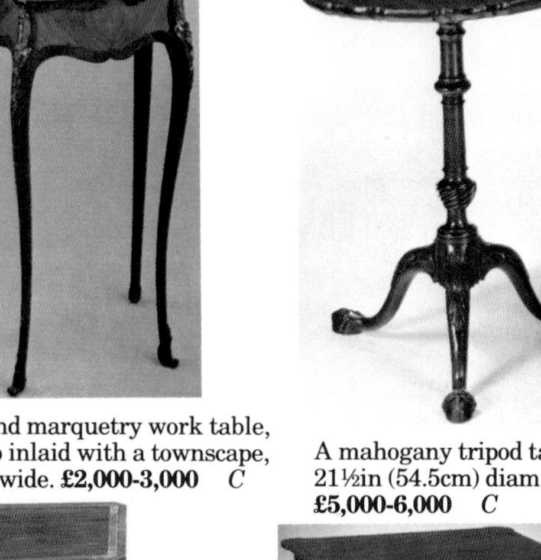

A mahogany tripod table, 21½in (54.5cm) diam.
£5,000-6,000 *C*

A George III mahogany tripod table, the tripartite triangular stem with moulded incurved side, ending on hoof feet, 29in (73cm) wide.
£2,000-3,000 *CNY*

A pair of Regency brass-inlaid rosewood tables, 18in (45cm). **£13,000-15,000** *C*

A Regency mahogany work table, 23in (58cm) wide.
£10,000-15,000 *CNY*

A pair of George III painted and gilt penwork tea tables, 36in (92cm) wide. **£65,000-75,000** *C*

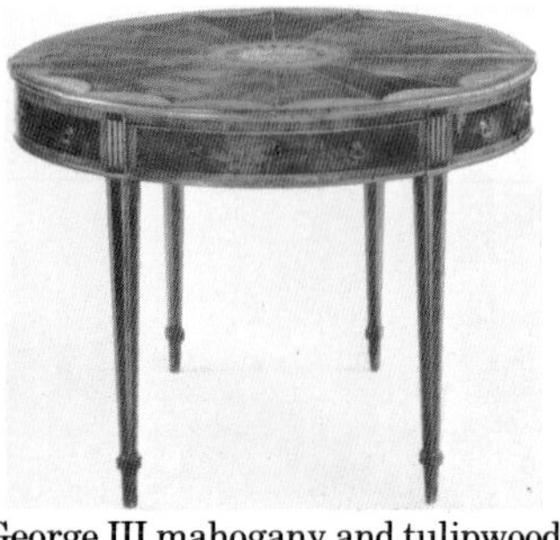

A George III mahogany and tulipwood tea table, with D-shaped folding top, divided by boxwood lines, 40in (101cm).
£8,000-10,000 *C*

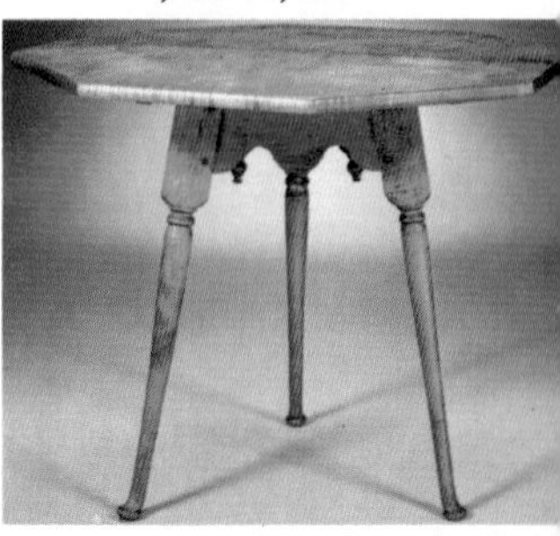

A Queen Anne figured maple tilt-tc tea table, Connecticut, c1735, 33in (84cm) wide.
£12,000-15,000 *CNY*

A Chippendale carved cherrywood tilt top tea table, repaired, inscribed E.B.W.Parsons, Hartford, Conn., c1765, 36in (92cm) diam. **£12,000-15,000** *CNY*

A George II faded mahogany library writing table, c1730, 48in (122cm) wide. **£6,000-9,000** *CNY*

A Continental neo-classical simulated porphyry and parcel gilt jardinière, possibly Italian, 19thC, 48in (121cm) wide. **£6,000-8,000** *CNY*

A Directoire mahogany cellaret, the hinged top with canted corners enclosing a fitted interior, 23in (59cm) wide.
£1,500-2,000 *C*

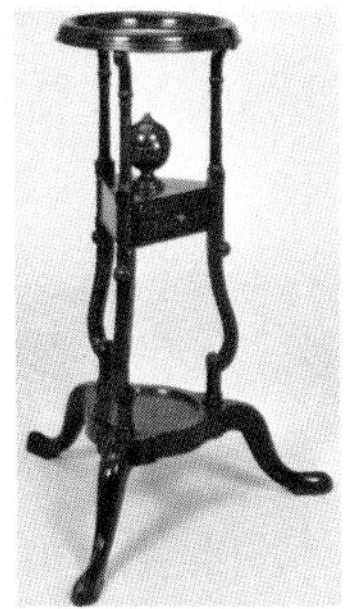

A George II mahogany basin stand, with frieze drawer and domed covered box, 29in (73.5cm) high.
£3,000-4,000 *C*

A Regency brass and rosewood étagère, the top tray with pierced border, 16½in (42cm) wide. **£8,000-10,000** *C*

A pair of George III satin-wood cheveret tables, with boxwood line inlay, 19½in (50cm). **£7,000-9,000** *C*

An early Victorian slate snap top table, painted and gilded with flowers and birds, on turned wood vase shaped stem, 36in (91cm) wide.
£4,000-5,000 *WW*

A Regency mahogany wine cooler of sarcophagus shape, with lead lined interior, 32in (82cm) wide.
£8,000-10,000 *C*

An early Victorian low table, with out-curving foliate border and gadrooned frieze, on legs carved with foliage and bellflower clasps, 29½in (75cm) wide.
£4,000-6,000 *C*

A nest of 4 Chinese scarlet and gold lacquer quartetto tables, decorated with dragons, flower and bamboo sprays and butterflies, 19thC, largest 22in (56cm) wide.
£4,000-6,000 *C*

An Irish George III mahogany wine waiter, with divided and undulating galleried top, 26in (66cm) wide.
£8,000-10,000 *C*

A pair of early George III giltwood torchères in the Thomas Johnson style, 50in (127cm) high.
£12,000-15,000 *C*

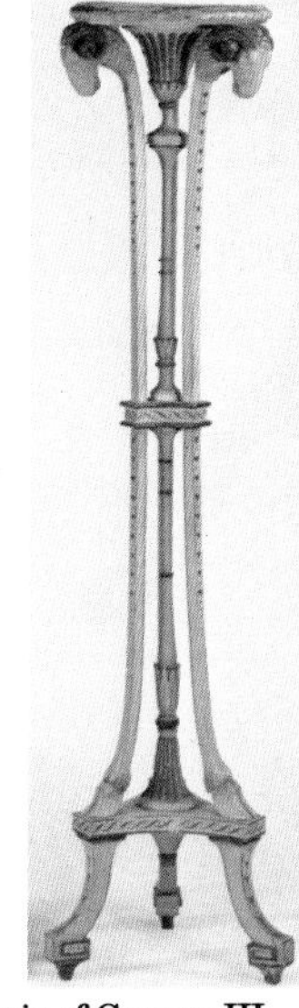

A pair of George III painted torchères, re-decorated, 55in (140cm). **£5,000-6,000** *C*

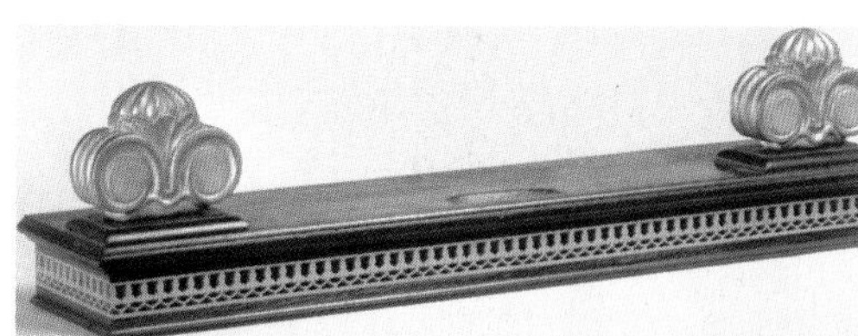

A set of 5 ebony and rosewood wall brackets, the shelf inlaid with Gothic-pattern bands, wit giltwood finials, 22in (56cm) wide.
£1,500-2,000 *C*

A pair of early Louis XVI ormolu chenets, wit silvered rockwork on partly ribbed bun feet, 12in (30cm) high. **£4,000-6,000** *C*

A pair of Continental rococo limewood blackamoors, possibly German, early 18thC, 57½in (146cm).
£10,000-15,000 *CNY*

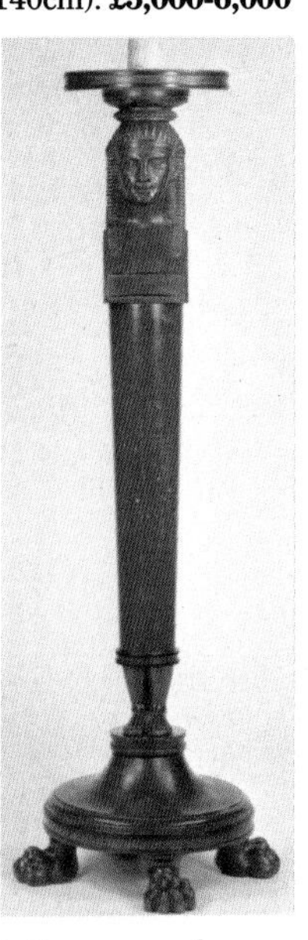

A Regency mahogany torchère, fitted for electricity, 54in (137cm) high.
£9,000-10,000 *C*

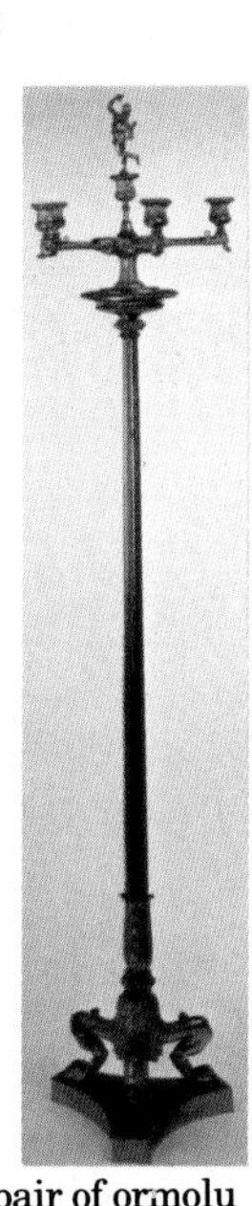

A pair of ormolu torchères, c1830, now on ebonised circular plinths, 68in (173cm) high, plinths 4½in (11cm) high. **£7,000-9,000** *C*

Right. A Regency Cork teapoy, with 2 metal canisters, 43in (108cm) high.
£10,000-12,000 *C*
Left. A pair of George III giltwood torchères, with later inset tops, 49in (124cm) high.
£25,000-30,000 *C*

A pair of ormolu chenets, after Claude-Jean Pitoin, the concave fronted base with lion masks, on ball feet, 16½in (42cm) wide.
£5,000-6,000 *C*

A pair of Louis XV giltwood corner wall brackets, with specimen marble tops, possibly German, 21in (54cm) wide. **£5,000-6,000** *C*

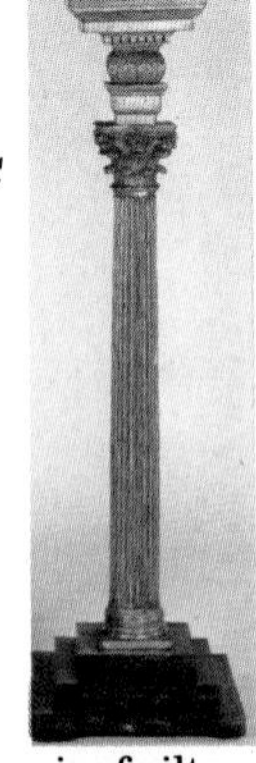

A pair of giltwood torchères, on square simulated porphyry stepped bases, 48½in (123cm) high.
£3,000-4,000 *C*

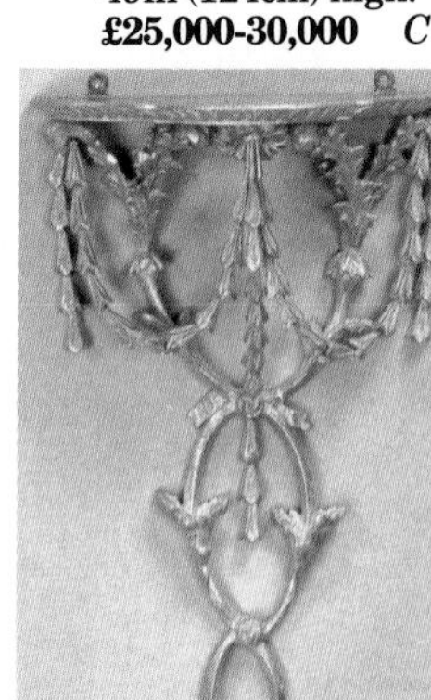

A pair of George III giltwood and composition wall brackets, 16½in (42cm) high.
£6,000-7,000 *C*

A Louis XVI giltwood fauteuil with padded oval back and circular seat covered in green damask, fluted turned tapering legs, later blocks.
£1,500-2,000 *C*

A pair of Louis XV style parcel gilt and cream painted fauteuils, upholstered in blue and white striped silk, the moulded frame with shell cresting and centre to the seat rail.
£1,000-1,500 *C*

A set of 6 Louis XV style beech fauteuils.
£4,000-5,000 *CSK*

A Louis XVI stained beechwood fauteuil.
£700-900 *C*

A Louis XVI giltwood bergère, with stuffover serpentine seat, on fluted tapered legs.
£600-800 *P*

A set of 4 Louis XVI style giltwood fauteuils, upholstered in tapestry, mid-19thC.
£1,500-2,000 *C*

A pair of Louis XVI style giltwood fauteuils, upholstered in machined floral tapestry, the moulded frames carved with berried foliage.
£1,500-2,000 *C*

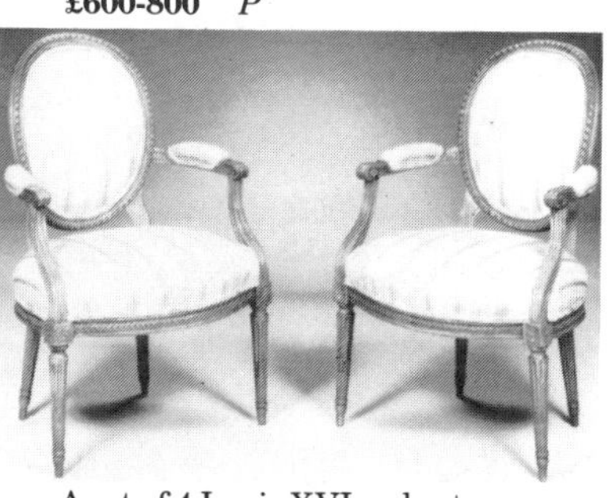
A set of 4 Louis XVI walnut fauteuils, late 18thC.
£4,500-5,500 *CNY*

A French walnut fauteuil, early 18thC.
£1,000-1,500 *P*

A French carved beechwood fauteuil, upholstered in petit point needlework, 18thC.
£650-750 *P*

A matched pair of Charles X carved mahogany fauteuils, with curved upholstered panel backs and scroll arm supports.
£800-1,000 *P*

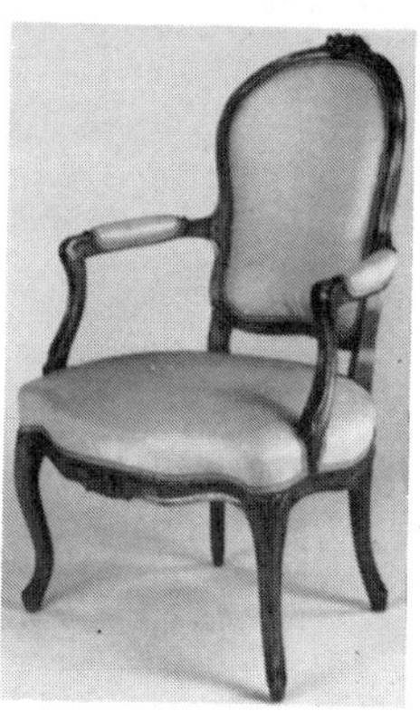
A set of 4 fruitwood fauteuils, with cabriole legs, restorations, later blocks, mid-18thC.
£3,500-4,500 *C*

A pair of French walnut chairs, 19thC.
£1,200-1,500 *RIP*

A pair of Empire mahogany fauteuils, upholstered in green silk, the curving arms with dolphin supports, on sabre legs.
£2,000-2,500 *C*

An Empire mahogany fauteuil, upholstered in striped silk.
£500-800 *C*

A walnut fauteuil, upholstered in gros and petit point needlework.
£1,000-1,500 *C*

A late Empire mahogany fauteuil, with high scrolled back and bowed seat, covered in dark red horsehair.
£1,500-2,000 *C*

A Dutch cream and grey painted fauteuil, with cartouche shaped caned back and seat.
£700-1,000 *C*

A pair of Italian carved beechwood and stained elbow chairs in the Louis XVI style, late 18th/early 19thC.
£600-800 *P*

A set of 4 Italian Directoire parcel gilt elbow chairs.
£350-450 *P*

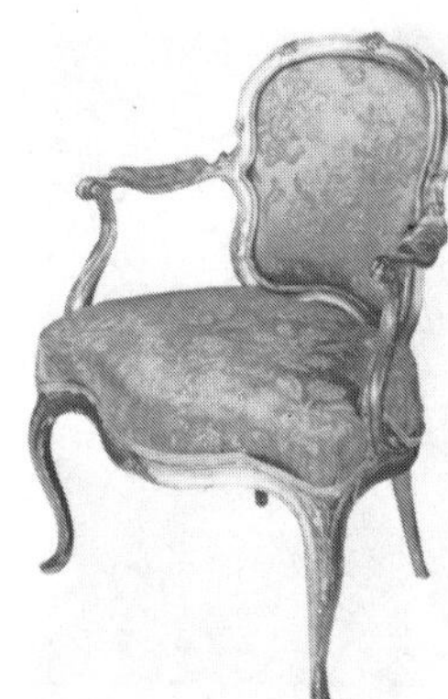

A giltwood fauteuil, later block mid-18thC.
£600-800 *C*

A Continental fruitwood open armchair, 18thC.
£350-450 *HCH*

An Empire mahogany fauteuil upholstered in yellow velvet,
£400-600 *C*

A pair of Spanish walnut armchairs with close nailed leather backs and seats.
£1,500-2,000 *C*

Continental walnut X-frame
air, with lions heads and warrior
pports, on paw feet.
400-500 *MGM*

A blue painted and parcel gilt fauteuil, possibly Scandinavian, late 18thC.
£3,000-4,000 *C*

A pair of Venetian green and white painted fauteuils, upholstered in pale blue linen, redecorated, late 18thC.
£1,500-2,000 *C*

Upholstered Armchairs

A set of 12 Spanish walnut open armchairs with padded backs and seats, 7 upholstered in distressed gilt leather, 5 in cream cotton.
£5,000-6,000 *C*

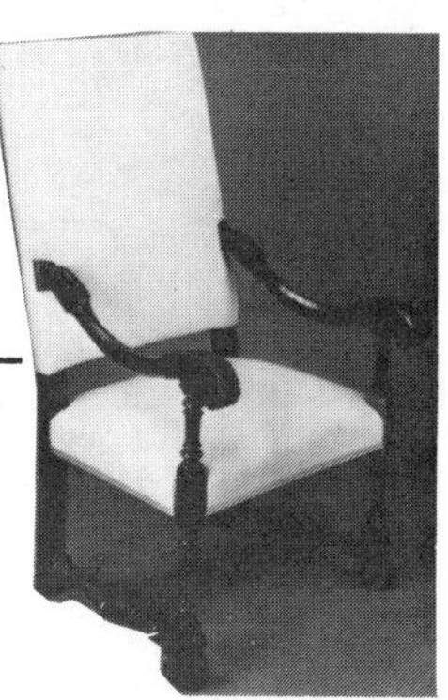

A pair of George I style walnut armchairs, the seats upholstered in beige velvet and red figured brocade, on cabriole legs with claw-and-ball feet.
£1,000-1,500 *CSK*

Georgian mahogany framed wing
rmchair, in Chippendale taste.
1,300-1,600 *TW*

A Georgian mahogany wing library chair, on reeded square supports, with brass casters.
£1,000-1,200 *HOD*

A Georgian wing armchair, re-upholstered in green leather.
£1,200-1,500 *RIP*

A George III mahogany armchair with serpentine back and outscrolled arms, upholstered in leather.
£1,500-1,800 *C*

A George III mahogany wing armchair, with padded back, re-railed.
£1,500-1,800 *C*

A pair of George II style walnut wing armchairs, upholstered in gros point with leaves and flowerheads.
£2,500-3,000 *CNY*

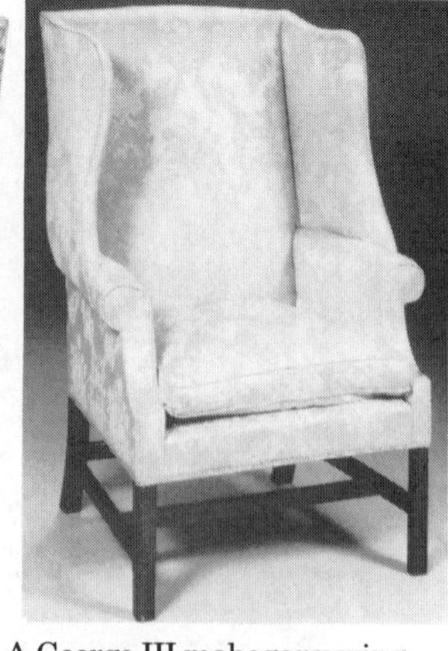

A George III mahogany wing armchair, upholstered in yellow damask.
£1,000-1,200 *CNY*

A George III mahogany bergèr with brass feet and casters.
£1,800-2,000 *CNY*

A George III white and green painted bergère, upholstered in pale green cloth, the decoration later.
£650-750 *C*

An early Georgian beechwood wing armchair, with high arched back, outscrolled arms and squab covered in pale green velvet, with later stretchers.
£3,000-3,500 *C*

A George III mahogany wing armchair, on square chamfered le joined by later stretchers.
£1,500-1,800 *C*

A George III mahogany wing armchair, the shaped back, arms and squab cushion upholstered in pale blue repp, on fluted square legs joined by an H-shaped stretcher.
£2,500-3,000 *C*

A George IV rosewood library armchair, with ratcheted buttoned padded back.
£1,400-1,600 *C*

A George IV rosewood bergèr armchair, with loose cushion.
£1,400-1,600 *CSK*

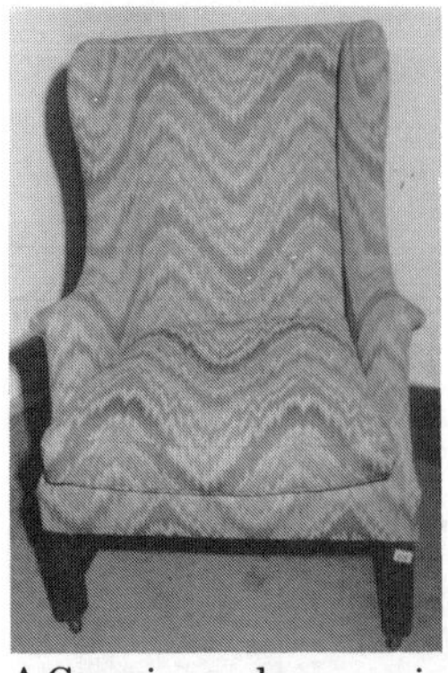

A Georgian mahogany wing armchair, on square supports united by plain stretchers.
£450-550 *TM*

A Regency mahogany library chai with cane filled back, arms and se with squab cushions, and another library chair.
£1,000-1,500 *CSK*

. Regency mahogany bergère.
400-600 *CSK*

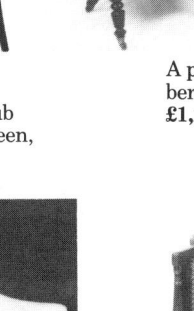

A pair of Regency mahogany tub shape chairs, upholstered in green, with sabre legs, one repaired.
£1,600-2,000 *GC*

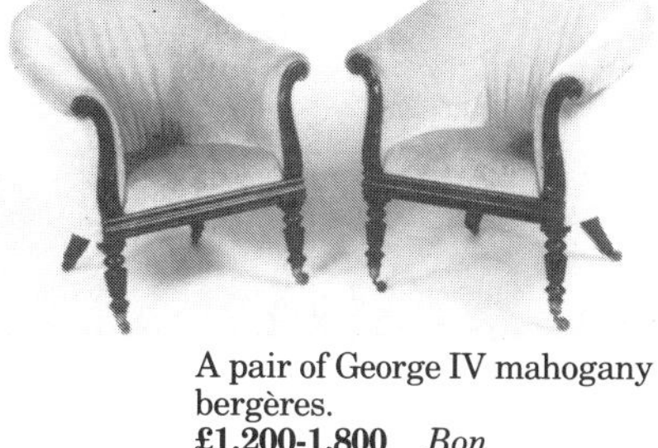

A pair of George IV mahogany bergères.
£1,200-1,800 *Bon*

. Regency mahogany bergère.
1,500-1,800 *C*

A Regency mahogany double library armchair.
£4,500-5,000 *C*

A Regency mahogany library armchair, with cane filled back and seat with red leather squab cushions.
£2,000-2,500 *C*

A Victorian mahogany armchair, the spoon back with a C-scroll carved frame headed by a flower and acanthus carved crest.
£700-800 *Bon*

. pair of Regency mahogany wing rmchairs, upholstered in hide.
1,500-5,000 *C*

pair of walnut bergères, ie padded backs and rcular seats upholstered ı green velvet.
1,000-1,200 *C*

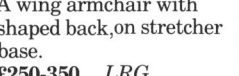

A wing armchair with shaped back,on stretcher base.
£250-350 *LRG*

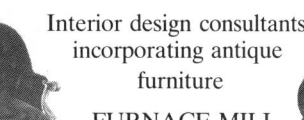

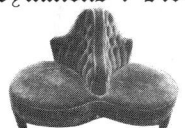

A late Regency mahogany framed bergère.
£650-750 *Bon*

A late Regency mahogany bergère library armchair.
£1,200-1,500 *CSK*

A pair of Regency design mahogany bergères with caned backs, sides and seats with upholstered squab cushions.
£1,200-1,500 *CSK*

A wing easy chair with reclining action, late 19thC.
£500-600 *LRG*

A Victorian rosewood scroll back nursing chair.
£200-300 *LRG*

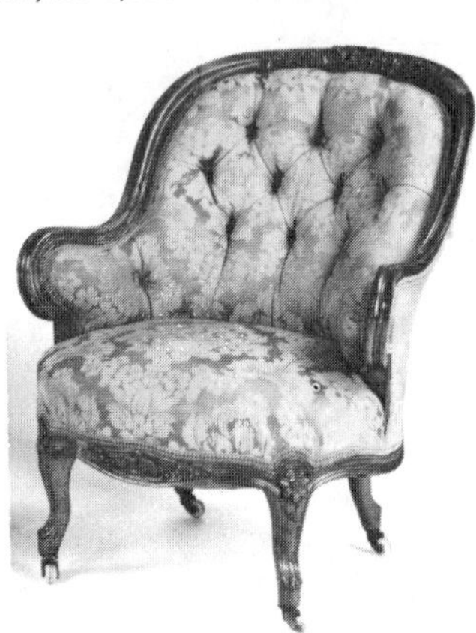

A pair of Victorian walnut armchairs.
£1,400-1,800 *CSK*

A library chair, with buttoned leather upholstery, on reeded legs.
£450-550 *LRG*

A suite of upholstered furniture comprising a two-seat sofa, 2 small armchairs with shaped backs and 4 matching chairs, 19thC.
£550-650 *LRG*

A Victorian spoon back nursing chair, the walnut frame with a flowerhead carved surmount abo a deep buttoned back and seat, upholstered in pale blue silk damask.
£600-800 *OL*

A pair of French walnut bergère chairs, re-upholstered in silk moire, mid-19thC.
£1,800-2,000 *RIP*

A pair of French wing armchair with carved gilded frames, 19th
£1,500-2,000 *DWB*

A pair of Italian painted and parcel gilt armchairs, 19thC.
£800-1,000 *CSK*

Corner Chairs

yew wood turned
ıair of traditional
esign, with ring
ırned bobbin back and
lats, and triangular solid
eat on turned
ıderframing, early 19thC.
650-650 *P*

A George II mahogany corner chair, with drop-in seat, on cabriole front leg headed by acanthus and claw-and-ball foot.
£1,100-1,300 *CNY*

A Louis XV beechwood and caned fauteuil, with arched moulded caned back and padded arms, the caned seat with loose cushion above flower carved seat rail, on cabriole legs headed by flowers.
£1,300-1,600 *CNY*

)ining Chairs

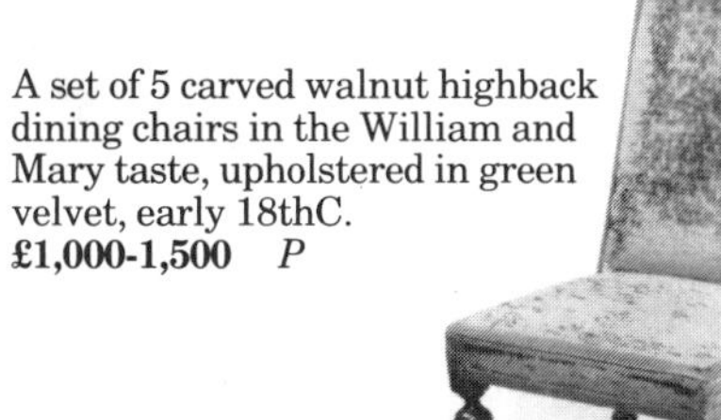

A set of 5 carved walnut highback dining chairs in the William and Mary taste, upholstered in green velvet, early 18thC.
£1,000-1,500 *P*

A set of 6 George I carved walnut, veneered and elm dining chairs, with restorations.
£5,000-8,000 *P*

pair of carved walnut high back
ning chairs, with pierced
bochon and foliate scroll crestings
ıd pierced cartouche shaped splat
ith lambrequin and strapwork
nament between column uprights.
00-1,200 *P*

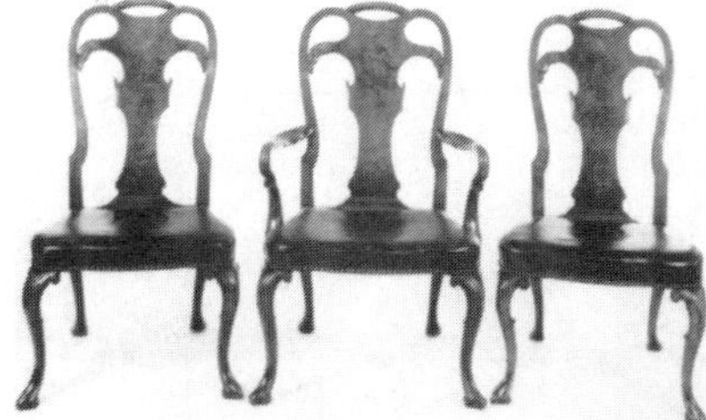

A set of 14 George I style faded walnut dining chairs, including 2 armchairs, each with triple arched pierced crest above a baluster shaped splat carved with volutes and flanking eagles' heads, upholstered in nailed green leather.
£10,000-12,000 *CNY*

A George I carved red walnut dining chair, with pierced Gothic splat with scroll ornament, upholstered in gros point and petit point.
£2,500-3,000 *P*

set of 10 stained beechwood
ning chairs in the William and
ary taste, upholstered in gros
int foliate needlework.
,000-1,500 *P*

A set of 8 George III mahogany dining chairs, including 2 carvers.
£2,000-2,500 *CSK*

A pair of George I walnut dining chairs.
£1,600-2,000 *P*

A set of 8 George I style mahogany dining chairs, including 2 carvers, with shell and eagles' mask headed cabriole legs and claw-and-ball feet.
£3,500-4,500 *CSK*

A set of 8 George III mahogany dining chairs, including a pair of open armchairs, re-railed and on armchair with a later beechwood leg.
£5,000-6,000 *C*

A George I green lacquer elbow chair, with woolwork tapestry stuffover seat, decorated with gilt chinoiserie figures, buildings and flowers.
£800-1,000 *HCH*

A pair of George III cream painted dining chairs, each with a shield shaped back with ribbon tied plume splat.
£1,100-1,300 *C*

A set of 4 George III dining chairs including two armchairs.
£900-1,000 *SAg*

A set of 6 George III mahogany dining chairs, including one open armchair, on square tapering legs with later blocks, the armchair partly re-railed, one chair with later legs.
£1,800-2,000 *C*

A set of 8 George III mahogany chairs.
£3,500-4,000 *SAg*

A set of 8 George III mahogany dining chairs, including 2 carvers, the carving later, renovations.
£2,500-3,000 *CSK*

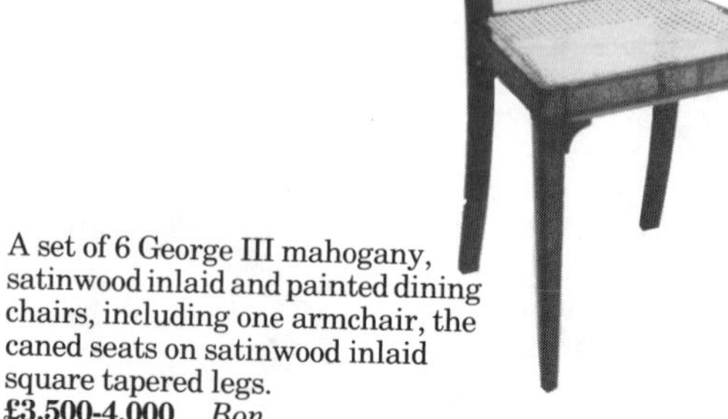
A set of 6 George III mahogany, satinwood inlaid and painted dining chairs, including one armchair, the caned seats on satinwood inlaid square tapered legs.
£3,500-4,000 *Bon*

A set of 6 George III black japanned dining chairs, including 2 armchairs, the pierced oval backs with radiating splats painted with an urn and husk chains, the caned seats with urn and foliate scroll painted rails.
£3,500-4,000 *Bon*

A matched set of 10 George III mahogany dining chairs, including 2 armchairs.
£3,000-3,500 *Bea*

A set of 4 George III carved mahogany dining chairs in the Chippendale taste.
£1,200-1,500 *P*

A set of 6 George III mahogany dining chairs, upholstered in stamped velvet, adaptations.
£2,000-2,500 *CSK*

A set of 8 George III mahogany dining chairs, including 2 armchairs.
£3,000-3,500 *Bea*

A set of 6 George III mahogany dining chairs, including 2 armchairs, the seats on fluted square tapered legs with spade feet.
£2,000-2,500 *Bon*

A set of 4 George III mahogany dining chairs.
£900-1,200 *P*

A set of 8 George III carved mahogany dining chairs, including a pair of elbow chairs with urn shaped arm supports.
£7,000-8,000 *P*

A set of 6 George III Hepplewhite design mahogany dining chairs.
£1,600-2,000 *LBP*

A set of 8 George III carved mahogany dining chairs, including one elbow chair, the backs with turned bar top rails and paterae decorated interlaced oval splats.
£3,000-4,000 *P*

A set of 8 George III mahogany dining chairs, including a pair of elbow chairs, the backs with brass and ebony strung curved bar top rails.
£3,500-4,500 *P*

A set of 6 George III mahogany dining chairs.
£2,000-2,500 *DWB*

A set of 10 George III mahogany dining chairs, repaired.
£11,000-12,000 *DN*

A set of 6 George III mahogany dining chairs, stuffed needlework seats.
£2,600-3,000 *DN*

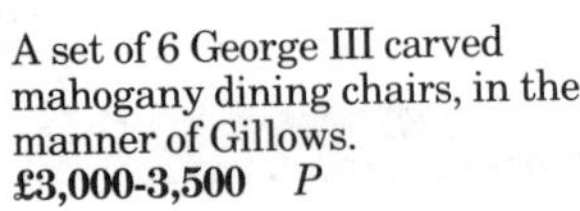

A set of 6 George III carved mahogany dining chairs, in the manner of Gillows.
£3,000-3,500 *P*

A set of 4 George III mahogany dining chairs, inlaid with rosewood, on square tapering legs.
£2,000-2,500 *C*

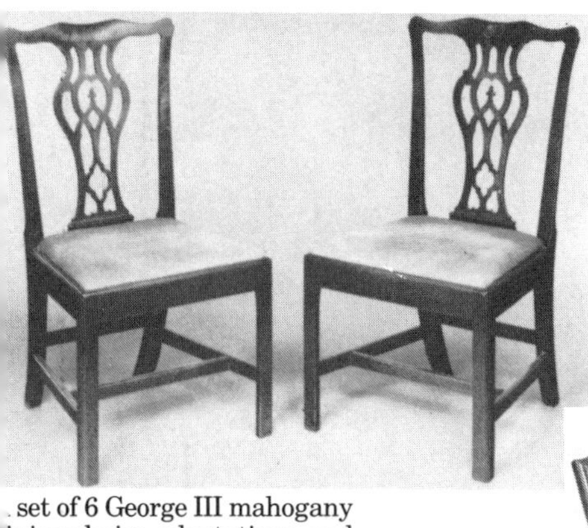

. set of 6 George III mahogany
ining chairs, adaptations, and
similar dining chairs.
3,000-3,500 *CSK*

Eight George III mahogany dining chairs, with pierced vase shaped splats, drop-in seats on straight legs with stretchers, including a pair of similar chairs with restored legs.
£2,000-2,500 *DN*

. set of 7 George III mahogany
oxwood strung dining chairs,
ncluding an elbow chair.
:1,200-1,500 *P*

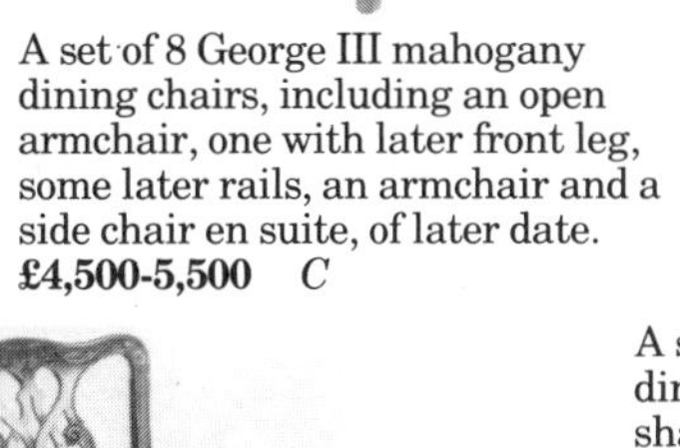

A set of 8 George III mahogany dining chairs, including an open armchair, one with later front leg, some later rails, an armchair and a side chair en suite, of later date.
£4,500-5,500 *C*

A set of 6 George III mahogany dining chairs, with pierced shield shaped backs, bowed padded seats and square tapering legs, later blocks.
£3,000-3,500 *C*

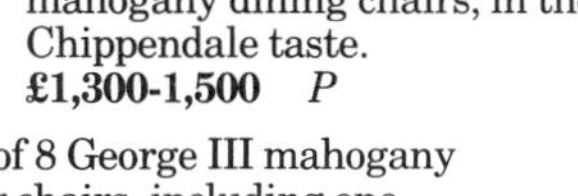

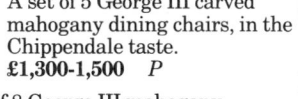

A set of 5 George III carved mahogany dining chairs, in the Chippendale taste.
£1,300-1,500 *P*

A set of 8 George III mahogany dining chairs, including one armchair.
£4,000-4,500 *C*

A set of 6 George III mahogany dining chairs, renovations.
£5,000-5,500 *CSK*

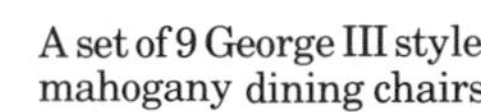

A set of 9 George III style mahogany dining chairs, including 2 armchairs.
£1,300-1,600 *Bea*

A set of 12 late George III carved mahogany dining chairs, 3 of a later date.
£7,000-8,000 *P*

A George III mahogany dining chair, with later blocks.
£400-600 *C*

A set of 6 George III style mahogany dining chairs.
£1,800-2,000 *P[Re]*

A set of 8 George III style mahogany ladderback dining chairs, including 2 armchairs, bearing the labels 'Druce and Co., Baker St. London'.
£2,500-3,500 *Bon*

A set of 8 George III style mahogan dining chairs, inlaid in satinwood.
£4,000-4,500 *CSK*

A set of 12 mahogany dining chairs of George III design, with serpentine padded backs and seats, upholstered in green leather.
£2,000-3,000 *CSK*

A set of 3 George III style mahogar chairs, including 2 open armchair each with a loose seat squab.
£1,000-1,500 *CSK*

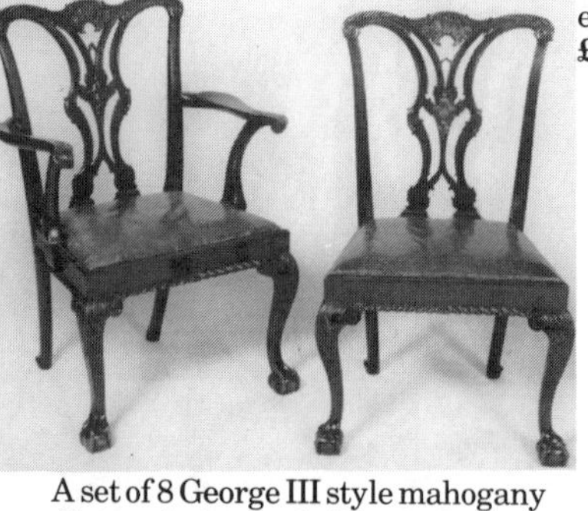

A set of 8 George III style mahogany dining chairs, including 2 elbow chairs, with elaborately carved and pierced splats and crest rails.
£5,500-6,500 *DN*

A set of 8 George III style mahogany dining chairs.
£1,500-2,000 *Bea*

A set of 4 George IV mahogany dining chairs, with bowed tablet top rails and pierced scrolling foliate splats, each stamped MT & MA within an oval.
£800-1,200 *C*

A set of 7 George IV simulated rosewood dining chairs, 5 stamped Gillows, Lancaster.
£3,000-3,500 *C*

A set of 6 George IV mahogany dining chairs.
£1,000-1,200 *CSK*

Use the Index!

Because certain items might fit easily into any of a number of categories, the quickest and surest method of locating any entry is by reference to the index at the back of the book. This has been fully cross-referenced for absolute simplicity

set of 7 George IV mahogany
ıning chairs, including
armchairs.
1,700-2,000 *CSK*

A set of Georgian mahogany Hepplewhite style dining chairs.
£1,200-1,500 *FHF*

A pair of Georgian mahogany Hepplewhite style carver chairs.
£500-800 *FHF*

set of 6 mid-Georgian mahogany
ıning chairs, the drop-in seats on
ıbriole legs with pad feet, later
ocks.
1,500-5,500 *C*

A set of 6 mid-Georgian walnut dining chairs, the drop-in seats covered in striped silk.
£3,000-3,500 *C*

A set of 5 late Georgian mahogany dining chairs, on reeded legs and with carved decoration to backs.
£500-1,000 *MGM*

set of 6 mid-Georgian walnut
ıning chairs, including one open
'mchair.
,500-4,500 *C*

A set of 8 Georgian mahogany dining chairs, including 2 carvers, with reeded backs within wrythen and bobbin turned cross rails.
£2,000-3,000 *M*

A set of 7 late Georgian mahogany dining chairs, including 2 carvers, with turned and carved supports and wide top rail.
£900-1,200 *P[EDH]*

A set of 8 late Georgian mahogany dining chairs, including 2 carvers, on reeded legs with drop-in seats.
£2,000-2,500 *MGM*

A set of 6 mid-Georgian style mahogany dining chairs, including 2 carvers.
£1,500-2,000 *CSK*

A pair of Regency beechwood dining chairs, the moulded stiles with geometric brass tablets, stamped GEE.
£500-700 *C*

A set of 10 Georgian style shield back dining chairs, including 2 elbow chairs, the shields decorated in Chinese manner with pagodas and central oval flowerheads, stamped Maple & Co.
£2,600-3,000 *P[CW]*

A set of 6 Regency mahogany dining chairs, including 2 elbow chairs, with scrolled reeded bar backs, drop-in seats, on sabre supports.
£2,700-3,000 *P[Pea]*

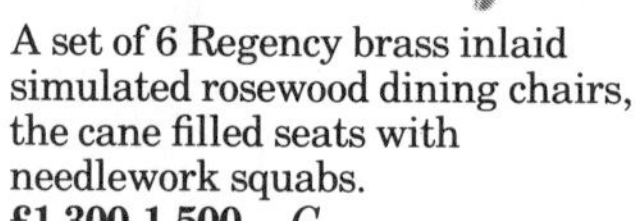
A set of 6 Regency brass inlaid simulated rosewood dining chairs, the cane filled seats with needlework squabs.
£1,300-1,500 *C*

Six Regency carved mahogany dining chairs.
£3,000-3,500 *HP*

A set of 6 Regency mahogany dining chairs.
£1,400-1,600 *CSK*

A set of 8 Regency mahogany dining chairs, with brass inlaid cresting rails, some replaced by wood.
£3,000-4,000 *P[Pea]*

A set of 8 Regency mahogany dining chairs, including 2 armchairs, the panelled top rails above moulded horizontal splats.
£2,500-3,000 *CEd*

A set of 6 Regency mahogany dining chairs, including an armchair.
£1,700-2,000 *Bea*

A set of 8 Regency mahogany dining chairs, including a pair of elbow chairs, re-railed.
£3,200-3,500 *P*

A set of 7 Regency mahogany dining chairs, including one elbow chair with scroll supports, with upholstered slip-in seats on moulded sabre legs.
£3,500-4,500 *P*

A set of 8 Regency mahogany dining chairs, including a pair of elbow chairs.
£4,000-5,000 *P*

A set of 8 Regency mahogany and ebony strung dining chairs, including a pair of elbow chairs.
£2,500-3,000 *P*

A set of 8 Regency mahogany and brass inlaid dining chairs, some requiring restoration.
£2,200-2,500 *DWB*

A set of 4 Regency rosewood and brass inlaid dining chairs.
£1,500-2,000 *P*

A set of 8 Regency mahogany dining chairs, including 2 armchairs, upholstered in brocade.
£3,500-4,000 *CNY*

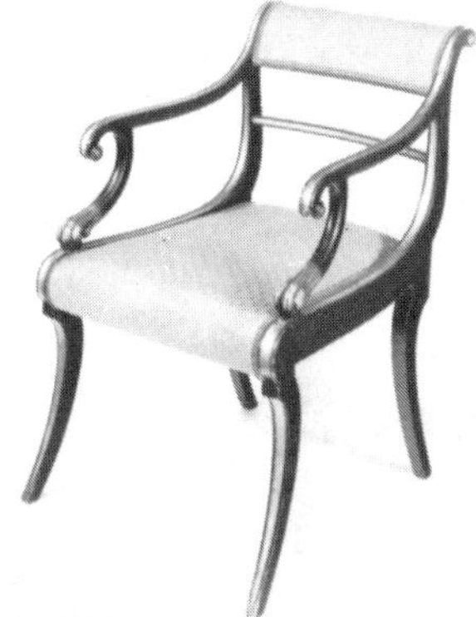

A set of 5 Regency brown painted and parcel gilt dining chairs, including a pair of armchairs with padded toprails.
£4,000-5,000 *C*

A set of 7 Regency mahogany and inlaid dining chairs, including a pair of elbow chairs, and one chair of a later date.
3,000-3,500 *P*

A set of 10 Regency ebonised dining chairs, with cane filled seats and squab cushions on channelled sabre legs, one now painted white.
£4,500-5,500 *C*

A set of 8 Regency brass inlaid mahogany dining chairs.
£8,000-10,000 *C*

A set of 7 Regency style mahogany dining chairs, including one armchair, early 19thC.
£1,700-2,000 *C*

A set of 6 Regency carved mahogany dining chairs, with slip-in seats on sabre legs.
£2,500-3,000 *P*

A set of 6 Regency mahogany dining chairs.
£1,500-2,000 *Bea*

A set of 8 Regency dining chairs, including 2 carvers, upholstered with rexine seats.
£4,000-4,500 *Wor*

A set of 6 late Regency mahogany dining chairs, with curved back rails, on ring turned tapering legs.
£800-1,000 *LRG*

A set of 6 late Regency mahogany dining chairs.
£1,200-1,500 *PB*

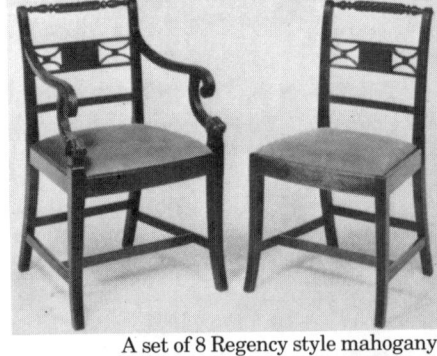

A set of 8 Regency style mahogany dining chairs, including 2 carvers, the arms terminating in lions' paws.
£2,000-2,500 *CSK*

A set of 12 William IV mahogany dining chairs, including 2 carvers, the curved top rails and horizontal splats with reeded decoration.
£13,000-15,000 *PB*

A set of 6 William IV mahogany dining chairs, with brass line inlay to crest rails.
£1,300-1,600 *DN*

A set of 6 early Victorian mahogany dining chairs.
£800-1,000 *CSK*

A set of 6 early Victorian mahogany dining chairs.
£1,200-1,500 *Bea*

A set of 3 William IV simulated rosewood dining chairs, the tops of the seat rails pierced with slits for squabs, one reduced, and a similar pair.
£1,000-1,200 *C*

A set of 4 Victorian mahogany dining chairs.
£300-400 *HCH*

A set of 5 rosewood dining chairs, with turned vertical splats and supports, early 19thC.
£700-1,000 *LRG*

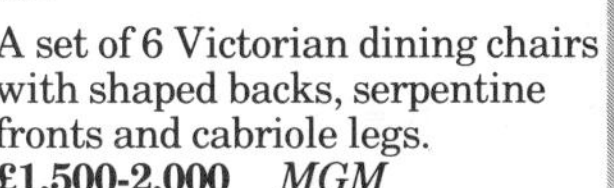

A set of 6 Victorian dining chairs with shaped backs, serpentine fronts and cabriole legs.
£1,500-2,000 *MGM*

A set of 6 Victorian mahogany dining chairs, with stuffover serpentine shaped seats.
£900-1,000 *BWe*

A set of 8 Victorian mahogany dining chairs.
£2,500-3,000 *CSK*

A set of 6 Victorian rosewood balloon back dining chairs.
£1,700-2,000 *CSK*

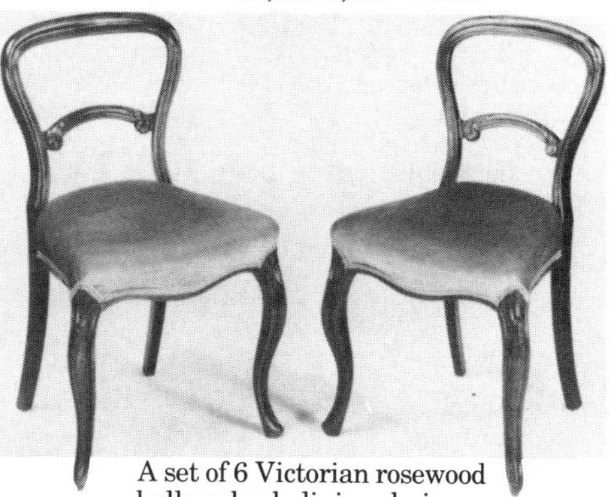

A set of 6 Victorian rosewood balloon back dining chairs.
£1,000-1,200 *CSK*

A set of 6 Victorian walnut dining chairs, the scrolling balloon and pierced foliate splat backs above upholstered serpentine seats on cabriole legs with knob feet.
£1,100-1,300 *CSK*

A set of 6 Victorian walnut framed dining chairs, with carved decoration to back, on cabriole legs.
£1,300-1,500 *MGM*

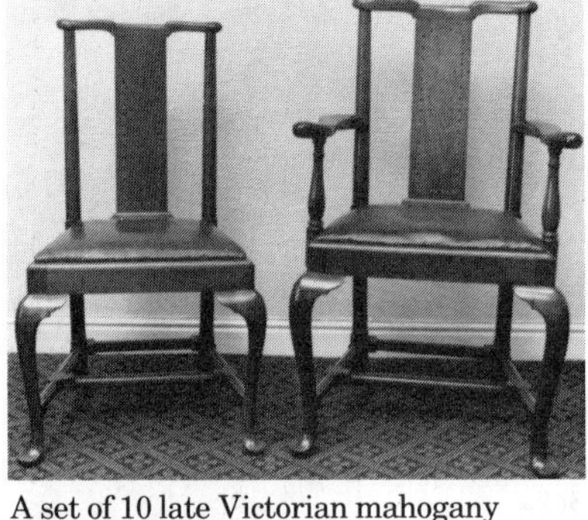

A set of 10 late Victorian mahogany dining chairs of Queen Anne influence, including 2 carvers, the central splats inlaid with satinwood and ebony stringing.
£2,000-2,500 *M*

A set of 8 Victorian cabriole leg dining chairs, with carved decoration.
£1,500-1,800 *MGM*

A set of 6 Victorian rosewood dining chairs.
£1,300-1,500 *MGM*

A set of 10 Edwardian mahogany and satinwood crossbanded dining chairs, inlaid with boxwood and ebony lines.
£2,600-3,000 *P*

An Edwardian mahogany dining room suite, comprising 12 chairs, including 2 carvers, a mahogany draw leaf dining table, 96in (243.5cm), a mahogany and brass sideboard of stepped form, 85in (216cm), and a mahogany three-tier buffet, 48in (122cm).
£5,000-6,000 *CSK*

A pair of Dutch mahogany and floral marquetry chairs, early 19thC.
£550-650 *DN*

A pair of Continental walnut and gilt embellished dining chairs in the Queen Anne taste, Spanish or Italian, 18thC.
£800-1,000 *P*

A harlequin set of 3 Indian silvered and brass repoussé covered dining chairs in Regency taste, the curved bar top rails with ram's head terminals, one with all over meandering floral repoussé decoration.
£1,000-1,500 *P*

A Dutch floral marquetry inlaid carver chair, 19thC.
£400-500 *MGM*

A set of 4 Dutch walnut and floral marquetry dining chairs in the Queen Anne taste, the balloon shaped backs inlaid with vases of flowers and birds, with slip-in serpentine floral gros point needlework seats, 19thC.
£1,700-2,000 *P*

Hall Chairs

A George III mahogany hall chair, the pierced oval back centred by a foliate rosette and edged with fluting, later blocks, stamped W.S.
£1,200-1,500 *C*

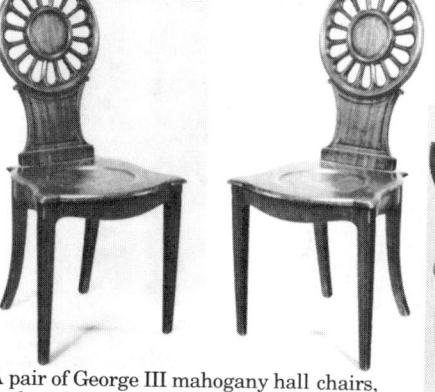

A pair of George III mahogany hall chairs, each with pierced wheel back with tapering splats, and shaped plank seat.
£1,500-2,000 *CNY*

A pair of late George III mahogany hall chairs, with shield panel backs and shaped seats with oval moulding.
£350-450 *LBP*

A set of 4 Regency mahogany hall chairs, with pierced wheel shaped splats, the central oval panel with a gilt monogram 'P'.
£4,500-5,500 *C*

. William IV mahogany hall chair, ith a ferret/weasel crest.
120-150 *Ph*

A Regency mahogany hall chair, with scroll and shell carved shaped back, requiring restoration.
£300-350 *P[Re]*

A pair of Regency carved mahogany hall chairs, with solid seats and sabre legs.
£250-350 *P*

Lord Kitchener's campaign chair, the headrest embroidered with a crown above a wreath with (S) H.K.K, 1896, with letter of authentication.
£300-350 *Bea*

A pair of Continental walnut and beech hall chairs, decorated with simulated marquetry vignettes etched with figures and animals in landscape settings, late 19thC.
£150-200 *LBP*

Side Chairs

A harlequin pair of walnut side chairs, 17thC and later.
£550-650 *C*

A pair of George III white painted side chairs, with close nailed padded oval backs and bowed seats covered in pale blue silk.
£900-1,200 *C*

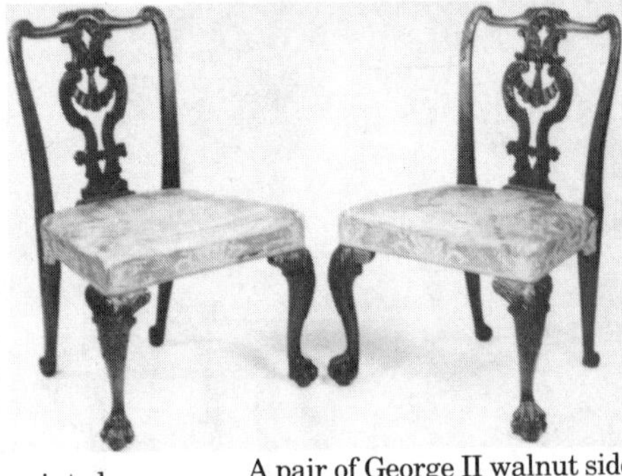

A pair of George II walnut side chairs.
£3,000-3,500 *CSK*

A pair of George III mahogany side chairs, upholstered in blue and gold striped velvet.
£2,000-2,500 *CNY*

A pair of Chippendale chairs with carved back splats.
£900-1,200 *IM*

A set of 4 Regency blue painted and parcel gilt side chairs, with cane filled backs and seats with squabs.
£1,500-2,000 *C*

A Regency painted chair, with trellis back and decorated with flowers and acorns, on a dark ground.
£100-150 *DN*

A mahogany chair, 19thC.
£80-120 *PCA*

An Edwardian bedroom chair with cane seat.
£50-80 *Ph*

A set of 6 Victorian walnut balloon back side chairs.
£1,200-1,500 *P[Re]*

A set of 6 Victorian walnut side chairs, on French cabriole legs.
£1,500-2,000 *P[Re]*

A set of 3 Edwardian satinwood chairs, including one elbow chair, the backs with cane panels and painted with an oval miniature portrait of a lady.
£1,500-2,000 *P[Pea]*

A pair of Charles X giltmetal mounted mahogany side chairs.
£1,400-1,600 *C*

An Edwardian inlaid chair with upholstered seat.
£120-150 *Ph*

A cane campaign chair, with folding legs and carrying handles.
£350-400 *MGM*

Small Chests

A William and Mary walnut and marquetry chest, on later bun feet, 37in (94cm).
£1,000-1,500 *Bea*

A William and Mary walnut oyster veneer and crossbanded chest, 30½in (78cm).
£4,500-5,000 *P*

An Indian carved chair, 19thC.
£350-450 *RIP*

A Queen Anne burr walnut chest, the quarter veneered and crossbanded top with feather inlay and cushion edge, 37½in (94.5cm).
£900-1,200 *P*

An oyster walnut and crossbanded chest of drawers, late 17th/early 18thC, 39in (99cm).
£7,500-8,000 *DN*

A William and Mary style miniature chest of drawers, the top crossbanded in satinwood, with brass drop handles and lock escutcheons surrounded by a half round moulding, 15½in (40cm).
£1,500-2,000 *HSS*

A George I walnut chest, with crossbanded and quartered chamfered top, 35in (89cm).
£3,500-4,500 *C*

A George I oyster veneer walnut chest with moulded top, later crossbanded and inlaid with geometric stringing, 37½in (95cm).
£5,000-5,500 *C*

A George I walnut chest, with quartered crossbanded moulded top, adapted, 38in (96.5cm).
£2,000-2,500 *C*

A George I walnut tall chest, with crossbanded top, alterations, 29in (74cm).
£2,000-2,500 *Bon*

A George II mahogany chest, with brushing slide, above 4 graduated drawers, 28½in (72.5cm).
£5,000-5,500 *C*

A George II mahogany chest with brushing slide, 36½in (92.5cm).
£1,500-2,000 *P[Re]*

A George III mahogany serpentine chest, the top drawer partly fitted, 38in (96cm).
£3,000-3,500 *C*

A George III mahogany dressing chest, the top drawer fitted with lidded compartments and bottles, 38½in (97cm).
£1,500-2,000 *P*

A George III mahogany chest in the style of Gillows, with 3 graduated drawers banded with satinwood, flanked by reeded pilasters, 40in (102cm).
£3,000-3,500 *C*

A George III mahogany and inlaid serpentine chest, the crossbanded top with projecting angles, 35½in (90cm).
£2,500-3,000 *P*

A George III mahogany serpentine chest with a moulded edge, fitted with a slide, on ogee bracket feet, 44½in (112cm).
£2,500-3,000 *P*

A George III mahogany secretaire, inlaid throughout with boxwood stringing and parquetry lines, the crossbanded central drawer fitted with a cupboard, drawers and pigeonholes, lacking one interior drawer, 48½in (123cm).
£800-1,200 *Bea*

A George III mahogany chest, the 4 long drawers with foliate cast brass handles and escutcheons, 36in (91.5cm).
£800-1,200 *Bea*

A George III mahogany dressing chest, with a brushing slide, 31½in (80cm).
£1,500-2,000 *Bea*

An early George III mahogany chest, on ogee bracket feet, 46½in (118cm).
£7,000-7,500 *P*

A George III mahogany chest of drawers with satinwood banded top, inlaid edge, 4 crossbanded graduated drawers, the second drawer with sliding inset leather writing surface, 41in (104cm).
£2,000-2,500 *DSH*

A George III mahogany secretaire chest, the boxwood and ebony strung fall with inset panel and fitted interior, 37in (94cm).
£2,000-2,500 *P*

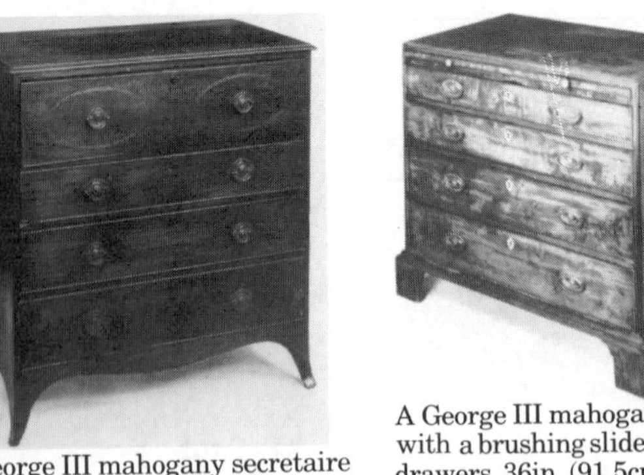

A George III mahogany chest, with a brushing slide and 4 drawers, 36in (91.5cm).
£1,000-1,500 *CSK*

A George III faded mahogany chest of drawers, with eared moulded burr yew banded top, 4 graduated drawers between engaged pilaster angles inlaid with stop fluting, 38in (97cm).
£3,000-3,500 *CNY*

A George III mahogany chest of drawers, with serpentine top above 4 well figured drawers, between canted angles, 49in (124.5cm).
£2,500-3,000 *CNY*

A George III mahogany chest, with moulded serpentine top, 44½in (112cm).
£2,000-3,000 *C*

A George III mahogany chest with moulded top, 38in (96.5cm).
£1,500-2,000 *C*

A George III satinwood, rosewood crossbanded and ebony strung secretaire chest, the baize lined fall enclosing a fitted interior, 46in (116cm).
£2,500-3,000 *P*

A mid-Georgian walnut miniature chest, with crossbanded top above 5 drawers, the base with one long drawer, 13½in (34cm).
£1,500-2,000 *C*

A Georgian mahogany serpentine fronted chest, the 4 graduated drawers with brass swan neck handles, 45in (114cm).
£2,500-3,000 *JD*

An early Georgian burr yew chest with moulded cornice, on later bracket feet, 43in (109cm).
£5,000-5,500 *C*

A small Georgian mahogany chest of 4 drawers.
£1,200-1,500 *HP*

. Georgian mahogany Lancashire
hest, with hinged lid and 5 false
rawer fascias, 4 short drawers
nder, all with brass drop handles,
eet cut down, 64in (162.5cm).
1,000-1,500 *JRB*

walnut crossbanded and
atherstrung chest, early 18thC, on
ter feet, 35in (89cm).
,000-5,500 *P*

walnut chest, 18thC, 39in (99cm).
,000-3,500 *SD*

Regency mahogany bowfront
est, with waved
ron on splayed
et, 42in
06.5cm).
,500-3,000 *C*

A Georgian Sheraton style mahogany chest, crossbanded in satinwood with ebony line inlay, the drawers with brass loop handles on splay feet.
£1,000-1,500 *JD*

A George III mahogany chest, previously a barrel organ, inlaid with boxwood lines, the hinged lid with a label of the 4 barrels and 15 tunes, the front carved with parcel gilt musical pipes, the apron with brass plaque inscribed 'Josephus Beloudy Londini Fecit', flanked by the date 1778, 'In Lewkners Lane, Near Drury Lane', previously fitted with musical works, 34½in (87cm).
£1,500-2,500 *C*

A mahogany dwarf chest, fitted with 3 drawers inlaid with boxwood lines, 18thC.
£800-1,200 *CSK*

A Georgian mahogany secretaire chest, 54in (137cm).
£1,500-2,000 *HOD*

A walnut and marquetry chest, the top inlaid with a shaped panel of an urn, birds and foliage, the drawers and sides similarly inlaid, early 18thC, 37½in (95cm).
£2,000-2,500 *P[CW]*

A mahogany chest, with a brushing slide, basically 18thC, 33in (84cm).
£2,500-3,000 *CSK*

A Regency mahogany chest, inlaid with ebonised and boxwood lines, the top with rosewood banded borders, 37½in (94cm).
£1,500-2,000 *CSK*

A pair of Hepplewhite period mahogany bowfront chests, the 4 drawers with oval plate brass handles, 39in (99cm).
£3,500-4,000 *P[Pea]*

A Regency satinwood chest, inlaid with ebonised lines and escutcheons, 36in (91.5cm).
£1,500-2,000 *C*

A Regency cream painted chest, the drawers decorated with Oriental figures fishing, framed by simulated bamboo mouldings, 39in (99cm).
£3,500-4,000 *C*

A Regency mahogany chest, with 5 drawers between square reeded pilasters, inlaid with ebony and mounted with giltmetal paterae and anthemions, later feet, 45in (114cm).
£600-800 *C*

A Regency mahogany satinwood crossbanded and boxwood lined chest, 47½in (120cm).
£500-800 *CEd*

A Regency mahogany chest of 4 drawers, with shaped apron and reeded turned feet, 41in (104cm).
£300-500 *Bea*

A Regency mahogany chest, with dressing slide and 3 graduated drawers, 36½in (92cm).
£1,200-1,500 *C*

A Victorian mahogany chest of 5 drawers, with bun feet.
£300-500 *MGM*

A walnut veneered crossbanded chest of 5 drawers, on bracket feet, 19thC.
£800-1,000 *MGM*

A brass bound military chest, comprising a chest of 5 drawers with countersunk handles, flanked by 2 cupboards, 19thC, 82in (208cm).
£1,000-1,500 *GC*

A Dutch walnut, marquetry and boxwood strung chest, the bombé front with 4 long drawers flanked by projecting hinged angles enclosing 4 short drawers, late 18th/early 19thC, 40in (101cm).
£3,000-3,500 *P*

A mahogany secretaire chest of 4 drawers, with fitted interior, on bracket feet.
£800-1,000 *MGM*

A late Victorian teak military chest in 2 sections, fitted with a secretaire drawer with easel supported maple writing slope and lidded interior, on turned feet, labelled Army & Navy C.S.L. Makers, 44in (112cm).
£1,000-1,500 *C*

A burr yew wood miniature chest inlaid with lines, 11in (28cm).
£3,000-3,500 *C*

A Dutch mahogany chest, inlaid with marquetry, fanned ovals and chequered geometric lines, on fluted square tapering legs with block feet, early 19thC, 34in (86cm).
£1,500-2,000 *CSK*

An Italian scarlet japanned chest, painted 'en grisaille' with insects, animals and birds amongst scrolling foliage, the 3 drawers with lions' mask and ring handles, 23in (58.5cm).
£1,500-2,000 *CSK*

A Dutch mahogany and marquetry chest, with overhanging frieze drawer above 5 further drawers, decorated with oval shell medallions and scrolling foliage, early 19thC, 38in (96.5cm).
£1,500-2,000 *C*

A Dutch walnut bombé chest of 4 graduated drawers, with urn and festoon handles, shaped apron, on claw-and-ball feet.
£1,000-1,500 *MGM*

A French marquetry serpentine fronted chest of 2 drawers, inlaid with floral designs, on cabriole legs.
£800-1,000 *MGM*

A Dutch walnut, mahogany and floral marquetry bombé fronted chest, the 4 long drawers with flowers and foliage, late 18th/early 19thC, 36in (91cm).
£2,500-3,000 *P*

A Louis XVI style kingwood chest, inlaid with marquetry in boxwood line borders, the rouge royale marble top above 5 drawers, 20½in (52cm).
£700-1,000 *CSK*

A French giltmetal mounted velvet and leather cartonnier, with 6 drawers with scarlet morocco fronts, the bases of the drawers stamped L. Dromard F.cant Paris, 18, Rue St. Lazare, Ft. de Siéges, 12in (30.5cm).
£600-1,000 *C*

A North African ivory and hardwood inlaid walnut chest, inlaid with geometric patterns and crossbanded, early 19thC, 40½in (102cm).
£1,500-2,000 *C*

A Portuguese palisander chest of drawers, with eared moulded serpentine top, the 3 drawers with shaped brass handles with pierced back plates, the angles applied with bellflowers, late 18thC, 51in (130cm).
£2,000-2,500 *CNY*

A Russian Karelian birch chest with stepped top, the recessed arched front with 3 drawers, mid-19thC, 40½in (102cm).
£2,500-3,000 *C*

Chests-on-Chests

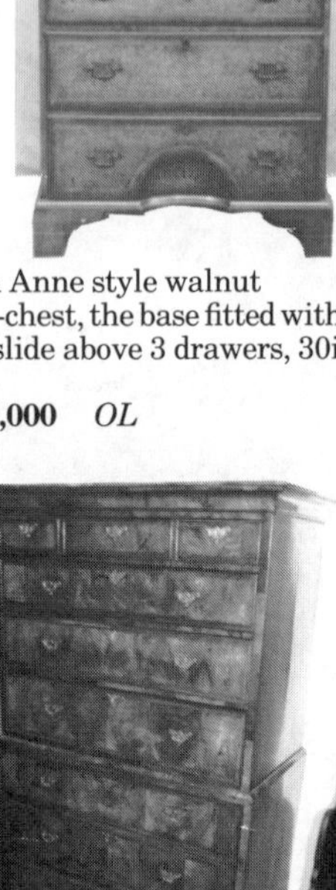

A Queen Anne style walnut chest-on-chest, the base fitted with writing slide above 3 drawers, 30in (76cm).
£2,500-3,000 *OL*

A Queen Anne style figured walnut and yew banded tallboy, inlaid with chequered featherbanding and stars, on a stand fitted with 3 short drawers, on pointed pad feet, 39in (99cm).
£2,000-2,500 *CSK*

A George I walnut tallboy, with moulded cavetto cornice, the upper part with fluted chamfered angles, 43in (109cm).
£8,000-9,000 *C*

A walnut tallboy, with 3 short and 6 long featherbanded drawers, early 18thC, 40½in (102cm).
£2,000-2,500 *PWC*

A walnut tallboy, c1730, 40in (103cm).
£5,000-5,500 *PCA*

A George I walnut cabinet-upon-chest, the upper part with 2 doors with shaped herringbone banding, on a separate chest of 3 drawers, 40in (101.5cm).
£3,000-3,500 *B*

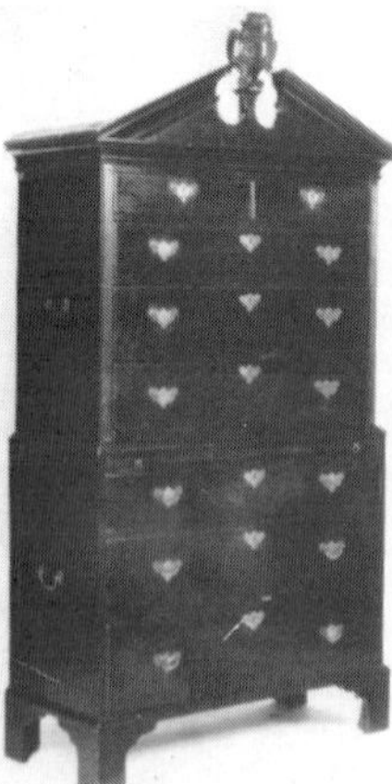

A George I figured walnut tallboy, with 6 long and 3 short featherbanded and crossbanded oak-lined drawers, on bracket supports, 42in (106.5cm).
£4,500-5,000 *P[WSW]*

A George II mahogany tallboy, the broken architectural pediment with a cartouche above a cavetto cornice, the lower section with a brushing slide and 3 long drawers, 48in (122cm).
£3,000-3,500 *Bon*

A George II period red walnut tallboy, fitted with a secretaire drawer, 44½in (111.5cm).
£2,000-2,500 *GC*

n early George III carved ahogany tallboy, the upper part ith a moulded dentil cornice and ind fret decorated frieze, 45in 14cm).

3,500-4,000 *P*

George III mahogany chest-on-est, on shaped bracket feet, 42½in 08cm).
,000-1,500 *P*

George III style mahogany llboy, inlaid with satinwood and xwood lines, 19thC, 44in 11.5cm).
00-1,200 *CSK*

A George III mahogany tallboy, with rosewood banded cornice, 43in (109cm).
£2,500-3,000 *CSK*

A George III mahogany tallboy, with a dentilled cavetto cornice and a blind fret frieze, 45in (114cm).
£2,500-3,000 *CSK*

A George III mahogany tallboy, with 2 short and 6 long graduated drawers, 46in (116.5cm).
£1,000-1,500 *CSK*

A George III mahogany secretaire tallboy, the base with a leather-lined fitted secretaire drawer with pigeonholes and short drawers, surrounding a prospect door, 44in (111.5cm).
£1,500-2,000 *C*

A George III mahogany tallboy, with dentilled cornice and fluted frieze interspersed with roundels, 47in (119cm).
£2,500-3,500 *C*

A George III mahogany tallboy, with key pattern cornice and fretwork frieze, 49in (125cm).
£2,500-3,000 *C*

A George III mahogany secretaire tallboy, with central writing drawer, 47½in (120cm).
£2,500-3,000 *CSK*

A mid-Georgian mahogany chest-on-chest with dentil cornice.
£2,000-2,500 *OSA*

A Georgian mahogany tallboy, with 6 long and 2 short drawers with brass loop handles and pierced back plates, 40in (101.5cm).
£2,500-3,000 *JD*

A Georgian mahogany tallboy, fitted with brass butterfly handles, 42in (106.5cm).
£1,500-2,000 *P[Pea]*

A Georgian mahogany tallboy, with 2 short and 6 long drawers with brass handles, 45in (113cm).
£1,000-1,500 *PWC*

A late Georgian burr walnut tallboy, the drawers with oval brass plate handles and escutcheons, and herringbone crossbanding, 44in (111cm).
£2,500-3,000 *M*

A walnut crossbanded chest-on-chest, with 9 drawers, on ogee bracket feet, 19thC.
£2,000-2,500 *MGM*

A mahogany tallboy, the top section with a dentil moulded cornice above 2 short and 3 long drawers, between fluted canted angles, late 18thC, 45in (113cm).
£1,500-2,000 *CSK*

A mahogany chest-on-chest, with 9 drawers, canted corners and a brushing slide.
£1,600-2,000 *MGM*

Chests-on-Stands

A George II leather mule chest, the top decorated with the initials MDG and dated 1734, the associated George III pine stand with one long drawer and cabriole feet, 47½in (120cm).
£1,000-1,500 *C*

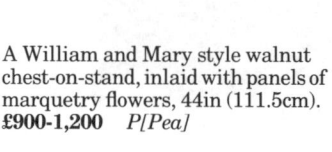

A William and Mary style walnut chest-on-stand, inlaid with panels of marquetry flowers, 44in (111.5cm).
£900-1,200 *P[Pea]*

Queen Anne walnut chest-on-
ınd, with barley twist supports
d flat shaped stretcher, 40in
)1.5cm).
,000-2,500 *CH*

George I crossbanded walnut
est-on-stand, on later cabriole
pports, 39in (99cm).
,500-3,000 *P[Pea]*

valnut tallboy, with 3 small and
ng drawers, on an arched stand
h 3 frieze drawers, part early
hC, 41in (104cm).
500-2,000 *CSK*

Miller's is a price Guide not a price List

The price ranges given reflect the average price a purchaser should pay for similar items. Condition, rarity of design or pattern, size, colour, pedigree, restoration and many other factors must be taken into account when assessing values

A William and Mary design walnut veneered chest-on-stand, with reeded chamfered sides.
£900-1,200 *Wor*

A George II fruitwood chest, on later stand, with cabriole legs and pad feet, 40in (101.5cm).
£1,000-1,200 *Bon*

A walnut chest-on-stand, 18thC.
£3,000-3,500 *SAg*

A William and Mary walnut chest-on-stand, on trumpet turned legs, 38½in (97cm).
£3,500-4,000 *C*

An early George III mahogany chest-on-stand, the two frieze drawers applied with blind fret, the stand carved with foliage on a punched trellis ground, 31in (78cm).
£5,500-6,000 *C*

A black japanned chest-on-stand, decorated with gilt chinoiserie figures, birds and houses, the stand with one long drawer, early 18thC, the stand later, 42in (106.5cm).
£1,700-2,000 *Bon*

A burr walnut and inlaid chest of 2 short and 3 long drawers, the separate stand with shaped apron and later turned feet, early 18thC, 37in (94cm).
£1,000-1,500 *DSH*

Wellington Chests

A Victorian walnut Wellington chest, with 7 graduated drawers, the top drawer with fragment of maker's label, 22½in (57cm).
£1,500-2,000 *Bea*

A walnut and marquetry hall chest with marble top, mid-19thC, 20in (51cm).
£1,200-1,500 *SWO*

A Victorian walnut secretaire Wellington chest of 5 drawers, a double fronted fitted drawer, 23i (58cm).
£1,500-2,000 *JD*

A French rosewood, tulipwood and maple semainier, crossbanded and veneered with a cube parquetry design, the rounded corners applie with ormolu floral mounts, c1860, 21½in (54cm).
£1,500-2,000 *Bon*

Coffers

An Italian painted and gilded cassone, the front painted with 4 circular mythological scenes framed by heraldic shields, on griffin feet, 65½in (166cm).
£2,500-3,000 *C*

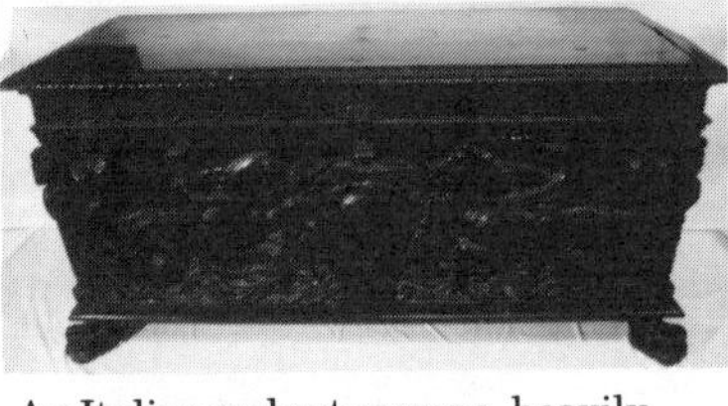

An Italian walnut cassone, heavily carved to front and sides, with putti riding seahorses with a coat of arms, late 17thC, 85in (216cm).
£1,800-2,000 *BM*

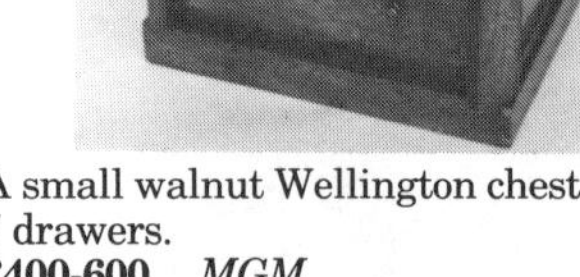

A small walnut Wellington chest 7 drawers.
£400-600 *MGM*

A Spanish rosewood and ivory inlaid table cabinet, the fall enclosing 11 drawers, on later bun feet, some replacements, 17thC, 15½in (40cm).
£2,000-2,500 *P*

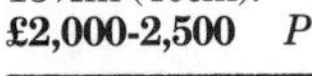

A Mediterranean ivory inlaid olivewood coffer, the front decorat with geometric compass stars and urns of flowers, late 18thC, 67in (170cm).
£2,000-2,500 *C*

Commodes

A George III mahogany bowfront commode, the bowed top above a slide, 42in (106.5cm).
£1,000-1,500 *Bon*

A George III mahogany night table/bedside steps, with one cupboard and two drawers, one converting to a commode drawer, 19in (48cm).
£700-1,000 *Bon*

A George III mahogany commo with crossbanded top, the sides applied with flowerheads, scroll and foliage, re-polished, 45in (114cm).
£2,000-3,000 *Bea*

n early Georgian design walnut ›mmode, 42in (106.5cm).
10,000-12,000 *LRG*

A set of Regency mahogany commode steps with leather lined treads, the lower step with fitted sliding commode and china pot, 21in (53cm).
£1,300-1,500 *C*

A marble top parquetry commode of tulipwood, c1850, 22in (56cm).
£1,000-1,200 *RIP*

mahogany and marquetry ›rpentine commode, banded and ılaid with boxwood lines, with ıclosed shelves, basically late 8thC, 58in (147cm).
2,000-2,500 *CSK*

A mahogany step commode, 19thC.
£700-1,000 *P[CW]*

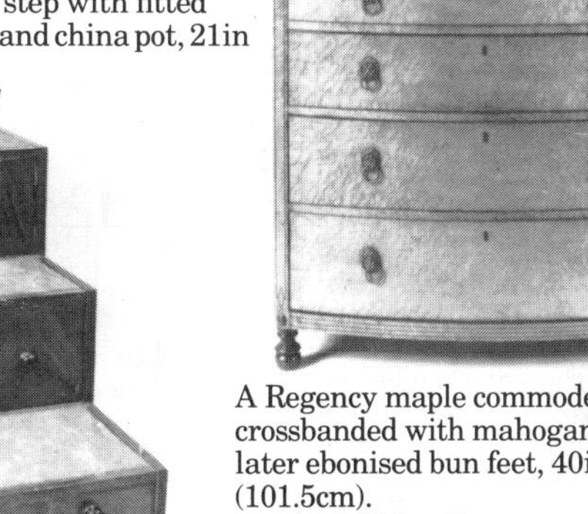

A Regency maple commode, the top crossbanded with mahogany, with later ebonised bun feet, 40in (101.5cm).
£2,000-2,500 *C*

satinwood, tulipwood ›ssbanded, gilt heightened and ›corated commode, painted with ›ags and stems with husks, the top ith acanthus scrolls and central ›al medallion with cherubs, 19thC, ›in (191cm).
,000-8,000 *P*

A walnut and ormolu commode with marble top, late 19thC.
£3,500-4,000 *SWO*

A mahogany and brass line inlaid commode, stamped and with inventory number to the reverse, damage, 19thC. 32in (81cm).
£1,700-2,000 *GC*

Dutch amboyna serpentine and ›mbé commode, with kingwood ›ssbanding and ormolu mounts, ›thC, 34in (86cm).
00-1,000 *CDC*

A Dutch mahogany bombé commode, with satinwood banding and boxwood and ebony stringing, the canted corners carved and inlaid with husk chains, stamped Edwards & Roberts, mid-18thC, inlay later, 43in (109cm).
£2,000-2,500 *Bea*

A Tyrolean walnut commode, inlaid with starred roundels in chequered boxwood line borders, late 18thC, 50in (127cm).
£1,500-2,000 *CSK*

A satinwood and marquetry commode, the top with tulipwood and kingwood crossbanding, the frieze with central drawer, 54in (138cm).
£3,500-4,000 *P*

A Louis XVI ormolu mounted amaranth and tulipwood commode, the drawers inlaid with quarter veneered tulipwood panels within chequered lines, 36½in (92cm).
£2,000-3,000 *CNY*

A Dutch kingwood and tulipwood commode, the top inlaid with 2 quartered panels with geometri borders, mid-18thC, 53in (134.5cm
£3,000-4,000 *C*

A Dutch mahogany crossbanded giltmetal moulded bombé commode, with quarter veneered top, 18thC, 54in (137cm).
£1,700-2,000 *P*

A Louis XV ormolu mounted kingwood and amaranth commode, with brown and grey marble top, the 3 drawers with ormolu handles, escutcheons, chutes and sabots, some mounts with the C couronné poinçon, 40in (101cm).
£5,000-7,000 *CNY*

The C couronné poinçon was a tax mark used between March 1745 and February 1749, on any alloy containing copper.

A Louis XV ormolu mounted tulipwood commode with breccia marble top, stamped Mondon Jm restorations, 38½in (97cm).
£7,000-9,000 *C*

François Mondon, maître c1728.

A Louis XVI ormolu mounted mahogany commode, with white marble top above a fielded panelled frieze drawer, 50½in (128cm).
£2,000-3,000 *CNY*

A Louis XVI style mahogany commode, outlined with plain bra mouldings, the later top with a pierced brass gallery, 49in (124.5cm).
£4,500-5,000 *Bea*

A Louis XV style rosewood and foliate marquetry bombé commode, inlaid with satinwood and applied with ormolu mounts, 53½in (134cm).
£1,500-2,000 *CSK*

A French rosewood commode, inlaid in marquetry, with bronze gilt handles and mounts, rouge marble top, early 19thC, 27in (68.5cm).
£700-1,000 *P[Pea]*

A Louis XV/Louis XVI Transitional commode, parquetry veneered in kingwood, tulipwood, ebony and other woods, marble repaired, and small pieces of veneer missing, 33in (84cm).
£2,500-3,000 *GC*

Louis XVI style ormolu mounted
ıhogany and marquetry
nmode, after Beneman, with
rieze drawers and 3 cupboard
ors, on toupie feet, 61in (155cm).
,000-5,000 *CNY*

Continental crossbanded bombé
mmode, with gilt metal mounts.
,500-2,000 *MGM*

South German walnut and
ssbanded commode, late
th/early 19thC, 42in (107cm).
,500-3,000 *P*

South German walnut and
nded commode, 18thC, 47in
9cm).
,500-3,000 *CSK*

Italian walnut crossbanded
nmode, 18thC, 43in (110cm).
500-2,000 *P*

A Charles X mahogany commode, with moulded concave top, above 3 drawers, flanked by fluted pilasters, 36in (91.5cm).
£1,500-2,000 *C*

A South German rococo parcel gilt and white painted commode, possibly Munich, with simulated marble top, above 2 drawers with rocaille lockplates and applied with gilt flowerheads, wave pattern, C-scrolls and handles, mid-18thC, 39½in (100cm).
£10,000-12,000 *CNY*

A South German bombé serpentine commode, 18thC.
£9,000-10,000 *P[CW]*

A North Italian walnut and marquetry commode, late 18thC, 48½in (123cm).
£6,000-8,000 *C*

A French chinoiserie commode in black lacquer and gilt with marble top, mid-19thC.
£2,000-2,500 *RIP*

A fruitwood commode, with later marble slab, probably German, late 18thC, 32½in (81cm).
£1,200-1,500 *C*

An Italian rococo painted commode, probably Venetian, with marble top above 2 conforming drawers, mid-18thC, 25in (63.5cm).
£2,500-3,500 *CNY*

A pair of Italian walnut bedside commodes, with galleried tops, crossbanded with fruitwood and inlaid with boxwood lines, late 18th/early 19thC, 16in (41cm).
£3,000-4,000 *C*

A North Italian rosewood bombé commode, with damaged marble top, 18thC, 59in (149.5cm).
£7,000-9,000 *DN*

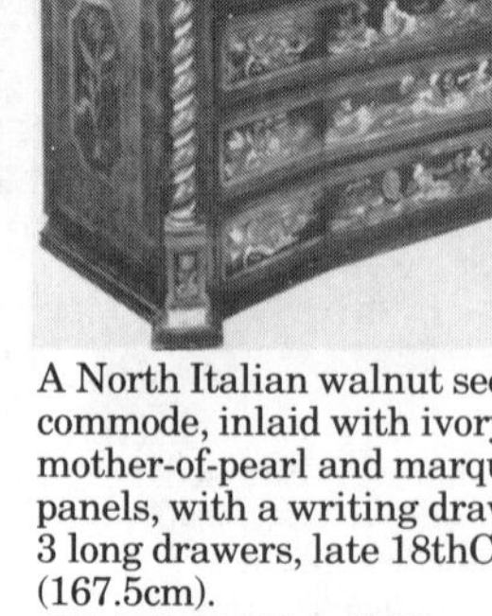

A North Italian walnut secretaire commode, inlaid with ivory, mother-of-pearl and marquetry panels, with a writing drawer above 3 long drawers, late 18thC, 66in (167.5cm).
£10,000-12,000 *CSK*

A North Italian walnut and parquetry commode, with frieze drawer, 50½in (128cm).
£3,500-4,500 *C*

A pair of Italian cream painted and decorated bombé commodes, with breccia marble tops with moulded edges, 41½in (105cm).
£3,000-3,500 *P*

A South Italian walnut and marquetry commode, the top inlaid with strapwork and foliage, 73in (185cm).
£3,500-4,000 *C*

A North Italian rosewood and marquetry commode, with canted top centred by a floral medallion above a frieze drawer and 2 drawers inlaid 'sans traverse', 39½in (100cm).
£6,000-7,000 *C*

A North Italian walnut and marquetry bedside commode, the top with a centred flower within a tulipwood banded foliate border, 22in (56cm).
£3,000-3,500 *C*

Cupboards – Armoires

A Dutch carved mahogany armoire, the upper part with a spindle gallery and moulded dentil cornice, fitted with shelves and drawers enclosed by a pair of paterae decorated panel doors, early 19thC, 66in (167cm).
£2,000-2,500 *P*

A Dutch neo-classical mahogany armoire, inlaid with kingwood and marquetry, the top section with 2 moulded panel doors enclosing shelves, late 18thC, 71in (180cm).
£3,500-4,000 *CSK*

Make the most of Miller's

When a large specialist well-publicised collection comes on the market, it tends to increase prices. Immediately after this, prices can fall slightly due to the main buyers having large stocks and the market being 'flooded'. This is usually temporary and does not affect very high quality items

A decorative Italian green painted and parcel gilt armoire, 18thC, 73½in (184cm).
£4,000-4,500 *Bon*

. Batavian carved teak armoire, ɪrved with acanthus and massive :anthus scrolls, 79in (200.5cm).
2,000-2,500 *Bon*

A French chestnut armoire, 18thC, 62in (157cm).
£3,500-4,000 *DN*

A Tyrolean green painted dowry armoire, the frieze dated 1781 and inscribed 'Maria Lemgauer', 46in (116.5cm).
£3,500-4,500 *C*

'upboards – Bedside

A Charles X bird's-eye maple and inlaid armoire with paterae, foliate swag and scroll ornament, fitted with a drawer, 44in (112cm).
£1,500-2,000 *P*

A Tyrolean cream and black painted armoire, mid-18thC, later bun feet, 55in (139.5cm).
£3,000-3,500 *C*

. pair of French mahogany bedside ıbinets, mid-19thC, 21in (53cm).
1,800-2,000 *C*

A Georgian mahogany tray top commode, 19in (48cm).
£600-800 *LBP*

A Regency mahogany commode stool, with hinged leather lined top, converting into bedside steps with one leather lined tread, 16½in (41.5cm).
£400-600 *C*

A Georgian mahogany tray top commode, with fitted double cupboard and drawers to base, 21½in (54.5cm).
£400-500 *LBP*

Make the most of Miller's

Every care has been taken to ensure the accuracy of descriptions and estimated valuations. Price ranges in this book reflect what one should expect to pay for a similar example. When selling one can obviously expect a figure below. This will fluctuate according to a dealer's stock, saleability at a particular time, etc. It is always advisable to approach a reputable specialist dealer or an auction house which has specialist sales.

Cupboards – Corner

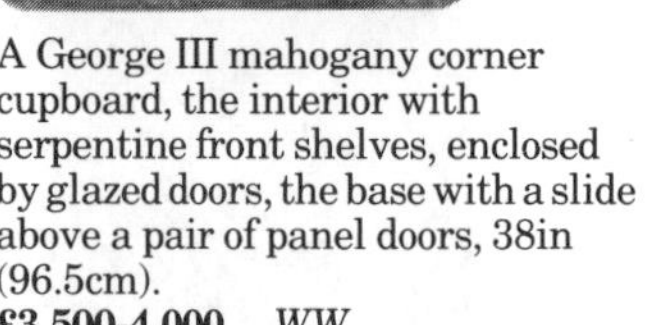

A George III mahogany corner cupboard, the interior with serpentine front shelves, enclosed by glazed doors, the base with a slide above a pair of panel doors, 38in (96.5cm).
£3,500-4,000 *WW*

A late Georgian mahogany bowfront corner cabinet, the doors inlaid with boxwood lines and flowers to the frieze, 30in (76cm).
£700-900 *LRG*

A pair of painted corner cupboards, with arched pediments, the panelled doors enclosing shelves, possibly Scandinavian, late 18th/early 19thC, 26in (66cm).
£2,000-2,500 *C*

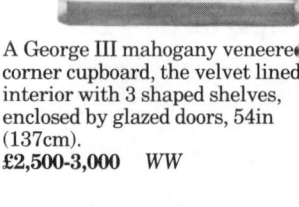

A George III mahogany veneered corner cupboard, the velvet lined interior with 3 shaped shelves, enclosed by glazed doors, 54in (137cm).
£2,500-3,000 *WW*

A Georgian painted corner cupboard, 36½in (92cm) high.
£400-600 *RIP*

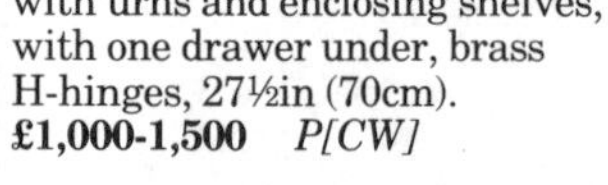

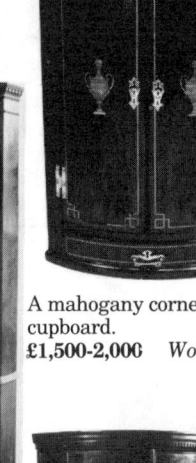

A George III mahogany bowfront corner cupboard, the doors inlaid with urns and enclosing shelves, with one drawer under, brass H-hinges, 27½in (70cm).
£1,000-1,500 *P[CW]*

A mahogany corner cupboard.
£1,500-2,000 *Wor*

A Georgian mahogany bowfront corner cupboard, 39in (99cm) high.
£900-1,000 *RIP*

A Continental kingwood and marquetry bowfront corner cupboard, fitted with a frieze drawer, recessed panel stiles with brass sunburst boss ornament, basically French, 18thC, parts later, 30½in (78cm).
£700-900 *P*

CORNER CUPBOARDS

- ★ these cupboards were made right through the 18thC in various woods including walnut and mahogany, as well as oak
- ★ examples in oak are usually 'country' versions of the more sophisticated pieces made in walnut or mahogany
- ★ corner cupboards with glazed doors, that are suitable for the display of porcelain or other objects, are the most sought after type. They are, however, far more difficult to find and are consequently more expensive
- ★ bow fronted examples are usually considered the most desirable, especially if they are fitted inside with two or three small drawers and the shelves are shaped
- ★ these cupboards are usually constructed in two parts; 'marriages' do exist and whilst these may be acceptable, it should be reflected in a lower price. Check that the backboards of the two parts match and that the quality of timber and style of construction correspond

Cupboards – Linen Presses

A George III mahogany linen press, the doors with fielded panels enclosing sliding trays, 52½in (133cm).
£1,200-1,500 *Bea*

A George III mahogany secretaire press, the baize lined fitted secretaire drawer above 4 graduated drawers, the panels in the doors possibly later, 46in (116.5cm).
£2,000-2,500 *C*

An early George III mahogany clothes press, the base with 2 short and one long drawer, on reduced bracket feet, 54½in (138cm).
£3,000-3,500 *C*

A George III mahogany linen press, with satinwood banding, the panelled doors enclosing trays, 51in (130cm).
500-700 *Bon*

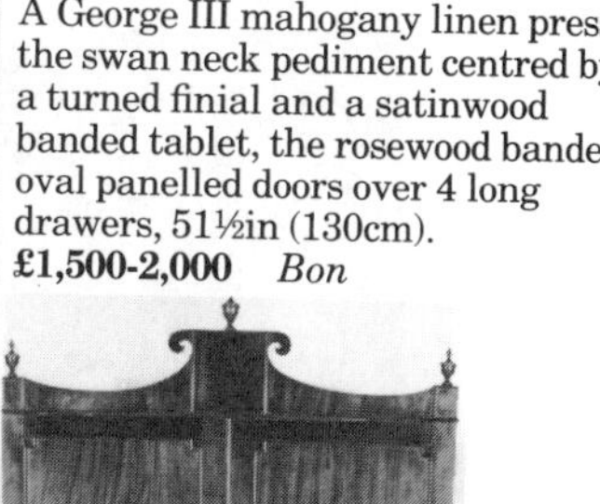

A George III mahogany linen press, the swan neck pediment centred by a turned finial and a satinwood banded tablet, the rosewood banded oval panelled doors over 4 long drawers, 51½in (130cm).
£1,500-2,000 *Bon*

A George III mahogany clothes press, the base with 2 short and one long drawer, on ogee bracket feet, 53in (134.5cm).
£2,000-2,500 *C*

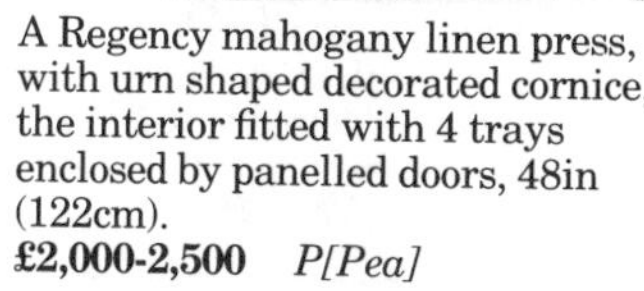

A Regency mahogany linen press, with urn shaped decorated cornice, the interior fitted with 4 trays enclosed by panelled doors, 48in (122cm).
£2,000-2,500 *P[Pea]*

Regency mahogany clothes press th eared cornice, above panelled ors with acorn angles, the base th 2 short and 2 long drawers on w feet, stamped 'Wilkinson, dgate Hill', 56in (142cm).
,000-4,500 *C*

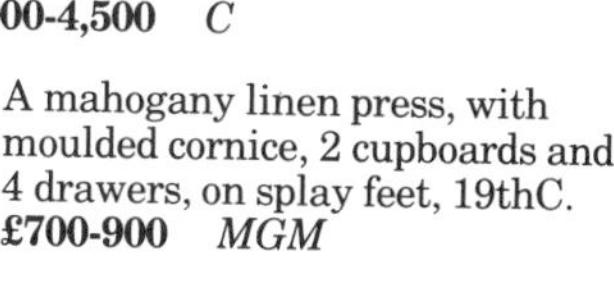

A mahogany linen press, with moulded cornice, 2 cupboards and 4 drawers, on splay feet, 19thC.
£700-900 *MGM*

An early Victorian mahogany clothes press, inlaid with satinwood bands, spandrels and patera banded and inlaid geometric line borders.
£1,200-1,500 *CSK*

Cupboards – Wardrobes

A Sheraton inlaid mahogany bowfront wardrobe, with 2 short and 2 long drawers, on shaped feet.
£3,000-3,500 *TW*

A George IV mahogany wardrobe, the panelled doors enclosing cedar shelves, the sides with panelled doors, on bun feet, 55in (139.5cm).
£1,400-1,600 *C*

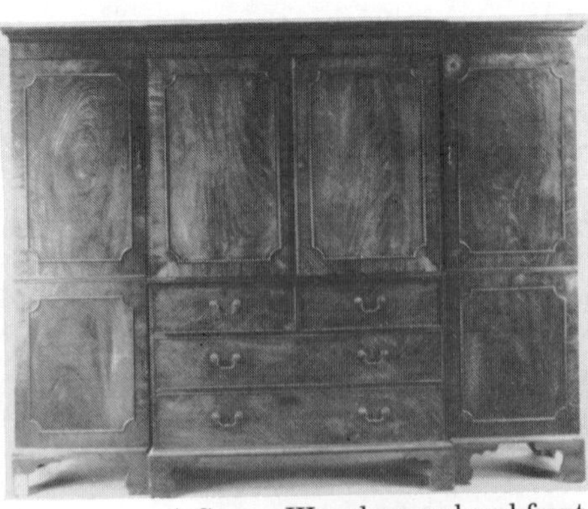

A George III mahogany breakfront wardrobe, the dentilled moulded cornice above 4 fielded radial panel doors, 101in (256.5cm).
£1,500-2,000 *CSK*

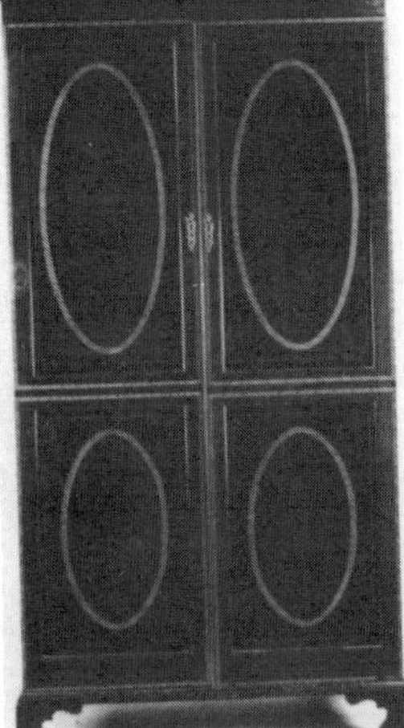

A mahogany wardrobe, with satinwood banded and boxwood line borders and dentil moulded cornice, basically early 19thC, 47½in (119cm).
£500-800 *CSK*

A Dutch mahogany and floral marquetry wardrobe, decorated with boxwood and chequer lines, with a moulded cornice and cushion frieze, on moulded turned feet, early 19thC, 71in (181cm).
£3,500-4,500 *P*

An early Victorian mahogany breakfront wardrobe, the bolection moulded cornice above 4 inset panelled doors, on plinth base, 92in (233.5cm).
£800-1,000 *CSK*

A Dutch mahogany and marquetry wardrobe, decorated with scrolling floral stems, vases of flowers and birds, with chequer strung cornice and moulded cavetto frieze, 19thC, 60½in (154cm).
£2,000-2,500 *P*

A Dutch mahogany wardrobe, with 2 panelled doors enclosing shelves and drawers, late 18thC.
£1,500-2,000 *DN*

Davenports

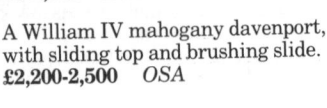

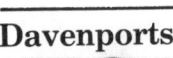

A late Regency rosewood davenport, with a leather inset fall, with a fitted interior, on a column of 4 graduated drawers to one side, 20½in (51cm).
£1,500-2,000 *Bon*

A William IV mahogany davenport, with sliding top and brushing slide.
£2,200-2,500 *OSA*

A George IV mahogany davenport, with a lined writing slope enclosing a fitted interior, with panel door to the right enclosing 4 short drawers, 20in (50cm).
£2,000-2,500 *CSK*

A Regency rosewood davenport, with leather lined sloping flap enclosing a fitted interior with an ink drawer to the right hand side and a slide opening to the left, the right hand side fitted with 4 drawers, on bun feet, 20½in (51cm).
£2,500-3,000 *C*

A Regency mahogany davenport, with fitted interior, two slides and 4 graduated drawers opening to the right with a small pen drawer above, the front, back and left with false drawers, 20in (51cm).
£4,500-5,000 *C*

A George IV rosewood davenport, the sliding top section with a lined writing surface enclosing a fitted interior, with a writing slide to the right above a door enclosing 5 drawers, on casters, 22in (56cm).
£1,300-1,500 *CSK*

An early Victorian calamander davenport with leather lined sloping top, the front and sides with scrolling foliate panels, one side with a door enclosing 4 short and 2 long drawers, with beaded turned feet, 21in (53cm).
£1,500-2,000 *C*

A mid-Victorian amboyna and ebony davenport, the superstructure with a pair of cupboard doors enclosing a fitted interior, the cedar lined frieze drawer with leather lined easel with panelled front and sides, the right hand cupboard with 3 drawers, on bun feet, 22in (56cm).
£800-1,000 *C*

A William IV rosewood davenport, the sliding boxed top with a pierced three-quarter brass gallery, enclosing a hinged leather lined writing slope, above a brushing slide and 4 long graduated drawers, the reverse with simulated drawer front, 19in (48cm).
£1,500-2,000 *CSK*

A walnut davenport, c1885, 21in (53cm).
£1,200-1,500 *BA*

A Victorian inlaid figured walnut davenport, with hinged stationery compartment, writing slope and 4 side drawers, and 4 dummy drawers to the reverse, 21in (53cm).
£1,400-1,800 *P[WSW]*

A Victorian walnut davenport, with raised stationery compartment, tooled leather inset to the sloping flap, enclosing pigeonholes and small drawers, a panelled side door enclosing 4 drawers, 21½in (54cm).
£1,200-1,500 *Bea*

A Victorian burr walnut davenport, with carved shaped supports, 21in (53cm).
£1,000-1,500 *JD*

A Victorian walnut inlaid davenport, with brass gallery, 4 real and 4 dummy drawers, on scroll supports and casters.
£1,200-1,500 *MGM*

A Victorian figured walnut veneered davenport, with fitted interior, 4 enclosed drawers and inlaid decoration.
£800-1,000 *MGM*

A Victorian burr walnut davenport, having sliding desk top, internally lined with satinwood, inset green tooled leather desk top, with Jack-in-the-box having drawers and pigeonholes, c1850, 24in (61cm).
£1,000-1,200 *GH*

An early Edwardian walnut davenport desk, 21in (53cm).
£1,000-1,200 *Ph*

A Victorian figured walnut davenport, with sprung compartment of 3 short drawers, flanked by pigeonholes above a piano front lifting to a fitted interior, with 4 short drawers to the right opposing 4 dummy drawers.
£2,000-2,500 *CSK*

Desks

A George I walnut feather crossbanded kneehole desk, with slide, the kneehole incorporating sliding kneehole cupboard with arched door, c1720, 32in (81cm).
£5,500-6,500 *GH*

A George II red walnut kneehole desk, with folding leather lined top enclosing a flap with divided interior, 37in (94cm).
£3,000-4,000 *C*

A George II style mahogany kneehole pedestal desk, with inset leather lined top, 54in (137cm).
£1,000-1,500 *CSK*

A George III mahogany kneehole desk, the crossbanded top inset with a panel of red tooled leather, 48in (122cm).
£3,000-3,500 *P*

A George III satinwood and mahogany banded writing desk, with domed tambour shutter front enclosing a fitted interior, 36in (91.5cm).
£3,500-4,500 *CSK*

A George II style mahogany kneehole pedestal desk, applied with carved acanthus mouldings in riband flowerheaded borders, 54in (137cm).
£1,000-1,500 *CSK*

. George III mahogany cylinder
esk, with tambour shutter
nclosing a fitted interior, 37½in
)5cm).
3,000-4,000 *C*

A George III mahogany kneehole desk, the frieze drawer over an arched kneehole fitted with a cupboard door, 43in (109cm).
£800-1,000 *Bon*

A George III mahogany partners' kneehole writing desk, the crossbanded top inset with a tooled leather panel, with 5 drawers to either side, on square tapered legs, with brass carrying handles to the sides, 58in (148cm).
£9,000-10,000 *P*

. George III mahogany desk, with
rossbanded top, 34½in (87cm).
2,500-3,000 *CSK*

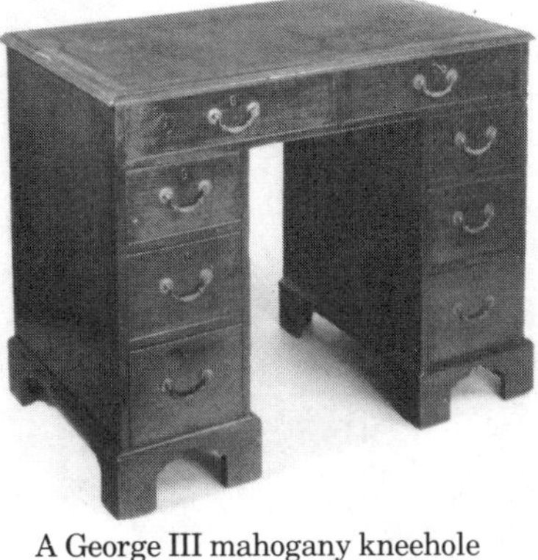

A George III mahogany kneehole desk, with a moulded edge and inset with a panel of green leather.
£1,700-2,000 *P*

A mid-Georgian walnut kneehole desk, the crossbanded top with re-entrant front corners, the recessed arched kneehole with a cupboard, restored, 34in (86cm).
£2,000-2,500 *C*

\ late George III mahogany
edestal writing table, attributed to
Gillows of Lancaster, with scarlet
nset leather top above arched fitted
rieze drawer forming sham side
lrawers, above 6 small drawers
surrounding the kneehole, 49in
125cm).
£1,500-2,000 *CNY*

. George III mahogany
ımbour cylinder desk,
ith satinwood fitted
nterior with pigeonholes,
rawers and slide, with a
aize lined ratcheted
djustable slope, 39in
)9cm).
3,000-4,000 *P*

An early George III style walnut partners' desk, with bellflower and C-scroll headed cabriole legs, on claw-and-ball feet, 67½in (171cm).
£3,500-4,000 *CSK*

A mahogany desk, with long frieze drawer and 6 small drawers flanking a kneehole cupboard panel door, basically 18thC, 35in (89cm).
£500-800 *CSK*

A mid-Georgian style partners' mahogany kneehole pedestal desk, the inset leather lined top above 6 drawers and a simulated panel cupboard door, 66in (167.5cm).
£1,500-2,000 *CSK*

A Georgian mahogany kneehole desk, with central recessed cupboard and secret frieze drawer, surrounded by 7 further drawers, 38in (96.5cm).
£1,500-2,000 *P[Pea]*

A Georgian style pedestal partners' desk, c1840, 92in (233.5cm).
£5,000-5,500 *DDS*

A Regency mahogany roll top desk with ebony stringing, the cylinder enclosing a fitted interior with leather lined slide, 37in (94cm).
£1,500-2,000 *C*

An English rosewood pedestal writing table, with gilt tooled green inset leather crossbanded top, above 9 drawers surrounding the kneehole, the opposing 3 frieze drawers above cupboard doors, mid-19thC, 59in (149.5cm).
£5,000-7,000 *CNY*

A Regency mahogany pedestal desk with leather lined top, the frieze with one central drawer and 2 side drawers, the kneehole flanked by a pair of panelled cupboard doors, 61in (155cm).
£2,000-2,500 *C*

A Regency mahogany partners' desk, one side with 9 drawers, the other with 3 drawers and 2 panelled cupboards, 54in (137cm).
£2,000-3,000 *C*

A Regency mahogany partners' desk with 9 drawers around a kneehole each side, 67in (170cm).
£3,000-4,000 *C*

A padouk and featherbanded kneehole desk, with a fitted interior, above a single frieze drawer, and a recess panelled cupboard door, 19thC, 37½in (95cm).
£700-1,000 *CSK*

An early Victorian mahogany partners' desk, 60in (152cm).
£5,000-5,500 *P[EDH]*

A William IV mahogany pedestal desk, fitted with 3 frieze drawers and 6 pedestal drawers, 48in (122cm).
£6,000-7,000 *C*

A mahogany desk, with 3 frieze drawers opposed by 3 dummy drawers, on pedestals each with 3 short drawers, 19thC, 43in (109cm).
£2,000-2,500 *CSK*

An early Victorian burr yew kneehole desk, with 2 panelled doors, the left enclosing slides, the right enclosing 4 drawers, 48in (122cm).
£2,500-3,000 *C*

A mid-Victorian burr walnut and mahogany kneehole desk, the kneehole flanked by 2 drawers and 2 fielded cupboard doors, 51in (129.5cm).
£10,000-12,000 *C*

A Victorian walnut desk, 37in (94cm) high.
£4,000-5,000 *SD*

A Victorian figured walnut kneehole writing desk with 5 drawers, the top with 8 green tooled leather faced drawers, the centre drawer impressed with maker's name, Grunden, Brighton, 54in (137cm).
£2,500-3,000 *P[WSW]*

A Victorian mahogany rolltop kneehole pedestal desk, with fitted interior and sliding leather lined writing plateau, 60in (152cm).
£900-1,200 *CSK*

A Victorian mahogany pedestal desk, in partners' style, the front frieze with 3 drawers, the pedestals each with 3 drawers, the reverse with false drawers, 60in (152cm).
£2,500-3,000 *WW*

A Victorian mahogany pedestal desk, 58½in (148cm).
£1,000-1,500 *Bon*

A Victorian mahogany writing desk, inlaid and crossbanded in satinwood, 48in (122cm).
£2,000-2,500 *M*

A Victorian mahogany kneehole desk, with leather incised top.
£500-800 *M*

A Victorian partners' pedestal desk, 81in (205cm).
£20,000-25,000 *P*

A Victorian mahogany writing desk, 53in (134cm).
£1,200-1,500 *Bon*

A Victorian walnut writing desk inlaid with ebony and kingwood, with ormolu mounts.
£2,500-3,000 *MGM*

A small Victorian mahogany twin pedestal writing desk, with 9 drawers.
£700-1,000 *P[EDH]*

A Victorian mahogany desk, c1870, 60in (152cm).
£1,600-1,800 *DDS*

A Victorian carved mahogany writing desk of Carlton House type, the top inset with panels of tooled green leather centred by an adjustable ratcheted slope, stamped W. Priest, 1 & 2 Tudor St, Blackfriars, 75½in (192cm).
£5,000-7,000 *P*

A late Victorian mahogany kneehole writing desk, inlaid with harewood foliate marquetry, satinwood bands and boxwood lines, 41½in (105cm).
£2,000-2,500 *CSK*

A Sheraton Revival rosewood and marquetry desk, stamped Maple & Co. Ltd., late 19thC.
£800-1,000 *DWB*

An Edwardian mahogany ladies writing desk, decorated with satinwood inlay and rosewood banding, 48in (122cm).
£1,000-1,500 *BWe*

An Edwardian inlaid rosewood desk, with 2 mirror panels, two-door cupboard and 4 small drawers, hinged reading flap and 8 drawers to pedestals.
£700-1,000 *CH*

An Edwardian Wootton style mahogany desk, with fielded panel front and sides opening to an interior fitted with short drawers and stationery compartments, with upholstered tread, 28in (71cm).
£2,000-2,500 *CSK*

A Wootton Desk Company American Bankers' desk, with fitted interior.
£2,000-2,500 *MGM*

A burr walnut and cockbeaded pedestal partners' desk, with bowfront pedestals and shaped top, c1920, 60in (152cm).
£2,600-2,800 *DDS*

A Chippendale style mahogany pedestal desk, the leather lined top with a gadrooned edge above a blind fret carved frieze, 54in (137cm).
£1,500-2,500 *CSK*

A mahogany Carlton House desk, with crossbanding and yellow stringing, 20thC, 41in (104cm).
£700-1,000 *WIL*

A mahogany partners' desk, each side 9 drawers inlaid with fruitwood letters, 70in (177.5cm).
£5,500-6,500 *CSK*

A mahogany library desk, the top inset with embossed leather, the sides with 8 drawers, on gadrooned ogee bracket feet, 61½in (156cm).
£10,000-12,000 *C*

A mahogany partners' desk, one side with 9 drawers, the other side with 3 drawers and cupboards, with carrying handles, 61½in (155cm).
£4,500-5,500 *C*

A Dutch satinwood marquetry rolltop desk, the superstructure with 2 drawers above a solid cylinder and an oak fitted interior, early 19thC, 42in (106cm).
£3,000-3,500 *C*

A Chippendale design mahogany pedestal desk, with scale carved border and blind fret decoration to drawer fronts, 48in (122cm).
£2,500-3,000 *P[Pea]*

DESKS

- ★ desk correctly describes a piece of furniture on which to read or write and which has the top sloping at an angle. In this form it has medieval origins, but the term now embraces various types, such as bureaux, secretaires and the flat top 'kneehole'
- ★ the davenport desk is highly sought after. Found after the 1790s, the earliest have the upper desk part sliding forward or swivelling to accommodate the knees of the sitter
- ★ later Regency and Victorian models have column supports to the desk. Look out for the rising nest of drawers that works on weights and pulleys, when a secret button is depressed. After the 1840s, the 'piano front' became fashionable and is still most in demand. While it matters not if the price is right and the description fair, remember that single sided kneehole desks have been made out of Victorian washstands
- ★ kneehole desks have also been made out of 18thC chests of drawers. Because of cost these are rare and can be detected by incompatible drawer sides
- ★ an original leather top in good condition is desirable, but a fine new one is better than a bad old one
- ★ a bureau made to take a bookcase on top will have a steeper angle to the fall front to accommodate the case or cabinet

A brass mounted mahogany writing desk, with a tambour rolltop enclosing 3 short drawers, 26½in (67cm).
£1,500-2,000 *C*

A kneehole desk, 47½in (120cm).
£1,000-1,200 *Bea*

Dumb Waiters

An early George III mahogany dumb waiter, the graduated trays revolving on turned waisted spiral cut stems, 24in (61cm) diam.
£1,700-2,000 *WW*

A George III mahogany two-tier dumb waiter, each tier with drop leaves, brass terminals.
£1,700-2,000 *DN*

A George III style mahogany dumb waiter, the tiers with chip carved borders, 46in (116.5cm) high.
£700-1,000 *CSK*

A late Georgian mahogany two-tier dumb waiter, 41½in (105cm) high.
£600-1,000 *C*

A mid-Georgian mahogany dumb waiter, 43½in (110cm) high.
£2,200-2,800 *C*

An early Victorian mahogany three-tier dumb waiter, 32in (81cm).
£300-500 *CEd*

DUMB WAITERS

- ★ there is some controversy about when dumb waiters made an appearance
- ★ they were certainly produced in the 1720s but are rare until the 1750s
- ★ defined by Sheraton (Cabinet Dictionary 1803) as 'a useful piece of furniture, to serve in some respects the place of a waiter, whence it is so named'
- ★ 18thC dumb waiters *generally* consist of three tiers
- ★ made usually from mahogany
- ★ in Chippendale period supports often carved with foliage, acanthus leaves, broken scrolls, etc
- ★ Robert Adam's neo-classical style radically changed the design
- ★ the pillars now tended to become plainly cylindrical with turned collars at top and bottom
- ★ the late 18thC and early 19thC saw the introduction of pierced galleries often made of brass
- ★ during the Regency period some dumb waiters made from rosewood
- ★ marriages are around so beware
  - – differing turning on 3 trays
  - – two-tier examples (they can be right but are often 'naughty')

Regency mahogany two-tier
ımb waiter, 38in (96.5cm) high.
,500-2,000 *C*

William and Mary stained
ıitwood mirror, with later plate,
e frame carved with pierced
iage, 47½ by 27½in (119 by 70cm).
,000-1,500 *C*

Queen Anne black and gold
panned toilet mirror, the base
ith 3 short drawers and
serpentine long drawers, on later
acket feet, redecorated, 18in
6cm).
00-1,200 *C*

Lowboys

A walnut lowboy, the crossbanded top with re-entrant corners above a frieze fitted with 3 small drawers, adaptations, early 18thC, 29½in (75cm).
£1,700-2,000 *CSK*

A William III carved giltwood picture frame, inset with later plate, remounted and re-gilt, 56 by 45in (142 by 115cm).
£1,500-2,000 *P*

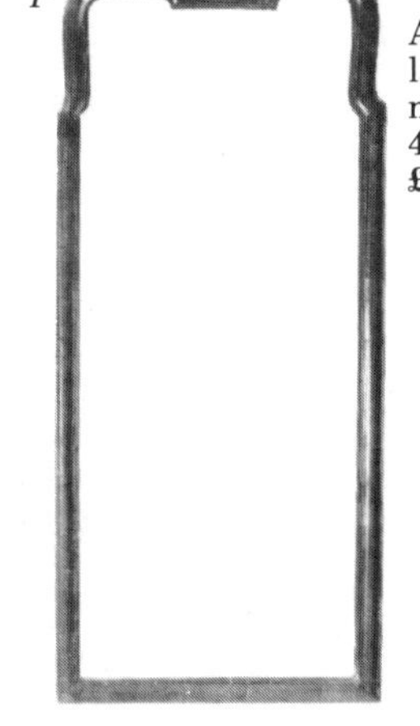

A George I giltwood mirror, the frieze centred by a shell, 40 by 29in (102 by 74cm).
£1,000-1,500 *C*

Mirrors and Frames

A William and Mary looking glass, the walnut cushion shaped frame with cross grained moulded borders.
£1,500-2,000 *DN*

A Queen Anne wall mirror, with arched bevelled plate, 36 by 25in (92 by 64cm).
£6,500-7,500 *P*

A Queen Anne walnut mirror, with later shaped bevelled plate, in moulded frame, 34 by 16in (88 by 40cm).
£500-800 *C*

A George I giltwood and gesso wall mirror, with later plate, with a scallop shell and outlines for girandoles below, 42 by 25in (107 by 64cm).
£1,700-2,000 *P*

A Queen Anne style walnut mirror, restored, 24in (61cm) high.
£400-600 *RIP*

A George I walnut toilet mirror, the base with 3 short drawers and a concave long drawer, 17in (43cm).
£1,500-2,000 *C*

A George I giltwood and gesso wall mirror, fitted with a later plate wit bevelled edge, 45in (114cm) high.
£4,500-5,000 *PB*

A pair of giltwood mirrors, 18thC, 38 by 20in (96.5 by 51cm).
£5,500-6,500 *CSK*

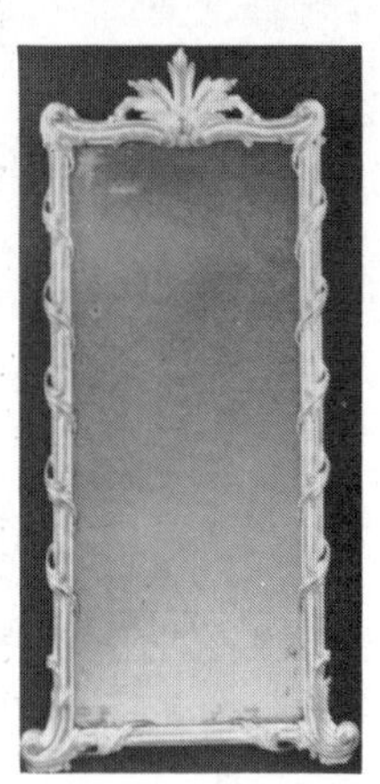

A cream painted and gilded mirror, redecorated, late 18thC, 55 by 27in (139.5 by 68.5cm).
£2,000-2,500 *C*

A George I style walnut and parcel gilt mirror, carved on the back wit an armorial crest and the initials A.H. London, 40 by 21½in (101.5 b 54cm).
£800-1,000 *CSK*

A George II giltwood mirror, 40 by 27in (101.5 by 68.5cm).
£2,000-2,500 *CSK*

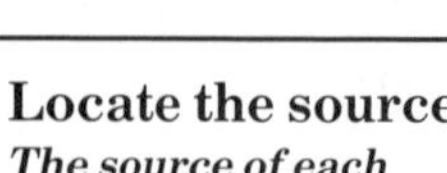

Locate the source
The source of each illustration in Miller's can be found by checking the code letters below each caption with the list of contributors.

An early George III mahogany and parcel gilt fret carved wall mirror, inset with a contemporary bevelled plate, 51 by 26½in (130 by 67cm).
£5,500-6,500 *P*

A George III giltwood mirror, the frieze with an églomisé panel, late plate, 44½ by 24in (111.5 by 61cm).
£1,400-1,800 *C*

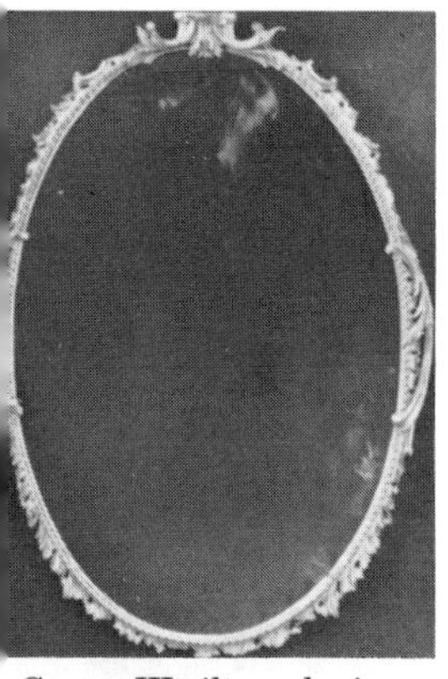

George III giltwood mirror with ıter oval plate, re-gilded, 44½ by 2in (112 by 81cm).
1,500-2,000 *C*

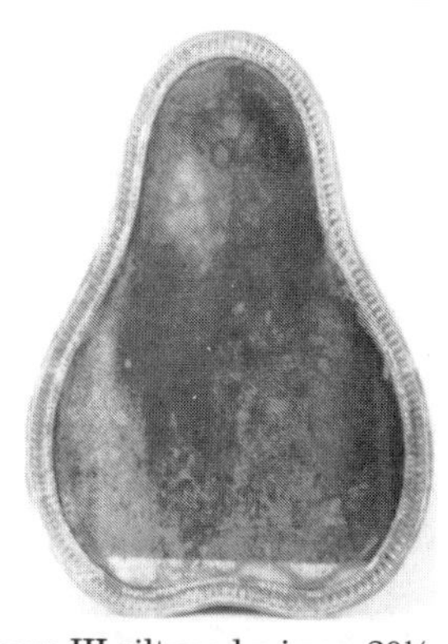

A George III giltwood mirror, 20½ by 15½in (52 by 38cm).
£800-1,000 *C*

A George III giltwood mirror, with later plate, 55 by 25in (140 by 63cm).
£2,500-3,500 *C*

George III giltwood mirror with ʼal plate, re-gilt, 34 by 26in (86 by 5cm).
,600-2,000 *C*

A pair of giltwood mirrors of George III style, 46 by 23½in (117 by 59.5cm).
£2,000-3,000 *C*

A gilt mahogany mirror of George III style, with divided cartouche shaped plate, the frame carved with C-scrolls, rockwork, and a ho-ho bird foliage, 53 by 27in (134.5 by 68.5cm).
£1,700-2,000 *C*

mid-Georgian walnut and parcel lt mirror, 53½ by 26in (135 by 5cm).
,000-5,000 *C*

A mid-Georgian walnut and parcel gilt mirror, with later plate, 50 by 27in (127 by 68cm).
£6,000-8,000 *C*

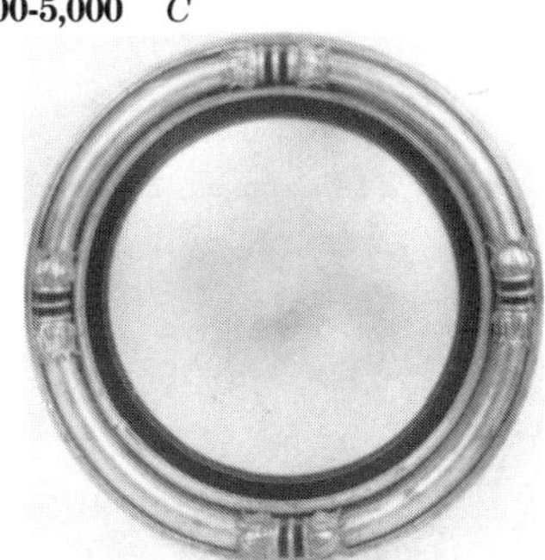

A Regency giltwood convex mirror, 25½in (64.5cm).
£700-1,000 *C*

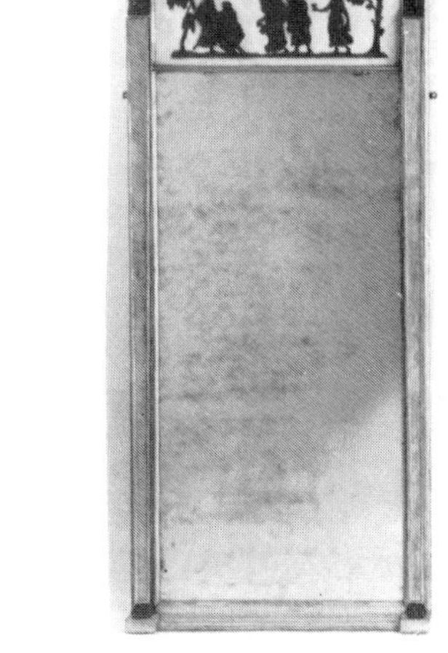

A Regency parcel gilt and ebonised pier glass, the frieze with classical figures on a cream painted ground, 70½ by 33in (177.5 by 84cm).
£1,600-2,000 *C*

A Regency carved giltwood girandole, 35½ by 19in (90 by 48cm).
£1,500-2,000 *P*

A Regency giltwood convex mirror, 35 by 25in (89 by 63.5cm).
£1,000-1,500 *C*

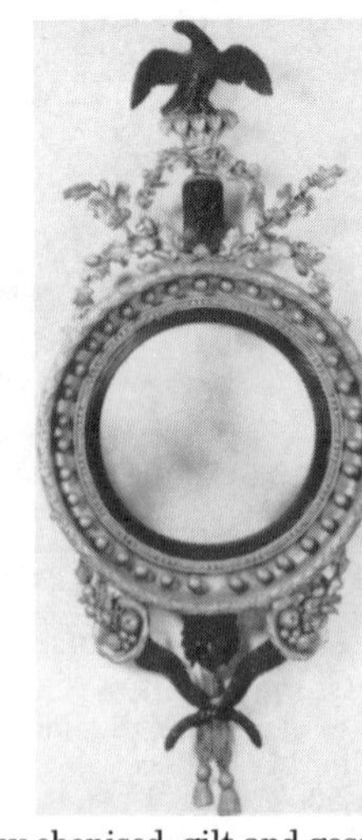
A Regency ebonised, gilt and gess convex mirror, 51½ by 23½in (131 by 59cm).
£2,000-2,500 *P*

A Regency giltwood girandole, the later flat mirror plate within a leaf moulded and sphere applied frame.
£2,500-3,000 *Bon*

A Regency giltwood convex mirror, 43 by 26in (109 by 66cm).
£1,000-1,500 *C*

A Regency giltwood convex mirro 40 by 24in (101.5 by 61cm).
£3,000-3,500 *C*

A pair of Regency giltwood pier glasses, 71 by 21in (180 by 53cm).
£2,000-2,500 *C*

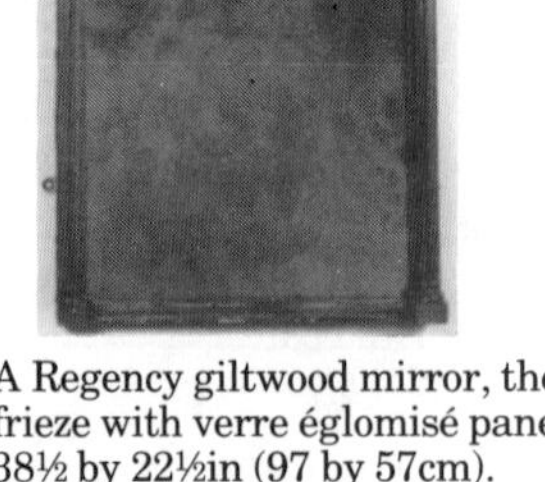
A Regency giltwood mirror, the frieze with verre églomisé panel, 38½ by 22½in (97 by 57cm).
£800-1,000 *C*

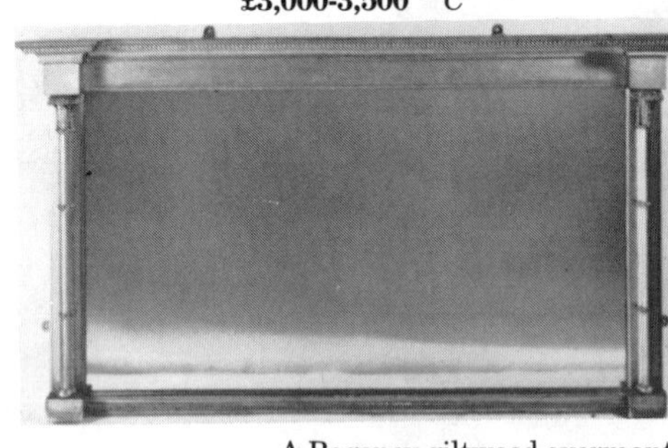
A Regency giltwood overmante 29½ by 53in (75 by 135cm).
£1,200-1,500 *C*

A Regency style ebony inlaid mahogany overmantel, stamped TT 1824, 44in (111cm).
£1,000-1,500 *C*

. Victorian mahogany dressing
ıirror, the roll front opening as a
rawer, 27in (68.5cm).
200-250 *Ph*

An Edwardian mahogany cheval mirror, inlaid with chequered stringing and boxwood lines, 68in (172.5cm).
£700-1,000 *CSK*

A giltwood and gesso convex mirror, early 19thC, 52 by 32in (131 by 81cm).
£2,000-2,500 *P*

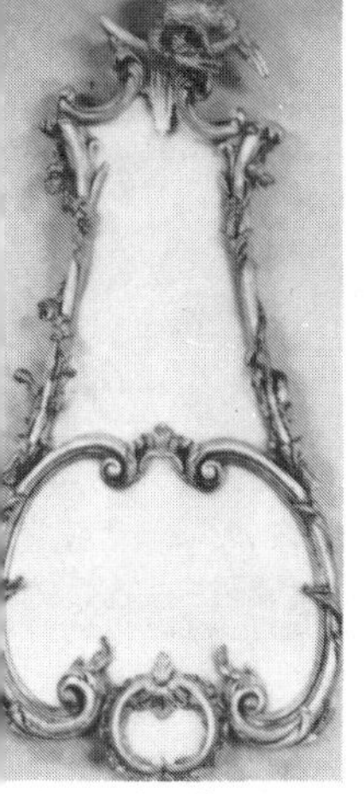

giltwood wall mirror, early 19thC,
1½ by 24in (130 by 61cm).
1,500-2,000 *CSK*

A pair of carved giltwood girandoles, in the manner of Thomas Johnson, surmounted by ho-ho birds and scrolls, 19thC, 31½ by 12in (80 by 31cm).
£2,000-3,000 *P*

An oval girandole wall mirror, with ribband cresting and 3 tulip sconces, 19thC, 42in (106.5cm).
£700-1,000 *LRG*

A gilt frame convex mirror, 19thC.
£600-800 *TM*

A carved giltwood picture frame, 19thC, 86 by 67in (220 by 170cm).
£1,000-1,500 *PB*

. pair of giltmetal girandoles, late
9thC, 21in (53cm).
1,000-1,500 *C*

A Louis XIII giltwood mirror, the cresting with putti supporting the arms of France, 21½ by 12in (54 by 30cm).
£1,000-1,500 *C*

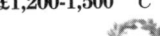

A giltwood mirror with bevelled plate, possibly Irish, 53 by 43 (134 by 109cm).
£1,200-1,500 *C*

A giltwood mirror of Régence style, 50 by 44in (127 by 112cm).
£2,000-2,500 *C*

An easel mirror with bevelled plate, makers J.D. W.D., Chester 1898, 19 by 12½in (48 by 31cm).
£600-800 *GSP*

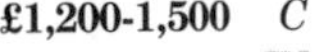

An Empire giltmetal frame, the back inscribed 'The Honble Mrs Duff', 12 by 8in (30.5 by 20.5cm).
£1,300-1,600 *C*

A Flemish red tortoiseshell and ebonised picture frame, distressed, late 17thC, 48 by 41in (122 by 104cm).
£9,000-11,000 *C*

A giltwood mirror, possibly German, late 18thC, 49 by 29in (124.5 by 74cm).
£4,500-5,500 *C*

A Venetian giltwood picture frame, painted with a sleeping boy, the frame late 17thC, 29 by 16in (73 by 41cm).
£1,600-2,000 *C*

An Italian neo-classical giltwood mirror, Liguria or Emilia, with divided plate, re-gilt, restorations, c1775, 69in (175cm) high.
£2,000-3,000 *CNY*

A German parcel gilt and ebonised mirror, late 18thC, 65 by 29in (165 by 73cm).
£1,500-2,000 *C*

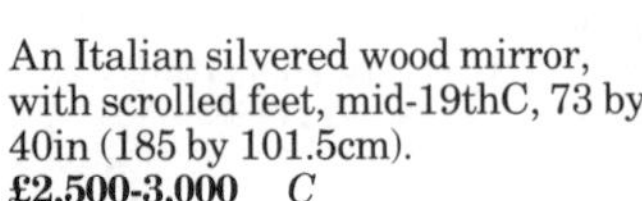

An Italian silvered wood mirror, with scrolled feet, mid-19thC, 73 by 40in (185 by 101.5cm).
£2,500-3,000 *C*

An Italian giltwood wall mirror, 19thC, 43 by 27in (109 by 68.5cm).
£700-1,000 *CSK*

A fruitwood and ebonised pier glass, with bevelled plate, possibly Russian, early 19thC, 48 by 24in (122 by 61cm).
£2,200-2,500 *C*

A pair of parcel gilt and white painted mirrors, probably Scandinavian, 41 by 28in (104 by 71cm).
£2,500-3,500 *C*

A Spanish giltwood mirror of 17thC design, 39½ by 27in (100 by 68cm).
£800-1,000 *C*

Screens

A four-leaf screen covered in Brussels verdure tapestry, the tapestry 17thC, each leaf 84½ by 25½in (214 by 63.5cm).
£7,000-8,000 *C*

A George II style firescreen, on scrolling foliate tripod base, 64in (162.5cm) high.
£400-600 *C*

A Georgian mahogany polescreen, with turned column, 58½in (148cm) high.
£300-400 *PWC*

A pair of William IV rosewood polescreens, 41in (104cm) high.
£900-1,200 *W*

A Regency mahogany firescreen, with sliding panels and gilt capitals, on arched tapering feet, 25in (63.5cm).
£300-400 *C*

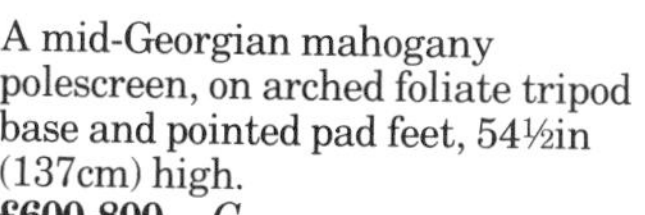

A mid-Georgian mahogany polescreen, on arched foliate tripod base and pointed pad feet, 54½in (137cm) high.
£600-800 *C*

A Regency carved giltwood three-fold freestanding firescreen, incorporating 10 mirrored glass panels, 42in (106.5cm).
£600-700 *GH*

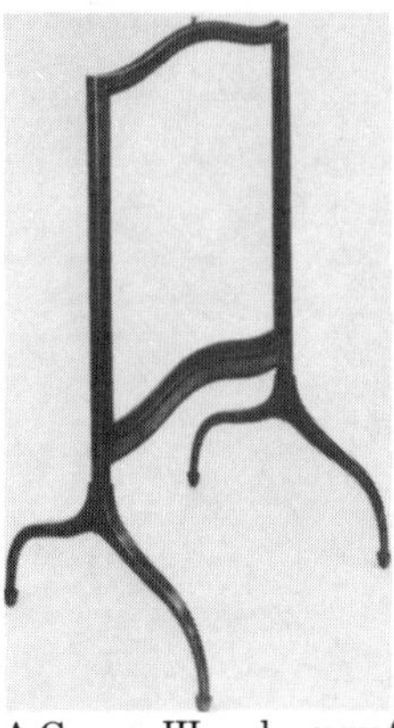
A George III mahogany firescreen, with arched glazed sliding panel in a boxwood lined frame with satinwood band, distressed, 19in (48cm).
£300-500 *C*

A late Victorian scrapwork four-leaf screen, the leaves with gilt slips and scrolling cornices.
£1,000-1,500 *C*

A pair of papier mâché and ebonised polescreens, on a ring turned column and splayed tripod supports, 19thC.
£500-700 *P*

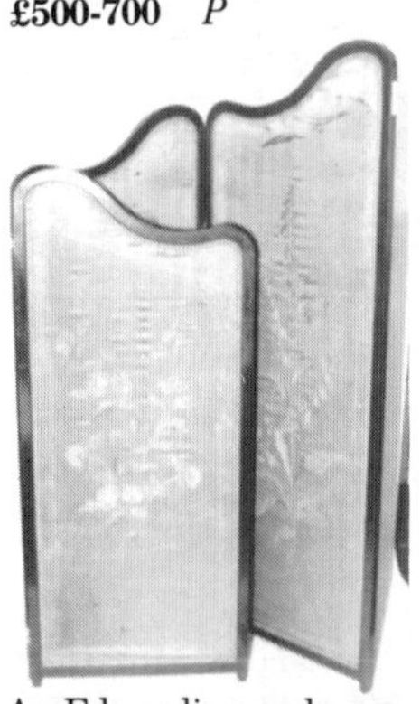
An Edwardian mahogany screen, with silk embroidered panels, c1910, 66in (167.5cm) high.
£150-200 *Ph*

An early George III carved mahogany polescreen, with petit point needlework banner, 60in (152cm) high.
£2,000-3,000 *Bon*

A late Victorian ebonised, parcel gilt and scrapwork three-leaf screen, the back with green patterned paper, distressed, each leaf 70 by 24in (177.5 by 61cm).
£2,000-3,000 *C*

A parcel gilt and gesso polescreen on tripod base, with silk embroidered panel, 53in (134.5cm) high.
£400-500 *Wor*

A Victorian crewel work four-fold screen, 54in (137cm) extended.
£50-80 *LRG*

A Victorian giltwood and gesso firescreen, 38in (96.5cm).
£450-650 *Bea*

A giltwood three-fold screen of rococo form, with shaped glazed panels and embroidered silk panels, 19thC, 76in (193cm) high.
£1,500-2,000 *CSK*

. French style rosewood firescreen, 1900, 21in (53cm).
150-200 *Ph*

A mahogany framed firescreen, c1900.
£200-250 *WIL*

. white painted three-leaf screen, ie arched leaves with needlework, ich leaf 37½ by 19in (94 by 48cm).
300-400 *C*

A painted leather three-leaf screen, 36 by 48in (91 by 122cm).
£500-700 *C*

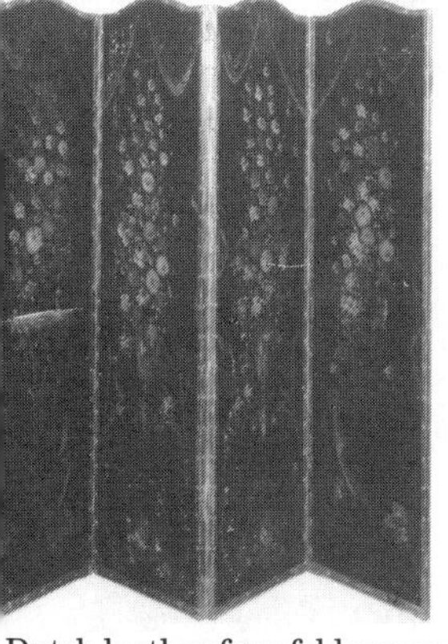
Dutch leather four-fold screen, ch leaf 72½ by 21in (183 by 53cm).
,500-2,000 *C*

A Louis XVI grey painted firescreen, with silk panel, 17in (43cm).
£1,200-1,500 *C*

A painted leather four-fold draught screen, with brass studs, 84in (213cm).
£600-700 *HCH*

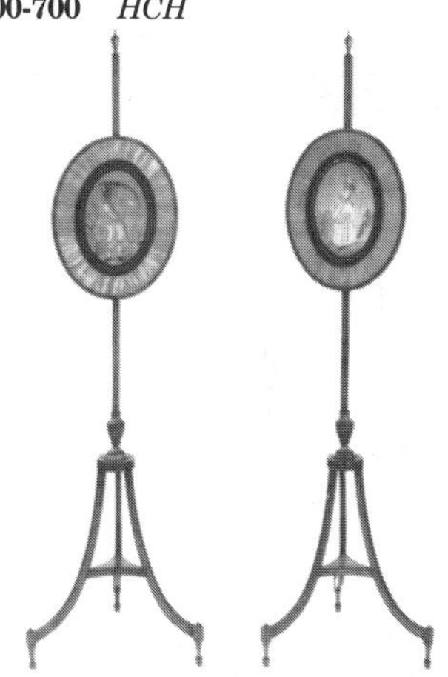
A pair of satinwood polescreens, each with a sliding oval panel banded with rosewood and with a central embroidered figure, 56½in (143cm) high.
£12,000-15,000 *C*

ettees

George I style mahogany vo-seater sofa, upholstered in rose nk velour, on cabriole legs with d feet, 49in (122cm).
,000-1,500 *CSK*

A George II style walnut settee, with triple carved vase splat and shaped arms, on carved cabriole supports with claw-and-ball feet, 62in (157cm).
£500-700 *CH*

A Sheraton Revival satinwood framed sofa, 78in (198cm).
£1,300-1,600 *DN*

Make the Most of Miller's

CONDITION is absolutely vital when assessing the value of an antique. Damaged pieces on the whole appreciate much less than perfect examples. However a rare, desirable piece may command a high price even when damaged

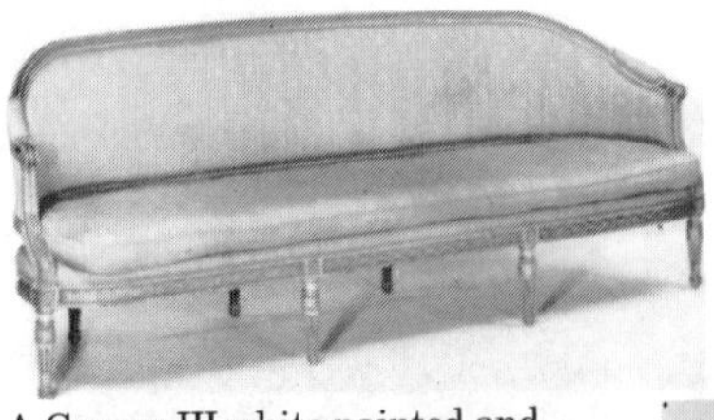

A George III white painted and parcel gilt sofa, with rounded arched back, sides, seat and squab covered in green repp, on turned tapering fluted legs, 98½in (250cm).
£1,500-2,000 *C*

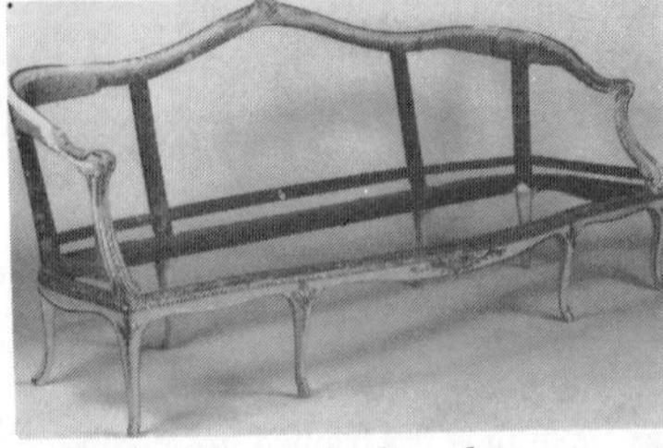

A George III parcel gilt and cream painted sofa, on cabriole legs headed by foliage, later blocks, redecorated, 84in (213cm).
£3,000-4,000 *C*

A George III style humpback sofa, covered in yellow moiré, on chamfered legs, carved with blind fretwork and pierced angles, 47½in (119cm).
£3,000-4,000 *C*

A Regency parcel gilt and ebonised sofa, with moulded frame and ring turned legs, reinforced seat rail, 72in (182.5cm).
£1,000-1,500 *C*

A Regency mahogany hall settee, the drop-in seat covered in green striped silk, on square tapering legs and spade feet, 77½in (196cm).
£3,000-4,000 *C*

A George III mahogany window seat, covered in blue and cream striped material, on moulded cabriole legs, 45½in (114cm).
£5,000-6,000 *C*

A George III cream painted and parcel gilt sofa, with spirally turned spreading arm supports and conforming tapering legs, the seat rails strengthened, 77in (195.5cm).
£1,500-2,000 *C*

A George III white painted and parcel gilt sofa with moulded ribbed frame and fluted seat rail, on square tapering legs headed by paterae, 75½in (190.5cm).
£3,500-4,500 *C*

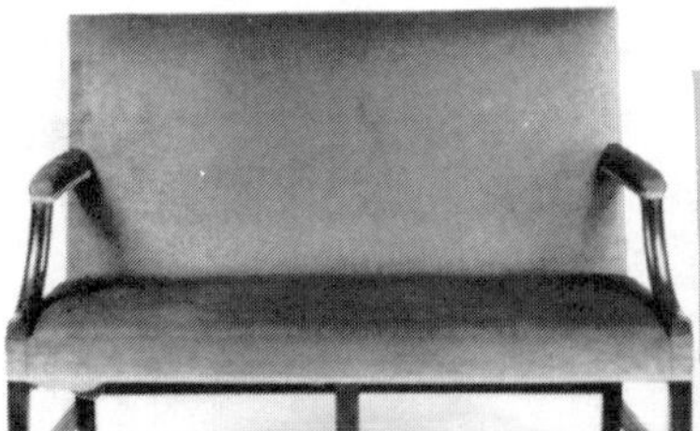

A George III mahogany sofa, re-railed, 49in (124.5cm).
£2,000-3,000 *C*

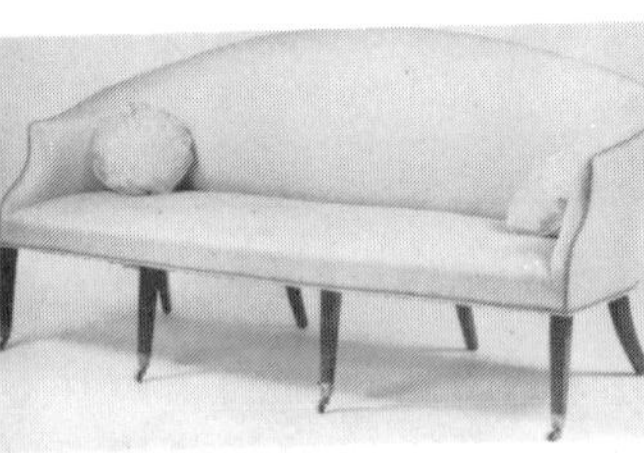

A George III mahogany sofa, upholstered in yellow repp, on square tapering legs, 3 back legs spliced, one replaced, 74in (188cm).
£1,500-2,000 *C*

A Georgian style carved mahogany settee, with stuffover arched back with outswept scroll arm supports terminating in eagles' heads, on cabriole legs with C-scroll and foliate shell decorated knees, terminating in paw feet.
£2,000-3,000 *P*

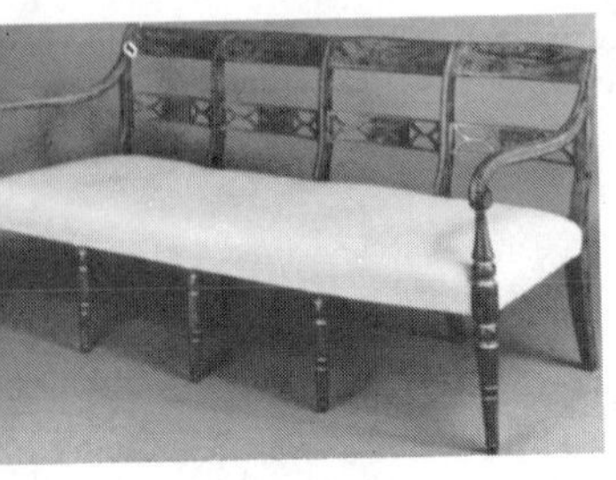

A Regency simulated rosewood and parcel gilt quadruple chairback settee, the white calico covered seat flanked by scrolled arms on turned tapering legs, 71in (180cm).
£1,500-2,000 *C*

A satinwood veneered and mahogany banded chaise longue, upholstered in blue brocade, on square tapering legs, early 19thC, 75in (190.5cm).
£800-1,000 *CSK*

A Victorian rosewood frame sofa, with serpentine seat, on flower carved cabriole legs with scrolled feet, 71½in (181cm).
£1,000-1,500 *Bon*

A Victorian oak framed conversation settee, on carved cabriole legs with knurl feet, 57in (144.5cm).
£1,200-1,500 *Bea*

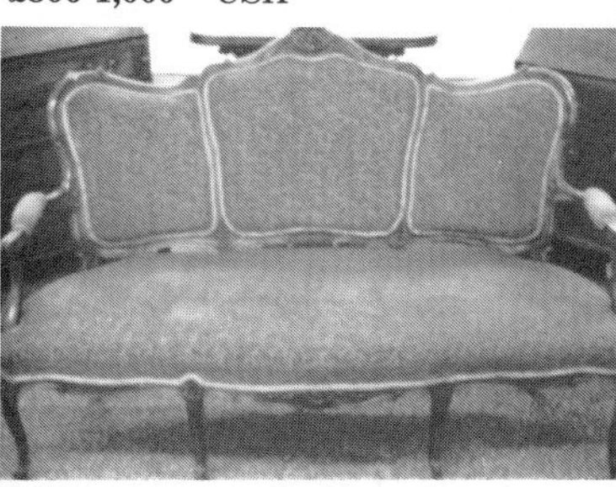

A Victorian carved walnut three piece suite.
£900-1,200 *HP*

A Victorian walnut conversation sofa, the seats and backs upholstered in figured damask, on scrolling feet, 50in (127cm).
£800-1,000 *CSK*

A Victorian walnut chaise longue, upholstered in green velvet, on cabriole legs with knob feet, 66in (167.5cm).
£1,200-1,500 *CSK*

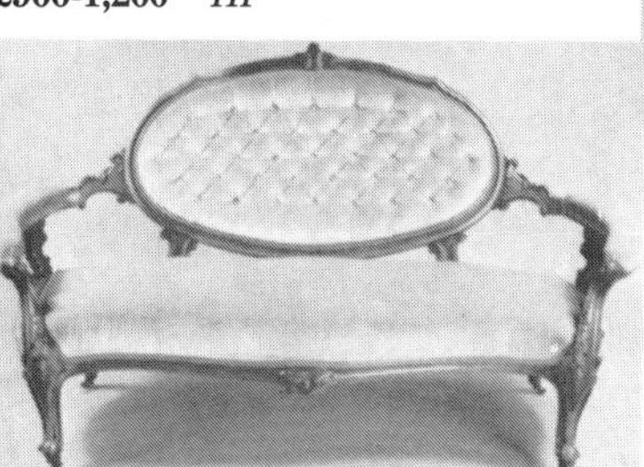

A Victorian walnut settee, upholstered in green in a moulded frame decorated with stylised foliage, the arms terminating in scrolls on cabriole legs, scroll feet and casters, 70in (177.5cm).
£1,500-2,000 *CSK*

A Victorian carved walnut framed chaise longue, with buttoned back.
£1,200-1,600 *MGM*

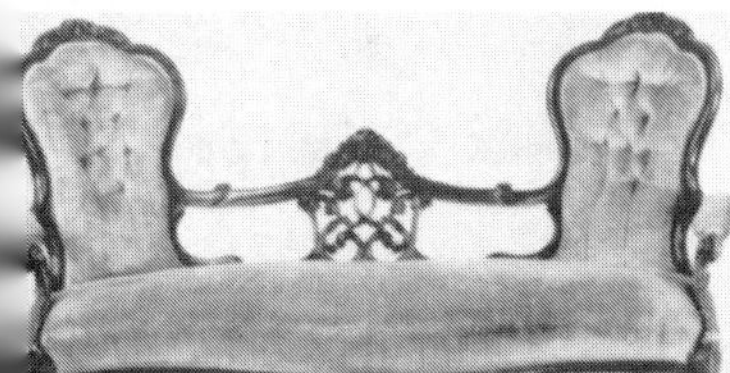

Victorian walnut sofa, with twin spoon back, 66in (167.5cm).
1,500-2,000 *CSK*

An Anglo-Indian carved rosewood four piece suite, comprising a pair of pierced framed sofas, 69in (175cm), and 2 side chairs, late 19thC.
£2,500-3,000 *CSK*

walnut chaise longue, upholstered in yellow velvet, on cabriole legs with knob feet, late 19thC, 70in (177.5cm).
1,200-1,500 *CSK*

A mid-Victorian carved rosewood settee, 78in (198cm).
£1,000-1,200 *DSH*

A seven-piece Edwardian mahogany parlour suite, with boxwood stringing and rosewood panels, comprising a settee, 2 carver chairs and 4 other chairs.
£2,200-2,600 *P[EDH]*

A mid-Victorian walnut sofa, upholstered in buttoned slate blue velvet, on cabriole legs, 80in (203cm).
£1,200-1,500 *C*

A mid-Victorian walnut sofa, upholstered in bottle green velvet, within a moulded frame with scrolling arm terminals, on cabriole legs, carved with foliage and strapwork, on scrolled toes, 79½in (202cm).
£1,500-2,000 *C*

An Edwardian inlaid mahogany parlour suite, comprising a two-seater settee with foliate inlaid splat, padded back and rounded arms, on cabriole legs, 2 armchairs and 4 side chairs.
£1,200-1,600 *Bea*

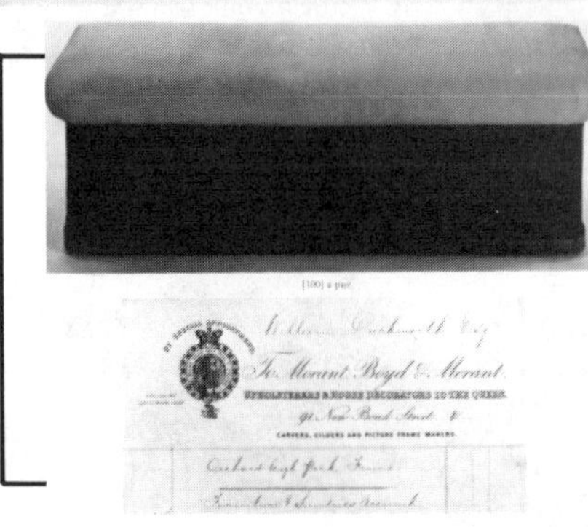

A pair of mid-Victorian amboyna ottoman window seats, by Morant, Boyd & Morant, each with a calico covered hinged seat and red velvet covered sides, on a plinth base and casters, 49in (124cm).
£1,500-2,000 *C*

Invoiced on 20 December 1858 – £10.18s.

A Louis XV walnut duchesse brisee, with rounded sloping back and flowerhead crestings, the moulded seat rail carved with flowerheads, on moulded cabriole legs, 73½in (186cm).
£1,700-2,000 *C*

A Louis XV parcel gilt and grey painted canapé, with moulded frame carved with foliage, on cabriole legs joined by an X-shaped stretcher, restored, 77in (195.5cm).
£2,800-3,400 *C*

A Biedermeier walnut sofa, covered in striped silk with 2 bolsters on scrolling legs, 62½in (158cm).
£3,000-4,000 *C*

A Louis XVI style giltwood sofa, on brass caps and casters, 19thC, 75in (190.5cm).
£1,500-2,000 *CSK*

A Louis XV style beech framed settee, upholstered in camel corded velvet, 81in (205.5cm).
£2,500-3,000 *Bea*

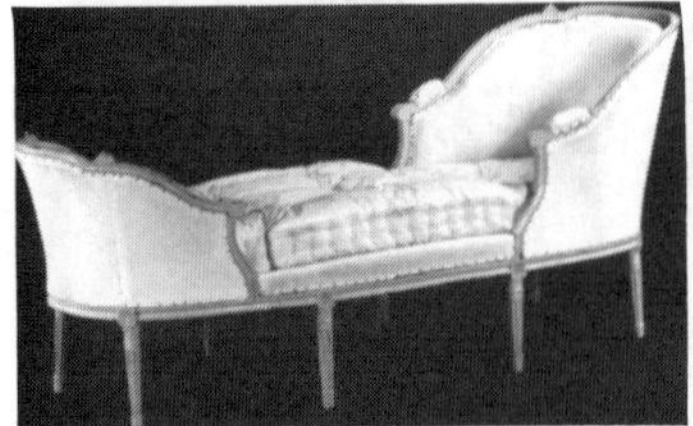

A Louis XVI grey painted lit-en-bateau, one leg later, the rails partly reinforced, 78½in (198cm).
£3,000-4,000 *C*

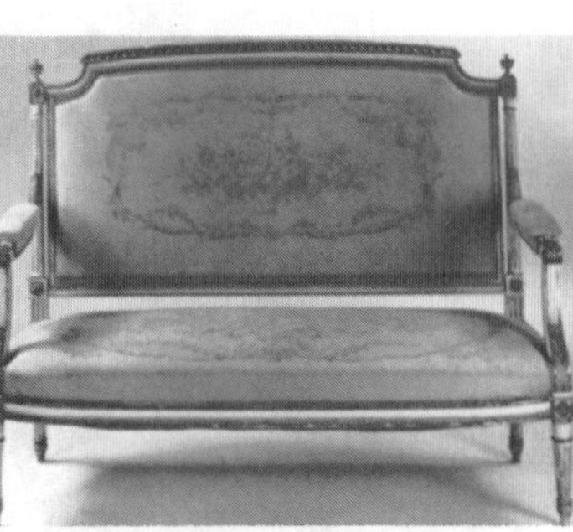

A Louis XVI style cream painted and parcel gilt suite, variously upholstered, comprising: a pair of chaises, a pair of fauteuils and a canapé with machined tapestry, the canapé 56in (142cm).
£2,000-3,000 *C*

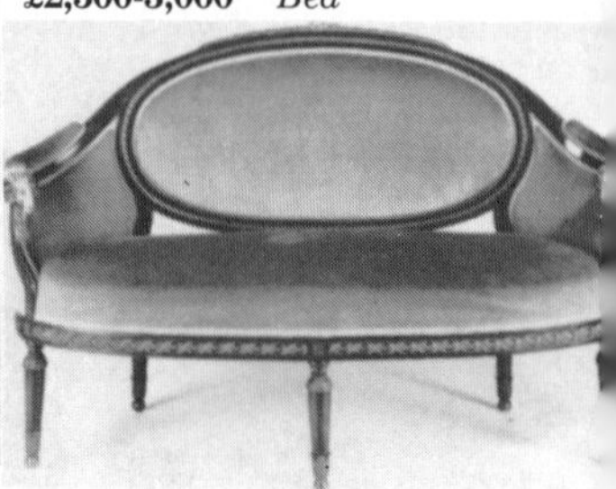

An Empire style mahogany canapé en cabriolette, upholstered in gold velvet with rams heads terminals, on turned tapering legs with sabots and paterae headings, 62in (157cm).
£1,200-1,600 *CSK*

An Italian Louis XV style salon suite, including a chair back settee and 4 occasional chairs with cane panel backs and floral and foliate crestings, late 18th/early 19thC, later green painted and gilt.
£2,000-2,500 *P*

A German Empire mahogany and boxwood strung sofa, with an upholstered panel arched back and padded scroll arm supports, a stuffover seat and panel frieze with a classical scene, on outswept feet.
£800-1,200 *P*

Shelves

A set of Regency mahogany and brass mounted twin hanging shelves, with beaded edges, on turned baluster uprights, 29½in (74cm).
£800-900 *P*

A pair of late Regency mahogany standing bookshelves, supported by ball, spiral turned and fluted tapering legs with paw feet, 48in (122cm).
£4,000-5,000 *CNY*

A pair of Regency parcel gilt and mahogany open corner étagères, with white marble tops and pierced three-quarter galleries, mirror glazed backs, flanked by lappeted moulding, on bobbin turned tapering legs, 23in (58cm).
£1,600-2,000 *C*

A set of Regency mahogany hanging shelves, with turned finials and feet, 28½in (72cm).
£700-800 *C*

Sideboards

A Georgian bowfront sideboard, with string and sunburst inlay in fruitwood.
£2,500-3,000 *FHF*

A Georgian mahogany bowfront sideboard, decorated with an American eagle and 'E. Pluribus Unum', on 6 tapered supports with spade feet, 74in (188cm).
£2,000-2,500 *HOD*

A Georgian mahogany serpentine sideboard, decorated with pollarded bandings, with brass curtain rail, 72in (182.5cm).
£2,000-2,500 *P[WSW]*

A George III mahogany serpentine front sideboard, with satinwood banding, replacement brass plate ring handles, the square tapering legs on socket feet, 53in (134.5cm).
£3,500-4,500 *WW*

A George III mahogany sideboard, with triple bowed top, on tapering legs and spade feet, 90in (228.5cm).
£3,000-4,000 *C*

A George III mahogany and satinwood crossbanded bowfront sideboard, fitted with drawers, cellaret and cupboard, 55½in (140cm).
£4,000-5,000 *P[Re]*

A George III mahogany and rosewood banded sideboard, with brass gallery, on boxwood strung square tapered legs with spade feet, 84in (213cm).
£2,000-3,000 *Bon*

A George III mahogany sideboard, with D-shaped top crossbanded with satinwood, 47½in (120cm).
£5,000-5,500 *GSP*

A George III mahogany kneehole sideboard, the centre drawer flanked by cellaret, small cupboard, one larger cupboard fitted with 4 sliding trays and decorated with a triple reeded moulding, 46in (116.5cm).
£4,000-5,000 *P[WSW]*

A George III mahogany and inlaid serpentine sideboard, with rosewood crossbanded top fitted with a central bowed drawer flanked by dummy front, addition to cellaret drawer apron.
£4,000-4,500 *P*

A George III mahogany and inlaid serpentine sideboard, with ebony and boxwood lines, on square tapered legs and block feet, 38in (98cm).
£2,000-2,500 *P*

A George III mahogany sideboard, 68in (172.5cm).
£3,500-4,000 *C*

A Regency mahogany bowfront sideboard, inlaid with shells, leafy spandrels, satinwood bands and boxwood lines, 85½in (217cm).
£1,500-2,000 *CSK*

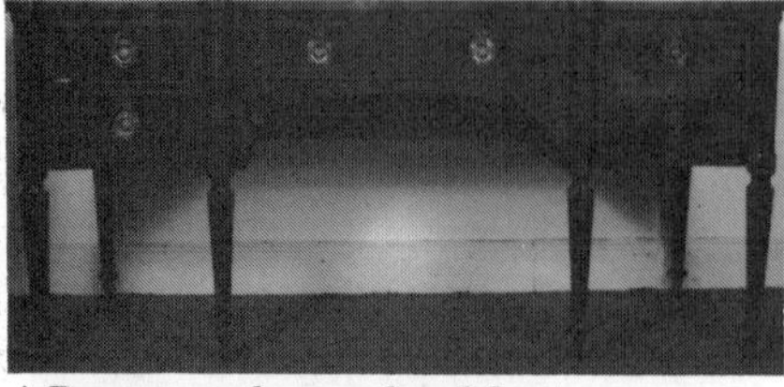

A Regency mahogany breakfront sideboard, crossbanded and boxwood line inlaid, divided by fluted turned columns, on fluted turned tapering supports, 80½in (204cm).
£2,500-3,500 *P[Re]*

A Regency mahogany sideboard, inlaid with ebony, 72in (182.5cm).
£1,200-1,500 *GH*

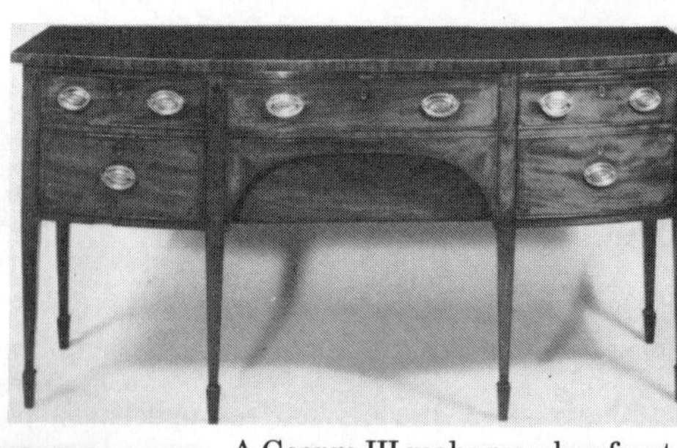

A George III mahogany bowfront sideboard, inlaid with radial boxwood lines, with square tapering legs and spade feet, 72in (182.5cm).
£6,000-7,000 *CSK*

A George III mahogany and crossbanded serpentine sideboard, decorated with boxwood stringing, the raised back with a brass gallery and 5 false drawers, 83½in (211cm).
£3,200-3,600 *DN*

A Regency mahogany veneered breakfront sideboard, banded in satinwood with stringing, with brass lion mask plate ring handles and later brass escutcheons, 72in (182.5cm).
£2,000-2,500 *WW*

A late Georgian marquetry mahogany bowfront sideboard, crossbanded in satinwood with a shell inlaid top, on square tapered legs and spade feet, 72in (183cm).
£4,000-5,000 *P*

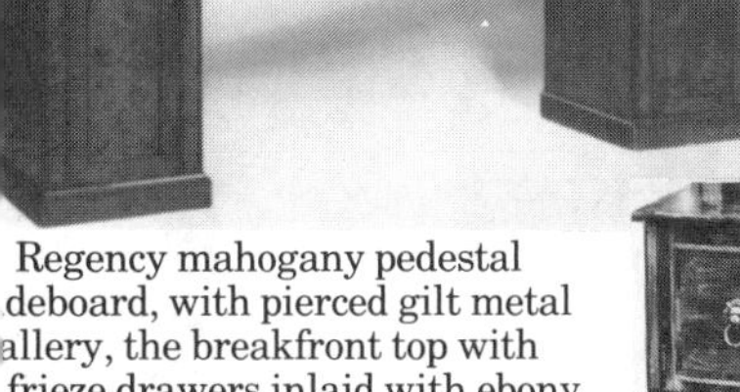

Regency mahogany pedestal deboard, with pierced gilt metal allery, the breakfront top with frieze drawers inlaid with ebony rolls and foliate designs, with oony inlaid panelled doors, 100in 254cm).
1,000-5,000 *Bon*

A Regency mahogany bowfront sideboard, with ebony and satinwood stringing, 72in (182.5cm).
£900-1,200 *Wor*

A Regency mahogany breakfront sideboard, in the manner of Thomas Hope, c1810, 96in (243.5cm).
£13,000-16,000 *N*

A Victorian Gothic Revival mahogany and satinwood pedestal sideboard, 82½in (210cm).
£300-500 *Bea*

A Sheraton period kneehole sideboard, with brass swan neck handles, on 6 inlaid tapered supports with spade feet, 57in (144.5cm).
£4,000-5,000 *HOD*

A Victorian rosewood and inlaid sideboard, with mirrored superstructure and doors, 54in (137cm).
£500-700 *LRG*

. mahogany Sheraton Revival arquetry breakfront sideboard ith satinwood crossbanding, eeding some restoration, 19thC, 4in (213cm).
1,000-5,000 *P[Re]*

A sideboard on turned legs with central drawer, celaret drawer and cupboard, slight damage, early 19thC, 60in (152cm).
£900-1,200 *LRG*

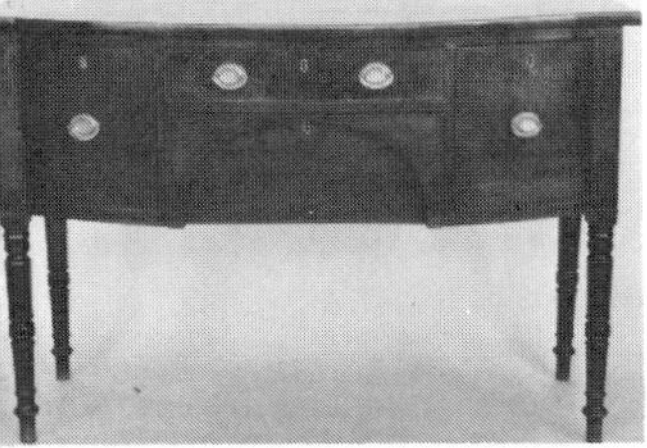

A Victorian ebonised sideboard, inlaid with marquetry arabesques, in various woods and in bone, on graduated plinth base, 80in (203cm).
£2,200-2,500 *CSK*

A late Victorian rosewood veneered sideboard, with ivory and boxwood marquetry inlay, 66in (167.5cm).
£2,000-2,500 *WW*

mahogany bowfront sideboard, ith 2 drawers and cupboards.
1,000-1,500 *MGM*

A mahogany mirror back sideboard, with open and blind fretwork panels, in the Moorish style, 52in (132cm).
£200-300 *MJB*

A mahogany breakfront sideboard, with central drawer, flanked by cellaret and napery.
£1,500-2,000 *MGM*

Stands

An early George III mahogany reading stand, with adjustable elevating ratcheted slope with candleslide, on knopped column and tripod legs, terminating in pad feet, 25in (63cm).
£1,600-2,000 *P*

An early George III style mahogany urn stand, 11in (28cm).
£1,000-1,500 *CNY*

A Regency mahogany pedestal, with stepped top and tapering panelled sides with canted angles, on a plinth base, 50in (127cm) high.
£1,700-2,200 *C*

A George III mahogany reading stand, on fluted column and splayed tripod legs, terminating in blocks, brass cappings and casters.
£2,000-3,000 *P*

A George IV rosewood folio stand, with later base.
£900-1,000 *C*

A Regency style gilt jardinière, with marble top, 45in (114cm).
£400-500 *W*

A rosewood adjustable folio stand, 19thC.
£1,500-2,000 *MAI*

A rosewood lamp stand, early 19thC, 28in (71cm) high.
£1,200-1,500 *DB*

A mahogany duet stand, on telescopic hexagonal column and tripod base with brass ball terminals, with boxwood ebony and satinwood inlay, late 19thC, 48in (122cm) high.
£2,500-3,000 *P[CW]*

A Victorian French easel, with gilt decoration, 76in (193cm) high.
£700-800 *Ba*

An Edwardian mahogany circular revolving book stand, on quadruple support with brass claw feet and casters, 18in (46cm).
£2,200-2,500 *JD*

A Victorian mahogany folio stand, with adjustable ratcheted and slatted slopes and book rests, 27½in (70cm).
£2,500-3,000 *P*

rosewood stand, the top inlaid ith composite marble, 18in (46cm) am.
,500-2,000 *Wor*

A heart-shaped étagère, c1920, 30in (76cm) high.
£300-350 *RIP*

A pair of giltwood plant stands in the French style, 40in (101.5cm) high.
£2,000-2,500 *McC*

teps

set of Regency mahogany leather ıed library steps, with panelled des, on ring turned tapering legs ith casters, 38in (96.5cm).
,500-3,000 *CNY*

A set of Regency mahogany leather lined library steps, early 19thC.
£1,500-2,000 *CNY*

Stools

A pair of giltwood window seats, with different upholstery, flanked by ring turned foliate rails, c1800, later blocks, redecorated, 26½in (67cm).
£2,500-3,000 *C*

A William and Mary walnut stool, upholstered in close nailed gros point needlework, on later turned feet, 25in (63.5cm).
£2,000-2,500 *C*

pair of walnut long stools, with se nailed upholstered top, on aluster supports joined by a ulded stretcher, basically early thC, 78½in (199cm).
,200-1,500 *CSK*

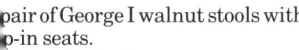

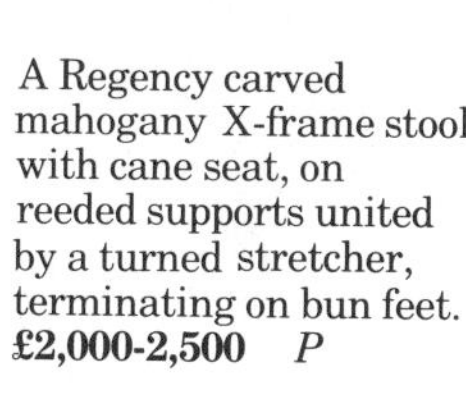

A Regency carved mahogany X-frame stool with cane seat, on reeded supports united by a turned stretcher, terminating on bun feet.
£2,000-2,500 *P*

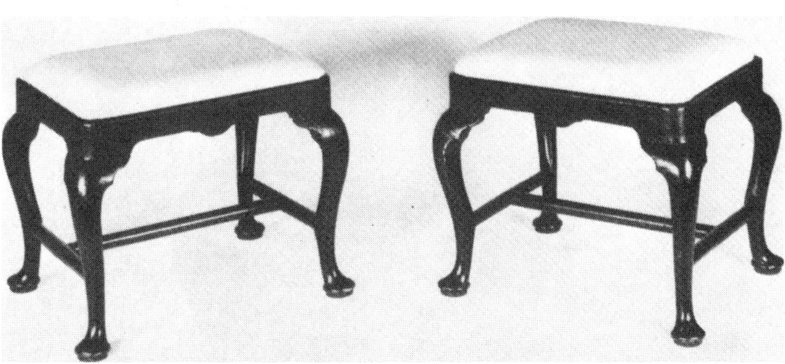

pair of George I walnut stools with p-in seats.
,000-9,000 *P*

A Regency rosewood X-frame stool, with padded blue velvet seat, the seat rail strengthened, 21½in (54.5cm).
£700-1,000 *C*

A Regency mahogany piano stool, with adjustable leather lined seat, on ribbed tapering legs joined by a concave sided stretcher, 14in (35.5cm) diam.
£600-800 *C*

A George II mahogany stool covered in yellow velvet, 24i (61cm).
£2,500-3,000 *C*

A pair of rosewood foot stools, 19thC.
£400-450 *RIP*

A Regency style low fender stool, covered in leopard skin on giltmet scrolling hoof feet, 42½in (106.5cm
£900-1,200 *C*

A carved mahogany stool, mid-19thC, 24in (61cm) high.
£700-750 *RIP*

An early Victorian parcel gilt and cream painted stool, the seat with needlework vine leaves, on cabriole legs headed by flowerheads, with scrolled feet, stamped 4 times Saunders & Woolley, 20½in (52cm).
£400-500 *C*

A Victorian walnut stool, upholstered in cut velvet, above a projecting scroll moulded rail, on cabriole legs, scroll feet and casters, 62½in (158cm).
£500-600 *CSK*

A walnut music stool, c1860, 24in (61cm) high.
£500-550 *RIP*

A Victorian rosewood stool, with loose needlework seat, 18in (46cm square.
£250-300 *WIL*

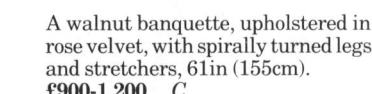

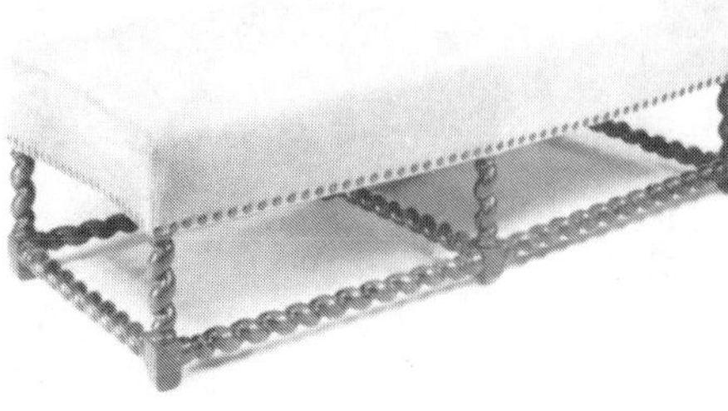
A walnut banquette, upholstered in rose velvet, with spirally turned legs and stretchers, 61in (155cm).
£900-1,200 *C*

. walnut stool with padded drop-in ›eat, 26½in (67cm).
1,500-2,000 *C*

A walnut stool, covered in floral needlework, on turned baluster legs joined by turned stretchers, on scrolled feet, 18in (46cm).
£2,000-3,000 *C*

Tables – Architects

A George I burr walnut architect's table, with moulded hinged crossbanded easel top, inlaid with chevron pattern banding and with pop-up book rest and swivelling brass candlestands, early 18thC, 34in (86cm).
£3,500-4,500 *CNY*

. George II mahogany architect's able, the top with re-entrant orners, and a pop-up book rest, bove a frieze fitted with a baize ned writing slide and ompartments, mid-18thC, 36in 91.5cm).
2,500-3,500 *CNY*

A Georgian mahogany architect's table, on twin supports with splayed legs with brass feet and casters, and adjustable rising top, 40in (101.5cm).
£350-450 *JD*

A Regency mahogany architect's table, with elevating superstructure and adjustable leather lined slope top, containing 2 ebony strung frieze drawers, 45in (114cm).
£4,500-5,000 *P*

.n early George III mahogany rchitect's table, the top ratcheted nd fitted with a sprung ledge above sliding drawer, fitted with a lined riting surface, 35in (89cm).
3,000-4,000 *CSK*

A mid-Georgian mahogany architect's table, with twin flap top and central easel supported slope, the sides with 2 slides and inkwell drawer, on square chamfered legs, 42in (106.5cm) open.
£1,500-2,000 *C*

. William IV mahogany architect's able, the double hinged top nclosing fitted and lidded ompartment, with hinged, atcheted tooled leather lined slope, earing a label 'Purchased at the Iamilton Palace Sale 1919', 38in 96cm).
'2,500-3,000 *P*

Make the most of Miller's

When a large specialist well-publicised collection comes on the market, it tends to increase prices. Immediately after this, prices can fall slightly due to the main buyers having large stocks and the market being 'flooded'. This is usually temporary and does not affect very high quality items

A George III mahogany architect's table, with a spring operated reading rest, on split front legs with quadrant column mouldings, lacking candle arms, 35½in (90cm).
£3,500-4,000 *Bea*

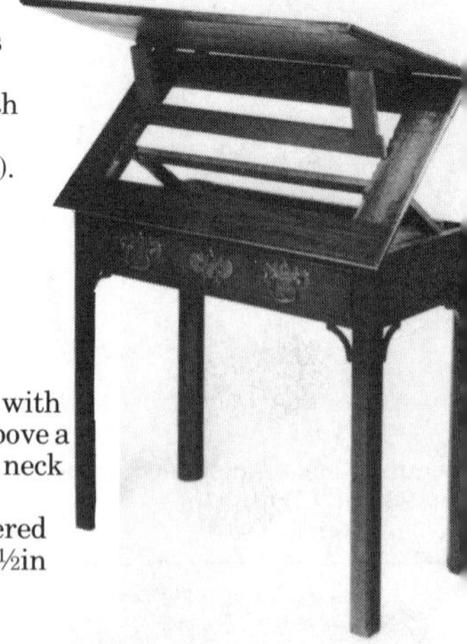

A mahogany architect's table, with double hinged ratcheted top, above a frieze drawer with brass swan neck handles and pierced brass escutcheons, on square chamfered legs with C-scroll brackets, 34½in (87cm).
£2,000-2,500 *CSK*

Tables – Breakfast

A George III mahogany breakfast table, with twin flap rounded top, frieze drawer, on baluster shaft and ribbed splayed legs, with brass paw feet, 43in (109cm).
£1,000-1,500 *C*

A George III mahogany breakfast table, with crossbanded top, on rin turned spreading shaft and shapec moulded tapering quadripartite base, with gilt metal claw feet, re-supported, 52in (132cm).
£2,000-2,500 *C*

A Regency mahogany breakfast table with tilt-top, on turned baluster shaft and downswept quadripartite base, with foliate brass caps and casters, 60in (152cm).
£2,000-2,500 *C*

A Regency mahogany breakfast table, with tip-up top and baluster shaft, moulded splayed quadripartite base and brass claw feet, 53in (134.5cm).
£2,500-3,000 *C*

A Regency mahogany breakfast table, the snap top crossbanded in rosewood, on a turned column and quadruped base, terminating in brass cappings and casters, 52in (133cm).
£1,600-2,000 *P*

◀
A Regency mahogany breakfast table, the tip-up top crossbanded ir rosewood with brass inlay, 65in (165cm).
£3,000-4,000 *C*

A Regency rosewood pedestal breakfast table, inlaid with satinwood bands and boxwood lines, with brass paw terminals, 52½in (133cm).
£5,000-6,000 *CSK*

A Regency rosewood and gilt metal mounted breakfast table, the snap top with a cut brass crossbanded border, on gilt paw feet and casters, 50in (127cm) diam.
£8,500-9,500 *P*

A Regency mahogany breakfast table, the tip-up top with ribbed border on a ring turned pedestal and quadripartite ribbed splayed legs with brass feet, 48in (122cm).
£1,200-1,800 *C*

A Regency mahogany breakfast table, with tip-up top, on a square pedestal inlaid with ebonised lines and 4 splayed legs with paw feet, restorations, 53½in (135cm).
£1,500-2,000 *C*

 Regency mahogany boxwood
trung and crossbanded breakfast
able, the snap top with beaded
rieze, 51½in (130cm).
4,500-5,500 *P*

A Regency rosewood breakfast table, the top with brass stringing, on a rosewood grained column with an overlapping leaf carved collar and concave triform plinth raised on anthemion carved feet, 48in (122cm) diam.
£3,500-4,000 *Bon*

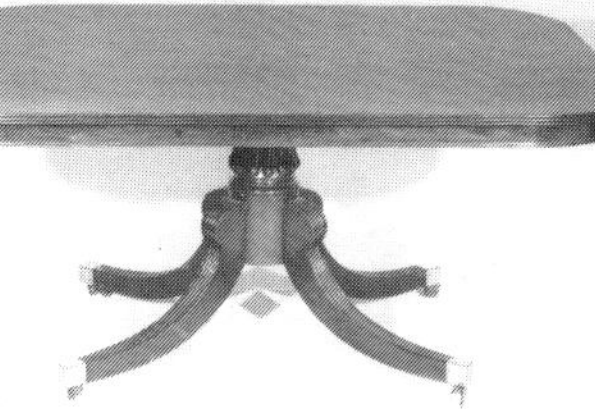

A Regency mahogany tip-up breakfast table, the top made from a single piece of figured mahogany, raised on gadrooned column and 4 reeded sabre legs with brass terminals, 63in (160cm).
£4,000-5,000 *DN*

 late Regency mahogany breakfast
able, the tilt top with bead moulded
dge, on a square pedestal support,
3in (134.5cm).
2,000-2,500 *CSK*

A George IV mahogany breakfast table, the crossbanded and flamed tilt top on a faceted tapering column and triform base with acanthus carved scroll feet, 51in (129.5cm).
£1,500-2,000 *CSK*

A mid-Victorian burr walnut breakfast table, the quarter veneered inlaid marquetry tilt top with carved gadrooned borders, on fluted and beaded quadruple column supports, labelled Hewetson & Milner, Manufacturers, The Exchange, 211-213 Tottenham Court Road, London, 60in (152cm).
£2,500-3,000 *CSK*

 William IV rosewood pedestal
reakfast table, 54½in (138cm).
1,000-1,500 *CSK*

 Victorian walnut and
arquetry breakfast
ble, with inlaid top,
7in (144cm) diam.
2,500-3,000 *Bon*

A Victorian figured walnut breakfast table, the tilt top inlaid with chequered boxwood lines in rosewood banded borders, 58in (147cm).
£1,600-2,000 *CSK*

An early Victorian rosewood breakfast table, 57in (144.5cm).
£1,500-2,000 *CSK*

A George I red walnut card table, with enclosed guinea wells and candlestands, 33in (84cm).
£2,000-2,500 *Bon*

A mahogany breakfast table, with crossbanded top and ring turned columnar shaft, with quadripartite base and brass feet, 58in (147cm) diam.
£1,000-1,500 *C*

A George II carved mahogany card table, 34in (87cm).
£5,000-6,000 *P*

Tables – Card

A William and Mary scarlet japanned and gilt chinoiserie decorated half round card table, on later supports, 30in (76cm).
£500-1,000 *P*

A George II carved mahogany card table, on cabriole front legs headed with acanthus ornament and terminating in claw-and-ball feet, 34in (87cm).
£3,000-3,500 *P*

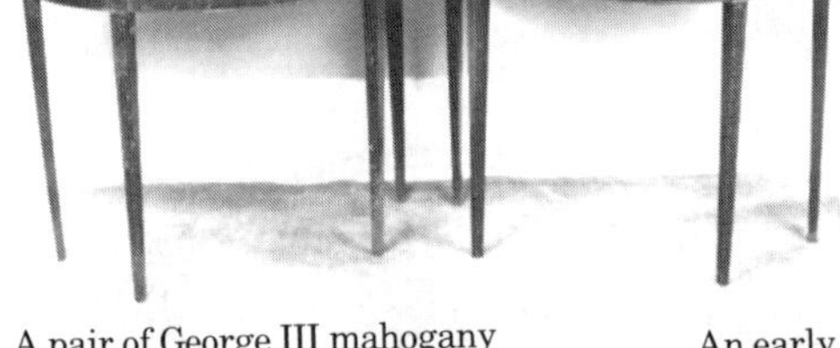

A pair of George III mahogany demi-lune card or tea tables, with fold-over tops and inlaid ruling, on square tapering supports, 36in (91cm).
£4,000-5,000 *P[Pea]*

An early George III mahogany card table, on blind fret carved square chamfered legs headed by fretwork brackets, 36in (91cm).
£1,200-1,800 *Bon*

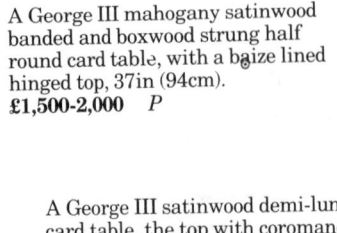

A George III mahogany satinwood banded and boxwood strung half round card table, with a baize lined hinged top, 37in (94cm).
£1,500-2,000 *P*

A George III mahogany serpentine card table, with later egg-and-dart carved edge, 36in (91cm).
£1,000-1,200 *Bon*

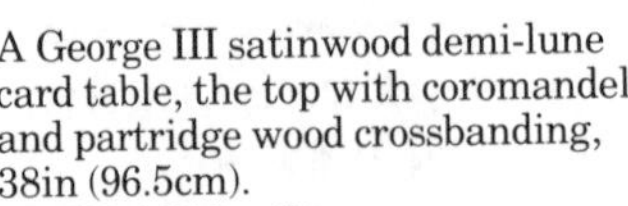

A George III satinwood demi-lune card table, the top with coromandel and partridge wood crossbanding, 38in (96.5cm).
£3,500-4,000 *Bea*

A George III mahogany, inlaid and crossbanded D-shaped card table, with fold-over top, square tapered legs and spade feet, 36in (91cm).
£1,000-1,500 *DSH*

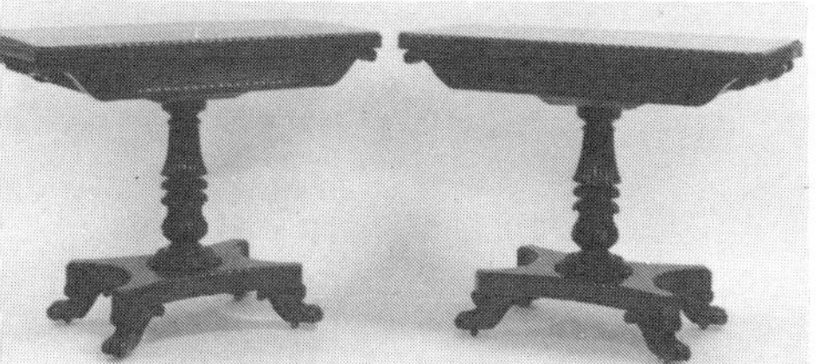

. pair of late Regency rosewood
ılding card tables, with bead and
eel carving to border, 36in (91cm).
2,000-2,500 *HCH*

pair of William IV rosewood card
ıbles, with baize lined D-end tops,
ı foliate knopped columns and
ıatrefoil platform bases, on reeded
ın feet.
2,500-3,500 *P*

A Regency mahogany fold-over card table, the top banded with rosewood, the frieze inlaid with a marquetry panel, with brass lion paw casters, 36in (91cm).
£1,000-1,500 *TM*

A Regency rosewood card table, the crossbanded top inlaid in cut brass, with brass paw caps and casters, 36in (91cm).
£2,000-2,500 *Bea*

A William IV rosewood swivel fold-over D-end card table, with green baize lining, on original brass casters, 36in (91cm).
£500-550 *GH*

. pair of William IV rosewood card
ıbles, with square section columns,
eneers distressed, 36½in (92cm).
800-900 *Bon*

A pair of William IV rosewood card tables, 36½in (92cm).
£5,500-6,500 *P*

A pair of Adam style D-shaped tables, comprising a side table and fold-over card table, 19thC, 36in (91cm).
£5,000-6,000 *DSH*

A satinwood, rosewood and harewood crossbanded and inlaid half-round card table, with brass cappings and casters, early 19thC, 44in (112cm).
£4,500-5,500 *P*

mahogany card table with carved
edestal and platform base with
roll feet, 19thC.
500-600 *MGM*

. rosewood folding card table, on
ırved pedestal with petal base and
paw feet, 19thC.
600-700 *MGM*

An early Victorian burr walnut fold-over swivel card table with green baize lining, on original brass casters, 39in (99cm).
£650-700 *GH*

A Victorian burr walnut fold-over card table, the shaped top decorated with satinwood foliate inlay, with ceramic casters, 39in (99cm).
£1,500-2,000 *BWe*

A Victorian rosewood card table, with a serpentine sided fold-over top, 36in (91cm).
£700-900 *Bea*

A Victorian burr walnut card table, the hinged demi-lune top above a plain frieze, on a turned and fluted column, with an overlapping leaf carved collar, 36½in (92cm).
£800-1,000 *Bon*

An Edwardian envelope top card table.
£650-700 *P[CW]*

A Louis XV style ebonised and boulle card table, applied throughout with gilt brass mouldings and inlaid in red tortoiseshell and cut brass, 36½in (92cm).
£750-1,000 *Bea*

A Victorian burr walnut serpent fronted card table, with a hinged swivel top and plain frieze, on a carved bulbous column with 4 sp legs, 26in (66cm).
£1,200-1,500 *AG*

A burr walnut card table, the figured top with outset corners, above a plain frieze, on cabriole le with pad feet, 30in (76cm).
£1,000-1,300 *Bon*

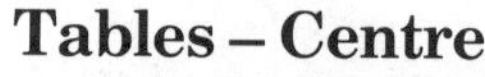

Tables – Centre

A George IV rosewood centre table, with baluster shaft, on scrolled tripartite base, 51in (129cm).
£2,500-3,500 *C*

A George I walnut centre table, 35in (89cm).
£3,000-4,000 *C*

A pair of Regency ebonised centre tables, the brass edged tops inlaid premier partie and contre partie in cut brass and white metal with strapwork and scrolling foliage, 35in (88cm).
£3,000-4,000 *Bea*

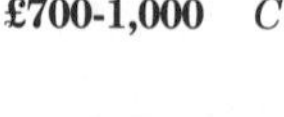

A Regency mahogany centre table with baluster shaft and arched moulded quadripartite base, 42in (106cm).
£700-1,000 *C*

A late Regency rosewood centre table, the leather inset top with gadrooned border, 44in (111cm).
£1,500-2,000 *CW*

A late Victorian satinwood two-tier centre table, with a removable two-handled glass tray to the top and on square legs, with splayed feet joined by a curved X-stretcher, 35in (89cm).
£3,000-3,500 *Bea*

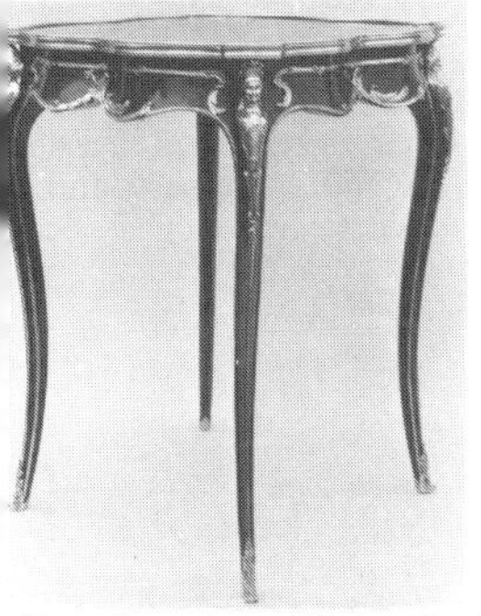

A French centre table, profusely decorated with giltmetal mounts and figure heads, on cabriole legs.
£600-700 *MGM*

An Italian slate and marble inlaid top on carved and parcel gilt base, the oval inset top inlaid with Pliny's doves in various coloured marbles and hardstones, including lapis lazuli and malachite, within a lunette carved border, on baluster column and quadruped scroll supports, with acanthus leaves and birds, 19thC, 40½in (103cm).
£3,500-4,000 *P*

A mahogany centre table, with marble top, 19thC, 36in (91cm).
£7,000-8,000 *P*

A Victorian ebonised marquetry and ormolu mounted centre table, the snap top with ebony ground, 54in (138cm) diam.
£5,000-6,000 *P*

A walnut centre table, 25½in (65cm).
£1,500-2,000 *C*

A Flemish ebony and marquetry centre table, the top inlaid in various woods with green stained ivory highlights, the spandrels and frieze drawers similarly inlaid, on spiral turned legs joined by a double Y-stretcher, 43in (109cm).
£3,000-4,000 *Bon*

A Victorian walnut centre table on carved and turned stretcher supports.
£800-900 *BM*

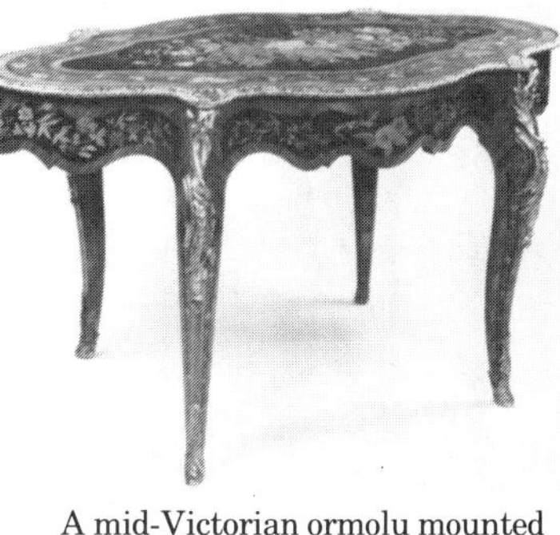

A mid-Victorian ormolu mounted marquetry inlaid centre table, 58in (147cm).
£3,000-4,000 *C*

A mahogany centre table, with specimen marble top and ring-turned shaft, flanked by C-scroll supports with concave sided tripartite base and ebonised bun feet, 19½in (49.5cm).
£1,200-1,600 *C*

A Dutch mahogany and ebony centre table, the crossbanded top with a quartered panel centred by a shell, on square tapering legs headed by rosettes, on ball feet, 36in (91cm).
£1,200-1,600 *C*

Tables – Console

A Victorian burr walnut centre table, with serpentine edge, on carved cabriole legs with turned stretcher.
£1,000-1,200 *MGM*

A giltwood console table, the marble top above a beaded, gadrooned and key patterned banded frieze, on carved eagle support, on a rocky plinth base, part 18thC, 38in (96.5cm).
£3,000-4,000 *CSK*

A giltwood demi-lune console table, with neo-classical ornament, late 18thC, with later decorated top, 18in (48cm).
£600-700 *P*

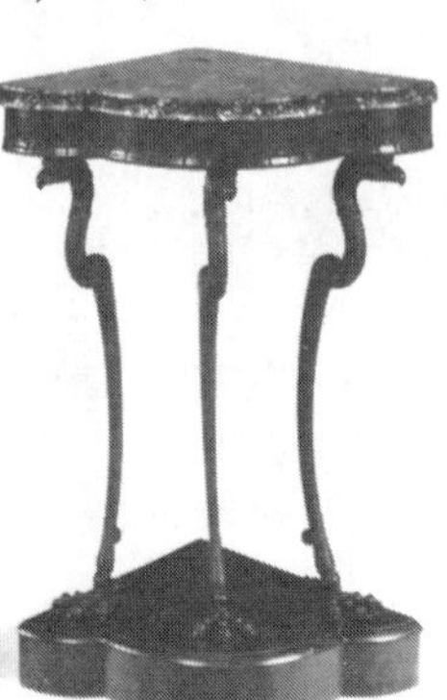

A pair of William IV mahogany and bronze corner console tables, with moulded mottled green scagliola tops, 28in (71cm).
£3,000-4,000 *C*

A Regency parcel gilt and rosewood console table, with white marble top and frieze carved with egg-and-dart, on scrolling foliate supports and paw feet, with mirrored back, 48in (124cm).
£2,000-3,000 *C*

A Swedish parcel gilt and blue painted console table, with white marble top, on simulated grey marble plinth base, 31in (78cm).
£4,000-5,000 *C*

A Regency parcel gilt and ebonised console table, with mottled black marble top and divided mirrored back, with plinth base and bun feet, 39in (99cm).
£3,000-4,000 *C*

A carved silvered wood baroque console table, with a serpentine pink marble top, on 4 bold carved cabriole legs, with S-scroll stretchers, 55in (140cm).
£2,500-3,000 *TM*

A Continental gilt gesso console table, the serpentine shaped marble top on rococo style base, 19thC, 54in (137cm).
£250-350 *LRG*

A Venetian giltwood console table, with moulded serpentine breccia marble top, restorations, mid-18thC, 43½in (111cm).
£4,000-5,000 *C*

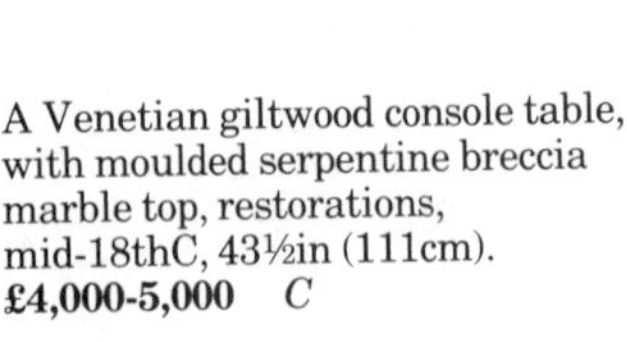

A French giltwood and gesso console table, 19thC, 52in (132cm).
£1,000-1,300 *P[Re]*

'ables – Dining

Georgian mahogany snap-top
ning table, bordered with a broad
tinwood band, 62in (158cm).
,000-7,000 *P[Pea]*

A George II mahogany drop-leaf dining table, with elliptical leaves, on cabriole legs, carved with scallop shells and husks and claw-and-ball feet, 49in (125cm).
£1,500-2,000 *Bon*

A Chippendale mahogany drop-leaf dining table, mid-18thC, 63in (160cm) long extended.
£1,600-2,000 *WW*

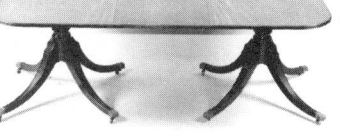

A George III style mahogany twin pedestal dining table, the top on plain turned columns and moulded outswept legs with brass casters, including one leaf, 91in (231cm) long.
£2,500-3,000 *Bon*

George III mahogany two-pillar
ning table, with thumb moulded
lge, 66in (168cm) long including
ngle extra leaf.
1,800-2,000 *HCH*

A Regency style mahogany twin-pillar dining table, on reeded quadruple supports, with brass claw feet and casters, 77in (195.5cm) extended, including one extra leaf.
£2,000-2,500 *JD*

Regency mahogany patent
xtending dining table, with
-shaped folding top, dividing to
eveal a telescopic action, inset with
brass plaque engraved 'Titter &
o.,/Inventors and Manufacturers
o.32/Pottergate St. Norwich',
ncluding 3 extra leaves, 111in
83cm) extended.
6,000-7,000 *P*

A Regency mahogany dining table, with Cumberland action, on turned supports and splayed legs with paw feet, 103½in (263cm).
£15,000-17,000 *C*

A mahogany triple pillar extending dining table, on quadruple supports with casters, early 19thC, 98in (248cm).
£4,500-5,000 *JD*

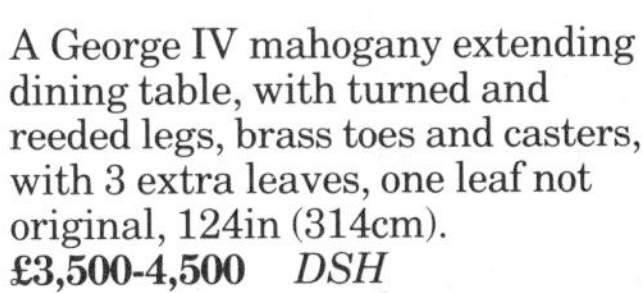

A George IV mahogany extending dining table, with turned and reeded legs, brass toes and casters, with 3 extra leaves, one leaf not original, 124in (314cm).
£3,500-4,500 *DSH*

A George IV dining table.
£3,500-4,000 *SWO*

George IV mahogany extending
ining table, on 8 ring turned
upports with brass casters, with
extra leaves, 92in (233cm)
xtended.
1,500-2,000 *P[Pea]*

A mahogany dining table, on waisted, faceted ribbed support, with finialled cruciform platform base, on casters, early 19thC, 53in (134.5cm).
£1,500-2,000 *CSK*

A George IV mahogany extending dining table, with twin flap top, on spiral twist legs, brass caps and casters, including 2 extra leaves, 80in (203cm) extended.
£1,500-2,000 *CSK*

A three-part mahogany D-end dining table, the centre section wit drop leaves, on 12 reeded turned tapering legs, early 19thC, 89in (226cm) extended.
£2,500-3,000 *CSK*

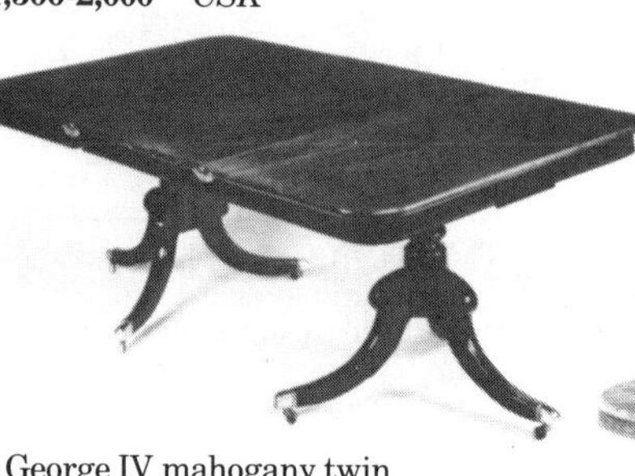

A George IV mahogany twin pedestal D-end dining table, on turned columns and hipped splayed legs, terminating in brass cappings and casters, including one extra leaf, 74in (189cm) extended.
£5,000-6,000 *P*

A Victorian mahogany dining table, on 5 reeded turned tapering legs, including 4 extra leaves, 142in (360cm) extended.
£2,000-2,500 *CSK*

A Victorian walnut pedestal dining table, with quarter veneered tilt-top, 54in (137cm).
£1,000-1,200 *CSK*

A Victorian walnut floral marquetry tilt-top dining table with carved pedestal and tripo base.
£3,500-4,000 *MGM*

Tables – Display

A Regency mahogany vitrine table, with moulded top and sides filled with glass panels, the front with a door, inlaid with ebonised lines, on square tapering legs, 20½in (52cm).
£3,500-4,500 *C*

A rosewood display table, inlaid with satinwood, 29in (73cm) high.
£800-1,000 *RIP*

A Louis XV style rosewood and brass mounted vitrine table, on cabriole supports and cast brass sabots joined by a mirrored undertier, 36in (91cm).
£1,500-2,500 *CEd*

Tables – Dressing

A George III satinwood kneehole dressing table, with crossbanded top, on tapering legs with brass casters, 40in (101.5cm).
£4,000-5,000 *Bea*

A George III mahogany dressing table, with folding top enclosing a divided and lidded interior, previously with a mirror, 22in (56cm).
£800-1,000 *C*

A rosewood bijouterie table, with ormolu mounts, on cabriole legs, late 19thC, 24in (60cm).
£700-800 *LRG*

A George III mahogany and inlaid gentleman's enclosed dressing table, stamped Gillows, Lancaster, inlaid with boxwood and ebony lines, 31in (79cm).
£3,000-3,500 *P*

A Danish satinwood and rosewood dressing table, the crossbanded top enclosing a fitted interior, including a mirror, with square tapering legs, late 18thC, 27½in (70cm).
£2,500-3,000 *C*

Tables – Drum

A Regency mahogany revolving pedestal drum table, with inset leather lined top, on down curving legs with brass block terminals, 38in (96cm).
£2,200-2,600 *CSK*

An inlaid mahogany kneehole dressing table, with reeded lift-up top enclosing fitted interior, with boxwood stringing and brass knob handles, on turned stump supports, 19thC, 49in (124.5cm).
£700-900 *HCH*

An Empire mahogany dressing table, with hinged lid enclosing a mirrored and divided interior, 21½in (54.5cm).
£500-700 *C*

A Regency rosewood drum table, with egg-and-dart carving, on a pillar and tripod base, 30in (76cm) high.
£2,600-3,000 *SBA*

A William IV mahogany drum table, with green leather inset top, above 4 true and 4 false frieze drawers, on turned lobed legs, 59½in (151cm).
£1,000-1,500 *Bon*

A Victorian burr-walnut Duchesse dressing table, with concave platform base, 54in (137cm).
£700-900 *CSK*

Tables – Dropleaf

A George II mahogany drop-leaf dining table, on plain cabriole legs, with pointed pad feet, 46in (116.5cm).
£700-1,000 *Bon*

A George II mahogany drop-leaf dining table, on turned tapering legs with pad feet, 72in (182cm) open.
£5,000-6,000 *GC*

A mahogany drum table, with inset gilt tooled leather top, on turned pillar and tripod base, with brass terminals and casters, 19thC, 52in (132cm).
£2,500-3,000 *HOD*

Tables – Games

A Regency style rosewood and satinwood banded sofa games table, fitted with a dummy and a frieze drawer, on standard and dual splayed end supports, terminating in brass capping and casters, 45in (115cm) extended.
£2,500-3,000 *P*

A Regency mahogany games table, with baize lined twin flap top, on ring turned tapering legs, 35in (89cm) open.
£600-800 *C*

A Regency mahogany games table, the top with a sliding centre section, inlaid to the reverse with a chessboard and enclosing a backgammon board, 35in (89cm).
£1,700-2,200 *CSK*

A giltwood and composition games table, with square pietra dura top inlaid with chess squares, mid-19thC, 21in (53cm).
£1,500-2,000 *C*

A Victorian rosewood games table, the top inlaid with chessboard, flanked by cribbage scorers, 20in (51cm).
£400-600 *DN*

A Victorian rosewood games table, on a barley twist column, and hipped cabriole legs with scrolled feet, 20in (51cm).
£350-450 *Bon*

A Regency black and white penwork games table, with concave sided platform base and bun feet, 16in (40.5cm).
£2,000-2,500 *C*

A Victorian burr walnut and marquetry games/work table, the shaped folding swivel top inlaid and banded in amboyna, fitted with one drawer and a sliding bag, on end supports with splayed feet, 26½in (67cm).
£900-1,200 *DN*

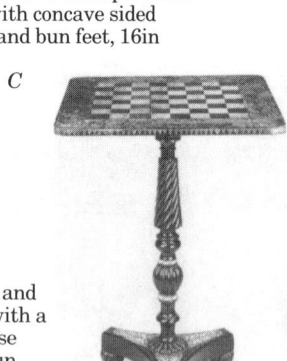

An Anglo-Indian ebony, ivory and penwork games table, inlaid with a chess board, the triangular base inlaid with ivory, on reeded bun feet, adapted, 21in (53cm).
£2,000-2,500 *C*

Tables – Gateleg

A gateleg table, on chamfered legs, joined by curvilinear stretchers, 36½in (92cm).
£500-600 *Bea*

A George II mahogany gateleg table, on slightly splayed turned legs with pad feet, 57in (145cm) diam.
£2,000-2,500 *Bon*

Tables – Library

A Regency mahogany library table, on an ebonised spirally fluted baluster pedestal, with paw feet, redecorated and possibly associated, 46½in (118cm).
£2,000-2,500 *C*

A William IV rosewood and brass inlaid library table, 55in (140cm).
£4,500-5,000 *P*

A Regency mahogany library table, with a tooled leather lined hinged ratcheted slope, on ebony banded dual splayed supports, 36in (91cm).
£3,500-4,000 *P*

A Victorian mahogany table, on 4 reeded and shaped legs, with 2 short and one through drawer, with leather-lined writing surface, 54in (137cm).
£800-1,200 *LRG*

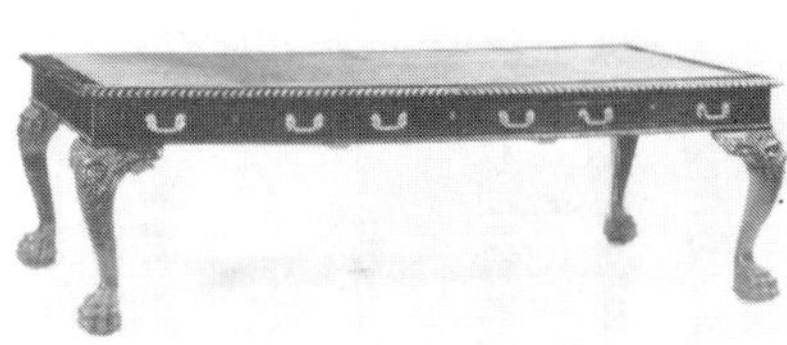

A mahogany library table, the leather lined top with a gadrooned edge, above 3 frieze drawers on each side, on cabriole legs with lions' masks with hairy paw feet, 97in (246cm).
£3,000-3,500 *CSK*

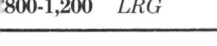

An early Victorian mahogany library table, 54in (137cm).
£800-1,200 *C*

Tables – Loo

A walnut loo table, c1820, 54in (137cm) diam.
£5,500-6,500 *Ba*

A Victorian walnut loo table, 47in (119cm).
£1,600-2,000 *JeM*

A Victorian marquetry inlaid loo table, supported on carved base.
£7,000-8,000 *MGM*

Nests of Tables

A set of Regency rosewood quartetto tables, with cockbeaded mouldings, the larger 22in (56cm).
£2,500-3,000 *P*

A set of 4 mahogany quartetto tables.
£900-1,000 *Wor*

Tables – Occasional

A George III satinwood occasional table, with hinged top, on square tapering legs, 21in (53cm).
£600-700 *C*

A walnut jardinière with burr walnut top, within kingwood crossbanding and gilt bronze gallery, on ormolu mounted supports, mid-19thC.
£1,000-1,500 *SWO*

A French rosewood and ormolu three-fold occasional table, 19thC.
£500-600 *SAg*

A pair of French style satinwood ormolu mounted tables, by Donald Ross of Denmark Hill, c1870, 16in (40.5cm).
£4,000-5,000 *GSP*

Tables – Pedestal

A rosewood pedestal table, the breccia specimen marble top on a faceted column and scrolling down curved legs applied with paterae, early 19thC, 25½in (64.5cm).
£1,500-2,000 *CSK*

A mahogany pedestal table, the circular moulded tilt-top mounted on a revolving bird cage and reeded tapering column, the down curving legs with claw-and-ball feet and carved acanthus leaf headings, part 18thC, 30in (76cm).
£1,200-1,500 *CSK*

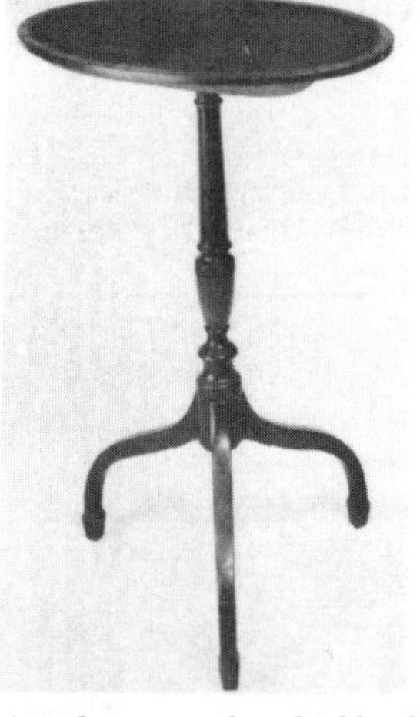

A mahogany pedestal table, the tilt-top inlaid with boxwood lines, with satinwood banded borders, basically late 18thC, 21½in (54.5cm).
£400-600 *CSK*

An Anglo Ceylonese ebony pedestal peacock table, with segmented panels of various woods in ivory chevron and white metal borders, 19thC, 58½in (148.5cm).
£10,000-12,000 *CSK*

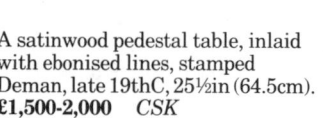

A satinwood pedestal table, inlaid with ebonised lines, stamped Deman, late 19thC, 25½in (64.5cm).
£1,500-2,000 *CSK*

Make the most of Miller's

When a large specialist well-publicised collection comes on the market, it tends to increase prices. Immediately after this, prices can fall slightly due to the main buyers having large stocks and the market being 'flooded'. This is usually temporary and does not affect very high quality items

Tables – Pembroke

A Georgian mahogany Pembroke table, with a drawer at each end, on ring turned tapering legs with brass cappings and casters, 42in (106.5cm).
£600-800 *LRG*

A George III mahogany Pembroke table, stamped Gillows of Lancaster, the top banded with amaranth and boxwood, 23in (58cm) open.
£2,500-3,000 *C*

A George III crossbanded Pembroke table, on 4 tapering legs and casters, with end drawer.
£400-600 *LRG*

A George III mahogany Pembroke table, with crossbanded serpentine twin flap top and one bowed frieze drawer, on square tapering legs, 38in (96.5cm) open.
£2,500-3,500 *C*

A George III mahogany and marquetry Pembroke table, crossbanded in rosewood, on square tapered legs, terminating in brass cappings and casters, 35in (90cm).
£3,000-4,000 *P*

A George III mahogany Pembroke table, the satinwood crossbanded top with ebony and boxwood stringing, on square tapered legs, brass cappings and leather casters, bearing a label George Simson No. 19, Smithside, St. Paul's Church Yard, 37½in (96cm).
£1,500-2,000 *P*

A Regency mahogany Pembroke table, the top above an ebony lined frieze drawer, on a turned baluster shaft and moulded splayed quadripartite support, ending in cast brass paw feet, 48in (122cm) open.
£800-1,000 *CEd*

PEMBROKE TABLES

- ★ became popular in the mid to late 18thC, possibly designed and ordered by Henry Herbert, the Earl of Pembroke (1693-1751)
- ★ on early examples the legs were square which are by far the most desirable
- ★ later tables had turned legs
- ★ the turned and reeded legs are much less popular
- ★ those with oval or serpentine tops more desirable
- ★ flaps should have three hinges
- ★ rounded flaps and marquetry again increase desirability
- ★ satinwood was greatly favoured, particularly with much crossbanding and inlay
- ★ many 18thC Pembroke tables have chamfering on the insides of the legs
- ★ the Edwardians made many fine Pembroke tables which have been known to appear wrongly catalogued at auction
- ★ Edwardian tables now in great demand

A Sheraton style Pembroke table with rosewood banded D-shaped flap top, on square tapering supports, 32in (81cm).
£1,500-2,000 *P[Pea]*

A Regency mahogany Pembroke table, inlaid with ebonised lines, the quadruple down-curving legs with brass paw feet, 33in (84cm).
£2,000-2,500 *CSK*

A William IV Pembroke table, with brass terminals.
£900-1,200 *DN*

Tables – Pier

A Regency parcel gilt and simulated rosewood pier table, with grey mottled marble top and later rosewood back, 29in (74cm).
£1,200-1,700 *C*

An Empire ormolu mounted mahogany pier table, with white marble top and a frieze drawer, on square tapering neo-classical monopodia and plinth base, 32in (81cm).
£4,000-5,000 *C*

Tables – Serving

A George III mahogany serving table, on stop fluted square tapered legs, headed by carved patera and terminating with spade feet, 66in (168cm).
£1,700-2,000 *Bon*

A George III mahogany serving table, with crossbanded serpentine top, on moulded tapering legs, 57in (145cm).
£3,500-4,000 *C*

A Regency plum pudding mahogany serving table, 96in (243cm).
£3,000-3,500 *Wor*

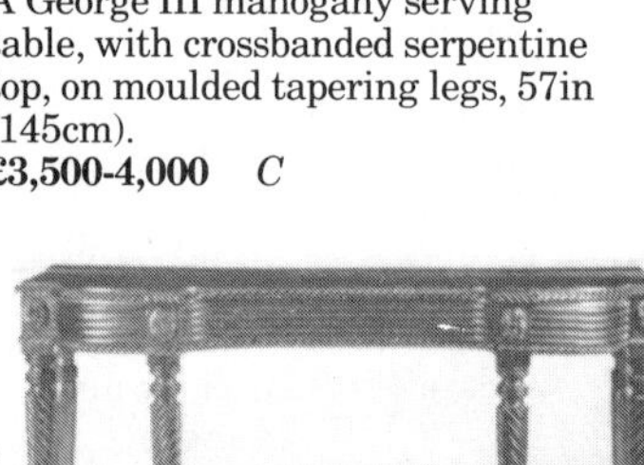

A late Regency mahogany serving side table, with rope carved borders and tapering legs, on paw feet with foliate paterae headings, adaptations, 75in (190cm).
£1,500-2,000 *CSK*

A George II mahogany side table with one drawer and original brass handles, on cabriole legs with pad feet, 40in (101cm).
£4,000-5,000 *DN*

Tables – Reading

A George III mahogany pedestal reading table, with 2 small oak lined drawers, on revolving pedesta and tripod supports, 24in (61cm).
£1,500-2,000 *P[WSW]*

A late Regency mahogany readin table, 22in (56cm).
£700-800 *Bon*

Tables – Side

A George II mahogany side tabl fitted with a frieze drawer, on turned tapered legs with pad fee 35½in (90cm).
£700-1,000 *P*

A Regency mahogany and fruitwoo side table, the top crossbanded in rosewood, with one frieze drawer, the pierced trestle ends filled with spindles, on splayed feet, 27in (68cm).
£1,700-2,000 *C*

A pair of George III style giltwood ide tables, with moulded white narble tops inset with conforming udding stone panels, 36in (91cm).
3,000-4,000 *CNY*

A mid-Georgian mahogany side table, the feet with later blocks, the legs possibly replaced, 29in (73.5cm).
£1,000-1,200 *C*

A George III mahogany side table, 39in (100cm).
£3,000-3,500 *P*

pair of William IV rosewood side bles, one as a card table, the other a tea table, 38in (97.5cm).
3,000-9,000 *HSS*

A satinwood side table, with a tray top and 2 frieze drawers, wood handles on lyre shaped end supports with a turned stretcher, 19thC, 48in (121cm).
£700-800 *DN*

A Regency mahogany side table, the top with brass Greek key pattern quarter gallery, the frieze with a Greek key pattern, with reeded edge, the corners applied with gilt brass lion masks, 58in (148cm).
£5,500-6,000 *HSS*

A pair of tortoiseshell D-shaped side ables, with crossbanded and fan nlaid tops and panelled friezes, on quare tapered legs with spade feet, 8in (97cm).
2,500-3,000 *P*

A French marquetry side table, in kingwood and various other woods, early 19thC, 29in (73.5cm) high.
£900-1,200 *RIP*

A pair of fruitwood side tables, with bun feet, basically early 19thC, 20½in (53cm).
£5,500-6,000 *C*

A Victorian inlaid burr walnut able, on twin turned supports, rnately carved splay feet with asters, 48in (121cm).
1,500-2,000 *JD*

A Dutch marquetry side table, the top with a pierced gallery, above a waved frieze drawer, on cabriole legs, inlaid with foliage and flowerheads, 36½in (92.5cm).
£2,000-2,500 *C*

A tortoiseshell, ebony and mahogany side table, the top and frieze inlaid with geometric strapwork, on square tapering legs, 36in (91cm).
£1,700-2,000 *C*

An Italian grey-painted side table, with moulded mottled yellow and pink marble slab, 39½in (100cm).
£3,000-3,500 *C*

Tables – Silver

A mahogany silver table, the rimmed top with a blind fret frieze, and chamfered square moulded legs with crenellated paw block feet, parts late 18thC, 30½in (77cm).
£8,000-10,000 *CSK*

Tables – Sofa

A Regency rosewood and brass inlaid sofa table, with stylised foliate and brass marquetry, with splayed legs terminating in brass cappings and casters, restored, 60in (153cm) extended.
£2,500-3,000 *P*

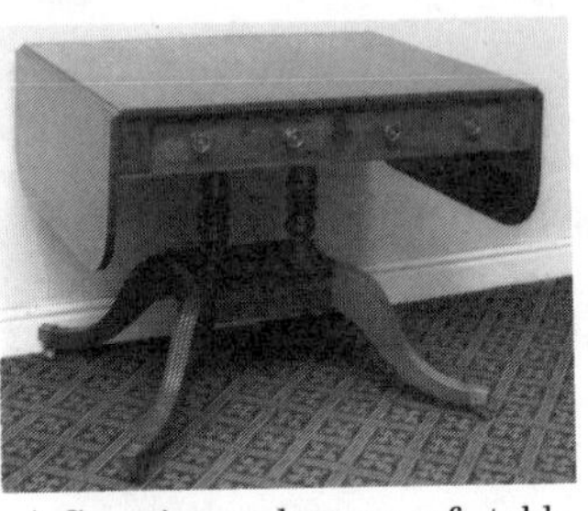

A Georgian mahogany sofa table, crossbanded in coromandel, 34in (86cm).
£1,500-2,000 *M*

A Regency mahogany and ebony inlaid sofa table, the rosewood and satinwood crossbanded hinged top with cut corners, 57in (145cm).
£2,500-3,000 *P*

SOFA TABLES

- ★ an elegant feminine writing table, usually with two shallow drawers
- ★ genuine ones are rarer than it might appear
- ★ either had two vertical supports or a central pillar
- ★ many fine examples made in mahogany with satinwood or rosewood stringing and crossbanding
- ★ rosewood examples can be of exceptional quality
- ★ examples with stretchers tend to be later
- ★ lyre end supports, particularly with a brass strip, are likely to increase value
- ★ many sofa tables have been made from old cheval mirrors
- ★ if the stretcher rail is turned and has a square block in the centre, it could be from a converted cheval mirror
- ★ many good sofa tables have been carved with Egyptian heads in the manner of Thomas Hope
- ★ long drawers are undesirable but many have been cut down

A Regency rosewood brass inlaid sofa table, with crossbanded top, 35in (89cm).
£2,200-2,600 *JD*

A Regency rosewood sofa and writing table, with a crossbanded and satinwood strung top, 61in (157cm).
£3,000-4,000 *P*

A Regency rosewood brass inlaid sofa table, with plate glass top, 34in (86cm).
£1,000-1,200 *P[WP]*

A Regency rosewood sofa table.
£2,000-2,500 *SWO*

A William IV rosewood sofa table, fitted with 2 short frieze drawers and 2 dummy drawers, on scrolled supports, 60in (152cm).
£950-1,200 *LRG*

A Regency rosewood sofa table, with crossbanded top, 58in (147cm).
£1,200-1,600 *C*

A Regency rosewood sofa table, crossbanded and with original ormolu decoration and feet, with brass line inlay to the top and drawer fronts, the drawers cockbeaded with satinwood.
£6,500-7,000 *OSA*

A mahogany sofa table, with hinged top, on square column, stepped concave supports terminating in brass cappings and casters, early 19thC, 37½in (96cm).
£3,500-4,500 *P*

A rosewood sofa table, the top crossbanded in satinwood with canted angles, on splayed legs terminating in brass paw cappings and casters, 19thC, 59in (150cm).
£5,000-6,000 *P*

A Charles X mahogany sofa table, on solid trestle ends, joined by a shaped stretcher and splayed feet, 61in (154cm) open.
£1,500-2,000 *C*

A Sheraton period mahogany sofa table, with 2 alternate boxwood line banded drawers and dummy drawers, with brass knob handles, 60in (152cm) open.
£3,000-3,500 *GC*

Tables – Supper

A mahogany supper table, with pad feet profusely carved with foliage, basically 18thC, 27½in (68.5cm).
£1,200-1,600 *CSK*

A Georgian mahogany supper table, with richly inlaid D-shape top, with end drawer, 37in (94cm).
£1,200-1,500 *P[Pea]*

A Georgian style carved mahogany supper table, the scalloped snap top with dished recesses, 27in (70cm).
£700-800 *P*

Tables – Tea

A George III mahogany concertina action serpentine tea table, c1760, 36in (91cm).
£4,000-4,500 *N*

A French mahogany tea table, the twin flap top with a bead moulded edge, on a spiral twist pedestal support, stamped J. Bosdet and Le Marquand, 19thC, 37in (97.5cm).
£1,500-2,000 *CSK*

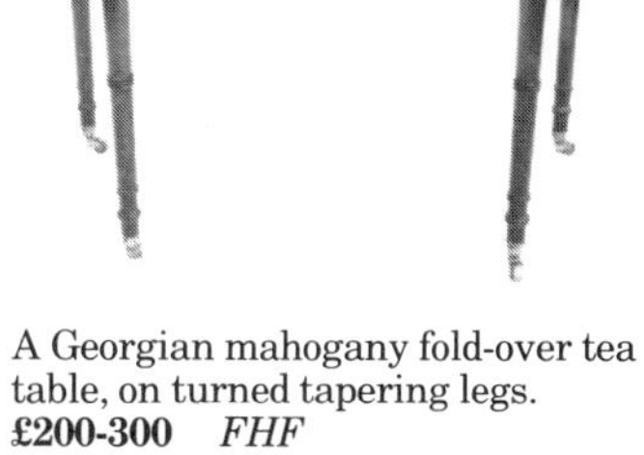

A Georgian mahogany fold-over tea table, on turned tapering legs.
£200-300 *FHF*

A Victorian oval tip-up table with ebonised and satinwood banding, and a chased brass mounted border, on ebonised and gilt base, 50½in (128cm).
£900-1,200 *DN*

Tables – Tripod

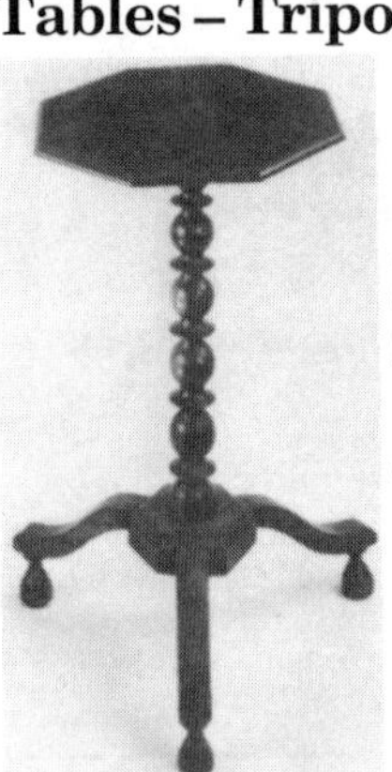

A yew wood table, on bobbin turned shaft, with hexagonal platform and splayed triple supports with baluster feet, late 17th/early 18thC, 16in (41cm).
£900-1,200 *P*

A George III mahogany tripod table, with moulded tip-up top, the arched legs carved with husks, on claw-and-ball feet, 29in (73.5cm).
£3,500-4,000 *C*

A mid-Georgian mahogany tripod table, the tilt top with scalloped edge, on columnar shaft, 34in (86.5cm).
£1,500-2,000 *C*

Tables – Toilet

A French marquetry enclosed toilet table, on fluted square tapering supports, 32in (80cm).
£400-500 *P[Pea]*

A yew wood and elm tripod table, c1760, 26in (66cm) high.
£1,000-1,500 *SBA*

An ebony tripod table, the top with a partly fluted pedestal, on a baluster support carved with foliage on a pounced ground, 18th/19thC, 24in (60.5cm).
£1,800-2,200 *CNY*

Tables – Tray

A George III mahogany butler's tray, with pierced three-quarter gallery, on later stand, with chamfered square legs and moulded stretchers, 33in (84cm).
£3,000-3,500 *C*

A George III mahogany tray, with inverted corners and pierced gallery, on a later mahogany stand with square channelled chamfered legs, joined by an H-shaped stretcher, 22½in (57cm).
£1,000-1,500 *C*

A George III mahogany tripod table c1760, adapted from a polescreen, 18in (45.5cm).
£2,500-3,000 *CNY*

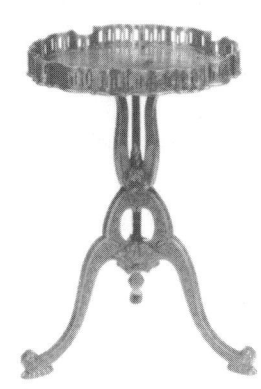

A Regency black and gilt japanned tripod table, 23in (58cm).
£1,500-2,000 *C*

A Regency rosewood tripod table, the top edged with boxwood, on spirally fluted baluster column and scrolling legs with giltmetal bun feet, 17in (43cm).
£2,000-2,500 *C*

A mahogany tripod table, with a serpentine arcaded gallery, 21in (53.5cm).
£5,000-6,000 *C*

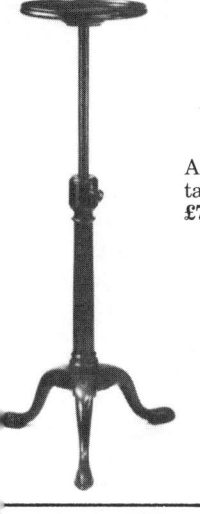

A mid-Georgian mahogany tripod table, 11½in (29cm).
£700-1,000 *C*

A Georgian mahogany tripod table, with pie crust rim, on carved legs with claw-and-ball feet.
£600-700 *MGM*

An Italian carved giltwood occasional table, with inset black marble top, 19thC, 24in (62cm).
£1,500-2,000 *P*

Tables – Wine/Lamp

A mahogany lamp table, inlaid with boxwood and ebonised lines, 20in (50.5cm).
£1,000-1,200 *C*

A mahogany wine table, with a reeded galleried edge and hinged ends, early 19thC, 63in (160cm).
£3,000-3,500 *P*

A mahogany lamp table with gallery, 25in (63.5cm) high.
£500-600 *RIP*

A late Regency mahogany demi-lune wine table, in the manner of Gillows, with brass curtain rail and moulded edge, on turned reeded legs, 81in (205cm).
£3,000-3,500 *CSK*

Tables – Work

A Regency inlaid rosewood work table, 16in (40cm).
£1,500-2,000 *P[WSW]*

A Georgian inlaid mahogany two drawer drop-leaf work table, 20in (50.5cm).
£800-1,000 *JD*

A bird's-eye maple work table, with parquetry top in various timbers, mother-of-pearl interior and accessories, stamped in the drawer by Tappell & Holland of London, c1820, 30in (76cm) high.
£3,500-4,000 *SBA*

A George III partridgewood and rosewood banded work table, with sliding panel back with yellow silk, 20in (50.5cm).
£2,000-2,500 *C*

A Regency rosewood pedestal workstand, of sarcophagus form, inlaid with marquetry in boxwood lined borders, with enclosed fitted upholstered interior, 17½in (44cm).
£900-1,200 *CSK*

A late George III thuya and rosewood crossbanded work table.
£6,500-7,500 *DN*

A late George III mahogany work table.
£3,500-4,500 *DN*

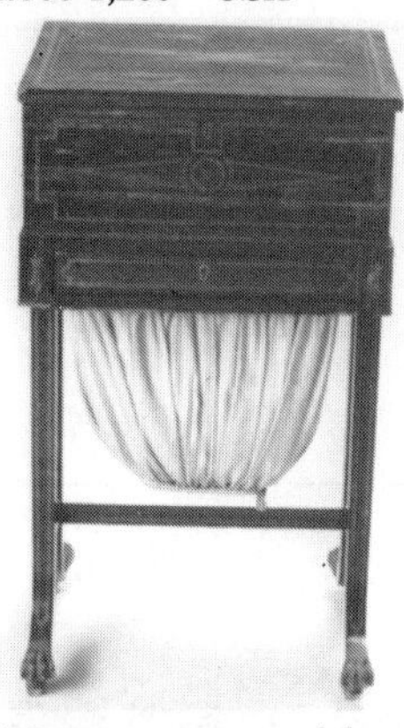

A Regency coromandel work table.
£2,000-3,000 *DWB*

A Regency rosewood work table, with easel top and frieze drawer, above a leather lined slide, formerly fitted with a work basket, 24½in (62cm).
£3,000-4,000 *C*

A William IV mahogany work table, 33½in (85cm).
£500-600 *DN*

A Regency rosewood work table, the top with gadrooned border, enclosing a baize lined interior, 17in (43cm).
£1,200-1,500 *C*

A Regency ladies rosewood writing/work table, with boxwood stringing, the corners and centre with harewood and satinwood shell inlays.
£1,200-1,500 *P[Wor]*

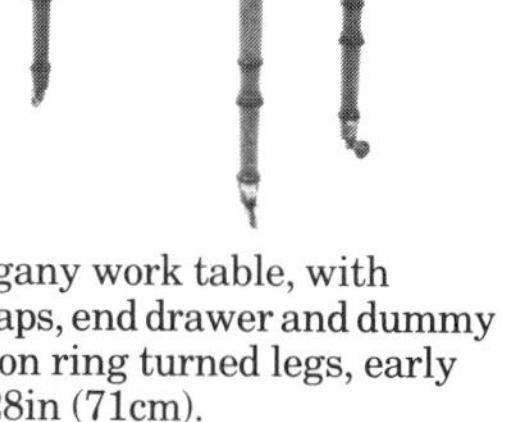

. mahogany work table, with drop flaps, end drawer and dummy rawer, on ring turned legs, early 9thC, 28in (71cm).
400-500 *LRG*

.n Empire mahogany work table, 0in (50cm).
600-900 *C*

'ables – Writing

tulipwood and marquetry table à rire, with a side drawer and ather lined slide, on slender ıbriole legs, 18thC, 18in (47cm).
,200-1,500 *P*

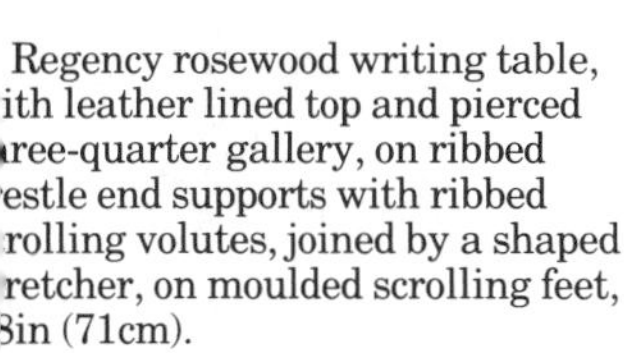

Regency rosewood writing table, ith leather lined top and pierced ıree-quarter gallery, on ribbed estle end supports with ribbed rolling volutes, joined by a shaped retcher, on moulded scrolling feet, 3in (71cm).
,000-3,000 *C*

A Victorian walnut work table, the burr wood veneered top inlaid with boxwood lines, enclosing a fitted interior, 25in (63.5cm).
£400-500 *Bea*

A Victorian rosewood sewing table, 17½in (49.5cm).
£1,500-2,000 *Ba*

A Regency carved rosewood writing table, the crossbanded top inset with a tooled green leather panel, 44in (112cm).
£4,000-5,000 *P*

A mid-Victorian parcel gilt, painted and sycamore work table, with fitted interior, on a tripod base, 19½in (49.5cm).
£1,000-1,500 *C*

A Victorian burr walnut veneered work table, with fret work interior, inlaid decoration, on carved cabriole legs.
£800-900 *MGM*

A Regency rosewood and brass mounted writing table, after a design by Gillows, with crossbanded top, 42in (108cm).
£12,000-15,000 *P*

A George IV rosewood writing table, on twin turned and lotus carved end column supports with oval plinths and gilt paw feet, joined by similarly turned and carved stretchers, 51in (129cm).
£1,200-1,500 *Bon*

A William IV mahogany writing table, with turned and reeded supports, 42in (106cm).
£4,500-5,500 *P[Pea]*

A ladies writing table in kingwood, banded and mounted in ormolu, 19thC, 36in (91cm).
£2,000-2,500 *RIP*

A Dutch ebonised and lacquer writing table, 34½in (87.5cm).
£3,000-3,500 *C*

An inlaid walnut, amboyna and ebonised writing desk, on turned fluted giltmetal mounted supports, and wavy stretcher rails, 19thC, 26½in (67cm).
£800-1,000 *P[Re]*

A French style floral marquetry inlaid ladies writing desk, on cabriole legs with giltmetal mounts.
£650-750 *MGM*

An Edwardian mahogany writing table, with satinwood banding, 29½in (75cm).
£500-600 *PL*

A French ladies writing table, with parquetry panels, giltmetal mounts and inset leather top.
£1,000-1,500 *MGM*

Teapoys

A burr ash teapoy with fitted interior, on a lobed pedestal with platform base and bun feet, 19thC.
£600-700 *MGM*

A Regency rosewood and brass inlaid teapoy, with brass carrying handles to side, on a lyre shaped column, quatrefoil platform and outswept supports, terminating in brass paw cappings and casters, 16½in (42cm).
£2,500-3,000 *P*

A William IV rosewood pedestal teapoy, the telescopic top enclosing a fitted interior, 17½in (44.5cm).
£600-700 *CSK*

An early Victorian rosewood teapoy c1840, 32in (81cm) high.
£900-1,200 *SD*

Dutch mahogany teestof, the
ver with urn finial enclosing a
rass liner, late 18thC, 11in (28cm)
am.
,000-1,200 *C*

Washstands

A George III black japanned corner washstand, variously gilt and decorated in colours, c1800, 51in (129cm) high.
£1,500-2,000 *CNY*

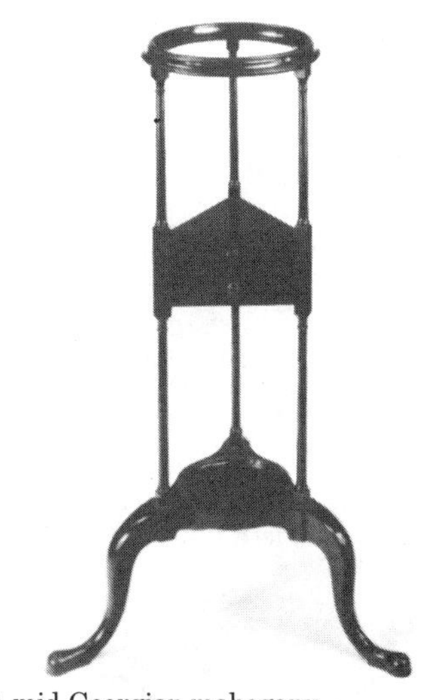

A mid-Georgian mahogany washstand, fitted with 2 drawers, the cabriole tripod base with dished centre, 31in (79cm) high.
£600-700 *C*

A late Georgian mahogany bowfront corner washstand, 25in (63.5cm).
£400-500 *LBP*

An inlaid mahogany washstand, stamped Edwards & Roberts, with satinwood crossbanding and boxwood and ebony stringing, 18½in (47cm).
£1,000-1,500 *Bea*

/hatnots

mahogany four-tier whatnot,
th frieze drawer, with casters.
,500-2,000 *JRB*

Victorian mahogany three-tier
hatnot, 36in (91cm) high.
200-250 *SAg*

A Victorian figured walnut whatnot, on scroll feet, 29in (74cm).
£400-500 *HCH*

A walnut three-tier whatnot, c1880, 24½in (62cm).
£2,000-2,500 *Ba*

Wine Coolers

A Georgian mahogany cellaret, on carved bun feet.
£1,800-2,200 *MGM*

A George III mahogany and brass bound wine cooler on stand.
£3,500-4,000 *P*

A George III mahogany and brass bound wine cooler on stand, with a hinged top and lions' masks handles to the sides, on square tapered legs with brass cappings and casters.
£1,800-2,200 *P*

A George III mahogany brass bound cellaret, the rising top inlaid with chequer bands, 15in (38cm).
£1,200-1,500 *GSP*

A Regency mahogany wine cooler, the framed panel sides each inset with flame veneer mahogany, on carved paw feet and casters, 15½in (38cm).
£800-900 *HCH*

A late Georgian mahogany decanter box, with lift-up top, fitted interior, above 2 short drawers with brass drop ring handles, on bracket feet, 21½in (54.5cm).
£1,000-1,500 *HCH*

A pair of Georgian mahogany wine coolers, the bodies strung with boxwood and lead lined, the domed lids with later finials, on spreading feet and square plinth bases, 27in (69cm) high.
£3,500-4,000 *P*

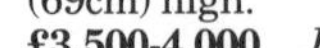

WINE COOLERS

- ★ cisterns for cooling wines were noted back in the 15thC and as objects of furniture became popular after about 1730. The cellaret is basically a cooler with a lid and fitted with a lock
- ★ there are two main types: those made to stand on a pedestal or sideboard and those with legs or separate stands to stand on the floor
- ★ octagonal, hexagonal, round or oval, the commonest form is of coopered construction with a number of brass bands
- ★ a cooler made to stand on a pedestal will often have the lowest brass band as near to the base as possible; a cooler made to fit into a stand will have the band slightly up the body to allow a snug fit
- ★ it is important that all mounts are original and condition should be good, but the absence of the old lead lining is not serious. An octagonal cooler or cellaret on stand may command a slightly higher price than a hexagonal model, but both are much in demand
- ★ after 1800, the sarcophagus shape became popular and later Regency models were made with highly figured mahogany veneers and large carved paw feet
- ★ there were not many new designs after the 1850s

A Regency mahogany wine cooler, with lead lined interior, the shaped body with spreading plinth base, formerly with a lid, 39in (99cm).
£4,000-4,500 *C*

A George III mahogany wine cooler, 25in (63.5cm).
£3,000-4,000 *WW*

. William IV mahogany wine ɔoler, with coffered gadrooned lid nd lead lined interior, on scrolled ɛet, 27½in (70cm).
900-1,200 *C*

Regency mahogany wine cooler, ɩe top banded and inlaid with an ɔonised line, enclosing a lined ıterior, on brass lions' paw feet, ith trade label Spillman & Co.
300-1,000 *CSK*

A green leather covered and close nailed folding library ladder, 91in (231cm) high, closed.
£900-1,200 *C*

A George III mahogany hunting table, on folding X-shape square section stand, joined by stretchers, 35in (90cm).
£800-1,000 *L*

A George IV mahogany pedestal cellaret, the coffered top above a panelled door and deep cellaret drawer, applied with radial mouldings, on a plinth base, 19½in (49.5cm).
£1,800-2,200 *CSK*

Miscellaneous

A mahogany waste paper basket, with waved toprail and pierced Gothic sides, 14in (35.5cm).
£3,000-4,000 *C*

A George IV mahogany bootjack, with reeded supports and shaped base, 32½in (82.5cm) high.
£450-500 *DSH*

A Dutch green painted and parcel gilt sleigh of rococo design, the padded back, arms and seat upholstered in red velvet, distressed, 52in (132cm) long.
£2,000-3,000 *C*

A George IV mahogany jardinière, the brass carrying handle and liner in a pierced urn shaped body and ribbed socle, the concave sided tripartite base with paw feet, 21in (53cm) high.
£1,000-1,200 *C*

A Victorian bath chair, the mahogany frame button upholstered in black cloth, with a brass trade plate inscribed F.H. Miller, Maker, Newark Street, Bath, the wooden spoke wheels with a rubber rim, the seat on front turned mahogany legs to a carpet covered folding footboard, a fitment for a hood missing.
£600-700 *WW*

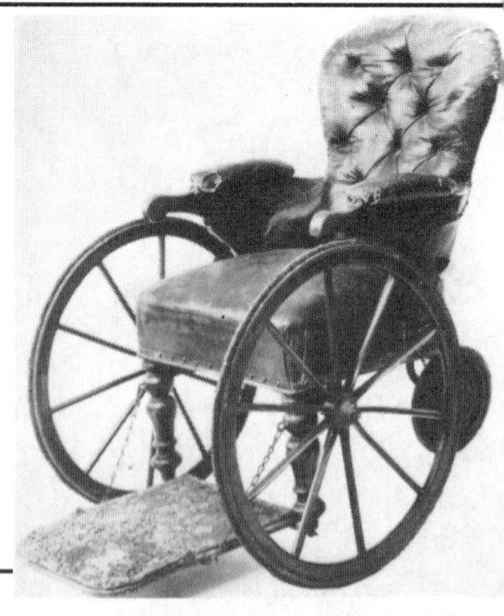

A mid-Victorian child's see-saw, with chair at either end, flanking an open aperture and split cane shelf, 68in (172.5cm).
£2,500-3,000 *C*

ARCHITECTURAL ANTIQUES

Fireplaces

A George III Coadestone chimneypiece, with the arms of Beaumont and Wentworth, signed Coade 1796 London, distressed, 102in (259cm).
£9,500-11,000 *C*

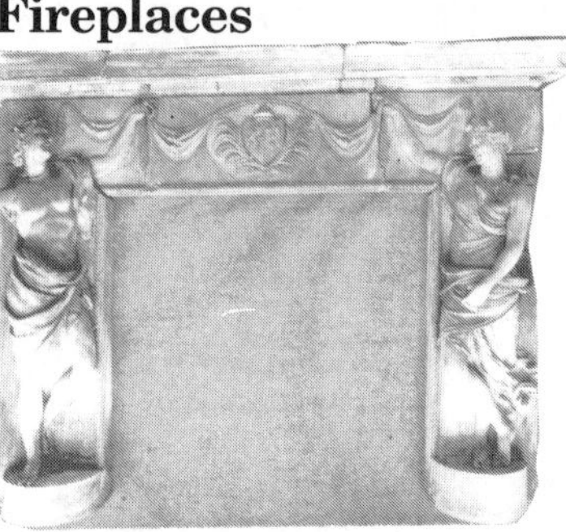

A George III stripped pine mantel, 73in (185cm).
£700-900 *CNY*

A pine fireplace, a 1920 copy of a Georgian style, 65in (165cm).
£400-500 *Ph*

A George III marble chimneypiece, with breakfront moulded overhanging cornice, above a frieze of Siena marble, 75in (190.5cm).
£18,000-20,000 *C*

A stripped pine fire surround, with tiled grate and iron doors.
£450-500 *ARC*

A Coalbrookdale grate, with adjustable hearth, c1840.
£300-400 *ARC*

A carved oak fire surround and overmantel, 48in (122cm) high.
£300-350 *GH*

A pine and gesso fire surround in Regency style, with cast iron grate, mid-19thC.
£550-650 *ARC*

A Regency giltwood overmantel, with 'verre églomisé' panel painted with a rustic scene, 55in (139.5cm).
£1,700-2,200 *C*

A Regency giltwood overmantel, 56in (142cm).
£500-700 *C*

▲ A Regency giltwood and composition overmantel, with later divided triple plate with a frieze, centred by a soldier in a chariot drawn by lions with attendants, 68in (172.5cm).
£700-900 *C*

A carved oak chimneypiece, 19thC.
£1,100-1,600 *CAN*

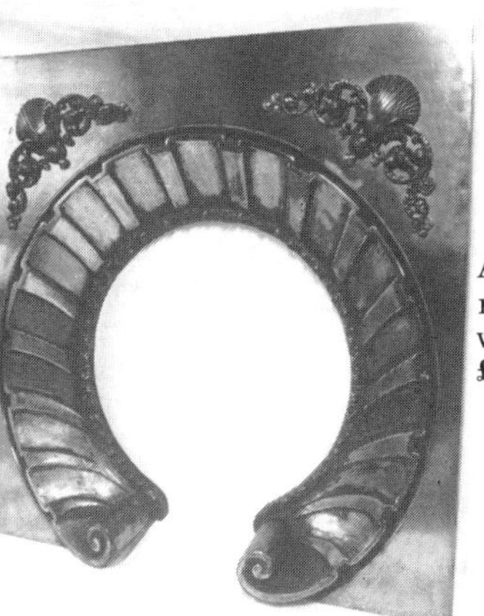

A burnished steel register plate, with shell motifs.
£500-750 *CAN*

A Victorian cast iron and brass grate.
£600-800 *ASH*

A Victorian cast iron interior with floral tiles.
£400-600 *ASH*

A Victorian cast iron and brass grate.
£500-700 *ASH*

A carved rosewood surround, inlaid with ivory and mother-of-pearl, 19thC, 78in (198cm) wide.
£2,000-2,200 *ASH*

A Victorian oak surround and shelf, 84in (213cm) wide.
£900-1,100 *ASH*

A cast iron and tiled grate.
£350-450 *CAN*

An ornately carved oak chimneypiece, 19thC.
£1,100-1,600 *CAN*

A George III brass fender, 56in (142cm).
£3,000-4,000 *C*

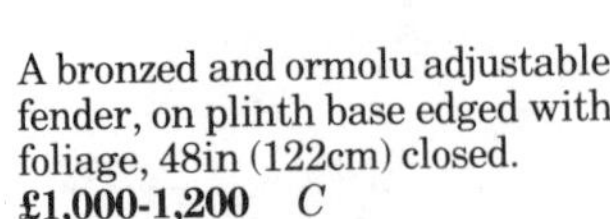
A bronzed and ormolu adjustable fender, on plinth base edged with foliage, 48in (122cm) closed.
£1,000-1,200 *C*

A George III brass serpentine fender, on claw feet, 54in (137cm).
£2,200-2,600 *C*

A giltmetal fender, stamped 1232 VI, 63in (160cm).
£600-800 *C*

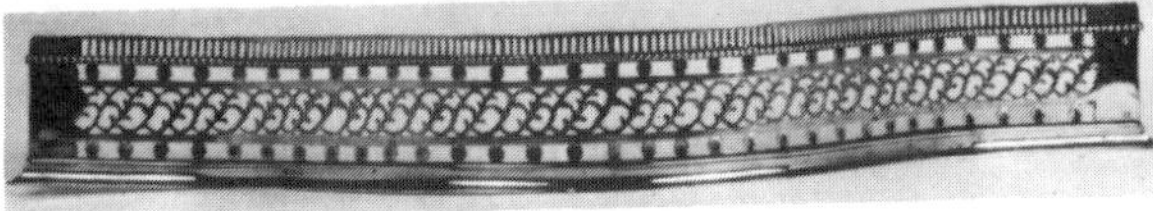
A George III brass serpentine fender, 45½in (115cm).
£2,000-2,500 *C*

A marble surround with Sienna columns, the frieze with carved rosettes, the tiled inset with brass canopy and fire front.
£4,500-5,500 *ASH*

A gilt and composition overmantel, in the manner of Robert Adam, with bevelled oval plate and cavetto ribbon-tied frame filled with entrelacs, 56 by 67½in (142 by 171cm).
£1,500-2,000 *C*

A pair of bellmetal chenet, with foliate and ball knops, spreading pierced shafts and arched bases, 17thC, 18½in (47cm) high.
£400-600 *C*

A Regency black painted cast iron and brass basket grate, on tapering legs with claw feet, 40in (101.5cm).
£3,500-4,000 *C*

A pair of 16thC style firedogs, c1880, 14in (35.5cm).
£100-150 *KEY*

A pair of wrought iron spit firedogs, late 17th/early 18thC.
£250-300 *KEY*

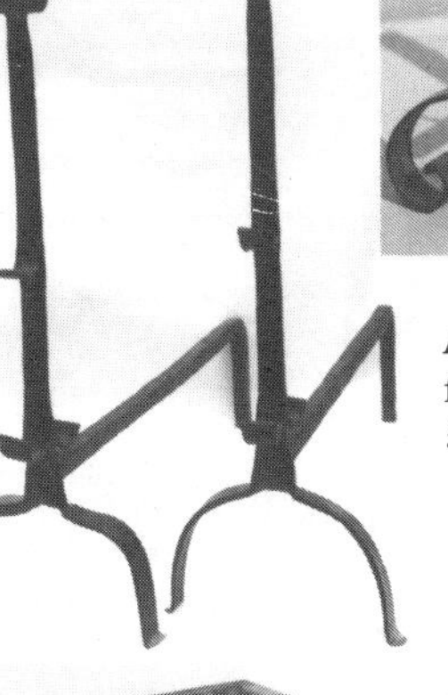

A pair of wrought iron firedogs, 18thC.
£100-150 *KEY*

A pair of Regency iron and brass mounted fire grates, 25½in (64cm).
£4,500-5,000 *P*

A pair of heavy brass andirons, with steel ball finials, 23in (58.5cm) high.
£350-400 *HOD*

A cast iron fireback, late 18thC.
£300-400 *ARC*

A pair of brass and enamelled andirons, each moulded in relief in the form of the Royal coat of arms, supported by 2 naked men, with circular boss feet decorated with foliage and flowerheads, 26in (66cm) high.
£2,500-3,000 *C*

A Regency black painted cast iron basket grate, in the manner of George Bullock, with claw feet and plinth base, with an associated shovel, 31in (79cm).
£3,000-3,500 *C*

A George III cast iron blacken steel basket grate, one finial lacking, 28½in (72cm).
£1,000-1,500 *C*

A Louis XVI style cast iron and brass fire basket, 22in (56cm).
£600-700 *LRG*

A Turtle stove, c1920, 30in (76cm).
£90-120 *ARC*

Miscellaneous

A circular window, 36in (91.5cm) diam.
£50-100 *CAN*

A pair of cast iron gable finials, 42in (107cm).
£100-150 *CAN*

A 'marbled' corner basin, with decorative cast iron bracket.
£200-300 *CAN*

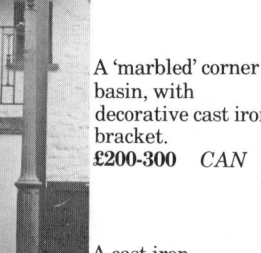

A cast iron lamp-post.
£120-220 *CAN*

A set of 18 oak mullioned and leaded glass windows of various sizes.
£3,000-4,000 *CAN*

A Coalbrookdale wrought iron stick stand, designed by Christopher Dresser, with metal liner, stamped No. 412, 29in (74cm).
£700-800 *P*

A collection of decorated and parcel gilt neo-classical interior panels, comprising a pair of doors painted with female figures depicting the Continents, Europe, Asia, America and Africa, 81 by 49in (206 by 124cm), a pair of larger doors depicting the Elements, 94 by 30in (238 by 76cm), and overmantels and arches applied with gilt metal rococo scroll hinges and floral ribband borders, 19thC.
£4,500-5,500 *P*

A pair of decorative cast iron brackets, 15 by 18in (38 by 46cm).
£200-300 *CAN*

A late Victorian black porcelain door plate, 7½in (19cm).
£7-10
and a pair of black porcelain handles, 2½in (6cm) diam.
£15-20 *WRe*

A pair of Regency black painted cast iron urns, redecorated, 24in (61cm) diam.
£2,000-3,000 *C*

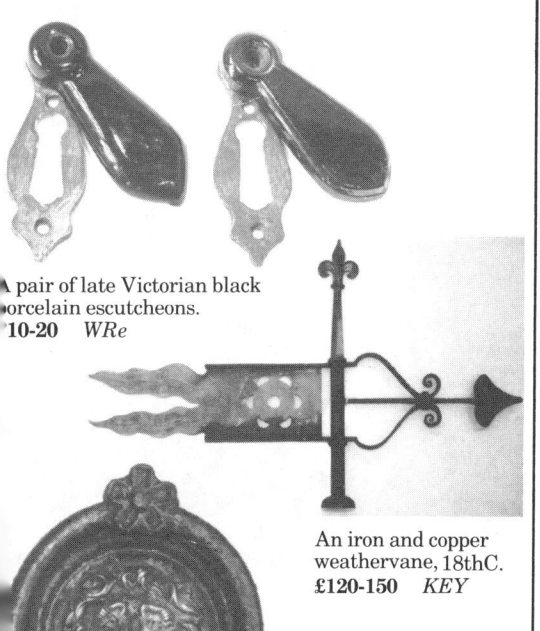

pair of late Victorian black orcelain escutcheons.
10-20 *WRe*

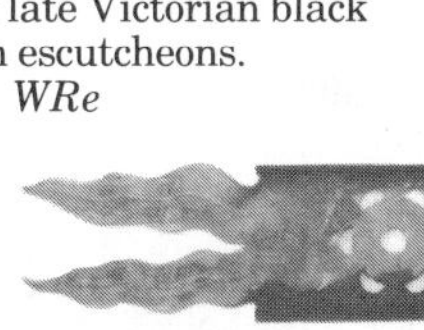

An iron and copper weathervane, 18thC.
£120-150 *KEY*

iron and brass door knocker, 330.
0-60 *KEY*

A pair of brass handles from an Edwardian chest.
£30-40 *WRe*

A rare Coadestone clock face, indented 'Coade London 1794', 38in (96.5cm) high.
£3,500-4,000 *MD*

Coade is an artificial stone; Mrs. Eleanor Coade set up her factory at Lambeth in 1769. This item was recently found adapted as a garden fountain.

A hand painted porcelain door plate, 11½in (28cm).
£20-25 *WRe*

A cast iron door knocker in the form of a goats head, c1870.
£35-40 *KEY*

A brass lion's head door knocker, c1880.
£70-80 *KEY*

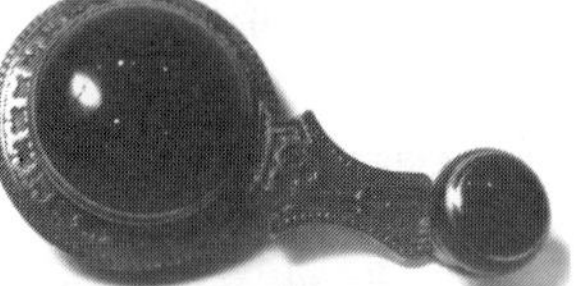

A black porcelain and brass servants bell pull.
£40-50 *WRe*

A brass bell pull.
£120-150 *WRe*

A brass bell push, 5½in (14cm).
£50-60 *WRe*

A pair of Georgian brass door stops, with moulded bases with weighted iron insets, inscribed with a sun mark and W.T.&S, 14in (35cm).
£500-600 *WW*

A black porcelain bell push, with gilt decoration.
£35-50 *WRe*

Late Victorian transfer printed floral patterned door knobs.
From **£20 per pair** *WRe*

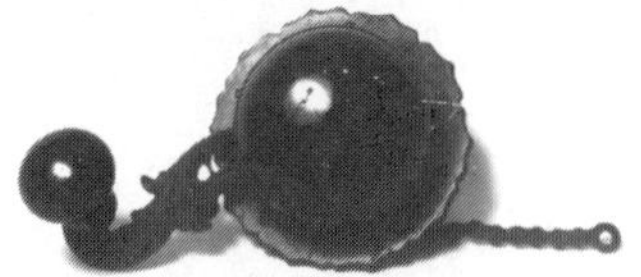

A black porcelain and brass bell pull.
£30-40 *WRe*

A set of 6 brass coat hooks
£50-60 *WRe*

A brass bell push, 3½in (9cm).
£40-50 *WRe*

A porcelain bell push, with red and blue flowers.
£30-40 *WRe*

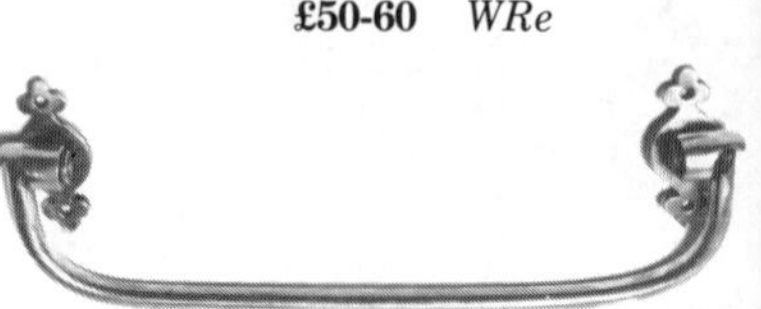

A brass towel rail, 11½in (29cm)
£25-35 *WRe*

A lead garden fountain of a cherub with a dolphin, 26in (66cm) high.
£700-750 *LRG*

A brass letter box with porcelain handle, 9½in (24cm) wide.
£85-95 *WRe*

A brass door knocker, 9in (23cm).
£55-65 *WRe*

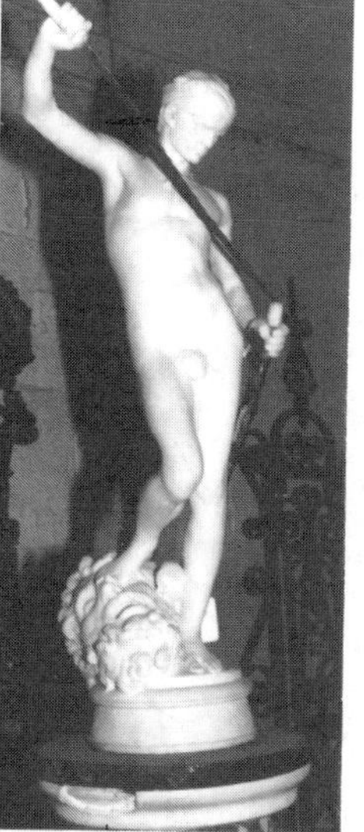

'David Van Quer', by Mercie, c1874.
£6,000-7,000 *DB*

A pair of cast stone garden figures, of classical females in fruiting vine headdresses and diaphanous drapes, 51in (130cm) high.
£2,000-3,000 *P*

A terracotta bust of Greek Philosopher, named 'Seneco', 8in (20.5cm).
£70-80 *DB*

A lead garden fountain statue, 23in (58.5cm) high.
£500-550 *GC*

A brass ceiling hook.
£8-10 *WRe*

A lead figure of a child, 19in (48cm) high.
£500-550 *WRe*

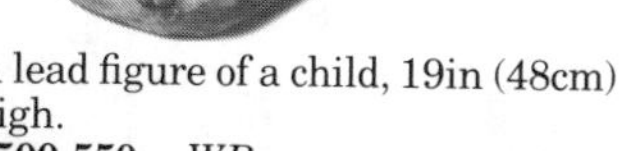

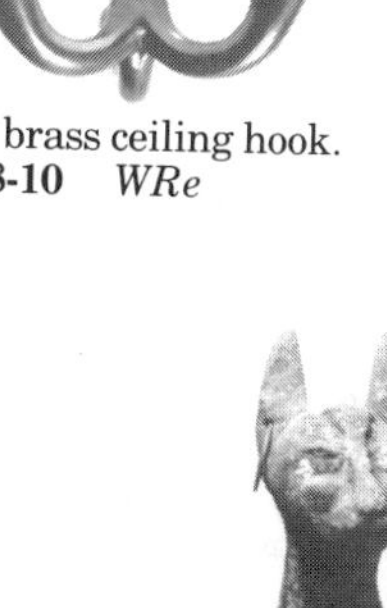

A pair of Abyssinian cats, 32in (81cm).
£900-1,000 *WRe*

Continental stone planter, 19 by 28in (48 by 71cm).
£750-850 *DB*

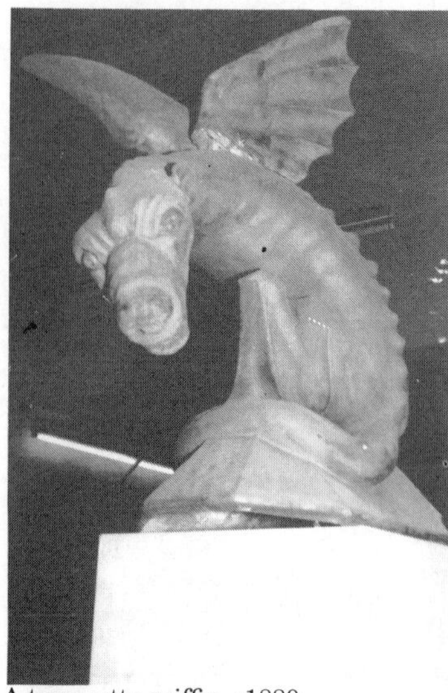

A terracotta griffin, c1880.
£400-500 *DB*

A pair of stone troughs, early 19thC, 24in (61cm) wide.
£90-130 *DB*

A composition stone and bronze sundial, in the style of Coade, with bronze dial, inscribed Austin, Seeley & Co., New Road, London, the support carved with the three Muses, the plinth with stylised key pattern, mid-19thC, 50½in (128cm) high.
£3,000-4,000 *C*

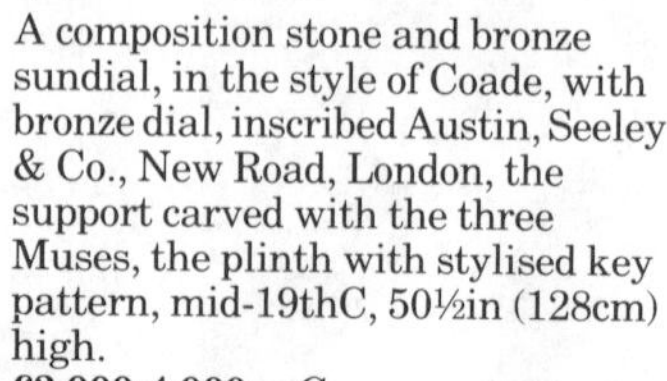

Victorian decorative railings.
£12-15 per foot *ARC*

An Italian garden vas 19thC, 28in (71cm).
£400-500 *DB*

A pair of garden urns, early 19thC, 40in (101.5cm) high.
£1,100-1,300 *ARC*

Two Regency wrought iron garden chairs wit penny feet, c1820.
£1,600-2,000 *RYA*

Decorative railings.
£20-25 per foot *ARC*

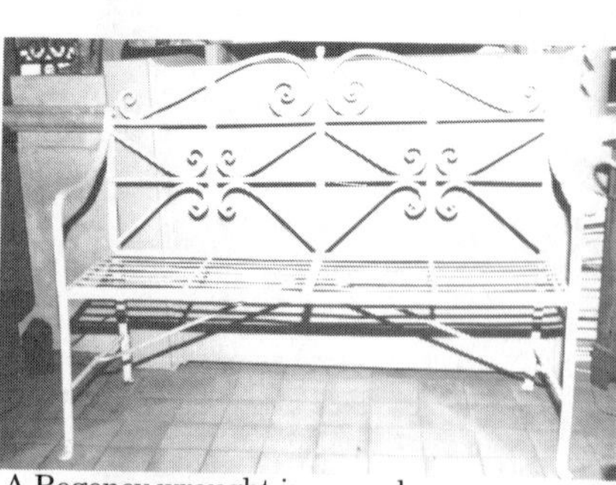

A Regency wrought iron garden bench, with geometric arcaded back, c1810, 56in (142cm).
£2,500-2,700 *MD*

A cast iron garden fountain, c1880, 60in (152cm) high.
£1,500-1,800 *ARC*

A white painted iron stickstand, modelled as a boy holding a serpent, 19thC, 34in (86cm).
£300-350 *LRG*

An English lead life-size statue of a young woman, 'The Haymaker', by John Cheere, complete with stone pedestal, c1766, 99in (251.5cm).
£25,000-30,000 *MD*

Only two identical figures have been traced in Britain, one at Bicton Gardens, Exmouth, and the other at Okeover, Ashbourne, Derbyshire, where John Cheere is known to have supplied a lead figure in 1741 — see Country Life, *23rd January, 1964, p. 175.*

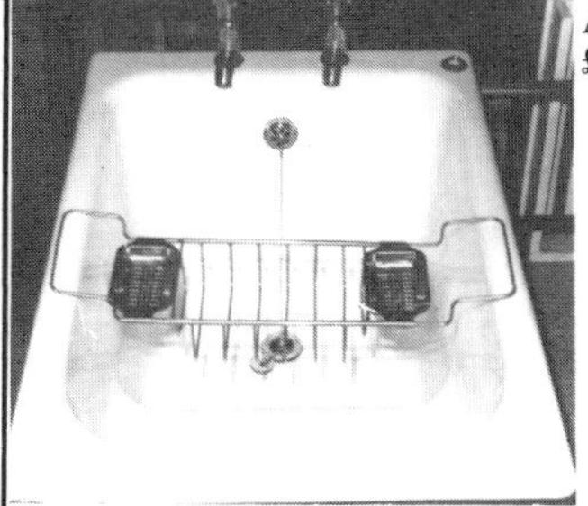

A French bath, 37in (94cm) long.
£150-200 *WRe*

A 'New Slipper' bed pan, 16in (41cm).
£35-55 *WRe*

A Victorian decorated W.C.
£275-300 *WRe*

Two carved oak fragments, 16thC.
£60-80 each *KEY*

A Victorian W.C., damaged, suitable for flower container, 16in (41cm) high.
£50-60 *WRe*

A Victorian 'waterfall' blue and white W.C., with wooden seat.
£300-350 *LRG*

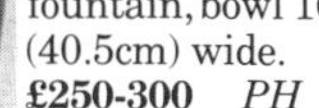

An enamelled tin water fountain, bowl 16in (40.5cm) wide.
£250-300 *PH*

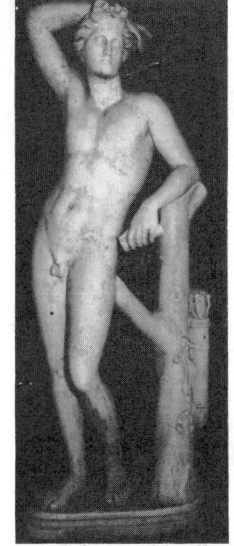

A figure of Apollo, c1960, 58in (147cm).
£500-600 *RP*

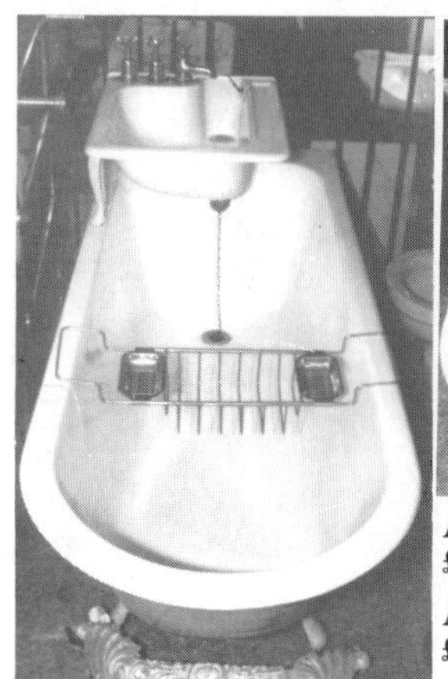

A combined cast iron bath and basin, 66in (167.5cm).
£550-600 *WRe*

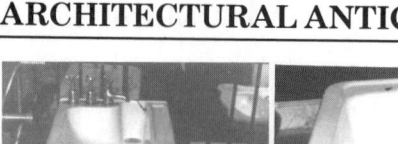

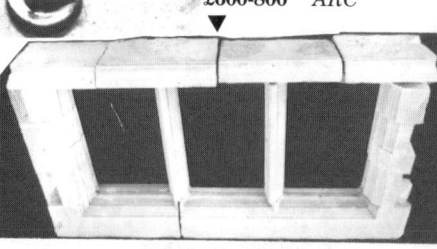

A roll top bath, 76in (193cm).
£350-400

A brass and copper soap rack.
£45-55 *WRe*

A carved oak bracket, from a church.
£400-500 *ARC*

A pair of mahogany newel posts, 60in (152cm).
£220-250 *ARC*

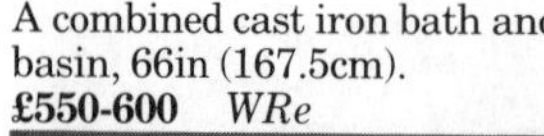

A Gothic pitch pine pulpit, 19thC.
£480-520 *ARC*

A Continental carved oak bar, c1900, 96 by 60in (243.5 by 182.5cm).
£5,500-6,500 *ARC*

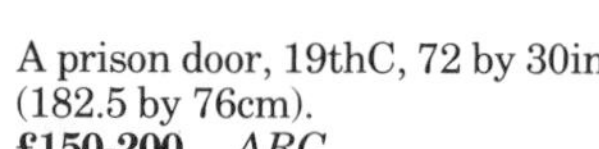

A prison door, 19thC, 72 by 30in (182.5 by 76cm).
£150-200 *ARC*

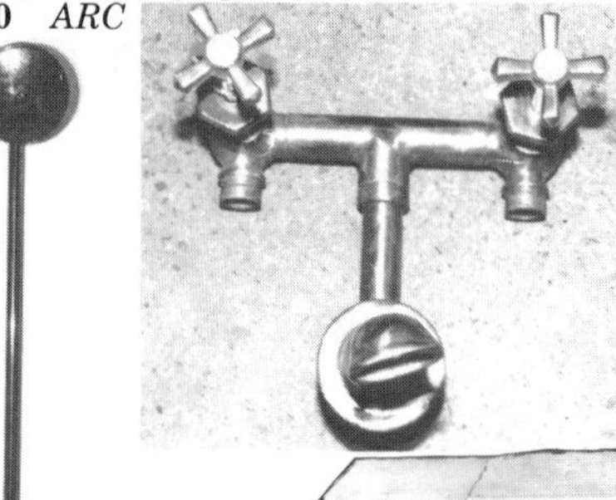

A brass mixer tap unit.
£150-200 *WRe*

A sandstone window, complete with leaded casements, 19thC, 60 by 108in (182.5 by 274cm).
£600-800 *ARC*

Telephone kiosks.
£300-400 each *ARC*

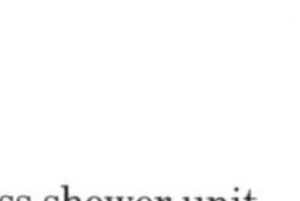

A copper and brass shower unit, 35in (89cm).
£225-250 *WRe*

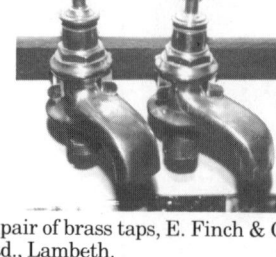

A pair of brass taps, E. Finch & Co. Ltd., Lambeth.
£60-80 *WRe*

A pitch pine bar counter, 19thC, 108in (274cm).
£600-800 *ARC*

A pitch pine pulpit, c1880.
£3,300-3,500 *AT*

hardware shop counter, 120in
04.5cm).
450-550 *ARC*

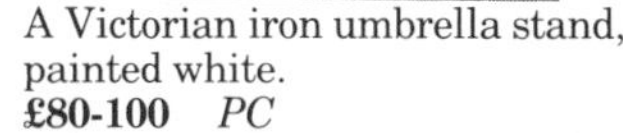

A Victorian iron umbrella stand, painted white.
£80-100 *PC*

A grocer's shop fitting, 108 by 252in (274 by 640cm).
£3,000-3,400 *ARC*

A stained glass panel, c1880.
£140-160 *DB*

Part of 2 stained glass hall windows, c1860, 192in (488cm).
£1,000-1,200 *DB*

rgan woodwork in dark stained
tch pine, heavily carved, c1870.
2,200-2,500 *AT*

rgan woodwork used for fretwork.
pes are often melted down for scrap
etal.

ılpit frontage in pitch pine with
rds eye effect panelling, c1870.
,800-2,000 *AT*

ılpits are often used in restaurants
example as cashiers' desks.

A Victorian cast iron rustic garden seat, 52in (132cm).
£400-500 *DN*

A late George III wrought iron bench, 48in (122cm).
£450-550 *DN*

A pair of Victorian cast iron urns, 25in (64cm) diam.
£400-500 *DN*

A Coalbrookdale cast iron garden seat, with the Fern and Blackberry pattern, 19thC, 59in (150cm).
£750-850 *DN*

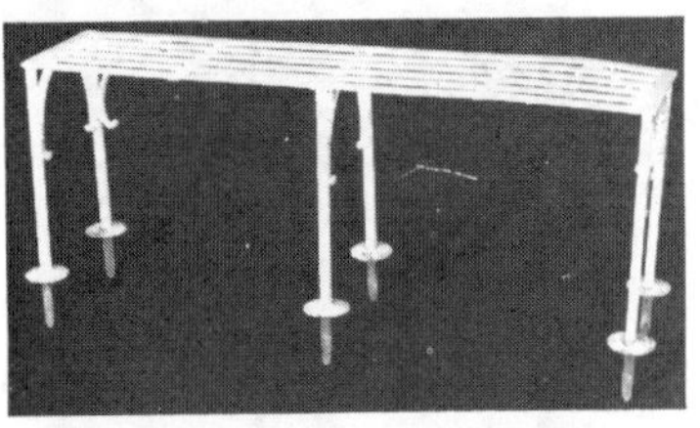

A wrought iron plant stand, 19thC, 54in (137cm).
£300-400 *DN*

An ornate painted iron garden seat, 48in (122cm).
£700-1,000 *JD*

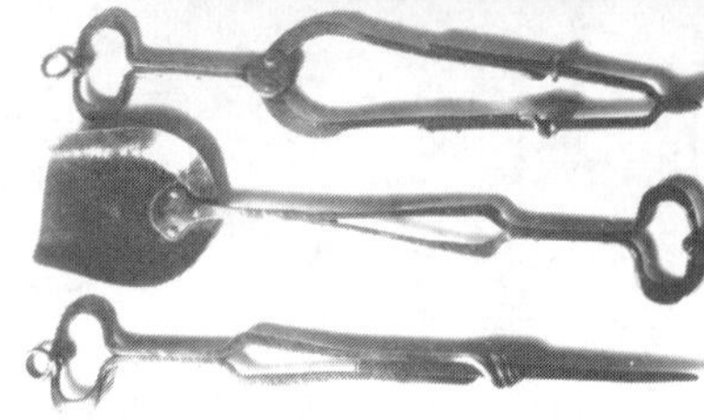

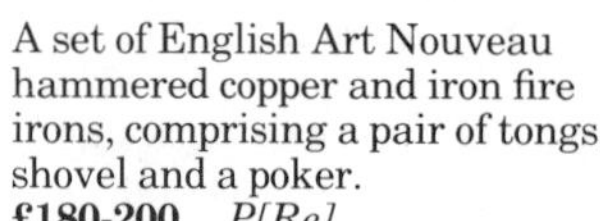

A set of English Art Nouveau hammered copper and iron fire irons, comprising a pair of tongs, shovel and a poker.
£180-200 *P[Re]*

A pair of gilt metal chairs, c1930, 35in (89cm).
£400-500 *RIP*

A cast iron chimney ornament, 6in (15cm).
£35-40 *KEY*

A bronze leopard, modern, 32in (81cm).
£1,500-2,000 *WRe*

CLOCKS

Longcase

A George III mahogany longcase clock, the brass dial with raised chapter ring and foliate spandrels, signed John Brand, London, with subsidiary seconds, date aperture and strike/silent ring in the arch, the 8-day movement striking on a bell, 100in (254cm).
£4,000-4,500 *CSK*

A walnut longcase clock, the arched brass dial with engraved wheatsheaf border and silvered chapter ring, with subsidiary seconds and date aperture and signed on a cartouche Hen. Batterson, London, with strike/silent in the arch, the movement with internal rack striking and anchor escapement, 18thC, with later gilt mounts to the hood 90in (229cm).
£2,000-3,000 *P*

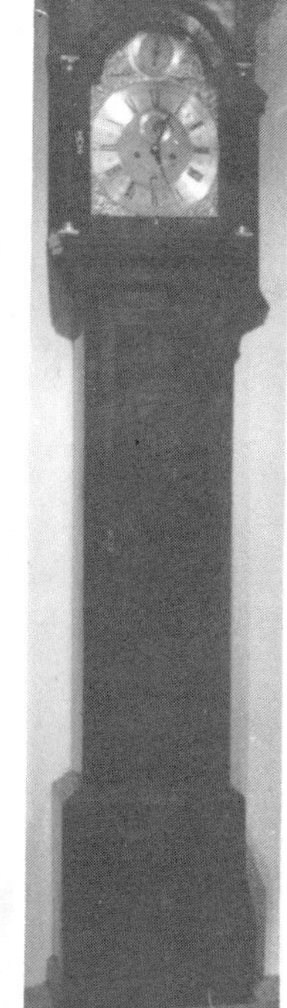

A walnut longcase clock, 8-day movement, brass dial, silvered chapter ring, subsidiary dial for seconds, calendar aperture, the figured walnut case by John Blake of Fulham.
£4,500-5,000 *SBA*

An oak longcase clock, by Thomas Clare, Warrington, with 12in (30.5cm) brass dial, with engraved and spandrelled dial centre, subsidiary seconds and date aperture, 8-day 4-pillar rack striking movement with anchor escapement, 18thC, 82in (208cm).
£1,000-1,500 *P[Re]*

An oak and mahogany crossbanded longcase clock, by David Collier, Gatley, the brass dial with subsidiary seconds and date crescent with rolling moon in the arch, 8-day rack striking 4-pillar movement with anchor escapement, c1800, 86½in (219cm).
£1,500-2,000 *P[Re]*

A George III musical longcase clock, by Corban Cranefield, Sherringham, 3-train movement.
£3,500-4,000 *DN*

A Georgian oak longcase clock with brass face, by John Baddeley of Tong, 83in (210.5cm).
£2,300-2,700 *FHF*

A walnut and seaweed marquetry longcase clock, with 12in (30.5cm) brass dial, signed Claudius du Chesne, Londini, with subsidiary seconds and date aperture, the 5-pillared movement with anchor escapement, early 18thC, 88in (224cm).
£6,000-8,000 *P*

A mahogany longcase clock, by W. B. Cornforth, Macclesfield, with 14in (35.5cm) convex enamelled dial, with rolling moon in the arch, subsidiary seconds and date crescent, 8-day rack striking movement with anchor escapement, c1820, 95in (241cm).
£700-1,000 *P[Re]*

An oak longcase clock, the dial with applied chapter ring and spandrels, signed Creighton B-Mena No. 120, ringed date aperture and winding holes, phases of the moon in the arch with lunar calendar and time of high tide scale, 91in (231cm).
£600-700 *CSK*

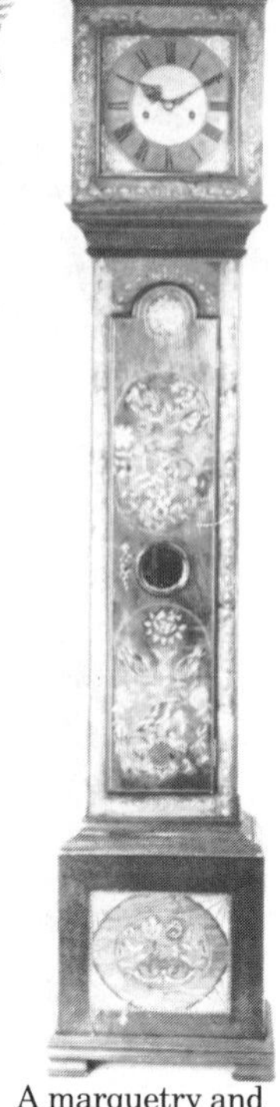

A marquetry and oak longcase clock, the 11in (28cm) dial with raised chapter ring, with inner quarter-hour ring, half-hour divisions and engraved Roman numerals with chased and faceted hands, signed A.M. Cressener, London, the movement with 4 ringing pillars and inside countwheel striking on a bell, 83in (210.5cm).
£2,000-2,500 *CSK*

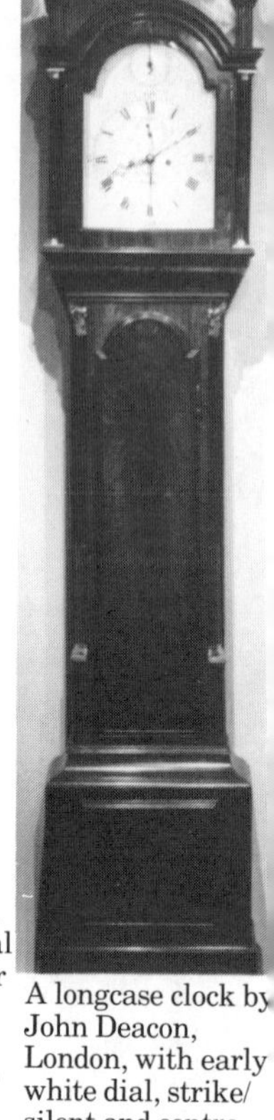

A longcase clock by John Deacon, London, with early white dial, strike/silent and centre sweep hand for the calendar, subsidiary dial for seconds, 8-day movement, c1760, the case in the pagoda design, with inlaid brass columns, all brasswork original.
£7,500-8,000 *SBA*

A George III 8-day longcase clock, by John Darke, Barnstaple, with 12in (30.5cm) brass dial, signed silvered chapter ring, seconds dial, calendar aperture, phase of the moon in the arch and 'High Water at Barnstaple Key', the 4-pillar movement with anchor escapement striking on a bell, with pendulum and weights, in mahogany case, 89in (226cm).
£1,200-1,500 *Bea*

A Dutch oak longcase clock, the silvered chapter ring signed De Wancker TotLoo, with inscription, the gilt spandrels with vases amid scrolling foliage, the door with glazed apertures, slightly distressed, 18thC, 98in (249cm).
£800-1,000 *C*

A country oak longcase clock with mahogany crossbanding, the 11in (28cm) dial engraved Wm. Edmunds, Madeley, the 30-hour movement striking on a bell, extensively restored, c1760, 77in (195.5cm).
£300-400 *MJB*

A Georgian mahogany longcase clock, the 12in (30.5cm) brass dial with brass chapter ring, subsidiary seconds and date aperture, the painted arch fitted with a rocking ship and signed around John Fearnley, Trowbridge, the twin-train movement with anchor escapement, 90in (228.5cm).
£2,000-3,000 *P*

A Victorian mahogany longcase clock, the brass dial with raised chapter ring and spandrels, subsidiary seconds ring and date aperture, signed in the arch Edmond Gibbs, London, the 8-day movement striking on a bell, 81in (205.5cm).
£1,000-1,500
CSK

A Regency mahogany longcase clock, the 12in (30.5cm) silvered dial with subsidiaries for seconds and for date, signed Grant, London, the 5-pillared movement with anchor escapement, 84in (214cm).
£4,000-5,000 *P*

A walnut month-going longcase clock, the movement with 11in (28cm) brass dial, signed at the base Christop Gould Londini fecit, with brass chapter ring, the centre with subsidiary seconds, date aperture and harboured winding holes, the 7-ring pillared movement with outside countwheel and anchor escapement, 18thC, with later arch to dial, 82in (208cm).
£3,500-4,500 *P*

A George III mahogany longcase clock, the hood and trunk with basal brass insets, the 8-day striking movement with anchor escapement and silvered metal dial, inscribed Grant, Fleet Street, London, 85½in (217cm).
£3,000-3,500 *GC*

John Grant of Fleet Street, London, was an eminent maker. He was free of the Clockmakers Company in 1781, and was warden. He died in 1810. His son, born in 1796, was also a clockmaker.

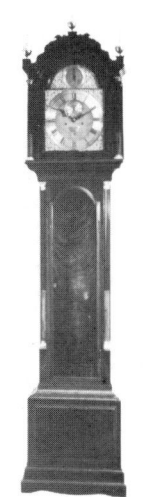

A walnut longcase clock, the 8in (20.5cm) brass dial with raised chapter ring, scallop shell spandrels and matted centre, signed L. Gray Westover, 18thC, with later 8-day movement striking on a bell, 65in (165cm).
£2,000-2,500
CSK

A George III mahogany longcase clock, inscribed Daniel & Thomas Grignon, 3-train movement.
£3,000-3,500 *DN*

A mahogany longcase clock, the brass dial signed Jas. Heron, New Town, subsidiary dial for seconds, date aperture, the 8-day movement striking on a bell, lacking bell, 87in (221cm).
£900-1,200 *CSK*

A Georgian mahogany longcase clock, with 12in (30.5cm) brass dial, silvered chapter ring, with subsidiary seconds and date aperture, signed on a cartouche William Haughton, London, with strike/silent in the arch, chiming the quarters on 8 bells, 97in (246cm).
£4,500-5,500 *P*

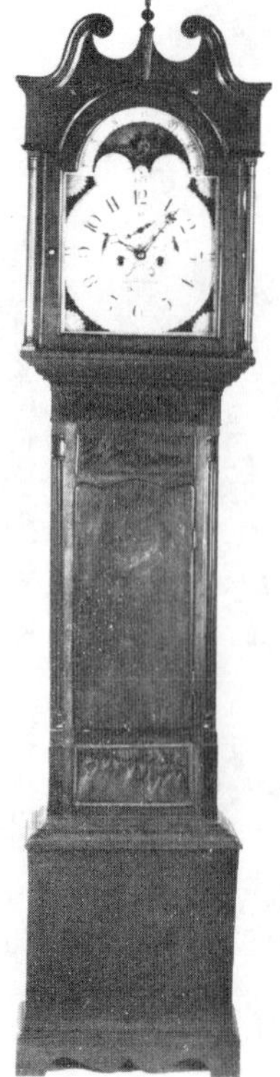

A mahogany longcase clock, the painted dial signed Geo. Hutchinson, Dullaghy, with subsidiary ring for seconds and date sector, rolling moon in arch with lunar calendar, the 8-day movement striking on a bell, 86in (218.5cm).
£1,000-1,500
CSK

An oak and mahogany banded longcase clock, the arched brass dial with pierced foliate spandrels and silvered chapter ring by Jonathon Ivison, fitted with an 8-day movement, 86in (218.5cm).
£1,300-1,600 *OL*

Longcase Clocks

Longcase clocks are generally ordered alphabetically by the makers name

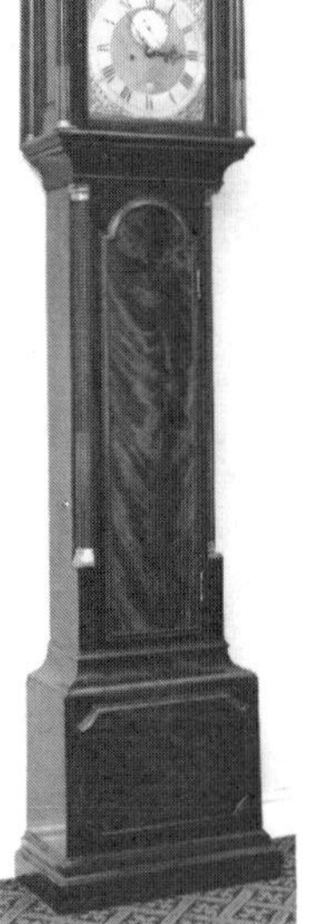

A George III mahogany longcase clock, the brass dial with silvered chapter ring, subsidiary seconds dial, date aperture and strike/silent in the arch, with brass cased weights and pendulum, 8-day strike, maker James Ivory, London, c1765, 97in (246cm).
£4,000-4,500 *M*

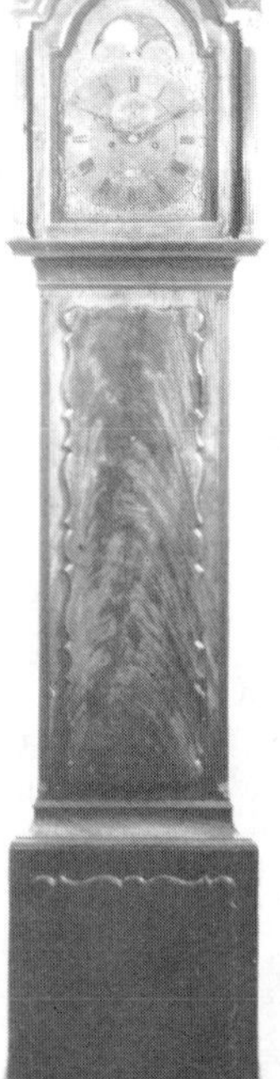

A mahogany longcase clock, the brass dial with engraved border and brass chapter ring, signed Philip Lloyd, Bristol, the engraved centre with subsidiary seconds and date aperture, with moon phase in the arch calibrated around and inscribed High Water at Bristol Key, the twin train movement with anchor escapement, 18thC, 88in (224cm).
£3,000-4,000 *P*

A mahogany 8-bell chiming longcase clock, the gilt brass dial with raised silvered chapter ring, subsidiary seconds and date aperture, strike/ silent ring in the arch and signed on a silvered sector Willm and Jno. Kipling, London, the 8-day 3-train movement with 5 ringed pillars chiming the quarters on 8 bells with 12 hammers and a separate bell for the hours, 88in (224cm).
£5,000-6,000
CSK

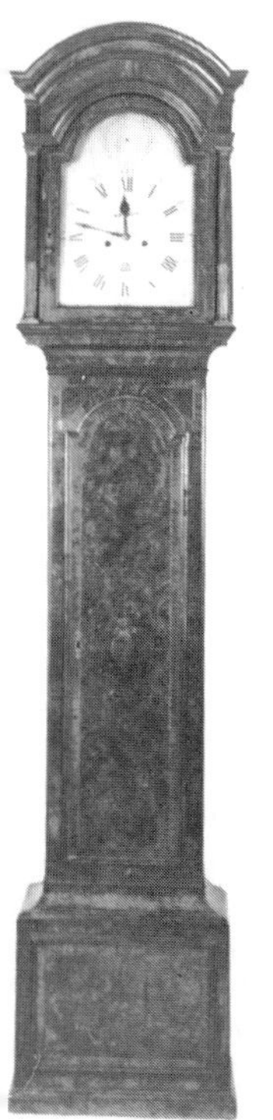

A burr walnut longcase clock, the silvered dial with strike/silent regulation in the arch, seconds dial, date aperture, inscribed Robt. Maisley, London, 18thC, 90in (228cm).
£3,500-4,000
P[PWC]

A 30-hour oak longcase clock, with brass capitals and hand painted dial, maker John Kent, Monmouth, c1790, 19in (48cm) wide.
£250-350 *GH*

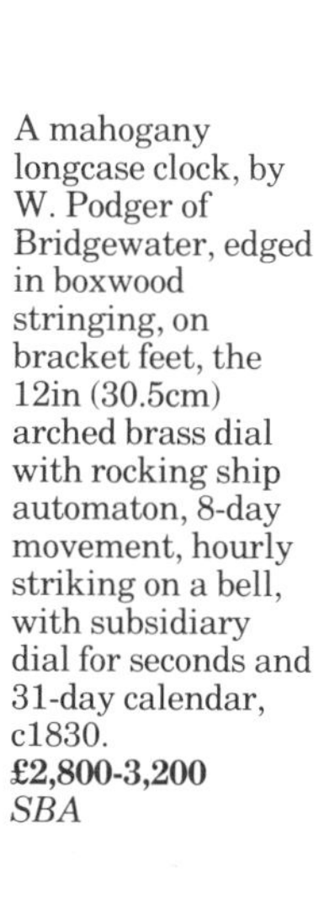

A mahogany longcase clock, by W. Podger of Bridgewater, edged in boxwood stringing, on bracket feet, the 12in (30.5cm) arched brass dial with rocking ship automaton, 8-day movement, hourly striking on a bell, with subsidiary dial for seconds and 31-day calendar, c1830.
£2,800-3,200
SBA

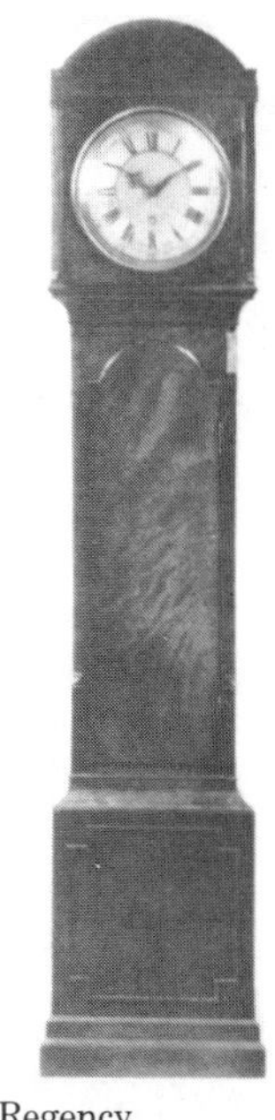

A Regency mahogany longcase clock, now fitted with a 30-hour posted movement with 11in brass dial and silvered chapter ring, signed Jno. Mercer, Hythe, 78in (198cm).
£800-1,000 *P*

A Victorian mahogany longcase clock, the silvered dial signed W. Ransone, London, with Roman numerals and blued steel hands, the weight-driven timepiece movement with 4 ringed pillars and anchor escapement, 69in (175cm).
£2,000-2,500
CSK

A Victorian mahogany and satinwood crossbanded longcase clock, the brass dial and silver chapter ring with Roman numerals, seconds dial and date aperture, with a silvered boss to the arch engraved William Patterson of Hamiltoun, fitted with an 8-day movement, 81in (206cm).
£750-1,000 *AG*

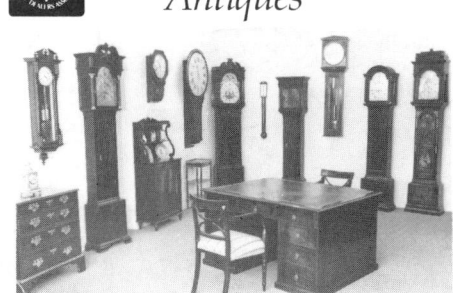

An oak and mahogany chiming longcase clock, signed Hugh Lough, Penrith, with Roman numerals, half-hour divisions and Arabic 5-minute numerals, sweep centre calendar, the massive 8-day movement playing a tune every 3 hours on 8 bells with 8 hammers and changing automatically every 24 hours, late 18thC, 93in (236cm).
£6,000-7,000
CSK

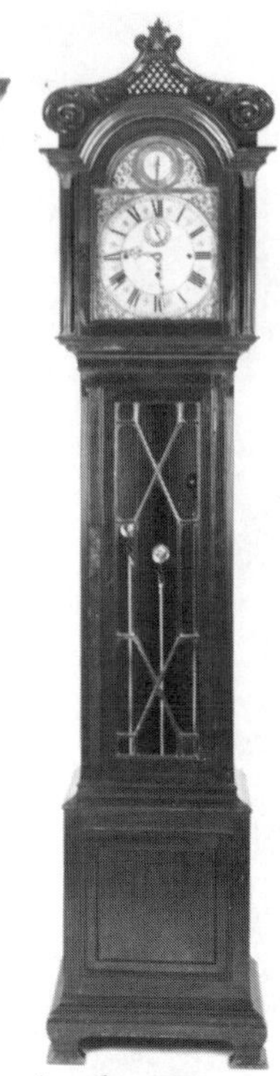

A mahogany longcase clock, the brass dial with silvered chapter ring, inscribed Maple & Co. Ltd., London, seconds dial, chime/silent ring in the arch, gilt metal cherub head and dolphin spandrels, the 3-train chiming 8-day movement with brass coated weights, 95in (241cm).
£800-1,000
P[PWC]

HINTS TO DATING LONGCASE CLOCKS

Dials

8in square	to c1669	Carolean
10in square	from c1665-1800	
11in square	from 1690-1800	
12in square	from c1700	from Queen Anne
14in square	from c1740	from early Georgian
Broken-arch dial	from c1715	from early Georgian
Round dial	from c1760	from early Georgian
Silvered dial	from c1760	from early Georgian
Painted dial	from c1770	from early Georgian
Hour hand only	to 1820	
Minute hand introduced	c1663	
Second hand	from 1675	post-Restoration
Matching hands	from c1775	George III or later

Case finish

Ebony veneer	up to c1725	Carolean to early Georgian
Walnut veneer	from c1670 to c1770	Carolean to mid-Georgian
Lacquer	from c1700 to c1790	Queen Anne to mid-Georgian
Mahogany	from 1730	from early Georgian
Softwood	from c1690	from mid-Georgian
Mahogany inlay	from c1750	from mid-Georgian
Marquetry	from c1680 to c1760	from Carolean to mid-Georgian
Oak	always	

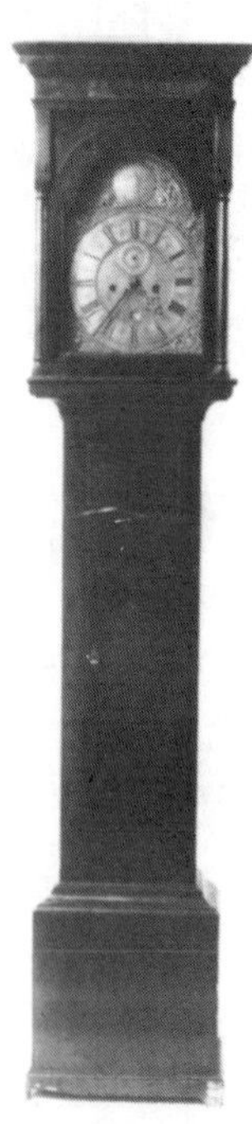

A Georgian 8-day longcase clock with brass dial, signed Polglase, Helstone, with seconds dial, calendar aperture and pierced gilt spandrels, the 4-pillar movement with anchor escapement striking on a bell, with pendulum, weights, bell and keys, 2 hands missing, 85in (216cm).
£700-900 *Bea*

A green and gilt lacquered longcase clock, the brass dial with raised silvered chapter ring, recessed seconds disc and date aperture, gilt foliate spandrels, and strike/silent ring in the arch, signed Thos. Palmer, London, the 8-day movement with strike on bell, 93in (236cm).
£1,500-2,000
CSK

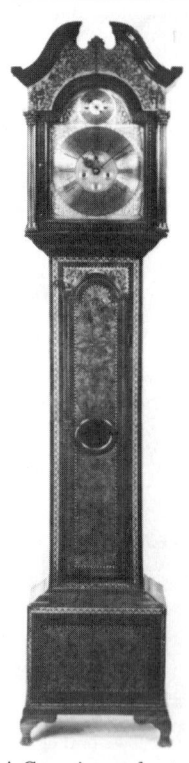

A Georgian walnut and inlaid longcase clock, signed Jon Sales, Dublin, with subsidiary seconds, date aperture and harboured winding holes, with an age of the moon dial in the added arch, the twin train movement with inside countwheel and anchor escapement, 102in (258cm).
£2,500-3,500 *P*

A walnut and panel marquetry longcase clock, with 11in (28cm) brass dial, with silvered chapter ring signed Thos Stubbs, London, with subsidiary seconds and date aperture, the movement with ringed pillars, internal rack striking and anchor escapement, early 18thC, 82½in (210cm).
£12,000-14,000 *P*

A Scottish mahogany longcase clock, by D. Robinson, Airdrie, with painted dial, 8-day movement with seconds and date, 19thC, 84in (213cm).
£1,000-1,200 *CH*

A walnut longcase clock, with 12in (30.5cm) brass dial with brass chapter ring, signed G. A. Smith, Barthomley, with subsidiary seconds and date aperture, the 6-ring pillared movement with inside countwheel strike and anchor escapement, the case with alterations, 18thC, 84in (213cm).
£1,500-2,000 *P*

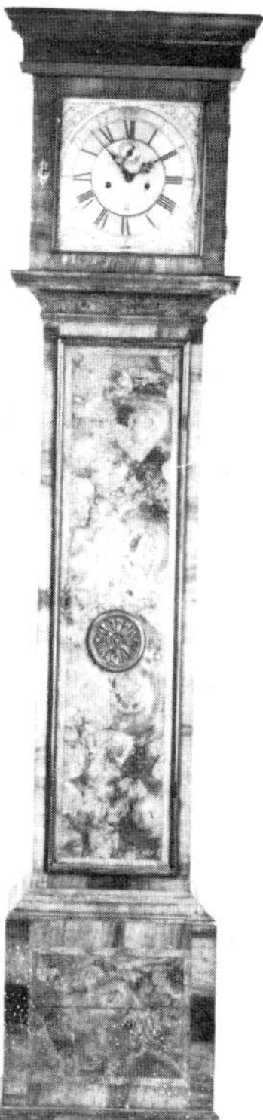

A burr walnut longcase clock, the 12in (30.5cm) dial with raised chapter ring and spandrels, Roman numerals, Arabic numerals for the 5 minute divisions, subsidiary ring for seconds, date aperture, the chapter ring signed Sadler, London, the 8-day movement with rack strike, lacking bell, 18thC, 87in (221cm).
£3,000-4,000
CSK

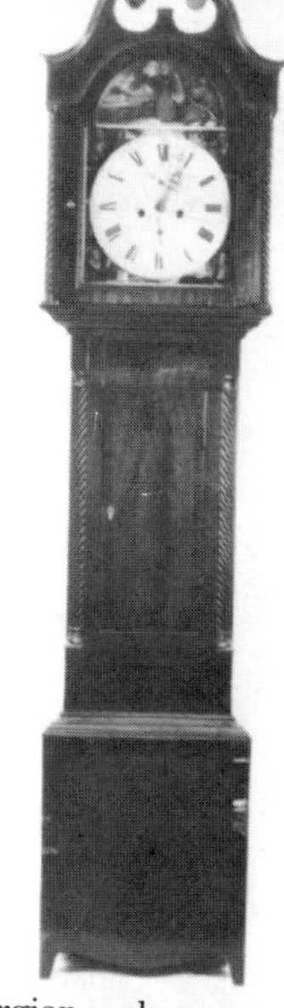

A Georgian mahogany longcase clock, the hood with swan neck pediment and spirally turned columns, the arched painted dial with subsidiary seconds and date, signed Geo. Ritchie, Arbroath, the twin train movement with anchor esapement, 82in (208cm).
£900-1,200 *P*

A German walnut cased pedestal clock, the pedestal fitted with a polyphon metal disc player, stamped 'Schutz -Marke', 19thC, 102in (258cm).
£5,000-5,500 *HOD*

A green lacquered longcase clock with caddy top, the brass dial with raised silvered chapter ring signed Sam Townson, London, half and quarter-hour marks and half-quarter divisions, silvered seconds ring, date aperture, and blued steel hands, hour hand broken, the 8-day movement with ringed pillars and outside countwheel striking on a bell, early 18thC, 94in (238cm).
£3,500-4,500
CSK

An oak 8-day longcase clock, with 10in (25.5cm) engraved brass dial, applied brass chapter ring and the 4 season spandrels with date indicator, maker William Webb, Wellington, with key, mid-17thC, 78in (198cm).
£900-1,000 *GH*

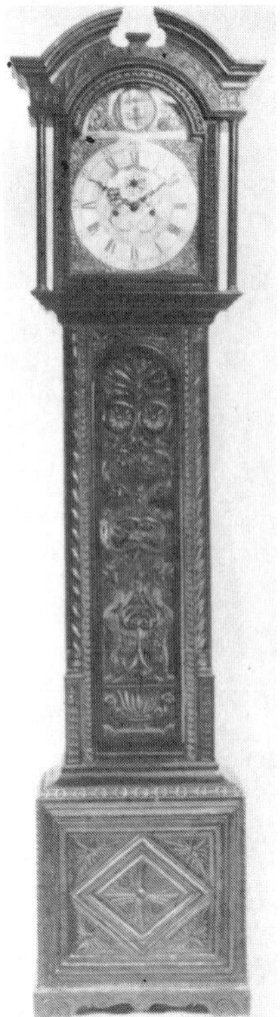

A carved oak longcase clock, signed on a silvered plaque in the arch Edw. Whitehead, Wetherby, with subsidiary seconds disc and engraved silvered centre, the 8-day movement striking on a bell, 86in (218.5cm).
£700-900 *CSK*

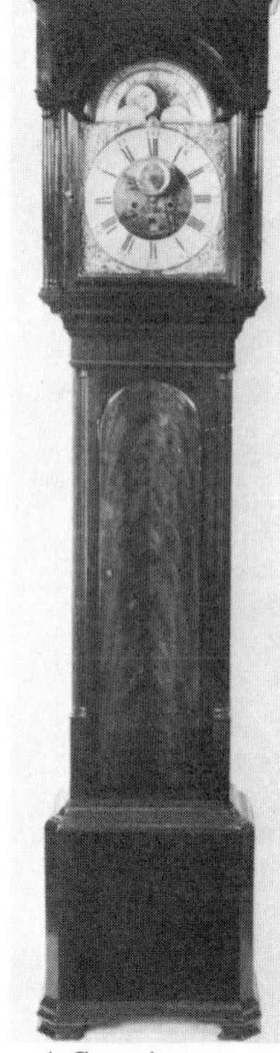

A Georgian mahogany longcase clock, the 13in (33cm) brass dial with silvered chapter ring, subsidiary seconds and date aperture, the arch with moon phase signed Williams, Preston, the twin train movement with anchor escapement, 90in (230cm).
£3,000-4,000 *P*

A walnut longcase clock, the silvered chapter ring signed E. Williamson, London, with subsidiary seconds, date aperture, harboured winding holes, the 5-ring pillared movement with inside countwheel strike and anchor escapement, late 17thC, with restoration, 81in (206cm).
£3,000-4,000 *P*

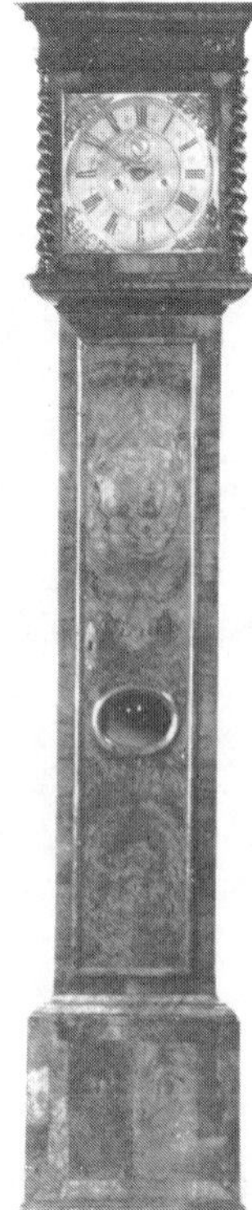

A walnut longcase clock, the 11in (28cm) brass dial with replaced winged cherub spandrels, and brass chapter ring, signed Jno Wise, London, with subsidiary seconds, date aperture and harboured winding holes, the movement with outside countwheel and later wheelwork, 18thC, with restorations and alterations, 82½in (210cm).
£1,700-2,200 *P*

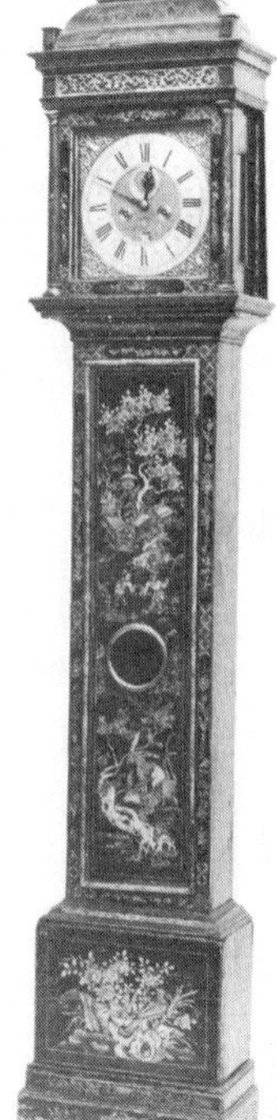

A George III black and gilt japanned longcase clock, by John Wimble, Ashford, the 8-day 5-pillar movement with square brass dial, 90in (229cm).
£1,800-2,200 *PB*

A George III mahogany longcase clock, the brass dial with silvered chapter ring, centre date and subsidiary seconds within the engraved centre, with moon phase in the arch, signed Samuel Young, Bonebury, the twin train movement with anchor escapement, 93in (235cm).
£3,500-4,000 *P*

A mahogany longcase clock, with 8-day 2-train movement striking on a bell, the white enamelled dial with subsidiary seconds dial and calendar aperture and painted rotating moon phase dial in the arch, late 18th/early 19thC, 84in (213cm).
£1,000-1,200 *LBP*

An Edwardian Chippendale Revival longcase clock, Whittington with Westminster chimes, 3-train movement, chiming on tubular bells, c1905, 102in (259cm).
£6,000-7,000 *N*

An Edwardian electric combination longcase clock, with 6in (15cm) brass dial, silvered chapter ring, the movement with alternative electric motor and 8-day chain fusee going train, striking the hours and the quarter hours on 9 gongs, in mahogany and inlaid case with concealed spirit level, strike/silent lever and glazed trunk door, with pendulum brass cased weight and 4 keys, 72in (182cm).
£2,500-3,000 *Bea*

An Edwardian longcase clock, with 3-train movement chiming on 9 tubular bells, with engraved dial.
£3,000-3,500
MGM

A late Georgian oak longcase clock, crossbanded in mahogany, with 8-day movement, 89in (226cm).
£1,400-1,700 *JRB*

A Dutch floral marquetry longcase clock, 18thC.
£4,000-5,000
LRG

A Lancashire mahogany longcase clock, with 15in (38cm) painted dial and rolling moon in the arch and centre date sweep, the dial centre with painted scene of the Death of Nelson, 8-day 4-pillar rack striking movement with anchor escapement, early 19thC, 94in (238cm).
£1,500-2,000 *P[Re]*

A mahogany longcase clock with 8-day movement, the painted dial depicting Rent Day, c1800.
£600-700 *P[EDH]*

A mahogany longcase clock with boxwood inlay and stringing, the 12in (30.5cm) brass dial with early added arch, half and quarter-hour divisions and blued steel hands, the arch with silvered plaque flanked by dolphin spandrels, the 8-day movement with 5 ringed pillars, internal countwheel striking on a bell, 96½in (245cm).
£3,000-3,500 *CSK*

A mahogany longcase clock, the 7in (18cm) breakarch brass dial with raised chapter ring, Roman numerals, matted centre and applied spandrels, inscribed Tempus Fugit, the 8-day spring wound 3-train movement chiming quarter hours on 5 rods, 59½in (150cm).
£2,000-2,500 *CSK*

Regulators

A floor standing Vienna regulator, finished in walnut and ebony, with 8-day movement, maintaining power and deadbeat escapement, c1850, 95in (241cm).
£6,000-7,000 *SBA*

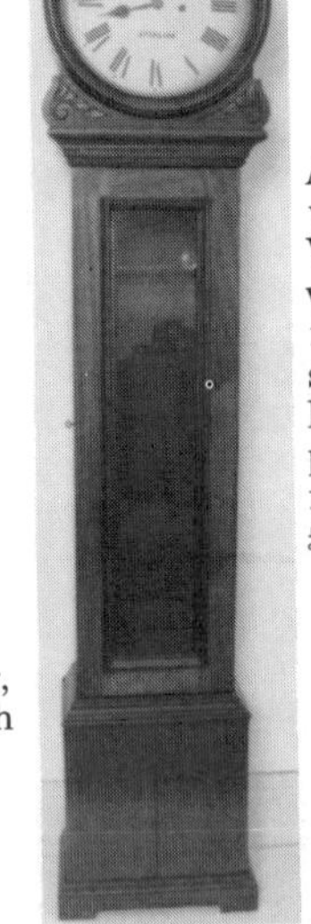

A small mahogany regulator, with white dial, signed Hepting, Stirling, 8-day 4-pillar movement with deadbeat escapement and Harrison's maintaining power, 19thC, 75in (190.5cm).
£700-1,000 *P[Re]*

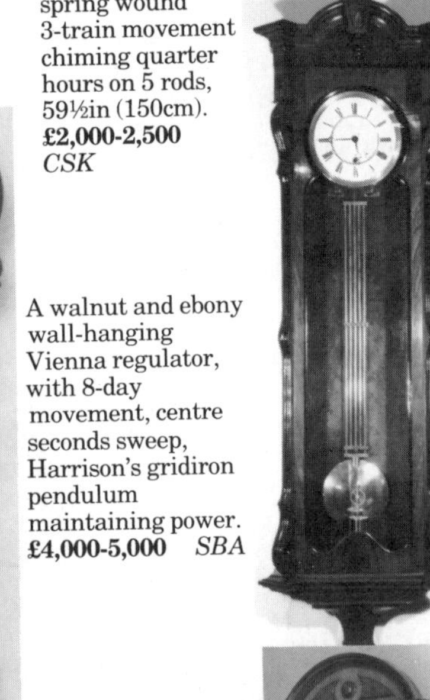

A walnut and ebony wall-hanging Vienna regulator, with 8-day movement, centre seconds sweep, Harrison's gridiron pendulum maintaining power.
£4,000-5,000 *SBA*

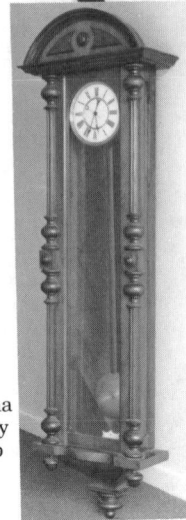

A mahogany regulator longcase clock, the painted dial inscribed 'Thos Moreland, Chester', c1840, 89in (226cm).
£2,000-2,500 *HOD*

A Victorian walnut cased Vienna regulator wall clock, with 10-day deadbeat escapement and sweep second hand.
£700-900 *MGM*

Bracket Clocks

A single fusee bracket clock in ebony, by John Berry of London, 8-day movement, c1690, 14in (35.5cm).
£4,500-5,000 *SBA*

A verge bracket clock by Charles Gabrier of London, with applied gilt spandrels, c1740, 34in (86cm).
£8,000-9,000 *SBA*

An ebony and gilt brass mounted bracket clock, the brass dial with silvered chapter ring, signed Claudius du Chesne, London, with date aperture and harboured winding holes, and with strike/silent, early 18thC, with alterations, 17½in (45cm) high.
£4,000-5,000 *P*

An ebonised bracket clock, with brass dial, strike/silent, by Thomas Gardner, London, the verge movement with 6 bell quarter repeating movement and engraved backplate, requires repairing, early 18thC, 18½in (47cm).
£1,500-2,000 *GSP*

A mahogany bracket clock with alarm, by Perigal, Coventry Street, London, c1775, 9½in (24cm).
£3,000-4,000 *TCW*

An ebony bracket clock, the square brass dial with silvered chapter ring signed John Miller, London, now converted to anchor escapement, and originally with pull quarter repeat, now removed, the engraved backplate signed Johannes Miller, Londini fecit, early 18thC, on later bun feet, 16in (40cm) high.
£3,000-4,000 *P*

An ebonised bracket clock, with inverted bell top, cast brass carrying handle, inscribed Richard Rayment, Bury St. Edmunds, with date aperture, mask and rococo spandrels, the movement converted to anchor escapement and with a backplate inscribed by the maker, feet replaced, 18thC, 19½in (49cm).
£1,000-1,500 *P[PWC]*

HINTS TO DATING BRACKET CLOCKS

Dials

Square dial	to c1770	pre-George III
Broken arch dial	from c1720	George I or later
Round/painted/silvered	from c1760	George III or later

Case finish

Ebony veneer	from c1660 to c1850	Carolean to mid-Victorian
Walnut	from c1670 to c1870	Carolean to Victorian
Marquetry	from c1680 to c1740	Carolean to early Georgian
Rosewood	from c1790	from mid-Georgian
Lacquered	from c1700 to c1760	Queen Anne to early Georgian
Mahogany	from c1730	from early Georgian

An ebony bracket clock, signed Thomas Science, London with mock pendulum and date apertures, and with strike/silent in the arch, the 5-pillared movement with fully engraved backplate and verge escapement, 18thC, 16in (41cm).
£2,500-3,000 *P*

A George III bracket clock in ebonised case, inscribed Thomas Wagstaffe, 3-train striking fusee movement.
£2,000-2,500 *DN*

A George III mahogany bracket clock, with carrying handle to each side, with enamel dial, signed Biddell, London, with brass hands and with enamel subsidiaries above for regulation and for strike/silent, the twin fusee movement with anchor escapement, 21in (53cm).
£1,500-2,000 *P*

A French bracket clock, the case ebonised with tortoiseshell and brass inlays, the case with velveted brass dial and silvered chapter, with a gilt bronze figure of Father Time, signed beneath Gribelin, Paris, early 19thC, now with later spring driven movement, 21in (53cm).
£200-300 *P[Re]*

A Regency mahogany bracket clock with brass inlay, silver dial with strike, on 4 brass feet, by In. Lamb, London, 19½in (49cm).
£1,000-1,500 *IM*

A Regency ebonised bracket clock, with white painted dial with Roman numerals and subsidiary date ring, signed Handley and Moore, London, with strike/silent ring in the arch, the 8-day repeating fusee movement striking on a bell, with engraved borders to the backplates, the pendulum with lock, 16in (40.5cm).
£1,000-1,500 *CSK*

A Regency mahogany quarter chiming bracket clock, on gilt brass ball feet, the white painted dial with Roman numerals, signed Hanson, Windsor, with strike/silent ring in the arch, the 8-day 3-train movement similarly signed, one foot detached, 17½in (45cm).
£1,600-2,000 *CSK*

A Regency Gothic mahogany bracket clock, the painted dial signed Manners & Sons, Stamford, with glazed cast brass bezel, the twin fusee movement with anchor escapement and strike on bell, the backplate with securing brackets to the case, 21½in (54.5cm).
£1,000-1,500 *C*

A Regency mahogany and brass inlaid bracket clock, with 8-day striking fusee movement, by Frodsham, London.
£1,200-1,500 *MGM*

A Georgian green lacquered bracket clock, with mock pendulum and date apertures, signed on a cartouche Stepn. Rimbault, London, and with strike/silent in the arch, the twin fusee movement converted to anchor escapement, with engraved backplate, 20in (51cm).
£2,000-2,500 *P*

A Regency mahogany bracket clock, the painted dial signed Metcalfe, London, the twin fusee movement with strike/silent setting and anchor escapement, 23½in (60cm).
£1,200-1,500 *P*

An ebonised and brass mounted bracket clock, the silvered dial signed Payne, 163 New Bond St. London, and with strike/silent above, the twin fusee movement with anchor escapement, 19thC, 14½in (36.5cm).
£1,200-1,500 *P*

A Regency mahogany bracket clock, the painted dial signed P. Grimalde, London, the twin fusee movement with arched plates and engraved border and with anchor escapement, 17in (43cm).
£3,000-3,500 *P*

A tortoiseshell and cut brass inlaid bracket clock, the chased brass dial with enamel numerals, signed on a panel below Lepeltier a Paris, 19thC, 26½in (67cm).
£1,000-1,500 *P*

A French bracket clock, mercury gilded with painted panels, 8-day movement, hourly and half-hourly striking, c1840, 17in (43cm).
£1,500-2,000 *SBA*

A bracket clock with 8-day movement, chimes on 8 bells and Westminster chimes, brass and ormolu dial in ebonised case with ormolu decoration, 19thC, 29½in (75cm).
£1,000-1,200 *DSH*

An English double fusee bracket clock, 8-day movement, hourly strike on the bell, in mahogany with fish-scale brass fretwork, by T. Farr, Bristol, c1830, 16in (41cm).
£1,500-2,000 *SBA*

A small French bracket clock, hourly and half-hourly striking on a gong, with porcelain and enamel dial, c1860, 12in (30.5cm).
£700-900 *SBA*

A French bracket clock, 8-day movement, hourly and half-hourly striking, in mahogany case, c1860, 13in (33cm).
£300-400 *SBA*

An English double fusee bracket clock in oak, with ormolu mounts, with 8-day movement, quarter striking on 2 gongs, ting-tang, c1860, 17in (43cm).
£1,200-1,500 *SBA*

A black marble bracket clock with applied gilt, 8-day movement and half-hourly striking, c1880, 11in (28cm).
£180-220 *SBA*

An oak cased ting-tang, fully restored and cleaned, c1890, 15½in (39cm).
£300-350 *SBA*

A mahogany 8-day bracket clock, with silvered dial with rise and fall regulator, quarter chiming on 2 gongs, with key, 19thC, 12in (31.5cm).
£250-300 *GH*

A Victorian pollard oak Gothic Revival bracket clock, with silvered brass dial with strike/silent in the arch, signed Muller, Twickenham, with substantial spring driven twin fusee mechanism, striking on a single gong, 42in (106.5cm) including bracket.
£800-900 *P[Re]*

A Victorian walnut bracket clock, with silvered dial engraved with scroll decoration and with subsidiaries for regulation and strike/silent above, the twin fusee movement with anchor escapement, 26in (66cm).
£500-700 *P*

A Victorian pollard oak Gothic cased 3-train bracket clock, chiming on 8 bells, by Thomas Myers, Sheffield.
£700-1,000 *MGM*

A striking bracket clock with white enamel dial with Roman numerals and Arabic 5-minute divisions with unusual pendulum regulation, being achieved by a small arbour below the disc, the movement of unusual lay-out signed on the backplate Ellicott, London, with twin chain fusees, 5 turned pillars, deadbeat escapement striking on a bell mounted to the side, the second wheel recessed into the backplate with a separate bridge, 15½in (39cm).
£1,000-1,500 *CSK*

An early Louis XV ormolu mounted polychrome contre-partie boulle bracket clock, signed on dial and backplate Chastelain a Paris, distressed, 38½in (98cm).
£3,000-3,500 *C*

A bracket clock with 8-day chiming movement and engraved brass dial, in mahogany Gothic style case, 24in (61cm).
£500-600 *P[WSW]*

John Carter, Cornhill, London – apprenticed 1829-42, afterwards Lord Mayor in 1857, Master C.G. 1856, 1859 and 1864, died 1878.

French boulle bracket clock, in aisted case with gilt metal mounts ıd cherub finial, 8-day striking ovement, 19thC.
'00-800 *MGM*

An ormolu mounted scarlet boulle bracket clock, the glazed dial with Roman enamel numerals, 48in (122cm).
£2,500-3,000 *C*

:arriage Clocks

An ebonised English carriage clock, the twin fusee movement with lever platform escapement, striking on a gong, with strike/silent lever on the backplate, signed Dent, London 477, 19thC, 9½in (24cm).
£3,000-4,000 *P*

A silver and tortoiseshell cased carriage clock, maker William Comyns, London 1909, 4½in (11.5cm) in original fitted case.
£1,200-1,500 *HOD*

A gilt bronze English carriage clock, striking on a gong and signed on the backplate James McCabe, London, 3463, the signed silvered dial with subsidiary seconds, and with push repeat fitted through the top glass, 19thC, 10½in (26cm).
£5,000-6,000 *P*

An English carriage timepiece, in gilt brass case, with mother-of-pea[rl] register plate, engraved silvered dial, the 8-day movement with leve[r] beneath the balance wheel, the do[or] inscribed Howell James & Co., Regent Street, London, 19thC, 6½i[n] (16.5cm).
£2,000-2,500 *DN*

A miniature oval carriage timepiece, with engraved mask, white enamel dial, Roman numerals, the 8-day movement with lever escapement, 3in (7.5cm).
£550-750 *CSK*

An English carriage timepiece, in gilt case, with Roman numerals and gilt halberd hands, the 8-day fusee movement signed on the backplate Bell and Sons, 131 Mount Street, Berkeley Square No. 14477, with platform escapement.
£900-1,200 *CSK*

A gilt repeating carriage clock, wit[h] ivory chapter ring, signed J.W. Benson, Ludgate Hill, London, the 8-day movement with silvered leve[r] platform escapement striking on a gong, with the maker's stamp Drocourt, with original red leather numbered case, 6½in (16.5cm).
£1,000-1,500 *CSK*

A striking carriage clock, the case with bevelled glass window to the top, silvered mask with ivorine chapter ring, the 8-day repeating movement striking on a gong and with large silvered pointed lever platform escapement, 6in (15cm).
£450-550 *CSK*

An alarm carriage timepiece, in gilt case with gilt mask to the white enamel dial, with subsidiary alarm dial, the 8-day timepiece movement with gilt lever platform escapement and bimetallic balance, the alarm ringing on a bell in the base, with red leather travelling case, 3in (8cm).
£250-350 *CSK*

An English petit sonnerie carriag[e] clock with white enamel dial, inscribed Lund & Blockley (to the Queen), No. 4095, with repeat button and silent/strike lever on t[he] base, 6in (15cm).
£2,000-2,500 *GSP*

Clocks
All clock measurements refer to height unless otherwise stated

A small striking alarm carriage clock, with white enamel dial and alarm ring, the 8-day movement with Drocourt stamp striking on a gong with silvered lever platform escapement and bimetallic balance, alarm hand missing, 4in (10cm).
£700-900 *CSK*

A brass carriage clock with enamel dial, with urn finials framing a statuette of Napoleon, 19thC, 8in (20cm), with case.
£500-600 *C*

A striking carriage clock, the white enamel dial signed Reid, with black Roman numerals, the 8-day movement striking on a gong with gilt lever platform escapement and bimetallic balance, 5in (12.5cm).
£350-450 *CSK*

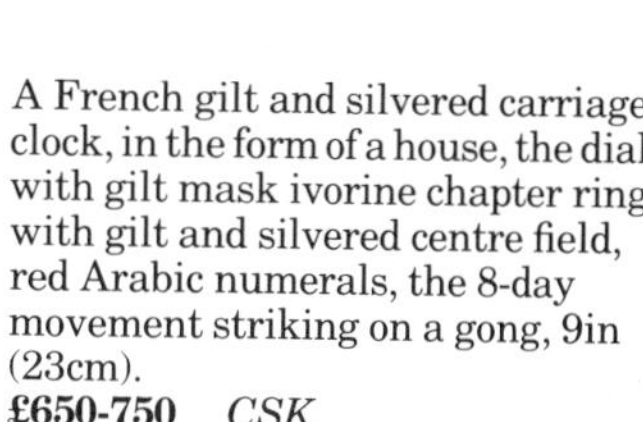

A French gilt and silvered carriage clock, in the form of a house, the dial with gilt mask ivorine chapter ring with gilt and silvered centre field, red Arabic numerals, the 8-day movement striking on a gong, 9in (23cm).
£650-750 *CSK*

A French alarm carriage clock, with white enamel dial, subsidiary ring for the alarm below the 6, the 8-day timepiece movement with gilt lever platform escapement ringing the alarm on a bell, 5½in (14cm).
£400-450 *CSK*

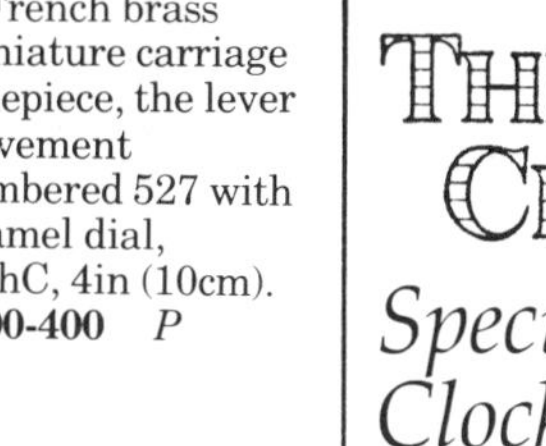

A French brass miniature carriage timepiece, the lever movement numbered 527 with enamel dial, 19thC, 4in (10cm).
£300-400 *P*

A French gilt brass carriage clock, the lever movement with grande sonnerie striking on 2 gongs, with alarm and push repeat and bearing the Drocourt trademark, signed Medaille D'or Idrac le Roy, Paris, the case with twisted corner columns, with a numbered key, 19thC, 7½in (19cm).
£2,700-3,000 *P*

. French gilt brass carriage clock, ıe lever movement striking on a ong, with push repeat and bearing ıe Richard trademark, the enamel ıal, damaged, within an engraved ilt mask, in an 'anglaise' case, 9thC, 7½in (19cm).
600-700 *P*

A French brass carriage clock, the lever movement striking on gong with push repeat, the enamel chapter ring within an engraved gilt mask, in an 'anglaise' case, 19thC, 8in (20cm).
£600-700 *P*

A French brass carriage clock, the lever movement striking on a gong, with push repeat and with the Margaine trademark on the backplate, with enamel dial, in an 'anglaise' case,19thC, 7in (18.5cm).
£550-650 *P*

A French gilt brass carriage clock, the lever movement striking on a gong and bearing the Drocourt trademark, with enamel dial, 19thC, 7in (18cm).
£900-1,000 *P*

A French gilt brass miniature carriage timepiece, the lever movement with enamel dial in an engraved case, 19thC, 4in (9.5cm), with a leather travelling case.
£900-1,200 *P*

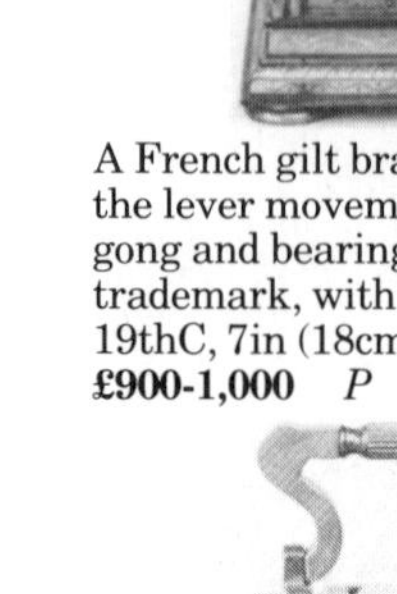

A French gilt brass carriage clock, the lever movement striking on a gong with push repeat and enamel dial, in a bamboo style case, 19thC, 7½in (19cm).
£600-700 *P*

A French miniature brass carriage timepiece, the lever movement bearing the Margaine trademark and numbered 15556, with enamel dial, 19thC, 3½in (9.5cm).
£450-600 *P*

A French brass carriage clock, the lever movement striking on a gong, 19thC, 7in (18cm).
£550-600 *P*

A French brass carriage clock, the lever movement striking on a gong, with alarm and push repeat and bearing the Drocourt trademark, numbered 44663, with enamel dial, in a numbered case, 19thC, 6½in (16.5cm), together with a travelling case.
£550-600 *P*

A French gilt brass carriage clock, the lever movement striking on a bell, with enamel dial, 19thC, 6in (15cm).
£300-400 *P*

A French gilt brass grande sonnerie carriage clock, the lever movement striking on 2 gongs with push repeat numbered 3017, with enamel dial, 19thC, 8in (20cm).
£1,500-1,700 *P*

A French gilt brass carriage clock, the lever movement striking on a gong with push repeat, with enamel chapter ring, 19thC, 7½in (19cm).
£600-650 *P*

An engraved and porcelain panel carriage timepiece, panelled to 3 sides with blue and white flowers on silvered background, the movement bearing the stamp of Richard et Cie, with cylinder escapement, 5in (13cm).
£1,200-1,500 *CSK*

A French brass cased carriage clock, with engraved and porcelain dial.
£200-250 *MGM*

A French brass carriage clock, the dial and sides set with porcelain plaques and signed LS, 8-day striking and repeating lever movement, 7½in (19cm).
£1,500-1,700 *DN*

A French brass carriage clock, with 8-day striking and repeating lever movement, 7in (18cm), with travelling case.
£600-700 *DN*

A grande sonnerie striking carriage clock, in gilt variant case, with silvered mask to white enamel dial, signed A. Jackemann, Paris, the 8-day movement striking on 2 gongs with lever platform escapement and change lever in base, 6in (15cm).
£1,500-2,000 *CSK*

Mantel Clocks

A black slate mantel timepiece, with gilt dial, the fusee movement with anchor escapement, signed Payne, 163 New Bond Street, 19thC, 8½in (22cm).
£300-350 *P*

A walnut mantel clock, the case with glazed top, side and back panels, the silvered dial with engraved spandrels, signed Chas. Frodsham, Clockmaker to the Queen, No. 2057, the fusee movement with anchor escapement, signed on the backplate, late 19thC, 12in (30.5cm).
£900-1,200 *P*

A gilt porcelain-panelled mantel clock, with Brocot escapement, 15in (38cm).
£2,200-2,500 *TCW*

A Regency rosewood and brass inlaid mantel timepiece, the silvered dial signed Carpenter, London, the fusee movement with shaped plates and anchor escapement, 9½in (24cm).
£2,000-2,500 *P*

A Regency burr walnut mantel clock, surmounted by a bronze gadrooned top with brass side frets and stringing to the front, the silvered dial signed C. Lupton, Cornhill, London, the 8-day fusee movement striking on a gong, the pendulum with fine regulation and lock, 11in (28cm).
£2,000-2,500 *CSK*

A Regency burr walnut, brass and ebony inlaid mantel timepiece, the silvered dial signed Grimalde & Johnson, Strand, London, the fusee movement with signed backplate and anchor escapement, damaged, 12in (31cm).
£2,500-3,000 *P*

A Regency mahogany and brass inlaid mantel timepiece, the enamel dial signed Scott, Horlr. to H.R.H. The Duke of Kent, 674, the fusee movement with anchor escapement and signed shaped plates, 10in (26cm).
£500-600 *P*

A Regency white marble and gilt bronze mantel timepiece, the gilt dial with engine turned centre, signed Viner, London, the fusee movement with anchor escapement, 8in (20cm).
£500-600 *P*

A Regency mahogany and brass inlaid mantel timepiece, the painted dial signed Thwaites & Reed, London, the fusee movement with arched plates and anchor escapement, 16½in (42cm).
£800-1,000 *P*

A mahogany and brass inlaid mantel clock, the painted dial signed Condliff, Liverpool, the twin fusee movement striking on a bell with anchor escapement, 19thC, 14in (35cm).
£800-1,000 *P*

A Regency mahogany and brass inlaid mantel timepiece, with enamel dial, damaged, the fusee movement with anchor escapement, 9½in (24cm).
£300-400 *P*

A Regency mahogany timepiece, with brass inlay to the front, with white painted dial, the 8-day fusee movement with shaped plates and pendulum lock, 16in (41cm).
£800-900 *CSK*

A mantel clock with 8-day striking movement, the painted dial marked Howell James & Co., London, with Meissen porcelain case, 19thC, 12in (30.5cm).
£1,000-1,200 *DSH*

A French brass mantel clock, with enamel dial and visible escapement, signed for Payne, Tunbridge Wells, the movement with twin glass mercury pendulum, 19thC, 20in (51cm).
£1,500-2,000 *P*

A Victorian mahogany mantel clock, the white dial signed Arnold and Dent, London, with Roman numerals and moon hands, the 8-day fusee movement striking on a bell, 12½in (32cm).
£500-700 *CSK*

An inlaid mantel clock, with 8-day striking movement.
£350-400 *MGM*

Make the Most of Miller's

CONDITION is absolutely vital when assessing the value of an antique. Damaged pieces on the whole appreciate much less than perfect examples. However a rare, desirable piece may command a high price even when damaged

Charles X ormolu mantel clock, th dial and striking movement, in oliate drum case with glazed ckplate, the stepped plinth with a ief panel of Cupid and Psyche er Gérôme, on block feet, 19in cm).
0-1,200 *C*

A Charles X bronze and ormolu mantel clock, with the seated figure of Cato with his helmet and sword amidst the ruins of Carthage, the stepped griotte marble base edged with foliage, on bun feet, 17½in (44.5cm) wide.
£1,500-2,000 *C*

A French ormolu and porcelain mantel clock, the decorated dial signed for Miller & Co., Bristol, 19thC, 17in (43cm).
£600-700 *P*

An ornate cast brass mantel clock, decorated with birds and mask heads, 8-day striking movement, and claw feet.
£250-300 *MGM*

A brass Eureka mantel timepiece, the movement with substantial compensated balance, numbered 7219, the signed enamel dial with subsidiary seconds, inscribed S. Fisher Ltd., 188 Strand, under a damaged glass shade, 13in (33cm).
£500-600 *P*

A French bronze and yellow marbl mantel clock, the engine turned silvered dial signed Duval a Paris, the 8-day movement with silk suspension, outside countwheel an striking on a bell, early 19thC, 24i (61cm).
£800-1,000 *CSK*

A French ormolu and porcelain mantel clock, 19thC, 15in (38cm).
£800-1,000 *P*

A French ormolu and bronze mantel clock, the gilt dial with enamel numerals, the movement with silk suspension and countwheel strike, 19thC, 22in (56cm).
£900-1,200 *P*

A French brass and porcelain mantel clock, 19thC, 14in (36cm).
£2,000-2,500 *P*

A French ormolu and enamel mantel clock, with polychrome champlevé decoration and circular gilt dial, 19thC, 12½in (32cm).
£600-700 *P*

A French ormolu and porcelain mounted mantel clock, the case with enamel dial, signed Chas. Frodsham, Paris, 19thC, 14in (36cm).
£1,200-1,500 *P*

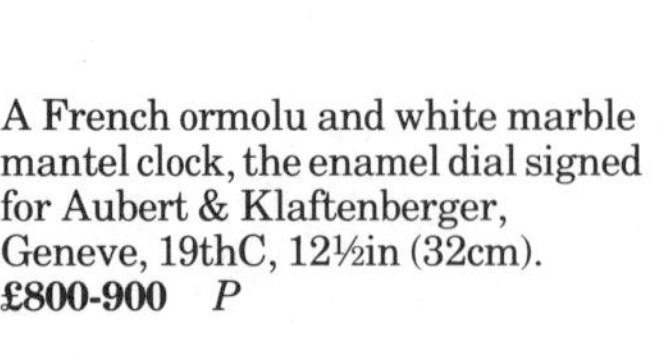

A French ormolu and white marble mantel clock, the enamel dial signed for Aubert & Klaftenberger, Geneve, 19thC, 12½in (32cm).
£800-900 *P*

A French ormolu and porcelain mantel clock, with enamel dial signed Vieyres & Repignon a Paris, 19thC, 11in (28cm).
£700-800 *P*

French white marble and bronze .antel clock, the case with ecorated enamel dial raised on a olumn with a naked putto, 19thC, 5½in (39cm).
600-700 *P*

A French gilt mantel clock, with 8-day striking movement, embossed with cherubs, 19thC.
£500-600 *MGM*

A French 8-day striking clock movement set in the stern of a ship, mounted on black marble base with glass dome, the pendulum moving a sailor and the ship's wheel, late 19thC, 13½in (34cm).
£900-1,200 *CW*

Charles X ormolu and porcelain ock, with silvered face and floral nd foliate bezel, the movement gned Le Roy Paris 1102, 16in 1cm) high.
800-1,200 *C*

A French mahogany 4-pillar clock in Empire style, with flame mahogany veneers, the movement with gilt cast bezel and white enamel dial, the 8-day movement with 9-rod pendulum, anchor escapement and outside countwheel striking on a bell, 23in (58cm).
£500-600 *CSK*

A French mantel clock, with annular chapter ring and 8-day movement, in gilt brass case, late 19th/early 20thC, 22½in (57cm).
£450-550 *Bea*

Louis XVI ormolu and biscuit antel clock, the glazed enamel dial gned A Paris, 13½in (34cm) wide.
1,200-1,500 *C*

A French red tortoiseshell and boulle mantel clock, the embossed gilt dial with blue Roman numerals on white porcelain cartouches with trefoil hands, the 8-day movement striking on a bell, 14in (36cm).
£550-600 *CSK*

A French bronze and gilt bronze mantel clock, with enamelled annual chapter ring with blue Roman numerals and regulator square above XII, and with 8-day movement by Japy Freres, 22in (56cm), with pendulum.
£1,500-1,700 *Bea*

A French ormolu mantel clock, the dial in green patinated frame surmounted by dying stag and 2 hounds, by Leroy & Fils, Paris, 10in (25.5cm).
£400-500 *WHB*

A French bronze white marble and ormolu mantel clock, in the form of a globe, on a gilt base, the dial of applied gilt Roman numerals with hands in the form of a snake, the 8-day movement striking on a bell, with lever platform escapement, 14½in (37cm).
£1,200-1,500 *CSK*

A French tortoiseshell and brass inlaid mantel clock, with 8-day striking movement and gilt metal mounts to case.
£350-400 *MGM*

An oak mantel clock, edged in boxwood, by W. H. of Germany, 8-day duration, striking on ting-tang chimes, c1880, 13in (33cm).
£200-250 *SBA*

An ormolu mounted white and red marble mantel clock, with glazed enamel dial signed Drouot à Paris, 15in (38cm) wide.
£2,000-2,500 *C*

Lantern Clocks

A late Stuart brass lantern clock of standard form, with anchor escapement and countwheel strike on bell above, with dolphin pierced frets above the dial, signed Nicholas Coxiter Londini fecit, within the florally engraved centre, 16in (41cm).
£1,000-1,200 *CAm*

An early Smith's lantern timepiece, c1920, 10½in (26cm).
£120-170 *SBA*

A brass lantern clock, with silvered chapter ring, half and quarter-hour divisions, engraved central field with single steel hand, signed Ninyan Burliegh, Durham, the weight driven movement with anchor escapement striking on a bell, early 18thC, with modern oak bracket, 15½in (39cm).
£1,200-1,500 *CSK*

A Georgian brass lantern clock, made for the Turkish market, the posted frame surrounded by a bell, with brass dial and chapter ring, signed on a cartouche in the arch Jno. Parks, London, the movement with verge bob pendulum escapement, 14½in (37cm).
£700-800 *P*

Locate the source

The source of each illustration in Miller's can be found by checking the code letters below each caption with the list of contributors.

A French brass lantern clock, the circular chased dial with enamel numerals, and pierced cresting, the movement with verge escapement and bob pendulum, originally designed for alarm, 16in (41cm).
£700-900 *P*

A brass lantern clock, the posted frame surmounted by a bell, the dial with brass chapter, signed Wilmshurst, Odiham, with engraved centre, the movement with verge bob pendulum escapement and countwheel strike, 15in (38cm).
£1,200-1,500 *P*

A Georgian brass miniature lantern clock, made for the Turkish market, signed on the cartouche in the arch Robt. Ward, London, the bell and bell cage missing, the movement with verge escapement, the pallet arbor and bob pendulum missing, 5½in (14cm).
£1,500-2,000 *P*

Skeleton Clocks

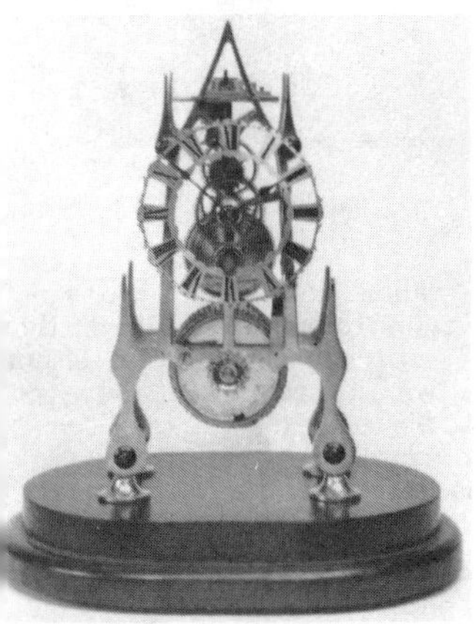

A brass skeleton timepiece, the pierced spired plates with pierced silvered chapter ring, the fusee movement with lever, platform escapement, on a mahogany base under a glass dome, 19thC, 13in (33cm).
£600-700 *P*

An English single fusee skeleton clock, in the Gothic style, with 8-day movement, passing strike, c1860.
£800-900 *SBA*

A Charles X ormolu and marble skeleton clock, signed Isidore Grenot, with enamel dial, on a black marble base, 18in (46cm).
£1,000-1,200 *CNY*

A brass cathedral skeleton clock, the pierced silver chapter ring with black Roman numerals, the fusee movement striking on a gong and Westminster chiming on 8 graduated bells at the quarters, on a white marble plinth, under a glass dome, late 19thC, 21½in (54cm).
£3,000-3,500 *HSS*

Wall Clocks

A Victorian skeleton clock, with passing strike, silvered chapter ring, the 8-day movement with chain fusee and deadbeat escapement, on wooden base with 4 bun feet, with a dome, 12in (30cm).
£400-500 *CSK*

A Swiss wooden wall clock, with arched side doors, the plates, wheels and pinions all of wood, with verge balance wheel escapement and outside countwheel strike, sounding on a bell mounted on top, 18thC, 11½in (29cm).
£4,500-5,000 *P*

A walnut Amsterdammertje, signed Etienne Hubert Amsterdam on the silvered chapter ring, the movement with anchor escapement and rack double strike, the wall case of standard form with figure finials, basically 18thC, 61in (155cm).
£700-1,000 *CAm*

A George III black lacquer Act of Parliament clock, painted with Roman chapters and Arabic minute numerals above signature Pet. Bargeau, London, fitted with later weight drive movement with deadbeat escapement, 60½in (152cm).
£2,000-2,500 *CNY*

A George III brass wall clock, the brass dial with date aperture, signed Edwd. Pashler, London, and with strike/silent lever at the IX, the twin fusee movement with anchor escapement, 18½in (47cm).
£1,500-2,000 *P*

An English inlaid mahogany dial clock, with brass bezel and convex 10in (25.5cm) circular dial, with twin fusee mechanism, striking on a bell with anchor escapement, early 19thC.
£450-500 *P[Re]*

A mahogany wall timepiece, the brass dial signed Mattw. & Thos. Dutton, London, the fusee movement with anchor escapement, 19thC, 26½in (67cm).
£2,700-3,000 *P*

A German carved wood wall clock, the brass movement striking the hours on a gong, and discharging an organ playing on 9 brass pipes, followed by a 4 air musical box, 19thC, 83in (211cm).
£7,000-8,000 *P*

Make the most of Miller's

When a large specialist well-publicised collection comes on the market, it tends to increase prices. Immediately after this, prices can fall slightly due to the main buyers having large stocks and the market being 'flooded'. This is usually temporary and does not affect very high quality items.

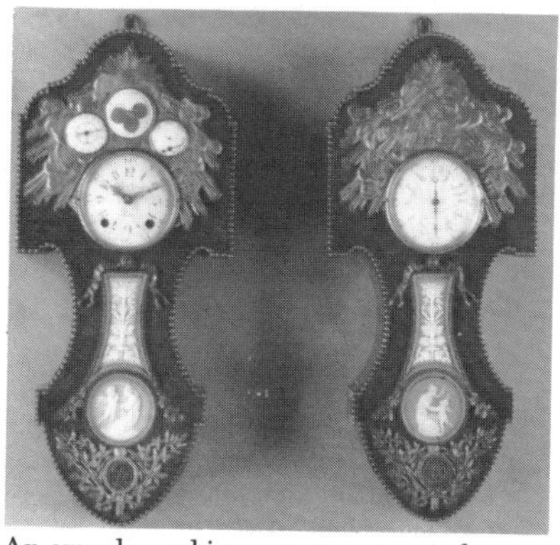

An ormolu and jasperware mounted wall clock and matching thermometer, with white enamel dials, the clock signed Du Quesne à Paris below 3 subsidiary dials for day, date and age of the moon, the signed movement late 18thC, the thermometer with single white enamel dial reading in degrees Celsius, mid-19thC, 25in (63.5cm).
£2,500-3,000 *CNY*

An oak Vienna wall clock, the enamel dial signed W. Schonberger, Vienna, the twin-train weight driven movement with deadbeat escapement, 19thC, 56in (142cm).
£650-750 *P*

An unusual wall clock for a gaming room, in mahogany frame surmounted by boxwood chess pieces, the 8-day spring wound movement with Brocot escapement, striking on a gong, late 19thC, 20in (51cm) square.
£800-900 *CSK*

A mahogany veneered wall clock by John Smith, Holborn, London, with drop pendulum case decorated with brass inlay, white enamelled dial over 8-day single fusee movement, 25in (63cm).
£300-400 *WIL*

HINTS TO DATING WALL CLOCKS

Dials

Square	to c1755	George II or later
Broken arch	from c1720 to c1805	early to late Georgian
Painted/round	from c1740	George II or later
Silvered	from c1760	George III or later

Case finish

Ebony veneer	from c1690	to William and Mary
Marquetry	from c1680 to c1695	from Carolean to William and Mary
Mahogany	from c1740	from early Georgian
Oak	always	

A German softwood wall clock, the case carved with oak leaves round a glazed door, white enamelled dial with 8-day movement, late 19thC, 13in (33cm).
£500-550 *WIL*

Garnitures

A French brass, enamel and porcelain mounted clock garniture, signed Lefranc, the enamel dial within an enamel bezel, the pendulum with similar decoration, 19thC, 15in (38cm), with a matching pair of side urns, on giltwood bases.
£1,800-2,000 *P*

An ormolu and porcelain garniture, the blue porcelain dial with gilt decoration, Roman numerals in white cartouches with seed pearl decoration, the 8-day movement striking on a bell, with 2 similarly decorated side pieces, the removable tops with painted scenes to the front and reverse, seed pearl decoration on circular gilt base, some damage, 18in (46cm) over the clock.
£1,700-2,000 *CSK*

A French green onyx, ormolu and enamel clock garniture, the gilt dial with enamelled bezel and centre signed for Sir John Bennett, the movement with decorated twin glass mercury pendulum, 19thC, 12½in (32cm), with a matching pair of side ornaments.
£700-800 *P*

A French porcelain and ormolu mounted clock garniture, the circular movement with enamel dial inscribed Le Roy & Fils, the bimetallic pendulum designed for a paste ring to oscillate outside the dial, the ring now missing, 19thC, 19in (49cm), with a matching pair of 4-branch candelabra.
£2,000-2,500 *P*

A French ormolu clock garniture, the clock movement mounted in an owl, with enamel numerals, 19thC, 19½in (49cm), with a matching pair of 3-branch candelabra.
£2,000-2,500 *P*

A gilt metal clock set, of Renaissance style, the clock with glazed enamel dial, indistinctly signed … Giuseppe…., the 8-light candelabra with cupid finials and scrolling branches, the pierced shafts supported by caryatids and putti with conforming bases, late 19thC, the clock 28in (71cm).
£2,500-3,000 *C*

A French red tortoiseshell and ormolu garniture, in the style of Louis XV, the inside of the case with red tortoiseshell, the gilt embossed dial with blue Roman numerals on white enamel cartouches, signed on an enamel cartouche Martino, Paris, the 8-day movement striking on a gong, with matching side pieces of 5-arm candelabra, on tortoiseshell bases with applied gilt mounts and gilt scroll feet, 24in (61cm).
£800-900 *CSK*

A German garniture of 3 comprising a clock, the movement by Roy a Paris, 17in (43cm), with 2-branch candelabra, modelled as musicians, adapted for electricity, some damage, late 19thC.
£900-1,200 *CEd*

A Sèvres style porcelain ormolu mounted clock set, stamped PH. MOUREY, comprising the clock with pink and white dial, 18in (46cm), and a pair of matching ormolu covered two-handled urns, each stamped Ph. Mourey, 14in (35cm).
£550-650 *CNY*

A French gilt marble and gilt metal garniture, in the Empire style, on green marble bases, the white enamel chapter ring with Roman numerals, engine turned gilt centre and moon hands, the 8-day movement under glass with outside countwheel striking on a bell, with matching 3-arm candelabra on fluted black columns, 18in (46cm) high over the clock.
£1,200-1,600 *CSK*

A French veined marble garniture, the white enamel dial indistinctly signed, the 8-day movement with outside countwheel striking on a bell, with matching side pieces consisting of a marble urn with gilt top and side pieces on square marble bases with gilt mounts and feet, 17in (43cm) over the clock.
£450-550 *CSK*

Prices

The never-ending problem of fixing prices for antiques! A price can be affected by so many factors, for example:
- ***condition***
- ***desirability***
- ***rarity***
- ***size***
- ***colour***
- ***provenance***
- ***restoration***
- ***the sale of a prestigious collection***
- ***collection label***
- ***appearance of a new reference book***
- ***new specialist sale at major auction house***
- ***mentioned on television***
- ***the fact that two people present at auction are determined to have the piece***
- ***where you buy it***

One also has to contend with the fact that an antique is not only a 'thing of beauty' but a commodity. The price can again be affected by
- ***supply and demand***
- ***international finance – currency fluctuation***
- ***fashion***
- ***inflation***
- ***the fact that a museum has vast sums of money to spend***

Miscellaneous

A Continental spelter mystery timepiece, the movement forming the upper part of the pendulum, which is supported in front of a cast figure of a kangaroo, 12½in (31.5cm).
£400-500 *P*

A carved oak cuckoo clock, the wooden dial with applied bone Roman numerals and bone hands, the skeletonised fusee movement striking on a gong, and operating 2 bellows and the cuckoo, 29in (74cm), with carved bracket.
£1,200-1,500 *CSK*

An ormolu and bronze clock, with glazed enamel dial, indistinctly signed ... Armentieres, the case surmounted by an eagle supported by a classical semi-nude figure upon a fruiting platform, 32½in (83cm).
£1,500-2,000 *C*

A French clock, 18½in (47cm).
£3,000-3,500 *Ba*

Provenance: Original for Burghley House, Stanford, property of Lady Isabella Cecil.

A South German giltmetal tabernacle clock or Turmuhr, basically early 17thC, associated and with restorations, 19in (48cm).
£6,500-7,000 *C*

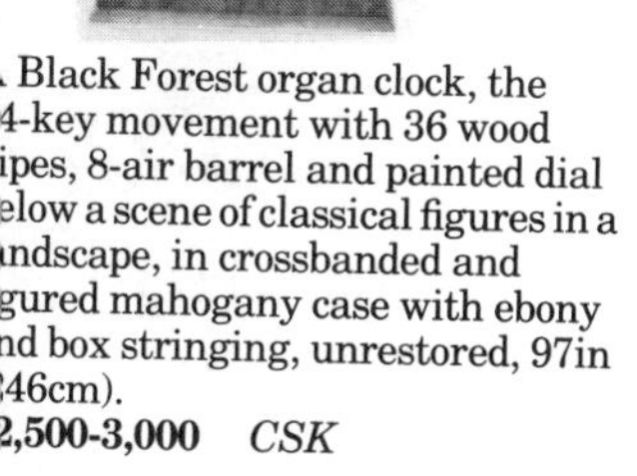

. Black Forest organ clock, the 4-key movement with 36 wood ipes, 8-air barrel and painted dial elow a scene of classical figures in a ndscape, in crossbanded and gured mahogany case with ebony nd box stringing, unrestored, 97in '46cm).
2,500-3,000 *CSK*

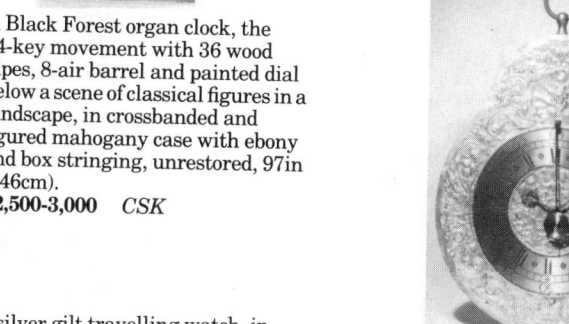

A German baroque brass and silvered Telleruhr, the circular plated movement with cylindrical pillars, resting barrel for the striking with pierced gates and numbered outside countwheel, chain fusee for the going with up-and-down ring engraved on the backplate signed Casper Sackerer, with loose ring suspension, basically early 18thC, with restorations, 17in (44cm) over pendant.
£1,200-1,500 *C*

silver gilt travelling watch, in gine turned case, with watch vealed by depressing the 2 sides, e matt silvered dial with Arabic merals and moon hands, the ovement jewelled to the centre th 17 jewels and signed Tavannes atch Company.
00-400 *CSK*

An ormolu mounted Sèvres pattern vase clock, the turquoise ground oviform vase inset with central glazed enamel dial, 23½in (59cm).
£800-1,000 *C*

An ormolu cartel clock, the glazed dial with Roman numerals, signed T. Martin, Paris, 27in (68.5cm) wide.
£1,000-1,500 *C*

A Louis XV cartel clock, with glazed enamel dial signed Joannes Biesta Paris, 32in (81cm).
£2,000-2,500 *C*

A Louis XV ormolu cartel clock, the glazed enamel dial signed Leroy a Paris, the movement with anchor escapement and rack strike planted on the backplate, the cartouche shaped case cast with upspringing foliage, 20in (51cm).
£1,200-1,600 *C*

A tôle piente Scwartzwald clockmaker figure, naturalistically painted, with a timepiece carried to his front and a dummy one, containing the key on his back, on wood base simulating maple, 15in (38cm).
£2,000-2,500 *CAm*

A Freise Stoelklok of standard form, with cast lead frets to the canopy and above the dial with moonphase, the movement with spiral angle posts, 18thC, 31½in (80cm).
£2,500-2,800 *CAm*

A Swiss silver and enamel miniature travelling timepiece, the case surmounted by a handle and decorated with purple guilloche enamel, fitted with a watch movement, 3.4cm, in a fitted travelling case in the form of a miniature briefcase.
£400-500 *P*

A brass mounted mahogany sedan clock, with glazed dial and moulded frame, early 19thC, 7in (18cm) diam.
£250-350 *C*

A Georgian gilt metal timepiece, th verge movement with engraved tapered plate signed Thomas Greenstreet, fecit, the signed 24-hour dial with movable centre disc engraved with 24 cities aroun the world, and held aloft by Father Time, 7½in (19cm).
£800-900 *P*

Watches

An 18ct gold half hunter watch by Connell, Cheapside, London, with button winding, the case hallmarked London 1877.
£500-600 *HCH*

An 18ct gold keyless lever watch, the movement with machined plates, signed Dent, Watchmaker to the King, 28 Cockspur St & 4 Royal Exchange, London, No. 58174, with gold hands, the case with thief proof pendant marked London 1921, 5.2cm.
£2,600-3,000 *P*

An 18ct gold open faced half hunter pocket watch, with blue Roman numerals on the front cover with white enamelled dial, signed Chas. Frodsham, 05745, 5cm.
£500-600 *CSK*

A silver pair cased verge watch, signed Jno Gammon, London 3398, the enamel dial with steel beetle and poker hands, early 18thC, 5.9cm.
£370-420 *P*

A Garrard & Co 18ct gold hunter pocket watch, with button winding and subsidiary seconds dial, the case hallmarked London 1913.
£400-500 *HCH*

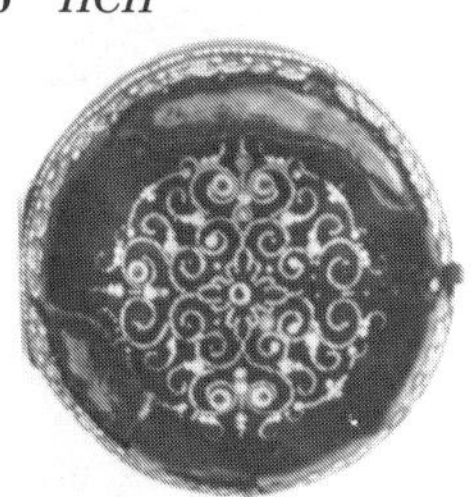

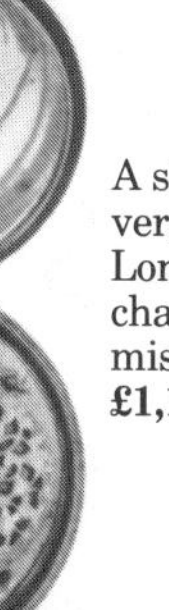

A silver and tortoiseshell pair cased verge watch, signed Chr. Gould, London, with signed silver champleve dial, some tortoiseshell missing, early 18thC, 5.6cm.
£1,100-1,300 *P*

A George III 18ct gold and enamel verge watch, the movement with pierced cock, signed J. Ireland, London 3385, the case with blue and white decorated bezels, marked London 1778, 4.3cm.
£800-1,000 *P*

A silver pair cased verge watch, the movement with square baluster pillars and pierced cock, signed Nicks Muddle, Lindfield, the inner case marked London 1750, 5cm.
£700-800 *P*

A Georgian gilt metal giant verge watch, the movement with pierced and engraved cock and ruby endstone, signed Wm. Robertson, London No. 4057, with later engraved silver dial, 8.5cm.
£1,800-2,200 *P*

A gold and enamel pair cased watch, the movement with square baluster pillars, steel cylinder escapement and pierced cock, signed Geo. Phi. Strigel, London, BBFM, the inner case marked London 1770, 4.8cm.
£2,100-2,500 *P*

A coaching watch, the cylindrical brass case contained within a brass bound mahogany box with recessed carrying handle, signed on the brass back 96 hours, Wregg, London No. 1649, Express No. 1., with unusual verge escapement, early 19thC, 12 by 9cm.
£2,500-3,000 *P*

A quarter repeating jacquemart watch, in gold drum case with dark blue enamel surround to dial, applied with gold mounts, striking on 2 gongs.
£2,000-3,000 *CSK*

A French gold and enamel verge watch, the movement with pierced bridge cock, signed L'Epine a Paris, with later enamel dial, 3.9cm.
£750-850 *P*

A Swiss gold and enamel cylinder watch, the gilt bar movement signed H. Capt. Geneve, with enamel dial, the signed gold cuvette numbered 19119, 3.7cm.
£1,000-1,500 *P*

A French silver quarter repeating verge watch, the movement with pierced Egyptian pillars and bridge cock, signed Jacques Gloria à Rouen, early 18thC, with later gilt dial, 6cm.
£2,000-3,000 *P*

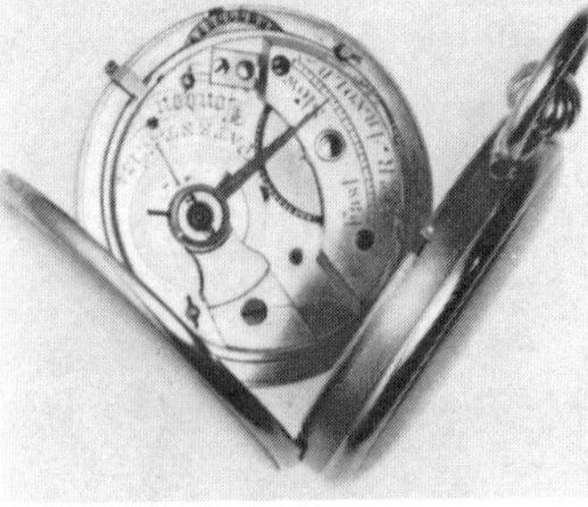

A gold Prest's keyless cylinder watch, by Jno. R. Arnold, Patent No. 134, London, the gilt movement signed on the bridge to the going barrel and on the top plate, casemaker TH, London 1825, 4.5cm.
£2,000-2,500 *C*

A German gold hunter cased keyless lever watch, the movement with compensated balance and overcoil spring, jewelled to the centre and signed Adolph Lange, Dresden 8667, the enamel dial, cracked, in numbered case, monogrammed to the front, 5.3cm.
£1,800-2,200 *P*

A Swiss gold minute repeating keyless lever dress watch by Cartier, the steel bar movement with compensated balance, signed Cartier, Paris 29, the signed silvered dial with subsidiary seconds, the case numbered 3088, with an inscription on the back to H. R. Coombs, Esq., 1917, 4.8cm.
£4,500-5,000 *P*

A Swiss gold and enamel cylinder watch, the movement signed Badollet a Geneve, with machined gold dial, the reverse decorated with a spray of lilies against a blue ground, 3.5cm.
£400-600 *P*

A Swiss gold and enamel cylinder watch, the gold cuvette inscribed Malignon a Geneve, No. 1805, 3.8cm.
£500-600 *P*

. gold and enamel form watch, the
erge movement with pierced
ridge cock, signed Fs Mayer a la
'ille de Karlsbaad a Vienne, the
ase in the form of a viola, damaged,
9thC.
1,500-2,000 *P*

A Swiss 8-day nickel cased keyless lever Goliath watch, the enamel dial signed Hy Moser & Cie, with subsidiary seconds, in a leather case, 10.3cm.
£400-500 *P*

A Swiss gold and enamel form watch, the keyless cylinder movement with enamel dial, contained in a jockey's racing cap decorated with black, blue and white designs, 2.7cm wide.
£1,700-2,000 *P*

. Swiss gold minute repeating
eyless lever watch, signed Touchon
: Co., Switzerland, with signed gilt
ial, the case with repeat slide in the
and, 4.4cm.
1,000-1,500 *P*

A Swiss 18ct gold hunter cased minute repeating keyless lever chronograph, the movement with visible stopwork, compensated balance and extra jewelling to the repeat train, 5.8cm.
£2,500-3,000 *P*

A Swiss gold miniature hunter cased pendant watch, the keyless cylinder movement with enamel dial, the case set with a diamond in a heart shaped setting, 2.6cm.
£270-320 *P*

Vristwatches

A lady's brilliant and baguette cut diamond bracelet watch, on a fan and scroll design tapering flexible link bracelet.
£3,200-3,600 *C*

A Swiss gold keyless lever dress watch, the movement jewelled to the centre, signed European Watch and Clock Co. Ltd, the silvered dial signed Cartier, 4.5cm, in a signed presentation case.
£2,000-3,000 *P*

A lady's Continental wristwatch, with rose diamond bezel and winding button, with pearl 3 row bracelet and diamond and pearl clasp.
£2,200-2,600 *CSK*

A lady's diamond and platinum wristwatch, with white enamel dial with white gold abstract chapters and hands, signed by Jaeger-LeCoultre.
£15,000-20,000 *CNY*

A lady's wristwatch with diamond bezel, the dial signed Kutchinsky on an 18ct gold integral bracelet.
£1,000-1,200 *CSK*

A lady's diamond, sapphire and yellow gold wristwatch, with 18ct gold stylised half moon band, enhanced by a calibré cut sapphire arc, mounted in platinum and yellow gold, c1940, signed Vacheron & Constantin.
£4,000-4,500 *CNY*

A lady's yellow gold wristwatch, signed by Concord, with quartz movement.
£600-800 *CNY*

A lady's yellow gold wristwatch with white enamel dial, gold chapters and brass hands, signed Waltham, with a blue snakeskin band.
£2,000-3,000 *CNY*

A gentleman's wristwatch by Vacheron & Constantin, Geneve, the matt white dial with applied gold numerals, the silvered movement signed, with certificate of origin and guarantee.
£1,700-2,300 *CSK*

An early chronograph wristwatch by Longines, with signed white enamel dial, blued steel moon hands, 24-hour ring in red Arabic numerals, red telemetric and black tachymetric scales, the central chronograph operated by a press button through the crown, movement numbered 5016649.
£2,500-3,000 *CSK*

A gentleman's wristwatch, signed on the matt silvered dial Rolex Oyster Elegante, Precision, with alternating baton and Arabic numerals, screwed down winder and screwed back.
£800-900 *CSK*

An 18ct gold Omega wristwatch, with gilt dial signed Constellation Automatic Chronometer Officially Certified, day, date, bar numerals, with integral flexible brick link bracelet, 3.7cm.
£700-900 *Bon*

A gentleman's steel automatic wristwatch, signed on the black dial Rolex Oyster Perpetual Datejust, applied gold batons and white date aperture, screw down crown and integral steel bracelet with Rolex clasp.
£250-300 *CSK*

An early Rolex Oyster, in water resistant plated case, signed on the white enamel dial, the case numbered 7966, 3cm long.
£450-500 *CSK*

A 9ct red gold cased wristwatch, with applied gold numerals, and subsidiary seconds ring, signed Rolex, with screwed back to case, the signed movement jewelled to the 3rd with 15 jewels. ▶
£600-800 *CSK*

A gentleman's yellow gold wristwatch, with grey enamel dial and gold hands, signed by Piaget, in a black leather fitted case.
£2,500-3,000 *CNY*

◀ A German pilot's wristwatch of World War II, in grey metal case, with black dial and luminous minutes and hours, sweep centre seconds, hand lacking, the gilt three-quarter plate movement signed A Lange & Sohne, number 216339, 5.5cm.
£600-700 *CSK*

A gold wristwatch, with club foot lever escapement, the signed metal dial with Arabic numerals and batons formed from inset mother-of-pearl, with subsidiary seconds, c1935, 2.3cm.
£250-300 *PT*

▼

A gentleman's wristwatch in gold bubble back case, signed Rolex Oyster Perpetual, Chronometre, the back numbered 46258 3131, with leather strap and gilt Rolex buckle, and a link mesh strap and clasp.
£2,600-3,000 *CSK*

Barometers

Stick

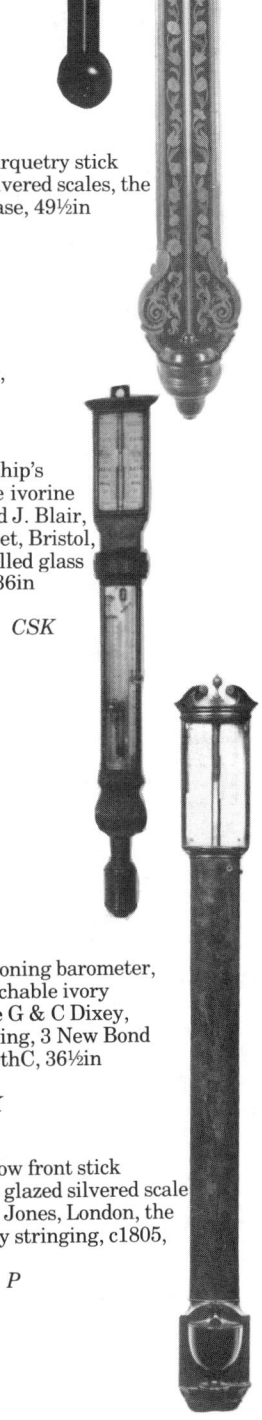

A mahogany stick barometer, with domed cistern and broken pediment, the register signed Rizzi Fecit, with thermometer and pressure scales, early 19thC, 37in (94cm).
£450-500 *P[Re]*

A walnut floral marquetry stick barometer, with silvered scales, the case with oak carcase, 49½in (126cm).
£1,800-2,000 *P*

A stick barometer with painted dial, the mahogany case inlaid with Sheraton shells and boxwood stringing, c1820, 37½in (95cm).
£800-1,000 *SBA*

A carved oak stick barometer, c1840, 46in (116.5cm).
£500-550 *SBA*

A mahogany ship's barometer, the ivorine plates stamped J. Blair, 45 Prince Street, Bristol, behind a bevelled glass plate, 19thC, 36in (91.5cm).
£1,500-2,000 *CSK*

An oak fishery or sea coast stick barometer, with twin glazed ceramic scales, by J. C. West, 92 & 93 Fleet Street, London, 19thC, 40½in (103cm).
£450-500 *P*

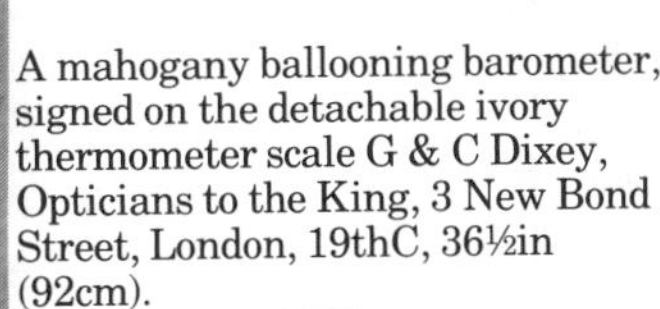

A mahogany ballooning barometer, signed on the detachable ivory thermometer scale G & C Dixey, Opticians to the King, 3 New Bond Street, London, 19thC, 36½in (92cm).
£900-1,000 *CSK*

A walnut veneer fishery or sea coast stick barometer, with twin glazed ceramic scales, by R & J Beck, 31 Cornhill, London, 19thC, 39in (99cm).
£420-460 *P*

A mahogany bow front stick barometer, the glazed silvered scale signed W. & S. Jones, London, the case with ebony stringing, c1805, 39in (99cm).
£1,800-2,200 *P*

A stick barometer, by Gilbert & Wright of London, with swan arch pediment, edged in ebony stringing, silvered dial, c1800, 41in (104cm).
£1,200-1,500 *SBA*

Wheel

A Georgian mahogany barometer, c1820, 38½in (97cm).
£1,000-1,200 *SBA*

A mercury banjo barometer, by J. Stopan of Aberdeen, with inlaid Sheraton shells, edged in ebony and boxwood stringing, c1820, 38in (96.5cm).
£450-550 *SBA*

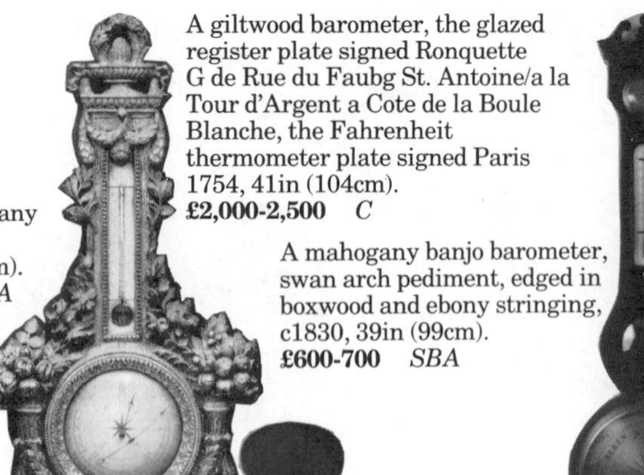

A giltwood barometer, the glazed register plate signed Ronquette G de Rue du Faubg St. Antoine/a la Tour d'Argent a Cote de la Boule Blanche, the Fahrenheit thermometer plate signed Paris 1754, 41in (104cm).
£2,000-2,500 *C*

A mahogany banjo barometer, swan arch pediment, edged in boxwood and ebony stringing, c1830, 39in (99cm).
£600-700 *SBA*

An oak banjo clock barometer, c1870, 39in (99cm).
£1,000-1,500 *SBA*

An inlaid mahogany banjo barometer, with silvered dials, by I. Somalvico, Hatton Garden.
£500-600 *MGM*

A lacquered brass aneroid barometer, signed J. Goldschmid, Zurich, fitted with a thermometer 3in (7.5cm).
£400-450 *CSK*

Chronometers

An 8-day marine chronometer, the movement with separate subplate, with Arnold type spring detent escapement, Arnold stud, helical spring and later compensated balance and signed on the mainplate Jno R. Arnold, London, Invt. et fecit 294, the 3½in (9cm) silvered dial signed Arnold, London 294, in a brass case, possibly the original bowl, now fitted with carrying handle, on ball feet, early 19thC.
£1,500-2,000 *P*

The Chronometer Ledgers at Greenwich show that this piece was issued to the Beagle in 1837 and transferred to Erebus where it was presumed lost in the Arctic with the Franklin Expedition, see V. Mercer, John Arnold & Son, *p237.*

An 8-day chronometer, by Charles Frodsham, with spring detent escapement, c1930.
£2,500-3,500 *DN*

A silver pocket chronometer, signed John Carter, Cornhill, London, No. 1573, the signed and numbered enamel dial with subsidiary seconds, the numbered case marked London 1842, 5.3cm.
£700-900 *P*

A 2-day marine chronometer, the movement with Earnshaw type spring detent escapement, the silvered dial signed Chadwick, Liverpool, No. 392, in a brass bowl hung in gimbals, with a safety key in a brass bound mahogany box, set with a signed and numbered ivory plaque, 19thC.
£1,200-1,600 *P*

A 2-day marine chronometer, signed on the frosted white dial Glashutte, number 12638, with gold hands, the movement with Earnshaw escapement, in gimballed dust cover, with rachet winder, diam of dial 10.2cm, with rating certificate and travelling box.
£600-700 *CSK*

A 2-day marine chronometer, in 2-tier box with glazed upper section signed on the silvered dial Thomas Mercer, No. 28266, with mahogany travelling box and rating certificate.
£500-600 *CSK*

Miscellaneous

A George III diagonal or 'yardarm' barometer and thermometer by Charles Zappa, with silvered engraved plates inlaid in mahogany case.
£2,200-2,600 *P[WSW]*

A brass cased desk aneroid barometer, the silvered dial with altitude scale and thermometer, in a silver case, maker W.F.W. London, 1907/8, the cover engraved with a monogram, 2½in (6.5cm).
£200-300 *CSK*

A Palais Royal noon cannon, by Lafontaine, 19thC.
£2,000-3,000 *HA*

Scientific Instruments

Dials

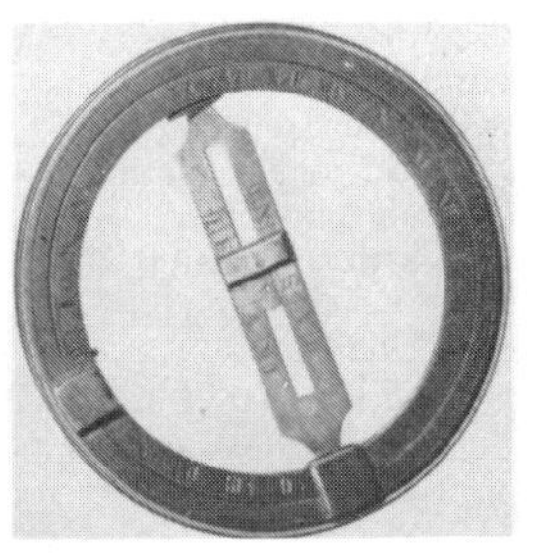

A brass universal equinoctial ring dial, unsigned, the meridian ring engraved on one side with a 0°–90° scale, the other side graduated with a 0°–83° scale read from the equinoctial, 18thC, 8.6cm diam.
£500-600 *CSK*

A silver and silver gilt equinoctial automatic dial, unsigned, but of the Johan Willebrand type, the horizontal plate engraved Gradus Poli, the compass with silvered dial engraved for variation, the blued steel needle with brass cap on pivot, the latitude dial engraved for 30°–65°, dial pointer and base plate missing, 18thC.
£2,500-3,000 *CSK*

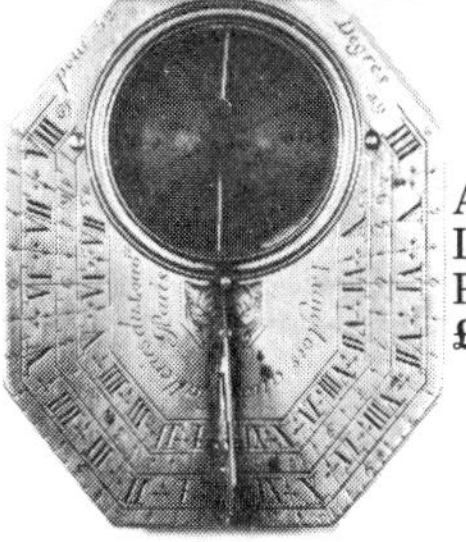

A brass Butterfield dial, signed Langlois aux Galleries du Louvre a Paris, slight damage, 8cm long.
£350-400 *P*

MAKE THE MOST OF MILLER'S

Price ranges in this book reflect what one should expect to pay for a similar example. When selling one can obviously expect a figure below. This will fluctuate according to a dealer's stock, saleability at a particular time, etc. It is always advisable to approach a reputable specialist dealer or an auction house which has specialist sales

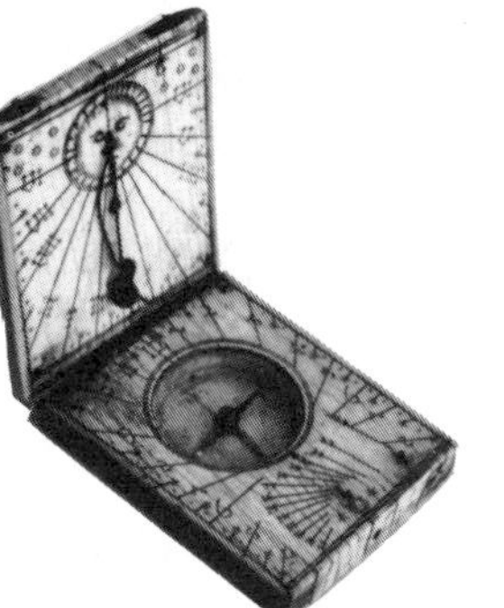

A German ivory sundial with moonphase indications, early 17thC.
£2,000-3,000 *HA*

A German ivory diptych dial, the cover engraved with a compass dial, the base with calendar dial and stamped with LM and a crown, the upper face with string gnomon dial and plumb bob, showing length of day against the zodiac signs, the lower inner face signed Lienhart Miller and dated 1628, inset with a compass, the needle on jewelled pivot, 9.2cm long, with glazed mahogany display case.
£1,500-2,000 *CSK*

Globes

A miniature terrestrial globe, inscribed within a cartouche 'A/New/Terrestrial/Globe/by/ Nath.Hill/1754', with fishskin case, depicting the major constellations, 3in (7cm) diam.
£1,500-2,000 *Bea*

A Georgian 18in (46cm) terrestrial globe, by W. & A.K. Johnston, on mahogany tripod stand with scroll feet and casters, later map.
£2,500-3,000 *JD*

A pair of 12in (30cm) J. & W. Cary globes, with coloured and varnished paper gores, set in divided brass meridian circles, titled 'Cary's New Terrestrial Globe . . . Made and Sold by J. & W. Cary, Strand, Septr 2nd 1816, with additions and corrections to 1818' and 'Cary's New Celestial Globe . . . precisely defined by Mr. Gilpin of the Royal Society . . . Jan.1, 1818', paper dial compass box, lacking one needle, 25in (63cm) high.
£9,000-10,000 *P*

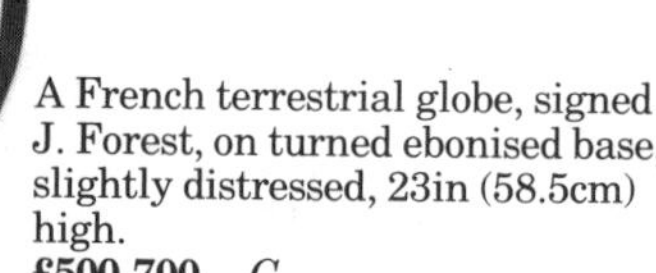

A 14in (36cm) Betts's Portable Terrestrial Globe, by George Philip & Son Ltd, the collapsible colour printed linen globe on umbrella pattern frame, with suspension ring, in original wooden box, late 19thC, 30½in (77cm) wide.
£250-350 *P*

A French terrestrial globe, signed J. Forest, on turned ebonised base, slightly distressed, 23in (58.5cm) high.
£500-700 *C*

Surveying

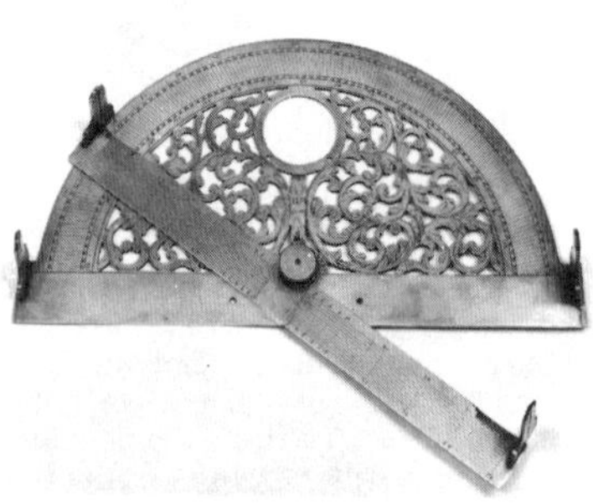

A brass graphometer, signed I L M Ad 1702, the scales divided 0°-180°/180°-0°, with 2 fixed sights, compass box missing, early 18thC, 14in (35cm) wide.
£900-1,200 *CSK*

A Newton's 15in (38cm) terrestrial globe, the sphere applied with hand coloured gores and inscribed 'Newton's New and Improved Terrestrial Globe. Accurately delineated from the discoveries of the most esteemed navigators and travellers to the present time, published 1 July 1815, manufactured by J. & W. Newton, No. 66 Chancery Lane, London, slight damage, 29½in (75cm) high.
£1,000-1,500 *Bea*

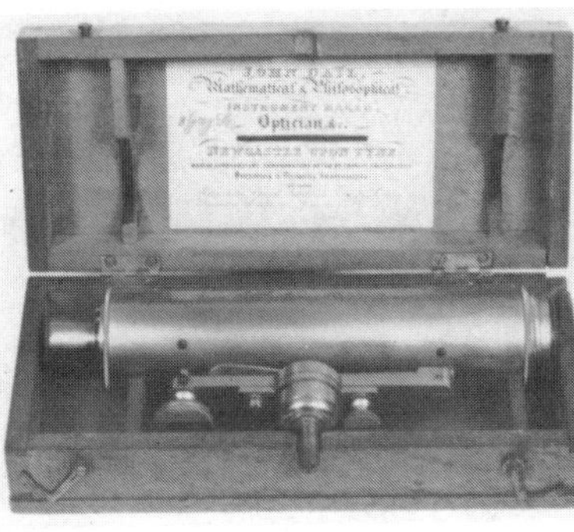

A surveyor's lacquered brass sighting level, signed John Cail Newcastle upon Tyne, with etched glass sights and maker's trade label, in mahogany case, 19thC, 9in (23cm) wide.
£200-300 *CSK*

A brass theodolite, signed on the plate Troughton & Simms, London, 19thC, 9½in (24cm) high.
£550-700 *CSK*

A brass folding arm protractor, signed Elliott Bros. London, with 2 verniers, fine adjustment tangent screw and clamp, late 19thC, 8in (20cm) wide, in mahogany case.
£250-300 *CSK*

A lacquered brass theodolite, by Troughton & Simms, some damage, mid-19thC, 11½in (29cm) wide, in the original mahogany case.
£850-1,000 *CSK*

A brass pantograph, by Watkins & Hill, London, in fitted wooden box with trade label, the box 26in (66cm) long.
£400-450 *C*

A lacquered brass 15in (38cm) 'Y' level, with 1in (2.5cm) diam lens and dust cap, pins replaced, 18thC, in oak case.
£250-350 *P*

Telescopes

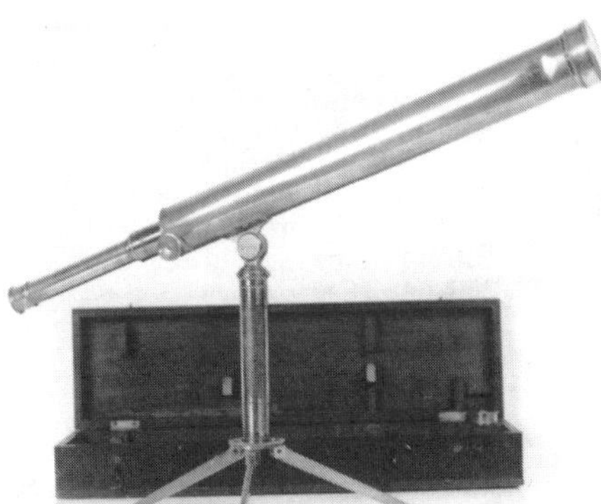

A rare Jesse Ramsden brass 2in (5cm) refracting library telescope mounted on tripod base, signed to the tube, with brass lens cap and accessories, c1800, in fitted mahogany case, 25½in (65cm) long overall.
£600-800 *P[Re]*

A brass 5in (13cm) astronomical telescope, with 52in (133cm) long white painted body tube, some damage, in mahogany case, applied with trade label of Dollond & Co, 1 Ludgate Hill, London, E.C., 19thC.
£600-700 *P*

A brass single-draw 1¼in (3cm) pocket telescope and stand, the draw-tube signed Dollond, London, with threaded dust cap, early 19thC, 7in (17cm) long extended, in pasteboard case.
£700-900 *P*

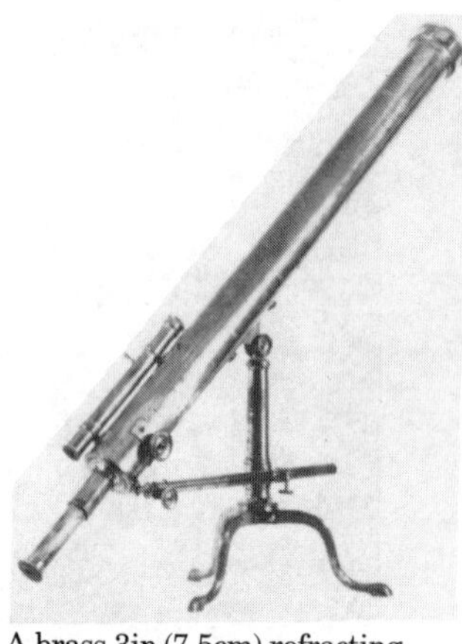

A brass 3in (7.5cm) refracting telescope, by Lewis & Brereton, 18 Preesons Row, Liverpool, with rack and pinion focusing, 19thC.
£650-750 *CSK*

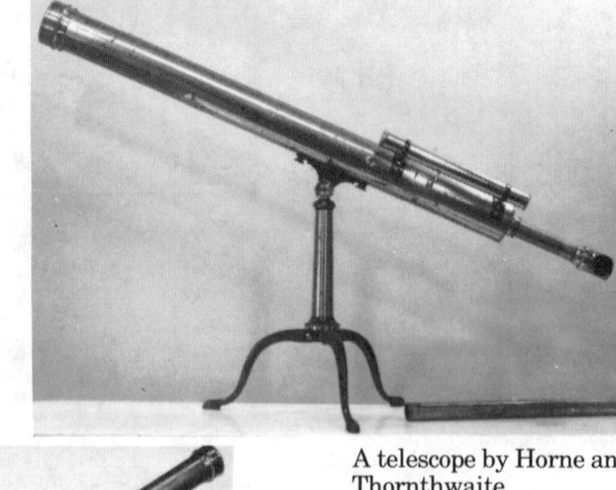

A telescope by Horne and Thornthwaite.
£450-500 *SAg*

A lacquered brass 3in (7.5cm) refracting telescope, signed Watson & Son, 313 High Holborn, London, with rack and pinion focusing and dust cap, in a Broadhurst & Clarkson case with 2 eye pieces, 45in (115cm) long.
£500-600 *CSK*

Microscopes

A lacquered brass botanical microscope, signed on the pillar Cary London, with accessories in a plush lined mahogany case, the lid with mounting ferrule, early 19thC, 5½in (14cm) wide.
£450-500 *CSK*

A rare lacquered brass solar microscope compendium, signed J. Cuff London on the rotating plate, one bead glass missing, 2 of 3 brass sliders numbered 1 x 2/3 x 4, and other items, 18thC, the case 9in (23cm) wide.
£2,000-3,000 *CSK*

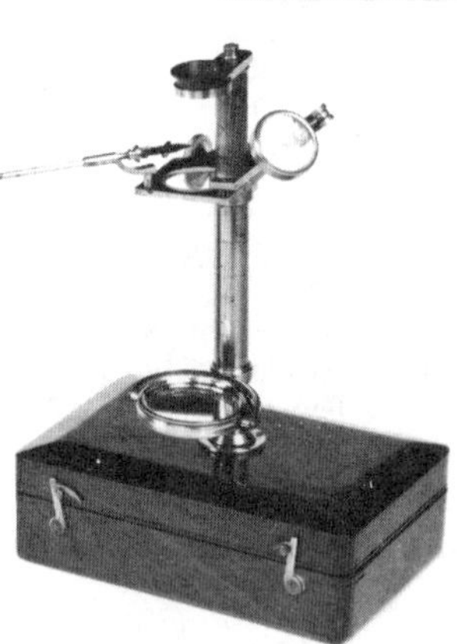

A lacquered brass botanical microscope, unsigned, with rack and pinion focusing, 3 objectives, bull's-eye condenser and swivel mirror, in a plush lined case, the lid with mounting ferrule, early 19thC, 5½in (14cm) wide.
£250-300 *CSK*

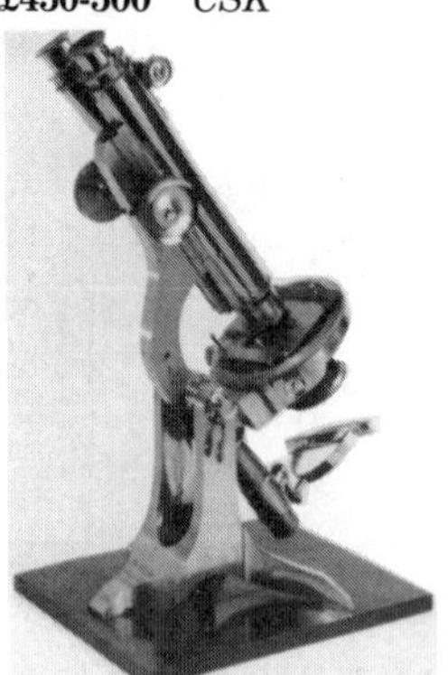

A lacquered brass Watson polarising compound binocular microscope, the 'Y'-shaped base signed T.W. Watson, 4 Pall Mall, London, 320, 19thC, in mahogany case, 17in (43cm) high, with an 18-drawer oak slide cabinet, with some slides, 11½in (29cm).
£700-800 *P*

Make the most of Miller's

When a large specialist well-publicised collection comes on the market, it tends to increase prices. Immediately after this, prices can fall slightly due to the main buyers having large stocks and the market being 'flooded'. This is usually temporary and does not affect very high quality items.

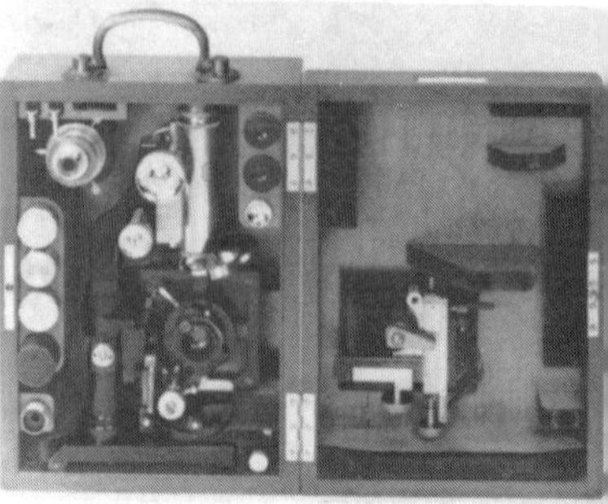

A black enamelled and lacquered brass compound monocular microscope, by E. Leitz Wetzlar, No. 29852, 12in (30.5cm) wide.
£500-600 *CSK*

Medical Instruments

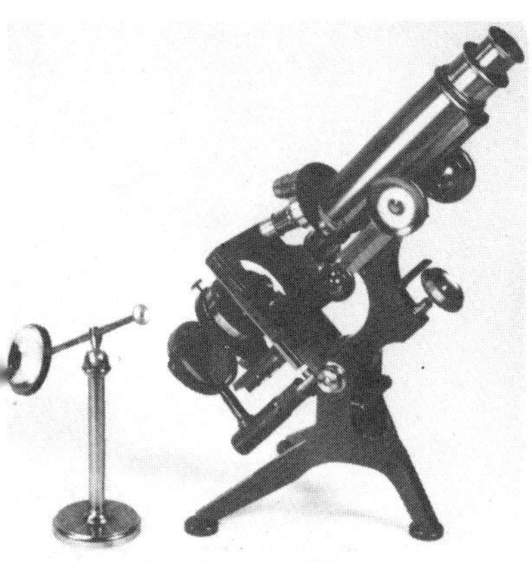

A lacquered and oxydised brass compound monocular microscope, by W. Watson & Sons Ltd, 313 High Holborn, London, with a comprehensive collection of accessories including 2 Abbe condensers, a wheel condenser, bull's-eye, polariser and other items in mahogany case, 13in (33cm) high.
£400-500 *CSK*

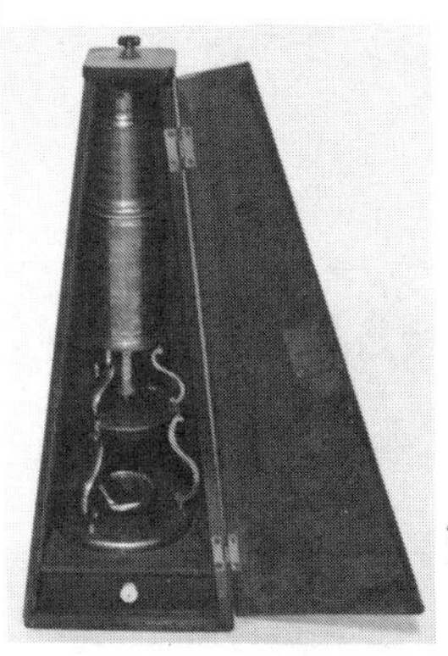

A brass Culpeper microscope by Lynch, Dublin, in original case, with a collection of eye pieces and slides.
£450-500 *MGM*

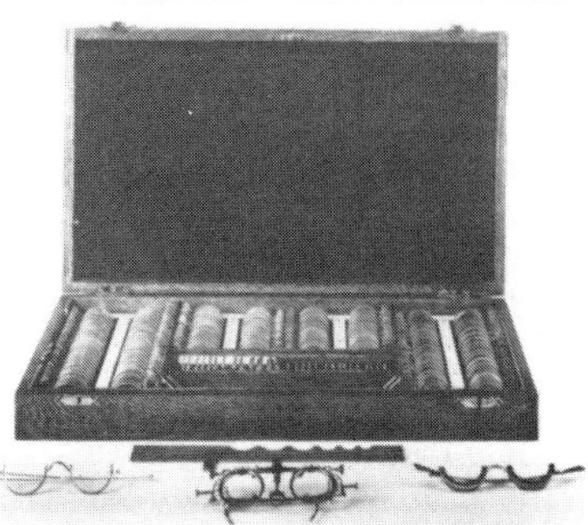

An optician's trial case in oak, containing lenses, coloured shades, 2 mirrors, 3 trial frames and an orthops rule, by Raphael Ltd London, the case 20½in (52cm) wide.
£150-200 *CSK*

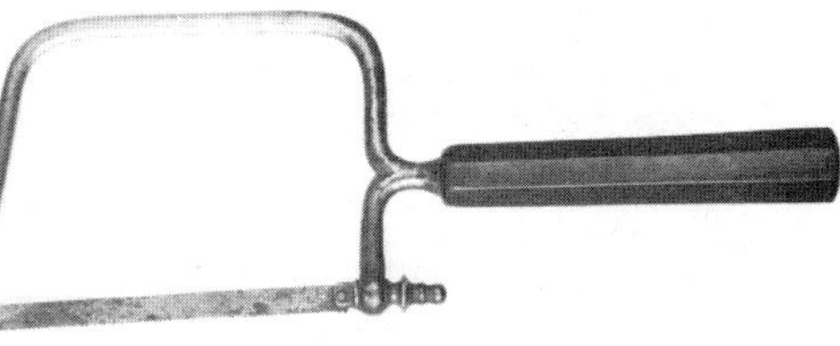

A bone saw and 3 dental elevators, 19thC.
£100-150 *CSK*

An amputation saw by Weiss, igned Weiss's Improved Saw, 3 Strand, London, on the blade ack, with anti-clog teeth and ebony andle, 19thC, 15½in (39cm) long.
:100-150 *CSK*

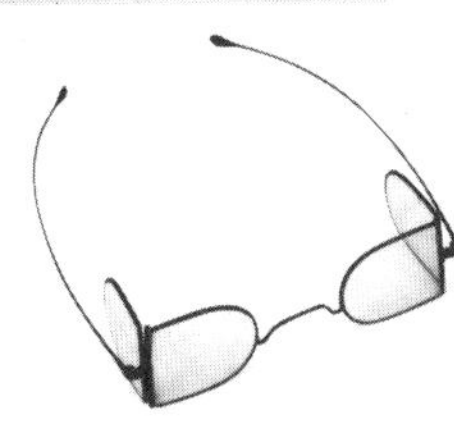

A pair of blued-steel framed 'D' folding sided spectacles, with blue tinted lenses, 19thC.
£70-80 *CSK*

A set of 6 folding trial spectacles, unsigned, numbered 2, 3, 4 and 5, with fractions ½ and ¾, the horn frame with centre brass interleaf and horn guards, 4¾in (12cm) long.
£250-300 *CSK*

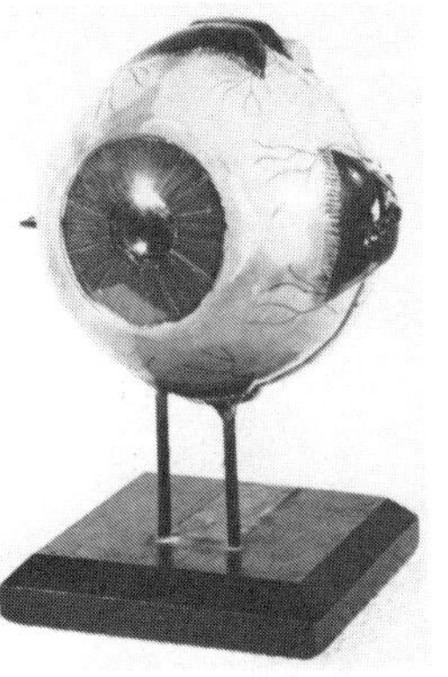

A sectional model of the eye, the laster body decorated in colours nd with glass lenses, mounted on n ebonised stand, late 19thC, 7in 17cm) high.
:400-500 *CSK*

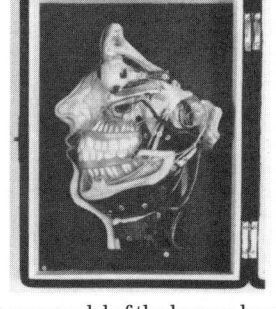

A wax model of the human head showing the nerves, arteries, veins and muscles, each numbered with identification sheet, mounted in an ebonised and glazed case, by Lehrmittelwerke, Berlin, 10in (25cm) high.
£250-350 *CSK*

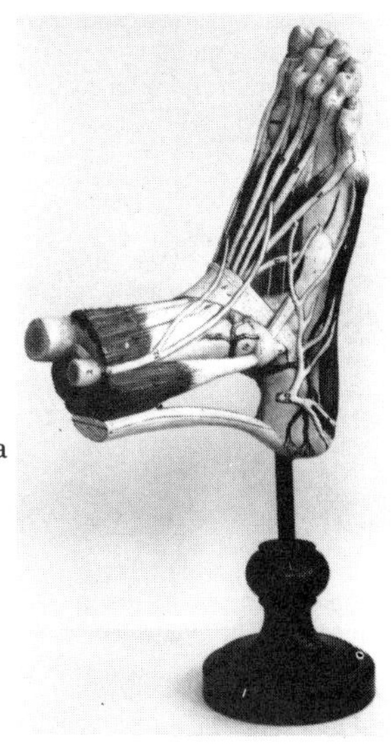

An anatomical plaster model of a human foot, 19thC.
£500-1,000 *HA*

A cupping set by Weiss, 62 Strand, London, with 2 glass cups in plush lined fitted case, 19thC, 5½in (14cm) long.
£350-400 *CSK*

A mahogany domestic medicine chest, the lid rising to reveal a fitted interior, 19thC, the case 7½in (19cm) high.
£350-450 *CSK*

A mahogany domestic medicine chest, with fully fitted interior, inset brass handles, engraved 'EC' with coronet, some damage, 19thC, 10½in (27cm) wide, contained in leather outer case.
£400-500 *P*

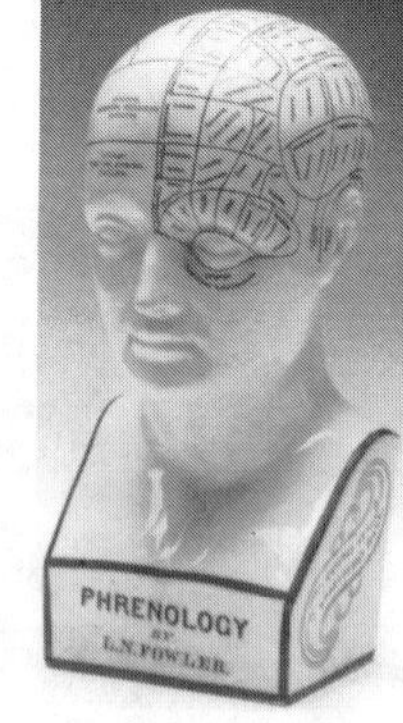

A Staffordshire pottery phrenology bust, inscribed L.N. Fowler, late 19thC, 12in (30.5cm), together with a book entitled *Brain and Mind*, published by L.N. Fowler & Co, London.
£400-500 *Bea*

Dental Instruments

A pocket dental scaling kit, the 7 burnished steel instruments with ivory handles, with mirror in a shagreen case, late 18thC, 2in (5cm).
£200-250 *CSK*

A set of wax demonstration models entitled 'The Development of the Human Set of Teeth', with reference card mounted in an ebonised and glazed case, by Lehrmittelwerke, Berlin, 16in (40cm) wide.
£200-250 *CSK*

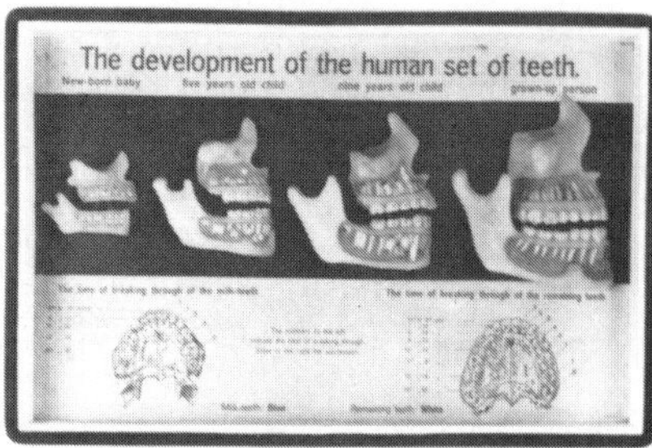

Miscellaneous

A lacquered brass siren on domed fruitwood base, 9in (23cm) high, and a Barlow's wheel on wood stand, 7in (17.5cm) wide.
£120-160 *CSK*

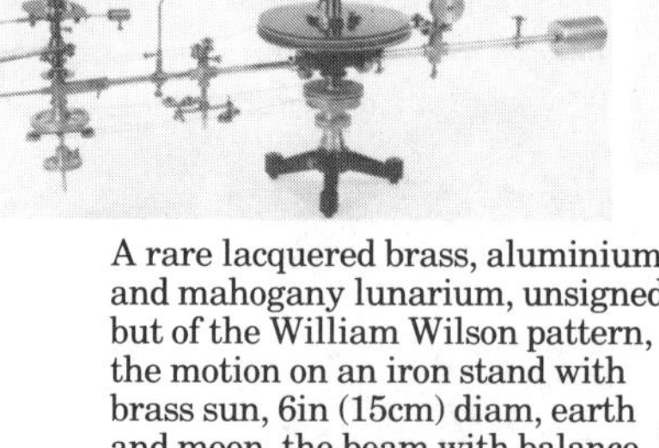

A rare lacquered brass, aluminium and mahogany lunarium, unsigned, but of the William Wilson pattern, the motion on an iron stand with brass sun, 6in (15cm) diam, earth and moon, the beam with balance weight and brass motion knob, 45½in (115cm) long.
£2,500-3,000 *CSK*

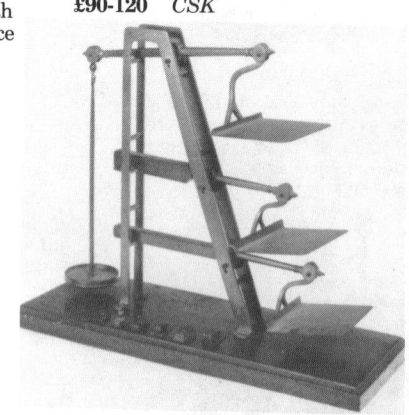

A mahogany inclined plane, unsigned, with arc engraved 0°-40°, brass pulley wheel, mahogany roller, cord, pan and 200g weight, 19thC, 28in (70cm) wide.
£90-120 *CSK*

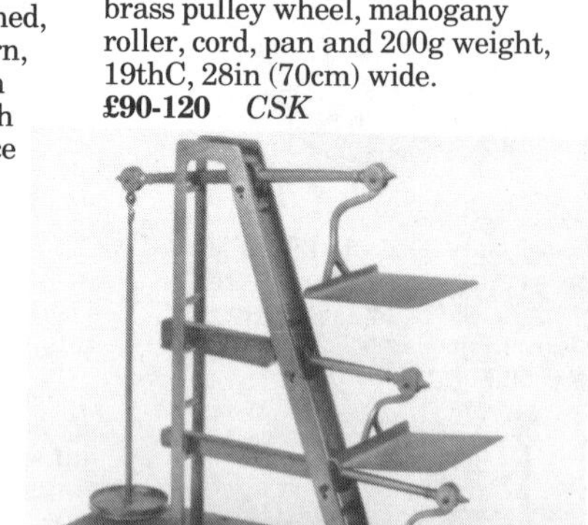

A lignum vitae scioptic ball, unsigned, with tinted lenses mounted in a mahogany frame, late 18thC, 5in (12.5cm) square, in a mahogany case, 8in (20cm) long.
£700-900 *CSK*

A double hour glass in a softwood frame, with bobbin turned pillars and pierced for an axis, 18thC, 7in (18cm) high.
£800-900 *CSK*

A 'Ladder Scale', 1oz and 2oz beams stamped De Grave & Co, London, the top beam weighted for 3oz with pan for additional weights, the frame with 6 weights mounted on a mahogany base, late 19thC, 16in (40cm) wide.
£550-650 *CSK*

A sheet brass letter balance, signed Parnell, London, and inscribed Hall's Patent, the shaped plate and pointer engraved, contained in the original plush lined and fitted leather case, 5in (13cm) wide.
£200-300 *CSK*

A Tate pump signed J.J. Griffin & Sons, Garrick St. London, 19thC, 23in (59cm) wide, together with 4 bell jars.
£350-450 *CSK*

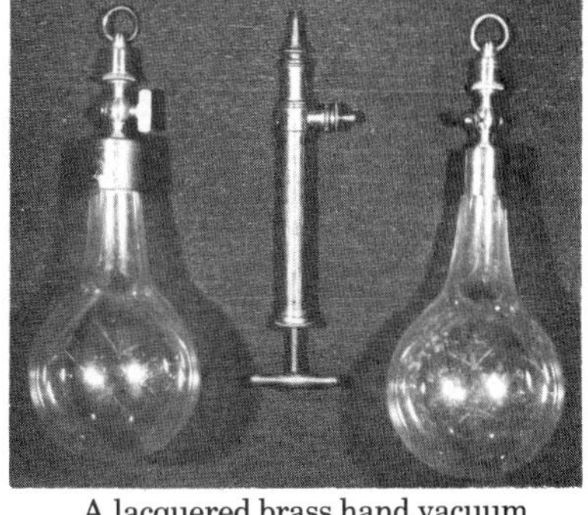

A lacquered brass hand vacuum pump, unsigned, with 2 glass bulbs, the brass bases with taps and end caps, 19thC, 12in (30.5cm) high.
£250-350 *CSK*

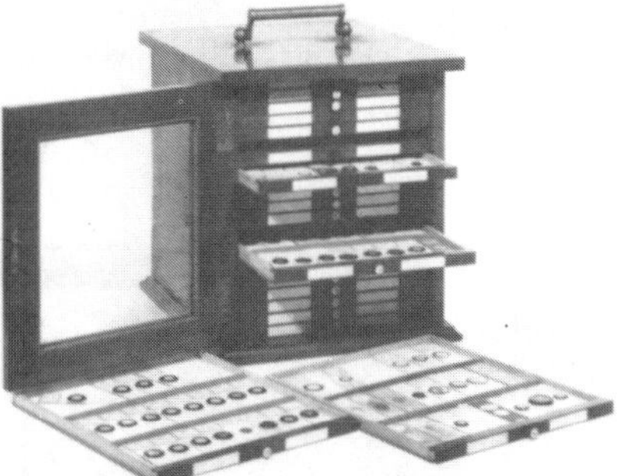

A mahogany microscope slide cabinet, with 21 drawers containing a collection of entomological, zoological and botanical slides by various makers, including F. Enoch, W.F. Stanley, E. Wheeler and others, the cabinet with brass carrying handle, late 19thC, 12in (30.5cm) high.
£800-900 *CSK*

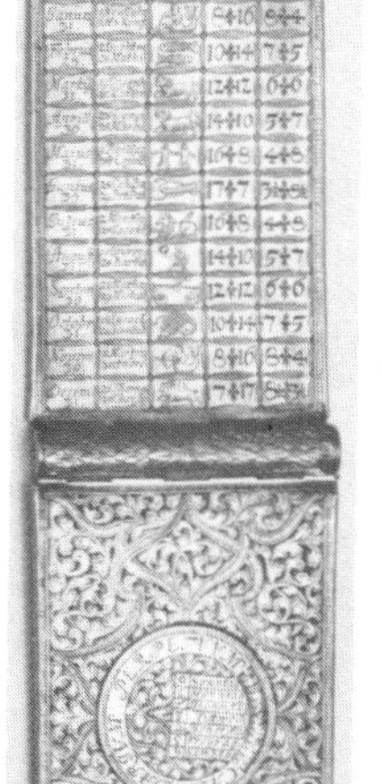

A German silver perpetual calendar, mounted on an ornately decorated chased scrollwork panel, 18thC, 8½ by 2½in (21 by 6cm), adapted as a notebook holder.
£750-850 *P*

A demonstration diffraction prism, mounted in brass frame, signed W. & S. Jones, 30 Holborn, London, early 19thC, 9½in (24cm) high.
£450-550 *P*

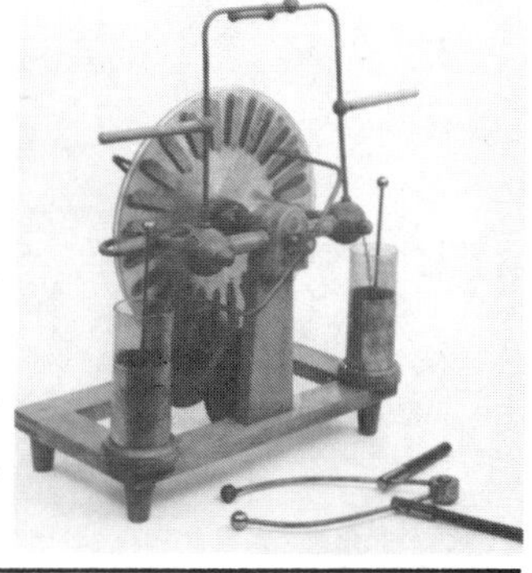

A Wimshurst pattern plate machine by Philip Harris Ltd, Birmingham, with 2 contra-rotating plates, 2 Leyden jars, collector brushes and combs, on a mahogany base, 22in (55cm) wide, and a pair of brass and ebonite discharge forks.
£550-650 *CSK*

Cameras

A rare underwater housing for a Leica camera, by Akustische und Kinogerate GmbH, Vienna.
£800-900 *CSK*

A 5 by 2½in (13 by 6cm) Heag IX Universal camera, with a pair of C. P. Goerz Dagor III f6.8 90mm lenses Nos. 253505 and 253496, and Ernemann magazine back.
£150-250 *CSK*

A 1½ by 1½in (4 by 4cm) grey Baby Rolleiflex camera No. 2056087, with a Schneider Xenar f3.5 60mm lens No. 7199161, by Franke and Heidecke, in case.
£150-200 *CSK*

A 7 by 5in (18 by 13cm) No. 5 Folding Kodak camera, early satchel type, with lens set into an early sector shutter and an E.K. Co. roll film pack stamped '7506'.
£350-450 *CSK*

A falling plate Svenska Express camera No. 2067 in black leather, stamped in gilt on reverse 'Hasselblad Svenska Express'.
£550-650 *CSK*

The camera was probably made by the German company Murer and bought in by Hasselblad's photographic department to sell under their own name.

A 28 by 28mm 'The Presto' camera by E. B. Koopman, with 4 glass plates in situ, and instruction book 'Presto Pocket Camera Primer'.
£550-650 *CSK*

A 2½ by 3½in (6 by 9cm) Rittreck IIa s.l.r. camera No. 2747 with a Musashino Koki Luminant f3.5 10.5cm lens No. 12001, extension tubes, a Luminant f4.5 21cm. lens No. 12108 and Rittreck roll film back and instruction book.
£300-400 *CSK*

A Leica I camera, No. 5640, with a Leitz Elmar f3.5 50mm lens, a Leitz rangefinder and cassette, all in Leitz leather case.
£1,000-1,200 *CSK*

The "TICKA"
Watch Pocket Camera.
HOUGHTONS LTD

A rare and unusual hallmarked silver Ticka camera with lens cap and engraved with 'A' monogram and crown motif, by Houghtons Ltd.
£900-1,200 *CSK*

The silver Ticka is hallmarked for London 1906. The monogram refers to Princess Alexandra who was one of the more talented Royal photographers.
Houghtons Ltd advertised the fact that Princess Alexandra was a Ticka user although the Royal Archives have no record of this. The camera belonged to Francis Henry Smith who was a Royal Marine and served on the Royal Yacht. He apparently left the Marines c1909 to become the Queen's Wardrobe man and later became a King's Messenger for George IV.

A Boowu copying gauge in maker's original box, and a Ozwto cable release in maker's box, by Leitz.
£50-60 *CSK*

A Leica I camera No. 3001, with a Leitz Elmar f3.5 50mm lens, c1926.
£500-700 *CSK*

A rare 'mountain' Elmar 10.5cm f6.3 lens No. 136450, with reversible lens hood and caps, by Leitz.
£500-700 *CSK*

Made in 1932 during the first year of production.

A Leica 1 (Model C) camera No. 52102, non-standardised with a matched Leitz Elmar f3.5 50mm lens and a matched Leitz Elmar f3.5 35mm lens, both engraved on barrel '102'.
£2,000-2,500 *CSK*

The Leica with interchangeable lens facility was introduced in 1930 from when this camera dates. Lenses had to be individually matched to a body. The total number of non-standardised Leicas with interchangeable lens mounts is 2995.

A Xenon 5cm f1.5 lens No. 289110 with 2 rings, by Leitz.
£150-200 *CSK*

An un-named tropical quarter plate detective camera with a built-in changing bag and seller's plaque 'Smith, Photo Chemist, Gosport'.
£300-400 *CSK*

A rare No. 1 concealed vest camera No. 8364 with glass plate inside camera and 2 other circular glass plates.
£600-700 *CSK*

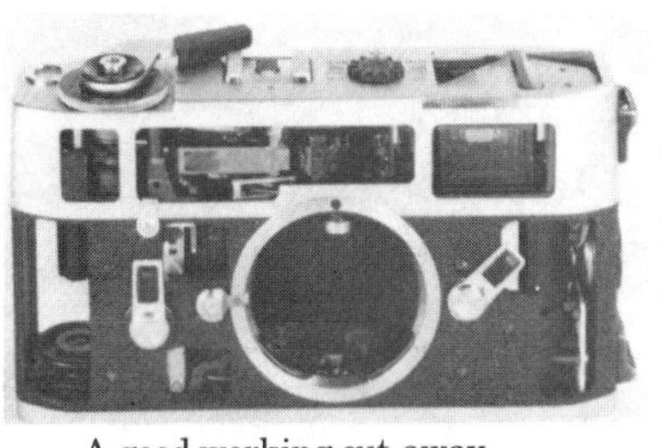

A good working cut-away demonstration Leica M5 camera, by Leitz.
£1,200-1,600 *CSK*

A rare 'The Rover Patent' detective camera, by J. Lancaster & Son, with wooden casing and leather case, a Lancaster Patent See Saw shutter and internal brass plate holders.
£350-450 *CSK*

The Rover camera was based on W. J. Lancaster's patent of 1 October 1890 and used an unusual form of falling plate design. The unexposed plates were stacked horizontally in the top of the camera and a release knob on the side of the camera allowed each to fall into the focal plane. Once exposed they moved backwards. The Rover was also a variant on the disguised/hidden camera.

A Leica Ic camera, converted to a If, No. 459934 with a Leitz Elmar 5cm f3.5 lens No. 805737, a 5cm brilliant viewfinder, in leather case and chrome FOKOS rangefinder in maker's box.
£500-700 *CSK*

A half plate brass and mahogany camera, with a brass bound lens and focusing cloth, camera with seller's plaque 'McGhie & Co, 75 St Vincent St, Glasgow', all in canvas case.
£250-300 *CSK*

Viewers

A Votra stereo transparency viewer.
£500-700 *CSK*

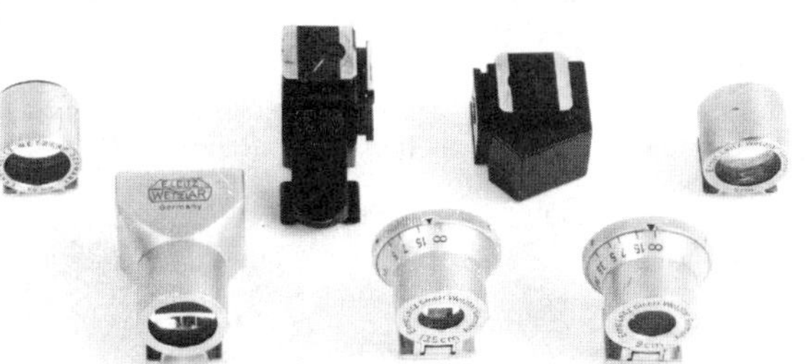

Five various direct vision viewfinders, including 13.5cm, 9cm, 5cm and others, 2 AUFSU waist-level finders, by Leitz.
£300-400 *CSK*

Make the most of Miller's

Every care has been taken to ensure the accuracy of descriptions and estimated valuations. Price ranges in this book reflect what one should expect to pay for a similar example. When selling one can obviously expect a figure below. This will fluctuate according to a dealer's stock, saleability at a particular time, etc. It is always advisable to approach a reputable specialist dealer or an auction house which has specialist sales.

ART NOUVEAU

Ceramics

An enamelled plaque, attributed to Harold Stabler, in soft cloisonné enamelled colours, within a silver coloured metal frame, 3in (8cm) diam.
£150-200 *P*

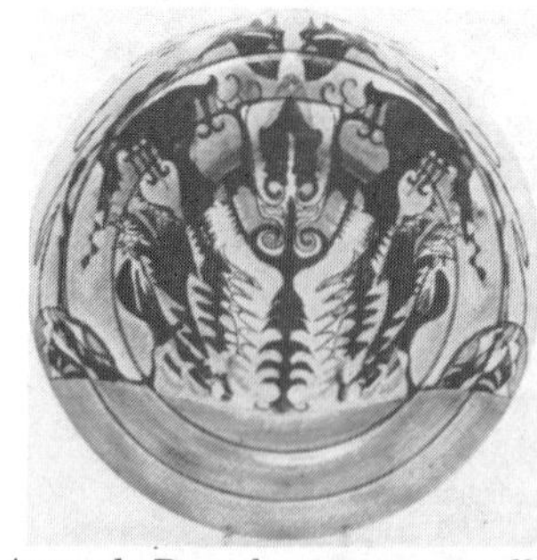

An early Rozenburg pottery wall plate, the design attributed to Th. A. C. Colenbrander, painted in bright colours, signed on base Rosenburg, den Haag, and date letter for 1890, 15in (38cm) diam.
£500-700 *P*

An early Rozenburg pottery wall plate, the design attributed to Th. A. C. Colenbrander, probably painted by W. F. Abspoel, painted W.G. mark for W. Von Gudenberg den Haag, date letter for 1888 and artist's device, 15in (38cm).
£500-700 *P*

An Austrian porcelain coffee set, painted in mauve, green and yellow with delicate flowers and further embellished with gilding, factory marks for Carl Knoll of Karlsbad, Austria.
£1,500-2,000 *P*

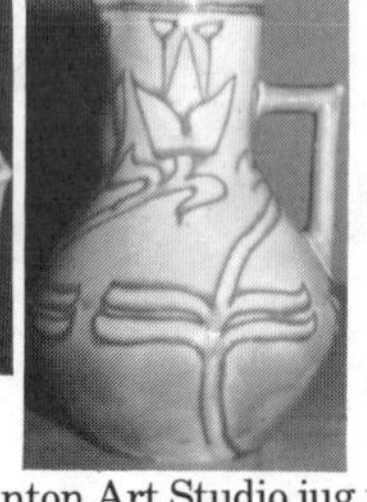

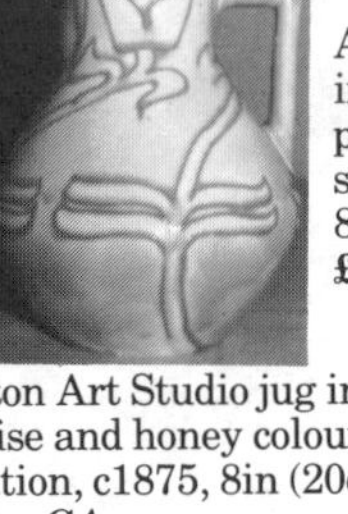

A Minton Art Studio jug in turquoise and honey colours, restoration, c1875, 8in (20cm).
£50-80 *CA*

A model of a parrot, brightly painted in ochre, green, iron red and brown, perched on a rocky mound base, signed E.D.M. Potterdale Pollie, 8½in (22cm).
£200-250 *CEd*

A William de Morgan red lustre tile panel, made from 2 large tiles, and painted in shades of red and pink lustres, framed.
£750-850 *P*

A Rookwood pottery 'Indian' flask and stopper, decorated by Harriet Elizabeth Wilcox, on a treacle coloured ground, impressed factory mark with date code for 1898, and artist's initials, 7½in (18cm).
£1,200-1,500 *P*

An Ault pottery vase, the base with raised Ault mark, impressed C. W. Dresser, signature and No. 246, 7in (18cm).
£550-650 *HOD*

An Eltonware vase, decorated with gold and platinum crackle glaze, base with signature, 21½in (54cm).
£800-900 *HOD*

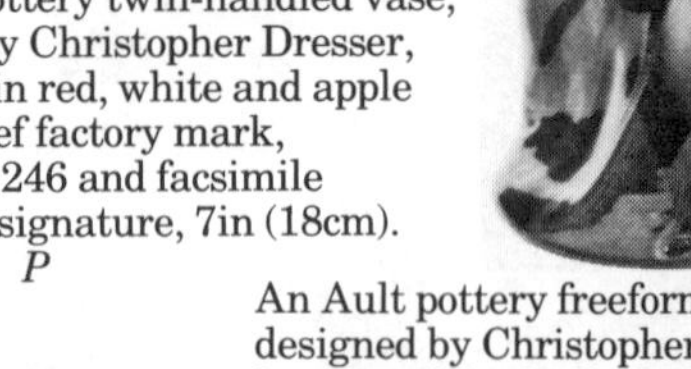

An Ault pottery twin-handled vase, designed by Christopher Dresser, decorated in red, white and apple green, relief factory mark, numbered 246 and facsimile designer's signature, 7in (18cm).
£700-800 *P*

An Ault pottery freeform vase, designed by Christopher Dresser impressed facsimile designer's signature, 12½in (32cm).
£300-350 *P*

A Brannam pottery vase, decorated in sgrafitto technique by James Dewdney, in red, blue and yellow glaze, giving the appearance of green and brown colouring, signed and dated 1898, 19½in (50.5cm).
£300-350 *P*

A small Dalpayrat high fired porcelain vase, glazed in mixed shades of sang-de-boeuf, mauve, eau-de-nil and pale blue with the white body showing through in places, signed Dalpayrat and numbered 12, 2in (5cm).
£150-200 *P*

A vase by Jessie Marion King, cracked, J.M.K. marks, 6in (15cm).
£150-200 *CEd*

A pair of Mettlach Villeroy and Boch vases, each incised and painted in ochre, red and green on a blue ground, rim chip to one, incised marks and 2416, 16in (40.5cm).
£420-500 *CEd*

A Linthorpe pottery vase, possibly designed by Christopher Dresser, decorated in brown slip against a rich turquoise ground, impressed Linthorpe, numbered 2201 and signed F.B. for Fred Brown, 20in (51cm).
£300-350 *P*

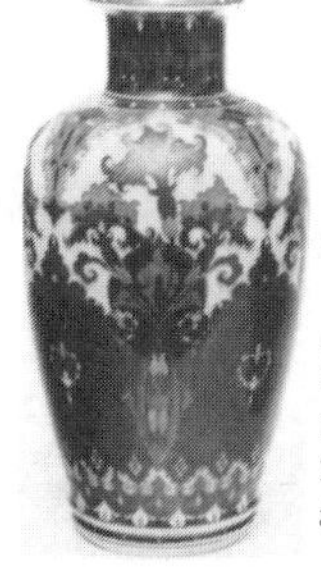

A Royal Bonn jardinière, with painted decoration, c1900, 18in (46cm).
£150-250 *ASA*

A pair of Rozenburg vases, painted in vivid colours, crown and stork marks, Rozenburg, Den Haag and numbered 332, 15½in (39.5cm).
£500-700 *P*

A Pilkington's Royal Lancastrian lustre vase, by Forsyth, decorated with dragons, maker's marks, c1900.
£400-600 *ASA*

A large Pilkington Royal Lancastrian vase, painted by Richard Joyce, in golden lustre and red against a powder blue ground, impressed rosette mark and artist's monogram, 12in (30.5cm).
£550-650 *P*

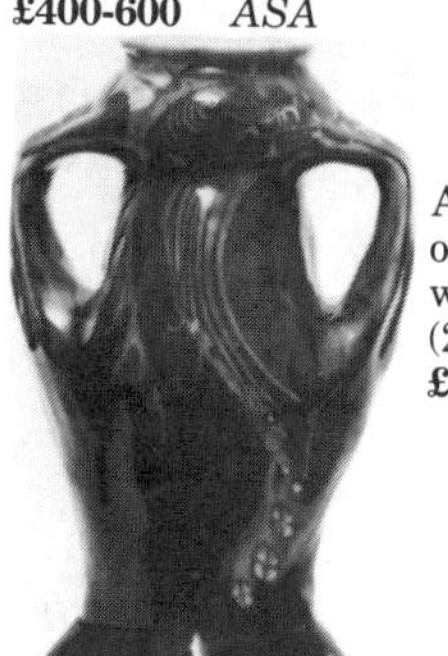

A pair of Rozenburg pottery vases, on a green ground, painted marks with a date mark for 1898, 9½in (24cm).
£450-550 *CAm*

Clocks

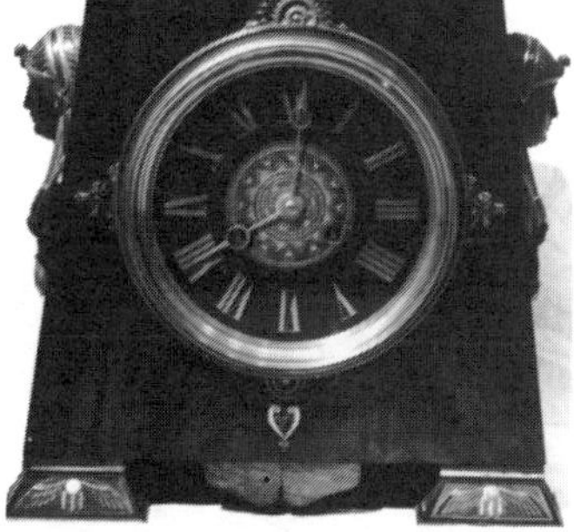

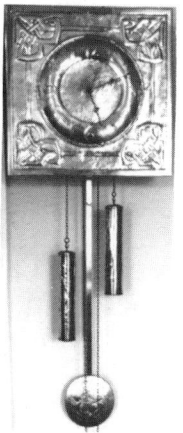

A French Empire style clock, c1880, 14in (35.5cm).
£450-500 *JeB*

A Liberty & Co., English pewter timepiece, designed by Archibald Knox, with copper coloured numerals and red enamelled berry forms against shaded blue and green enamelling, stamped on base English Pewter 0609, Made in England and Rd. 468016, 8in (20.5cm).
£2,000-2,500 *P*

An Arts and Crafts brass clock with chased Celtic motifs on face, pendulum and weights, with simple Black Forest movement, reminiscent of Knox designs for Liberty's Tudric pewter, c1900, 15in (38cm).
£1,200-1,500 *ST*

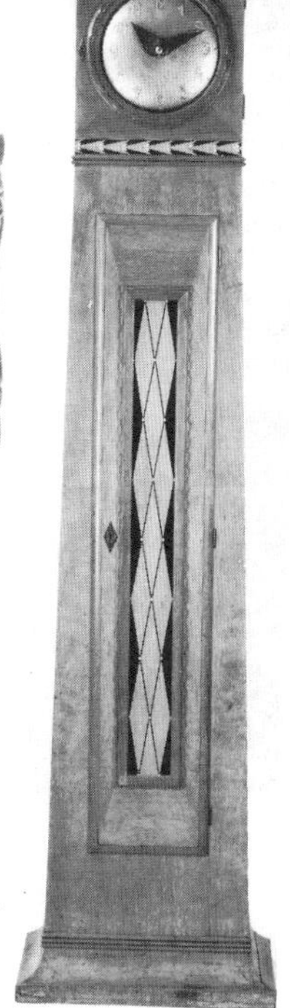

A Secessionist inlaid walnut longcase clock, inlaid in ebony and ivory, the movement by Gustav Becker, 77½in (197cm).
£950-1,000 *P*

A mantel clock in pottery case, printed in blue with pansies and convolvulus on a gold ground, indistinctly marked, late 19thC, 19½in (50cm).
£400-500 *Bea*

A Liberty & Co., pewter and enamel clock, marked Tudric and impressed no, c1900.
£800-1,200 *ASA*

A calendar clock in carved oak case
£350-450 *MGM*

An oak electric mantel timepiece, the case applied with pierced brass, on ball-and-paw feet, the enamel dial signed The Brush Co. Ltd., Loughborough, 19in (48cm).
£400-450 *P*

Figures

A Royal Dux figure, signed F. Otto, 24in (61cm).
£350-400 *PC*

A Royal Dux centrepiece, comprising 2 semi-nude nymphs with 2 leaves, on column decorated with water lilies, red triangular mark, 14in (35.5cm).
£400-450 *PC*

A Goldscheider porcelain figure, 12in (30.5cm).
£400-450 *JAD*

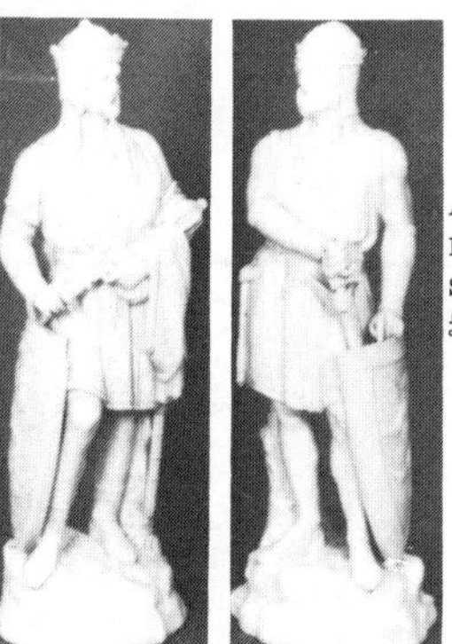

A pair of white glazed figures modelled as Bruce and Wallace, some damage, 19in (48.5cm).
£250-300 *CEd*

A French porcelain figure, based on a design by the illustrator Umberto Brunelleschi, in grey and pink with gilt, marked on reverse Brunelleschi and Radiguet Ceramiste, Oissels France, 13½in (34.5cm).
£600-700 *P*

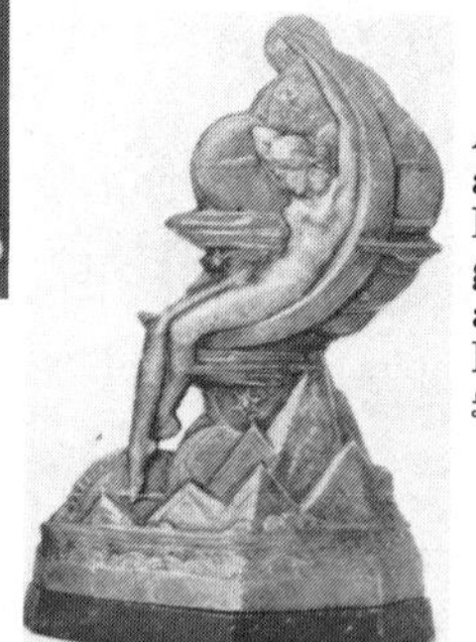

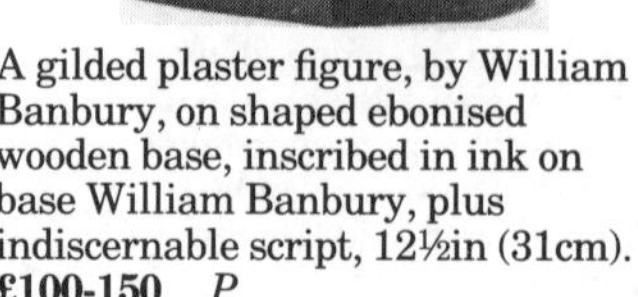

A gilded plaster figure, by William Banbury, on shaped ebonised wooden base, inscribed in ink on base William Banbury, plus indiscernable script, 12½in (31cm).
£100-150 *P*

A bronze figure of a naked girl, cast from a model by Küchler, inscribed Küchler and founder's mark of K and Vrais Bronce, Deposé, 14½in (37cm), with separate wooden base.
£800-900 *P*

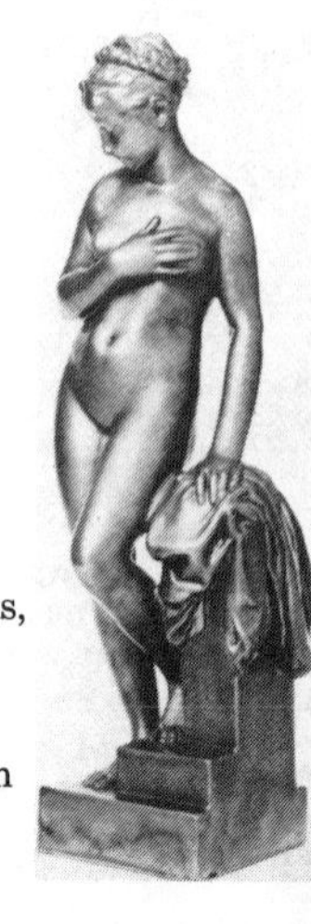

A Zsolnay lustre glazed classical figure, modelled as the nude Venus, covered overall in golden green lustre shading to tones of reddish gold in places, signed in lustre Zsolnay Pecs in circle, and made in Hungary, 18in (45.5cm).
£1,200-1,500 *P*

A gilt bronze group, cast from a model by Perrot, on marble base, inscribed Perrot, 10in (25.5cm).
£500-600 *P*

An abstract bronze figure of a woman, cast from a model by Willi Soukop, R.A., signed on the underside Soukop, 11in (28cm).
£500-700 *P*

An unusual Austrian bronze group, on marble base, inscribed Drah and marked Bronce M.N.F. Wien, 18½in (47cm).
£1,200-1,500 *P*

An amusing bronze figure of a poacher, wearing mediaeval costume and plumed hat, holding a knife between his teeth, wrestling with his 'prize' gripped between his legs, raised on marble base, unsigned but stamped 126/105, 9in (23cm).
£150-200 *P*

Furniture

An Arts and Crafts walnut armchair.
£400-500 *P*

An Arts and Crafts armchair, c1910.
£150-250 *ST*

A pair of mahogany armchairs, designed by Josef Hoffman, upholstered in buff textured velvet.
£2,000-2,500 *CAm*

An ebonised elbow chair, in the manner of Gimson, with lattice back and rush seat, on splayed supports.
£300-400 *P*

A bamboo drawing room suite, comprising a settee, 4 chairs, and an occasional table, each bearing a label Maison de Bamboos Perret et Vibert, 33 Rue du 4 Septembre, Paris.
£1,500-1,700 *P*

A nest of 2 tables, inset with tiles, largest 18in (46cm), and a shaped coffee table, 40½in (103cm). label Lazlo Hoenig, 54 South Audley St., Grosvenor Sq. London W1.
£250-300 *P*

An Arts and Crafts occasional table, with inlaid plank legs, probably made by Wylie & Lockhead, c1900, 23in (58cm) square.
£750-850 *ST*

An occasional table by Gallé, 17½in (44.5cm) square.
£650-750 *GAL*

An Arts and Crafts sideboard, 48in (122cm).
£450-550 *RP*

A Gothic style oak side table, in the manner of Pugin, 42½in (107cm).
£550-650 *P*

An Arts and Crafts oak sideboard, by Stanley Davis of Windermere, marked under top with maker's monogram SDW 1927, and J.E.O. monogram, 54in (137cm).
£800-900 *P*

A mahogany escritoire with marquetry panel, by Shapland Petter of Barnstaple, c1905.
£1,500-1,800 *ST*

An Austrian mahogany kneehole desk, attributed to Otto Wagner, the top inset with green leather, with brass gallery, on flared brass feet, 47½in (121cm), and a matching mahogany chair, drop-in seat, with revolving action, on similar brass supports.
£2,000-2,500 *P*

An Aesthetic Movement walnut hanging cabinet, with hand painted panel, c1875.
£350-380 *P[Re]*

An Aesthetic Movement corner cupboard, the bow fronted doors enclosing 3 shelves and painted in colours, one door unfinished, on three-legged base with a single drawer and undertier, 27in (69cm).
£300-400 *P*

A mahogany and marquetry buffet, attributed to Louis Majorelle, with bronze mounts and marble tops, the gallery with a narrow shelf at the top, 56in (143cm).
£900-1,000 *CAm*

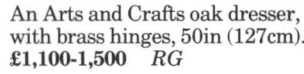

A Dutch Arts and Crafts tea buffet, designed by Jac. van den Bosch for 'het Binnenhuis', with metal tag 't Binnenhuis Raadhuisstraat, Amsterdam', and with branded monogram J. v.d. Bosch and the numbers 848, 61½in (156cm) high.
£1,300-1,500 *CAm*

An Amsterdam School sideboard, rosewood bordered in coromandel, 65in (165cm).
£350-450 *CAm*

An Arts and Crafts pollard oak bedroom suite of 8 pieces, in the manner of C. F. A. Voysey.
£2,000-2,500 *P[Re]*

An Arts and Crafts oak dresser, with brass hinges, 50in (127cm).
£1,100-1,500 *RG*

An Arts and Crafts oak bookcase, with unusual copper metalwork and leaded light panels in the doors, unstamped, but probably Liberty's, c1900, 85½in (217cm).
£1,800-2,500 *ST*

An Arts and Crafts Movement oak sideboard, by Liberty's, probably designed by Leonard Wyburd, with geometric leaded glass and copper strapwork handles, c1895, 94in (238cm).
£4,000-6,000 *ST*

A walnut cabinet, 66in (167.5cm) high.
£1,500-2,000 *RG*

A mahogany display cabinet, 48in (122cm).
£1,400-1,600 *CEd*

An inlaid mahogany display cabinet, with enclosed shelves, inlaid in fruitwoods with Art Nouveau foliage and flowers.
£800-1,000 *P*

A mahogany display cabinet, 54½in (138cm).
£2,000-2,500 *CEd*

An Arts and Crafts ebonised oak book cabinet, the top with brass panel inscribed 'Studies Serve for Delight', 50in (127cm).
£500-550 *P*

An Edwardian oak bureau, c1910, 54½in (138cm).
£500-600 *N*

An Arts and Crafts style mahogany display cabinet, the back with design registration mark 414768, 53in (134.5cm).
£600-700 *P[CW]*

A Limoges enamelled framed mirror, the bevelled glass flanked by panels enamelled in colours, 12½in (31cm).
£2,500-3,000 *P*

An Arts and Crafts plant stand, with copper strapwork, 36½in (92cm) high.
£150-250 *ST*

An oak hall stand, with mirror and embossed copper panels, 36in (91.5cm).
£400-500 *LRG*

Glass

A Daum etched and enamelled glass vase, etched Daum Nancy, 21½in (54cm).
£2,500-3,500 *CNY*

A Daum etched glass vase, the thick transparent brown ground deeply etched with wide zig-zag lines, inscribed, Daum Nancy, France, 9in (23cm).
£1,500-2,000 *CNY*

A Daum etched glass vase, in blue glass cut with thin vertical bands and small circles staggered throughout, inscribed Daum, Nancy France, 11in (28cm).
£600-700 *CNY*

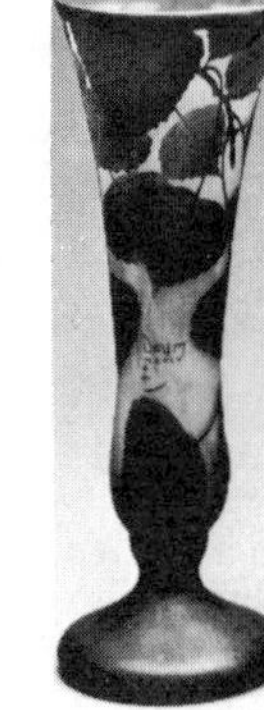

A Daum overlaid and etched glas vase, on white ground overlaid in deep brown etched to depict full autumnal leaves, etched Daum Nancy, 14in (35.5cm).
£650-700 *CNY*

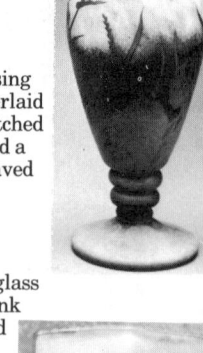

A Daum two-layer cameo glass landscape vase, enamelled signature, 4½in (12cm).
£700-800 *PSG*

A Daum overlay glass vase, in shades of yellow, orange and brown, 5in (13cm).
£800-850 *Bea*

A Daum clear glass vase encasing blue, yellow and white, and overlaid in deep blue and grey/green, etched and carved with Rudbeckia and a martelé ground, repairs, engraved Daum Nancy, 16in (41cm).
£3,000-4,000 *CNY*

A Daum mottled amber tinted glass vase, relief decorated in deep pink morning glory flowers, inscribed Daum, Nancy, 327, 7in (18cm).
£800-850 *GC*

A Daum glass vase, with enamel decoration, 4½in (11.5cm).
£200-250 *SWO*

A large Daum glass vase, of transparent pale turquoise tone, signed on footrim Daum Nancy France, 12in (30.5cm).
£350-450 *P*

A Gallé enamelled glass vase, enhanced with gilding, Cristallerie de Emile Gallé Nancy France in cameo, 13in (33cm).
£1,200-1,600 *CNY*

A Gallé glass vase, the cream coloured ground overlaid in red, with cameo signature Gallé, 5in (13cm).
£800-1,200 *CNY*

A Gallé 4 layer cameo glass vase, decorated with chrysanthemum, signed in cameo, 6in (15cm).
£1,400-1,600 *PSG*

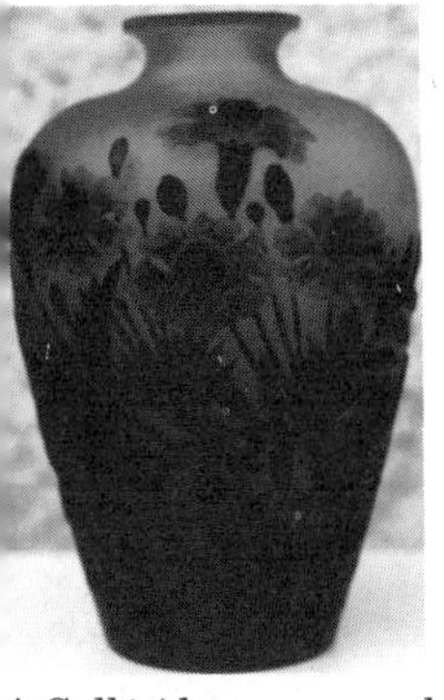

A Gallé 4 layer cameo glass vase, decorated with flowers and leaves, signed in cameo, 9½in (24cm).
£2,500-3,000 *PSG*

A Gallé glass vase, overlaid in pink and green, etched signature in the Chinese manner Gallé, 6in (15cm).
£1,000-1,500 *CNY*

A Gallé 4 layer cameo glass vase, signed in cameo, 14½in (37cm).
£2,500-3,000 *PSG*

A Gallé glass vase, the blue and white ground overlaid in olive green and brown, with cameo signature Gallé, 4in (10cm).
£1,000-1,300 *CNY*

A Gallé 4 layer cameo glass vase, decorated with flowering clematis, signed in cameo, 6½in (17cm).
£2,500-3,000 *PSG*

A Gallé 4 layer glass vase, decorated with clematis flowers, signed in cameo, 9in (23cm).
£800-1,000 *PSG*

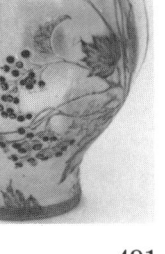

A Gallé 2 layer cameo glass solifleur vase, decorated with wild flowers, signed in cameo, 7in (17cm).
£550-600 *PSG*

A Gallé acid etched and enamelled vase, in green, amber, red and yellow, carved signature, 10½in (27cm).
£1,400-1,600 *CAm*

A Gallé glass vase, the white ground overlaid in light brown, with cameo signature Gallé, 9½in (24cm).
£1,200-1,500 *CNY*

A Gallé vase, the frosted and cream coloured ground overlaid with purple, with cameo signature Gallé, 5½in (14cm).
£1,500-2,000 *CNY*

A Gallé glass vase, the pinkish white ground overlaid in deep brown, with cameo signature Gallé, 5½in (14cm).
£1,000-1,300 *CNY*

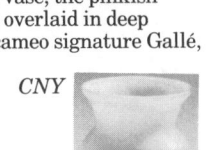

A Gallé cameo glass vase, in shades of purple, brown, blue and cream, 8in (20.5cm).
£900-1,200 *Bea*

A Gallé cameo glass vase, base signed Gallé Depose, 16in (40.5cm).
£4,500-5,000 *P[CW]*

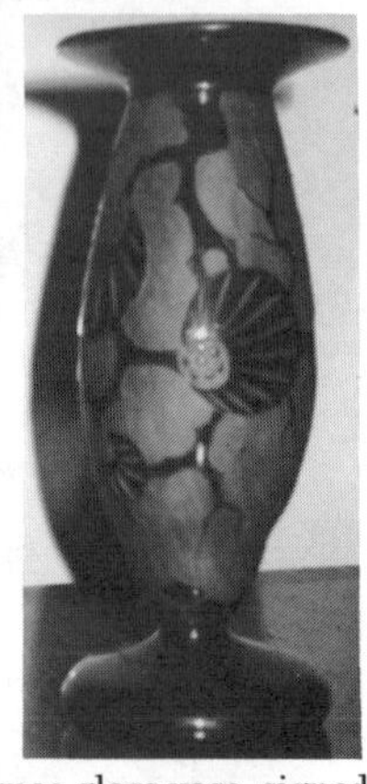

A French cameo glass vase, signed Le Vere Francais, c1900, 12in (30.5cm).
£400-600 *ASA*

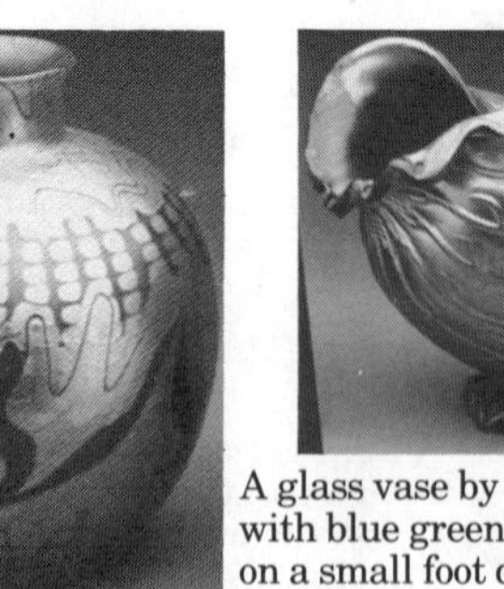

A glass vase by Loetz, with all-over silvery iridescence, inscribed Loetz Austria, 6in (15cm).
£3,000-4,000 *CNY*

A glass vase by Loetz, in pale green with blue green iridescence, raised on a small foot depicting a wave, c1900, 7½in (19cm).
£700-800 *CNY*

A Loetz glass vase, with random splashes of golden iridescence shading through pale turquoise and violet, and applied with a silver coloured metal collar, 13in (33cm).
£400-500 *P*

An overlaid and carved glass vase, inscribed D. Christian Meisenthal, 3½in (9cm).
£1,000-1,300 *CNY*

A glass vase, overlaid in green and aubergine, with finely etched leaves, vines and blossoms depicting passion flowers, inscribed D. Christian Meisenthal Loth, 7in (18cm).
£1,000-1,200 *CNY*

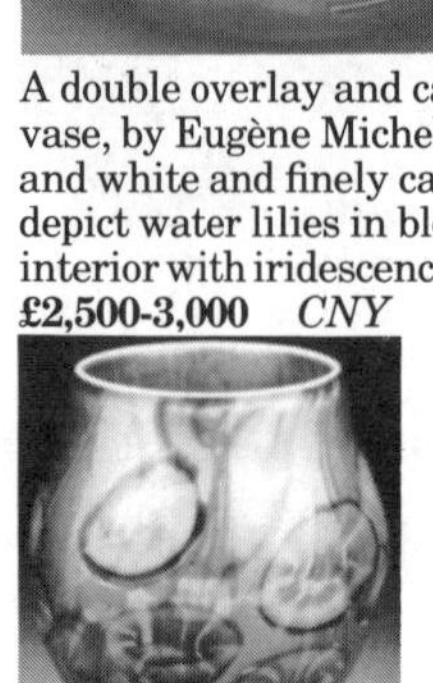

A double overlay and carved glass vase, by Eugène Michel, in green and white and finely carved to depict water lilies in blossom, the interior with iridescence, 5in (13cm).
£2,500-3,000 *CNY*

A blue iridescent Favrile glass vase inscribed X182, L.C. Tiffany-Favrile, 9in (23cm).
£1,000-1,500 *CNY*

A Favrile glass paperweight vase, with many stylised morning glory blossoms amidst streamers encased in the clear glass, the interior with iridescence, crack to foot, engraved U4113 Louis C. Tiffany, c1904, 7½in (19cm).
£500-550 *CNY*

An iridescent Favrile glass comport, inscribed L. C. Tiffany Inc. Favrile W41N, 3in (7.5cm).
£1,000-1,500 *CNY*

An iridescent Favrile glass comport in all-over blue and purple iridescence on a short stem and circular foot, inscribed 1531 2104 L L.C.T. Tiffany Favrile, 6½in (16.5cm).
£1,000-1,500 *CNY*

An iridescent gold Favrile glass flower bowl, with central detachable flower frog, both incised L.C. Tiffany Favrile 5344K, 14½in (36cm) diam.
£1,200-1,500 *CNY*

A Favrile glass centrepiece, the ribbed body with all-over blue iridescence, inscribed L.C. Tiffany Favrile 8412K, 10in (26.5cm).
£1,000-1,500 *CNY*

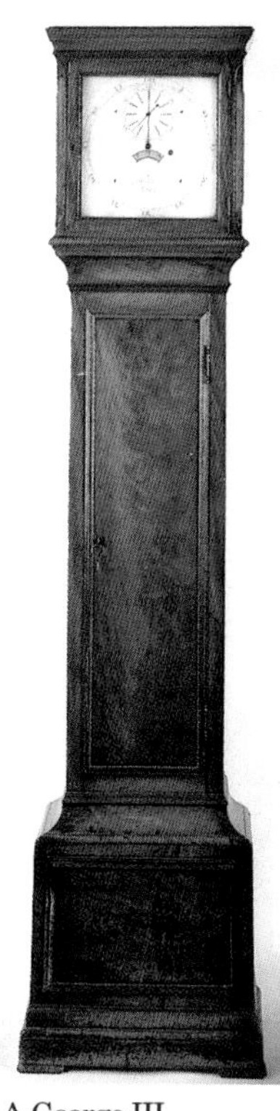

A George III mahogany regulator, the 10in silvered dial signed Holmes, London, later movement, 72in (182cm).
£6,000-8,000 *P*

A walnut longcase clock, 10in brass dial signed Bird, London, restored, late 17thC, 81in (204cm).
£13,000-16,000 *P*

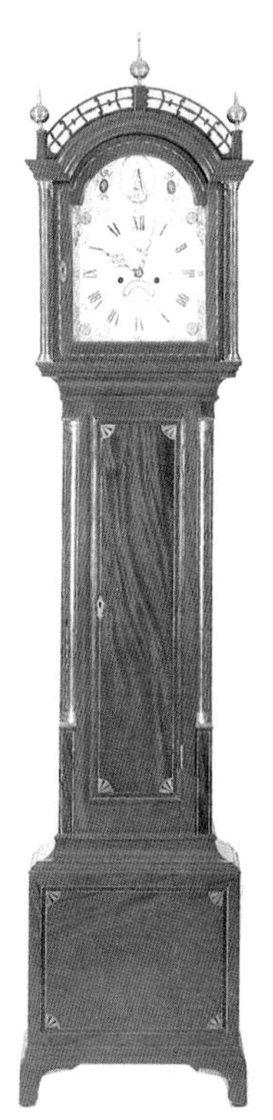

A Federal longcase clock, dial signed David Wood, Newbury-Port, Mass., c1790 damage, 90in (229cm).
£20,000-25,000 *CNY*

A walnut longcase 8-day clock, by Jacob Lovelace, Exeter, c1730, 101in (257cm).
£5,500-6,500 *DJM*

A walnut and floral marquetry longcase clock, 12in brass dial signed Jona Spencer, London, early 18thC, 84in.
£7,000-8,000 *P*

A floral marquetry longcase clock, 11in dial signed Thos. Bradford Londoni fecit, restorations, c1690, 78in (198cm).
£8,000-10,000 *CNY*

A mahogany longcase regulator, the dial signed Ollivant & Son Manchester, mid-19thC, 75in (190cm).
£15,000-18,000 *C*

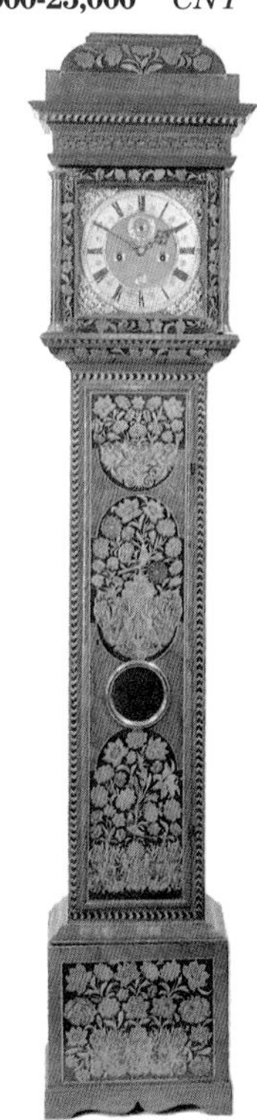

A walnut and panel marquetry longcase clock, with later pierced fret, 11in brass dial signed J. Windmills London early 18thC, 86in.
£10,000-12,000 *P*

A mahogany longcase sidereal regulator with break circuit work, signed Wm.Bond & Sons, Boston, c1858, 64½in (164cm).
£17,000-19,000 *CNY*

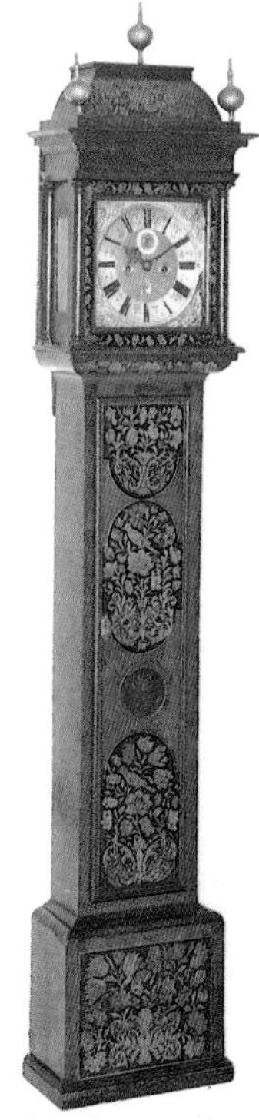

A walnut and marquetry longcase clock, dial signed Wm. Sharpe, Londini Fecit, late 17thC, 85in (216cm).
£8,000-10,000 *L*

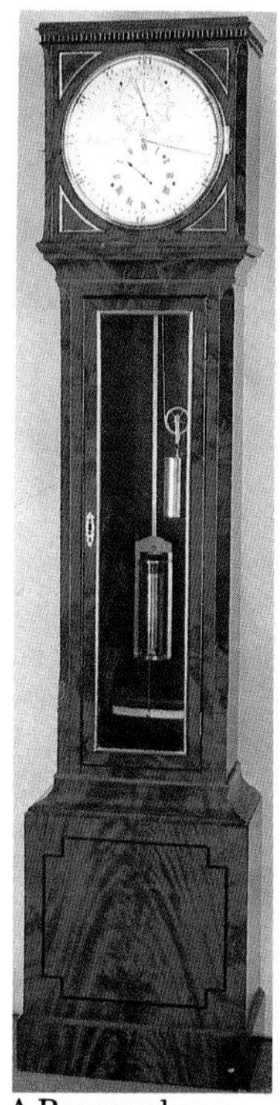

A Regency longcase regulator, with 12in engraved, silvered dial signed A. Samuel & Son, City London, No. 8388, 78½in (199cm).
£12,000-14,000 *DRA*

A Queen Anne twin-train month-going mean and sidereal longcase movement, by Daniel Quare and Stephen Horseman, London, No. 148, now in Regency pale mahogany case, 82½in (210cm) high.
£28,000-32,000 *C*

A mahogany 8-day longcase clock, the dial signed by Wm. Fletcher of Gainsboro', c1800, 91in (231cm).
£5,000-6,000 *DRA*

l. A Queen Anne clock by Jacob Godshalk, Philadelphia, restored, 96in. **£7,000-9,000**

r. A Chippendale clock by David Rittenhouse, Philadelphia, c1770, 80in. **£6,000-8,000** *CNY*

A giltmetal mounted Sèvres pattern vase clock and pedestal, late 19thC, vase 24½in (62cm) high.
£3,000-4,000
pedestal 45in.
£2,000-3,000 *C*

A Black Forest Biedermeier organ automaton clock, mid-19thC, 106in (270cm).
£9,000-11,000 *C*

A Federal maple and églomisé clock by Aaron Willard, Boston, Mass., c1815, No. 508, 35½in (90.5cm) high.
£7,000-9,000 *CNY*

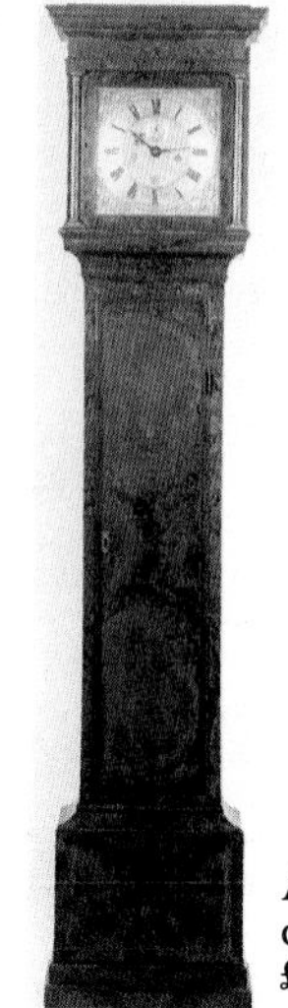

A burr walnut longcase clock, by Thomas Tompion.
£45,000-50,000 *Bon*

A walnut and marquetry long-case clock, the dial signed by James Wightman, London, 17thC, 78½in (199cm).
£16,000-18,000 *DRA*

A French ormolu-mounted porcelain clock set, comprising clock with striking movement, 18in (46cm) high, the candelabra with 4 foliate candle nozzles, 17in (43cm).
£4,000-5,000 *C*

A Louis XVI ormolu and terracotta mantel clock, the enamel dial with Roman numerals and days of the week, signed Sotiau A Paris, the case with figures of Minerva and attendants, 18in (46cm) wide. **£3,000-4,000** *C*

An ebony veneered bracket clock by Clarke & Dunster, London, with Dutch strike and alarm, 8-day movement, repaired, early 18thC, 17in (43cm) high. **£5,000-6,000** *CSK*

A Louis XVI ormolu-mounted Sèvres vase 'solaire' clock, cover restored, 18½in (47cm).
£10,000-12,000 *C*

An Empire ormolu-mounted marble mantel clock, the enamel dial signed 'a Paris', the movement with outside countwheel strike, 21in (53cm) high.
£5,000-6,000 *C*

An Empire bronze, ormolu and marble mantel clock, after a design by Thomas Hope, 21½in (55cm) high. **£6,000-7,000** *C*

A Louis XVI ormolu and alabaster rotunda clock, signed Festeau a Paris, 16½in (42cm) high, with later glass dome.
£4,000-5,000 *C*

A George III mahogany bracket clock, the 2-train movement with verge escapement, strike/silent regulation in the arch, a recessed plaque with maker's name William Garrett, London, c1785, 20in (51cm). **£5,500-7,000** *DRA*

A Louis XV ormolu mantel clock, the dial and movement signed Etienne Le Noir a Paris, 13½in (34cm) high.
£4,500-5,500 *C*

l. A Vienna regulator in walnut veneered case, by Lehrner in Pesten. **£5,000-7,000**
c. A late Biedermeier period Vienna regulator, by Mösslinger in Wien. **£3,000-4,000**
r. A lantern style Vienna regulator in fine mahogany case. **£12,000-18,000** *GeC*

A grande sonnerie striking Vienna regulator, by S. Glink, Pesten, Budapest, with burr elm case.
£4,000-6,000 *GeC*

A mantel clock, signed A. Duchesne, Lejeune à Paris, 18thC, 39in (99cm).
£2,500-3,000 *P*

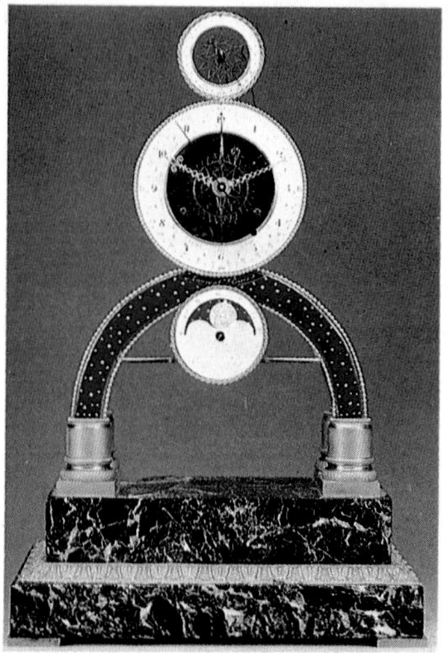

A French Directoire skeleton clock, by Laurent A Paris, c1790.
£20,000-25,000 *CG*

A Victorian bracket clock, the movement chiming on 8 bells with a gong, 30in (76cm) high. **£1,000-1,500** *WW*

An Empire mantel clock, with circular enamel dial in an urn-shaped case, 18in (46cm) high.
£4,000-5,000 *C*

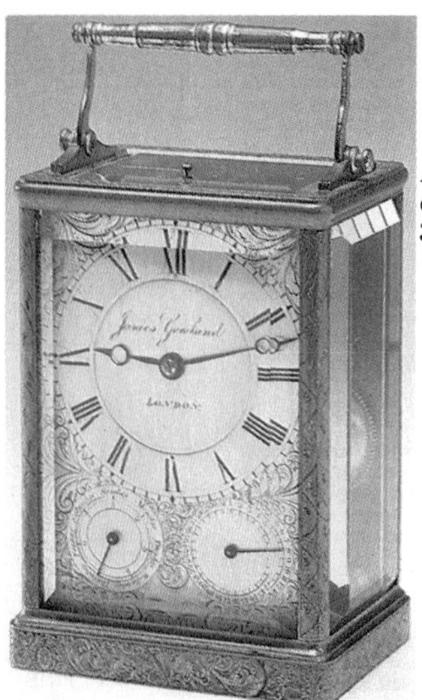

An 8-day carriage clock, signed in the centre James Gowland, London, the movement with lever escapement, in gilt brass case, 7in (18cm) high, with key and morocco travelling case. **£3,500-4,500** *Bea*

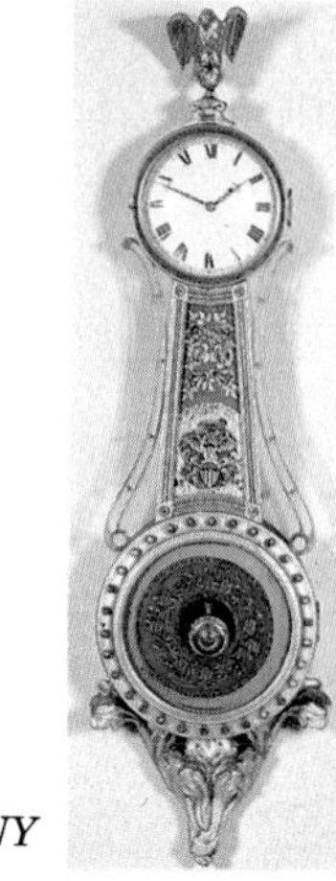

A Federal gilt and eglomisé girandole clock, by Lemuel Curtis, Concord, Massachusetts, c1816, base glass replaced, 46in (117cm) high.
£8,000-10,000 *CNY*

A gold, enamel and jewelled singing bird cage, with clock watch, musical movement and double singing bird mechanism, by Freres Rochat and G. Remond, with signature 'Fait par Stüber', c1815, 8½in (21.5cm) high.
£300,000+ *CG*

A pair of gold watches formed from a baroque repousse watchcase, attributed to Johann Andreas Thelot, movements Goldney St. James St, London Nos. 5398 and 5497, Thelot's work c1700, English movements c1820, 4.7cm diam.
£19,000-21,000 *C*

A gold double glazed half-quarter repeating Robin 'montre perpetuelle', signed Mugnier Horloger de S.M. l'Empereur et Roi No. 1009, mid-19thC, 5.6cm diam.
£17,000-19,000 *C*

A Regency mahogany wall regulator, the moulded case with oval mirror-glazed door, 65in (165cm) high.
£4,000-6,000 *C*

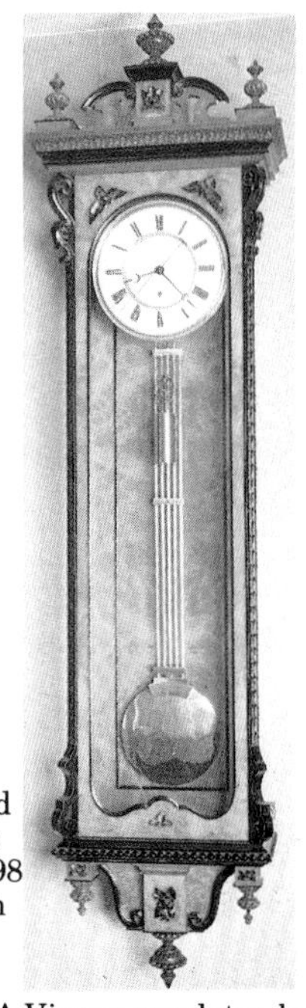

A Vienna regulator, by Camerer, Cuss & Co., established 1788 in London, with a seconds beating 5-rod gridiron pendulum, 11in (28cm) diam. enamelled dial, clock with finials, 77in (196cm) high.
£5,000-6,000 *DRA*

A George III giltwood cartel clock, with associated silvered dial signed William Linderby, London, the case surmounted by an eagle, 34in (86.5cm) high.
£5,000-6,000 *C*

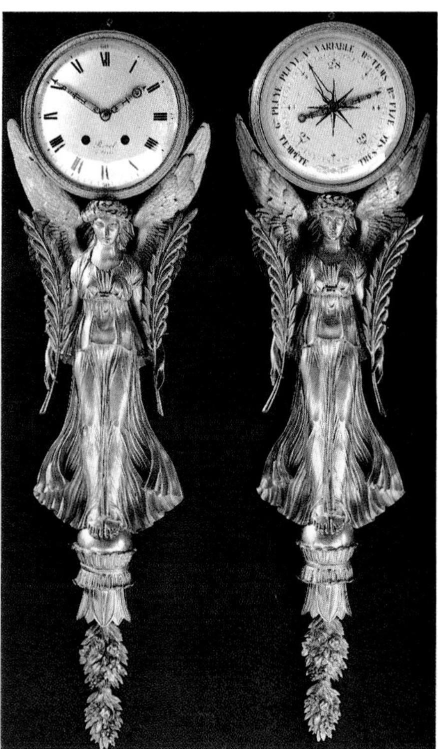

An Empire ormolu cartel clock and matching barometer, the clock with dial signed Revel a Paris, each supported by winged classical female figures holding laurel sprays, 37½in (95cm) high.
£60,000-70,000 *C*

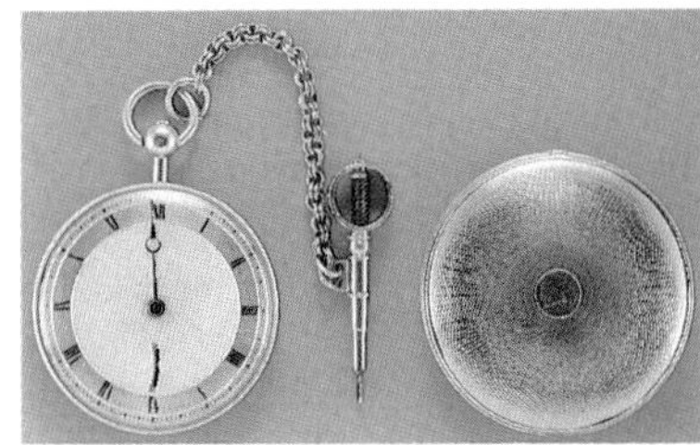

A gold double cased watch, by Breguet, No. 3876, the movement of Lepine calibre with ruby cylinder escapement, 4.1cm diam, with original gold chain and tipsy key.
£10,000-15,000 *CG*

A black enamelled and lacquered brass theodolite, the telescope with rack and pinion focusing, signed T. Cooke & Sons York, England, No. 2250, 16in (41cm) high. **£2,000-3,000** *CSK*

A gold perpetual calendar bracelet watch, signed Patek Philippe & Co, Geneve, No. 967639, 3.4cm diam. **£25,000-30,000** *CG*

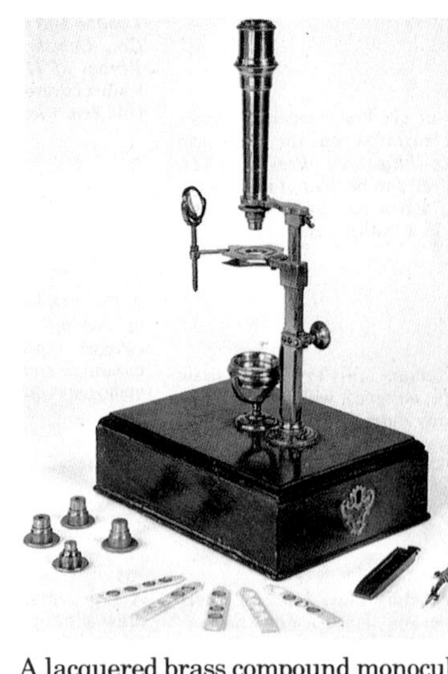

A lacquered brass compound monocul microscope, unsigned, with various accessories, in a fitted mahogany case, late 18thC, 9in (23cm) long. **£2,500-4,000** *CSK*

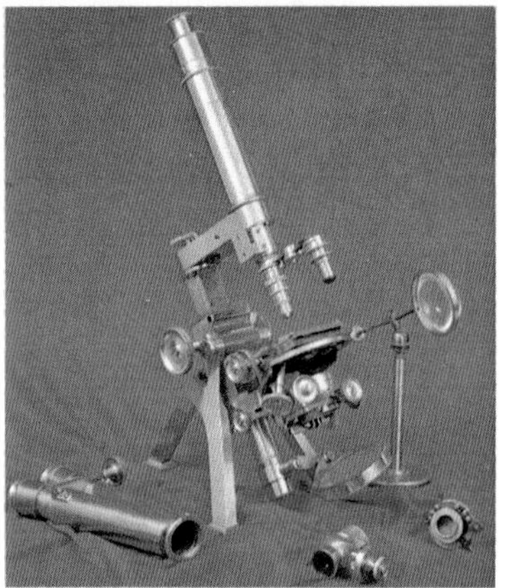

A lacquered brass compound binocular microscope, signed Powell & Lealand, 170 Euston Road, London, dated 1884, original mahogany case 19in (49cm). **£5,000-7,000** *CSK*

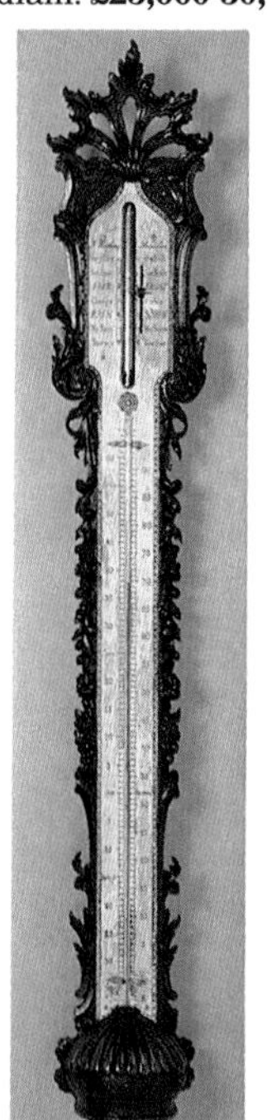

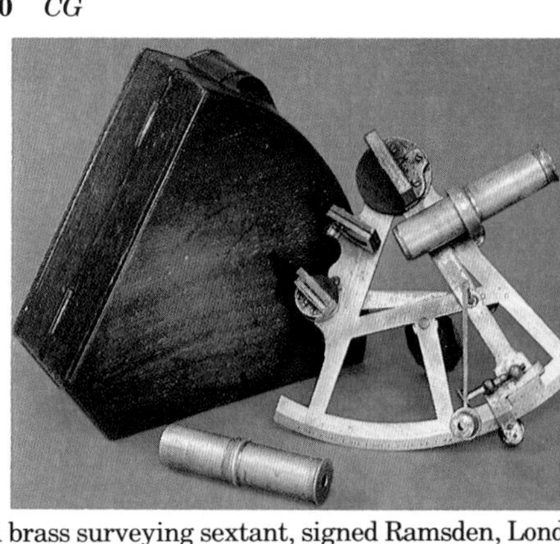

A brass surveying sextant, signed Ramsden, Lond index arm with vernier, magnifier, tangent screw and clamp, late 18thC, 4in (10cm) radius, in original fitted mahogany case. **£3,000-4,000** *CS*

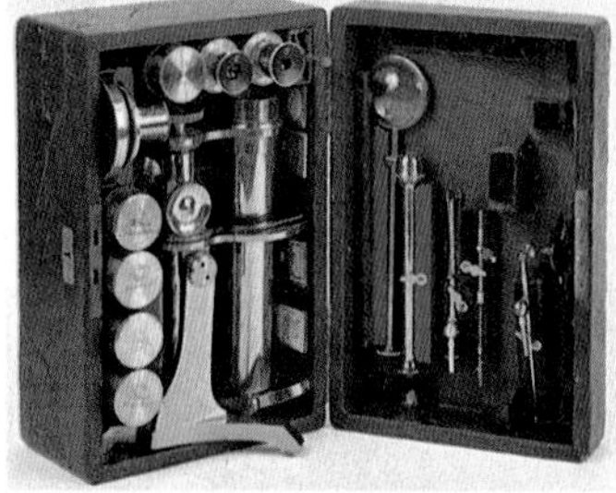

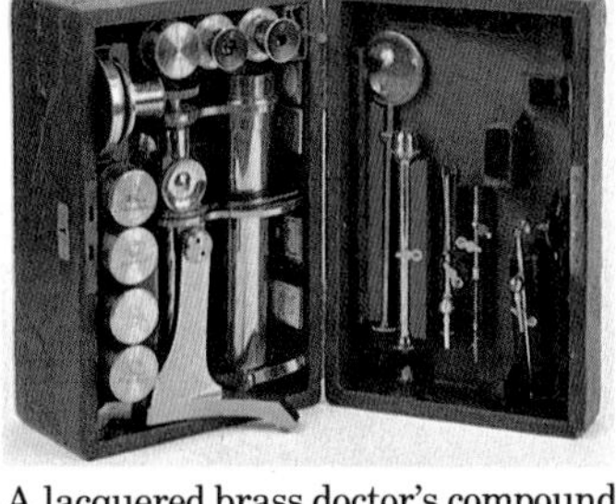

A lacquered brass doctor's compound monocular microscope, signed Ross, London 4089, 19thC, in fitted case, 11in (26cm) wide. **£1,200-1,500** *CSK*

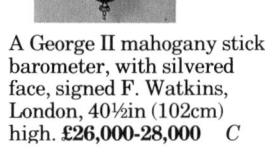

A George II mahogany stick barometer, with silvered face, signed F. Watkins, London, 40½in (102cm) high. **£26,000-28,000** *C*

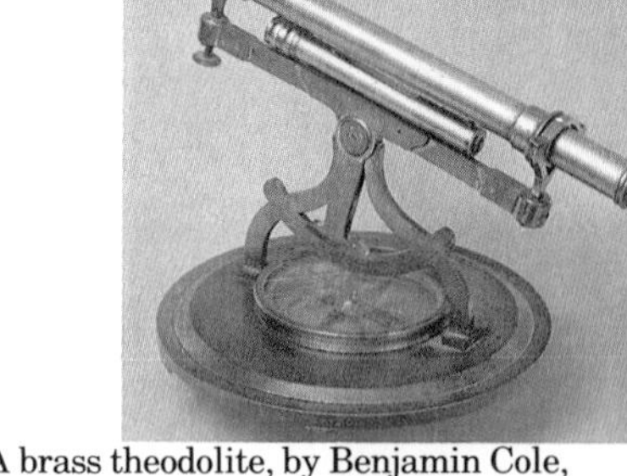

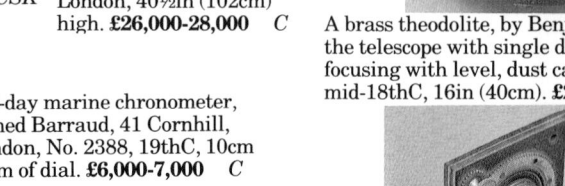

A brass theodolite, by Benjamin Cole, the telescope with single draw tube focusing with level, dust cap and slide, mid-18thC, 16in (40cm). **£2,000-3,000** *C*

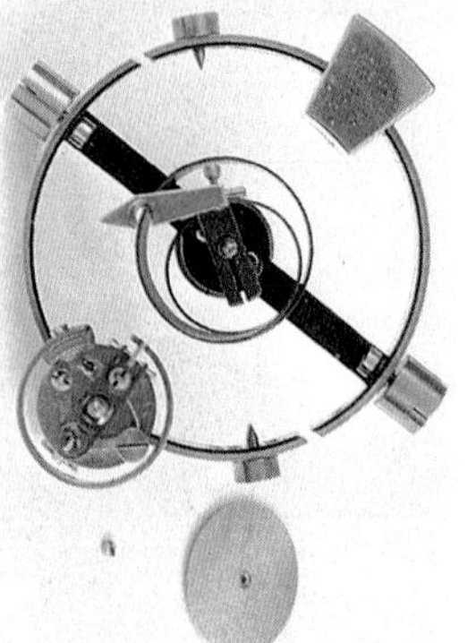

A 2-day marine chronometer, signed Barraud, 41 Cornhill, London, No. 2388, 19thC, 10cm diam of dial. **£6,000-7,000** *C*

A lacquered brass solar microscope, the draw tube stamped B. Martin, London, 18thC, the mahogany wall plate 5½in (14cm). **£2,000-3,000** *CSK*

A tulip leaded glass and bronze table lamp, impressed Tiffany Studios New York 1548 and 28620, 29½in (75cm) high. **£22,000-25,000** *CNY*

An overlaid and etched glass table lamp, the shade etched Daum Nancy France, the base with similar design on a circular foot, 13in (32cm) high. **£9,000-11,000** *CNY*

A cameo landscape table lamp, the shade carved with Daum Nancy with the Cross of Lorraine, the base carved with DN monogram, 25in (63cm) high. **£9,000-10,000** *C*

A pair of terrestrial and celestial globes, 'Ger et Leon Vath Amsterdam 1750', 19in high. **£10,000-12,000** *C*

A pair of William IV terrestrial and celestial globes, by W. Harris, London 1836, distressed, 40in (101cm). **£18,000-20,000** *C*

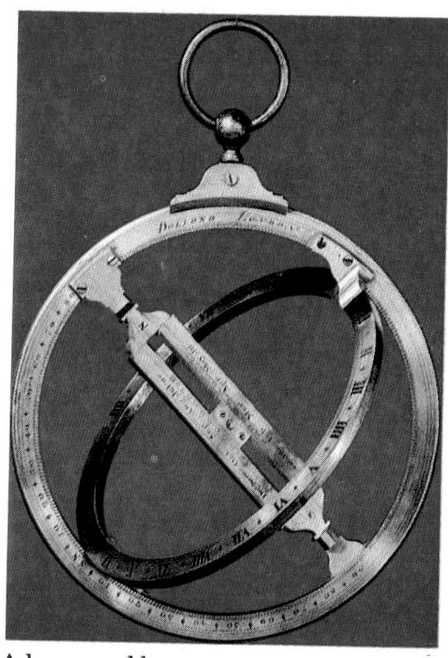

A lacquered brass universal equinoctial ring dial, signed Dollond London, early 19thC, 9½in (24cm), in original plush lined fishskin covered case. **£4,000-6,000** *CSK*

A lacquered brass azimuth sighting instrument, signed Narrien, London, c1820, 9½in (24cm). **£2,000-3,000** *CSK*

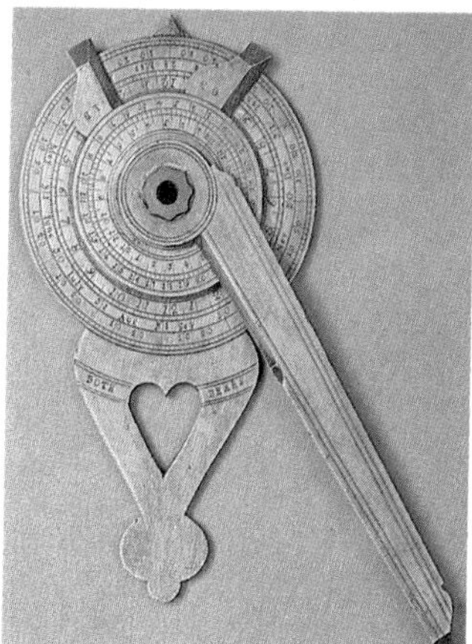

A fruitwood nocturnal dial, 17thC, index arm 7½in (19cm) long, main plate 4in (10cm) diam. **£2,000-4,000** *CSK*

A planetary motion compendium, unsigned, with 9 brass framed movements, early 19thC, 14in (35cm) wide, in fitted case. **£2,000-3,000** *CSK*

A copper and mica table lamp, the base of trumpet form, stamped Dirk Van Erp, c1915, 22in (56cm) high.
£12,000-15,000 *CNY*

A cameo glass table lamp, the conical shade acid-etched with pendant branches of honeysuckle, signed in cameo Gallé on shade and base, 8½in (21cm) high.
£10,000-15,000 *P*

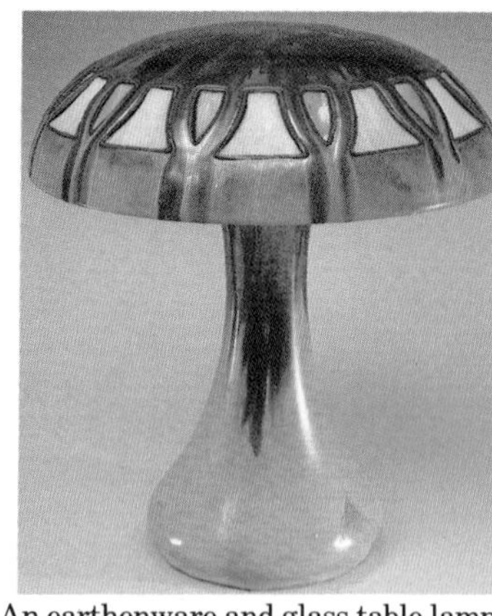
An earthenware and glass table lamp the shade of mirrored black glaze over green flambé inset with leaded glass, by Fulper, the base and shade printed with firm's logo and number 21,15½in (39cm) high. **£9,000-12,000** *CNY*

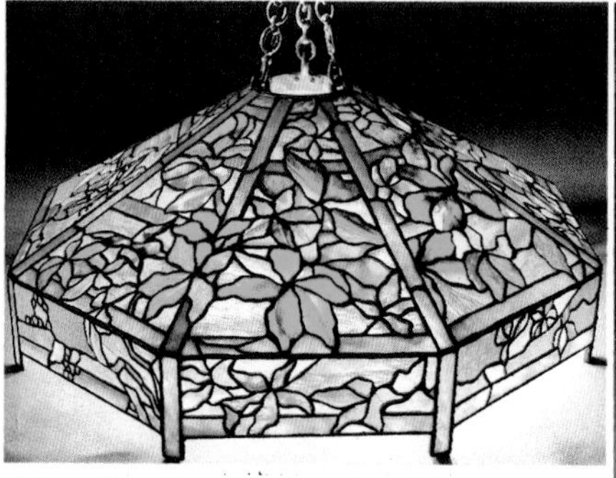
A 'woodbine' leaded glass chandelier, impressed Tiffany Studios New York 2-609, 27in (68cm) diam. **£12,000-15,000** *CNY*

A 'trumpet vine' double overlay and etched glass table lamp, with cameo signature Gallé, 26½in (67cm) high.
£30,000-35,000 *CNY*

A 'hanging head dragonfly' leaded glass and bronze table lamp, both shade and base impressed Tiffany Studios New York, 1507 and 7984, 32½in (82cm) high. **£30,000-35,000** *CN*

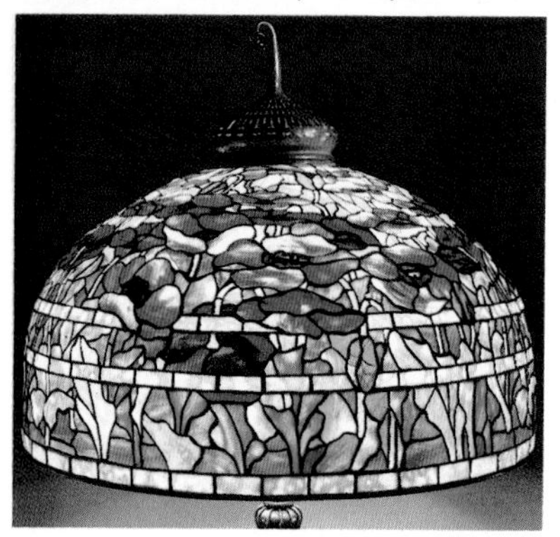
An 'Oriental poppy' glass and bronze floor lamp, shade and base impressed Tiffany Studios New York 2404 and 378, 76in. **£43,000-46,000** *CNY*

A 'woodbine' leaded glass and bronze table lamp, the shade stamped Tiffany Studios New York, 16in (40cm) diam, the base similarly stamped, 21in (53cm) high.
£30,000-33,000 *CNY*

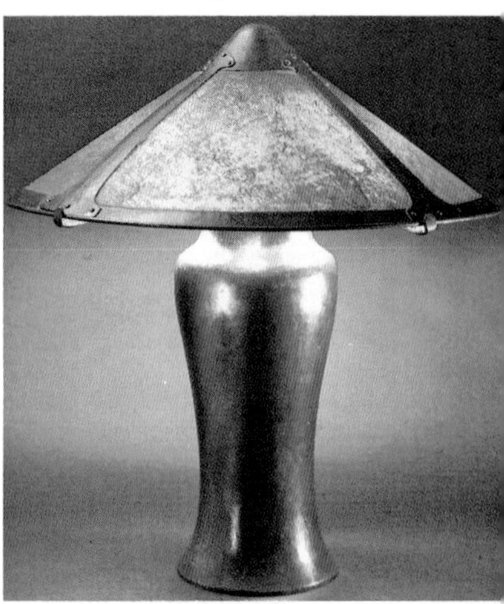
A copper and mica tabe lamp, stamped Dirk Van Erp, c1910, 25½in (65cm) high
£40,000-43,000 *CNY*

double overlay and etched glass harger, with cameo signature allé, 15½in (39cm) diam. **4,500-5,500** *CNY*

l. A Gallé carved acid-etched triple overlay landscape vase, carved signature Gallé, 20in (50cm). **£8,000-10,000** *C*

r. A blue cala-lily triple overlay mould-blown glass vase, cameo signature Gallé, 14in (35cm). **£25,000-30,000** *CNY*

A mould blown vase, carved and acid-etched with rhododendron, carved 'Gallé', 10in high. **£14,000-16,000** *C*

A Gallé double overlay vase, repaired, 9in (23cm) high. **£1,500-2,000** *EG*

A bronze mounted Gallé vase, engraved signature Gallé ft. 1891-93, bronze foot signed with EG monogram, 11½in (28.5cm) high. **£22,000-27,000** *C*

An acid-etched and enamelled vase, engraved Cristallerie d'Emile Gallé Nancy, 28in. **£4,000-5,000** *CAm*

A triple overlay carved and acid-etched vase, carved signature Gallé, 9in (23cm). **£12,000-15,000** *C*

An overlaid and etched glass vase, with 2 glass handles modelled as snails, etched Daum, Nancy, 8in (20cm). **£5,500-7,500** *CNY*

A triple overlay vase, 'Premier Gel d'Automne', carved signature Gallé, 13in (33cm) high. **£65,000-75,000** *C*

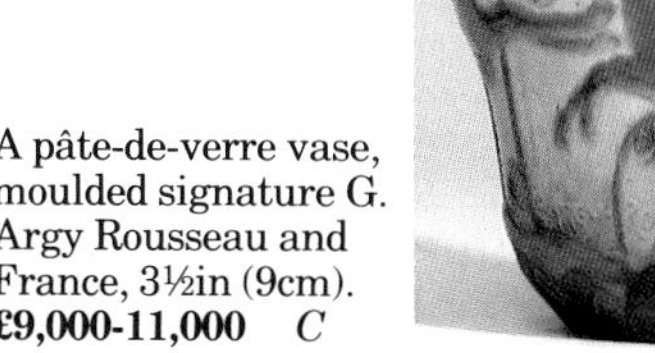

A pâte-de-verre vase, moulded signature G. Argy Rousseau and France, 3½in (9cm). **£9,000-11,000** *C*

A black vase, 'Martins Pecheurs', moulded with songbirds in flowering branches, with impressed signature R. Lalique, 9½in (23.5cm) high. **£6,000-7,000** *C*

A Carlo Bugatti ebonised and rosewood cabinet, with brass, pewter and ivory inlay, 35½in (90cm). **£9,000-10,000** *C*

A leaded glass window, designed by Frank Lloyd Wright, c1900, 41½ by 27in (105 by 68cm). **£3,500-4,500** *CNY*

An important oak dining table and 8 chairs, designed by Frank Lloyd Wright, c1903, table top 54½in (138cm) wide, chairs 46in (117cm) high. **£350,000+** *CNY*

A Daum pâte-de-verre figure by Almaric Walter, moulded monogram AW and carved Daum Nancy with Cross of Lorraine, 6½in (17cm). **£7,500-9,000** *C*

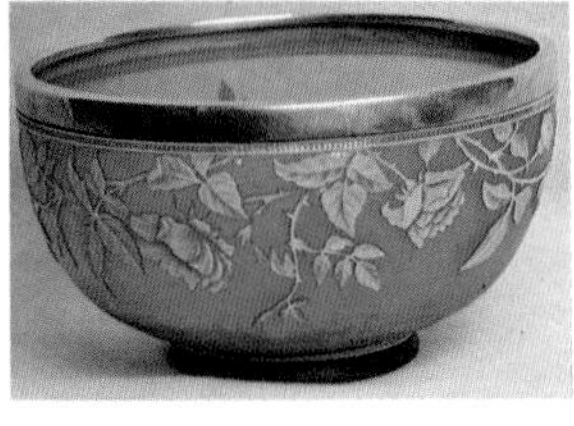

A cameo glass bowl by Thos. Webb & Sons, silver rim, H.M. London 1901, 8in (20cm) diam. **£1,700-2,000** *SWO*

An Almaric Walter pâte-de-verre paperweight, designed by H. Bergé, moulded signature A. Walter Nancy H. Berge, 3in (8cm) high. **£10,000-12,000** *C*

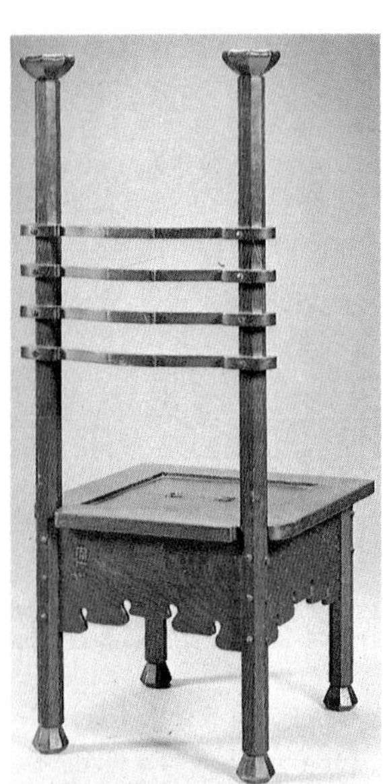

An oak side chair, by Charles Rohlfs, Buffalo, 1901, 47in (119cm) high. **£16,000-19,000** *CNY*

An oak side chair, designed by Frank Lloyd Wright, c1902, 40in (101cm) high. **£14,000-16,000** *CNY*

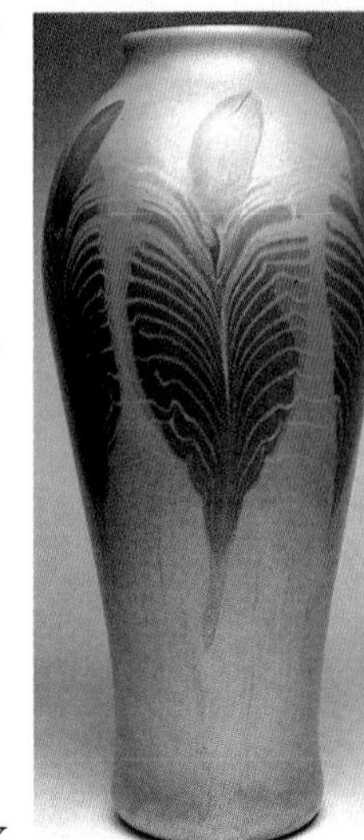

A Favrile glass vase, by Tiffany Studios, c1896, inscribed L.C. Tiffany E136, 20in (50cm) high. **£4,000-5,000** *CNY*

An Arts and Crafts mahogany secretaire, the panelled drop desk flap enclosing central cupboard with mother-of-pearl inlay, 48in (122cm). **£750-950** *P*

A walnut and marquetry revolving bookcase, the top inlaid with various fruitwoods with swallows and Gothic pinnacle, on later revolving base, inlaid Gallé signature, 20in (51cm) wide. **£7,000-9,000** *C*

A three-fold wood framed and leather covered screen, decorated across the top with a tooled and gilded frieze of seagulls, with sailing boats below, the lower frieze depicting fish, crabs and shells, 70in high. **£1,000-1,500** *P*

An Austrian mahogany kneehole desk, attributed to Otto Wagner, with ivory, satinwood stringing and bronze plaques, 48in, and a chair. **£2,500-4,000** *P*

Two jade table screens, carved in relief with birds in landscapes, Immortals gathered in groves and flowering peony, cracks to wood, 19thC, 7in high. **£18,000-20,000** *CHK*

An oak bookcase, model No. 700, designed by Harvey Ellis, executed by Gustav Stickley, c1903, 36in (91.5cm) wide. **£6,000-9,000** *CNY*

A Carlo Bugatti ebonised and rosewood ladies writing desk, with pewter and ivory inlay, signed Ricardo Telligrini 1897, 30in (76cm). **£4,500-6,000** *C*

An Art Nouveau silver vase by Gilbert Marks, London 1902, 13½in (34cm) high, 30oz. **£3,000-4,000** *DN*

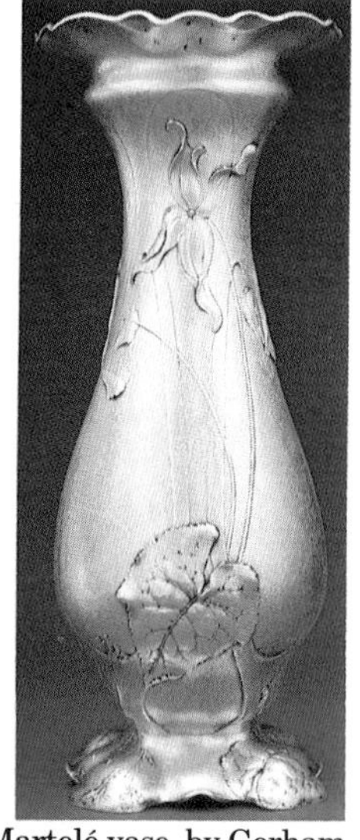

A Martelé vase, by Gorham Manufacturing Co, Providence, c1910, 15in, 61.5oz. **£4,000-5,000** *CNY*

A repoussé tankard by Tiffany & Co, New York, for the world's Columbian Exposition, Chicago, 1893, the lid with stylised monogram, touchmark on base, 10in (25cm) high, 52oz 10dwt. **£16,000-19,000** *CNY*

An early Ming gilt bronze figure of Vajrasattva, cast Yongle 6-character mark, 7in (18cm) high. **£14,000-16,000** *CHK*

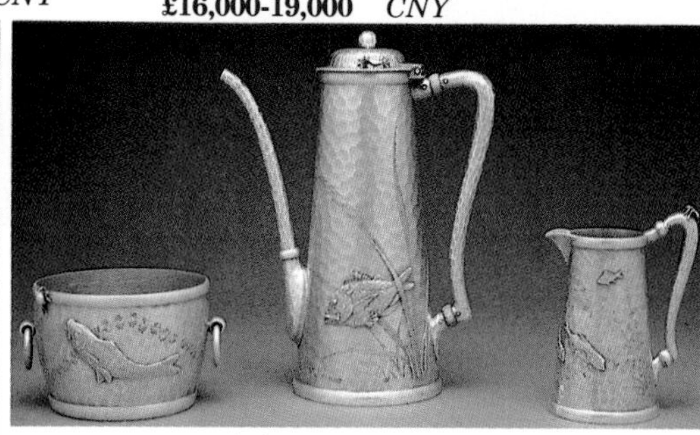

A three-piece demi-tasse service, by Tiffany & Co, New York, 1878-1891, coffee pot 8in (20cm) high, 23oz 10dwt. **£9,000-12,000** *CNY*

A silver and enamel lidded tankard by Liberty & Co, attributed to a design by Archibald Knox, c1900. **£4,000-5,000** *Bon*

A pair of pale celadon jade Mughal style tripod basins, 19thC, 7½in (18.5cm) wide, on pierced wood stands. **£5,000-6,000** *CHK*

A rare Yixing stoneware wrist-rest, modelled as a section of bamboo, impressed with potter's seal mark of Chen Mingyuan, slight chip, late 17th/early 18thC, 8in (21cm), fitted box. **£13,000-15,000** *CHK*

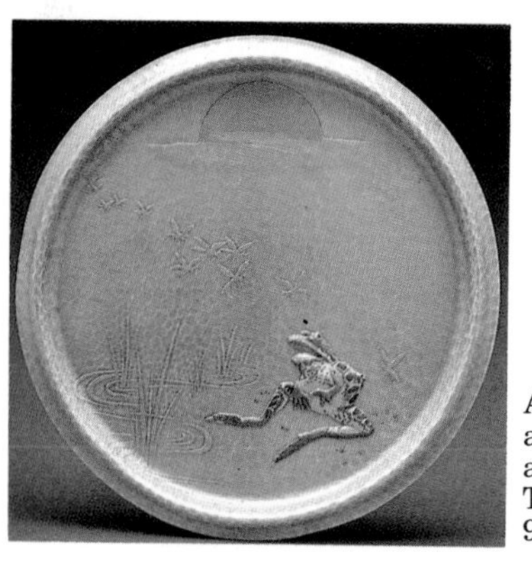

An inlaid waiter, decorated with an applied frog inlaid with gold alloy and copper, slight damage to sun, by Tiffany & Co, New York, 1878-1891, 9½in (24cm), 10oz. **£11,000-15,000** *CNY*

A 142-piece mixed metal flatware service, with cast applied decoration of silver, gold and copper, in the Japanese taste, by Tiffany & Co, New York, c1880, marked 'ETC', 201oz 10dwt. **£55,000-70,000** *CNY*

A Martele centrepiece bowl with scenes of the seasons, Gorham Man.Co. Providence 1906, English import marks of Birmingham 1908, 27in (68cm) long, 178oz 10dwt. **£22,000-25,000** *CNY*

A 'Navajo' vase, by Tiffany & Co. New York, 1900, for the Exposition Universelle, Paris 1900, and the Pan-American Exposition, Buffalo 1901, Exposition touchmarks, damage, 8½in (22cm) high, 89oz. **£25,000-30,000** *CNY*

A vase shaped ewer, by Tiffany & Co, New York, c1895, with applied sea motifs surrounded by seaweed, marked on base, monogram erased, 14in (36cm), 86oz 10dwt. **£10,000-15,000** *CNY*

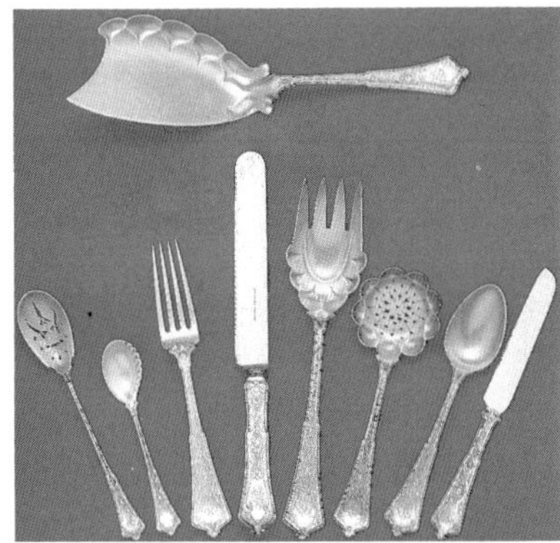

A 242-piece parcel gilt Persian pattern service, each engraved with a crest, by Tiffany & Company, New York, 1878-91, 332oz 10dwt. **£10,000-15,000** *CNY*

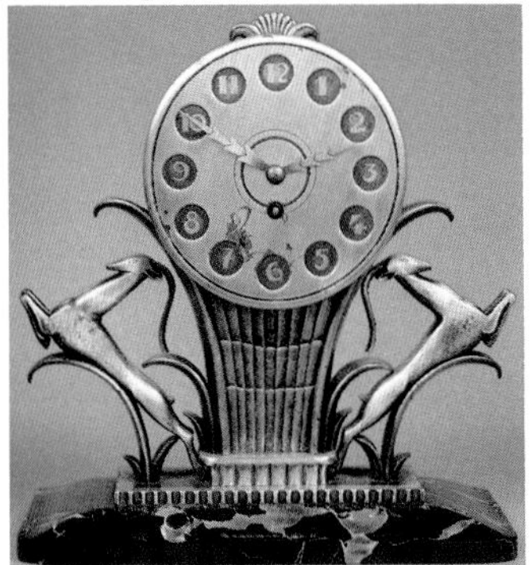

A silvered bronze mantel clock, the drum body with Arabic chapters, on marble base, stamped E. Brandt, France, 12in (30.5cm) high. **£2,000-3,000** *C*

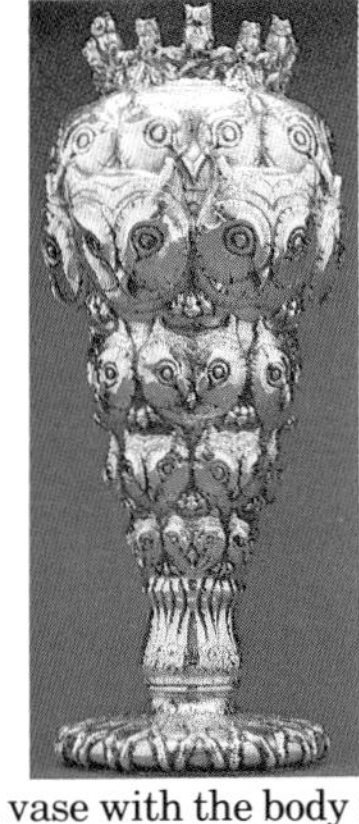

A vase with the body formed of 5 rows of owls' heads and talons, by Tiffany & Co, New York, Chicago Exposition 1893 touch, 10½in, 26oz. **£25,000-30,000** *CNY*

An Imperial inlaid ink cake box and cover, with mother-of-pearl inlay, the black ink cakes moulded with floral sprays and inscriptions, minor chips, Qianlong, 12in (31cm) wide. **£8,000-10,000** *CHK*

A pair of Liberty Cymric silver candlesticks, attributed to Archibald Knox, stamped maker's mark L & Co Cymric and Birmingham hallmarks for 1902, 8½in (22cm) high, 22oz 1dwt. **£4,000-5,000** *C*

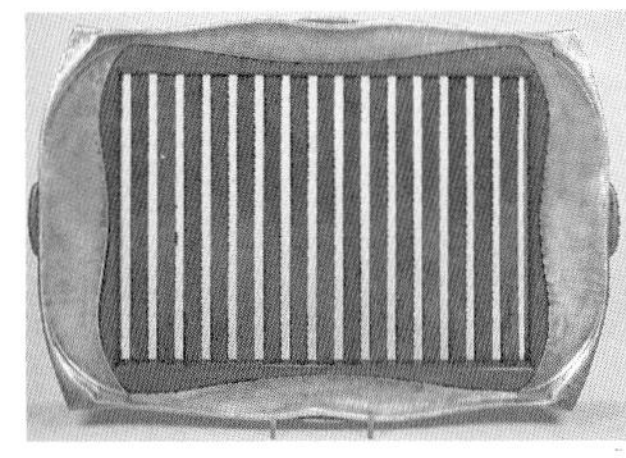

An 'Edelzinn' pewter and mahogany tray, designed by Joseph Maria Olbrich, c1904, unmarked, 22½in (57cm) long. **£3,000-4,000** *P*

A silver gilt carved ivory tusk flagon set with stones, by Tiffany & Co. New York, 1910, marked, 23in, 466oz gross. **£20,000-25,000** *CNY*

A green patinated bronze group, 'The Crowning of the Virgin', by T. B. Huxley Jones, 47in (120cm). **£1,700-2,500** *P*

A bronze figure, 'Needless Alarms', cast from a model by Frederic Lord Leighton, unsigned, 18½in (47cm) high. **£2,600-3,200** *P*

An early bronze statuette, 'Salomé', from a model by Carl Milles, signed, foundry mark for E. Colin & Cie, Paris, 12in (30cm). **£20,000-25,000** *P*

A Guild of Handicrafts silver and enamel brooch by C. R. Ashbee, stamped, London 1907, 7.8cm. **£12,000-15,000** *C*

A German bronze group, 'Europa and the Bull', cast by Georg Wrba, signed, C. Leyrer, München marks, 14in. **£2-3,000** *P*

An enamelled cigarette box, signed on the base Jean Goulden, numbered, dated LXVI28, 6½in long. **£1,600-2,000** *P*

A Martin Bros. stoneware vase, signed Martin Bros, London & Southall, 1891, 16in (40cm) high. **£3,000-4,000** *P*

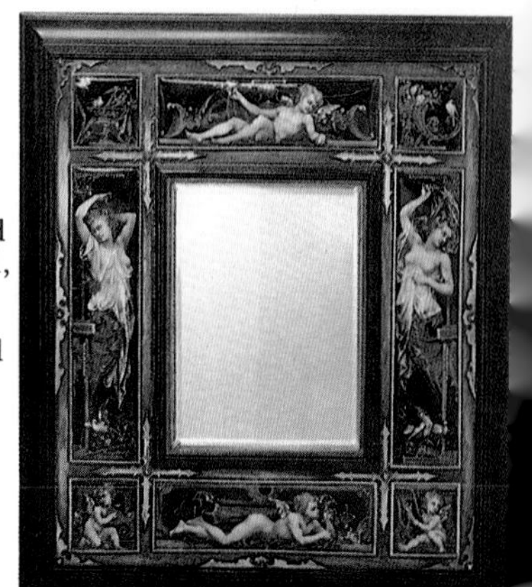

A Limoges enamelled framed mirror, 14 by 12in (36 by 31cm). **£2,500-3,500** *P*

A Sibyl Dunlop necklace, pendant 7cm long, original case. **£3-4,000** *P*

A Minton porcelain vase designed by Dr. Christopher Dresser, painted in colours, heightened in gilt, with bands of stylised Gothic foliage, damaged, 20in (20.5cm) high.
£5,000-6,000 *C*

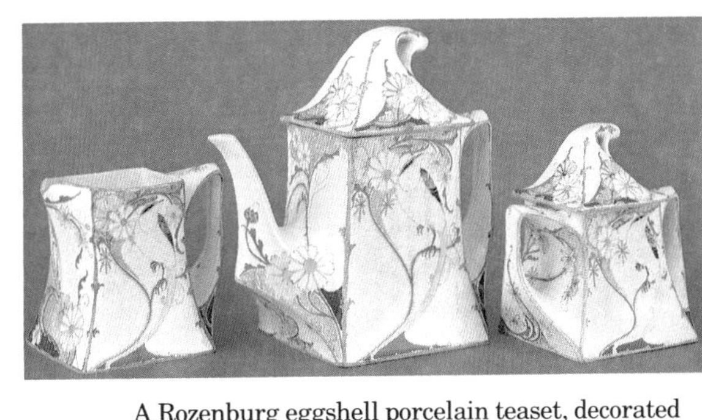

A Rozenburg eggshell porcelain teaset, decorated by H. G. A. Huyvenaar, with polychrome decoration of daisies and birds on a cream ground, cracks, painted marks Rozenburg Den Haag, painter's monogram H, datemark for 1900, teapot 7in (18cm) high. **£4,000-6,000** *CAm*

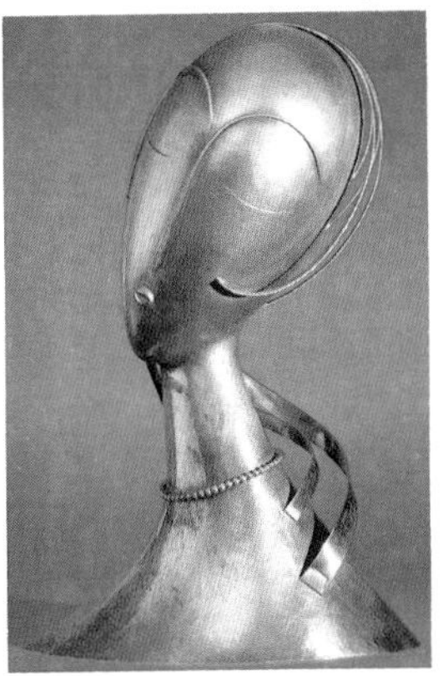

A brass bust of a young woman, the head with brass strip forming long flowing hair and features, stamped marks 1021 Franz Hagenauer Wien wHw Made in Austria RD, 17in (43cm) high. **£5,000-6,000** *C*

A bronze table mirror, the openwork base of overlapping fern leaves, impressed Tiffany Studios New York and engraved E.C.T. June 8th 1909, 21in (54cm) high.
£10,000-15,000 *CNY*

A William de Morgan four-tile panel, with two snakes amongst flowering foliage, each impressed with W de Morgan Merton Abbey, 16½in (42cm) square. **£6,500-7,500** *C*

A Salvatore Meli ceramic and glass centre table, the stoneware base in the form of a head of a mythical hound, the ceramic inscribed Meli.58 Roma, 47in (120cm) wide. **£8,000-9,000** *C*

A William de Morgan jar and cover, painted in the Isnik manner, underglazed blue inscription W. De. Morgan Fulham, 14½in (36.5cm) high.
£6,500-7,500 *C*

A Danny Lane float glass stack chair, formed by irregular cut and polished glass panels held by metal screws.
£3,500-4,500 *C*

A pair of birch laminated side chairs by Gerald Summers. **£4,000-5,000** *C*

The Bourne and Hollingsworth clock, with musical chimes on six bells by Gillett and Johnson, Croydon, England, the bells cast with the signature of Gillett and Johnson, Croydon, 1927.
£22,000-25,000 *C*

A bronze and ivory figure, 'Eastern Dancer', on a green marble base, inscribed in the bronze Schmidt-Cassel, 15½in (38.5cm) high.
£15,000-20,000 *C*

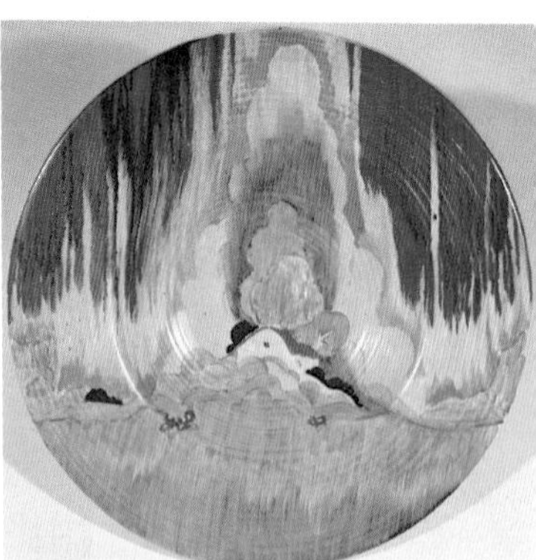

A Wilkinson Bizarre pottery charger, by Clarice Cliff, painted with cottages and trees, 18in (46cm).
£1,500-2,000 *DSH*

A Macassar ebony veneered stationery cabinet, by Ernest Gimson, 25in (63cm) high. **£10,000-12,000** *P*

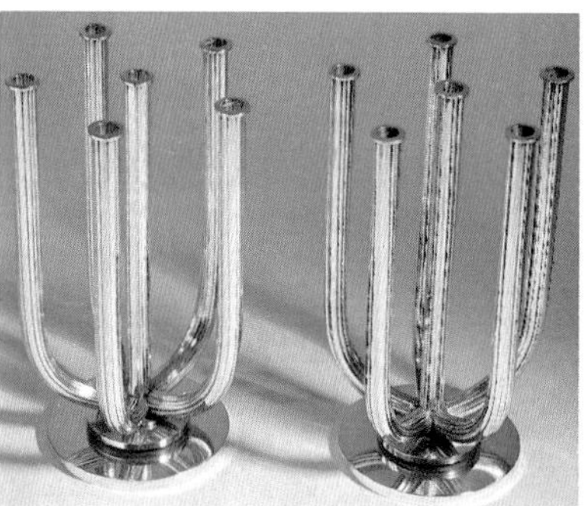

A pair of Georg Jensen 5-branch candelabra, designed by Harald Nielsen, with fluted cylindrical branches, stamped marks, 18in (46cm) high. **£17,000-20,000** *C*

A bronze and ivory figure, 'Bat Dancer', cold painted in red, turquoise and silver, on stepped marble base inscribed F. Preiss, 9½in (23.5cm) high.
£4,000-5,000 *C*

A silvered bronze group, 'Diana', on black slate base, the bronze inscribed Lorenzl, 18in (46cm) high.
£5,000-6,000 *C*

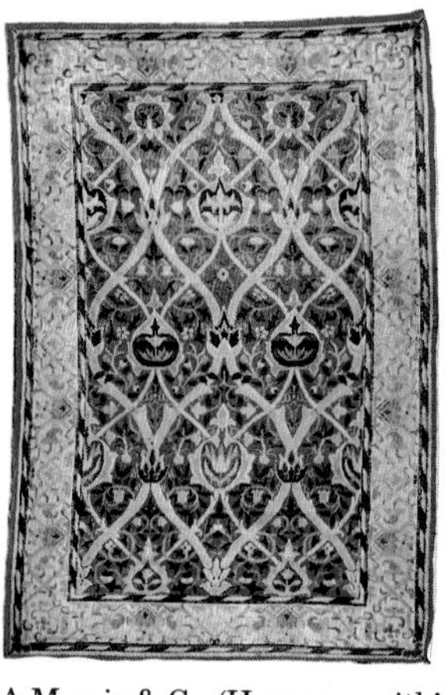

A Morris & Co. 'Hammersmith' hand-tufted woollen and mohair carpet, 122 by 169in (310 by 429cm).
£17,000-19,000 *P*

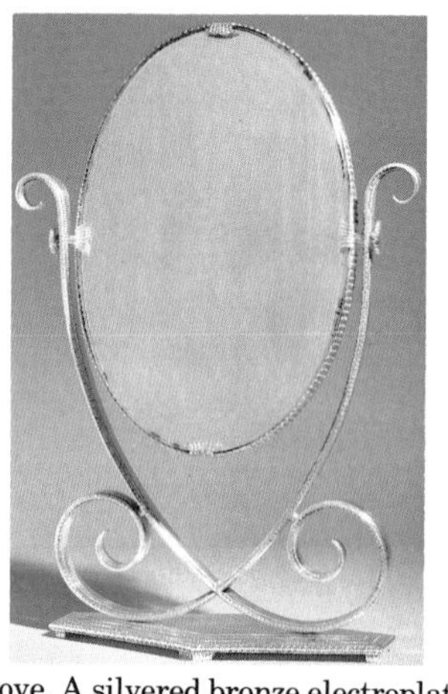
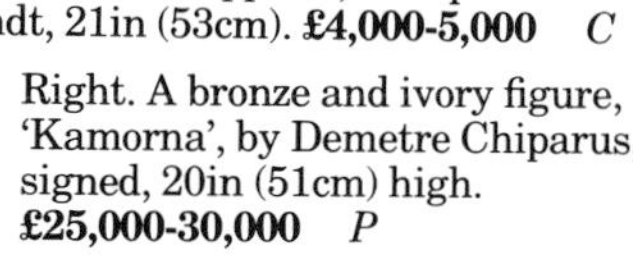

Above. A silvered bronze electroplated dressing table mirror, the swivel glass on scroll supports, stamped E. Brandt, 21in (53cm). **£4,000-5,000** *C*

Right. A bronze and ivory figure, 'Kamorna', by Demetre Chiparus, signed, 20in (51cm) high.
£25,000-30,000 *P*

A Clarice Cliff Bizarre pottery charger, painted in pastel shades with 2 gazelles in exotic tropical landscape, printed blue marks Hand Painted Bizarre by Clarice Cliff Wilkinson Ltd, England, 17½in (44.5cm).
£2,000-3,000 *C*

A bronze and ivory figure, 'Con Brio', cast and carved from a model by Ferdinand Preiss, cold painted in pink and gold, on green onyx tray, inscribed F. Preiss, 11½in (29cm) high. **£7,000-9,000** *C*

A painted bronze and ivory figure, 'The Butterfly Dancer', cast and carved from a model by Demetre Chiparus, signed, 17in (43cm). **£20,000-25,000** *P*

A parcel gilt bronze and ivory statue, 'Valkyrie Rider', cast and carved by Louis Chalon, signed in the bronze, 21½in (54.5cm).
£5,500-6,500 *C*

Left. A carved ivory figure on marble plinth, bow and arrow missing, some damage, signed F. Preiss, 7in (18cm) high. **£400-500**

Right. A carved ivory figure of a girl with feeding bowl and bird, on marble plinth, signed F. Preiss, 7in (18cm) high. **£550-650** *PC*

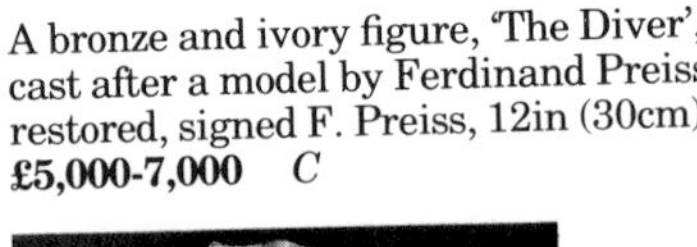

A bronze and ivory figure of a girl with clock, cast after a model by Ferdinand Preiss, base inscribed F. Preiss, 21½in (54.5cm) high.
£9,000-12,000 *C*

A Linthorpe pottery vase, designed by Christopher Dresser, impressed Linthorpe with facsimile signature and HT monogram for Tooth, numbered '449', damage, 16½in (42cm) high.
£4,000-5,000 *P*

A bronze and ivory figure, 'The Diver', cast after a model by Ferdinand Preiss, restored, signed F. Preiss, 12in (30cm).
£5,000-7,000 *C*

A cold painted bronze and ivory figure, 'Girl on a Wall', cast and carved from a model by Ferdinand Preiss, the girl on a green onyx 'wall', signed on the reverse F. Preiss, 9½in (23.5cm) high.
£7,000-8,000 *P*

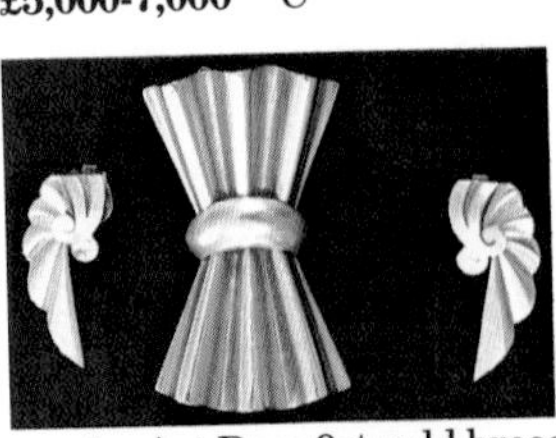

An Art Deco 9ct gold brooch in the form of a bow, with a pair of earrings. **£150-200** *PC*

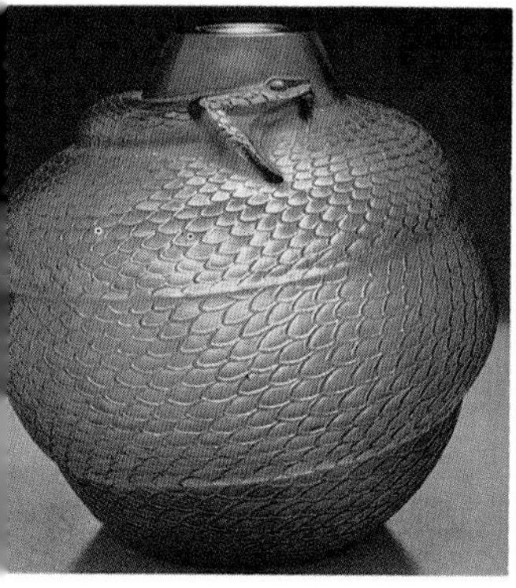

frosted amber glass vase, 'Serpent', ‹ René Lalique, moulded as a cobra, oulded R. Lalique, 10in (26cm) high. ‚,000-10,000 *CNY*

A Monart ginger jar, with bluish green whorls, c1929, 10in (25cm). **£500-600** *FA*

A scent bottle, 'Bouchon Cassis', moulded R. Lalique, France No. 494, bruised, 4½in (11.5cm). **£4,000-5,000** *Bon*

.n etched glass table lamp, shade and ase etched Daum, Nancy, France, 7in (43cm) high, shade 15in (38cm) iam. **£10,000-14,000** *CNY*

A Monart vase, in pale green, orange and brown with gold aventurine, c1930, 9in (23cm) high. **£250-350** *FA*

A Monart bowl in mottled orange with silver flecks, c1930, 13in (33cm). **£250-350** *FA*

. Ray Flavell glass sculpture, 'A Thought About .rt Deco', the smoky grey glass plate sandblasted 'ith curved bands supporting a cased amethyst owl with fluting, engraved Ray Flavell, 3in (32.5cm) high. **£1,200-1,500** *C*

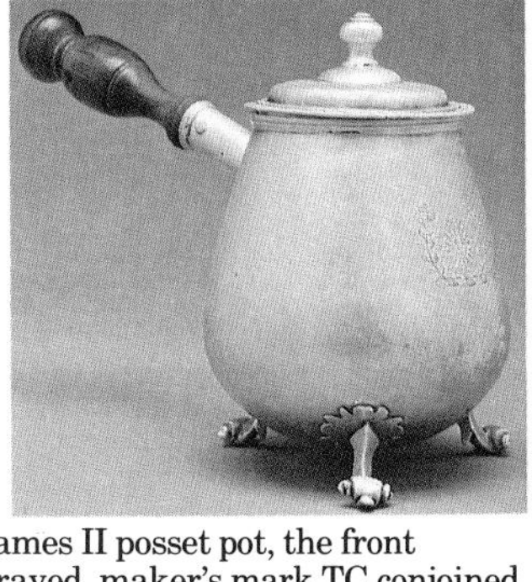

A James II posset pot, the front engraved, maker's mark TC conjoined, London 1686, 6½in long, 7oz. **£40,000-50,000** *CNY*

A George I Irish coffee pot, engraved with a coat-of-arms in a baroque cartouche, by John Hamilton, Dublin, 1715, 9½in (24cm) high, 29oz gross. **£5,000-6,000** *C*

George I bullet teapot, the hinged cover with .ter mother-of-pearl finial, marked on base and over, by John Eckfourd, London, 1727, later ivory roll handle, 7in (18cm) long, 9oz 10dwt. 2,500-4,000 *CNY*

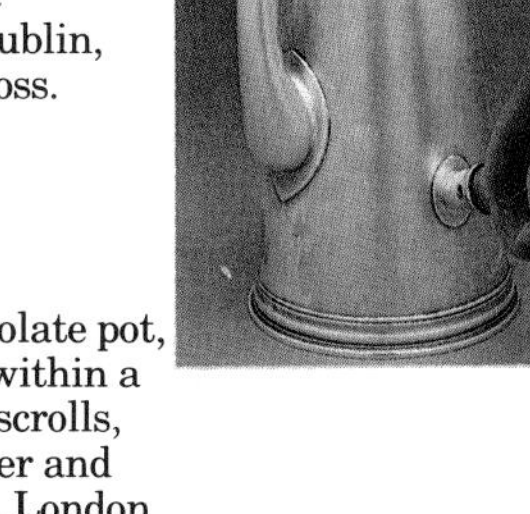

A Queen Anne chocolate pot, the front engraved within a cartouche of foliate scrolls, marked on side, cover and finial, Joseph Ward, London 1704, 10in (25cm), 25oz. **£6,000-8,000** *CNY*

Two Victorian 10-light candelabra, by Barnard Bros. 1846 and C. F. Hancock, 1895, the nozzles unmarked, 32in (82cm), 458oz. **£15,000-17,000** *C*

A Victorian 7-light candelabrum, by John S. Hunt 1846, No. 2792, 30in (76cm) high, 269oz.
£10,000-12,000 *C*

A pair of Queen Anne tapering baluster candlesticks, engraved with armorials, by William Turell, 1713, 7½in (19.5cm), with later nozzles, 30oz.
£15,000-17,000 *P*

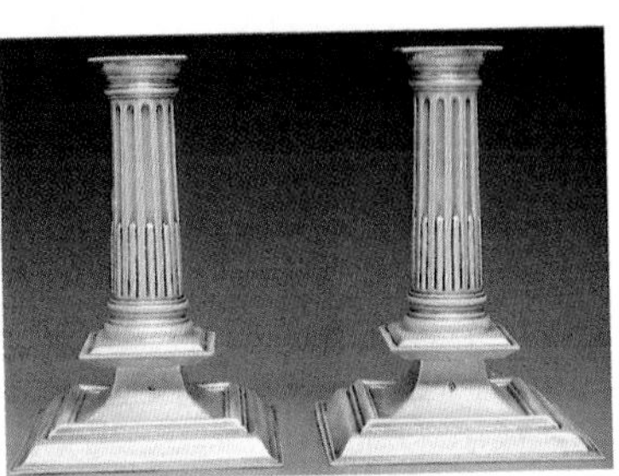

A pair of Charles II candlesticks, bases engraved with initials S over IE, London 1683, maker's mark TA, pellet below, in circular punch, probably for Thomas Allen, 6in, 17oz. **£14,000-16,000** *CNY*

A George III coffee pot, stand and lamp, engraved with crest, marked, by Paul Storr, London 1804, stand by Burwash and Sibley, 1806, 13in (32cm), 46oz 10dwt. **£3,000-4,000** *CNY*

An early George III cast figure taperstick, modelled as a British sailor in traditional uniform, shown also in reverse, by William Cafe, 1761, 6in (15.5cm), 5.5oz. **£4,000-5,000** *P*

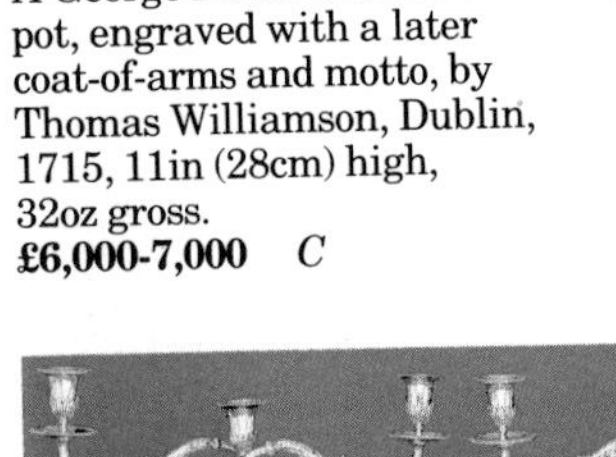

A George I Irish chocolate pot, engraved with a later coat-of-arms and motto, by Thomas Williamson, Dublin, 1715, 11in (28cm) high, 32oz gross.
£6,000-7,000 *C*

A George II chamber candlestick, engraved with a crest, by Paul de Lamerie, London 1746, 6in (16cm), 9oz 10dwt, the base with scratch weight 11*4.
£8,000-10,000 *CNY*

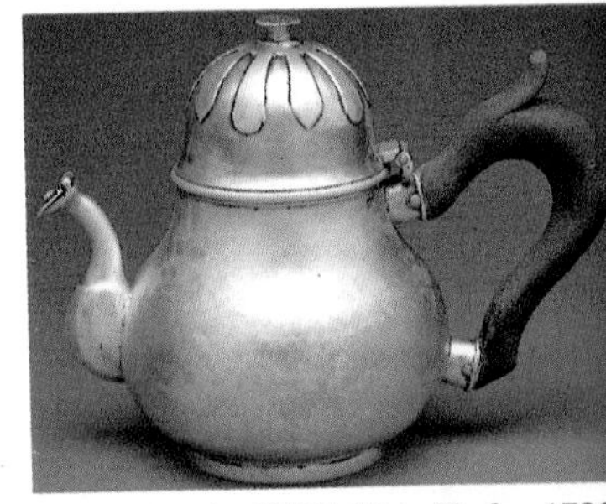

A teapot, marked HM, New York, c1720, engraved on base IM, mark struck near rim on either side of handle, 6in (15cm) high, 16oz 10dwt gross.
£24,000-26,000 *CNY*

A pair of George III 3-light candelabra, engraved with a crest, by Richard Cooke, 1800 and 1804, 17in (43cm) high, 128oz.
£12,000-15,000 *C*

Four George II table candlesticks, cast and chas[ed] with flowers, foliage and scrolls, engraved with a crest, by Samuel Courtauld, 1757, 11in (28cm), 86oz. **£8,000-10,000** *C*

George III basket, with ngraved coat-of-arms vithin a rococo cartouche, Villiam Kidney, 1745, 15in 38cm) wide, 83oz.
9,000-12,000 *C*

A set of 6 Charles II shell shaped dishes, by Samuel Hood, 1675, one with maker's mark and leopard's head crowned only, 5in (12.5cm) wide, 10oz 7dwt.
£37,000-42,000 *C*

A George I Irish monteith, with lion's mask and drop ring handles, with shaped detachable rim, by David King, 1715, 11in (28cm) high, 63oz. **£26,000-30,000** *C*

pair of George I basins, with gadrooned borders, he domed centres engraved with a coat-of-arms in calework, foliate scroll and laurel surround, by avid Willaume, 1726, 15in (38cm) diam, 112oz.
17,000-20,000 *C*

A pair of wine coolers, the plain bodies half-fluted and engraved with a frieze of leaves and flowers, lion mask drop ring side handles, detachable rims and tinned liners, c1775, 9in (23cm). **£3,000-4,000** *P*

pair of George II sauceboats, engraved vith a crest and coronet, by George Vickes, London, 1731, 9in (23cm) wide, he bases numbered and with scratch veights, 34oz. **£44,000-48,000** *CNY*

A George II Irish engraved punch bowl, by Robert Calderwood, Dublin 1732, 8in (20cm) diam, 23oz.
£9,000-12,000 *C*

George II style swing handled cake asket, on mask and scroll feet, by harles Stuart Harris & Sons, 1912, 6in (40cm) long, 101.5oz.
6,500-8,500 *P*

A George II basket, by Benjamin Godfrey, 1741, engraved with later coat-of-arms, coronet and motto, 12in (30cm) long, 51oz.
£9,000-12,000 *C*

A George III basin and Victorian ewer, the basin engraved, 1764, with maker's mark of John Jacob over-striking another, the ewer by Robert Garrard, 1841, 50oz. **£6,000-7,000** *C*

A pair of George III baskets and covers, by William Pitts, 1803, with frosted glass liners, 12½in (31.5cm) long, 95oz.
£12,000-15,000 *C*

A George II sauceboat stand from the Anson service, by Paul de Lamerie, London, 1739, 11in (28cm) long, 22oz.
£42,000-46,000 *CNY*

A William IV inkstand, with central taperstick and 2 mounted glass bottles, by Joseph & John Angell, 1830, 14in (36cm) wide, 42oz.
£4,000-6,000 *P*

A pair of George III vegetable dishes, covers and handles, by John Edwards, 1798, 12in (30.5cm), 85oz, and
A pair of George III sauce tureens and covers, by Robert Sharp, 1798, 10in, 47oz. **£5,000-7,000 each pair** *C*

A pair of George IV entrée dishes, covers and handles, by Philip Rundell, 1822, 12½in (31cm) wide, 148oz.
£6,000-7,000 *P*

A pair of donkey salts, by Mortimer and Hunt, fully marked, London 1840, each numbered 368, 4½in (11cm) high.
£9,000-10,000 *Bon*

A set of 3 Charles II casters, engraved with initials AP, the smaller casters 1682, the larger 1683, maker's mark WB, a mullet below 6 and 7in (15 and 18cm) high, 22oz.
£46,000-50,000 *C*

An Elizabeth I Communion cup and a cover paten, London 1571, maker's mark HW, the paten by John Jons, Exeter, c1576, 8in (21cm), 9oz 10dwt.
£4,000-6,000 *CNY*

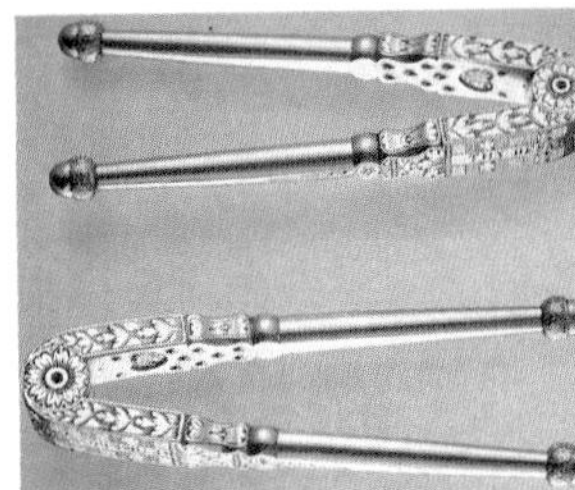

Two pairs of nut crackers, inscribed, probably English, c1716, 4½in (11cm) long, 8oz.
£6,000-7,000 *P*

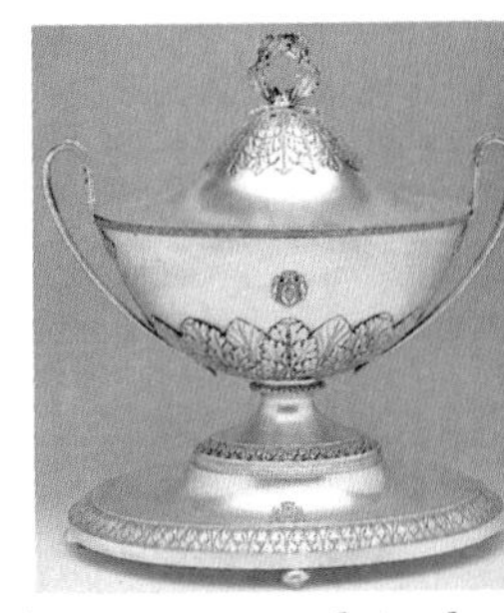

A soup tureen and stand, marked with initials of Carl Frederick Bredenberg St. Petersburg, 1801, 20½in (52cm) high, 8,775 gramme
£8,000-10,000 *C*

A French centrepiece, the rim inscribed, by Christofle, Paris, 25in (63.5cm) high, 8,947 grammes. **£8,500-10,000** *C*

A pair of George I toilet jars and covers apparently unmarked, but probably by Isaac Liger, c1728, 5i (12.5cm) high, 17oz, the bases wi scratch weights 8 14 and 8 12.
£17,000-20,000 *CNY*

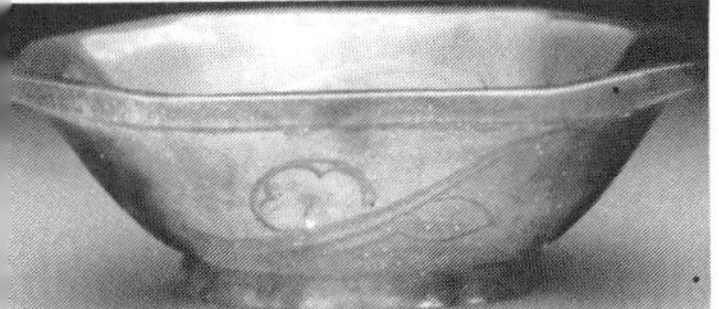

A pâté-de-verre dish, the ranslucent and red streaked round carved with stylised lossoms, leaves and sinuous stem, noulded Decorchemont, 3in (7.5cm) igh.
1,200-1,500 *CNY*

A Daum cameo glass vase, etched and enamelled with a design of violets, the rim gilded, with enamelled signature, 5in (13cm) diam.
£600-700 *PSG*

A Daum cameo glass box and cover, the greyish body overlaid with acid etched green glass, heightened with gilding, applied with a silver coloured metal collar, signed in gold on base Daum Nancy, 5in (12.5cm) diam.
£1,200-1,500 *P*

A pair of pink cameo glass jars with ilver screw top lids, 2in (5cm) high.
120-150 *PC*

A pâté-de-verre bust of a satyr, the bust modelled in amethyst glass, inscribed Despret and 1099, 6½in (16.5cm).
£500-600 *CNY*

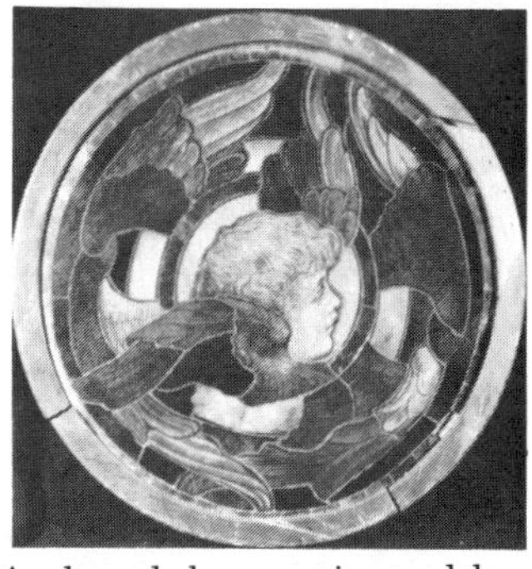

A coloured glass mosaic roundel, attributed to Powells and designed in the manner of Burne-Jones, 18in (45.5cm) diam.
£200-250 *P*

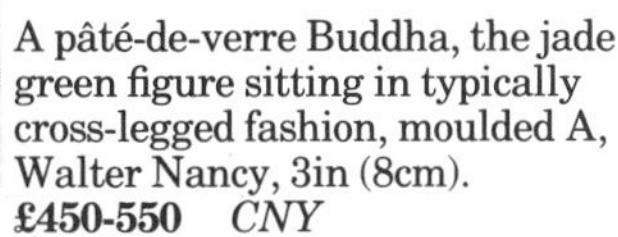

A pâté-de-verre Buddha, the jade green figure sitting in typically cross-legged fashion, moulded A, Walter Nancy, 3in (8cm).
£450-550 *CNY*

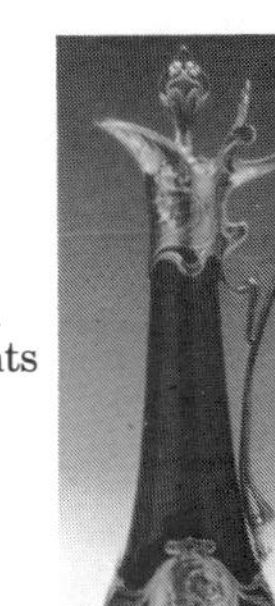

A W.M.F. claret jug, the emerald green glass jug with plated mounts incorporating female masks and flowerheads, 16in (40.5cm).
£500-600 *Bea*

Jewellery

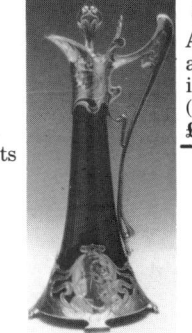

A glass and gold necklace, the green and violet woven cord necklace set with 9 moulded iridescent glass scarabs in 18ct gold, stamped Tiffany & Co, and 18ct, 16in (40.5cm) long.
£2,000-2,500 *CNY*

A Gip carved and pierced horn pendant, with bead link necklace, set with a silver backed moonstone, signed, 4½in (11cm).
£250-300 *P[Re]*

A cameo set, c1900, bracelet 6½in 16.5cm) long.
£5,000-5,500 *CJ*

A pâté-de-verre pendant, by G. Argy-Rousseau, with translucent ground, moulded with a bouquet of red and purple flowers on a fuchsia coloured cord, moulded A-R-G, 3in (7.5cm) diam.
£900-1,200 *CNY*

Make the most of Miller's

Every care has been taken to ensure the accuracy of descriptions and estimated valuations. Price ranges in this book reflect what one should expect to pay for a similar example. When selling one can obviously expect a figure below. This will fluctuate according to a dealer's stock, saleability at a particular time, etc. It is always advisable to approach a reputable specialist dealer or an auction house which has specialist sales.

Lamps

A brass and glass oil lamp, c1910, 40in (101.5cm).
£150-200 *COB*

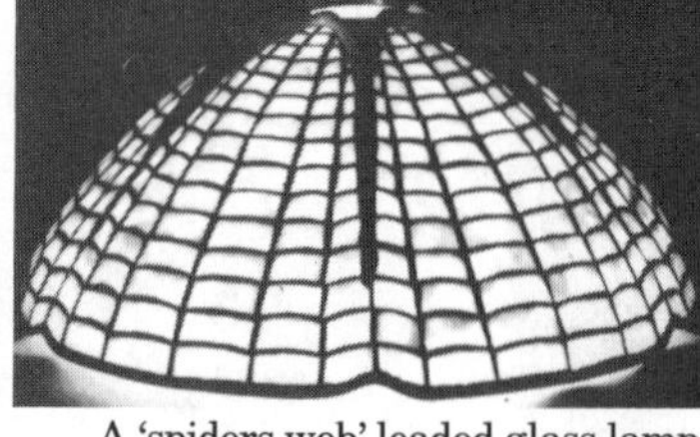

A 'spiders web' leaded glass lamp shade, impressed Tiffany Studios New York 337, 15in (38cm) diam.
£3,000-4,000 *CNY*

A Favrile glass and bronze bell desk lamp, inscribed L.C.T. Favrile, the bronze base with green patina, impressed Tiffany Studios, New York 419, 11in (28cm).
£3,000-3,500 *CNY*

A bronze table lamp base, impressed Tiffany Studios, New York 531, 26½in (67cm) high.
£1,000-1,500 *CNY*

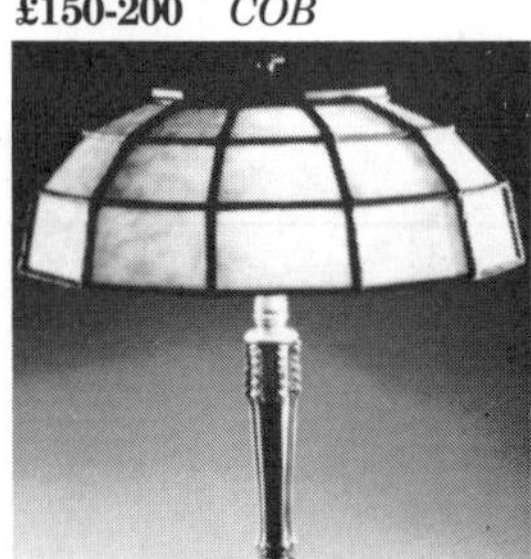

A leaded glass and gilt bronze table lamp, with white streaked amber and yellow panels, impressed Tiffany Studios, New York 1933, the gilt bronze base impressed Tiffany Studios New York 543, 21in (53cm) high.
£3,200-3,700 *CNY*

A leaded glass, bronze and Favrile glass table lamp, with tag impressed Tiffany Studios, New York, some damage, 26in (66cm) high.
£6,000-8,000 *CNY*

A stained and leaded glass table lamp, with a brass column cast with stylised foliage, on a leaf shaped base, the shade with a stylised floral border, 23in (58.5cm) high.
£700-800 *CEd*

A bronze figural lamp base, cast from a model by R. Sudre, modelled as a naked girl, with lamp fitment, signed R Sudre lere Epreuve and stamped Raymond Sudre, numbered 1910, 20½in (52cm) high.
£500-700 *P*

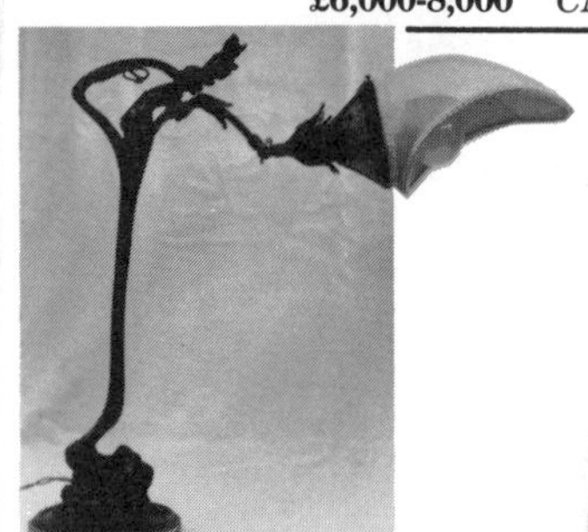

A bronze table lamp of a nude female figure, holding an adjustable lamp, on a circular base, not signed, 18in (46cm).
£2,300-3,000 *PC*

Martin Bros.

A Martinware grotesque ewer, signed Martin, London & Southall, 3in (8cm) high.
£400-500 *P*

A Martin Brothers stoneware jug/flask, glazed in green, pink, brown and blue, signed Martin Bros., London & Southall, 8½in (21.5cm) high.
£500-700 *P*

A Martinware egg cup set and stand, the cups signed Martin Bros, London, 7½in (19.5cm).
£300-500 *P*

Make the most of Miller's

Unless otherwise stated, any description which refers to 'a set' or 'a pair' includes a valuation for the entire set or the pair, even though the illustration may show only a single item.

Metal

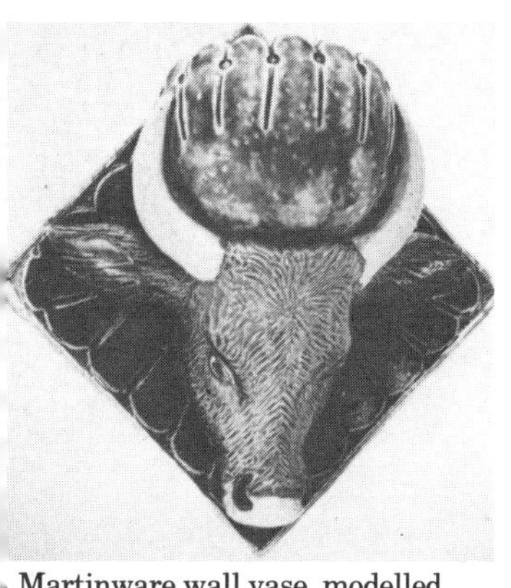

. Martinware wall vase, modelled s the head of a cow, on a diamond haped tile with blue ground, ncised mark R.W. Martin, outhall, 6½in (16.5cm).
450-500 *L*

. Jean Després plated bowl, with verall hammer textured finish, igned J. Després on base and JD oinçon on rim, 4in (10cm) high.
900-1,200 *P*

. WMF silvered pewter covered vo-handled punch bowl and ladle, amped, 21½in (54cm) high.
550-750 *CAm*

Georg Jensen 57 piece ontinental pattern table service, amped marks, London, import arks for 1934, 68oz not including eel.
,500-2,000 *CEd*

. set of Georg Jensen Cypress attern cutlery, comprising 61 ieces, designed by Tias Eckhoff, amped in oval Georg Jensen erling Denmark, 92oz gross.
,500-2,000 *P*

A German pewter bowl by Osiris, 5½in (14cm) high.
£150-180 *GAL*

A WMF pewter dish with figure, 9in (23cm) high.
£650-750 *GAL*

A David Anderson bowl, the silver coloured metal stamped David Anderson, 830S and numbered 5485, 16½in (42cm) wide.
£400-500 *P*

A set of Georg Jensen Scroll pattern cutlery, designed by Johan Rohde, comprising 79 pieces, stamped in oval Georg Jensen and Sterling Denmark, 136oz gross.
£1,500-2,000 *P*

An Arts and Crafts plated copper épergne, attributed to the Guild of Handicraft Ltd., and a design by Charles Robert Ashbee, 10½in (27.5cm).
£700-800 *P*

An Arts and Crafts stemmed bowl, attributed to John Paul Cooper, inscribed 'In memory of a Labour of Love, Ascension Day 1914', 6in (15cm).
£1,000-1,500 *P*

A Liberty & Co. English pewter and Clutha glass stemmed bowl, the mount marked English Pewter and 0276, 6½in (16.5cm) high.
£500-600 *P*

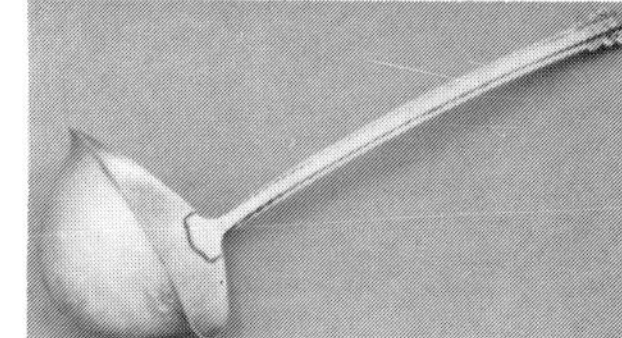

An Omar Ramsden silver soup ladle, stamped 'OR' with London hallmarks for 1924, 10½in (27cm), 6oz.
£500-700 *P*

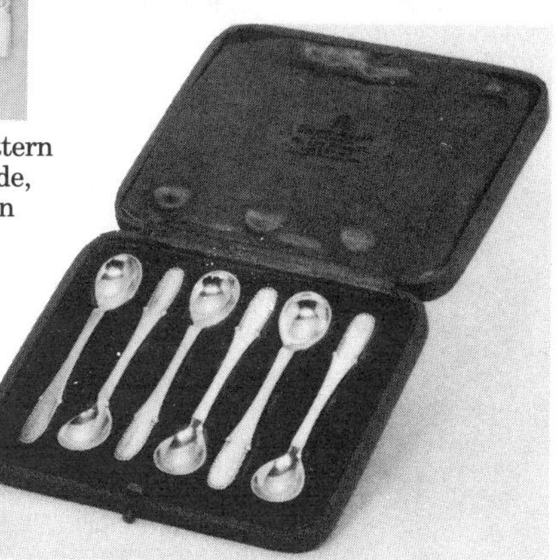

A set of 6 Georg Jensen silver coffee spoons, stamped maker's mark, G.S. and London import mark for 1925, cased.
£100-150 *CEd*

A Georg Jensen hammered teapot, with grooved ebony handle, stamped, 456 artists monogram GS and London import marks for 1929, 6in (15cm) high, 16oz gross.
£350-500 *CEd*

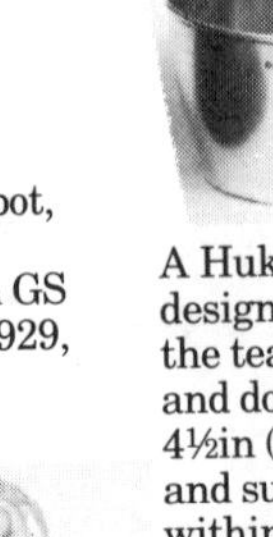

A Hukin & Heath silver teaset, designed by Christopher Dresser, the teapot with wickered handle and domed cover with button finial, 4½in (11.5cm) high, and a milk jug and sugar bowl, both contained within the pot, maker's marks for Birmingham 1880 and registration lozenge for 18th October 1879.
£1,500-2,000 *P*

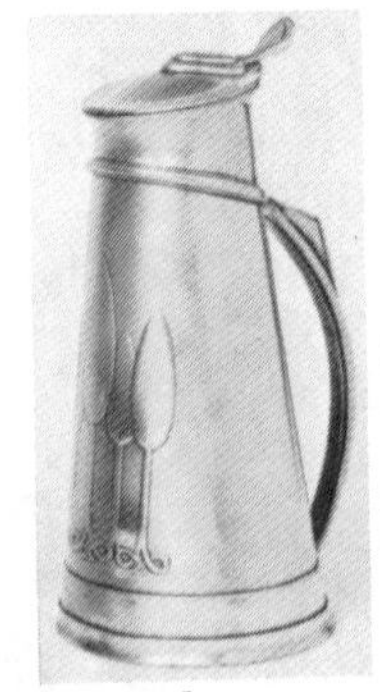

A large pewter ale jug and cover, showing the influence of the designs of C. F. A. Voysey, unmarked, but probably Liberty & Co, 14½in (36.5cm) high.
£200-250 *P*

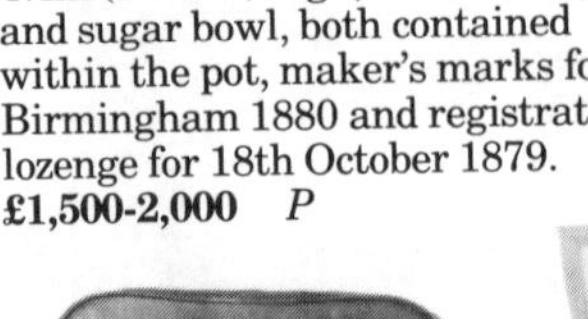

An Orfèvrerie Gallia plated tea and coffee set, stamped with factory marks, numbered 4643 and 4644, tray 20½in (52.5cm) wide.
£1,200-1,500 *P*

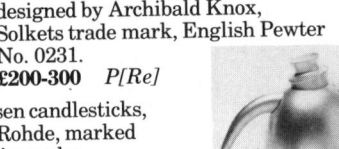

A Liberty's pewter tea service, designed by Archibald Knox, Solkets trade mark, English Pewter No. 0231.
£200-300 *P[Re]*

A Mappin & Webb silver coffee set, comprising: a coffee pot, 7in (18cm), hot milk jug and sugar bowl, maker's marks for Sheffield 1938.
£700-800 *P*

A pair of Georg Jensen candlesticks, designed by Johan Rohde, marked with Danish maker's marks, numbered 612 and with designer's monogram, 3in (7cm) high.
£500-600 *P*

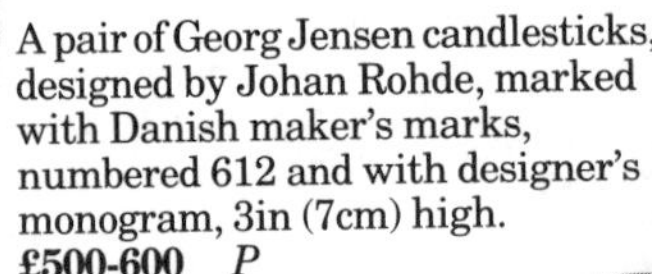

A Modernist teaset, the silver coloured metal stamped 800 and 210ff in shaped punch, teapot 5in (13cm) high.
£800-900 *P*

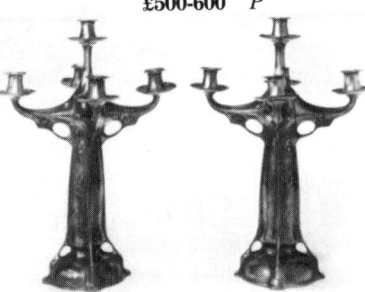

A pair of Liberty's Tudric pewter candlesticks, each with detachable driptray, No. 01769, 8in (20.5cm).
£150-200 *HCH*

A pair of pewter candlesticks, by Just Anderson, c1920, 9in (23cm).
£350-400 *GAL*

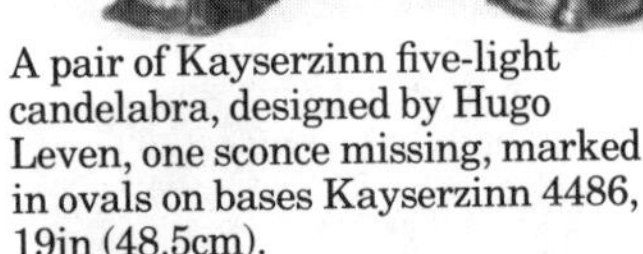

A pair of Kayserzinn five-light candelabra, designed by Hugo Leven, one sconce missing, marked in ovals on bases Kayserzinn 4486, 19in (48.5cm).
£2,000-2,500 *P*

▶ A silver goblet, Chester 1905, 8in (20.5cm).
£220-250 *TVA*

A Gothic style cup and cover, with Manchester Reform Club monogram, with gilt interior, inscribed 'Omar Ramsden Me Fecit', London 1923, 15in (38cm), on oak socle with silver plaques and strapwork decoration.
£2,500-3,000 *P[Re]*

A Gothic style goblet, with Manchester Reform Club monogram, inscribed 'Omar Ramsden Me Fecit', London 1923, 7in (18cm), on silver mounted oak socle. ▶
£450-500 *P[Re]*

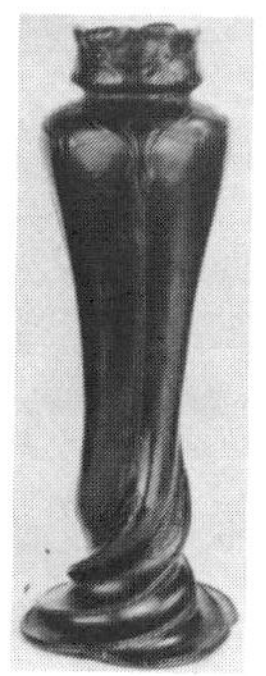

A Liberty & Co. Tudric Pewter flower vase, possibly designed by Archibald Knox, stamped marks, Tudric 0441, 4in (10cm).
£500-700 *P*

A bronze vase, signed J. Ofner, 13in (33cm).
£200-400 *CSK*

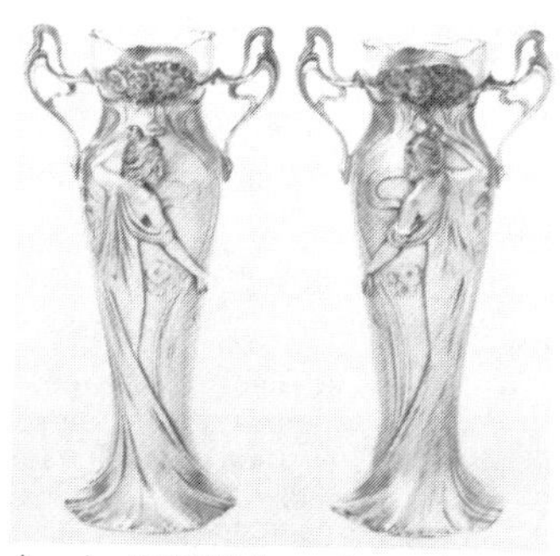

A pair of WMF figural metal vases, with glass liners, stamped marks on base, 14½in (36.5cm).
£1,200-1,600 *P*

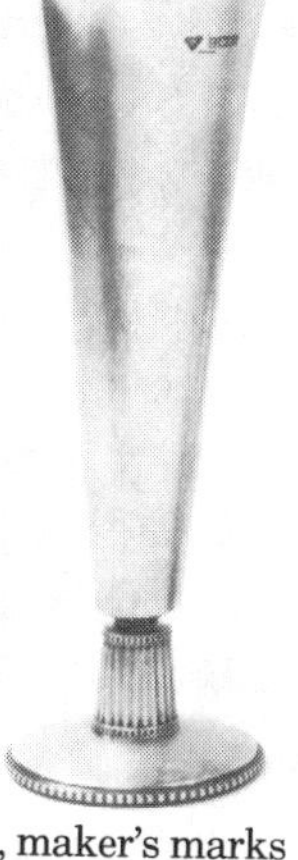

A silver vase, maker's marks G & Co. Ld, and Birmingham marks for 1963, 10½in (26cm).
£150-200 *P*

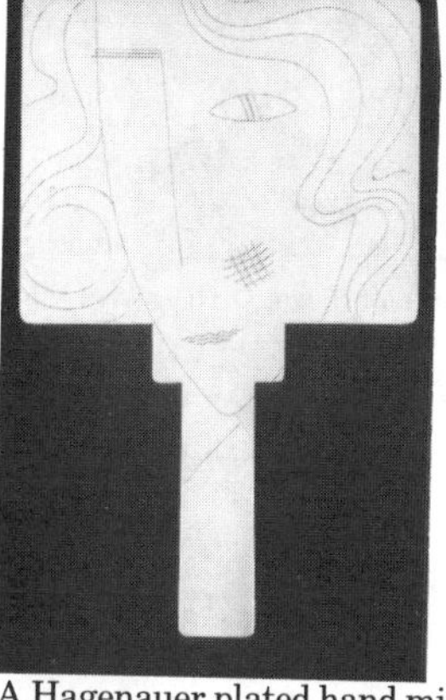

A Hagenauer plated hand mirror, with linear decoration on one side, stamped on reverse with WHW in circle, 9½in (23.5cm).
£250-350 *P*

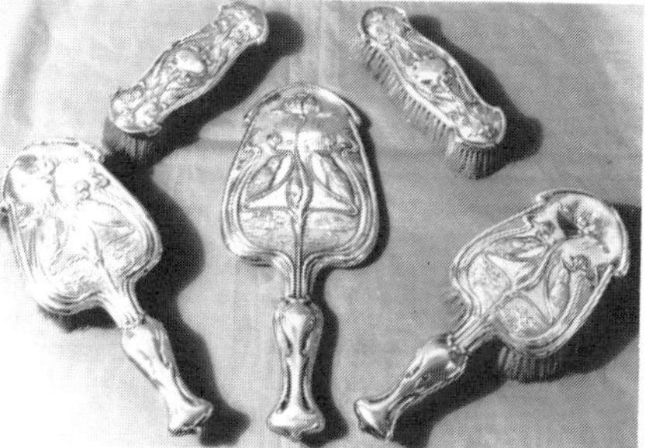

A silver backed brush set, embossed with kingfishers and water lilies, Chester 1909, cased by Oldfields, Liverpool.
£300-400 *P[CW]*

A hammered copper framed mirror, 21 by 15in (53 by 38cm).
£150-200 *ST*

An Arts and Crafts mirror, with moth enamelled in relief, 19 by 15in (48 by 38cm).
£200-250 *ST*

A silver and enamelled picture frame, marked H & A Birmingham 1904, 6½in (16.5cm).
£600-700 *P*

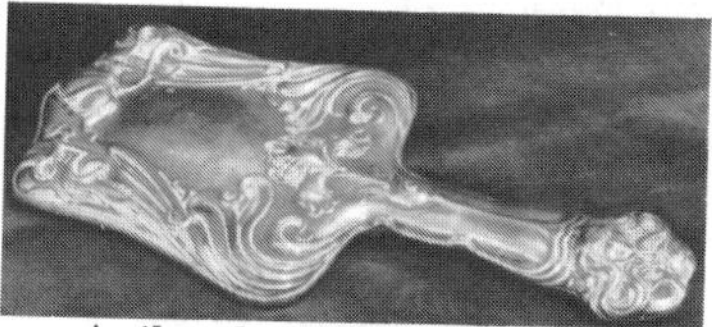

A silver backed hand mirror, 1907.
£50-70 *PC*

A brass flower, the petals remove to make individual ashtrays, c1900, 9½in (24cm).
£75-100 *GAL*

A pair of Liberty & Co., silver and enamelled picture frames, marked L & Co., Birmingham 1913, 5½in (13cm) diam, in original Liberty box.
£2,000-2,500 *P*

A pewter garniture by Margery Gilmore, comprising an oval mirror and a pair of double candle sconces, each piece embossed with a Celtic interlaced design, each stamped M.G., the mirror 30in (76cm) wide.
£600-650 *CEd*

A bronze desk set, by Tiffany Studios, with firm's marks.
£500-700 *CNY*

A Glasgow style pewter and enamel cigar box, the hinged cover inset with an enamel plaque, 9in (23cm) wide.
£200-250 *CEd*

A Continental brass and woo[d] tobacco jar.
£100-150 *GAL*

An Arts and Crafts copper and brass casket, 5½in (14cm) wide.
£45-65 *GAL*

Moorcroft

A Moorcroft Tudric candlestick, with pewter top, c1920, 4in (10cm).
£200-250 *SBA*

A Moorcroft tazza, with pewter base, 9in (23cm) diam.
£350-400 *SBA*

A Moorcroft bowl, c1920, 10in (25.5cm) diam.
£250-325 *SBA*

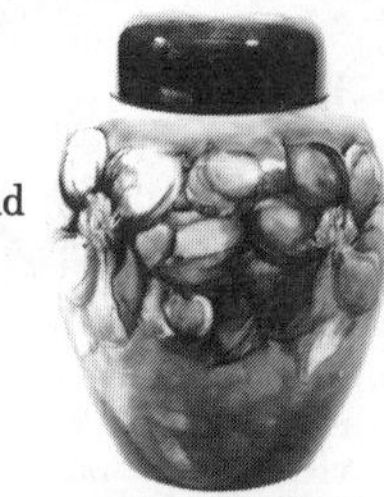

A Walter Moorcroft ginger jar and cover, with a turquoise and blue mottled ground, painted initials impressed facsimile signature, factory mark and potter to the Queen, c1945, 11in (28cm) high.
£350-450 *WIL*

A pair of Macintyre Florianware vases and covers, decorated by William Moorcroft with anemone-like flowers in blue and green on an ivory ground, one with slight hair crack, 8½in (22cm).
£700-800 *Bea*

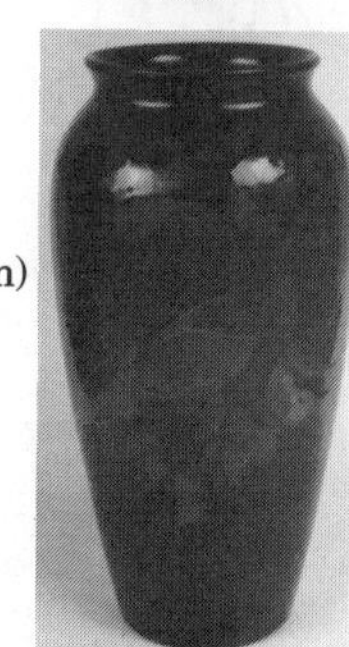

A Moorcroft vase, 10½in (26cm) high.
£350-400 *SBA*

A Moorcroft pottery vase, painted with green trees on a yellowy blue ground, green painted signature and printed Made for Liberty & Co., mark to base, 9in (23cm).
£900-1,000 *BWe*

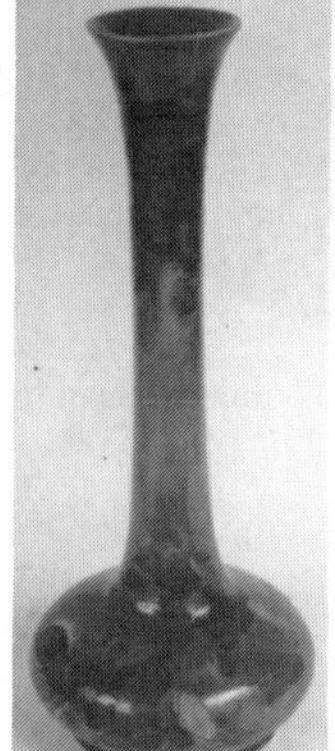

A Moorcroft vase, c1912, 10in (25.5cm) high.
£300-350 *SBA*

A Moorcroft Florianware vase, signed, c1895, 10in (25.5cm) high.
£450-550 *SBA*

A pair of Moorcroft Macintyre vases, signed, c1898, 10in (25.5cm) high.
£850-950 *SBA*

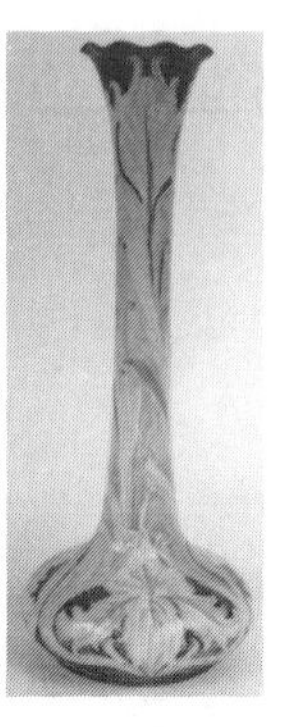

A Moorcroft Florianware vase, signed, 12in (30.5cm) high.
£550-650 *SBA*

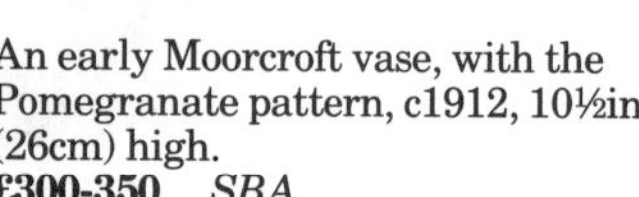

An early Moorcroft vase, with the Pomegranate pattern, c1912, 10½in (26cm) high.
£300-350 *SBA*

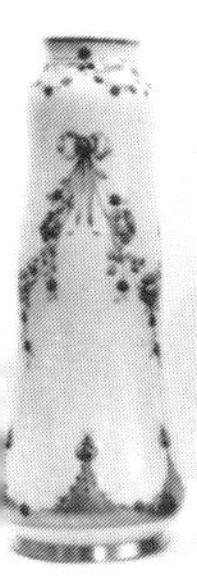

Moorcroft Macintyre vase, ainted with 18thC pattern, nriched with gilding, printed Iacintyre marks, signed in green /. Moorcroft, 16in (40.5cm) high.
500-600 *FHF*

A Moorcroft vase, painted on a tan brown ground, decorated in corn yellow, blue and green, with impressed facsimile signature W. Moorcroft Potter to H.M. The Queen, Made in England, also painted signature, c1935, 20in (51cm).
£550-600 *FHF*

Three Moorcroft Macintyre Florianware vases.
£2,500-3,500 *SWO*

A Moorcroft vase, painted with a ▶ rich ruby glaze with impressed mark, Made in Burslem, signed W. Moorcroft, and with original paper label, slight chip to base, 16in (42cm).
£1,200-1,500 *FHF*

Moorcroft pottery vase, painted on mottled blue green ground, blue gnature on base and impressed oyal marks, 7in (18cm).
400-500 *P[Re]*

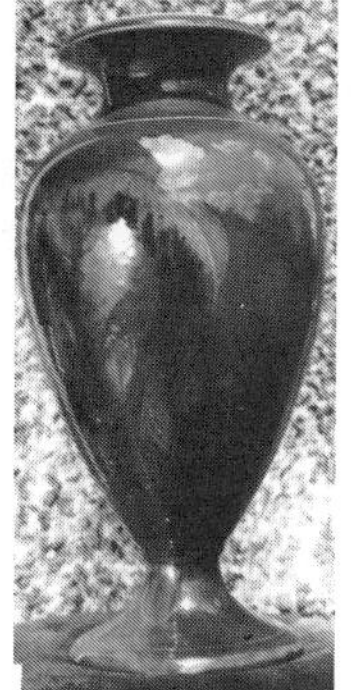

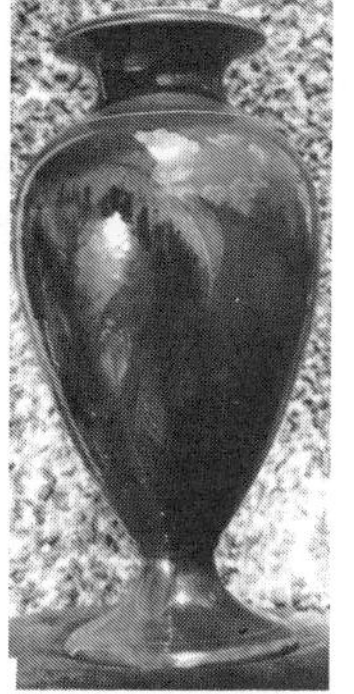

A Moorcroft Burslem vase, with a flambé fish design on blue/lilac ground, c1910, 12½in (31cm).
£800-1,000 *PGA*

A Moorcroft Macintyre peacock pattern candlestick, c1900, 13½in (33cm).
£250-350 *PGA*

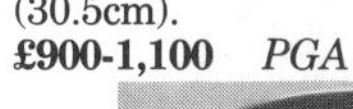

A Moorcroft vase with loop handles, with poppy design, c1925, 12in (30.5cm).
£900-1,100 *PGA*

large Moorcroft vase with isteria design, green signature, 1914, 10in (25cm).
600-800 *PGA*

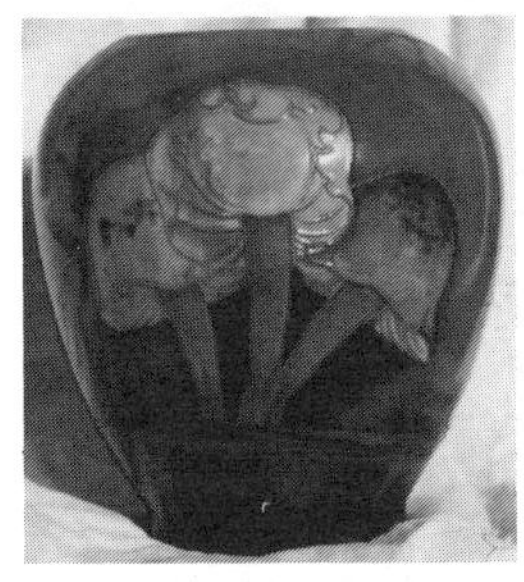

A Moorcroft vase with the toadstool design, under a rare brown lustre glaze, 8in (20cm).
£800-900 *PGA*

A vase with the Claremont toadstool design, on a mottled green ground, c1915, 9in (23.5cm).
£800-900 *PGA*

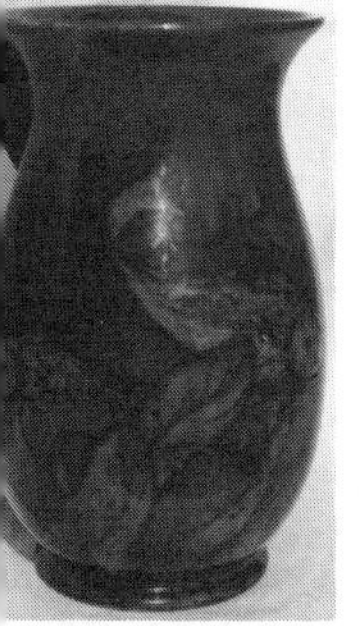

Moorcroft vase with a fish design n a pale flambé ground, c1930, 12in 31.5cm).
950-1,150 *PGA*

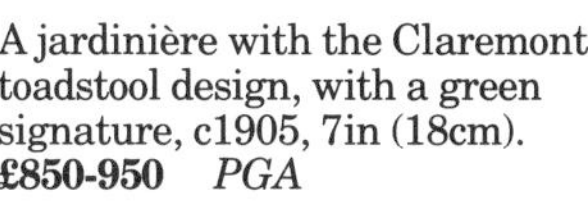

A jardinière with the Claremont toadstool design, with a green signature, c1905, 7in (18cm).
£850-950 *PGA*

Locate the source

The source of each illustration in Miller's can be found by checking the code letters below each caption with the list of contributors.

Posters

Louis Wain: 'A Day at the Seaside', pen and ink, signed in pencil, image area 7 by 5½in (18 by 14.5cm), framed and glazed.
£300-350 *P*

Louis Wain: 3 pencil drawings framed together and depicting a cat, a dog and another cat, entitled 'Sister Mary James Top Note', each picture signed, 30½ by 10½in (77 by 26.5cm), framed and glazed.
£300-350 *P*

Jules Chéret: 'Macassar de Naquet', a chromolithographic poster, signed en block, 53 by 38in (134.5 by 96cm), framed and glazed.
£450-500 *P*

Privat Livemont: 'Paintress', a chromolithographic panel signed en block and Brux. 1901, 19½ by 12½in (50 by 31.5cm), framed and glazed.
£250-300 *P*

Nan M. Moffat: 'Gypsy Rondo', oil on canvas, signed in pencil on back of frame, dated 1922 and GSA Glasgow School of Art, image area 36½in square, framed.
£450-500 *P*

E. McKnight Kauffer: 'You Can Be Sure Of Shell – Actors Prefer Shell', a chromolithographic poster for Shell petrol, signed en block, damaged, date '33, 30 by 45in (76 by 114cm).
£150-200 *P*

Privat Livemont: 'Sculptress', a chromolithographic panel signed en block, and Brux. 1901, image area 19½ by 12½in (50 by 31.5cm), framed and glazed.
£250-300 *P*

'Beatrice', a porcelain panel, painted by George Buttle, in natural colours, mounted in a silver plated frame, made by the Duchess of Sutherland's Cripples' Guild, and embellished in relief with theatrical figures and foliage and inscribed 'I was born to speak all mirth and no matter', signed on porcelain G. A. Buttle 1915, stamped on frame with crown and DSCG, 17½ by 13½in (45 by 34.5cm).
£2,000-3,000 *P*

George Buttle was a porcelain painter who worked for Wedgwood, Bishop & Stonier, Moore Brothers and Royal Doulton. The Doulton archives reveal him as a gifted figure painter in both the romantic and classical styles, whose other works also included miniatures, ceramic cameos and portrait heads of children. A large vase by Buttle was shown at the Brussels Exhibition in 1910. He left Doulton in 1911 to return to Bishop & Stonier as Art Director.

Walter Crane: engraved and printed by Duncan C. Dallas, Dallas Type Press, No. 5, Furnival St. London, J. M. Dent & Co., Aldine House 1893, a limited edition of 650, numbered 62, signed by the designer and the printer, in original box.
£400-450 *P*

Miscellaneous

A Belgian two-piece buckle, by Paul Dubois, unsigned, 4½in (11.5cm).
£150-200 *P*

A Belgian two-piece foliate buckle, in white colour metal with an openwork design of leaves, engraved Paul Dubois, 8½in (21.5cm) wide.
£500-550 *P*

A Perry & Co., chamber candlestick, designed by Christopher Dresser, painted overall in red, adapted, probably contemporary, maker's mark Dr. Dresser's design, and registration mark for 30th October, 1883, 7½in (19cm) high.
£350-450 *P*

A Perry & Co., chamber candlestick, designed by Christopher Dresser, and retailed through Liberty & Co., maker's mark, stamped Dr. Dresser's design, painted Liberty & Co., London and registration mark for 30th October, 1883.
£600-700 *P*

Doulton

Two Doulton Lambeth brown salt glaze stoneware figures by George Tinworth, impressed marks and artist's monogram G.T., 5in (12.5cm).
£700-900 *CSK*

A Doulton 'Reynard the Fox' coffee service, pattern No. H4927.
£500-600 *DN*

A pair of Doulton stoneware ewers, decorated by Hannah Barlow and Florence Roberts, impressed and incised marks, 11½in (29.5cm).
£650-700 *Bea*

A Doulton stoneware oil lamp, base with brass mounts, probably decorated by Florence Roberts, in shades of blue and green on a textured ground, complete with a frosted glass shade, impressed marks dated 1884, 18in (46cm).
£400-450 *Bea*

A Doulton Lambeth Isobath inkwell, stoneware glazed in shades of blue and brown, c1877, 6in (15cm).
£400-500 *PA*

A pair of Doulton Lambeth vases, impressed marks Frank A Butler and 1883, 16in (41cm).
£400-500 *DN*

A pair of Doulton faience Slaters Patent vases, late 19thC, 14½in (37cm).
£300-400 *Bea*

A pair of Doulton faience vases, decorated on a two-tone brown ground, dated 1885, 9½in (24cm).
£250-300 *GC*

Royal Doulton

'Sarah Gamp', a Royal Doulton character teapot and cover, circle mark, lion and crown, date code for 1939, introduced 1939, withdrawn 1960, 7in (18cm) high.
£600-800 *P*

'Old Charley', a Royal Doulton character teapot and cover, circle mark, lion and crown, date code for 1939, introduced 1939, withdrawn 1960, 6in (17.5cm) high.
£400-500 *P*

'Mephistopheles', small, D5758, designer H. Fenton, introduced 1937, withdrawn 1948.
£450-500 *LT*

'Granny', a Royal Doulton character jug, toothless version, D5521.
£500-700 *Bea*

'The White haired clown', large, no number, should be D6322, designer H. Fenton, introduced 1951, withdrawn 1955.
£450-500 *LT*

'The Clown', white hair, D6322, designed by H. Fenton, introduced in 1951, and withdrawn in 1955, 6in (15cm).
£300-600 *WIL*

'Mephistopheles', a large Royal Doulton two-sided character jug, withdrawn 1948.
£750-900 *Bea*

'Old King Cole', a Royal Doulton character jug, with yellow crown and grey/white hair, 6in (15cm).
£3,500-4,500 *P[Re]*

'Ginger haired Clown', a Royal Doulton character jug, 6½in (16cm).
£650-800 *PB*

'One of the Forty', designer H. Tittensor, ivory decoration, no number, should be HN494, second version, model 298, introduced 1921, withdrawn 1938, 7in (18cm).
£400-450 *LT*

'One of the Forty', designer H. Tittensor, ivory decoration, no number, should be HN492, 12th version, model 327, introduced 1921, withdrawn 1938, 7in (18cm).
£400-450 *LT*

'Quality Street', HN1211, introduced 1926, withdrawn 1938, 7in (18cm).
£600-700 *LT*

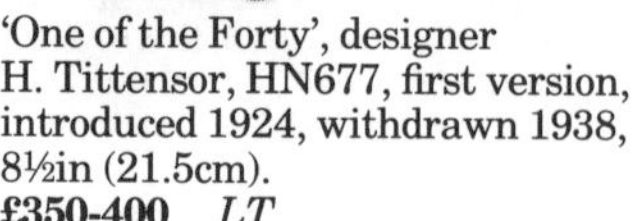

'One of the Forty', designer H. Tittensor, HN677, first version, introduced 1924, withdrawn 1938, 8½in (21.5cm).
£350-400 *LT*

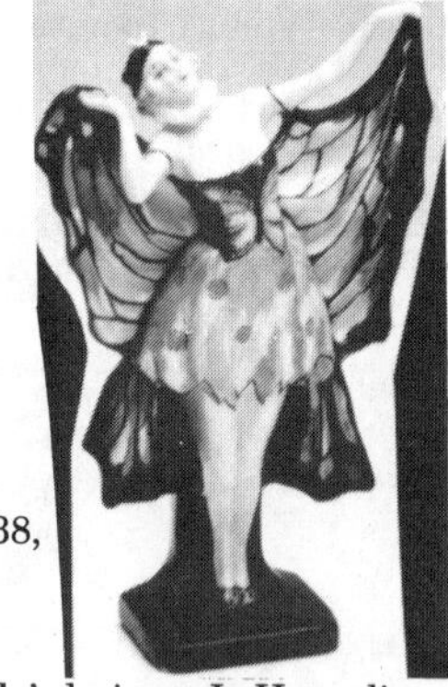

'Butterfly', designer L. Harradine, HN719, introduced 1925, withdrawn 1938, 6½in (16cm).
£500-600 *LT*

'Kathleen', a Royal Doulton porcelain figure, designed by L. Harradine, HN1252, printed and painted marks, 8in (20cm).
£300-350 *CSK*

'Columbine', designer L. Harradine, HN1439, first version, introduced 1930, withdrawn 1938, 6in (15cm).
£350-400 *LT*

'Sweet and Twenty', a Royal Doulton porcelain figure, designed by L. Harradine, HN1360, printed marks, 6in (15cm).
£200-250 *CSK*

Delight', a Royal Doulton figure, lesigned by L. Harradine, HN1772, printed and painted marks, 7½in 19cm), and 4 other pieces.
£100-120 *CSK*

'The Orange Lady', a Royal Doulton figure, green printed marks to base and HN1953, 8½in (21.5cm).
£100-120 *BWe*

'Young Miss Nightingale, a Royal Doulton porcelain figure, designed by M. Davies, HN2010, printed marks, 9½in (24cm).
£350-400 *CSK*

'Calumet', a Royal Doulton figure, green printed marks to base and HN2068, 6½in (16.5cm).
£200-250 *BWe*

Easter Day', a Royal Doulton figure, HN2039, withdrawn 1969.
£150-200 *Bea*

'The Gaffer', a Royal Doulton figure, green printed marks to base and HN2053, 7½in (19cm).
£150-200 *BWe*

'Promenade', designer Margaret Davies, HN2076, introduced 1951, withdrawn 1953, 8in (20cm).
£750-800 *LT*

Midinette', a Royal Doulton figure, lesigned by L. Harradine, HN2090, printed marks, 7in (18cm).
£150-200 *CSK*

'Uriah Heep', a Royal Doulton figure, green printed marks to base and HN2101, 7½in (19cm).
£90-120 *BWe*

'The Wardrobe Mistress', a Royal Doulton figure, HN2145, withdrawn 1967.
£200-250 *Bea*

'Queen Elizabeth The Queen Mother', a Royal Doulton figure, produced to celebrate her 80th birthday, HN2282, No. 1422 of a limited edition, complete with stand, certificate and original box.
£300-400 *Bea*

A rare pilot figure, girl with pink skirt and pail under right arm, 7in (18cm).
£1,500-2,000 *LT*

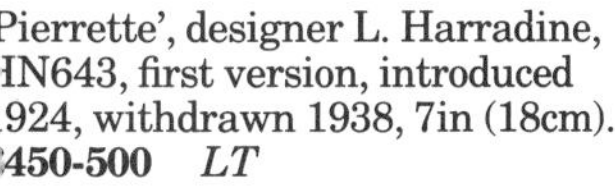

'Pierrette', designer L. Harradine, HN643, first version, introduced 1924, withdrawn 1938, 7in (18cm).
£450-500 *LT*

'Fortune Teller', a Royal Doulton figure, HN2159, withdrawn 1967.
£200-250 *Bea*

A rare pilot figure, lady in blue and pink ball gown, foot and left hand defective, hair cracks, 9in (23cm).
£900-1,200 *LT*

A pair of Royal Doulton stoneware vases, by Hannah B. Barlow & Florrie Jones, heightened in brown on a buff ground, the base with green and blue lappets, incised H.B.B. & F.J. monograms, 5½in (14cm).
£200-250 *CSK*

A pair of Royal Doulton stoneware vases, with panels of blue brown on green ground.
£100-150 *MGM*

A pair of Royal Doulton vases, initialled WB, c1925, 13in (33cm).
£150-200 *TVA*

A pair of Royal Doulton stoneware vases, incised monograms for Eliza Simmance & Bessie Newberry, 20thC.
£350-400 *WIL*

A pair of Royal Doulton vases, decorated in the Art Nouveau manner, in green and yellow on a gold decorated ivory ground, c1900, 10½in (27cm).
£150-200 *Bea*

A Royal Doulton vase, covered in a thick multi-coloured crackled glaze, bearing the marks for Charles John Noke and Harry Nixon, 5½in (13.5cm).
£300-400 *Bea*

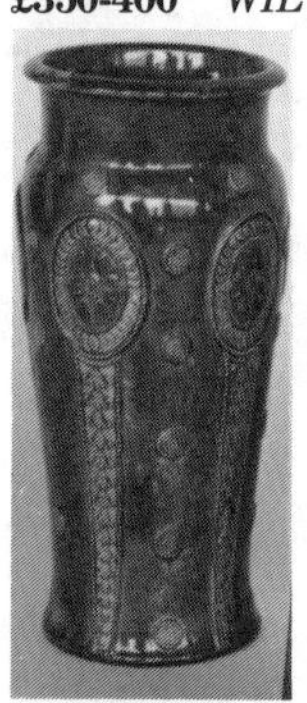

A pair of Royal Doulton blue ground stoneware vases.
£150-200 *MGM*

A Royal Doulton plate depicting Porchester, signed A. Holdcroft, c1925, 10in (25.5cm).
£120-140 *TVA*

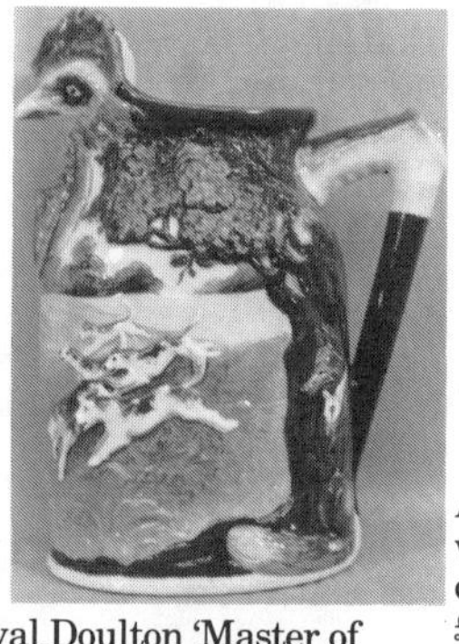

A Royal Doulton 'Master of Foxhounds' presentation jug, No. 248 of a limited edition of 500, with original certificate of verification, 13in (33cm).
£350-400 *OL*

A Royal Doulton stoneware Dewar whisky jug, with green collar, c1895, 6½in (16.5cm).
£130-150 *CA*

A Royal Doulton buff stoneware jardinière, by Hannah Barlow, with olive green glazed neck, incised with sheep in panoramic landscape, 9in (23cm) diam.
£300-350 *WHB*

A Royal Doulton stoneware jardinière and stand, painted with deep blue and mottled green, stand chipped, late 19thC, 37½in (95cm).
£400-450 *Bea*

A set of 5 Royal Doulton plates, signed A. Piper, with gilded rims, the centres painted with flowers and fruit, 9½in (24cm).
£450-500 *P[Re]*

ART DECO
Lalique Glass

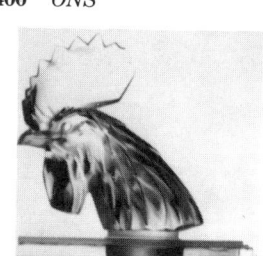

A clear and frosted glass car mascot of pale amethyst hue, Faucon R. Lalique, No. 1124, 6½in (16.5cm).
£900-1,200 *P[CW]*

A Lalique frosted glass car mascot, 'Coq Nain', with satin finish, moulded R. Lalique France, on circular base, 8in (20.5cm).
£600-700 *P*

A Lalique glass cockerel, script Lalique France marks, 8in (20.5cm).
£300-400 *ONS*

A glass cockerel's head, moulded Lalique France marks, chip to comb, 7in (18cm), on stepped Lalique glass base, script Lalique France marks.
£400-450 *ONS*

A topaz frosted and polished car mascot, 'Coq Nain', moulded R. Lalique, No. 1135, 8in (20.5cm).
£3,000-4,000 *Bon*

A satin and polished car mascot, 'Victoire', modelled as an open mouthed maiden with stylised windswept hair streaming behind her, relief moulded mark R. Lalique, 10½in (26cm) long.
£7,000-8,000 *Bon*

A Lalique glass car mascot, 'Grand Libellule', modelled as a large dragonfly, moulded and signed on tail Lalique and R. Lalique France, 8in (21cm), with original electrical mount with green cell inside.
£2,200-2,500 *P*

A frosted and polished car mascot, 'Petite Libellule', set in metal mount, moulded mark Lalique, 6½in (16.5cm) long.
£2,500-3,500 *Bon*

A clear and polished car mascot, 'Cinq Chevaux', relief moulded mark R. Lalique and wheel cut France, in bronze mount and ebonised wood stand.
£2,500-3,000 *Bon*

A clear and satin glass car mascot, 'Faucon', moulded R. Lalique, etched No. 1124, 6in (15.5cm).
£1,000-1,500 *Bon*

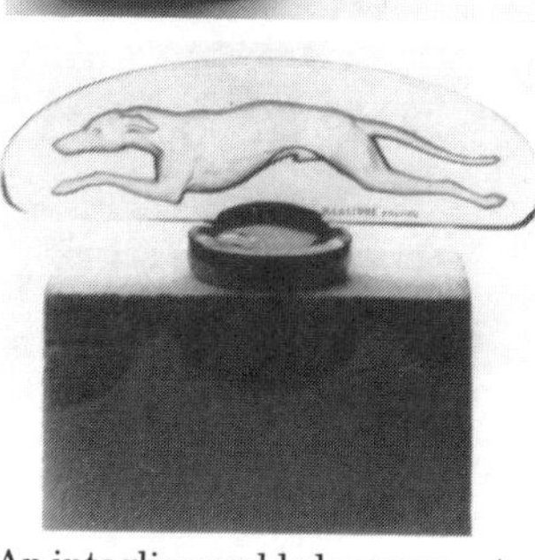

An intaglio moulded car mascot, 'Levrier', intaglio moulded mark R. Lalique France, 7½in (19.5cm) long.
£750-1,000 *Bon*

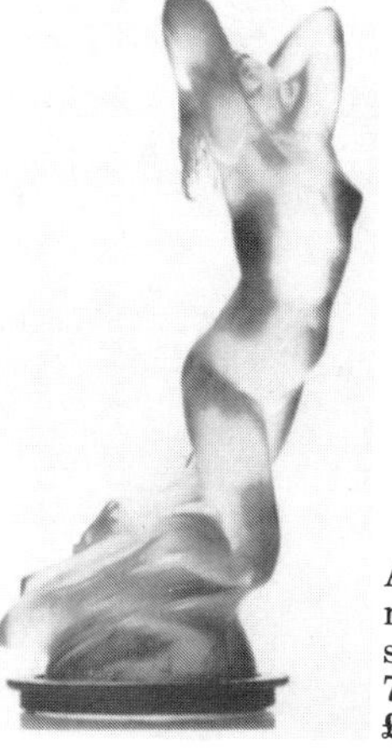

A frosted car mascot, 'Vitesse', moulded as a naked female figure, slight chip, moulded R. Lalique, 7½in (18.5cm).
£4,000-4,500 *Bon*

A Lalique opalescent glass statuette, 'Naiade', moulded faintly R. Lalique and signed on underside of base Lalique, 5in (12.5cm).
£5,000-5,500 *P*

A Lalique frosted glass statuette, 'Source de la Fontaine', on wooden base, incorporating lamp fitment, 21in (53cm) high.
£2,000-2,500 *P*

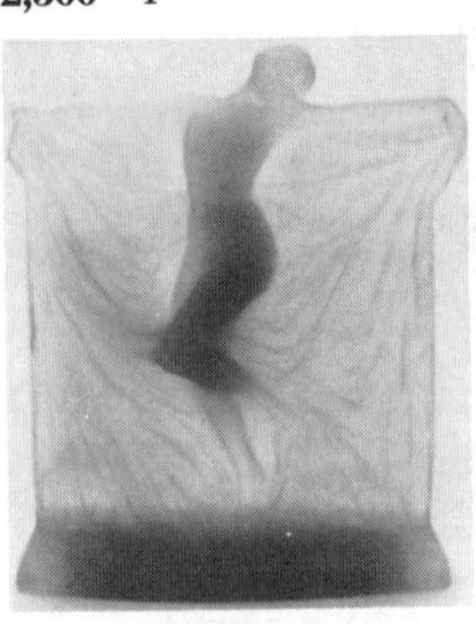

An opalescent and frosted glass figure of a nude female dancer, 'Thais', her right hand slightly reduced, etched script mark R. Lalique, France, 8½in (21.5cm).
£2,500-3,000 *Bon*

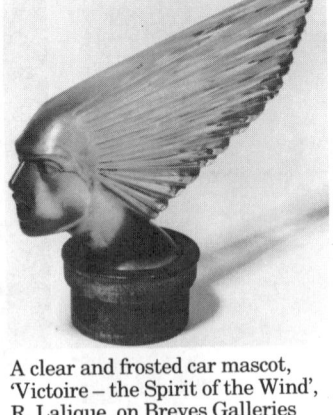

A clear and frosted car mascot, 'Victoire – the Spirit of the Wind', R. Lalique, on Breves Galleries chrome light mount, 10in (25.5cm) long.
£6,000-7,000 *P[Pea]*

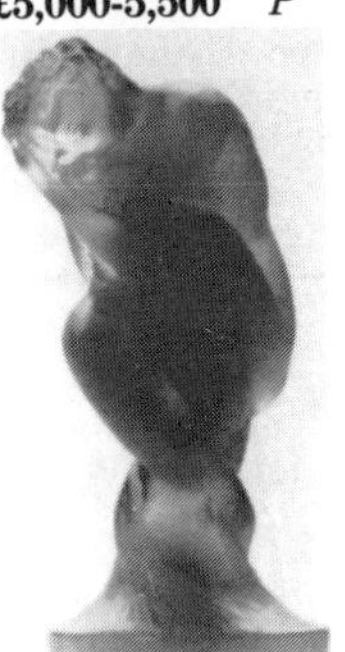

An opalescent statuette, 'Sirene', moulded as a water nymph tending her hair, small chip, moulded R. Lalique, etched script mark R. Lalique, France, No. 831, 4in (10cm).
£1,500-2,000 *Bon*

A frosted glass figurine of a naked young woman, 'Grande Nue, Longs Cheveux', etched script mark R. Lalique, France, No. 836, 16in (40.5cm).
£7,500-8,500 *Bon*

l. A Lalique 'Alicante' vase, blue tinted with moulded budgerigar heads and wheat ears, etched signature R. Lalique, France, with removable fittings for use as a table lamp, 10in (25.5cm).
£1,000-1,500
r. A Lalique 'Laurier' vase, in blued opalescent glass, incised mark and No. 947, 7in (18cm).
£400-600 *DN*

A Lalique frosted glass vase, moulded all over with a thistle design and stained in light blue, signed R. Lalique, France, No. 979, 8½in (21.5cm).**£600-700** *Bea*

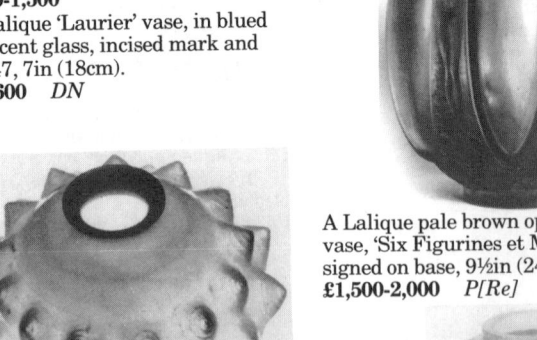

A Lalique pale brown opaque glass vase, 'Six Figurines et Masques', signed on base, 9½in (24cm).
£1,500-2,000 *P[Re]*

An opalescent vase, 'Dordogne', intaglio moulded and engraved script mark R. Lalique, France, 7in (18cm).
£1,200-1,500 *Bon*

A large Lalique frosted glass vase, 'Penthièvre', signed on base R. Lalique France No 1011, 10½in (25.5cm).
£2,500-3,000 *P*

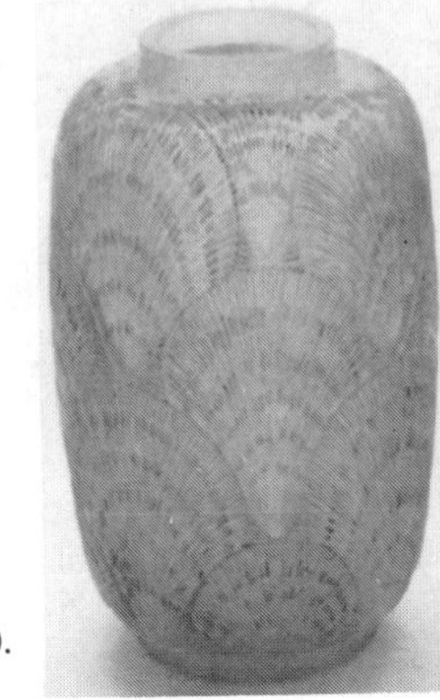

A blue stained opalescent vase, 'Coquilles', etched script mark R. Lalique, France, 7½in (18.5cm).
£700-800 *Bon*

A clear, frosted and blue stained vase, 'Bordures Epines', with everted rim moulded with trailing thorned branches, wheel cut mark R. Lalique, 8in (20cm).
£550-700 *Bon*

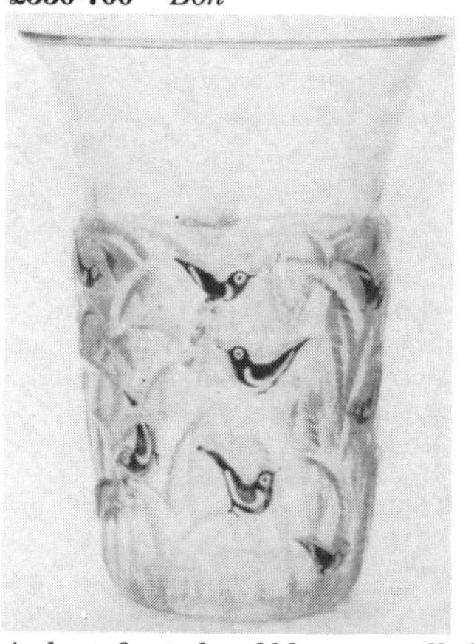

A clear, frosted and blue enamelled vase, 'Bornes', wheel cut mark R. Lalique, France, 9in (23cm).
£3,300-3,600 *Bon*

A Lalique opalescent glass vase, with frosted surface, etched R. Lalique on base, 7in (18cm).
£600-700 *P*

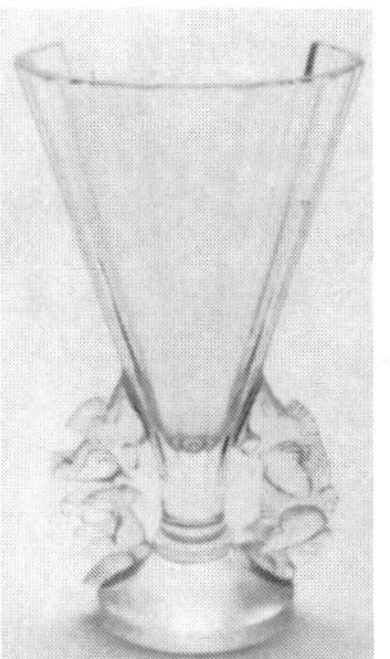

A clear and satin vase, 'Roitelets', stencilled R. Lalique, France, 11½in (29cm).
£1,000-1,200 *Bon*

A Lalique glass vase of trumpet shape, the sides moulded with ears of barley, with pale brown staining, marked on base R. Lalique, France, 6½in (16.5cm).
£450-550 *P*

A Lalique opalescent glass vase, 'Chardons', heightened with blue staining, marked R. Lalique France on base, 7½in (18.5cm).
£700-750 *P*

A smoked glass vase, 'Béliers', moulded at the rim with a pair of stylised rams, wheel cut R. Lalique, 7½in (19cm).
£1,500-2,000 *Bon*

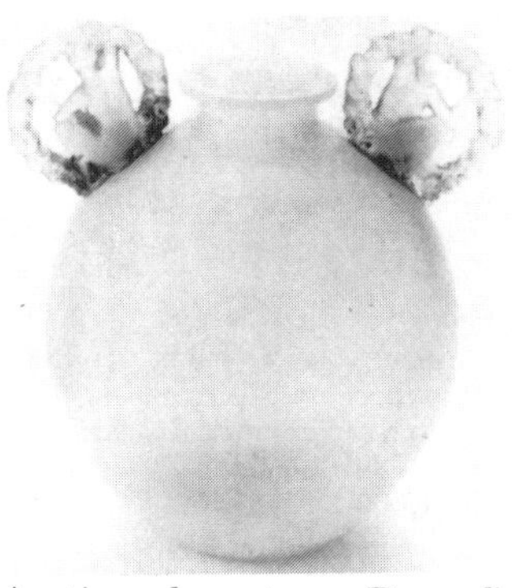

A satin opalescent vase, 'Ronsard', the 2 handles moulded as semi-circular garlands of flowers, each enclosing a seated nude female figure, fracture to one arm, stencilled R. Lalique, engraved France, 8½in (21cm).
£1,500-2,000 *Bon*

A blue stained frosted vase, the ground detailed with vertical ribbing, stencilled R. Lalique, France, 6½in (16cm).
£500-700 *Bon*

A clear and frosted vase, 'Yvelines', the handles moulded with deer amidst foliage, the leaves spreading onto the body of the vase, etched R. Lalique, France, 8in (20cm).
£750-800 *Bon*

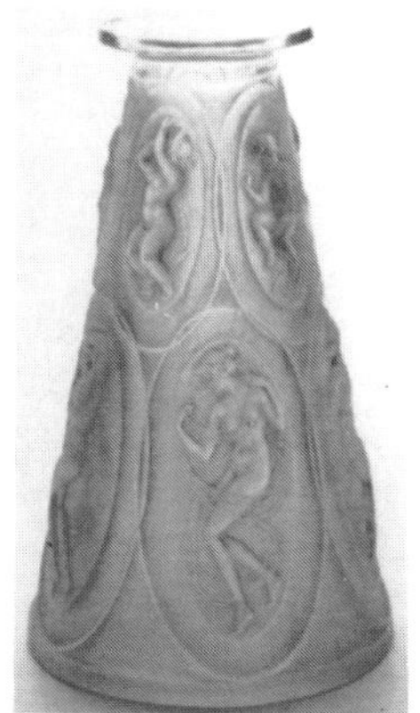

A frosted, clear and green stained vase, 'Camees', relief moulded mark R. Lalique, 10in (25.5cm).
£3,500-4,000 *Bon*

A Lalique glass vase, heightened with blue staining, signed on base R. Lalique, 9in (23cm).
£950-1,100 *P*

A frosted vase, 'Baies', heightened in black enamel, moulded mark R. Lalique, 10½in (26.5cm).
£3,000-4,000 *Bon*

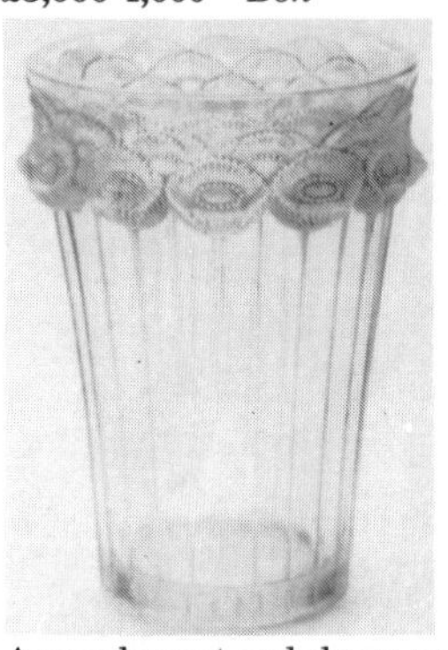

An opalescent and clear vase, moulded in relief beneath the rim with poppy flowerheads, stencilled mark R. Lalique, France, 5½in (14cm).
£1,200-1,500 *Bon*

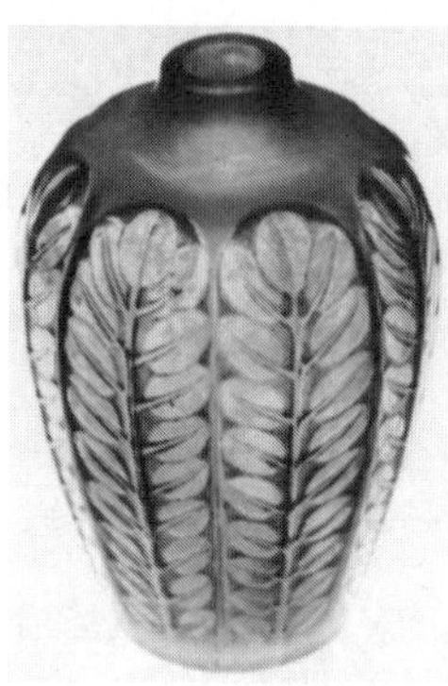

A blue stained opalescent vase, 'Tournai', moulded with vertical panels of leafy branches, stencilled R. Lalique, France, 5in (13cm).
£600-700 *Bon*

A frosted, clear and amethyst stained vase, 'Charmille', moulded with overlapping beech leaves, intaglio moulded R. Lalique, 14in (33.5cm).
£3,000-4,000 *Bon*

A blue stained, clear and frosted vase, 'Paimpol', moulded in high relief with 6 panels of graduating conical projections alternating with spiny ribbed panels, stencilled Lalique and La Marquise De Sevigne, Paris, 10in (25cm).
£1,500-2,000 *Bon*

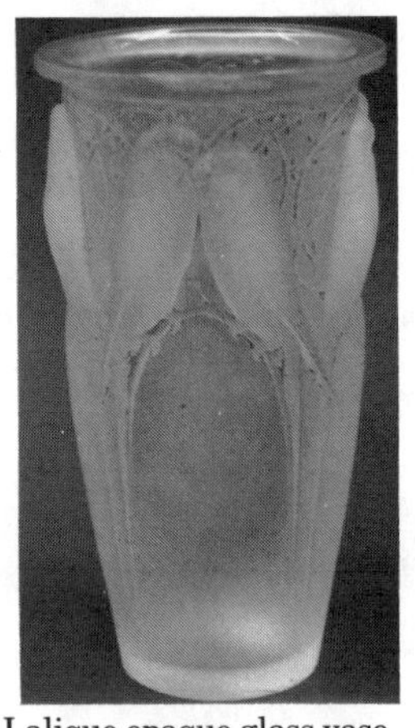

A Lalique opaque glass vase, 'Ceylan', with blue stained decoration, below a narrow slightly everted rim, base chipped, etched R. Lalique, 9½in (24cm).
£1,500-1,700 *HSS*

An amber vase, 'Ormeax', moulded with a carpet of beech leaves, engraved script mark R. Lalique, France, No. 984, 6½in (16.5cm).
£800-1,000 *Bon*

A grey stained opalescent vase, 'Oléron', moulded with a shoal of leaping fish, etched script mark R. Lalique, France, No. 1008.
£500-550 *Bon*

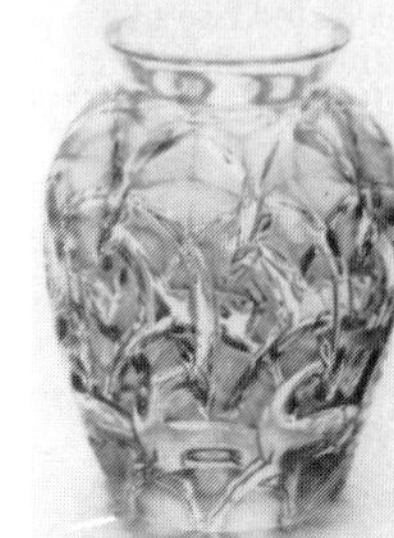

A rare, blue stained clear and frosted vase, 'Chamois', moulded with panels of chamois antelope with curving stylised horns, stencilled R. Lalique, France, 5½i (14cm).
£650-800 *Bon*

A frosted and opalescent vase, 'Pinson', moulded with sparrows amongst berried branches, all above a narrow foot, stencilled mark R. Lalique, 7in (18cm).
£1,000-1,200 *Bon*

A red-amber vase, 'Aras', moulded on the body with crested parakeets amongst berried branches, intaglio moulded R. Lalique, 9in (23cm).
£4,500-5,500 *Bon*

An electric-blue frosted and polished vase, 'Perruches', moulded with pairs of billing parakeets upon blooming prunus boughs, traces of white stain, etched script mark R. Lalique, with France, No. 876, 10in (25.5cm).
£5,000-6,000 *Bon*

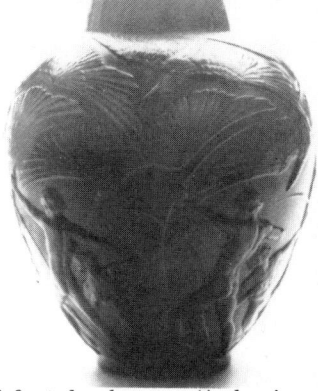

A frosted amber vase, 'Archers', moulded in relief with a design of nude male archers below swooping eagles, minor chip to rim, intaglio moulded mark R. Lalique, with France etched in script, 11in (28cm).
£3,500-4,000 *Bon*

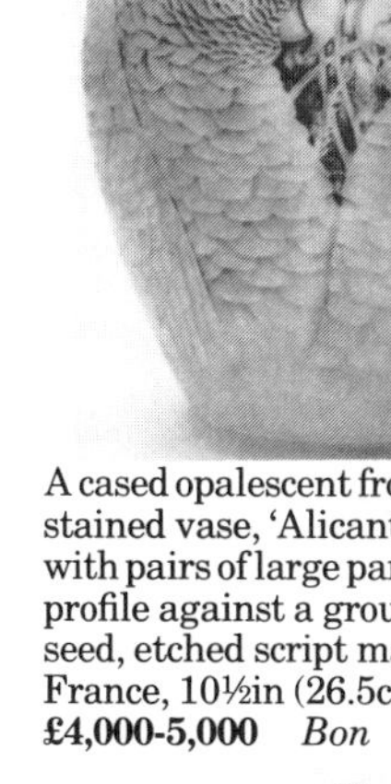

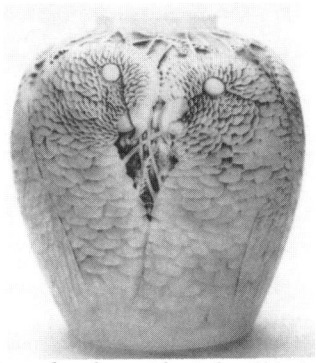

A cased opalescent frosted and black stained vase, 'Alicante', moulded with pairs of large parakeet heads in profile against a ground of millet seed, etched script mark R. Lalique, France, 10½in (26.5cm).
£4,000-5,000 *Bon*

A frosted, clear and blue stained vase, 'Aigrettes', moulded beneath the rim with egrets in flight, chips to footrim, wheel cut mark, R. Lalique, France, 10in (25cm).
£1,200-1,500 *Bon*

A large frosted opalescent vase, 'Sauterelles', moulded with grasshoppers perched on curving blades of grass, etched script mark R. Lalique, France, No. 888, 10½in (27cm).
£3,000-4,000 *Bon*

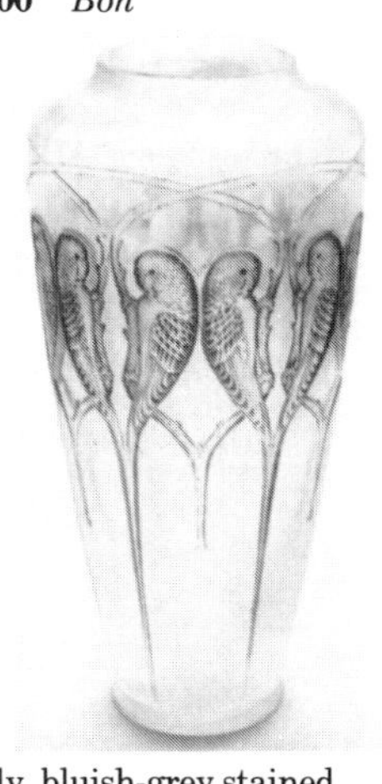

A rare early, bluish-grey stained frosted vase, 'Ceylan', moulded with facing pairs of budgerigars perched on budding branches, minute chips to rim, unsigned, 13½in (34.5cm).
£3,500-4,000 *Bon*

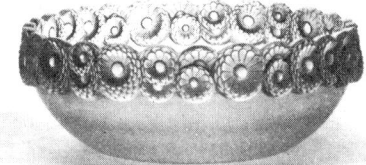

A frosted, clear and sepia stained surtout, 'Faisan', moulded with 4 panels each with an oriental pheasant and serpentine garland interspersed by slender panels with candle sconce surmounts, the base with stepped form, engraved script mark Lalique, France, 5in (14cm).
£750-1,000 *Bon*

A Lalique frosted glass bowl, heightened with blue staining, marked on base R. Lalique, France, 9½in (24cm) diam.
£500-600 *P*

A peppermint green and opalescent bowl, 'Muguet', the sides moulded with lily of the valley, stencilled mark R. Lalique, France, 9in (23cm) diam.
£3,000-3,500 *Bon*

A Lalique opalescent glass bowl, 'Coupe Calypso', marked on base in block R. Lalique France, 12in (30cm).
£2,500-3,000 *P*

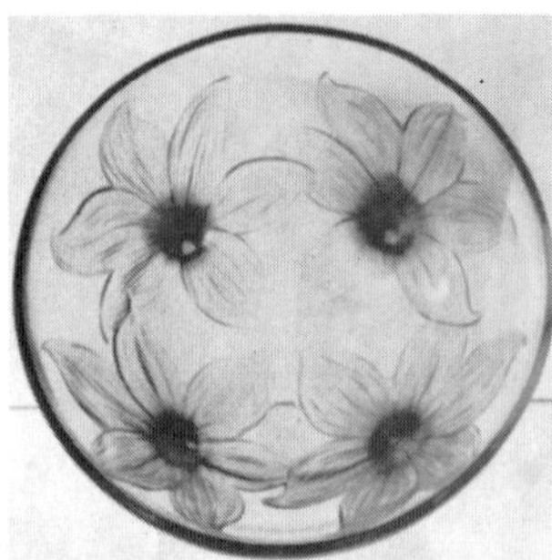

A Lalique bowl, inscribed R. Lalique, France, 9½in (24cm) diam.
£300-400 *WW*

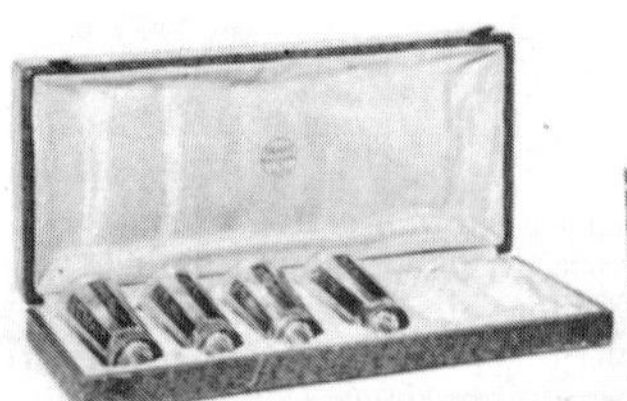

A Cristal Lalique glass paperweight, 'Perche', moulded as a fish resting on its dorsal fins, moulded on edge R. Lalique, and signed on base Lalique France, 4in (10cm) high.
£600-650 *P*

A set of 6 Lalique glasses, heightened with silver grey staining, signed in script R. Lalique France, 4in (10cm), in original Lalique fitted case for '24 Place Vendôme, Paris'.
£2,000-3,000 *P*

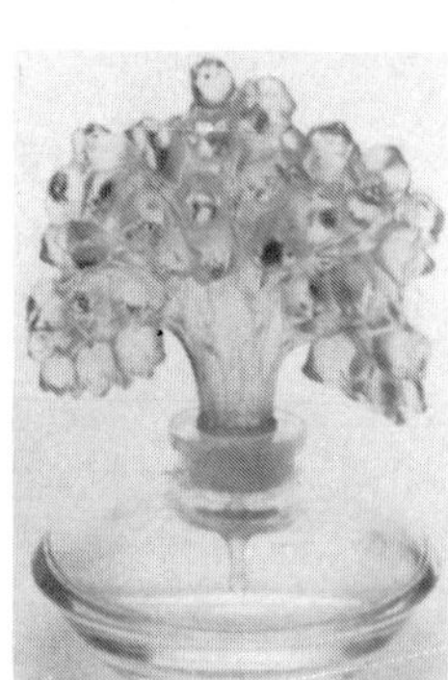

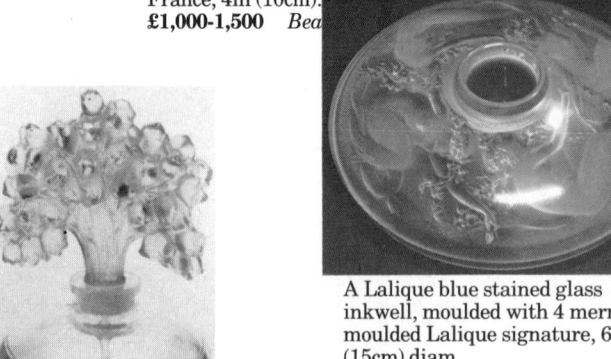

A rare amethyst and clear glass scent bottle, 'Flacon Muguet', the stopper formed as a spray of lily of the valley in frosted and polished glass, unmarked, 4in (10cm).
£3,000-3,500 *Bon*

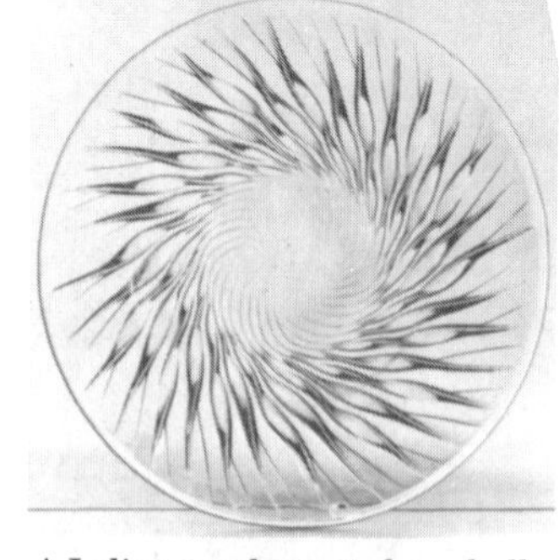

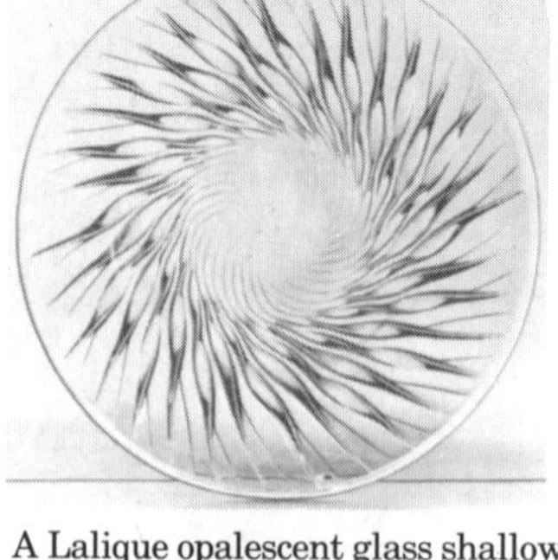

A Lalique opalescent glass shallow dish, etched mark, 14in (35.5cm).
£500-600 *WW*

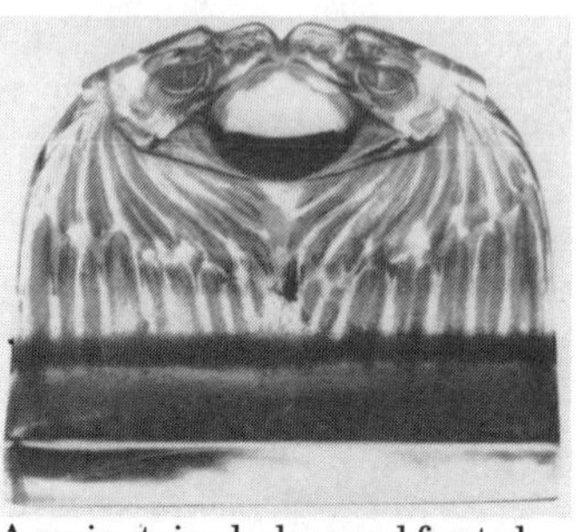

A sepia stained, clear and frosted presse-papiers, 'Deux Aigles', moulded as 2 eagle heads, jointly gripping a sphere in their beaks, moulded in intaglio R. Lalique, 3in (8cm) high.
£350-400 *Bon*

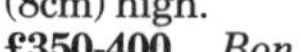

A Lalique blue stained scent bottle and stopper, catalogued 'Amphitrite', inscribed R. Lalique, France, 4in (10cm).
£1,000-1,500 *Bea*

A Lalique blue stained glass inkwell, moulded with 4 mermaids, moulded Lalique signature, 6in (15cm) diam.
£600-800 *P[Re]*

A Lalique clock, with Swiss 8-day movement set in a milky blue panel with naked female figures, in an onyx and malachite frame, marked Lalique in capitals, 5in (12.5cm) high.
£1,500-2,000 *GSP*

A grey stained clear glass cendrier 'Archers', the everted rim moulded with panels of kneeling archers, moulded R. Lalique, 4½in (11.5cm) diam.
£250-350 *Bon*

A Lalique glass carafe and stopper moulded in high relief, heightened with silver grey staining, the stopper moulded with a shell like spiral, moulded Lalique, with extended L and engraved France, 14½in (36cm).
£1,700-2,000 *P*

A frosted and clear glass scent bottle, 'Claire Fontaine', the stopper moulded as a spray of lily of the valley, etched Lalique, France, with Made in France and Cristal Lalique stickers, c1950, 4½in (12cm).
£100-150 *Bon*

A frosted clock, 'Sirènes', moulded with floating water nymphs, the gilt rimmed face with Arabic numerals, moulded R. Lalique, 11in (27.5cm) high.
£2,500-3,000 *Bon*

An opalescent clock, 'Inseparables', moulded R. Lalique, engraved France No. 760, 4½in (11cm).
£2,000-2,500 *Bon*

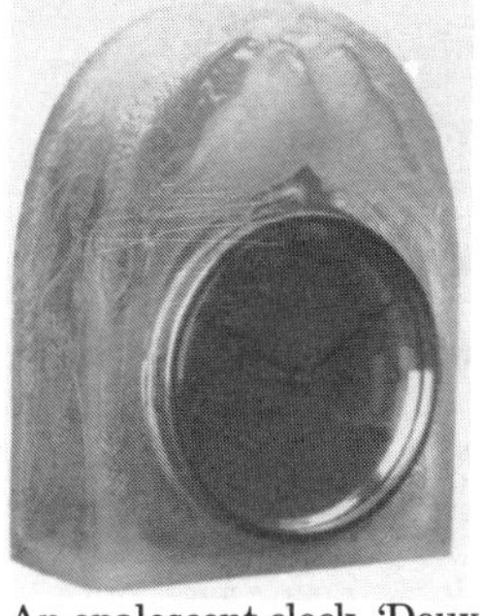

An opalescent clock, 'Deux Colombes' the glass face surmounted by a pair of doves perched on flowering prunus branches, moulded R. Lalique, France, 9in (22.5cm).
£2,200-2,500 *Bon*

A frosted clock, moulded with a pair of love birds amidst flowering sprays, moulded R. Lalique, 6in (15.5cm) high.
£1,300-1,600 *Bon*

A clear and frosted clock-luminaire, 'Deux Figurines', the bronze base enclosing the lighting fitment, wheel cut R. Lalique, France, 15in (38cm).
£5,500-6,500 *Bon*

A rare clear, frosted and stained table lamp, stencilled mark R. Lalique, France, c1931, 13in (32cm) high.
£9,000-10,000 *Bon*

A Lalique frosted glass ceiling light, moulded R. Lalique, France, 15in (38cm) diam.
£450-500 *CEd*

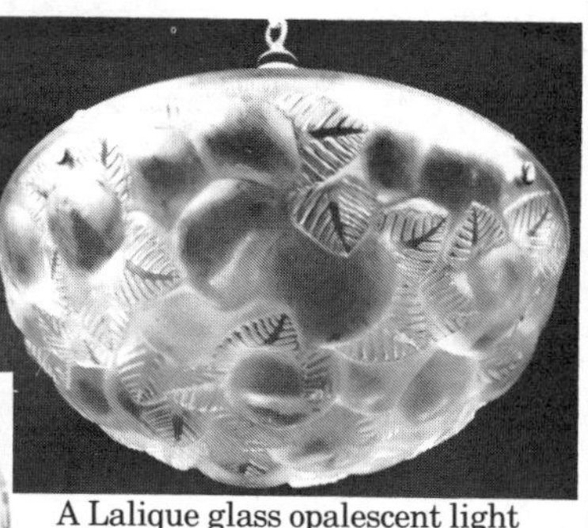

A Lalique glass opalescent light bowl, signed, c1930, 15in (38cm) diam.
£800-900 *N*

A sienna stained frosted and polished hand mirror, 'Narcisse Couché', engraved Lalique, 12in (30cm), in satin lined box with cover stamped Lalique, Place Vendôme 24, Paris.
£3,500-4,000 *Bon*

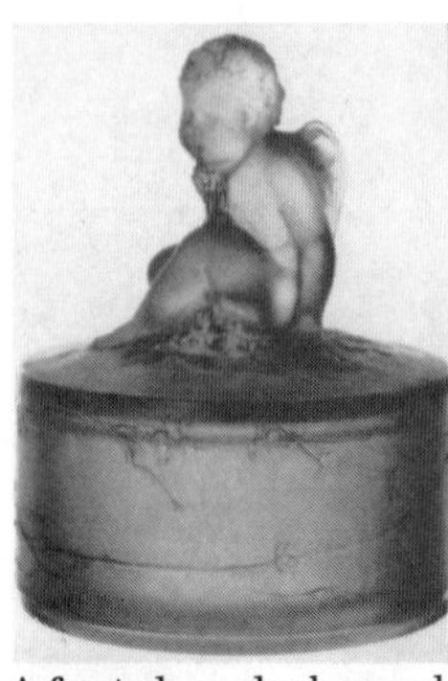
A frosted powder box and cover, 'Amour Assis', moulded mark, 5½in (14.5cm).
£900-1,000 *Bon*

A clear and frosted box, 'Roger', with a design of opalescent cabochons and exotic birds, moulded mark Lalique, 5½in (13.5cm) diam.
£600-800 *Bon*

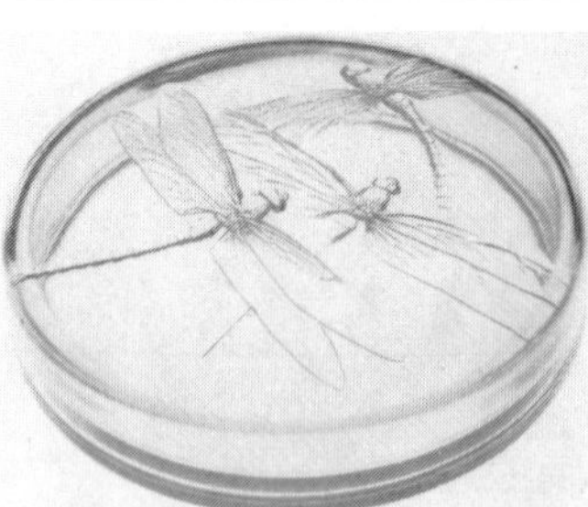
An opalescent and clear glass box and cover, 'Georgette', relief moulded mark, R. Lalique, and engraved in script at rim France, No. 51, 8½in (21cm) diam.
£800-1,000 *Bon*

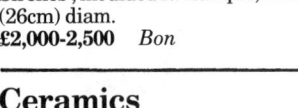

An opalescent box and cover, 'Deux Sirênes', moulded R. Lalique, 10½in (26cm) diam.
£2,000-2,500 *Bon*

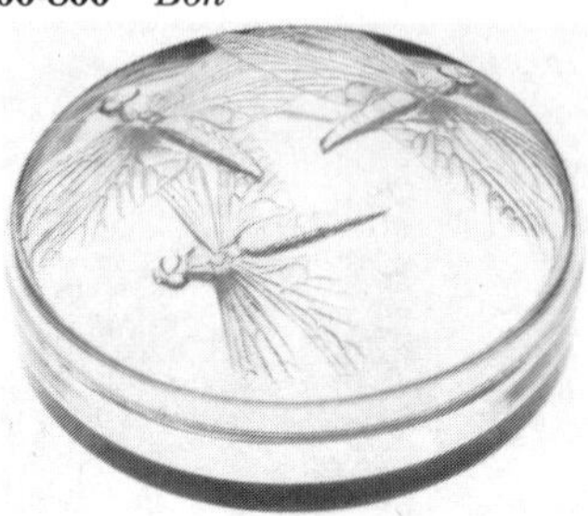
An opalescent box and cover, 'Libellules', moulded mark R. Lalique, 7in (17cm).
£600-800 *Bon*

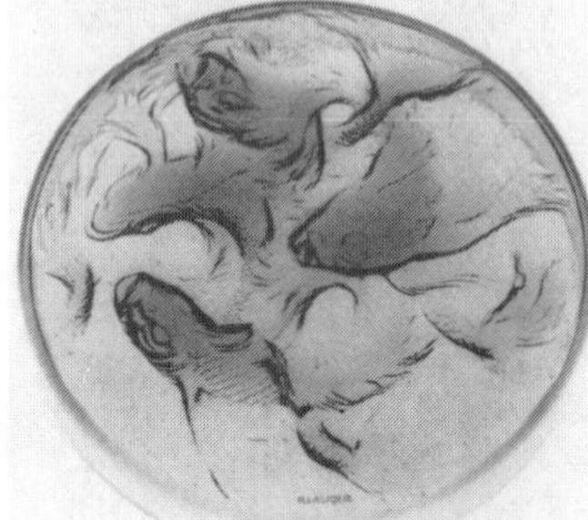
An amber glass box, 'Grande Cyprins', with silk lined card base, the cover moulded with entwined oriental carp, moulded mark R. Lalique, 10½in (26cm) diam.
£1,000-1,500 *Bon*

Ceramics

A large Goldscheider wall mask of a lady holding beads, various makers' marks, Austria, c1930.
£350-550 *ASA*

A Swedish pottery Modernist bust, modelled as a girl with green curly hair, orange lips and an orange necklace, covered in a speckled green glaze, impressed 'b' within a crowned shield, 12in (30.5cm).
£600-700 *P*

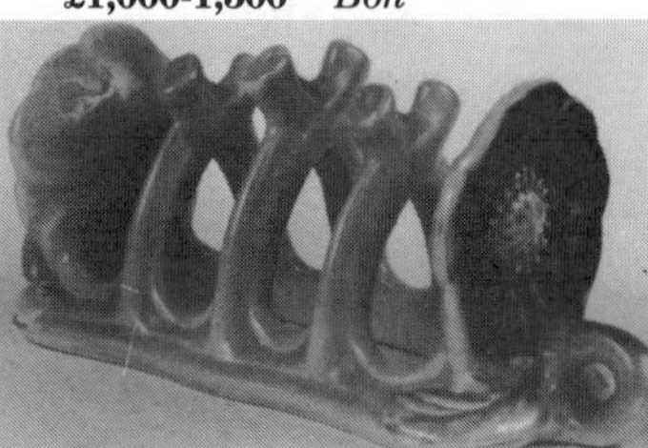
A toast rack by Shorter, with purple anemones on a green base, c1930, 6in (15cm) long.
£25-35 *BRI*

A Carltonware dish with clematis on a green ground, c1930, 7in (18cm).
£40-60 *BRI*

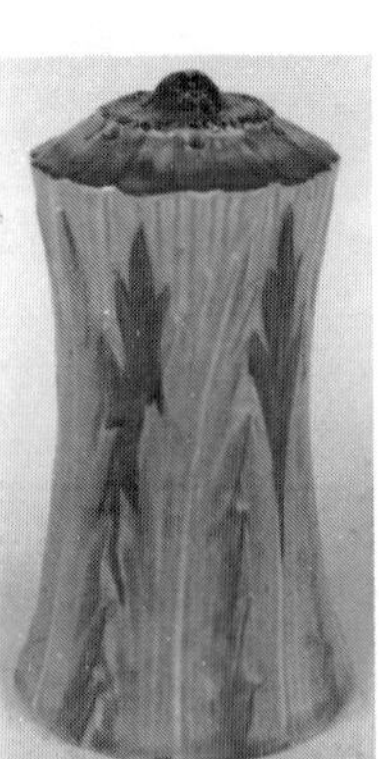
A Carltonware sugar sifter with flower and leaves in relief, c1930, 5in (13cm).
£50-70 *BRI*

A Carltonware beaker with a design of anemones on a yellow ground, c1930, 4in (10cm).
£30-70 *BRI*

A Carltonware dish designed as pear fruit, flowers and leaves, c1935, 4½in (11.5cm).
£30-60 *BRI*

A Carltonware china coffee service of 15 pieces with gilt interiors and highlights, all painted and gilded in bright colours with exotic birds and stylised clouds.
£200-250 *P[Re]*

A cream jug in Carltonware with anemones in relief on a yellow ground, c1930, 3in (7.5cm).
£40-70 *BRI*

A Carltonware lustre jug with gilt loop handle, the body painted and gilded with stylised floral and fan decoration, 5in (13cm).
£140-170 *P[Re]*

A Carltonware oviform vase, the dark and pale blue ground with purple, lavender and green zig-zag motif outlined with gilt decoration, printed marks Carltonware, Made in England, Handcraft 8490, 10½in (27cm).
£200-300 *C*

An Epiag porcelain part dinner service, painted in pale puce, yellow and red with stylised fuchsia and silver gilt rims, comprising: large tureen, cover and stand, a sauce boat with fixed stand, 6 dinner plates, 6 soup plates, a large fish plate, a circular serving dish, a square serving dish, a double salt with handle, 6 side plates, a tea and coffee pot, a milk jug, a sugar basin and cover, 12 cups and saucers, printed marks Epiag, Czechoslovakia, tureen 8in (19.5cm) high.
£400-600 *C*

Clarice Cliff

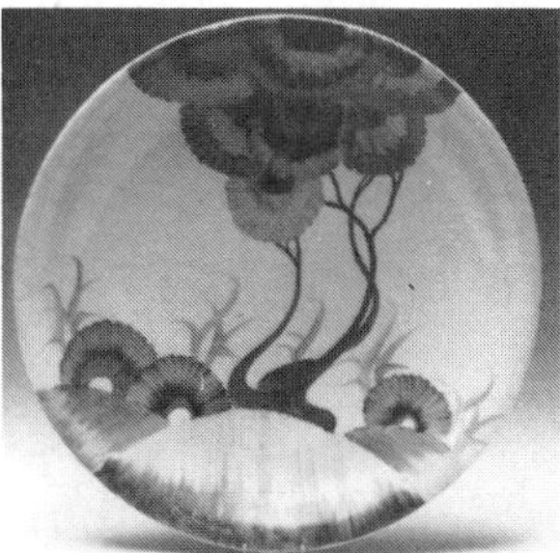

A Clarice Cliff Bizarre shallow dish, with slightly everted rim, boldly painted with brightly coloured flowers, 16½in (42cm).
£300-350 *Bea*

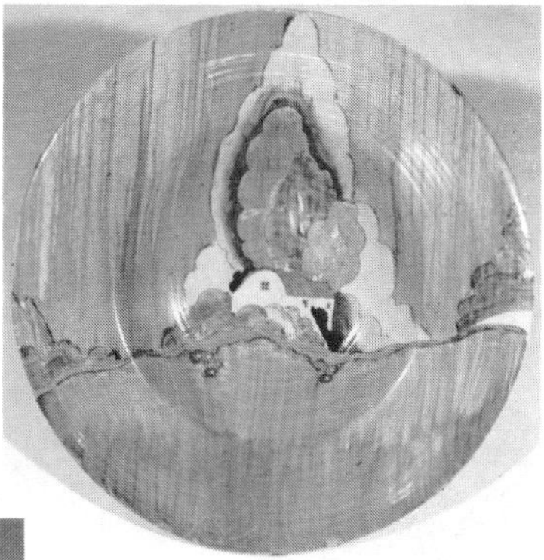

A Clarice Cliff breakfast set.
£100-120 *JAD*

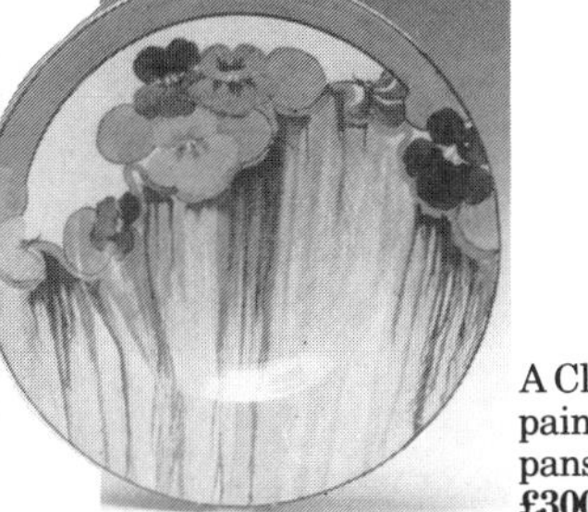

A Clarice Cliff Bizarre dish, brightly painted with streaky glazes and pansies, 13in (33cm).
£300-350 *Bea*

A Wilkinson Bizarre pottery charger by Clarice Cliff with dished centre, 18in (46cm).
£1,500-2,000 *DSH*

A Clarice Cliff Fantasque coffee set, painted in orange, black and green, against a cream ground, printed factory marks and facsimile signature.
£700-800 *P*

A Clarice Cliff breakfast set, with the Secrets pattern.
£300-400 *JAD*

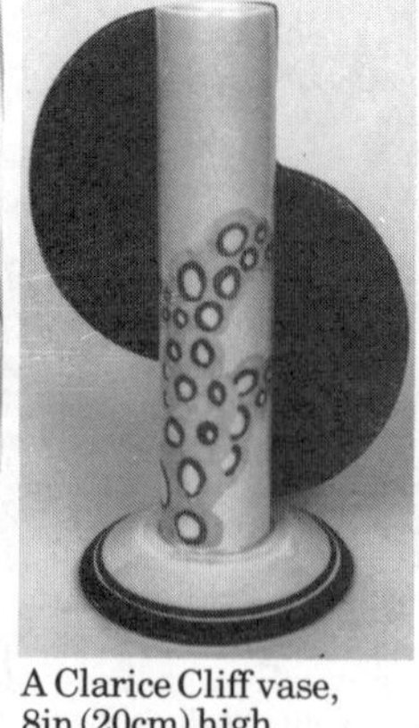

A Clarice Cliff vase, 8in (20cm) high.
£150-200 *JAD*

A Clarice Cliff Fantasque coffee service, 'Summer House', painted in red, yellow, green, black and blue, comprising: a coffee pot and cover, a milk jug, a sugar bowl and 6 cups and saucers, minor chips, stamped marks Fantasque Bizarre by Clarice Cliff, Newport Pottery, England, coffee pot 8in (20cm) high.
£1,600-1,800 *C*

A Clarice Cliff Bizarre tea service, painted with concentric light and dark brown rings on a cream ground, and a crocus preserve jar and cover, some damage.
£170-200 *Bea*

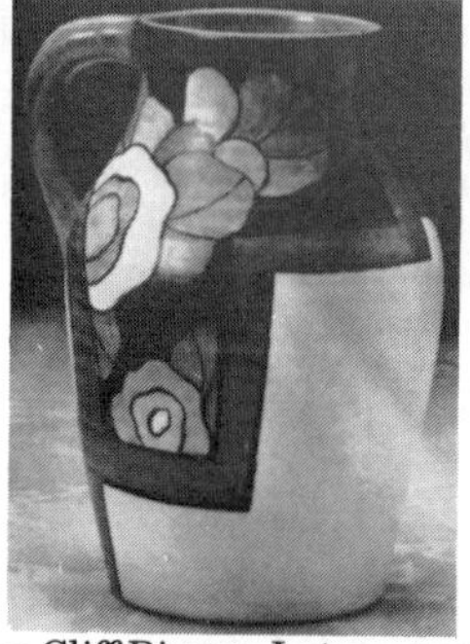

A Clarice Cliff Bizarre Latona vase, boldly painted in blue with stylised pink, purple, blue and green flowers in panels, 12in (30cm).
£700-900 *OT*

A Clarice Cliff Bizarre pottery coffee service, each piece boldly painted in colour.
£350-400 *Bea*

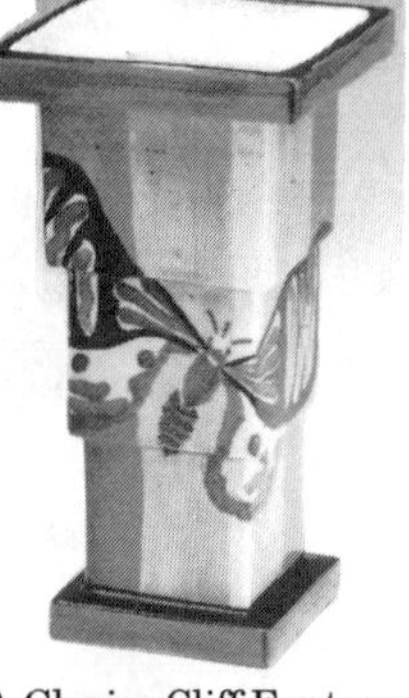

A Clarice Cliff Fantasque vase, boldly painted in colours, 7½in (19.5cm).
£250-300 *Bea*

A pair of Clarice Cliff bookends, 6½in (16cm).
£160-200 *Bea*

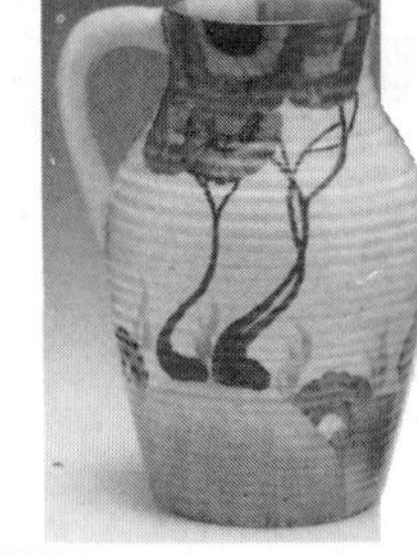

A Clarice Cliff Bizarre jug, painted in bright enamel colours, 11in (28.5cm).
£250-300 *Bea*

A Clarice Cliff Fantasque jug, boldly painted in bright enamel colours, 11½in (29cm).
£400-500 *Bea*

A Clarice Cliff Delicia patterned jug.
£400-450 *HP*

A Clarice Cliff Bizarre biscuit barrel, boldly painted in yellow and green against a blue and orange ground, with wicker handle, 6½in (16cm).
£150-200 *OT*

A Clarice Cliff wall pocket in the form of 2 budgerigars, painted in green, blue and yellow, 9in (23cm).
£70-100 *OT*

Ceramic Figures

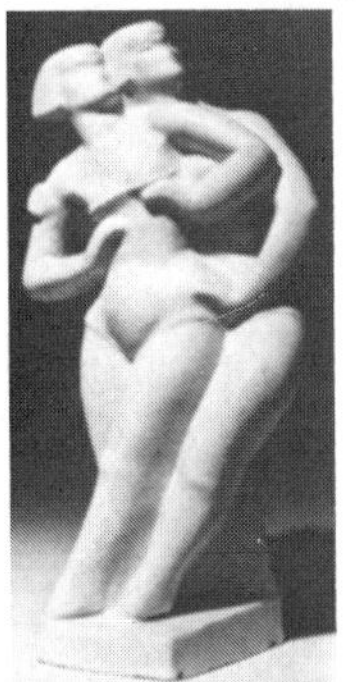

A stylish pottery group, modelled as 2 girls of ample proportions, covered in a crackled cream glaze, indistinct monogram, possibly French, 17in (43cm).
£200-250 *P*

A china figure, unmarked, c1930, 12½in (31cm).
£160-200 *GAL*

A Goldscheider porcelain figure of a lady with a fan, signed on base, Austria, c1930, 17in (43cm) high.
£400-600 *ASA*

A Goldscheider ceramic figure, 14½in (37cm).
£280-350 *JAD*

A Goebels figure, German, 6in (15cm).
£200-300 *GAL*

A Lenci figure with a box at the back with a frog on the lid, Italian, 10in (25cm).
£300-350 *JAD*

A Royal Dux figure, c1935, 12in (30.5cm).
£300-400 *GAL*

Metal Figures

A figure of a girl with a hoop, cast and iron, signed Bertrand, c1920.
£300-400 *SBA*

A gilded spelter figure, Con Brio, of a young maiden with arms outstretched.
£200-300 *P[Re]*

A table lighter decorated with a silver plated spelter figure of a woman golfer, marked on base Fashioned by Ronson 16270 G.M. Silox, 11in (28cm) wide.
£100-150 *HOD*

Bronze and Ivory Figures

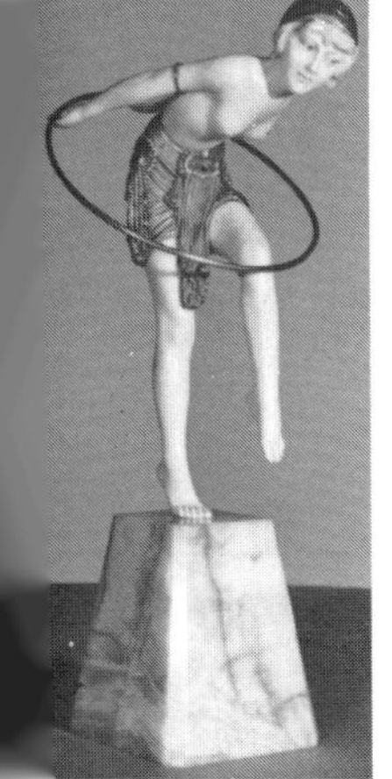

A bronze and ivory figure, 'Hoop Girl', by Chiparus, c1930.
£5,000-7,000 *ASA*

A gilt bronze figure cast from a model by Lorenzl, on green onyx base, bronze inscribed Lorenzl, 11in (28cm).
£500-600 *CSK*

A gilt bronze figure cast from a model by Lorenzl, on green onyx base, bronze inscribed Lorenzl, 10in (26cm).
£500-600 *CSK*

A cold painted bronze and ivory figure by Lorenzl, enamelled in colours, on an onyx base, hairlines to base and one thumb lacking, signed Crejo, 10in (25cm).
£400-500 *CEd*

A bronze and ivory figure of Harlequin by Lorenzl.
£800-1,200 *ASA*

A bronze and ivory figure by Lorenzl, c1930.
£700-1,000 *ASA*

A bronze figure cast from a model by Le Faguays, signed on base, 25in (64cm) high.
£900-1,000 *CSK*

A cold painted bronze figure, 'Sword Dancer', cast from a model by Nan Greb, inscribed Nan Greb, 21in (54cm).
£1,500-2,000 *CSK*

A cold painted bronze figure cast from a model by Nan Greb, inscribed Nan Greb, 11in (28cm).
£800-900 *CSK*

A bronze and ivory figure, 'Gamine', cast and carved after a model by Ferdinand Preiss, cold painted in green, on a green marble base, hairlines to head, arms and legs, inscribed F. Preiss, 13½in (34cm).
£5,000-6,000 *CEd*

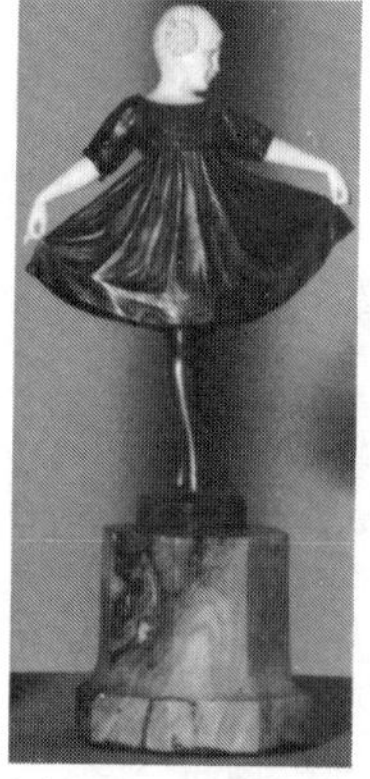

A bronze and ivory figure of a child by Preiss, c1930.
£800-1,300 *ASA*

A bronze figure of a dancer by Preiss, c1930.
£1,800-2,200 *ASA*

A bronze and ivory figure in the manner of F. Preiss, on black marble plinth, 11in (28cm).
£5,000-5,500 *BWe*

A bronze figure of a motorcyclist, unsigned but attributed to Bruno Zack, the marble base applied with metal tag stamped 'B. Zack Sculp. Argentor Vienna', 8in (20cm).
£2,000-2,500 *P*

Locate the source

The source of each illustration in Miller's can be found by checking the code letters below each caption with the list of contributors.

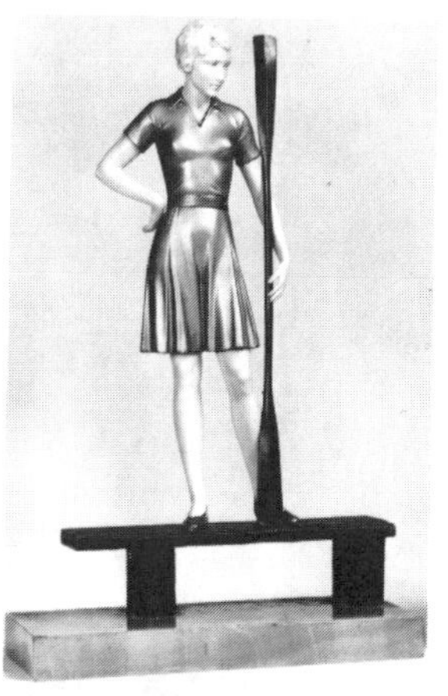

A bronze and ivory figure on a green marble base, 12in (30cm).
£2,500-3,000 *BWe*

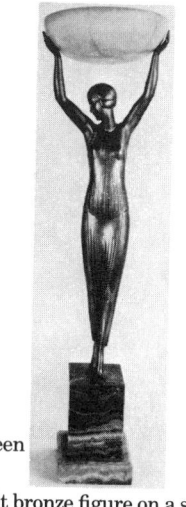

A gilt bronze figure on a stepped marble base, 27in (69cm).
£1,200-1,500 *CSK*

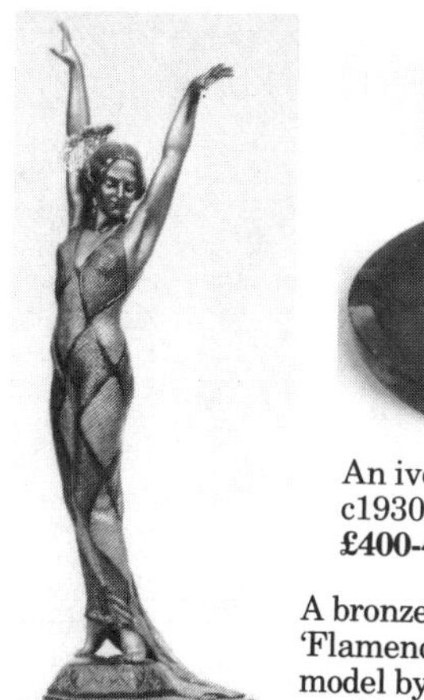

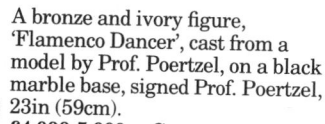

An ivory figure on an onyx base, c1930, 10in (25cm) diam.
£400-450 *JAD*

A bronze and ivory figure, 'Flamenco Dancer', cast from a model by Prof. Poertzel, on a black marble base, signed Prof. Poertzel, 23in (59cm).
£4,000-5,000 *C*

A bronze figure, 'Scarf Dancer', cast from a model by Demetre Chiparus, the marble base incised D.H. Chiparus, 27in (68cm).
£5,500-6,500 *C*

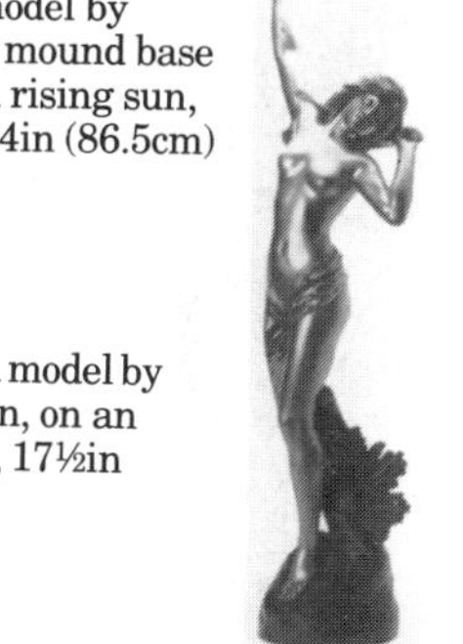

A gilded and painted bronze figure, 'Venus', cast from a model by Edouard Drouot, on a mound base cast with waves and a rising sun, inscribed E. Drouot, 34in (86.5cm) high.
£800-1,000 *Bon*

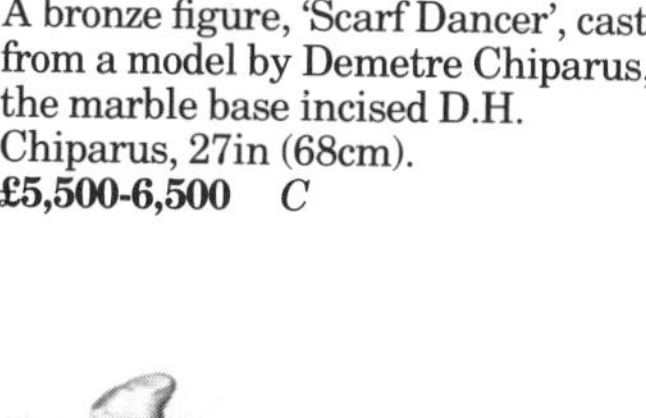

A bronze figure cast from a model by Lorenzl, patinated in green, on an onyx base, signed Lorenzl, 17½in (44cm).
£700-900 *P*

A bronze and ivory figure, 'Clown', cast and carved from a model by Jaeger, signed in the metal Jaeger R.v.M., 10in (25.5cm).
£3,000-4,000 *C*

A bronze and ivory figure, 'The Courtier', cast and carved from a model by Lorenzl, signed in the bronze Lorenzl, 7in (17.5cm).
£600-800 *C*

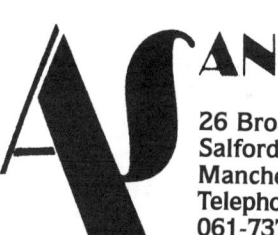

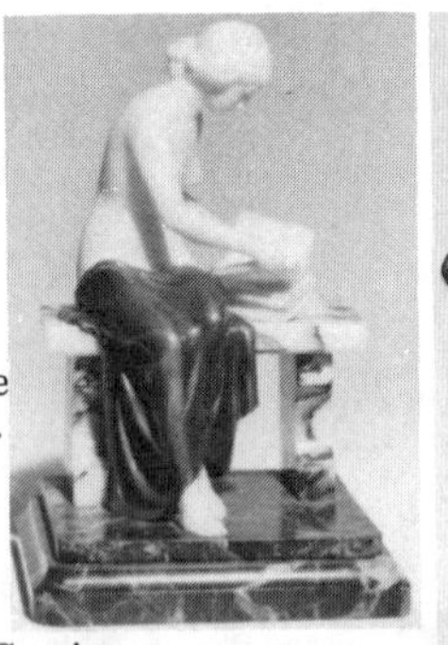

A bronze and polychrome marble figure, 'Reading', cast and carved from a model by Schumacher, signed in the bronze Henry, 10in (26cm).
£1,000-1,300 *C*

A bronze and ivory figure, 'Grecian with torch', cast and carved from a model by Ferdinand Preiss, on stepped pink striated base, signed in the bronze F. Preiss, 10in (25cm).
£3,000-4,000 *C*

A bronze and ivory figure, 'Dancing Girl', cast and carved from a model by Lorenzl, signed in the bronze Lorenzl, 9in (23cm).
£700-900 *C*

A bronze figure, 'Spanish Flamenco Dancer', cast from a model by Sonher, inscribed Sonher, 13½in (34.5cm).
£1,000-1,200 *C*

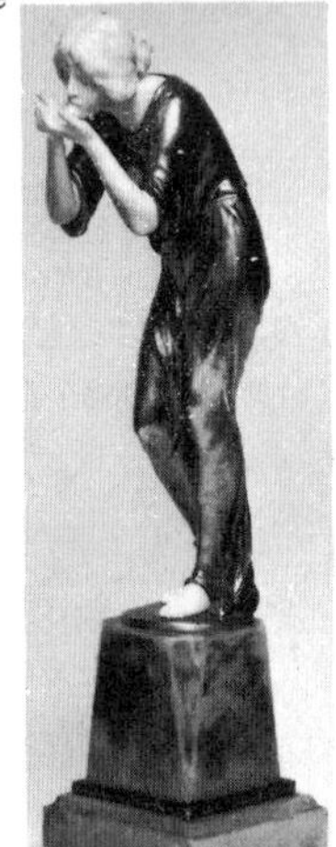

A gilt bronze and ivory figure, 'Mystery', cast and carved from a model by V. Seifert, signed in the bronze V. Seifert, 11½in (29cm).
£3,500-4,500 *C*

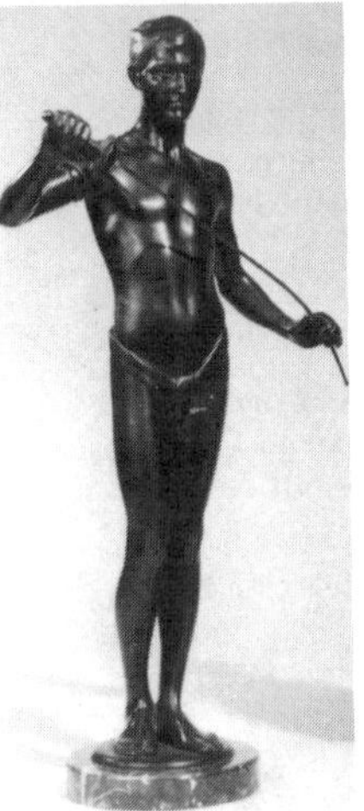

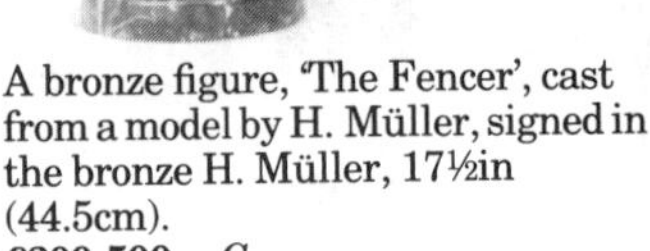

A bronze figure, 'The Fencer', cast from a model by H. Müller, signed in the bronze H. Müller, 17½in (44.5cm).
£300-500 *C*

A bronze figure, 'Athlete', cast from a model by H. Henjes, signed in the bronze H. Henjes fec.10, 14in (35.5cm).
£400-600 *C*

A bronze and ivory figure, 'Feeding the birds', cast and carved from a model by L. Barthelemy, signed in the bronze L. Barthelemy, 12in (30.5cm).
£2,500-3,500 *C*

A spelter and ivorine group, 'Pierrot and Columbine', cast from a model by D. Chiparus, on striated marble plinth, 30in (76cm) wide.
£2,500-3,500 *C*

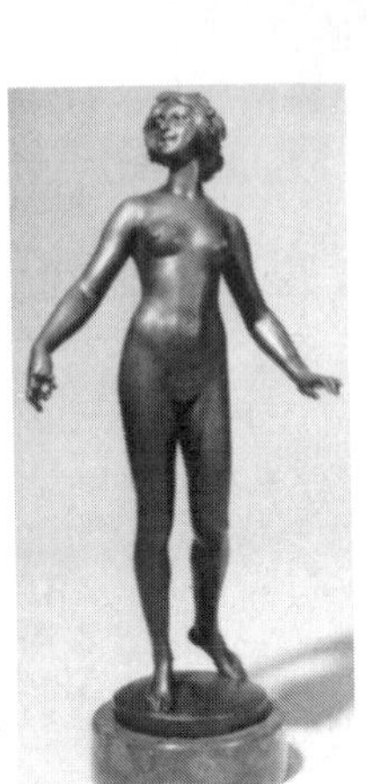

A bronze figure, 'Flower Girl', cast from a model by Tuch, a flower in her right hand, signed in the bronze Tuch, 17in (43.5cm).
£800-1,000 *C*

Make the most of Miller's

When a large specialist well-publicised collection comes on the market, it tends to increase prices. Immediately after this, prices can fall slightly due to the main buyers having large stocks and the market being 'flooded'. This is usually temporary and does not affect very high quality items.

Furniture

A Macassar ebony bedroom suite, the dressing table with marquetry and inlaid metal banding, with double bed, chest of drawers with swing mirror, a table and a pair of chairs with wicker seats, dressing table 47in (119cm).
£2,000-2,500 *CSK*

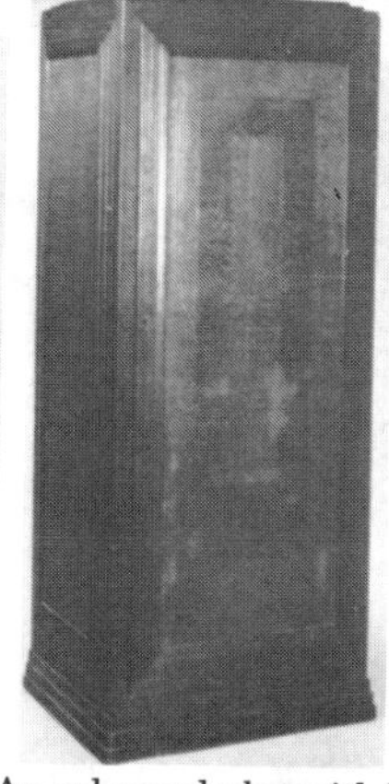

An oak wardrobe, with label Token hand made furniture, designed by Betty Joel, made by J. Renny, at Token Works, Portsmouth 1929, 73½in (187cm) high.
£100-150 *P*

A drawing room suite, comprising 2-seater sofa and 2 armchairs, with bird's eye maple frames.
£1,500-2,000 *LRG*

A contemporary 'Seige Tournant' chair, with chromium plated tubular frame, the seat and arm rails upholstered in red hide, by Le Corbusier, designed and made for the Salon des Artistes Decorateurs, 1928.
£4,000-5,000 *P*

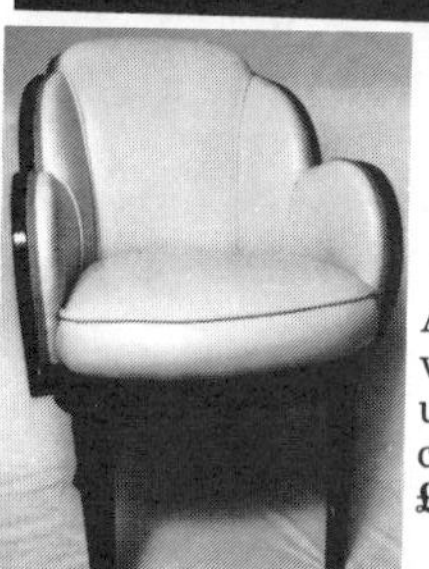

A six-piece cloud back lounge suite, veneered in walnut and re-upholstered in cream leather, c1930, settee 65in (165cm) wide.
£3,000-4,000 *ST*

An oak secretaire, with fitted interior, 41in (103cm) wide.
£550-600 *P*

A Clement Mère bird's eye maple secretaire, with ivory block feet, inscribed C. Mère, 50in (127cm) high.
£7,000-8,000 *CSK*

French putissandrede Rio buffet, ttributed to Rehulman, c1930, 86in 218.5cm).
2,200-2,600 *RG*

An Amsterdam School sideboard, designed by Richard Reens, in rosewood and coromandel, c1928, 119in (302cm).
£1,000-1,500 *CAm*

A walnut and mahogany centre table, designed by W. F. Crittall and made by E. W. Beckwith, 44in (112cm) square.
£2,000-2,500 *P*

A copper base table, incorporating an electric light, with glass top, 30in (76cm) diam.
£200-300 *JAD*

A nest of tables, 19in (48cm).
£400-500 *RG*

A chrome base table with black glass top, 16in (40.5cm) diam.
£70-100 *JAD*

A chromium frame and mirror glass two-tier tea trolley.
£70-100 *PC*

A sideboard enclosing satinwood interior shelves, and edged with satinwood.
£300-400 *P*

A mahogany dining table, designed by W. F. Crittall and made by E. W. Beckwith, 67in (170cm).
£3,000-4,000 *P*

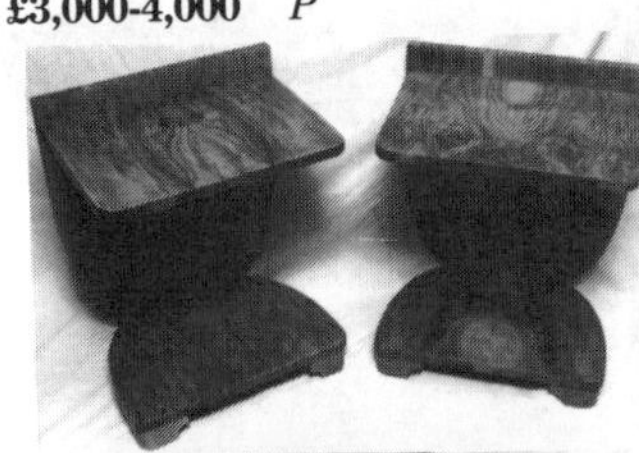

A coffee table and set of 4 occasional tables, 34in (86cm) wide.
£350-450 *JAD*

A Rawley Gallery mirror, with original label on the back, c1930, 29in (74cm) high.
£100-150 *JAD*

A green lacquer piano, with chrome trim, 57in (144.5cm), and stool.
£350-400 *JAD*

Glass

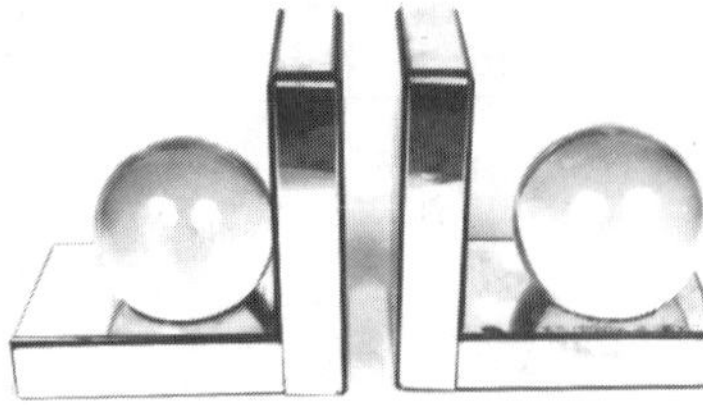

A pair of glass book ends, c1930, damaged, 5in (12.5cm) high.
£25-50 *JAD*

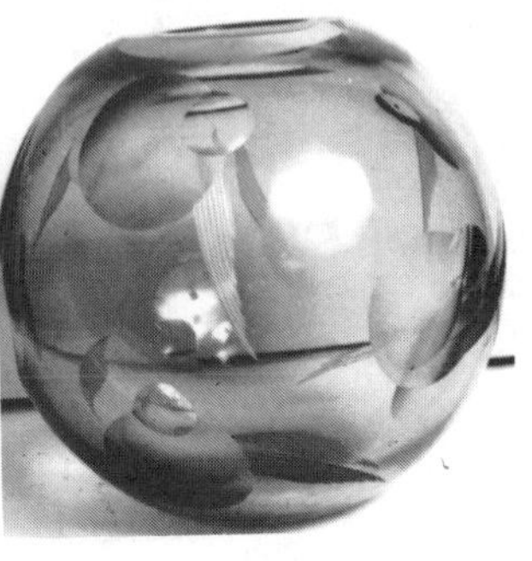

A blue English bowl, c1930, 7in (18cm).
£100-120 *GAL*

A Moser Unica bowl, with blue centre and rim decorated with red and milky white dotted striations, engraved marks Chris Lebeau, Jan.1926, Moser-Fecit-Tchecoslovaquie, 10½in (27.5cm).
£450-500 *CAm*

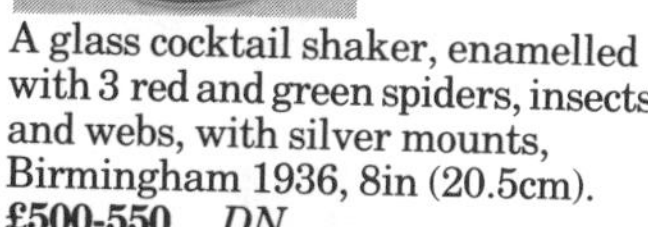
A glass cocktail shaker, enamelled with 3 red and green spiders, insects and webs, with silver mounts, Birmingham 1936, 8in (20.5cm).
£500-550 *DN*

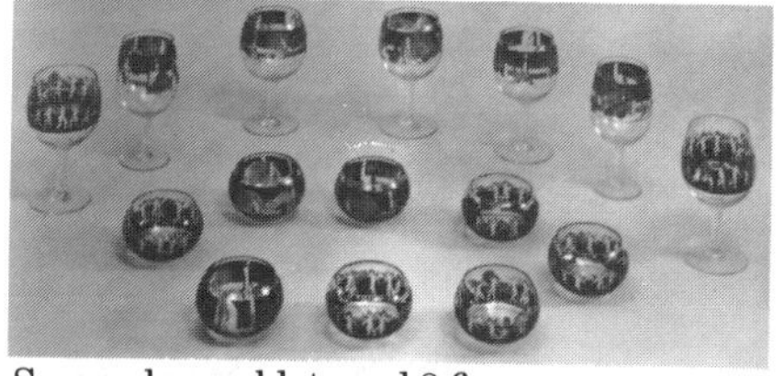

Seven glass goblets and 8 finger bowls, signed Verdar.
£700-900 *M*

Purchased from an Italian Count in 1930 for £15.00.

A glass decanter set, decorated with panels of black enamel, frosted and engraved linear decoration.
£450-500 *P*

A decanter and glasses, in clear glass faceted with square panels and alternately flashed with amber, one chipped.
£200-250 *P*

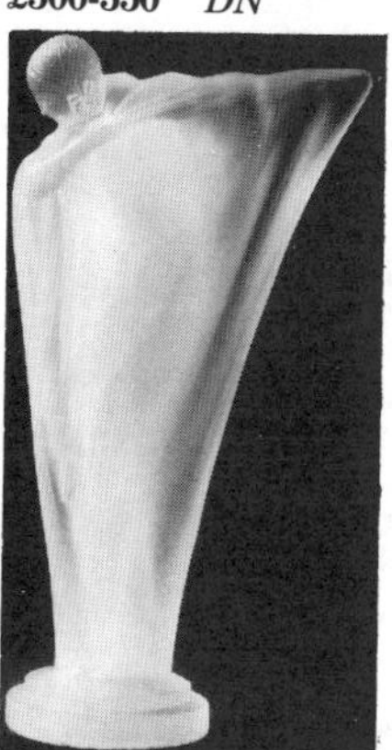

An Etling opalescent glass figure, moulded Etling France 50, 8in (20.5cm).
£800-900 *P*

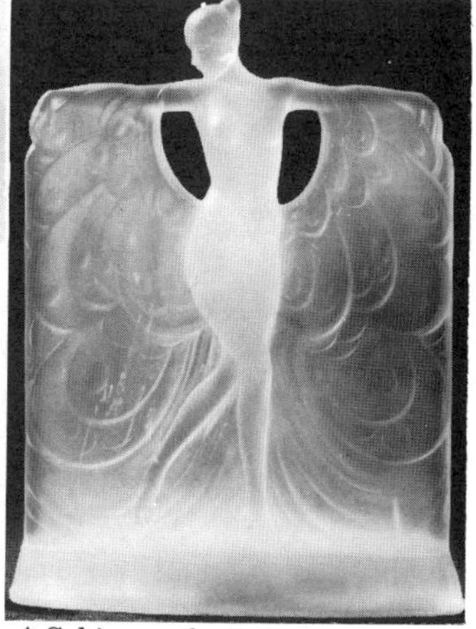

A Sabino opalescent glass figure, 'Suzanne Au Bain', unsigned, 9in (23cm), with wooden mount incorporating fitments for use as a lamp.
£1,800-2,000 *P*

A Venini patchwork vase, the clear glass internally decorated in red, green and blue, acid stamped Venini Murano Italia, 4½in (11cm) high.
£1,200-1,500 *CAm*

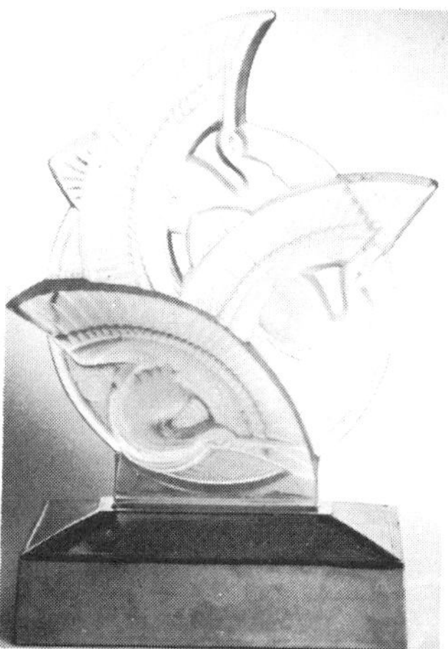

A Sabino opalescent glass lamp, signed on the glass Sabino France, 13½in (35cm) high, set in a chromed base incorporating lamp fitments.
£700-800 *P*

A vase with black sunburst design, c1930, 5in (12.5cm) high.
£50-70 *JAD*

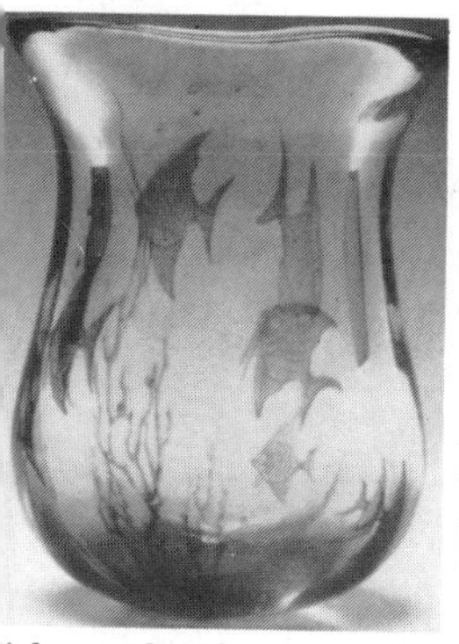

A heavy Orrefors green glass vase, by Edward Hald, inscribed on the base and dated 1938, 10½in (26.5cm).
£400-450 *Bea*

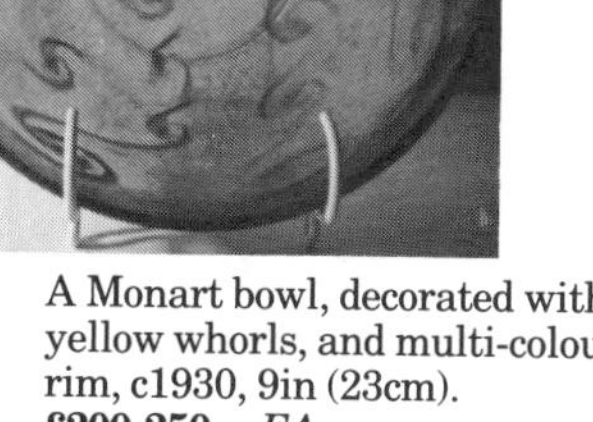

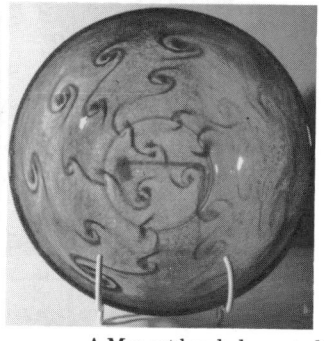

A Monart bowl, decorated with yellow whorls, and multi-coloured rim, c1930, 9in (23cm).
£200-250 *FA*

l. A Monart powder box and lid, in orange and blue with gold aventurine clear knob, c1930, 5in (12.5cm) diam.
£350-450

r. A Vasart vase, in white and pale green with gold aventurine, c1930, 4in (10cm).
Acid etched signature **£20-25**
Without signature **£10-12** *FA*

A Monart vase in pale green, brown and gold aventurine, c1930, 3½in (9cm).
£70-90 *FA*

A Monart vase, in lilac turquoise, paper label with the code VA.260, c1929, 9in (23cm).
£400-450 *FA*

Metal

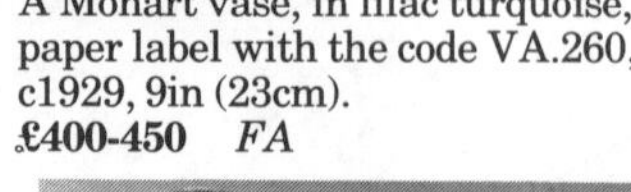

A pair of American bronze book ends, by Chase, 6in (15cm) high
£200-300 *GAL*

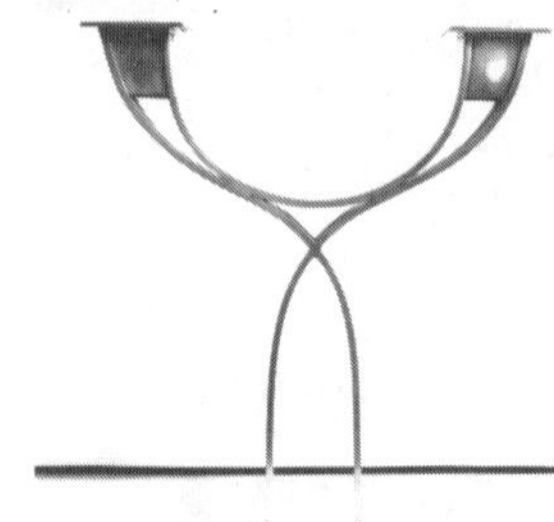

A pewter candlestick, c1955, 8½in (22cm).
£80-90 *GAL*

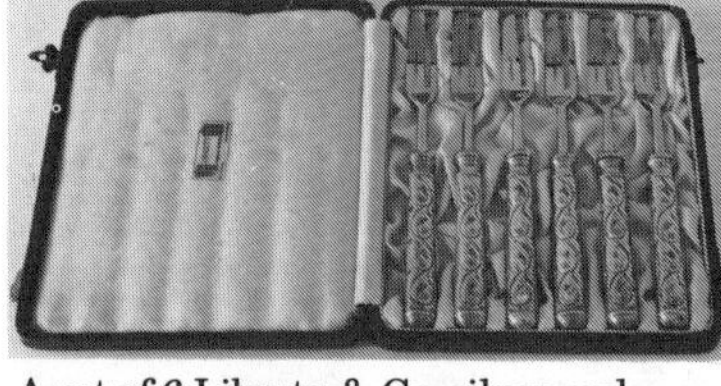

A chrome and enamel cigarette box, 9½in (24cm) wide.
£75-100 *GAL*

A pair of George V table candlesticks, with carved oak barley-twist stems, hammered silver square bases and circular nozzles, A. E. Jones, Chester 1922, 9in (23cm), loaded.
£450-500 *Bea*

A pair of chrome Art Deco style uplighters, 75in (190.5cm).
£180-230 *RG*

A set of 6 Liberty & Co. silver and enamel handled cake forks, Birmingham 1931.
£150-200 *HCH*

A four piece Art Deco style Walker & Hall teaset, Sheffield 1944, 50oz approx.
£450-500 *WIL*

A French electroplated tea and coffee service, with rosewood handles and finials, stamped marks GM, tray 21in (52cm) wide.
£1,000-1,200 *C*

A four piece tea service, by Edward Barnard and Sons Ltd., London 1934, 54oz gross.
£1,200-1,500 *DN*

A silver tea and coffee service by Mappin & Webb, with ivory handles, 1937 and 1939.
£2,500-3,000 *SWO*

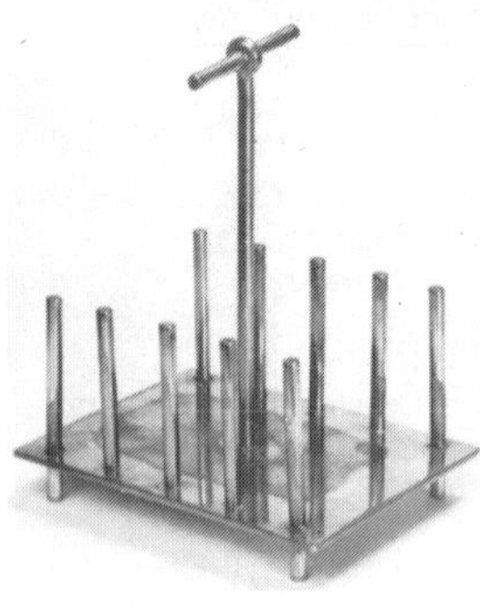

A Hukin & Heath electroplated toast rack, designed by Christopher Dresser, stamped maker's mark, 5in (13cm) high.
£1,600-2,000 *CSK*

Locate the source
The source of each illustration in Miller's can be found by checking the code letters below each caption with the list of contributors.

Miscellaneous

A French enamel stove, c1930, 36in (91.5cm) high.
£60-80 *COB*

A plaster owl, c1910, 19in (48cm) high.
£250-300 *JeB*

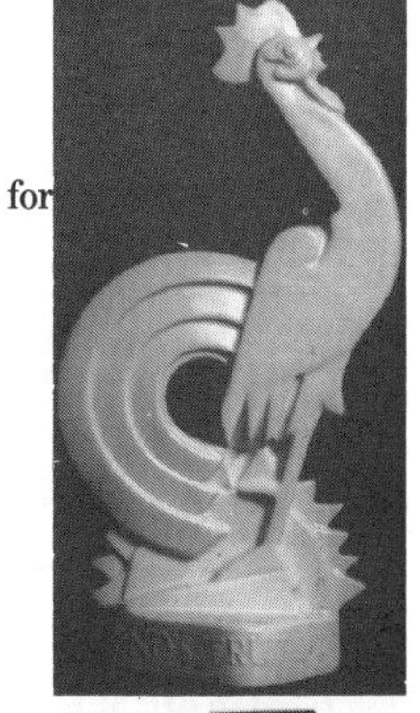

A ceramic advertising cockerel for Eno's Fruit Salts.
£70-80 *GAL*

A cigarette box, applied overall with square plaques of bleached petrified wood and a broad central band of red stained odonolite edged with brass, the interior lined with wood, 8½in (21cm) wide.
£500-550 *P*

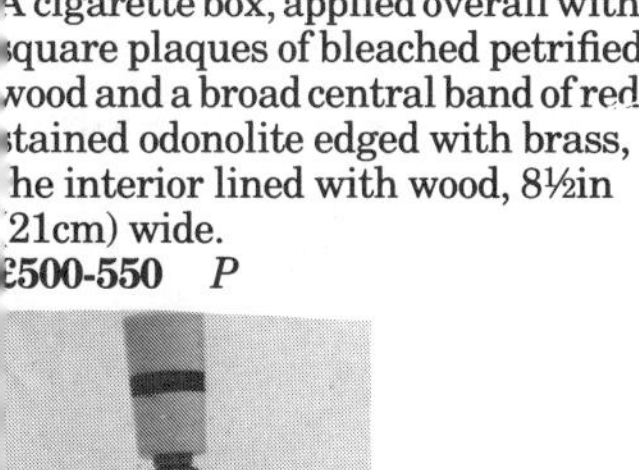

A marble box with clock in lid, damaged, 5½in (14cm) wide.
£20-30 *JAD*

An inkstand, with chrome trim, 14in (35.5cm) wide.
£80-100 *JAD*

A marble garniture, c1930.
£450-500 *Ba*

A Goebel figure table lamp, 9in (23cm) high.
£60-80 *PC*

A chrome clock, 9in (23cm) wide.
£20-25 *JAD*

A Brazilian gourd electric floor lamp, with mushroom shaped shade and tapering conical illuminated column, 64in (162.5cm) high.
£500-600 *P[Re]*

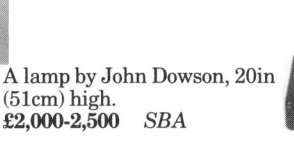

A spelter figure lamp, c1930, 22in (56cm).
£250-300 *GAL*

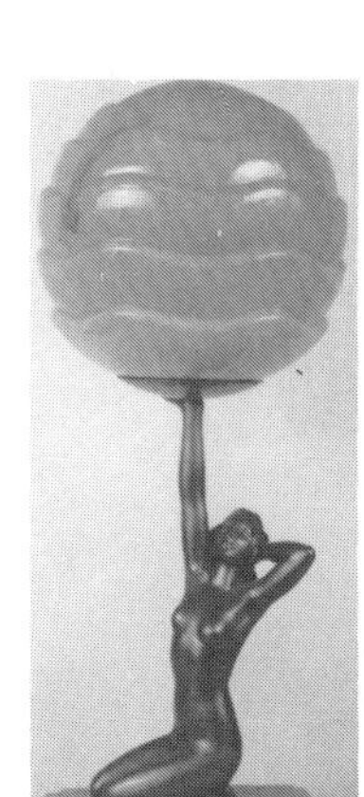

A lamp, 16½in (42cm) high.
£300-400 *SBA*

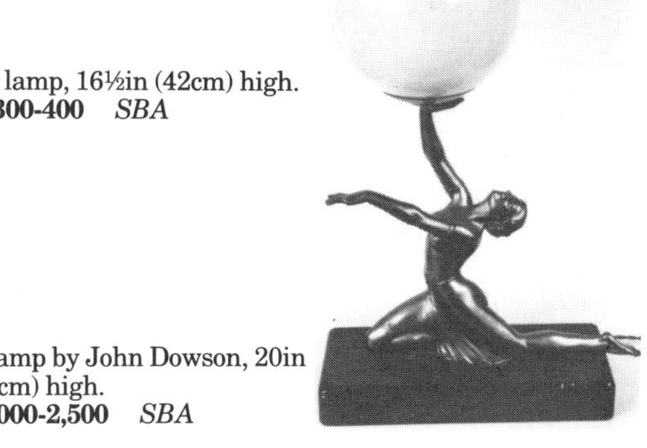

A lamp by John Dowson, 20in (51cm) high.
£2,000-2,500 *SBA*

Post War Design

A paperweight by Paul Ysart, decorated in bright blue, yellow, green, red, purple and white, with PY cane, 3in (7.5cm) diam.
£330-360 *FA*

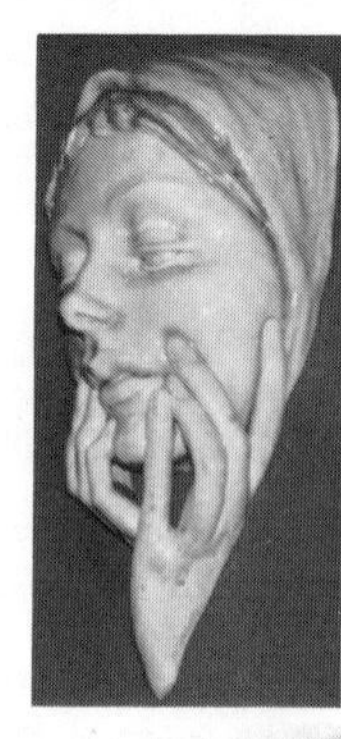

A pottery wall mask, signed H. R. Rhodes, dated 1943.
£100-200 *ASA*

Brass candlesticks, c1955, 5in (12.5cm) high.
£50-75 *GAL*

A Wedgwood Windsor grey Travel pattern dinner service, designed by Eric Ravilious, each piece decorated in black and light blue with trains, liners, sailing boats, balloons, aeroplanes and buses, printed factory marks and designer's name.
£2,500-3,000 *P*

SILVER

Baskets

A George III bread basket, engraved with a coat-of-arms within shield shaped cartouche, by William Plummer, 1782, 15in (38cm) long, 42oz.
£6,000-7,000 *C*

A George III cake basket, with beaded borders and reeded swing handle, by Thomas Chawner, London 1783, 16in (41cm), 29.25oz.
£200-250 *DN*

A George III cake basket, engraved with a coat-of-arms within a shield shaped cartouche, by Robert Hennell, 1787, 14in (35.5cm), 25oz.
£2,000-2,500 *C*

A George III sugar basket, with a band of bright cut engraving and a crest, by John Robins, London 1796, 7in (18cm), 8.33oz.
£550-600 *DN*

A George III sugar basket, the sides with pierced fret band, with a contemporary initialled cartouche, fitted with a blue glass liner, maker's mark Thomas Daniel and W.H. London 1789, 6.5oz.
£550-600 *WW*

A George III bread basket on spreading foot, by Henry Nutting or Hannah Northcote, 1801, 14in (35.5cm) long, 26oz.
£1,200-1,500 *C*

A George III crested sugar basket, with reeded swing handle on oval foot, by Peter and Anne Bateman, London 1791, 5½in (14cm), 5oz.
£600-700 *DN*

A George III cake basket, with reeded swing handle, on raised foot, Dublin 1806.
£460-500 *P[Re]*

A George IV fluted swing-handled ake basket, with applied rococo loral and foliate rim, the handle with similar decoration, Thomas Bradbury & Co., Sheffield 1826, 10in (25.5cm), 22oz.
500-550 *CSK*

An early Victorian sugar basket, maker's mark EE over JW, London 1846, 220 grammes.
£350-450 *HSS*

A Russian swing handled trompe l'oeil basket, applied with a red and blue enamelled Cyrillic monogram in one corner, by Ivan Chlebnikov, Moscow, c1885, 11½in (29.5cm) diam, 30.5oz.
£2,000-2,500 *P*

pair of late Victorian dessert askets, James Dixon & Sons, heffield 1896, 9½in (24cm), 21oz.
700-750 *P[Pea]*

A Victorian dessert basket, maker William Comyns, London 1893, 10in (25.5cm), 9½oz.
£250-300 *P[PWC]*

A dessert basket, on pierced and carved panel feet, James Deakin & Sons, Sheffield 1901, 9½in (24cm), 9.75oz.
£250-300 *P[PWC]*

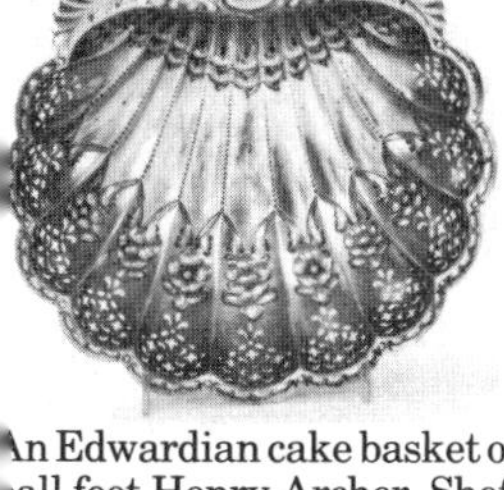

An Edwardian cake basket on fluted all feet Henry Archer, Sheffield 1902, 9½in (24cm), 12oz.
400-450 *CSK*

A dessert basket, the pierced trellis sides with portrait medallions and floral swags, cast rococo borders and side handles, on scroll feet, B. Muller, Chester import mark 1904, 12in (30.5cm), 20oz.
£500-600 *WW*

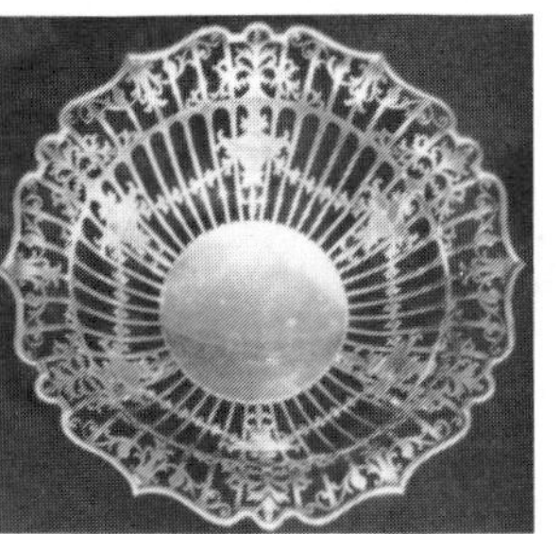

A dessert basket, maker's mark J.R., Sheffield 1913, 7½in (19cm), 7.5oz.
£200-300 *P[PWC]*

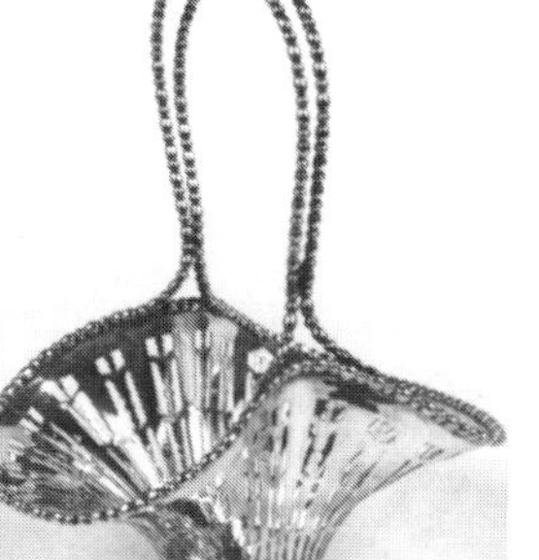

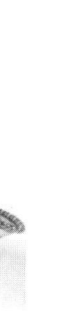

silver basket, Sheffield 1913.
190-200 *TVA*

A pierced and engraved fruit dish, Robert Hennell, London 1788.
£1,800-2,000 *BM*

Beakers

A pair of George III silver mounted horn beakers, Thomas & James Phipps II, London 1818, 6in (15cm).
£220-250 *P[PWC]*

A German beaker and cover, on 3 ball feet, with silver gilt rim, the base with inscription dated 15th June, 1711, by Philipp Stenglin, Augsburg, 1708-1710, 5in (12.5cm), 199grammes.
£3,000-3,500 *C*

Bowls

A George II Irish bowl, with a moulded rim, on a raised spread circular base, engraved with a contemporary cartouche and armorials, by David King, Dublin 1732, 6½in (17cm) diam, 14oz.
£3,500-4,000 *P*

A Queen Anne two-handled porringer, decorated with ropework girdle and band of fluting, engraved with armorial, Edward Wimans, 1704, 5in (12.5cm) diam, 10oz.
£1,000-1,200 *P*

A George II fluted bowl, engraved with a crest, by Benjamin Godfrey, 1739, 7in (18cm) diam, 12oz 7dwt.
£3,000-4,000 *C*

A pair of bowls, with stylised arms of James I, and the date '1610' and inscribed around the rim, one with 'Wine was made from the beginnings to make men glad and not for drunkennes (sic.). Wine measurably drunke and in time bringethe gladnesse and chearfulnesse of the mind', the other 'looke not thou upon the wine when it is red and when it sheweth his color in the cup or goeth downe pleasantly in the end thereof it will bite like a serpente and hurt like a cockatrice', 6in (15cm) diam, 31.5oz.
£2,500-3,000 *P*

A George III sugar bowl and cover, on spreading foot, later chased with rococo flowers and foliage, the cover with flower finial and engraved with a crest, probably John King, London 1769, 5in (12.5cm).
£450-500 *CSK*

A George III covered sugar bowl, with a detachable domed cover surmounted by a cast poupée finial, decorated all over with lobed fluting, reeded borders, by Rebecca Emes and Edward Barnard, 1814, 4½in (12cm) high, 12oz.
£700-750 *P*

A silver compote, with 2 applied and chased polar bears on the inverted rim, by Gorham 1872, impressed with firm's marks and Sterling 125 E 4, 11in (28cm), 24.5oz.
£5,000-6,000 *CNY*

A Victorian parcel gilt bowl and spoon, with beaded edging and frieze of classical and mythological figures on a matted ground, Martin Hall and Co., Sheffield 1870, 5.9oz, in fitted case.
£400-450 *Bea*

An Edwardian reproduction of a Charles II porringer, embossed with leaping lions and unicorns, with beaded caryatid handles, by Charles Stuart Harris, 1902, 20.5oz.
£450-500 *P*

A pair of Victorian rose bowls, decorated in Queen Anne Monteith style, on spreading bases and on wood plinth stands, Charles Stuart Harris, London 1891, 5in (12cm) high, 21.4oz.
£500-700 *Bea*

A late Victorian rose bowl, applied with scrolls and cherubs' masks, a cartouche with regimental initials, motto and crest, William Gibson & John Langman, London 1891, 11in (28cm), 36oz.
£1,000-1,200 *CSK*

A Continental bowl, on 4 shell and scroll feet, with 2 dolphins' masks and ring handles, import marks, 1902, 13in (33cm) long, 47oz.
£2,000-3,000 *C*

An Edwardian rose bowl on stand, Goldsmiths & Silversmiths, London, 1903.
£300-350 *TVA*

A two-handled bowl, on spreading foot with egg and dart border, engraved 'The Argentine Grand National Cup', by Elkington & Co., Birmingham, 1908, 13½in (34cm) diam, 100oz.
£2,000-2,500 *C*

A William IV parcel gilt pap boat, with rose, thistle, shamrock and ovolo border, by William Knight (II), 1831.
£250-300 *P*

A George V silver sugar bowl, with decorative edge, on 6 feet, maker's mark O.R. for Omar Ramsden, London 1935, 5in (12cm) diam, 6oz 2dwt.
£400-500 *GC*

A rose bowl, with pierced rim design, fluted sides and 2 serpentine handles, hallmarked, London 1921, 82oz.
£900-1,000 *BWe*

A Russian sugar bowl, with swing handle and gilt rim, Moscow 1894, 4½in (11cm), 8.5oz.
£360-400 *Bon*

An Edwardian hammered sugar bowl, A. E. Jones, Birmingham 1908, 4in (10cm) diam, 4.5oz.
£150-200 *HCH*

A Walker & Hall repousse dessert bowl, with winged figure handles, 13in (33cm), 52.5oz.
£1,800-2,200 *GSP*

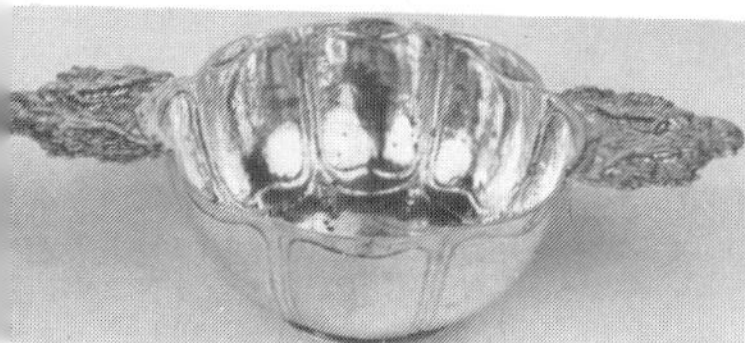

A Dutch brandy bowl, the flat handles cast and pierced with recumbent cherubs and foliage, by Volkaert Symonsz, Swaert, Haarlem, 1661, 10in (25.5cm) wide, 210grammes.
£2,000-3,000 *C*

SILVER

Some dates of importance in study of silver:–

- ★ 1660 restoration of Charles II – beginning of great era of domestic English silver
- ★ c1670 influence of acanthus leafage and fluted baroque
- ★ 1685 The Revocation of the Edict of Nantes – brought Huguenot silversmiths to England
- ★ 1697 introduction of Britannia standard. Lasted until 1702
- ★ 1740s early signs of rococo
- ★ 1750s revival of chinoiserie
- ★ 1760s influence of neo-classicism
- ★ 1800-20 tendency to add decoration to plainer style
- ★ 1820s revival of rococo style
- ★ by 1830s machines much in use
- ★ 1880s Arts and Crafts movement – influence of Art Nouveau

Boxes

An English silver gilt needle case, the hinged cover engraved with a cherub mask, maker's mark William South, London, c1690.
£650-700 *WW*

A tortoiseshell and silver tobacco box, the top inlaid with a silver crest of a rampant leopard, 18thC.
£500-550 *WW*

A George III silver wrigglework snuff box, by W. Edwards, London 1806.
£120-140 *TVA*

A George III bag-shaped vinaigrette, by Joseph Taylor, Birmingham 1817.
£100-150 *DN*

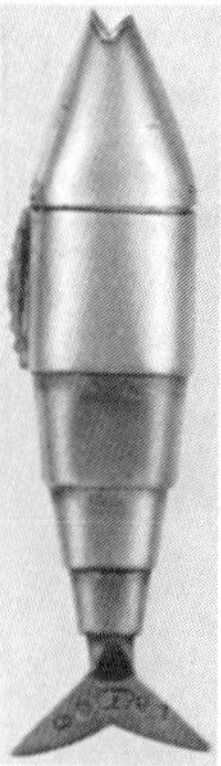

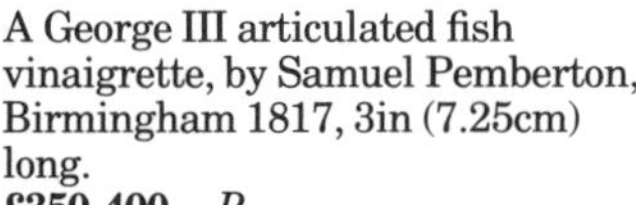

A George III articulated fish vinaigrette, by Samuel Pemberton, Birmingham 1817, 3in (7.25cm) long.
£350-400 *P*

A William IV engine turned snuff box, the lid chased with a castle landscape, Taylor & Perry, Birmingham 1835, 3in (7.5cm).
£200-250 *DN*

A chased baluster shaped paint box and lid, London 1690, 3½in (9cm) high, 3.5oz.
£600-700 *P[EDH]*

A box with mother-of-pearl base, the cover carved with huntsmen, dogs, scrolls and shells, engraved with monogram, unmarked, base damaged, early 19thC, 3in (7.5cm).
£80-100 *DN*

A George III crested box, the domed cover with a gadrooned border and a shield shaped armorial, by Thomas Halford, London 1809, 3in (7.5cm).
£200-240 *DN*

A silver gilt filigree box formed as a heart, with detachable cover and plain base, probably English, 17thC, 2½in (6cm) wide.
£350-550 *C*

A Continental niello box, decorated with 2 figures, flowers, leaves and birds, 19thC, 3in (7.5cm).
£170-200 *DN*

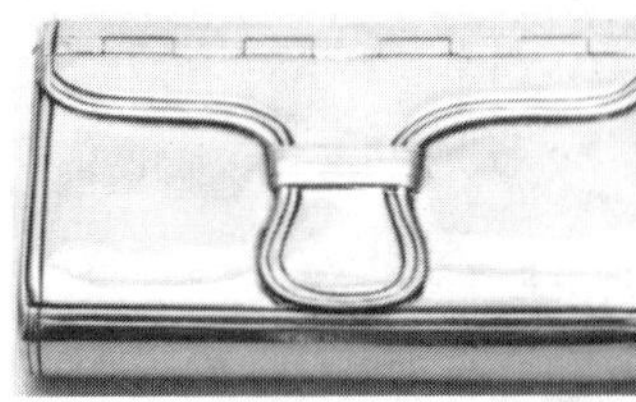

A George III bag-shaped snuff box inscribed inside 'From an Individual Whose good fortune is to have a sincere Friend', by Robert Butterfield, London 1814, 2½in (6cm).
£300-350 *DN*

A George III shaped vinaigrette, with central laurel wreath, ray engraving and bright cut bands of flowers, by Joseph Willmore, Birmingham 1819, 1½in (3.5cm).
£300-350 *DN*

A George IV table snuff box, the hinged cover decorated in a Fragonard style rococo scene, with gilt interior, the engine turned base engraved with a monogram, John Shaw, Birmingham 1828, 3in (7.5cm), 4.5oz.
£500-550 *WW*

A George V vesta box, the hinged lid enamelled depicting the cover of *Punch* magazine, maker's mark H.J. Birmingham 1931, 4.5cm.
£600-700 *Bea*

A William IV snuff box, the lid engraved 'Love thy Friends with all their faults, None are Without Imperfections', Edward Smith, Birmingham 1836, 3in (7.5cm).
£150-200 *DN*

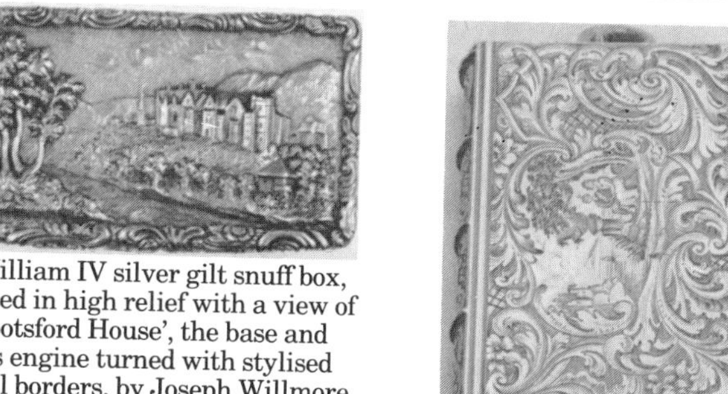

A William IV silver gilt snuff box, chased in high relief with a view of 'Abbotsford House', the base and sides engine turned with stylised scroll borders, by Joseph Willmore, Birmingham 1832, 8cm wide, 4.25oz.
£650-700 *P*

A Victorian book-shaped vinaigrette, Charles Rawlins and William Summers, London 1840, 4.5cm high.
£450-500 *DN*

A Victorian snuff box, with cross hatching, reeded sides and scroll chased borders, by W & R, Birmingham 1840, 2½in (6.5cm), 1.75oz.
£150-200 *DN*

A Victorian book-shaped vinaigrette, by Taylor & Perry, Birmingham 1847, 4cm.
£200-250 *DN*

An Austro-Hungarian silver gilt snuff box, the cover with a niello work panel of a carriage and horses, within a border of leaf scrolls, Johann Carl Klinckosch, Vienna 1855, 3in (8cm), 3.5oz.
£700-750 *DN*

A Victorian engraved bag-shaped vinaigrette, by H & T., Birmingham 1876, 2.5cm.
£200-250 *DN*

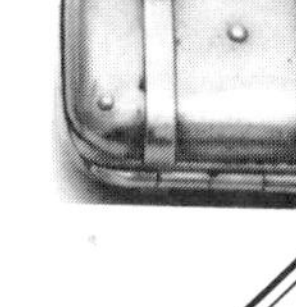

A Victorian portmanteau-shaped vinaigrette, by S. Mordan & Co., London, unmarked, 3cm.
£300-350 *DN*

An Austrian silver gilt box, profusely decorated in multi-coloured champlevé, c1880, 4in (10cm).
£650-700 *P*

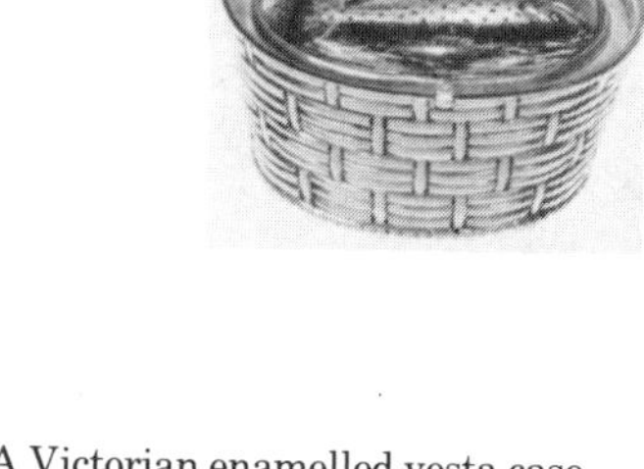

Victorian fisherman's creel vesta se, with name plate inscribed Taffin 1883', the interior with sex crystal depicting 2 trout laid t on the riverbank, chip to crystal, omas Johnson, 1882, 5.5cm.
,800-2,000 *P*

A Victorian enamelled vesta case, with snap cover, the front in white enamel, possibly by C. H. Cheshire, Birmingham 1887, 5cm long.
£250-300 *P*

A Victorian combined vesta case and tinder box, engine turned around a vacant oval cartouche, maker's mark HJ, Birmingham 1880.
£200-250 *P*

A Victorian table snuff box, flat chased with scrolling leaves, George Unite, Birmingham 1884, 3½in (9cm), 4oz.
£200-250 *DN*

A Victorian bell-shaped vesta cas with enamel panel of a floating bu on a calm sea, Birmingham 1893 4cm, 0.8oz.
£250-300 *Bea*

A cedar lined cigar box, with central cutter, tools and spirit light, London 1899.
£600-650 *BM*

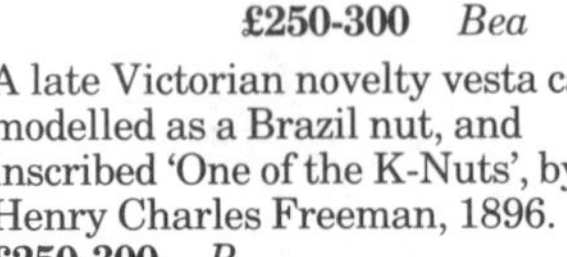

A late Victorian novelty vesta case, modelled as a Brazil nut, and inscribed 'One of the K-Nuts', by Henry Charles Freeman, 1896.
£250-300 *P*

A box with pierced and embosse lid, by William Comyns, Londor 1903, 6in (15cm), 4oz.
£200-250 *DN*

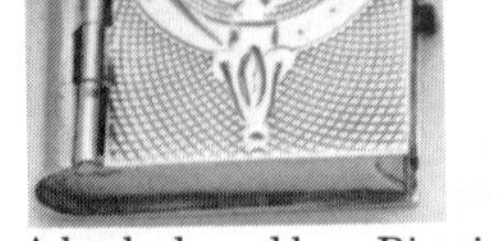

A book shaped box, Birmingham 1922, 3cm.
£50-70 *DN*

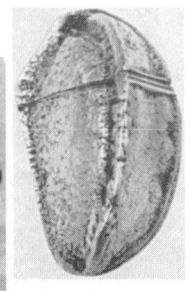

An Edwardian vesta case, enamelled on cover with 2 huntsmen and their pack, small chips to enamel, by George Randle, Birmingham 1901.
£300-350 *P*

A silver gilt and enamel cigarette case, the cover enamelled in black and white with an oval panel of putti with garlands of flowers in a landscape, with borders of leaf scrolls, .800 standard.
£300-350 *DN*

A mother-of-pearl and silver mounted box, the cover carved with a female bust beneath a canopy, trees, and animals, 7cm.
£150-200 *DN*

A silver snuff box, import marks, 4in (10cm), 6oz.
£200-230 *Bon*

A Russian cigarette case with hinged vesta compartment, an another compartment for a wic probably Dmitri Nikolaiev, Moscow, c1890.
£250-300 *P*

Candelabra

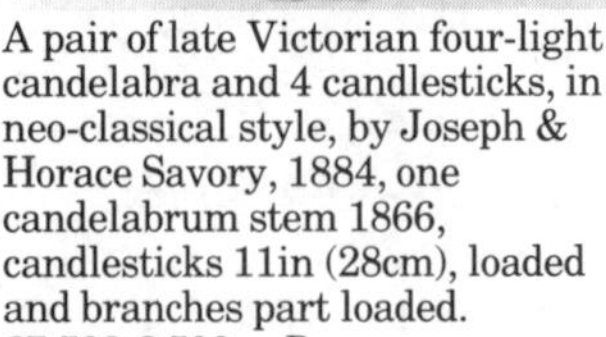

A pair of late Victorian four-light candelabra and 4 candlesticks, in neo-classical style, by Joseph & Horace Savory, 1884, one candelabrum stem 1866, candlesticks 11in (28cm), loaded and branches part loaded.
£7,500-8,500 *P*

A pair of German cast rococo styl seven-light candelabra, by J. D. Schleissner & Sons, Hanau, with Dutch import marks, c1895, 21½ (54cm), 234.5oz.
£3,500-4,500 *P*

A Victorian five-light candelabrum, engraved with a monogram, Robert Garrard, 1841, 30½in (77.5cm) high, 254oz.
£4,500-6,000 *C*

A pair of George V five-light candelabra, Sheffield 1915, loaded, 22½in (56.5cm).
£2,500-3,000 *HSS*

A pair of George I style two-light candelabra, Garrard & Co., London 1970.
£450-550 *P[Re]*

Candlesticks

A pair of Queen Anne cast candlesticks, Henry Lyon 1701, 5½in (14cm), 18oz.
£8,500-9,000 *P*

A William III cast taperstick, engraved with a crest, by Andrew Raven, 1701, 4in (10.5cm), 4.75oz.
£2,500-3,000 *P*

A pair of Queen Anne candlesticks, engraved with initials LMD and DL, by John Audry, Exeter 1704, 8in (20.5cm), 16oz 15dwt.
£4,000-5,000 *C*

A George II Scottish cast taperstick, by William Aytoun, Edinburgh 1739, 4½in (11.5cm), 4.25oz.
£1,200-1,500 *P*

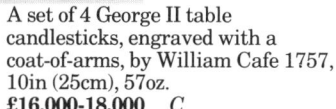

A set of 4 George II table candlesticks, engraved with a coat-of-arms, by William Cafe 1757, 10in (25cm), 57oz.
£16,000-18,000 *C*

A pair of Russian cast candlesticks, maker's mark apparently AFH or AIH in script, untraced, Assay Master Nikifor Moshshalkin, St. Petersburg, 1795, 8½in (21.5cm), 27oz.
£1,800-2,000 *P*

l. A George II silver taperstick, with detachable nozzle, knopped baluster column and shaped square base, by John Priest, London 1749, 5in (12.5cm), 5oz 3dwt.
£550-600

r. A George III silver taperstick, with gadrooned detachable nozzle, knopped column, spreading foot and square gadrooned base, by William Cafe, London 1763, 4½in (11.5cm), 5oz 15dwt.
£560-600 *DSH*

A set of 6 George III table candlesticks, with detachable nozzles, by J & T Settle, Sheffield 1817 and 1818, also struck with the maker's mark of Samuel Hennell, 12in (30.5cm).
£6,000-7,000 *C*

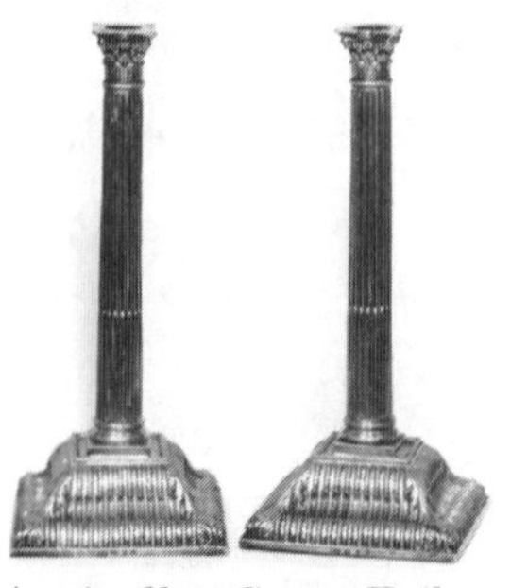

A pair of late George II silver classical column candlesticks, odd sconces, one damaged, maker W.A., 1759, weighted, 14in (35.5cm).
£2,000-2,500 *GSP*

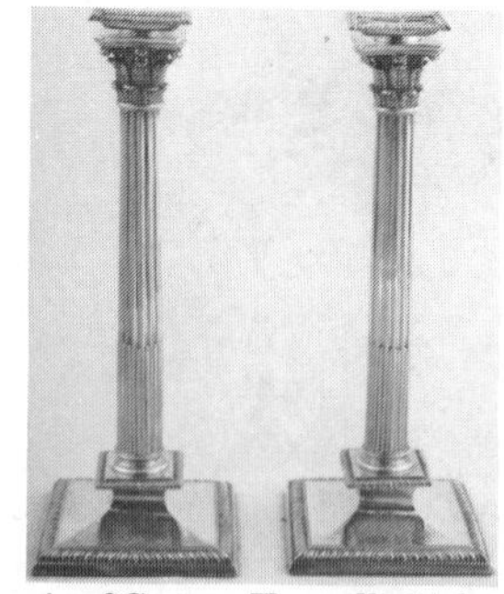

A pair of George II candlesticks, by John Robinson II, 1756 and 1766, 11½in (29cm).
£1,500-2,000 *DN*

A set of 4 George III cast candlesticks, by William Cafe, 1762, 10in (25cm), 84oz.
£5,000-5,500 *P*

A pair of George III cast candlesticks, with contemporary nozzles, engraved with a crest, by Ebenezer Coker, 1762, 42oz.
£3,000-3,500 *P*

A pair of George III table candlesticks, engraved with a crest, by Jonathan Alleine, 1777, 10½in (26cm), 56oz.
£4,500-5,500 *C*

A pair of George III candlesticks, with detachable sconces, engraved with crests, maker's mark I.P. & Co. (John Parsons & Co.), overstruck T.P.A.H., Sheffield 1783, 11in (28cm).
£900-1,200 *GC*

A set of 4 George IV cast candlesticks, with knopped columns, chased with birds and flowers and engraved initial H., one nozzle missing, by Hyam Hyams, London 1834, 6in (15cm), 52oz.
£2,500-3,000 *DN*

A pair of George III table candlesticks, one fractured at knop, makers George Ashforth & Co., Sheffield 1792, loaded, 11½in (29cm).
£1,100-1,500 *P[PWC]*

A pair of George IV table candlesticks, with detachable nozzles, chased overall with scrolls, shells and foliage, by S. C. Younge & Co., Sheffield 1821, 12in (30.5cm).
£2,000-2,500 *C*

A pair of George IV silver gilt candlesticks, with detachable nozzles, maker's mark perhaps of James Ellis & Co., Sheffield 1822, 12in (31cm).
£2,500-3,000 *C*

A pair of Portuguese candlesticks, maker's mark initials LARA in a monogram, Oporto, 1853, 10½in (27cm), loaded.
£700-750 *P*

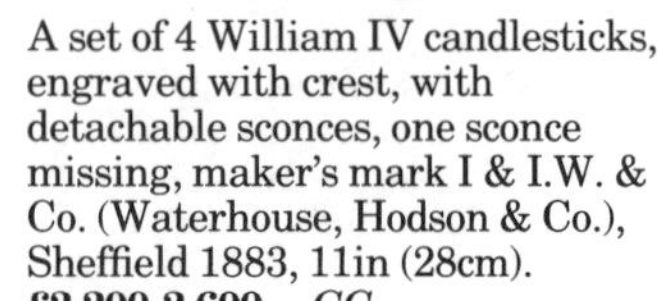

A set of 4 William IV candlesticks, engraved with crest, with detachable sconces, one sconce missing, maker's mark I & I.W. & Co. (Waterhouse, Hodson & Co.), Sheffield 1883, 11in (28cm).
£2,200-2,600 *GC*

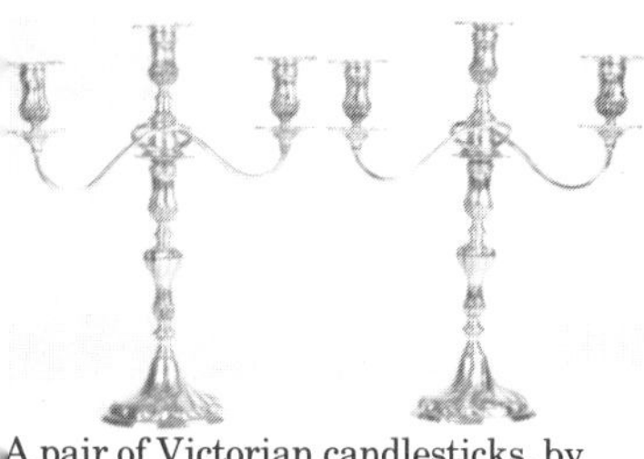
A pair of Victorian candlesticks, by Robert Garrard, 1844, with a pair of plated three-light branches to form candelabra, 12in (31cm), candlesticks 55oz.
£2,000-2,500 *C*

A set of 4 late Victorian candlesticks, in the neo-classical manner, by Hawksworth, Eyre & Co. Ltd., Sheffield 1894, 11½in (29cm), loaded.
£1,500-2,000 *P*

A Victorian heart shaped silver mounted tortoiseshell chamber candlestick, with fluted nozzle, gadrooned and pierced border, by William Comyns, London 1894, 5in (12.5cm).
£350-400 *DN*

A pair of Victorian table candlesticks, makers James Deakin & Sons, Sheffield 1898, loaded.
£800-1,000 *P[PWC]*

A pair of Edwardian candlesticks, T.A.S., Sheffield 1907, 7in (18cm).
£450-500 *CSK*

A pair of Corinthian column table candlesticks, Birmingham 1919, 8½in (21.5cm).
£400-500 *P[Re]*

A pair of late Victorian candlesticks, with detachable nozzles, by Charles Stuart Harris, London 1898, 11½in (29cm), weighted.
£850-900 *OT*

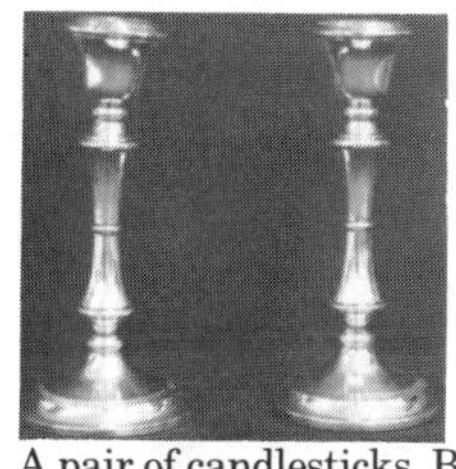
A pair of candlesticks, Birmingham 1920, 6½in (16.5cm).
£100-120 *PC*

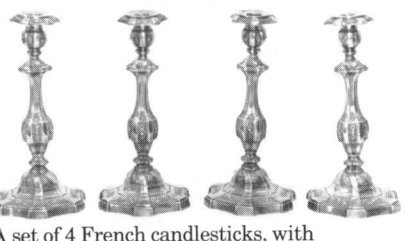

A set of 4 French candlesticks, with fluted panelled bodies and floral repousse decoration, on domed bases, all drilled for electricity, 59oz.
£1,400-1,600 *GSP*

Casters

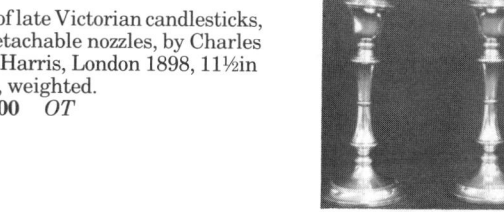

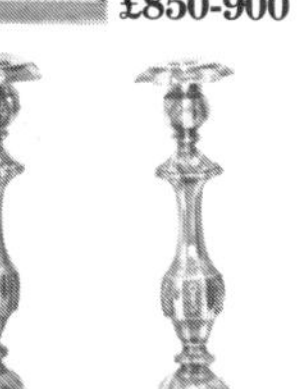
A set of 3 George I casters, engraved with a coat-of-arms in baroque cartouche, by Edward Vincent, 1716, largest 7½in (19cm), 27oz.
£7,000-8,000 *C*

A pair of George II casters, the pierced covers each with baluster finials, engraved with cyphers, by Thomas Bamford, 1728, 5in (13cm), 8oz.
£1,800-2,000 *CSK*

A pair of Dutch silver gilt casters, by Albert de Thomese, The Hague, 1733, chased later with scalework and scrolls and engraved with a coronet and cypher, 8in (20cm), 22oz.
£3,200-3,500 *C*

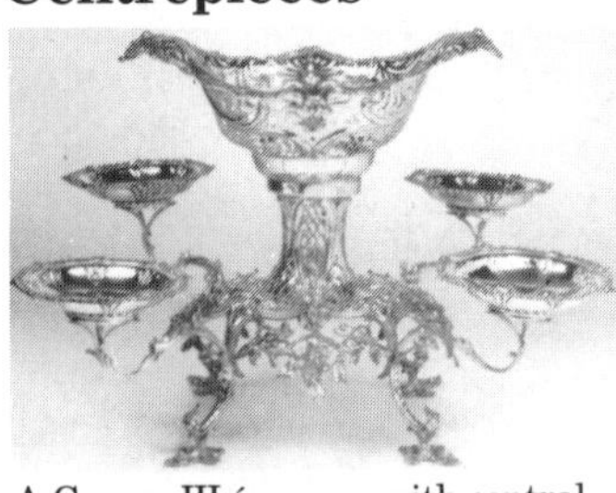

A pair of George II baluster casters, engraved with armorials, Jabez Daniell and James Mince, London 1759, 5½in (14cm), 6.3oz.
£400-500 *Bea*

A pair of George II sugar casters, engraved with armorials, by S. Wood, 1754, 6½in (17cm), 10.5oz.
£900-1,200 *P*

A George II Scottish caster, engraved with a crest and motto, by Charles Dickson, Edinburgh, 1744, the cover apparently unmarked, 5in (12.5cm), 5oz.
£450-500 *CSK*

Centrepieces

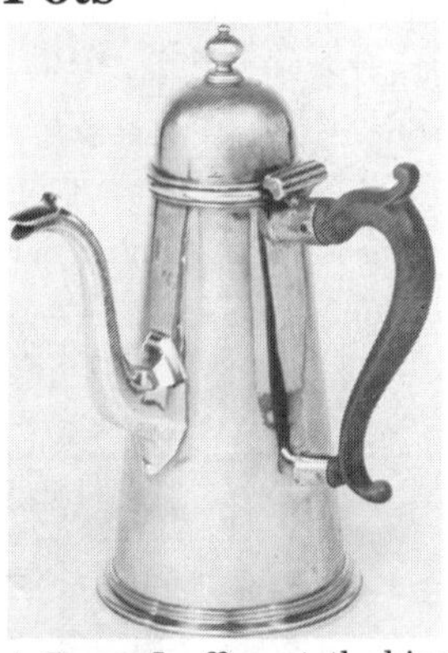

A George III épergne, with central oval basket pierced and chased, engraved with a crest, by Thomas Pitts 1766, the 4 branches unmarked, 98oz.
£9,000-10,000 *C*

A Victorian Imperial presentation centrepiece, engraved with initials and crown of Alexander II of Russia and with the inscription 'Ex Dono Imperatoris Russiae Alexandri II 1880', by Stephen Smith and William Nicholson 1856, on oval ebonised wood base, 11½in (29cm), 78oz.
£2,200-2,600 *C*

A Victorian six-light candelabrum centrepiece, engraved 'York, August Meeting 1847 Won by Mr. Gully's Mathematician 3yrs old', and with the names of the stewards by Charles Reily and George Store 1847, 24½in (62cm), 202oz.
£3,500-4,500 *C*

Coffee & Chocolate Pots

A George I coffee pot, the hinged domed cover with baluster finial, with wood scroll handle at right angles to the spout, by George Wickes, 1724, 9in (23cm), 22oz 10dwt gross.
£5,500-6,500 *C*

A Louis XV chocolate pot, with hinged flap to the moulded lip, the slightly raised cover with pivoting baluster finial and scroll thumbpiece, with baluster wood handle, by Jean Gouel, 1734, 10in (25cm), 840grammes without handle.
£3,600-4,000 *C*

A George II coffee pot, with domed hinged cover with turned finial, later foliate and scroll engraved decoration, London assay, marks rubbed, probably Richard Gosling entered 1739, 10in (25cm), 28oz gross.
£900-1,200 *P[Pea]*

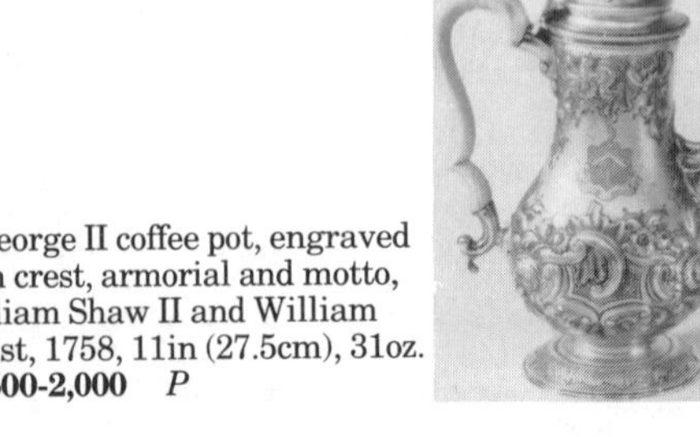

A George II coffee pot, engraved with crest, armorial and motto, William Shaw II and William Preist, 1758, 11in (27.5cm), 31oz.
£1,500-2,000 *P*

A George II coffee pot, with leaf capped scroll spout and hinged domed cover, chased with foliage and scrolls, by Daniel Piers, 1754 9in (23cm), 22oz gross.
£1,500-2,000 *C*

A George III coffee pot with engraved armorials, the domed lid with wrythen finial, wood handle, maker's mark rubbed, 1764, 25.5oz gross.
£1,500-2,000 *GSP*

A George III coffee pot, with polished wood double scroll handle and domed hinged cover with flower finial, Daniel Smith and Robert Sharp, London 1762, 11½in (29cm), 33.5oz gross.
£1,800-2,000 *CSK*

A George II coffee pot, with double scroll handle, Thomas Cooke and Richard Gurney, London 1752, 9in (23cm), 20.8oz gross.
£1,500-2,000 *Bea*

A George III chinoiserie coffee pot, T. Whipham and C. Wright, 1767, 12½in (31.5cm), 34oz.
£4,500-5,000 *N*

A George III coffee pot, with wood handle, the domed cover with fluted finial and on spreading foot, possibly John King, London 1778, 11in (28cm), 29.2oz gross.
£2,000-2,500 *Bea*

A George III pedestal coffee pot, with scroll handle, reeded borders and engraved with a band of wrigglework, with shaped finial, by Henry Chawner, initialled, London 1795, 10½in (26cm), 22oz.
£1,000-1,200 *P*

A George III cylindrical coffee biggin, stand and detachable lamp, the biggin with applied reeded bands, detachable domed cover and ball finial, by John Wakelin and Robert Garrard, 1798, 11in (28cm), 28oz.
£1,000-1,500 *C*

A William IV coffee pot on scroll feet, with simulated bark and oak leaf spout, hinged domed cover and later Victorian acorn and oak leaf finial, engraved with coats-of-arms, by Paul Storr, 1836, finial by J. S. Hunt, 9in (23cm), 32oz.
£2,500-3,000 *C*

An early Victorian coffee pot with rustic handle, on 4 fish mask supports, Joseph Wilson, London 1838, 36oz.
£500-550 *P[Pea]*

A Chinese export coffee pot, with dragon handle, dragon head finial, the body chased with elaborate battle scenes, on dragon mask and claw feet, the plain spout engraved with flowers and leafage, by Hung Chong of Canton and Shanghai, c1880, 8½in (22cm), 23.5oz.
£750-950 *P*

A Victorian coffee pot, probably William Cooper, London 1843, 10½in (27cm), 28.75oz.
£1,200-1,500 *CSK*

Cups

A Victorian coffee pot, E., E.J. & W. Barnard, London 1875, 11in (28cm), 27.8oz.
£450-500 *Bea*

A George I Irish two-handled cup, with harp shaped handles and moulded rim, engraved with a coat-of-arms within scrolling foliage cartouche, by Anthony Stanley, Dublin 1715, 9½in (24cm), 62oz.
£3,000-3,500 *C*

A Charles II plain cup, engraved with a coat-of-arms within plume mantling, the base with the name Henry Moore, MP, by Robert Williamson, York 1669, 3½in (9cm), 3oz 13dwt.
£3,000-3,500 *C*

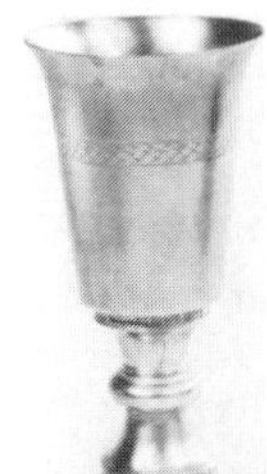

A Provincial ascribed communion cup, mark only for William Bayrheed (Barehead) of Durham, c1610, 8in (20cm), 10oz.
£2,000-2,500 *P*

A George I two-handled cup and cover, on circular foot with moulded girdle, leaf capped scroll handles and baluster finial engraved with crest and armorial, by Abraham Buteux, 1727, 13in (33cm), 98oz.
£4,500-5,500 *P*

A George III two-handled cup and cover, with entwined serpent handles and fluted cover with beaded bud finial, by Andrew Fogelberg and Stephen Gilbert, 1789, 18in (46cm), 104oz.
£4,000-5,000 *C*

A pair of George III goblets, inscribed and dated, Samuel and Edward Davenport, London 1796, 6in (15cm), 13.6oz.
£1,200-1,500 *Bea*

A pair of George III goblets, Charles Aldridge, London 1791, 7in (18cm), 14.8oz.
£1,200-1,500 *Bea*

A pair of George III wine goblets, by Story & Elliott, 1810, 6in (15cm), 26oz.
£1,500-2,000 *P*

A Victorian boar's head stirrup cup, by William Edwards, 1872, 4½in (11cm), 7.25oz.
£3,500-4,000 *P*

A Continental silver betrothal cup, in the form of Queen Elizabeth I wearing long robes, import marks for London 1881, possibly Dutch, 8in (20cm).
£350-400 *HSS*

A George III silver gilt fox mask stirrup cup, by Thomas Pitts, 1771, 5½in (14cm) long, 5oz 13dwt.
£3,000-3,500 *C*

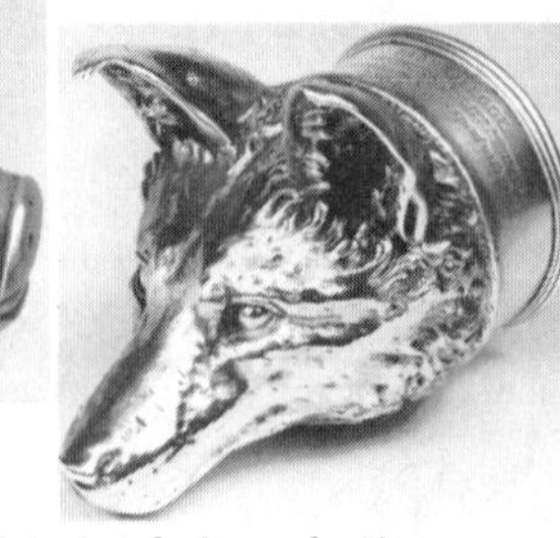

A Victorian fox's mask stirrup cup, engraved with the inscription 'Capt. Montague Legge To his Brother Officers 2nd. Batt. 1st Royals, in remembrance of 14 happy years spent with them, 1864', by John S. Hunt, 1850, 5in (12.5cm) long, 12oz 16dwt.
£2,000-2,500 *C*

A Victorian silver cup, by Robert Harper, London 1860, 5in (12.5cm), 6½oz.
£300-400 *P[PWC]*

An Australian goblet, engraved with a Greek key pattern border, on trumpet foot, inscribed 'Narracoorte Pastoral and Agricultural Society Show, 17th August 1882, Presented by H. Steiner, awarded to Mr. John Riddoch for the best 5 Merino Ewes', Adelaide, South Australia, c1880, 6½in (16.5cm), 5oz.
£800-900 *P*

A George IV silver gilt travelling wine cup, by John Riley, 1824, 4½in (11cm), 6oz.
£500-600 *P*

A Victorian commemorative goblet, engraved with a view of the St. Pancras Baths and Wash Houses, and inscribed 'St. Pancras – Presented to Mr. James Hoppey Commissioner for Public Baths and Wash Houses for St. Pancras to commemorate the laying of the first stone of the Baths and Wash Houses, Tottenham Court Road, May 8th, 1877', by D. & C. Hands, 1876, 6in (15.5cm), 5.75oz.
£600-700 *P*

A two-handled loving cup, Sheffield 1902, 6in (15cm), 30.5oz.
£250-300 *PC*

An Australian cup and cover, with horse finial, inscribed 'Mount Shank Cup presented by Capt. Gardiner to the Mount Gambier Turf Club, won by Mr. G. Riddoch's 'Mystery', January Meeting, 1875', by J. M. Wendt, Adelaide, South Australia, c1875, 13½in (34.5cm), 24.5oz.
£1,700-2,000 *P*

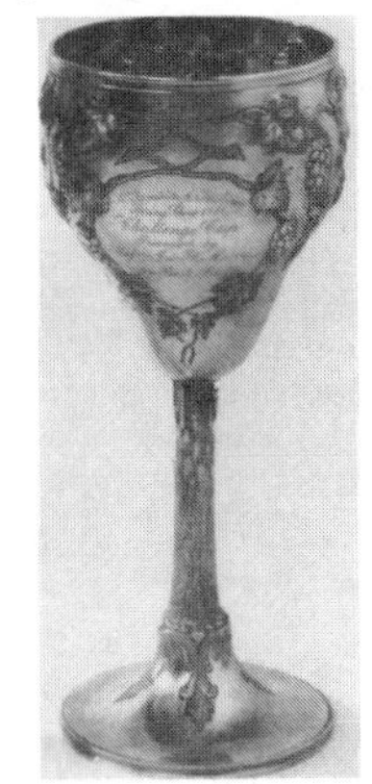

An Australian trophy cup, embossed with fruiting vines and standing on a simulated tree trunk support terminating in a trumpet foot, inscribed, by J. M. Wendt, Adelaide, South Australia, c1880, 9½in (24cm), 6.75oz.
£750-800 *P*

Cutlery

A Dutch silver gilt Apostle spoon, with faceted stem and fig shaped bowl, Alkmaar, probably 1652.
£700-800 *P*

A William and Mary spoon-cum-fork, engraved on both sides with foliate scroll plumage, maker's mark only partly struck on stem, I or HH with pillar between, probably London, c1690, 6in (15cm).
£450-500 *P*

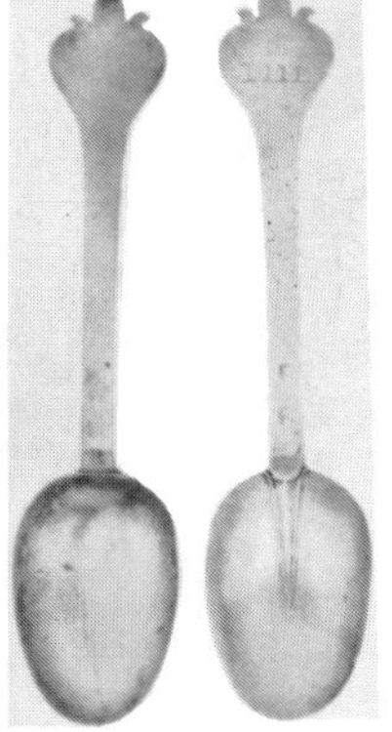

A pair of unascribed Channel Islands trefid spoons, the oval bowls with ribbed rat-tails, maker's mark I.T. in distinctly shaped cartouche punch, probably Guernsey, and prick dot initialled '$^{\text{M}}_{\text{ILM}}$', c1710.
£200-300 *P*

An Apostle spoon, with gilded finial, the bowl pricked with INNR 1661, and bearing an unascribed provincial spoked wheel and dot mark, c1640.
£300-350 *DN*

A George IV silver punch ladle, with silver mounted turned whalebone handle, London 1828. ▶
£100-120 *TVA*

A Victorian spatula-cum-spoon, with wide stem, by T. Johnson, 1856.
£150-200 *P*

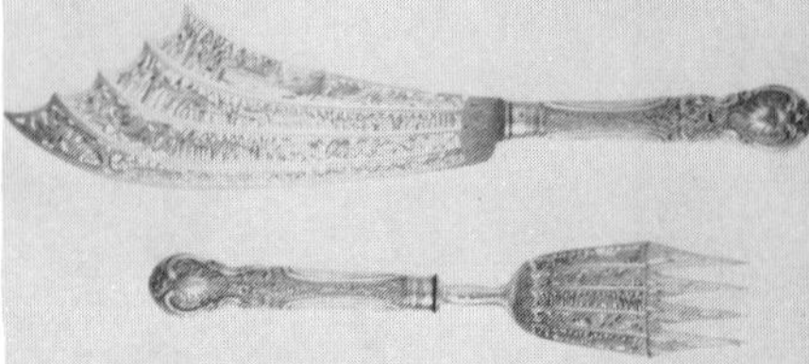

A pair of Victorian fish carvers, pierced and engraved with an underwater scene, by George Adams, 1856, the knife 14½in (37cm), in a fitted velvet lined leather case.
£1,000-1,200 *P*

A Victorian 6 piece fruit set, comprising a sifter spoon, ladle, and 4 serving spoons, makers Lias & Lias, London 1870, 11oz, the case labelled Carrington, Regent St.
£250-300 *P[Pea]*

A Victorian fish slice and fork, the handles cast as Bacchante, the slice with pierced and chased blade depicting a nymph astride a sea monster, indistinct maker's mark, London 1864, slice 14in (35.5cm), 16oz.
£900-1,200 *CNY*

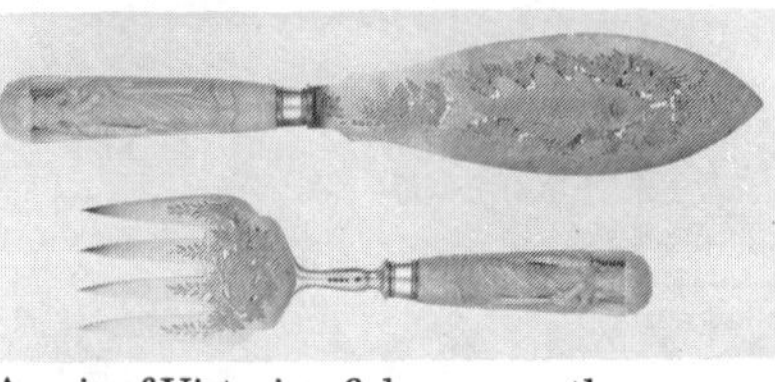

A pair of Victorian fish carvers, the unusual handles of ivory and finely carved in the neo-Gothic style with a full figure of a draped woman within an alcove, by George Adams, 1868, in a fitted and lined case.
£650-700 *P*

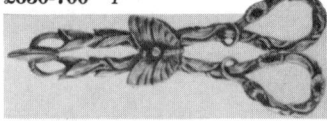

A pair of George III Irish sugar nips, with scroll decorated arms and floral engraved pivot, maker's mark rubbed, Dublin c1770.
£150-200 *P*

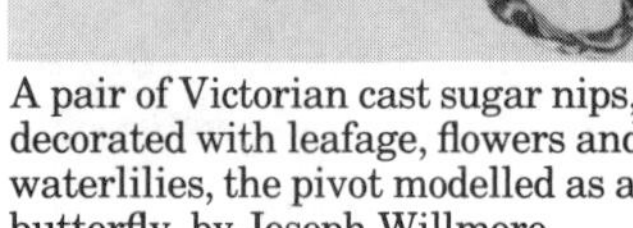

A pair of Victorian cast sugar nips, decorated with leafage, flowers and waterlilies, the pivot modelled as a butterfly, by Joseph Willmore, Birmingham, 1840, 2.25oz.
£200-250 *P*

A pair of Victorian cast sugar nips, the handles modelled as swans, the finger loops as serpents entwined round the birds' necks, the grips cast and chased in the form of lily pads, Francis Higgins, London 1853.
£400-500 *CSK*

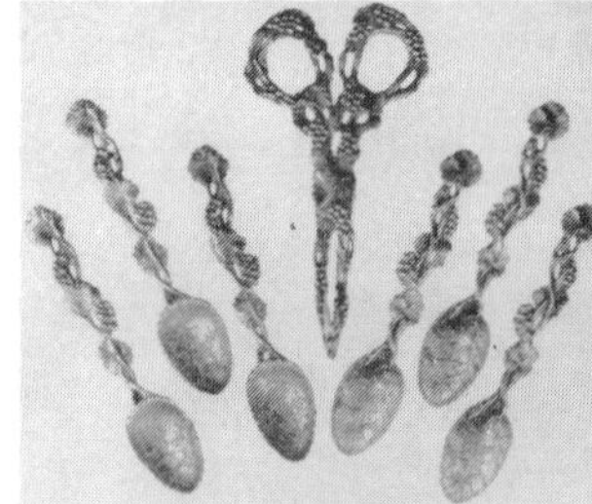

A matching set of 12 George IV teaspoons, and a pair of similar sugar nips, by Edward Farrell, c1826, 14oz, in fitted lined case.
£600-700 *P*

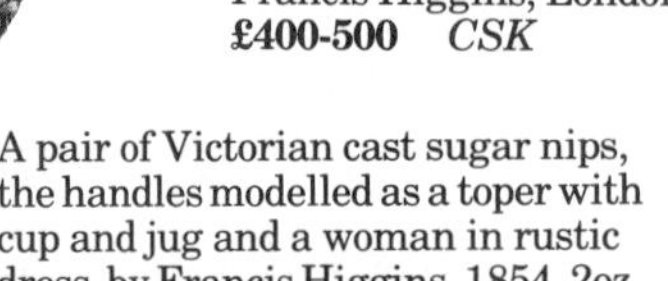

A pair of Victorian cast sugar nips, the handles modelled as a toper with cup and jug and a woman in rustic dress, by Francis Higgins, 1854, 2oz.
£250-300 *P*

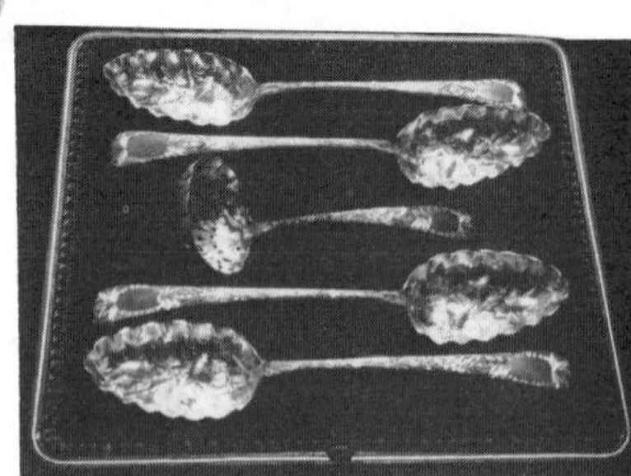

A set of 5 Regency silver gilt dessert spoons, the fluted bowls embossed and engraved, London marks for 1827, maker's marks JTH.JHM, 7oz 5dwt, in original case.
£230-260 *BOW*

A pair of Victorian novelty sugar nips, modelled as an outstretched monkey, by Albert William Barker, 1886, 2.5oz.
£300-350 *P*

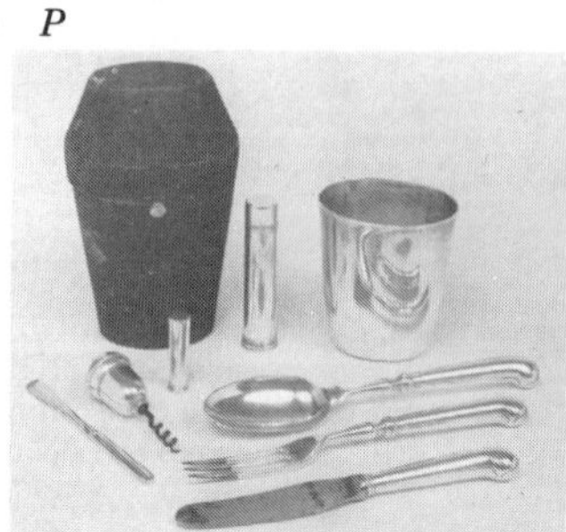

A travelling canteen, by Benjamin Pyne, 1722, unmarked, 12oz 11dwt gross, without knife blade, in fitted shagreen case.
£1,500-2,000 *C*

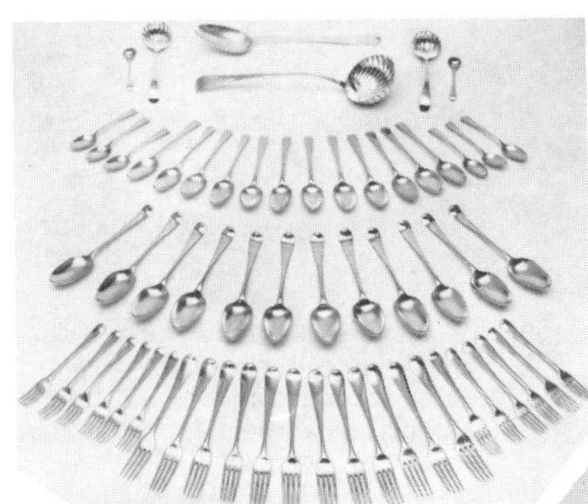

A Georgian Old English table service comprising 66 pieces, variously marked, London 1746-1810, 99.25oz, in mahogany case.
£2,000-3,000 *P[PWC]*

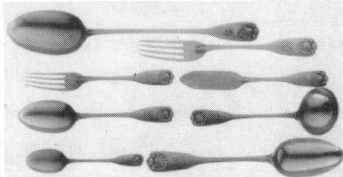

A Victorian Fiddle and Shell pattern part table service, comprising 64 pieces, London 1895, 136oz.
£1,500-2,000 *Bea*

A Victorian Queen's pattern table service, comprising 110 pieces, by George Adams, c1870, and 2 sauce ladles by Lias Bros, 1872, and a soup ladle, 1902, maker's mark M. Bros, 284oz.
£8,000-9,000 *C*

A Princess pattern table service, with engraved monograms, comprising 126 pieces, the table forks and salt spoons by George Adams, 1873, the remainder by Henry Holland, 1872, 267oz without fish slice and fork.
£8,000-9,000 *C*

An Old English Thread pattern table service, comprising 154 pieces, the table and cheese knives with steel blades, by C. J. Vander, modern, 216oz.
£6,000-7,000 *CSK*

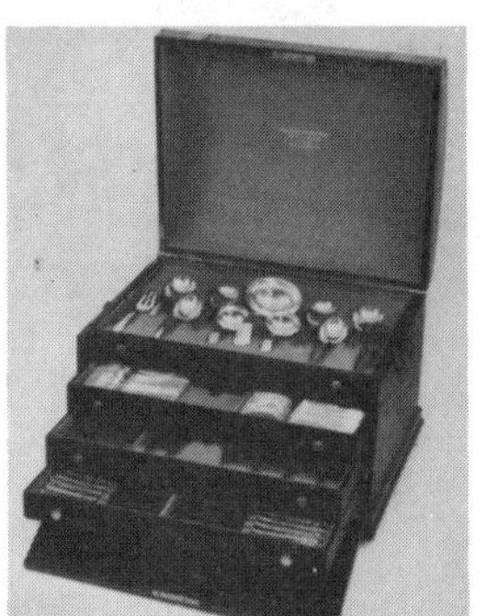

A canteen of cutlery, comprising 145 pieces, stamped for Begeer and hallmarks for Utrecht 1928.
£6,000-7,000 *CAm*

Spoons – Caddy

A caddy spoon, with hammered fig shaped bowl and stylised flower handle, set at the centre with a cornelian boss, Omar Ramsden, 1921.
£400-450 *P*

Dishes

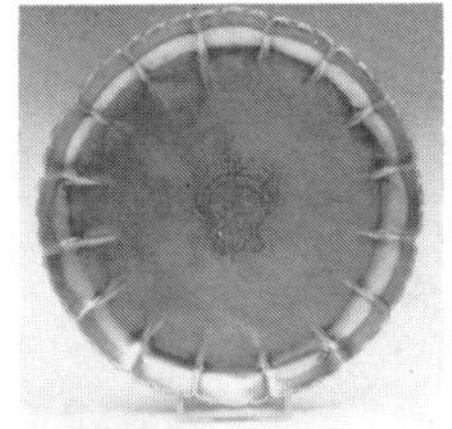

A George I strawberry dish, engraved with an armorial and with raised fluted sides, John Sanders I, London 1719, 6½in (16.5cm) diam, 7.9oz.
£3,500-4,000 *Bea*

A set of 4 George II cast shell butter dishes, engraved with leafy scroll oval cartouches, crested, no maker's mark, 1729, 22.5oz.
£3,200-3,500 *P*

Twelve George II shaped dinner plates, with gadrooned borders, engraved with 2 coats-of-arms, one later, by Edward Wakelin, 1749, 9½in (24.5cm), 212oz.
£9,000-10,000 *C*

A pair of George III silver soup plates, with later engraved coats-of-arms, and motto 'Recte et suaviter', by Paul Storr, London 1808, 38oz 11dwt.
£900-1,000 *DSH*

A George II meat dish, one side engraved with an armorial and motto, the other with a crest and different motto, Edward Wakelin, London 1754, 66.25oz.
£2,000-2,500 *CSK*

Did you know

MILLER'S Antiques Price Guide builds up year by year to form the most comprehensive photo-reference system available.

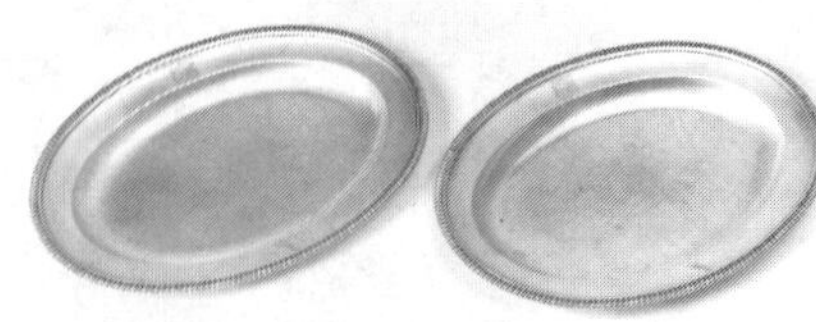

A set of 3 George III meat dishes, 2 with initials on undersides, William Bennett, London 1807, 13in (33cm), 67oz.
£1,500-2,000 *WW*

A George III meat dish, engraved with armorials and a similar cover with leaf scroll handle, London 1818, the dish by Paul Storr, 16½in (40.5cm), the cover by Philip Rundell, 14in (35.5cm), 115oz.
£4,500-5,500 *DN*

A Victorian breakfast turnover dish and 2 liners, the revolving cover monogrammed and reeded, on 4 tapering paw feet, London 1890, 14½in (35.5cm) wide, 106.9oz.
£1,500-2,000 *Bea*

A William IV meat dish, engraved with a coat-of-arms, crests and Earl's coronet, by Paul Storr, 1836, and a matching Old Sheffield Plate meat dish cover with detachable scroll handle, similarly engraved, by Waterhouse, Hatfield & Co., c1836, dish 25in (63.5cm) wide, 134oz.
£4,500-5,500 *C*

A set of 3 Victorian dishes, engraved with armorials, by Robert Garrard, London 1874, and inscribed Garrards, Panton Street, London, 10in (25cm), 64oz.
£700-750 *DN*

A suite of one large and 2 smaller dishes on stands, with triform winged mask and paw supports, hung with fruiting floral festoons, the bowls with beaded rims and applied medallions, by Mappin & Webb, London 1919, the larger 11in (28cm) diam, 71oz.
£1,200-1,500 *P*

An entree dish, with divider and detachable handle, Birmingham 1924, 54oz.
£550-600 *PC*

A pair of fluted hot water dishes, 7½in (19cm).
£300-350 *DN*

A bonbonnière, the sides chased with leaves and husk swags, the domed pull-off cover similarly chased, and with bud finial, Birmingham 1936, 8in (20.5cm) high, 11oz.
£250-350 *Bon*

A paua shell bon-bon dish, supported by silver and silver gilt cherub figure, London 1984, 6in (15cm).
£100-120 *PC*

A German parcel gilt sideboard dish, with detachable pierced floral handles, by Erhard (I) or Isaak Warnberger, Augsburg, c1680, 27in (68cm) wide, 48.5oz.
£4,500-5,500 *P*

Inkstands

A George III inkstand, with claw-and-ball feet, fitted with 2 pierced, beaded and bright cut mounts, each containing a cut glass inkwell, the central reeded wafer box with a detachable reeded and beaded taper stick with vase shaped socket, William Plummer, London 1774, 7in (18cm) wide, 9.75oz.
£800-900 *CSK*

A George III inkstand, modelled as a cube with 2 pull-out drawers, the lower one with integral pounce compartment, the hinged cover opening to reveal a glass inkwell, by Phipps & Robinson, 1787, 13.75oz.
£2,500-3,000 *P*

A George III Provincial inkstand, with 2 silver mounted cut glass inkwells, each with hinged covers, the covers each engraved with a monogram, by R. Cattle and J. Barber, York 1807, 11in (28cm) wide, 32oz.
£1,400-1,700 *C*

A late Victorian inkstand, the 2 cut glass wells with flat hinged covers with gadroon and shell borders, London 1891, 8½in (21.5cm) wide, 11.5oz.
£350-450 *Bon*

A skull and crossbones inkwell, on slate base, H.M. Edinburgh, 1859, 4½in (11.5cm) high.
£1,200-1,500 *SWO*

An Edwardian inkstand, with 2 cut glass inkwells with hinged covers, Henry Lambert, London 1903, 11in (28cm), 23.75oz.
£850-950 *CSK*

A George IV inkstand, probably Joseph Angell, the inkstand with indistinct maker's mark, London 1828 and 1829, stand 10in (25cm), 30oz.
£1,500-1,700 *CSK*

Jugs

A Queen Anne hot water jug, with scrolled thumbpiece, slightly domed cover, scrolled handle and flanged foot, London 1707, 23oz.
£1,200-1,500 *DSH*

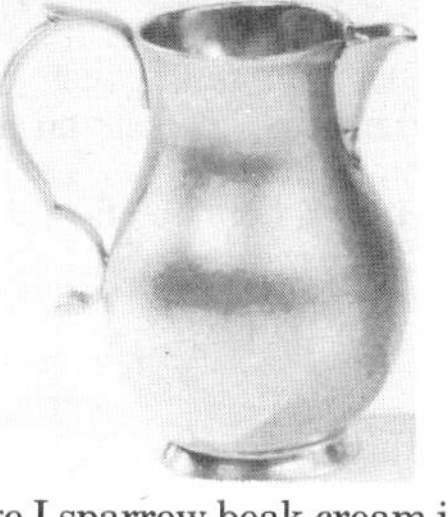

A George I sparrow beak cream jug, on a sloping collet foot, with scroll handle, by William Paradise, 1724, 3in (8cm), 2.5oz.
£800-900 *P*

A George II cream jug, monogrammed, with double scroll handle, Benjamin Sanders, London 1737, 3½in (9cm), 4.3oz.
£500-600 *Bea*

A George II bombé cream jug, the scroll handle with caryatid female head, by John Pollock, 4½in (11cm), 5oz.
£450-500 *P*

A George II cream jug, in rocaille manner, the handle with an entwined snake, its head forming the thumbpiece, gilt interior, by Peter Werritzer, 1756, 4½in (12cm), 5oz.
£1,500-1,700 *P*

A George III helmet shaped milk jug, by BM, probably Benjamin Mordecai or Benjamin Mountigue, London 1790, 6in (15cm), 3.75oz.
£250-300 *DN*

A George III hot water jug, the domed cover with acorn finial, engraved with armorial within foliate swags, by Daniel Smith & Robert Sharp, 1773, 12in (30cm), 32.5oz.
£1,500-1,700 *P*

A George III milk jug, by R. & S. Hennell, 1802, 6in (15cm) long, 5.75oz.
£250-300 *P*

A George III cream jug, monogrammed, Samuel and Edward Davenport, London 1808, 5in (12.5cm), 3.9oz.
£250-300 *Bea*

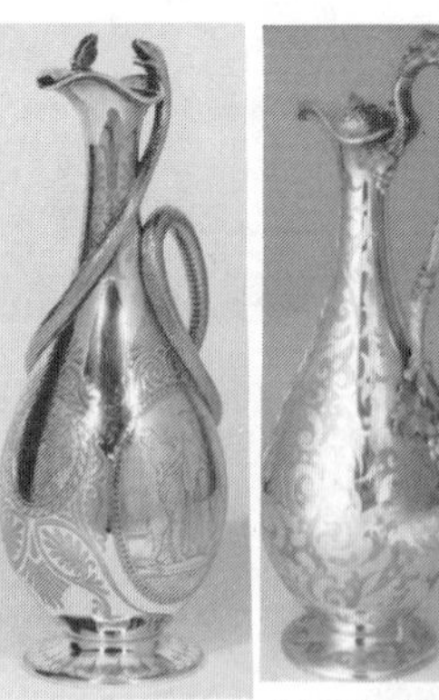

A Victorian claret jug, with hatched scroll work, by E. & J. Barnard, c1857, 14½in (37cm), 24.25oz.
£1,000-1,200 *DN*

A Victorian claret jug, the lid with a butterfly finial, the handle formed by a coiled snake, engraved with coat-of-arms and motto 'Industria et Probitate', by E. & J. Barnard, London 1855, and registration mark, 13½in (34cm), 27oz 13dwt.
£1,500-2,000 *DSH*

A Victorian jug and domed cover, with ivory pineapple knob, the handle with linen fold decoration, by George Fox, London 1875, 11in (28cm), 23oz gross.
£800-1,000 *DN*

A Victorian silver mounted glass claret jug, by W. & G. Sissons, Sheffield 1875, 10½in (26cm), in fitted oak case.
£1,200-1,600 *DN*

A Victorian spiral reeded jug with domed cover and finial, with ebonised handle, beaded and scroll spout and round foot, by Charles Stuart Harris, London 1880, 9in (23cm) 14oz gross.
£160-200 *DN*

A Victorian trophy flagon, the hinged cover surmounted by a cast finial representing a hound biting and grasping a fox, decorative cast lip and silver handle, by James Barclay Hennell, 1881, 13in (33cm), 69oz.
£3,000-4,000 *P*

The inscription reads: 'Maraquin, Winner of the West of Scotland Grand National Open Hunters Steeple Chase Ridden by Captn Smith, April 1881', and engraved with armorials.

A late Victorian glass claret jug, with silver mount to the rim, chased with a cartouche panel engraved with a monogram, flanked by foliage, the slightly domed hinged cover with pierced thumbpiece, inverted S-scroll handle, by W. & G. Sissons, Sheffield 1886, 11in (28cm).
£800-1,000 *HSS*

A Continental ewer and basin, the ewer with duck's head spout, hinged cover, shell thumbpiece and foliage finial, the basin with gadrooned rim, each bearing Paris marks for 1708-9, ewer 9½in (24cm), 2,053 grammes.
£15,000-17,000 *C*

A Spanish jug, with grotesque mask spout and reeded rim, the base engraved with a later crest, Medina del Campo, late 16thC, 6½in (16cm), 685 grammes.
£23,000-25,000 *C*

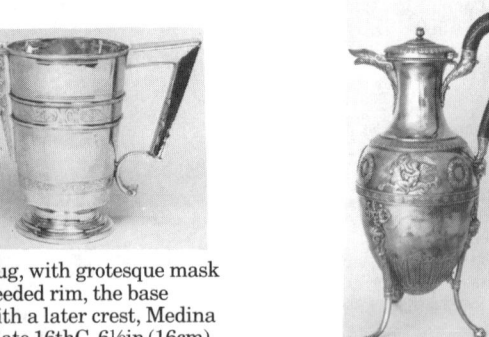

A French Empire silver gilt ewer, by Martin-Guillaume, Biennais.
£28,000-32,000 *DN*

A French ewer and basin, the basin with anthemion border and applied masks at either side, both by different makers, Paris, c1800, ewer 14½in (36.5cm), 68.75oz.
£2,700-3,000 *P*

Mugs and Tankards

A William and Mary tankard, with hollow handle, engraved with a later crest, by R. Timbrell, 1690, 6½in (17cm), 22oz.
£3,000-3,500 *P*

A George III tankard, small repairs, by William Caldecott, London 1759, 7½in (19cm), 25oz.
£1,500-2,000 *DN*

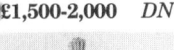

A George III tankard, by Solomon Hougham, 1792, 7½in (19cm), 27oz.
£1,500-1,700 *C*

A Victorian embossed presentation tankard, with rose pattern panels, London 1861, 4½in (11cm), 6.5oz.
£180-220 *PC*

An Edwardian waisted shaving mug, with a bracket handle, engraved with initials A.M.B., Birmingham 1904, 4in (10cm).
£200-250 *CSK*

A George I Britannia Standard tankard, maker I.S, hallmarked London 1719, 6in (15cm), 21oz.
£1,600-2,000 *HOD*

A George II tankard, inscribed and engraved with armorials, by William Soame, 1758, 10½in (26cm), 44.5oz.
£4,000-4,500 *P*

A George III tankard, with angular scrolled handle, maker's mark W.S., London 1819, 2½in (7cm), 3oz.
£120-150 *P[PWC]*

A Victorian christening mug, Chester 1898.
£100-150 *TVA*

A George II tankard, by John Langlands, Newcastle 1759, 5in (12.5cm), 11oz.
£450-500 *P[PWC]*

A George III tankard, initialled, the domed cover with scroll thumbpiece, William and James Priest, London 1772, 7in (18cm), 19.6oz.
£1,500-2,000 *Bea*

A pair of George III christening mugs, each with gadroon base and applied shell and anthemion band, cast leaf handles and raised on pedestal feet, by Emes and Barnard, London 1813, 4½in (11cm), 13oz.
£700-750 *OT*

A German parcel gilt tankard, the matted sides imitating shagreen, with C-scroll handle and double scroll thumbpiece, maker's mark QR (untraced), apparently Frankfurt-on-Main, c1680, 5½in (13.5cm), 16.75oz.
£4,000-4,500 *P*

A Scandinavian peg tankard, on fruit and foliage ball feet, the scroll handle with fruit and foliage thumbpiece, the hinged cover with Chiron and Achilles within guilloche border, maker's mark indistinct, probably 19thC, 8in (20.5cm), 1,295 grammes.
£2,500-3,000 *C*

A Norwegian peg tankard, the handle with eagle thumbpiece, the cover set with coins, by Anders Nielsen Borg, Trondheim, probably 1723, 6½in (16cm), 15.5oz.
£6,000-7,000 *P*

A Norwegian peg tankard, the stepped domed cover inset with a gilt coin of Christian VI dated 173 the barrel hinge surmounted by a cast crowned lion supporting a ball with beaded scroll handle, one foot damaged, by Peter Gabriel Aamunosen, Peter Michael Blyth (Warden), Bergen 1815, a 19thC reproduction of an 18thC style, 6½i (16cm), 12oz.
£1,200-1,500 *P*

Salts

A set of 4 George III two-handled boat-shaped salts, on pedestal bases, with gilt interiors, engraved with a crest, by William Fountain, 1778, 6in (15cm) wide, 17.5oz.
£800-900 *P*

Six George III salt cellars, each with reeded rim, 4 engraved with a crest, by Robert and Thomas Makepeace, 1794, 3½in (8cm) diam, 26oz.
£1,500-2,000 *CSK*

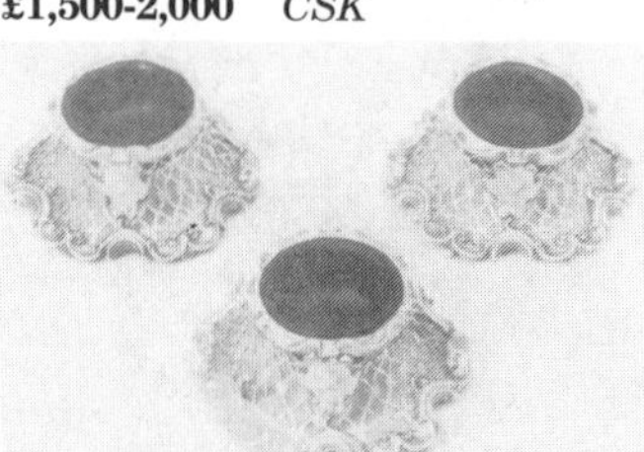

A set of 6 early Victorian salts, with blue glass liners, Charles Fox, London 1840, 24oz.
£1,000-1,200 *WW*

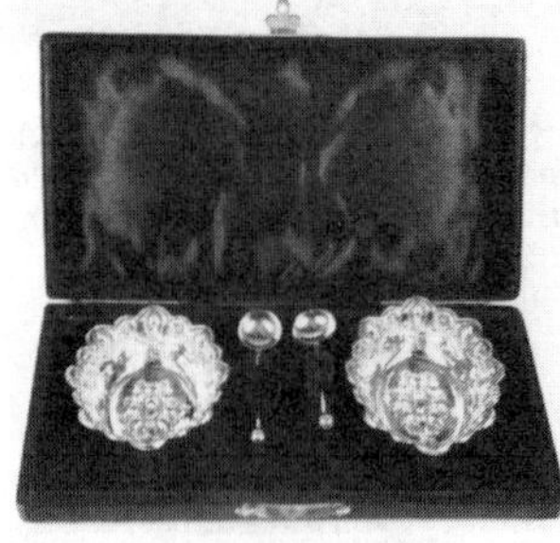

A pair of Victorian embossed salts and spoons, Birmingham 1900.
£100-120 *TVA*

A set of 4 George III salts, by Thos Robins, London 1819, 3in (7cm) diam, 18oz.
£450-500 *HCH*

A set of 4 Victorian salts, with white glass liners, apparently J. C. Eddington, 1849, 12oz.
£300-400 *P*

Salvers

A George II Scottish salver, with 3 hoof feet, scroll and foliage border, the ground chased with a similar band, by Robert Lowe, Edinburgh 1751, 9in (23cm), 16oz 7dwt.
£450-500 *C*

A pair of early George III salvers, by Richard Rugg, 1767, 7in (18cm), 23.5oz.
£1,200-1,500 *P*

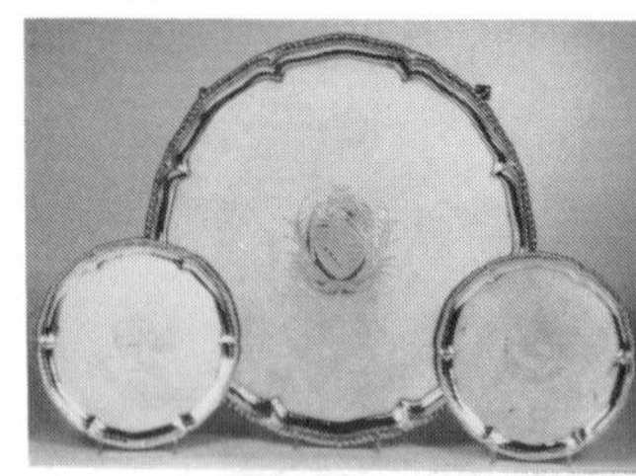

A George III salver, and a pair of matching smaller salvers, all engraved with the same coat-of-arms, by John Carter, 1772, the larger 14in (35.5cm), 65oz.
£3,500-4,000 *C*

A pair of early George III salvers, with claw-and-ball feet, engraved with armorials, maker's mark E. Pellet C., London 1767-8, 8in (20.5cm), 26oz.
£1,500-2,000 *P[PWC]*

A George III salver, with raised beaded border, on 4 claw-and-ball feet, maker possibly John Crouch, London 1772, 14½in (36.5cm), 44oz.
£650-750 *HCH*

A George III card tray, with shell and beaded border, on 3 claw-and-ball feet, engraved monogram to centre, by Robert Jones and John Schofield, London 1775, 6in (15cm), 7oz.
£300-350 *Bon*

A George III salver, with contemporary engraving of a coat-of-arms, maker's mark I.S. (John Schofield), London 1779, 12in (30.5cm), 28oz 2dwt.
£1,200-1,500 *GC*

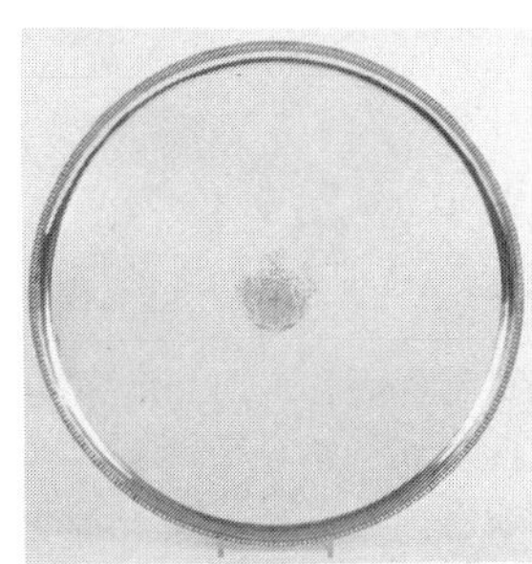
A George III salver, engraved with a coat-of-arms in a flower and scroll cartouche, by John Hutson, 1788, 18in (46cm), 68oz.
£4,000-4,500 *C*

A Victorian salver, on 4 cast scroll feet, by the Barnards, 1873, 16½in (41cm), 57oz.
£1,500-2,000 *P*

A silver salver, London 1876, 25oz.
£450-500 *BM*

A late Victorian dish, engraved Gilbert Marks 1900, 15in (38cm), 30oz.
£2,000-2,500 *C*

A salver with applied vine border, on 3 leaf chased and scroll pierced bracket feet, James Dixon & Sons, Sheffield 1900, 12½in (31.5cm), 31oz.
£500-550 *Bon*

An Edwardian beaded salver, on openwork legs, the border pierced with Gothic arches and cast with rams' masks and drapery swags, with a plain ground, William Comyns, London 1910, 11½in (29cm), 33.5oz.
£550-650 *CSK*

Sauceboats

A pair of George III cast sauceboats, with applied laurel leaf festooning and flowerhead tassies, on pedestal bases and with laurel frieze and gadroon borders, engraved with a crest, by John Parker and Edward Wakelin, 1769, 10in (25cm) wide, 47.5oz.
£7,000-8,000 *P*

A George III mustard pot, with hinged cover, acorn finial and reeded scroll handle, engraved with a crest with blue glass liner, by John Wakelin and William Taylor, 1786, 7oz.
£800-900 *CSK*

A George III mustard pot, engraved with reeded bands, with blue glass liner, by Robert and David Hennell, 1779, 4oz.
£500-600 *CSK*

A pair of Victorian sauceboats, with leaf capped scroll handles and quatrefoil and scroll borders, by Robert Garrard, 1853, 8in (20.5cm), 43oz.
£3,500-4,000 *C*

A pair of George II style sauceboats and ladles, the sauceboats on moulded feet with scroll handles, with reeded and shell rims, chased with scrolls, latticework and rocaille ornament, the ladles cast with fruits, foliage and scalework and with shell bowls, by D. & J. Welby, 1959 and 1960, 8in (20.5cm), 41oz.
£2,000-2,500 *C*

Scent Bottles

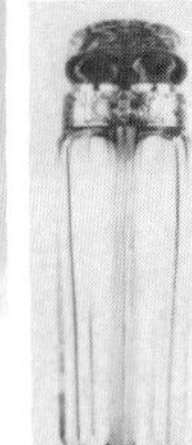

A Victorian clear glass scent bottle, the silver gilt double stoppers engraved with scrolling foliage, S. Mordan & Co., and inscribed 1st Sept. 1858, 4in (10cm).
£250-300 *Bon*

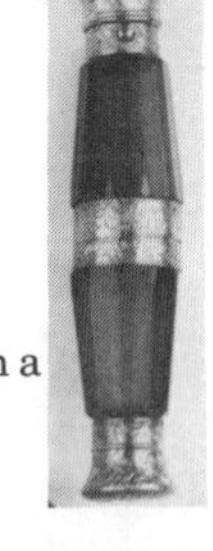

A Victorian silver gilt and blue glass scent bottle, the centre with a hinged vinaigrette, the stoppers engraved with scrolling foliage, S. Mordan & Co., 5in (13cm).
£200-250 *Bon*

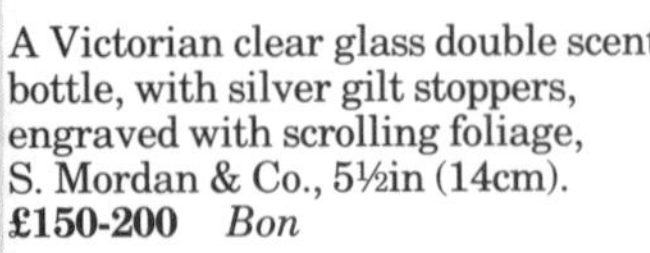

A Victorian clear glass double scent bottle, with silver gilt stoppers, engraved with scrolling foliage, S. Mordan & Co., 5½in (14cm).
£150-200 *Bon*

A Victorian overlay blue glass scent bottle, applied with gilt mounts and stopper, enamelled in champlevé technique, with blue beading and scrolling foliage, and set with a carnelian finial, 4in (10cm).
£150-200 *Bon*

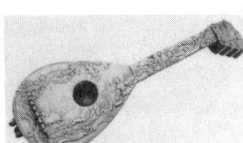

A Victorian silver gilt scent bottle, with engraved decoration depicting children playing in a meadow, S. Mordan & Co., London 1888, 2in (5cm), in fitted case.
£250-300 *Bea*

A Victorian ruby glass scent bottle, the body with canted corners, the base fitted with a vinaigrette, plain silver gilt mounts, S. Mordan & Co., London 1876, 3½in (9.5cm).
£300-350 *Bon*

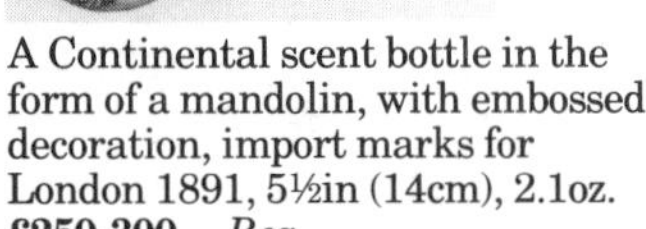

A Continental scent bottle in the form of a mandolin, with embossed decoration, import marks for London 1891, 5½in (14cm), 2.1oz.
£250-300 *Bea*

Services

A George III tea service, comprising a teapot with later scroll handle, a teapot stand on 4 fluted scroll feet, a sugar basin and a cream jug, by Peter, Ann and William Bateman, 1801 and 1802, teapot 7in (18cm) high, 41oz.
£1,800-2,200 *C*

A George III Scottish three-piece tea service, on ball feet, J. McKay, Edinburgh 1809, 42oz.
£900-1,000 *DN*

A Georgian matched tea and coffee service, the milk jug and sugar basin with snake handles, the teapot and hot water jug with wood handles, various makers and dates, 1810-1823, 97.5oz, in a fitted wooden chest.
£2,000-2,500 *Bea*

A Regency three-piece tea service, the milk jug and sugar basin with gilt interiors, Joseph Angell, London 1818, 39oz gross.
£800-1,000 *WW*

A George IV tea and coffee service comprising a coffee pot and teapot with domed hinged covers and flower finials, a sugar basin and a cream jug, each engraved with cre and motto, maker's mark IW, 182 coffee pot 7½in (19cm), 98oz.
£2,500-3,500 *C*

A George IV composite four-piece tea and coffee service, 74oz.
£1,400-1,700 *DN*

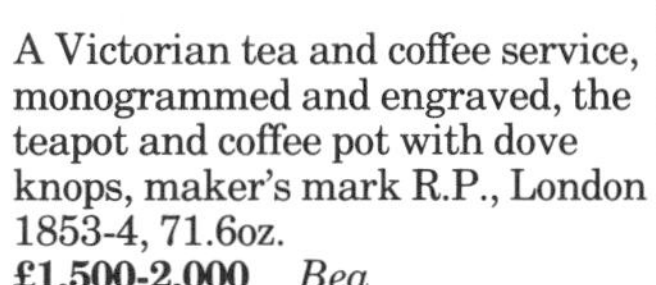

A Victorian tea and coffee service, monogrammed and engraved, the teapot and coffee pot with dove knops, maker's mark R.P., London 1853-4, 71.6oz.
£1,500-2,000 *Bea*

A composite tea and coffee service, comprising a teapot and coffee pot with later Victorian finials, a sugar basin and cream jug, each later engraved with initial P, the teapot by Matthew Boulton & Plate Co., Birmingham, the remainder by The Soho Plate Company, the successor company of Robinson, Edkins and Aston, 1833, coffee pot 7in (18cm), 82oz.
£3,000-4,000 *C*

A William IV tea service, the teapot and hot water jug with scroll chased silver handles and flower knops, on scrolling bracket feet, by Edward, Edward Jn., John and W. Barnard, London 1836, 79oz.
£2,300-2,600 *DN*

A Victorian tea and coffee service, the teapot and coffee pot with ivory pineapple finials and wood scroll handles, maker's mark C.E., London 1879, 46.6oz.
£1,500-2,000 *Bea*

A Victorian tea service, comprising a pumpkin-shaped teapot with embossed scroll decoration, 11½in (29cm) wide, and a matching sugar basin and cream jug, Edinburgh 1842, 65oz 10dwt.
£1,000-1,500 *DSH*

A Victorian tea and coffee service, the teapot and coffee pot with domed hinged covers and knopped finials, Henry Wilkinson, London 1857, 60oz.
£1,500-2,000 *Bon*

A Victorian tea and coffee service, Hyam Hyams, London 1866, the coffee pot London 1854.
£1,500-2,000 *P[Re]*

A Victorian tea and coffee service, in neo-classical style, the teapot and coffee pot with ebonised handles and pineapple finials, marked on base 'Wm. Angus, 27 and 29 Lord Street, Liverpool', by William and George Sissons, London 1882, 56oz.
£1,700-2,000 *DN*

A Victorian floral and foliate chased tea service, the milk jug and sugar basin gilt lined, W.S., London 1859, teapot 8in (20.5cm) high, 48.75oz.
£900-1,000 *CSK*

A Victorian tea and coffee service, the teapot and coffee pot with cast flower knobs, by Joseph II and Albert Savory, London 1851, the coffee pot by Walter and John Barnard, London 1885, 78.5oz.
£1,500-2,000 *DN*

A Victorian tea service, the sugar bowl and milk jug gilt lined, George Angell, London 1878, teapot 5in (12.5cm) high, 18oz.
£600-650 *CSK*

A tea service, engraved in the Aesthetic taste with bamboo and birds in water landscapes, crested, teapot inscribed, Elkington & Co., Birmingham 1884, 61.75oz.
£900-1,000 *P*

A Victorian tea and coffee service, comprising a teapot, coffee pot, hot water jug, sugar basin and cream jug, on scroll feet, on a two-handled tray with similar engraved decoration and moulded scroll border and handles, all engraved with a crest and motto, by Elkington & Co., Birmingham 1897 and 1898, the tray 25in (63.5cm) long, 234oz.
£7,000-8,000 *C*

A Victorian teaset, Messrs. Barnard and J. E. W. & J. Barnard, London 1889, 1891 and 1898, 47oz gross.
£500-600 *P[PWC]*

A Victorian tea service, London 1893, 28.7oz gross.
£500-600 *Bea*

A five-piece tea and coffee service and a Victorian tray, 1897, 70oz.
£1,400-2,000 *SWO*

A Victorian fluted and floral engraved tea service, Atkin Bros, Sheffield 1895, 58.5oz.
£900-1,200 *P[EDH]*

A silver teaset, maker's mark R.S. (perhaps R. Stewart), Glasgow 1901, 58.5oz.
£900-1,200 *P[PWC]*

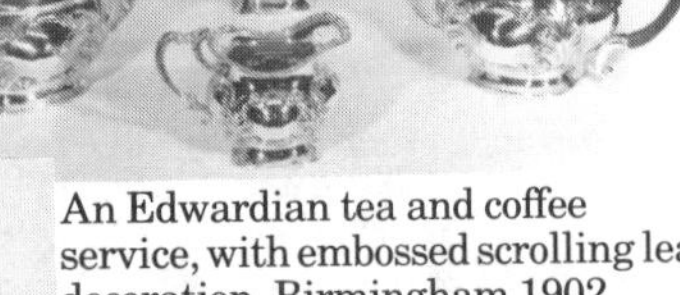

An Edwardian tea and coffee service, with embossed scrolling leaf decoration, Birmingham 1902, teapot 12in (30.5cm) wide, 68oz 19dwt.
£900-1,200 *DSH*

An Edwardian tea and coffee service, the milk jug and sugar basin gilt lined, Elkington, Birmingham 1904, coffee pot 10in (25.5cm), 69oz gross. ▶
£1,200-1,500 *CSK*

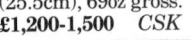

A silver gilt coffee service, London 1911, and a pair of silver gilt sugar tongs, Sheffield 1909, 20oz.
£500-700 *HCH*

An Italian gilt tea and coffee service and matching tray, with ivory scroll handles, domed covers and vase shaped finials, each engraved with a monogram and coronet, unmarked, coffee jug 12in (31.5cm), 4,938 grammes. ▶
£2,500-3,000 *C*

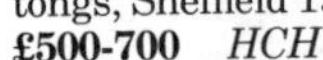

A six-piece tea and coffee service, including tray, by Garrard & Co., H.M. London, c1938, 196oz.
£2,800-3,000 *SWO*

An American coffee service, by Gale & Willis, New York, 19thC, .925 standard, 49.5oz.
£900-1,200 *DN*

Tea Caddies

A George I tea caddy, engraved with rocaille decoration, by Paul Crespin, 1724, 5in (13cm), 12.25oz.
£2,500-3,000 *P*

A George III tea caddy with central hinge, two covers and plain divider, engraved with wrigglework borders and a coat-of-arms and monogram, by Henry Chawner, 1788, 7in (18cm) high, 15oz 10dwt.
£2,500-3,000 *C*

A George III tea caddy, the underbase engraved with initials HA, by Henry Chawner, 1790, 4in (10cm) high, 14oz.
£3,500-3,700 *P*

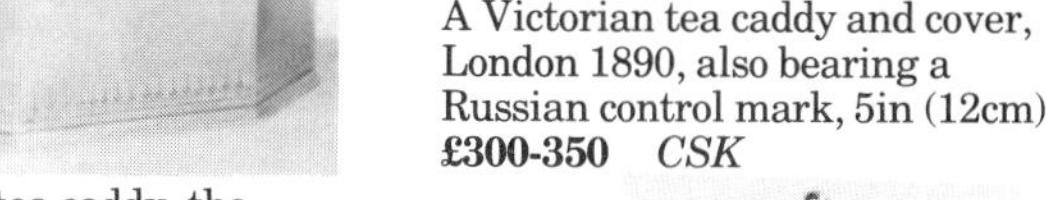

A Victorian tea caddy and cover, London 1890, also bearing a Russian control mark, 5in (12cm).
£300-350 *CSK*

A George IV tea caddy, cast and chased in the revived rocaille manner, with detachable raised cover surmounted by a cast floral bouquet, possibly by John Welshman, 1882, 6½in (16.5cm) high, 18oz.
£1,500-1,700 *P*

A mid-18thC style tea caddy, with sliding top and lift-off cover with baluster finial, chased with rococo flowers and foliage, with 4 vacant scroll cartouches, Chester 1911, 4½in (11cm).
£300-400 *CSK*

Tea Kettles

A Danish tea kettle on stand, with burner, by A. Dragstead, Copenhagen 1895, 66.25oz.
£600-700 *P*

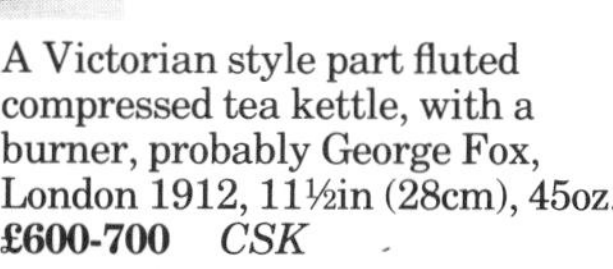

A Victorian style part fluted compressed tea kettle, with a burner, probably George Fox, London 1912, 11½in (28cm), 45oz.
£600-700 *CSK*

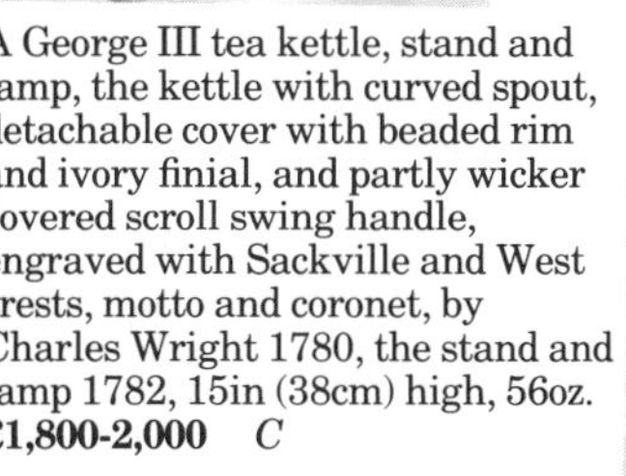

A George III tea kettle, stand and lamp, the kettle with curved spout, detachable cover with beaded rim and ivory finial, and partly wicker covered scroll swing handle, engraved with Sackville and West crests, motto and coronet, by Charles Wright 1780, the stand and lamp 1782, 15in (38cm) high, 56oz.
£1,800-2,000 *C*

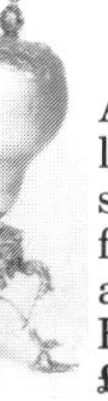

A Victorian tea kettle, stand and lamp, with swing handle and curved spout, the stand on 3 scroll and shell feet, and with pierced and cast apron, with circular lamp, by Harris Bros, 1896, 63oz.
£900-1,000 *C*

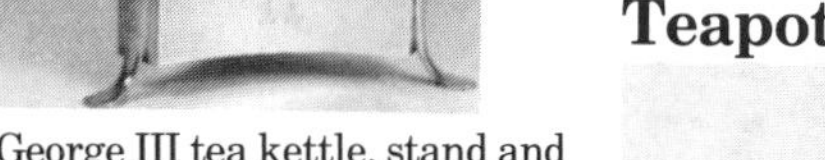

Teapots

A George III teapot, engraved in the rocaille manner, with gilt interior, by Augustin Le Sage, 1763, 4in (10.5cm), 10oz.
£800-900 *P*

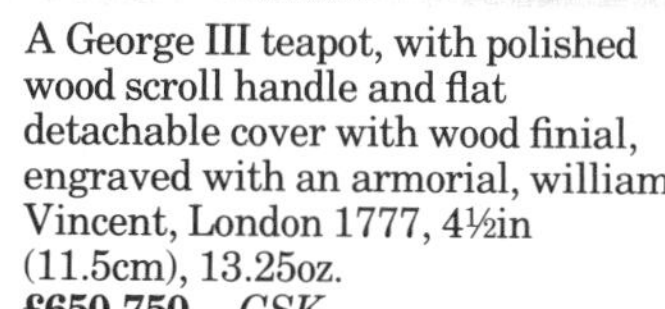

A George III teapot, with polished wood scroll handle and flat detachable cover with wood finial, engraved with an armorial, william Vincent, London 1777, 4½in (11.5cm), 13.25oz.
£650-750 *CSK*

A George III teapot, the domed cover with an ebony finial, scroll wood handle, spout repaired, Hester Bateman, London 1780, 13.75oz gross.
£500-550 *WW*

A George III teapot and stand, with ivory pineapple finial, by William Stephenson, 1790, 19.5oz.
£2,000-2,500 *P*

A George III Irish teapot with domed cover, and ebonised handle, by Peter Wills, Cork c1790, 20.5oz gross.
£800-900 *DN*

A George III teapot, the domed cover with stained ivory finial, by Urquhart and Hart, London 1798, 15oz.
£550-600 *P*

A George III teapot and stand, the cover surmounted by a green ivory bud finial, contemporary engraved monogram either side, reeded wood handle, by Peter, Ann and William Bateman, 1799, the stand reeded and with similar frieze decoration, on 4 feet, overall height 7½in (19.5cm) high, 20oz.
£1,200-1,500 *P*

A George III teapot, with engraved silver knob, wood handle, by Samuel Hennell and John Terrey, London 1815, 22oz gross.
£450-500 *DN*

A Victorian teapot, on leafy scroll feet, with bud finial and leaf capped scroll handles, by Robert Hennell, 1842, 7½in (18.5cm), 24.5oz.
£550-600 *P*

A George IV teapot, the finial modelled as a greyhound, by Edward Barton, London 1829, 27.5oz.
£500-550 *P[PWC]*

A Victorian teapot, by Edward, John & William Barnard, London 1844, 22.25oz.
£350-400 *P[PWC]*

A Victorian teapot in early 18thC style, with domed cover, ivory handle and knob, engraved with a crest, by Robert Garrard II, London 1851, 20oz.
£450-500 *DN*

Trays

A George III plain round waiter, by Elizabeth Jones, c1790, 7in (18cm), 8.5oz.
£350-400 *DN*

A Victorian two-handled tea tray, maker's mark J.H., probably of John Hall, London 1893, 15in (38cm) long, 119oz.
£1,700-2,000 *Bea*

A late Victorian tray, with shell and gadrooned chased border and 2 leaf chased handles, by Harry Wright Atkin, London 1893, 22½in (57cm) long, 89oz.
£1,500-2,000 *DN*

A George I spoon tray, engraved with an armorial and with raised fluted sides, maker's mark indistinct, London 1720, 6in (15cm) long, 2.8oz.
£1,200-1,500 *Bea*

Tureens

A George III soup tureen, with conforming pedestal foot, with engraved crest, lacking cover, by William Pitts, London 1787, 14in (35.5cm) wide, 31oz.
£600-650 *P[PWC]*

A set of 4 George III sauce tureens and covers, each on cast spreading foot with reeded loop handles, domed covers, engraved with coat-of-arms and crest, by Robert Sharp, 1788, 6in (15cm) high, 125oz.
£8,000-9,000 *C*

A George IV entree dish and cover, the fluted domed cover with detachable lion's mask and acanthus foliage ring handle, by Paul Storr, 1822, 12in (30.5cm) long, 73oz.
£3,000-4,000 *C*

A set of 4 George III entree dishes, covers and handles, engraved with coat-of-arms, crest and coronet, by Robert Sharp, 1788, 10½in (26cm) long, 155oz.
£8,000-9,000 *C*

A pair of George III sauce tureens, Birmingham 1816, 35oz.
£1,500-2,000 *DN*

A pair of George IV sauce tureens and covers, on foliage and scroll feet, the domed covers with similar chased decoration on a matted ground, with detachable foliage ring handles, engraved with a monogram, by Joseph Angell, 1825, 72oz.
£2,000-3,000 *C*

Wine Antiques

A pair of William IV coasters, by Henry Wilkinson & Co., Sheffield 1835, 7in (18cm) diam.
£1,200-1,500 *DN*

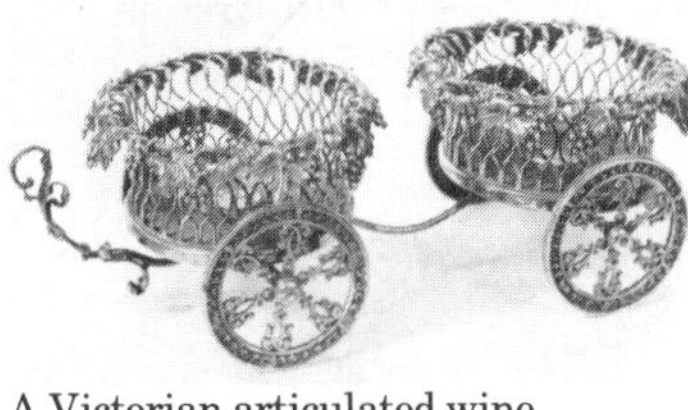

A Victorian articulated wine wagon, decorated with vines, maker's mark R & S, Roberts & Slater, Sheffield 1859.
£2,000-2,300 *GC*

A William IV claret jug, on shaped foot cast and chased with dolphins, foliage and shell ornament, with vine tendril handle, the hinged cover with crest finial, maker's mark IW overstriking another, perhaps that of Charles Fox, the foot with retailer's mark of J. Walker, Aberdeen, 1837, 17in (43cm), 65oz.
£3,800-4,200 *C*

A set of 4 William IV wine labels, with suspensory chains, maker's mark WR, London 1826.
£400-450 *Bon*

A pair of George IV cast wine labels, pierced 'Bucellas' and 'Madeira', by Edward Farrell, 1824 and 1825.
£850-900 *P*

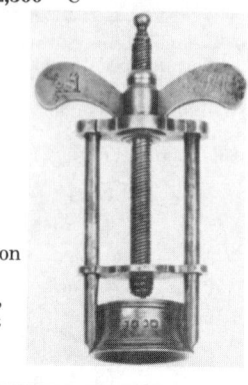

A pair of George III wine coasters, with turned wood bases, the sides with a monogram within oval cartouches, maker's mark indistinct, 1789, 5in (12.5cm) diam.
£2,000-2,500 *C*

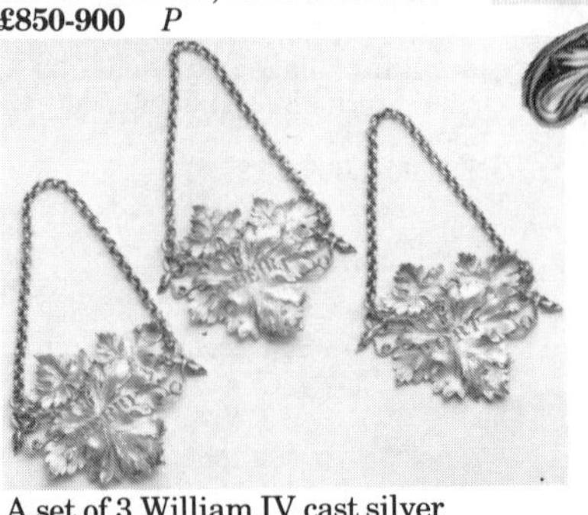

A set of 3 William IV cast silver wine labels for fortified wines, by Chas. Reily and Geo. Storer, London 1830.
£550-600 *WRo*

A Dutch corkscrew, with fluted kidney shaped handle and fluted baluster stem, probably Cornelis Hilberts, Amsterdam, 1749.
£400-450 *P*

A William IV Farrow & Thompson type corkscrew, engraved with boar's head crest and monogram, lacking helical worm, by Reily & Storer, 1830.
£1,500-1,700 *P*

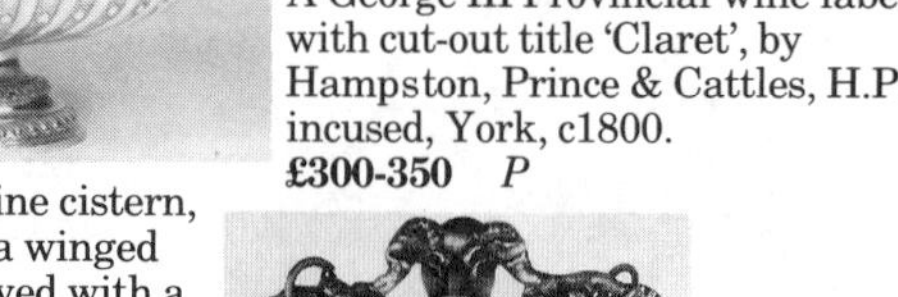

A George III Provincial wine label with cut-out title 'Claret', by Hampston, Prince & Cattles, H.P. incused, York, c1800.
£300-350 *P*

A claret jug, by The Goldsmiths & Silversmiths Co. Ltd., 1910, 14in (35.5cm), 42oz gross.
£1,200-1,500 *C*

A Queen Anne style wine cistern, the handles formed as a winged female caryatid, engraved with a coat-of-arms, maker's mark RR, Britannia Standard, 1936, 24in (61cm) wide, 239oz.
£14,000-16,000 *C*

A pair of George III cast wine labels, incised 'White' and 'Claret', probably by Thomas Hemming, c1770.
£750-850 *P*

A claret jug, with hinged domed cover and openwork scroll finial, by The Goldsmiths and Silversmiths Co. Ltd., 1902, 14in (35.5cm), 42oz gross.
£1,500-1,700 *C*

A set of 3 George III wine labels, with raised titles 'Port', 'Claret' and 'Sherry', by Paul Storr, 1815.
£1,800-2,000 *P*

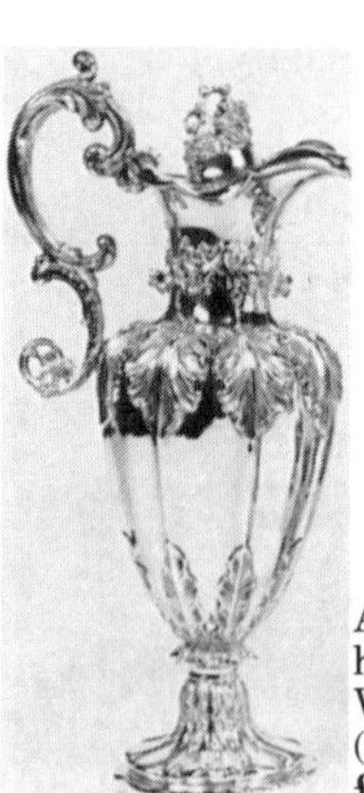

A Victorian claret jug, with scroll handle and grape finial, by Henry Wilkinson, Sheffield 1838, 13½in (34cm), 24oz gross.
£1,200-1,500 *C*

A pair of Victorian wine coasters, on a turned wood base, Charles Fox, London 1839, 5in (12.5cm) diam.
£2,000-2,500 *Bea*

A pair of George III wine coasters, with pierced sides, the silver bases with contemporary coats-of-arms, maker's mark W.B.R.S., William Burwash & Richard Sibley, London 1810, 6in (15cm) diam.
£3,500-4,000 *GC*

A George IV silver gilt wine ewer, in the style of François Briot, by William Eaton, 1827, 11½in (29cm), 37oz.
£1,700-2,000 *C*

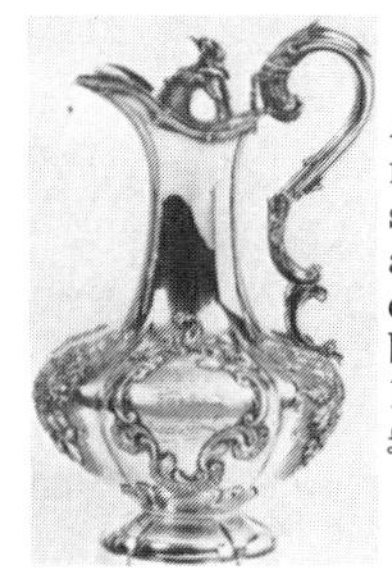

A Victorian silver mounted clear glass claret jug, with scroll handle, mask spout, hinged flat cover, by George Fox, 1864, 12in (30.5cm).
£1,500-1,800 *C*

A Victorian claret jug, chased on a matted ground, with leaf capped scroll handle, hinged domed cover and flower finial, engraved with a crest and presentation inscription, by Charles Reily and George Storer, 1838, 12in (30.5cm), 30oz gross.
£1,000-1,200 *C*

A George I brandy saucepan, with ebonised handle, maker's mark I.F., London 1723, 8½in (22cm).
£350-400 *Bea*

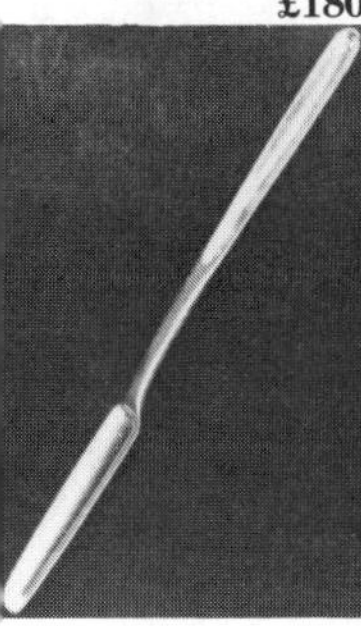

A Victorian silver gilt mounted glass claret jug, with scroll and figure handle and detachable grape and vine leaf stopper, by John Figg, 1866, 16in (41cm).
£3,000-3,500 *C*

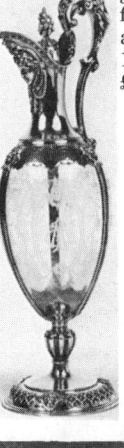

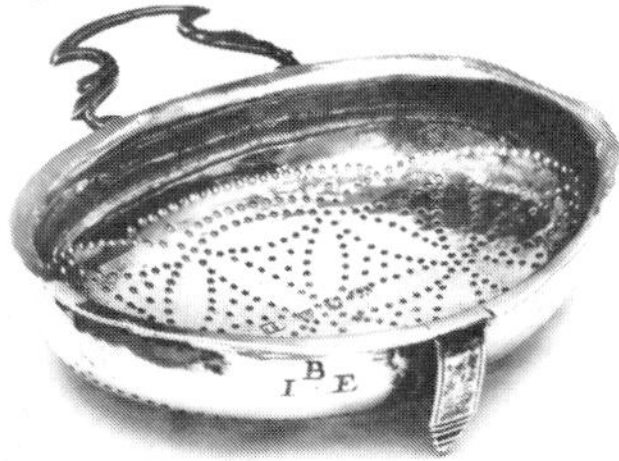

A George III lemon strainer with handle, maker's mark T.S., possibly Thomas Shepherd, London 1790, 2oz 10dwt.
£180-220 *GC*

Miscellaneous

A Victorian morocco leather desk folder, the silver mounts embossed with cherubs' heads and with pierced rococo borders, maker's mark H.M., Birmingham 1898, 11½in (29cm).
£200-250 *P[PWC]*

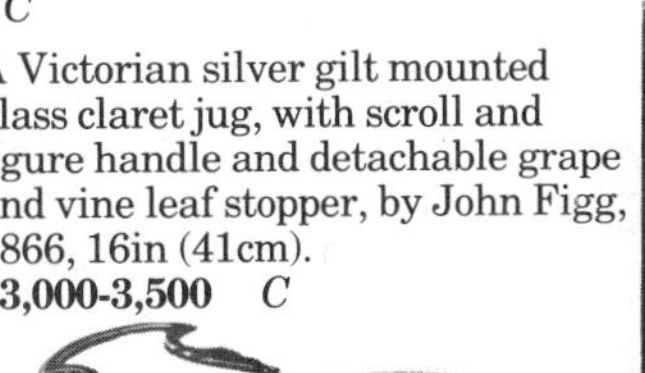

A George III plain ovoid nutmeg grater, with reeded band, marked inside top, Birmingham 1801, 1½in (4cm).
£100-120 *DN*

A Georgian marrow scoop, London 1810, 1oz.
£65-75 *PC*

A Victorian biscuit barrel, the hinged cover with ivory finial, engraved with flowers on integral stand with 2 handles and bun feet, by John, Edward, Walter and John Barnard, London 1876, 11in (28cm), 26oz.
£750-800 *DN*

A travelling clock, in scroll and flower embossed silver case with carrying handle, by Charles James Fox, London 1899, 3in (7.5cm).
£400-450 *DN*

A metal clock in an Edwardian silver mounted case, engraved with a monogram, W.H.S. Birmingham 1904, 4½in (11.5cm).
£230-260 *CSK*

A pair of Continental vases, modelled as double-ended cornucopiae, on 4 pierced scroll and flower supports, bearing English import marks for 1897, 8in (20cm) high, 41.5oz.
£1,800-2,000 *P*

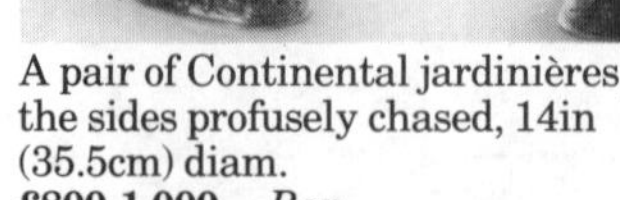

A pair of Continental jardinières, the sides profusely chased, 14in (35.5cm) diam.
£800-1,000 *Bon*

A Chinese vase, with matt textured finish, fruit and foliage handles, neck and base polished, foliage and birds on one side, vacant cartouche on reverse, polished Chinese marks under base, 10in (25.5cm), 11oz.
£250-300 *JM*

A Victorian silver thimble, Chester 1886, with original box.
£20-30 *TVA*

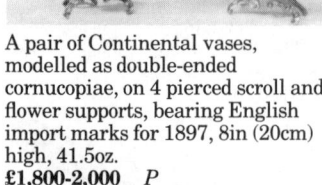

A Victorian table bell, with a putto finial, Birmingham 1886, 6in (15cm).
£500-550 *Bea*

A Victorian whistle, Birmingham 1894.
£60-70 *TVA*

Two Victorian coaching horns, each with moulded mouthpiece, engraved with a crest and presentation inscription, one by Augustus Kohler, 1884, the other maker's mark J.S., Dublin 1884, 36in (91.5cm), 32oz.
£2,000-2,500 *C*

A Dutch hand bell with baluster handle, probably by Christoffei Radijs, The Hague, 1740, 5in (13cm), 9oz.
£2,200-2,500 *P*

A Victorian table lighter, modelled as a monkey on a barrel, the raised arm detachable to form a match, by Jane Brownett, 1889, 4½in (11.5cm) high, 5oz.
£700-800 *P*

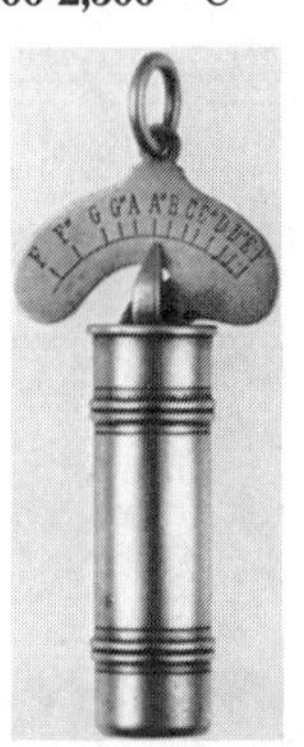

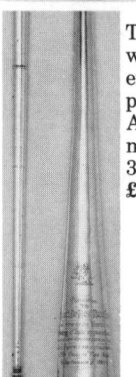

An Edwardian tuning whistle, with graduated scale of notes, by James Samuel Bell, 1907.
£450-500 *P*

A Victorian novelty perfume atomizer, modelled as a contemporary manual fire tender on wheels, by E. H. Stockwell, 1888.
£1,200-1,500 *P*

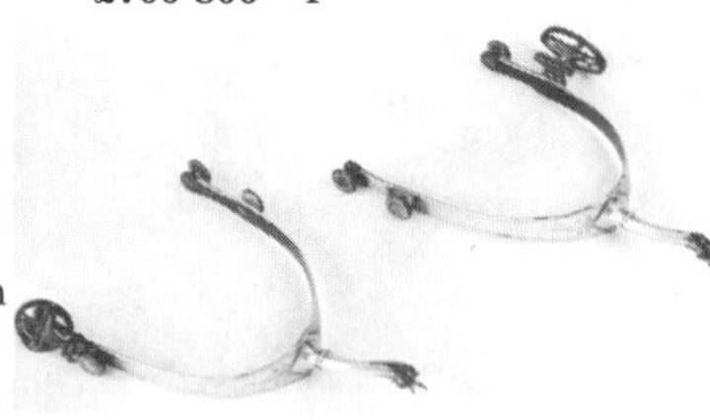

A pair of spurs, engraved with feather edged borders and foliate motifs, steel buckles, c1790, 5in (13cm) long.
£250-300 *P*

An eleven piece dressing table set, fully hallmarked London 1905 or 1906, the brushes and mirror also carry registration mark R2374817.
£700-800 *NUB*

A South American chamberpot, with cast handles and thumbpiece, the base inscribed Paul Augarte, possibly Argentinian, c1820, 5in (13cm) high, 25oz.
£1,200-1,500 *P*

A silver and leather mounted wooden shaving paper holder, stamped 'Shaving', W.D., Birmingham 1912, 6½in (16.5cm).
£130-160 *CSK*

A George III Irish dish ring, embossed with a classical urn, with blue glass liner, by Joseph Jackson, Dublin, c1775, 7in (17.5cm), 10oz.
£1,000-1,500 *P*

A silver handled dusting brush, Goldsmiths & Silversmiths Co., London 1895.
£40-60 *PC*

A George II Irish lemon strainer, applied with 2 openwork handles, one engraved with a crest, the reverse with initials, maker's mark only, struck twice, by George Cartwright, Dublin, c1735, 10in (25.5cm), 6oz 8dwt.
£1,500-1,700 *C*

A silver sovereign and half-sovereign case, Birmingham 1905, 1.25oz.

£50-80 *PC*

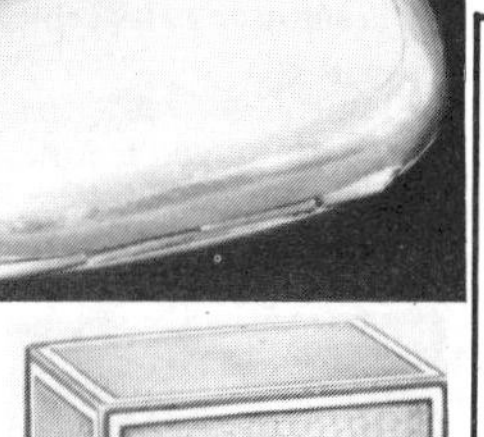

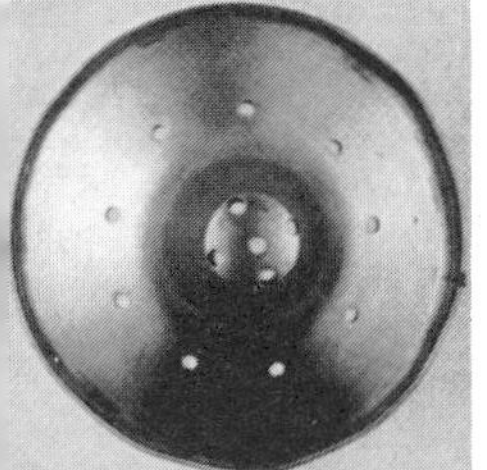

A George IV nipple shield, by T. & I. Phipps, 1821.
£300-350 *P*

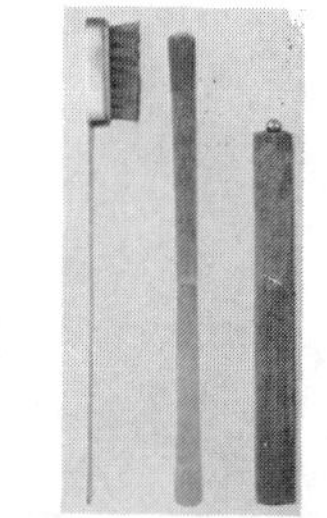

A Georgian toothbrush set, comprising a toothbrush, 4½in (12cm) long, a two-part covered paste box, an unmarked tongue scraper, by James Barber II (?), 1793, in a fitted red shagreen case.
£300-350 *P*

A Queen Anne baby's teether, the handle embossed in the baroque style, c1705, 5in (13cm) long.
£500-550 *P*

A Swiss travelling clock, with silver case, with translucent grey/blue guilloche and white enamelling, the white enamelled face inscribed Goldsmiths & Silversmiths Co. Ltd., 112 Regent Street, London, with London import marks for 1913, 2½in (6.5cm) high, in leather and gilt tooled case.
£650-700 *DN*

An altar cross, the knop set with 8 amethysts, the cross with fleur-de-lys and Tudor rose terminals, and applied twice with the lamb and flag, the base engraved 'To the Glory of God and In Memory of Ellen Bertha Tufnell 1867-1930', by Omar Ramsden, 1932, 31in (79cm) high, 110oz gross.
£3,000-4,000 *C*

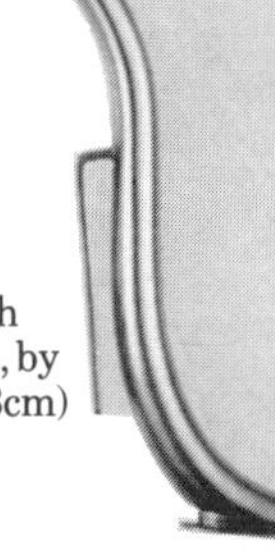

A Victorian feeding syphon, with hinged pierced strainer and clips, by William Saunders, 1875, 5in (13cm) long.
£200-250 *P*

Judaica

Victorian silver miniature Tephilin protective outer cases, 1in (2.5cm) high.
£4,000-7,000 *AnC*

A seven-light German brass Sabbath lamp, suspended from an ornate cast hook and chain, the oil tray with 7 spouts joined to the drip tray below by a short tapering column, the lower part of the drip tray with a serrated edge, some damage, c1790, 5½in (14cm) high.
£500-600 *AnC*

An English 18ct gold seal, of Judaica interest, inscribed 'Peace in Israel'.
£1,500-2,000 *AnC*

A Ridgway blue and white Seder plate, for use on Passover, with scenes from Amsterdam Haggedah, 12in (30.5cm).
£100-150 *AnC*

An olive wood Palestinian watch holder, signed Bezalel.
£100-200 *AnC*

A Swedish charity box, with lockable moulded hinged lid with a hinged cover over the slot for the money, mounted on the cover a cast bird of prey, marked on the base 'Nicolassen', slight damage, c1870, 4in (10cm) high.
£240-280 *AnC*

An Austrian siddur prayer book with silver mounts, printed on paper with Hebrew and German text on the same page in 2 columns, approx. 500 pages, the edges gilt, the cover in purple velvet with silver mounts, some damage, Vienna, c1864, 7½in (19cm).
£250-300 *AnC*

An Austrian alabaster and bronze bust of a Rabbi, the traditional Sephardic robes with long flowing sleeves finely formed in mottled white and beige alabaster, supported on an alabaster base, slight damage, late 19thC, 20in (51cm).
£2,400-2,600 *AnC*

A Syrian damascened brass table top, now used as a wall hanging plate, the surface of the plate profusely decorated with finely engraved silver and copper, some damage, c1870, 24½in (62cm).
£4,000-4,500 *AnC*

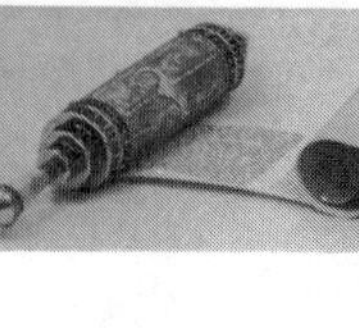

A Palestinian silver Bezalel Esther holder and scroll, the silver body finely chased and engraved with repousse work scenes taken from the Book of Esther, the Esther handwritten on 3 cemented pieces of parchment in 23 columns, retained by a silver keep with swivel catch, c1935, 9in (23cm).
£1,500-2,000 *AnC*

A Polish silver parcel gilt Esther holder and Esther scroll, the Esther handwritten on 4 sewn pieces of parchment in 19 columns, later metal keep with swivel catch inscribed 'Bezalel' in Hebrew, c1860, 9in (23cm).
£800-900 *AnC*

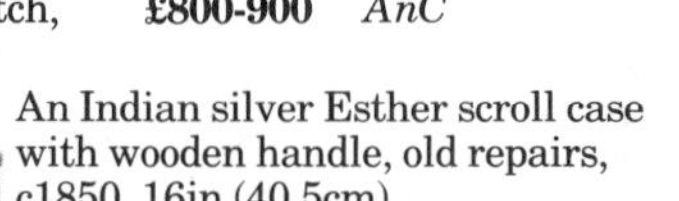

An Indian silver Esther scroll case with wooden handle, old repairs, c1850, 16in (40.5cm).
£600-700 *AnC*

The inclusion of hands in the design indicates that the original owner was probably a Cohen.

A Dutch silver table bell, maker's mark RH, Amsterdam 1792, 10oz.
£1,300-1,500 *DWB*

A Dutch Hanukah lamp, with fixed cast interior with 8 oval oil reservoirs, pierced back with cartouche, bearing the cast Hebrew inscription 'Hanukah', c1810, 11in (28cm).
£650-700 *AnC*

An American silver Art Deco 8-branch Hanukah lamp, with moulded square base with chased band, plain square section stem surmounted by a pierced Star of David finial, marked '925' on the star, c1930, 11in (28cm), 15oz.
£300-350 *AnC*

A late Victorian silver and silver gilt English Hanukah lamp, the removable silver gilt servant light is fitted centrally above the crown, a row of 8 silver gilt baluster candle holders, each with a removable silver gilt sconce individually mounted on the serpentine silver base, marked on the base, backplate and sconces, some restoration, hallmarked London 1897, 10½in (26.5cm), 32oz.
£3,000-3,500 *AnC*

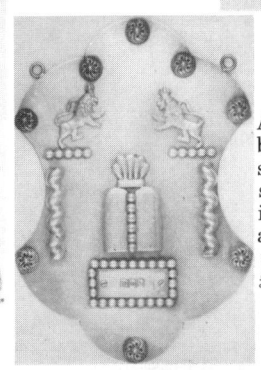

A Polish Hanukah lamp, late 19thC, 12in (30.5cm).
£1,500-2,500 *AnC*

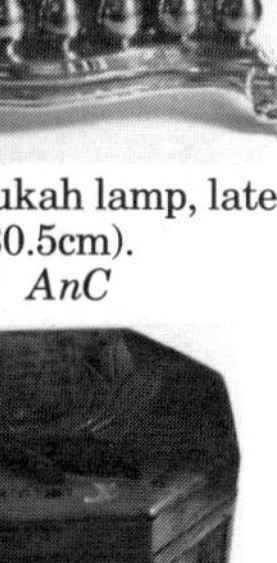

A Polish silver Torah pointer, c1880, 11in (28cm), 2.5oz.
£250-300 *AnC*

A Provincial Polish Torah breastplate, in plain silver plated cartouche shape, inscribed 'Pessach' in Hebrew, 2 rings are attached for a chain, c1860, 11½in (29cm).
£550-600 *AnC*

A Palestinian carved Ethrog box, signed 'Bezalel', Jerusalem.
£200-500 *AnC*

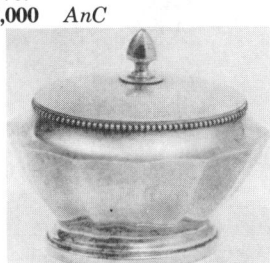

A French niello snuff box, depicting a scene of Elijah and Rebecca at the well, c1870.
£1,300-2,000 *AnC*

A European Torah and mantle, handwritten in black ink on sewn sheets of parchment rolled in 2 scrolls, with turned olive wood handles with ivory tips, the white silk mantle with an applied embroidered white Star of David on gilt Hebrew text, mid-19thC, with attached certificate from a scribe stating that the scroll is kosher, dated August 1985, 19in (48cm).
£2,500-3,000 *AnC*

A German silver Ethrog container, with hinged oval lid, gilt interior, marked on the base 800 and with crown and moon, c1895, 4½in (11.5cm) high, 9oz.
£250-300 *AnC*

An Israeli silver Ethrog container on 4 repousse feet, the edge of the raised lid pierced in the form of the Hebrew lettering 'And you shall take for yourself beautiful fruits', plain interior, the base with large decorative spotting, marked Esco-Sterling within an oval on base, c1950, 5½in (14cm), 14oz.
£400-500 *AnC*

A pair of English silver Torah bells, with matching breastplate, 12in (30.5cm), c1929.
£2,500-3,500 *AnC*

A Polish Torah pointer, 19thC.
£350-600 *AnC*

A French papier mâché box, with push fit lid painted with a Rabbi in red robes and hat, slight damage, c1830, 4½in (11.5cm).
£170-200 *AnC*

An English silver plated steeple spice box, with 4 bells, plain tapering spire and flag finial, c1870, 9½in (24cm).
£300-350 *AnC*

This is a very unusual design for an English spice container.

An Austro-Hungarian filigree spice box, marked on the spice compartment and the top, c1885, 6in (15cm), 1.9oz.
£550-600 *AnC*

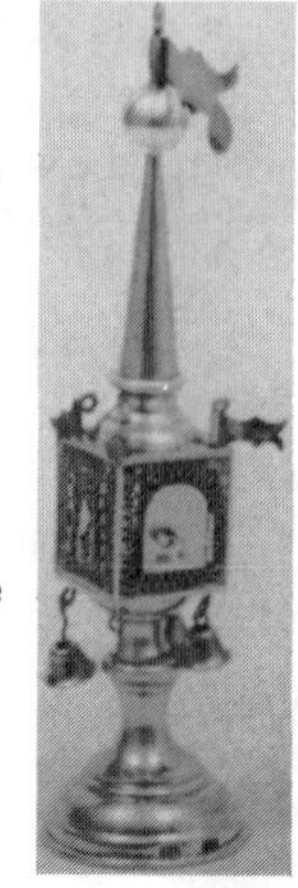

A Russian silver steeple spice box, marked on the base, bells, door and flag, hallmarked 1892, some damage, 9in (23cm), 4.5oz.
£670-700 *AnC*

A Palestinian silver steeple spice box, with hinged arched door, the small spire surmounted by a pierced ball and long wire stem for the flag, small filigree finial, marked on the base Silver Israel, minor damage, c1950, 8in (20.5cm), 2.3oz.
£200-250 *AnC*

An English silver steeple spice box, marked on base, bells, terminals and flag, hallmarked London 1913, some damage, 11in (28cm), 7.5oz.
£850-900 *AnC*

A German silver haudala and spice box holder, with pull-out drawer, c1860.
£2,000-2,500 *AnC*

A Polish Safed silver Kiddush beaker, engraved with 3 scenes from the Holy Land, titled in Hebrew 'Cave of Macpala – The Tower of David – Western Wall', marked 12 within a rectangle on the base, c1870, 3in (7.5cm), 2.4oz.
£1,300-1,600 *AnC*

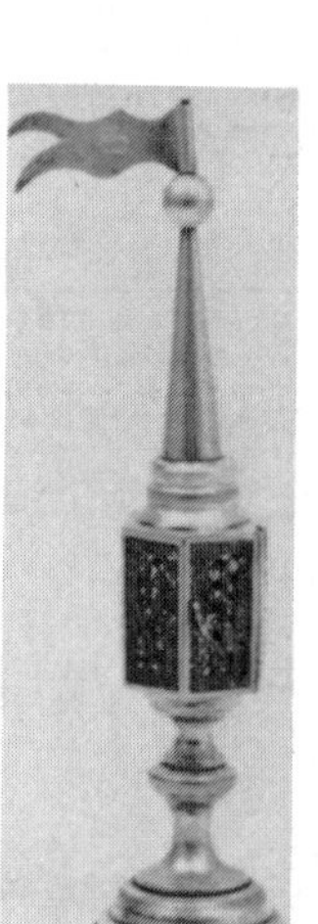

A Russian silver steeple spice box, slight damage, marked on the base and flag, hallmarked 1879, 9in (23cm), 5oz.
£600-650 *AnC*

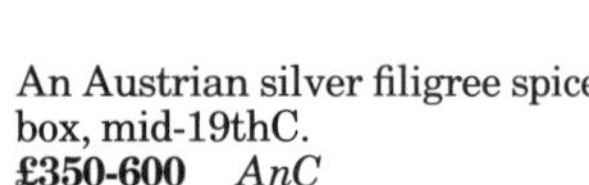

An Austrian silver filigree spice box, mid-19thC.
£350-600 *AnC*

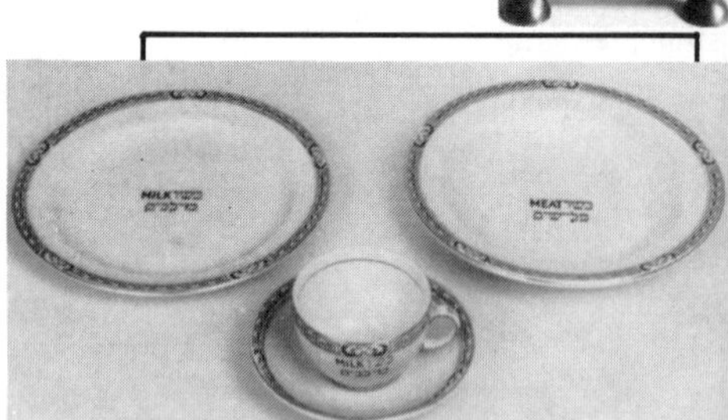

A china tea service made for use by Jewish passengers aboard a Cunard liner. The service comprises a soup dish, cup and saucer, each decorated with a black band of Greek key decoration with foliage and grapes at intervals and gilt lining, the dish inscribed 'Meat' in English and Hebrew, the plate and cup 'Milk' in a similar manner, marked 'The Cunard Steamship Company Limited', 'Ridgway Potteries Limited', the soup dish made by Booths and Colcloughs, c1910.
£400-450 *AnC*

The inclusion of the English text was probably for the benefit of the catering staff to avoid incorrect use.

An Austrian silver filigree spice box in the form of a locomotive, c1870.
£1,500-2,500 *AnC*

A combined spice box and Kiddush, Vienna, c1860.
£1,500-2,500 *AnC*

A German silver goblet, slight damage, maker's mark on the underside of the base, c1870, 4in (10cm), 2.5oz.
£120-150 *AnC*

A German silver goblet, with gilt interior, c1880, 4½in (11.5cm), 2.8oz.
£150-180 *AnC*

An Italian filigree spice box, 17thC.
£700-1,000 *AnC*

A late Victorian English silver filigree spice box.
£500-1,000 *AnC*

A French silver Kiddush cup, signs of gilding, maker's mark on the base, c1870, 3in (7.5cm), 2.3oz.
£150-200 *AnC*

A German Augsburg Kiddush cup, c1720, 4in (10cm).
£3,000-5,000 *AnC*

A German silver Kiddush cup, profusely chased with floral motifs, and small vacant cartouche, slight damage, c1840, 2½in (6.5cm), 1.7oz.
£120-150 *AnC*

A Turkish silver Kiddush cup, with gilt interior, c1850, 3½in (9cm), 3oz.
£120-150 *AnC*

Silver Plate

Candlesticks

A set of 4 George III Sheffield candlesticks, on square tapering beaded columns and square stepped beaded bases, engraved with a crest and motto 'Fear God in Life', of James, 14th Baron Somerville.
£1,200-1,500 *DN*

A pair of Victorian dressing table candlesticks, the stems designed as bound palms on stepped square bases with tongue and acanthus edging, Sheffield 1866, 5½in (14cm), loaded.
£450-500 *Bea*

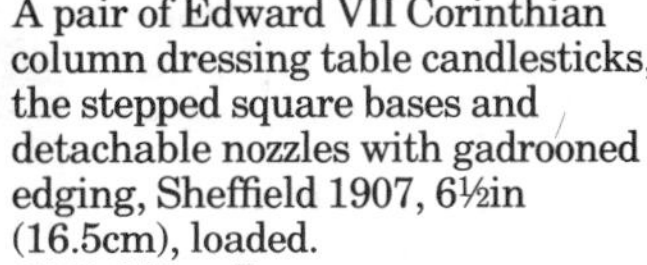

A pair of Edward VII Corinthian column dressing table candlesticks, the stepped square bases and detachable nozzles with gadrooned edging, Sheffield 1907, 6½in (16.5cm), loaded.
£500-550 *Bea*

A Sheffield plate oil lamp and shade, on 3 winged paw feet and supporting a glass reservoir, later converted for electricity, 26in (66cm).
£300-350 *Bea*

An electroplated Corinthian column oil lamp, with glass reservoir and shade, later converted for electricity, 23½in (60cm).
£300-350 *Bea*

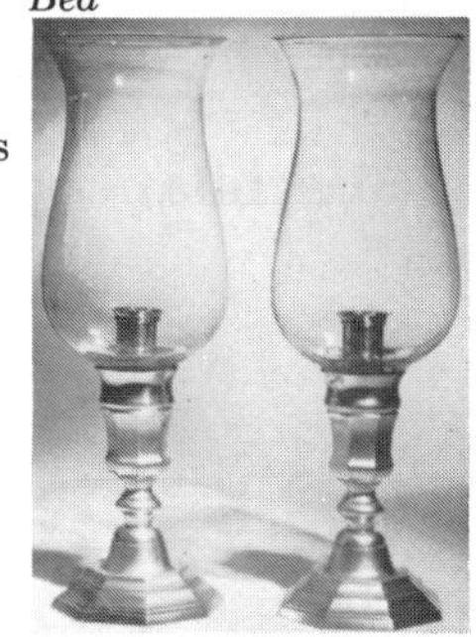

A pair of silver plated candlesticks, with tulip-shaped hurricane shades with lift-out nozzles, on faceted shafts and moulded octagonal bases, 15½in (39cm).
£2,500-3,000 *C*

A set of 4 Sheffield plate candlesticks, 9in (23cm).
£350-400 *Bea*

OLD SHEFFIELD PLATE

- ★ old Sheffield plate made from c1740-1840 when it was replaced by electroplating
- ★ a problem arises with electroplating being called Sheffield plate and hence the original plate should be notated 'old' Sheffield plate, although frequently this title is omitted
- ★ aid to dating Old Sheffield plate by edge identification; until 1785 edges merely turned over or with simple punched-in beading
- ★ by 1789 beading, reeding or gadrooning
- ★ 1800 shells, dolphins, oak leaves
- ★ 1815 vine leaves and flowers, altogether much more elaborate
- ★ check for a seam on hollow ware as electroplate completely covers the piece

A set of 4 Sheffield plate candlesticks, each stamped Danl. Holy/Wilkinson & Co., 12in (30.5cm).
£600-650 *Bea*

Services

A three-piece teaset, the handles with scroll mountings, gadroon borders, c1815.
£300-350 *P*

A Victorian electroplated tea and coffee service, with beaded edging decorated with cartouches and foliate bands.
£500-550 *Bea*

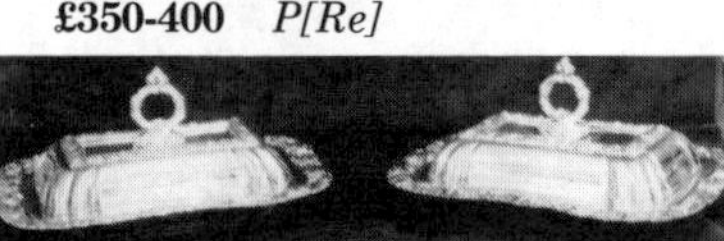

A five-piece electroplated tea and coffee service, on spreading circular bases, with beaded edging, Elkington & Co., 1859.
£700-750 *Bea*

A four-piece electroplated tea and coffee service, with bright cut foliage, tied festoons and fronds, on spreading bases.
£300-350 *Bea*

Tureens

A pair of Sheffield soup tureens, engraved with coat-of-arms and crest, c1820, 14in (35.5cm) high.
£3,000-3,500 *CNY*

The arms are those of Porter with Bothell.

An old Sheffield plate gadrooned sauce tureen and cover, on leaf capped paw feet, finely engraved with 2 armorials, the part fluted detachable cover engraved with 2 crests, 9in (23cm).
£350-400 *CSK*

A pair of French silver on copper raised sauce tureens, by Odiot of Paris, early 19thC, 7in (18cm).
£350-400 *P[Re]*

A pair of entree dishes, covers and liners, with chased borders, engraved with armorials, with griffon head handles, by Elkington & Co., 19thC, 14in (35.5cm).
£450-500 *DN*

A pair of plated entree dishes, with vine decorated borders, 10in (25.5cm).
£100-120 *PC*

An electroplated soup tureen and cover, 16in (40.5cm), and a matching dish.
£550-600 *Bea*

A pair of Victorian plated entree dishes, the domed covers with Egyptian Sphinx finials, the supports to the stands in the form of winged Egyptian female terms, with spirit burners, 11in (28cm).
£550-650 *P[PWC]*

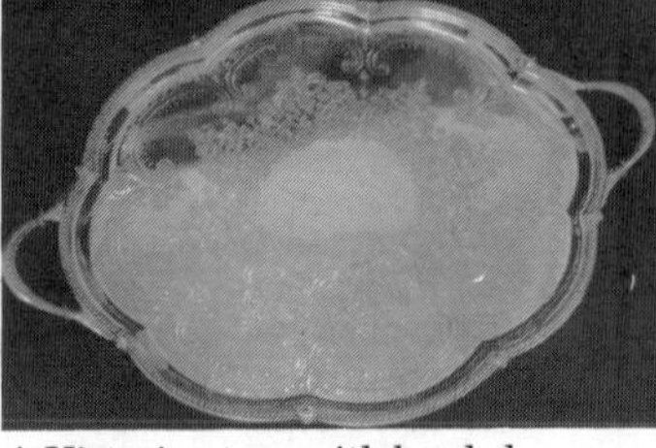

A Victorian tray with beaded handle and border, finely engraved centre, London 1874.
£3,000-3,500 *P[Re]*

Miscellaneous

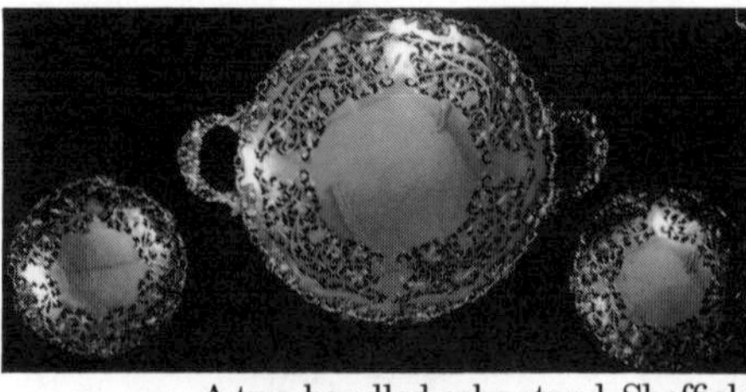

A two-handled cake stand, Sheffield 1923, 15½in (39cm) wide, with a pair of sweetmeat dishes, Sheffield 1922, 6½in (16.5cm) diam.
£850-900 *P[Re]*

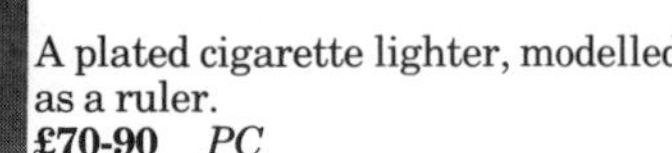

A plated cigarette lighter, modelled as a ruler.
£70-90 *PC*

Sheffield plated pint tankard with d, early 19thC, 7in (18cm).
60-80 *PC*

. George III Sheffield tea caddy, right cut engraved with swags of owers, cartouche and ribbon tie, in (12.5cm).
250-300 *DN*

. George III bullet-shaped teapot, ith baluster finial, floral border ngraving, cast spout, wood handle, y Francis Crump, London 1769.
300-350 *P[Re]*

silver plated and crystal decanter t, one decanter cracked, impressed 2459, E & Co., with crown in shield lkington & Co., 18½in (47cm) wide.
900-1,200 *CNY*

A plated breakfast dish, with strainer and lid, 14in (35.5cm) wide.
£140-180 *PC*

A silver plated kettle on stand, with spirit burner, c1890.
£350-400 *BM*

An old Sheffield plate tea urn, on 4 ball feet, with lions' mask and ring handles, the domed cover with ball finial and with gadrooned borders, c1820, 16in (40.5cm) high.
£600-650 *C*

An Edwardian novelty desk clip and pen brush in the form of a muzzled bear, on oak base, Birmingham 1908.
£300-350 *P[Re]*

A plated and engraved inkstand, with a pair of cut glass inkwells.
£120-150 *PC*

A George III Sheffield plate cruet, the 4 sauce bottles with stoppers, and a set of 4 Regency bottle labels, c1785.
£350-400 *WW*

A Victorian electroplated tea kettle on stand, with 3 scroll supports and burner, 14in (35.5cm) high.
£200-250 *Bea*

A glass claret jug, in the manner of Christopher Dresser, with angular plated mounts, flared star cut base, Hukin & Heath, 9in (23cm).
£300-350 *DN*

A Sheffield plate inkstand with pen rests, fitted with a chamberstick and snuffer, pounce pot and inkwell, all with acanthus cast rims, on paw feet, early 19thC, 9½in (24.5cm) wide.
£350-400 *P[Re]*

A plated ink stand, with presentation inscription and vine pattern edging, supporting 2 glass wells with central reservoir and taperstick with snuffer, 13in (33cm).
£450-500 *Bea*

A Victorian silver plate surtout d'table, liner marked Prevost & Co., 16in (41cm) high.
£20,000-25,000 *CNY*

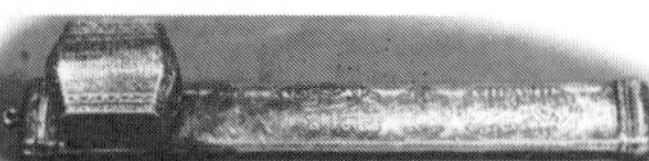

An Eastern silver coloured metal Scribes box, the engraved quill box with attached inkwell, engraved with stylised script and geometric patterns, with various marks.
£1,500-1,700 *P[CW]*

A silver lustre wig holder, by Bailey & Batkin, sole patentees, c1820, 9in (23cm).
£550-650 *DL*

A silver plated model of General Gordon by Adrian Jones.
£1,800-2,000 *SAg*

A pair of George III coasters, with wrigglework band decoration, turned mahogany bases, Robert Hennell, London 1792.
£900-1,200 *P[Re]*

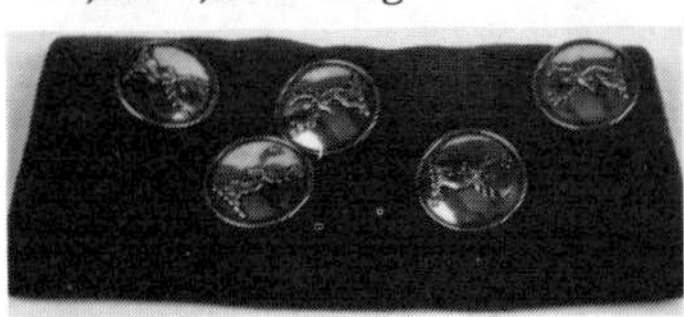

A set of 5 Georgian Sheffield plated and crested livery buttons, c1820.
£40-50 *TVA*

'The Milton Shield', an Elkington electrotype by L. Morel-Ladeuil, 1867, 33in (84cm) high.
£1,200-1,500 *N*

Gold

Miscellaneous

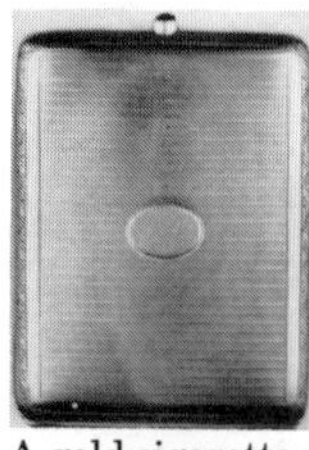

A gold cigarette case, the reeded panels bordered by scroll and foliate bands, with cabochon cut synthetic sapphire thumbpiece, 127 grammes.
£600-800 *CAm*

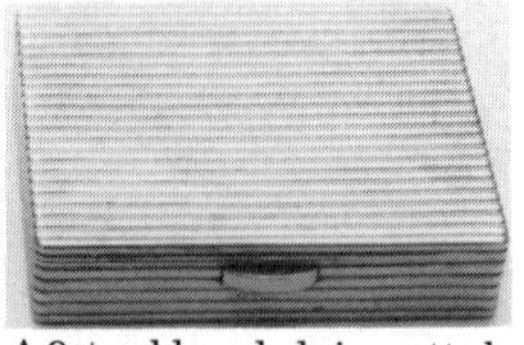

A 9ct gold reeded cigarette box, with plain thumbpiece, Cartier, London 1954, 2½ by 3in (6.5 by 7.5cm), 3.25oz.
£500-550 *DN*

A gold engine turned vinaigrette, with hinged lid, the thumbpiece inset with turquoise, the oval cartouche monogrammed, unmarked, c1830, 3 by 2.2cm.
£550-650 *P*

An English gold cigar box, the interior of the cover engraved with inscription dated 1933, wood lined, by Asprey, London, 1928, 18ct, 48oz 10dwt gross.
£8,000-9,000 *CNY*

A gold snuff box with engraved scroll and foliate decoration, the cover set with 3 plaques with multi-coloured flower arrangements on white ground, probably Vienna, early 19thC, 94 grammes.
£1,000-1,200 *CAm*

Metal

Brass

A brass and iron bed, 19thC, 55in (140cm).
£650-750 *MSM*

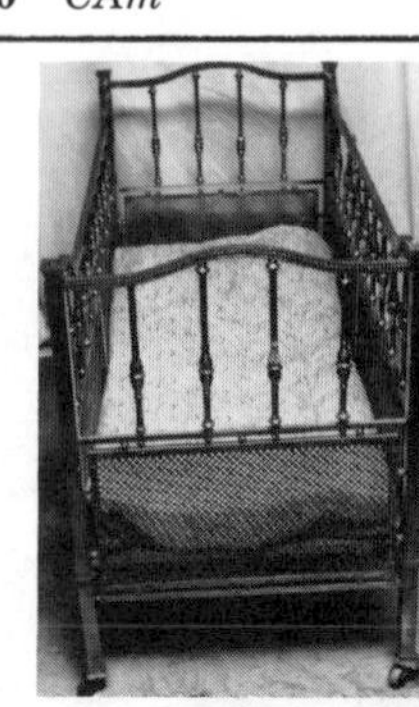

A brass cot, 19thC, 38in (96.5cm).
£550-650 *MSM*

A four-piece brass dressing table set, probably Austrian, Jugendstil, unmarked, candlestick 7in (18cm) high.
£150-200 *ST*

A set of 4 Charles II style brass candlesticks, 10in (25.5cm).
£1,200-1,500 *CNY*

A brassed metal bust of Wellington, in military dress, on wood base, 6½in (16cm).
£50-80 *P*

A set of 4 Charles II style brass candlesticks, 16½in (42cm).
£1,500-2,000 *CNY*

A brassed metal wall piece profile portrait bust of Wellington, 6½in (17cm).
£50-70 *P*

A Spanish brass candlestick, c1700.
£130-160 *KEY*

A pair of brass candlesticks, mid-18thC, 8in (20.5cm).
£450-500 *WW*

A pair of brass candlesticks, late 18thC.
£200-250 *PCA*

A pair of candlesticks with shell-shaped bases, 18thC.
£600-800 *KEY*

A pair of brass candlesticks, 19thC.
£50-70 *PCA*

A pair of brass candlesticks, c1830.
£65-85 *KEY*

A Regency brass desk lamp, with adjustable twin branches, shaped nozzles and drip pans, the base with twin rest for snuffers, lacking shades, 19in (48cm).
£700-750 *C*

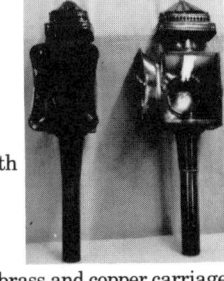

A pair of brass and copper carriage lamps, mid-19thC.
£90-120 *PC*

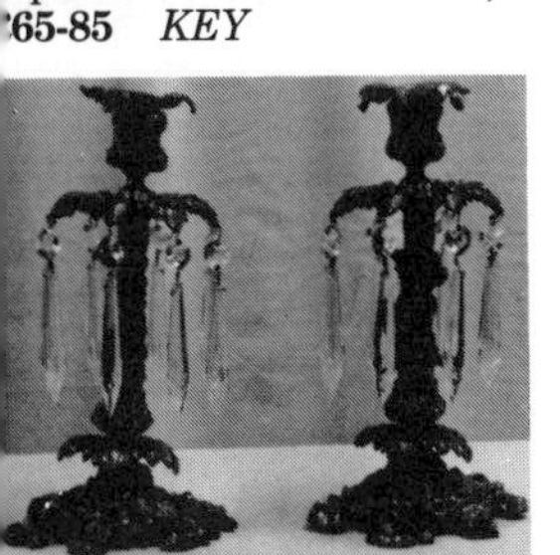

A pair of Victorian ornamental brass candlesticks, with glass lustre decoration.
£70-100 *PC*

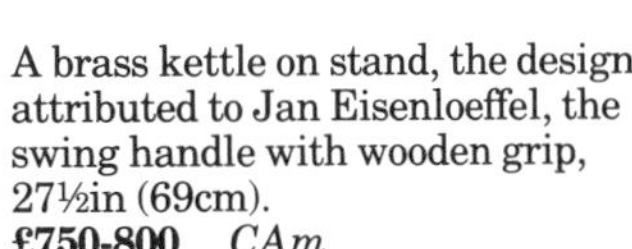

A brass kettle on stand, the design attributed to Jan Eisenloeffel, the swing handle with wooden grip, 27½in (69cm).
£750-800 *CAm*

A brass kettle and stand, 19thC.
£70-100 *PCA*

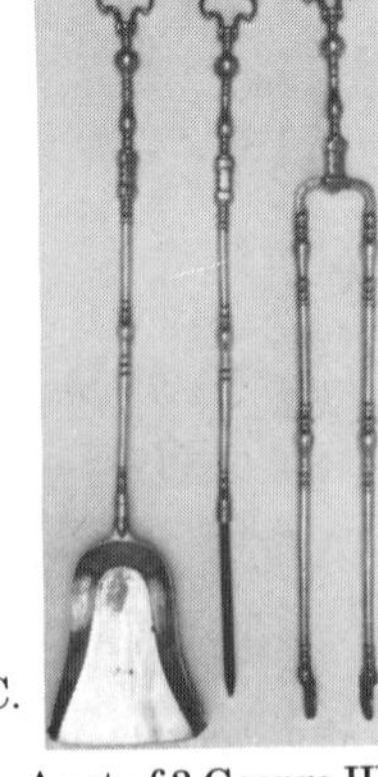
A set of 3 George III brass fire-irons, with shaped ring handles and baluster shafts, comprising a poker, a pair of tongs and a shovel, 24in (61cm).
£1,400-1,600 *C*

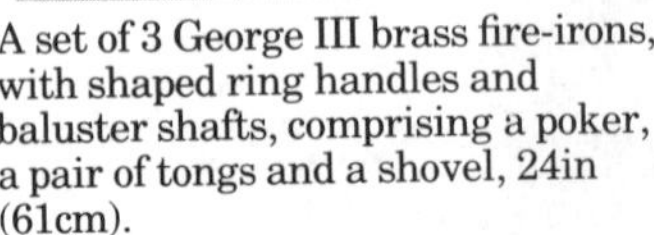
A brass coal scuttle, 19thC.
£100-130 *PCA*

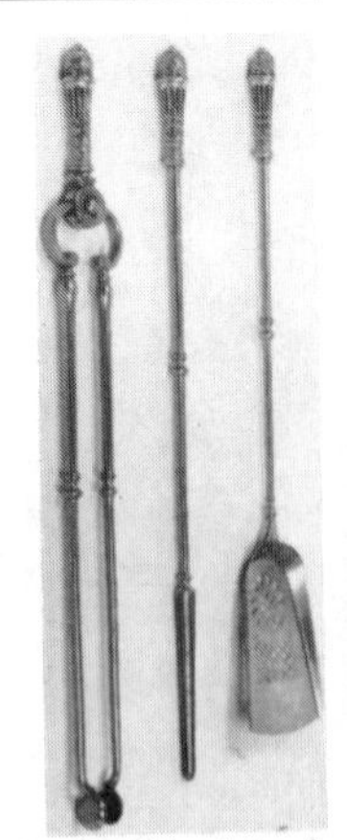
A set of 3 brass and polished steel fire-irons, with foliate bosses and fluted handles, 29½in (75cm) long.
£1,500-2,000 *C*

A steel balance with brass pans, by Charles De Grave, with some weights and label of values, in a fitted walnut case, 19thC, 6in (15cm) wide.
£350-400 *CSK*

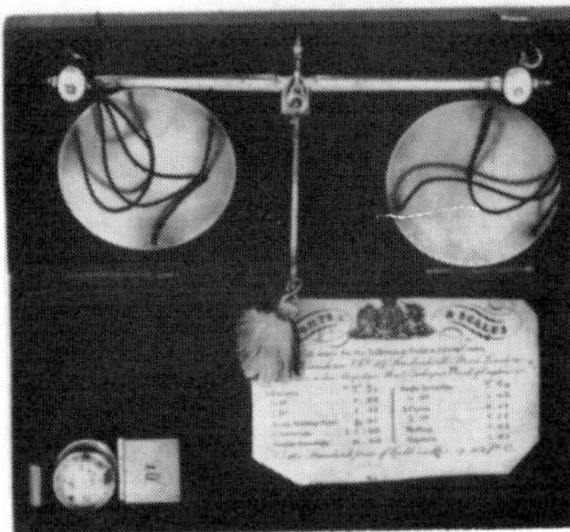
A steel balance with brass pans and weights, with trade label for Richard Vandome, in plush lined leather covered case, 19thC, 7in (18cm) wide.
£200-250 *CSK*

A pair of Dutch brass buckets, decorated with repousse fruiting foliage, and a brass 'cat and fiddle' brush.
£400-600 *C*

A Victorian brass postal balance, the beam signed Ortner & Houle, St. James's St. London, the 2 pans with painted porcelain plaques, 8in (20cm), and a set of 5 weights.
£1,000-1,200 *CSK*

A set of brass letter scales with 4 brass weights, on oak stand, 13in (33cm) wide.
£100-130 *PC*

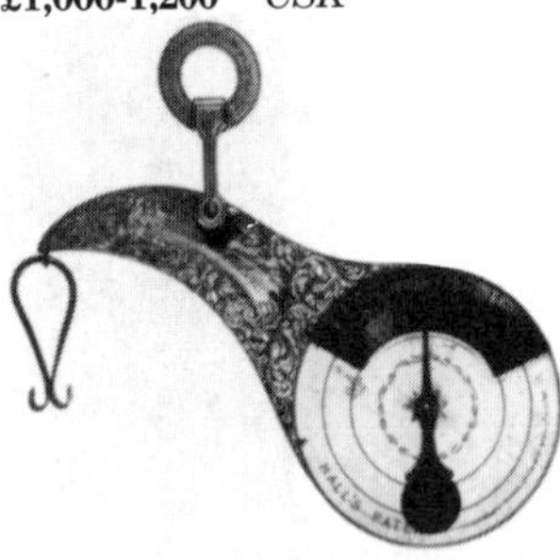
A sheet brass letter balance, signed Parnell London and inscribed Hall's Patent, in the original plush lined and fitted leather case, 5in (12.5cm) wide.
£150-200 *CSK*

A model brass and wooden cannon, c1830, 5in (12cm) long.
£60-70 *KEY*

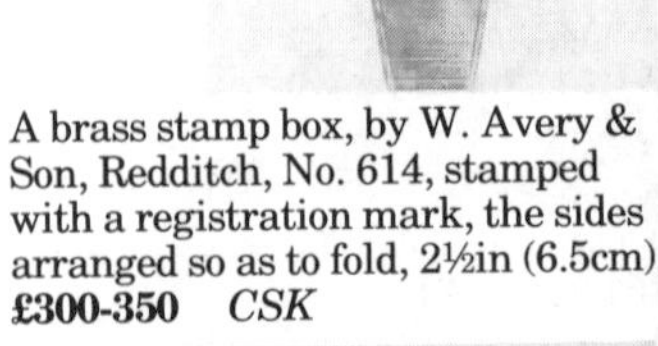
A brass stamp box, by W. Avery & Son, Redditch, No. 614, stamped with a registration mark, the sides arranged so as to fold, 2½in (6.5cm).
£300-350 *CSK*

A brass door stop, modelled as a saddled horse, 13in (33cm) wide
£350-400 *C*

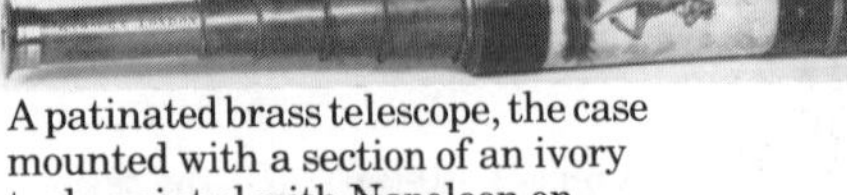
A patinated brass telescope, the case mounted with a section of an ivory tusk, painted with Napoleon on horseback with the Imperial Eagle, stamped Ramsden, London, 8in (20cm) long when closed.
£750-850 *C*

An English brass plate, the underside inscribed with ownership T, and with traces of silvering, 18thC, 10½in (26.5cm) diam.
£1,400-1,700 *P*

A Regency brass inlaid rosewood inkstand, with 2 bottles.
£350-400 *MGM*

A Victorian water bailiff's brass tipstaff, the handle unscrewing to reveal an oar, 5in (12.5cm).
£900-1,200 *DN*

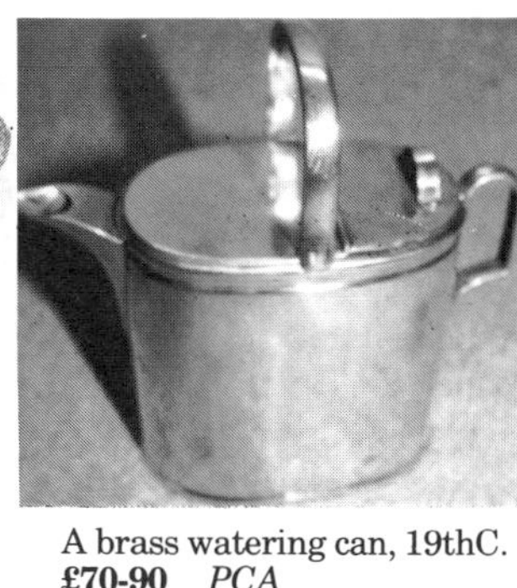

A brass watering can, 19thC.
£70-90 *PCA*

A Louis XVI style gilded brass chandelier with vase turned column, late 19thC, 44in (111.5cm).
£750-850 *P[Re]*

A pair of martingale horse straps, 19thC.
£100-120 *PCA*

Bronze

A pair of bronze busts of Sheakespear (sic) and Pope, on engraved gilt socles, on bronze pedestal columns, 19thC, 12in (30cm) high.
£1,800-2,000 *P*

A bronze bust of Napoleon as First Consul, mounted on veined marble half column, 19thC, 14½in (36cm) high.
£400-450 *C*

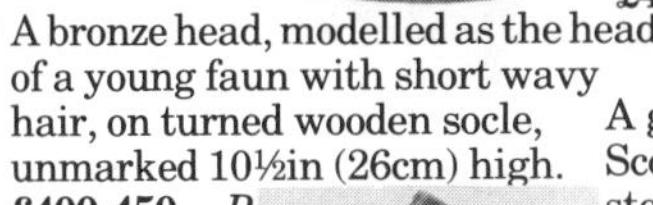

A bronze head, modelled as the head of a young faun with short wavy hair, on turned wooden socle, unmarked 10½in (26cm) high.
£400-450 *P*

A gilt bronze bust of Mary Queen of Scots, by Mathurin Moreau, on stepped socle, 19thC, 17in (43cm) high, with separate red marble plinth.
£700-900 *DSH*

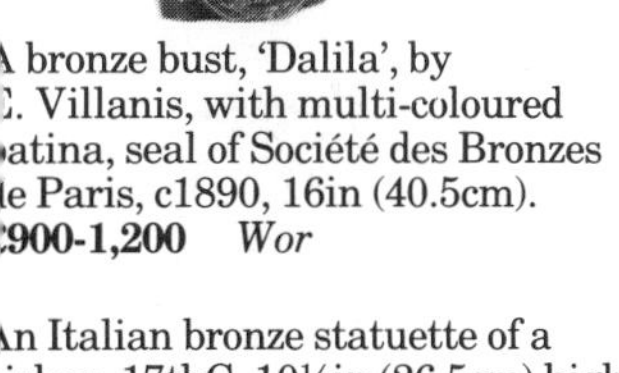

A bronze bust, 'Dalila', by C. Villanis, with multi-coloured patina, seal of Société des Bronzes de Paris, c1890, 16in (40.5cm).
£900-1,200 *Wor*

An Italian bronze statuette of a bishop, 17thC, 10½in (26.5cm) high.
£1,500-2,500 *C*

An Italian bronze of a lifesize blacksmith's apprentice, cast from a model by Commendatore Professore Rivalta, inscribed Fonderia Carradori, Pistoia, 19thC, 47in (120cm) high, on a carved wood pedestal.
£6,500-7,000 *C*

A German bronze group of Hercules and the Hydra, derived from a model by Giambologna, early 17thC, 17in (43cm) high.
£6,500-7,000 *C*

A bronzed spelter portrait bust desk ornament of Adolf Hitler, by Schmidt-Hoffer, Berlin.
£270-320 *GW*

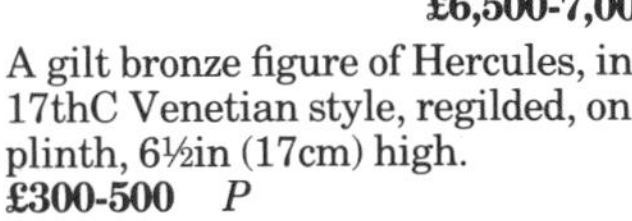

A gilt bronze figure of Hercules, in 17thC Venetian style, regilded, on plinth, 6½in (17cm) high.
£300-500 *P*

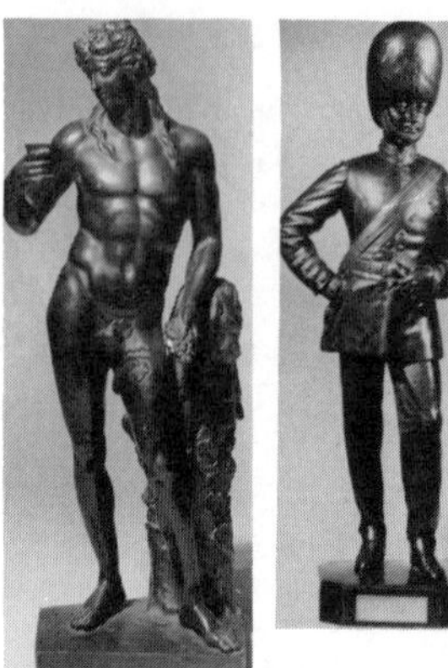

An English bronze figure of the young Prince of Wales, cast from a model by Thomas Fowke, standing on a bronze plinth inscribed T. Fowke Sc, London 1864, and bearing the silver label inscribed 'Honble. Artillery Company, Prince of Wales Prize, won by Corpl Hunt 1864', 33in (84cm) high.
£10,000-12,000 *C*

A French bronze group of the voyage of the Nations, cast from a model by Edouard Drouot, 19thC, 19½in (49cm) high.
£1,800-2,500 *C*

Drouot was born in France in 1859, he studied in Paris under the Moreaux family, and is best known as a genre painter, winning a medal at the salon of 1892 and receiving a honourable mention at the exposition of 1900.

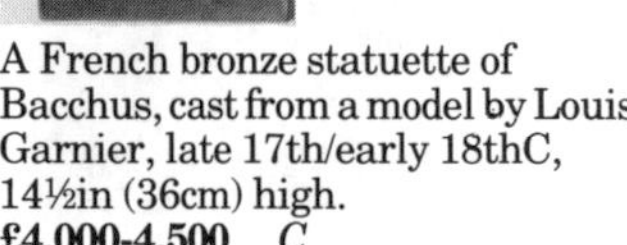

A French bronze statuette of Bacchus, cast from a model by Louis Garnier, late 17th/early 18thC, 14½in (36cm) high.
£4,000-4,500 *C*

A pair of Continental bronze figures, after Giambologna, of Mercury and Iris standing on a puff of wind, 19thC, 30in (76cm) high.
£600-700 *DN*

A pair of bronze figures of Mercury and Hebe, 19thC, tallest 32in (81.5cm) high.
£600-700 *LRG*

A 'new sculpture' bronze figure of The Catapult Boy, cast from a model by Sir William Reid Dick, signed Reid Dick, on a Siena marble base, string of catapult missing, 12½in (31cm) high.
£1,700-2,000 *C*

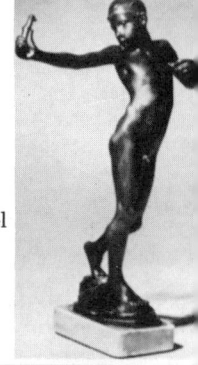

A pair of Italian bronze putti, late 19thC/early 20thC, 15½in (39cm).
£500-600 *CAm*

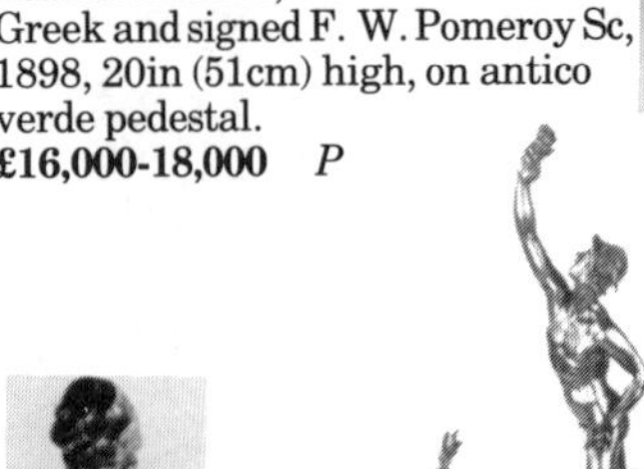

A bronze figure of Perseus, with the head of Medusa, the base incised in Greek and signed F. W. Pomeroy Sc, 1898, 20in (51cm) high, on antico verde pedestal.
£16,000-18,000 *P*

A bronze figure of a woman, signed Oscar Gladenbeck, c1900, 12in (30.5cm).
£200-300 *LRG*

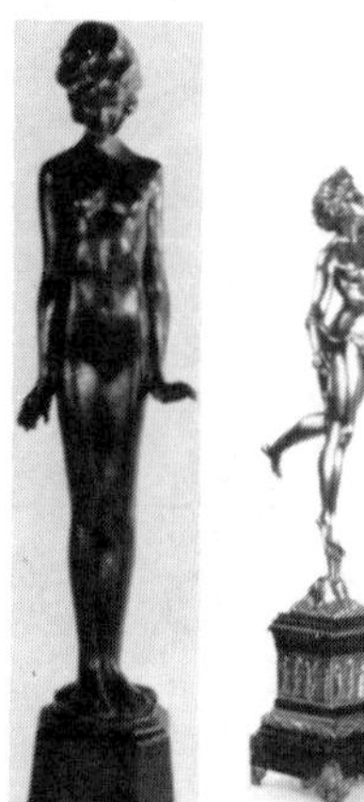

A pair of gilt bronze figures, of Mercury after Giambologna, and another of Fortune, both on marble and gilt bronze plinths, 34in (86cm).
£1,700-2,000 *P*

A French bronze statuette of a seated classical man, cast from a model by Charles René de St. Marceaux, signed St. Marceaux, and with Susse Frères, Paris, inscription, seated on a marble plinth, broken top right and overpainted gold, late 19th/early 20thC, 23½in (60cm).
£300-350 *C*

A bronze statue of a young hunter carrying a bow, his hound at his side, by Marcel Debut, signed, 30in (76cm) high.
£3,500-4,000 *P[CW]*

A bronze figure of a young naked girl, by Hester Cleminson, unmarked, 9½in (24.5cm) high.
£500-600 *P*

A bronze statuette of a French circus performer, holding a hoop and playing with a poodle, signed G. de Chemellier, 17in (43cm) high.
£150-200 *WD*

A pair of French bronze figures of Rousseau and Voltaire, 19thC, tallest 13in (33cm) high.
£1,200-1,500 *DN*

A French bronze figure of a retriever, inscribed E. Delabrierre, 19thC, 10in (25.5cm) high.
£450-500 *GC*

A bronze statue of a nude male, inscribed 'Honor Patria', and signed E Picault, 32in (81cm).
£500-600 *WD*

A French bronze figure of a racehorse, signed on the base I. Bonheur, 19thC, 11½in (29cm).
£1,800-2,500 *C*

An English bronze figure of a groom and a rearing horse, cast from a model by Joseph Edgar Boehm, the base incised, 19thC, 23½in (59cm) high.
£4,500-5,000 *C*

A bronze painted chicken and 3 chicks, late 19thC.
£100-130 *PC*

A bronze figure of a deer hound, possibly Austrian and later gilded, late 19thC, 11in (28cm) high.
£400-450 *P*

A bronze model of a seated bloodhound bitch, after Prince Paul Toubetskoy, the base bearing the signature Paolo Troubetskoy, early 20thC, 9in (22.5cm) high.
£1,000-1,500 *C*

A French bronze model of a roaring tiger, cast from a model by T. Cartier, on rocky mound, signed Cartier, late 19th/early 20thC, 11½in (29cm) high.
£900-1,500 *C*

An Austrian cold painted bronze figure of a bulldog, 4in (10cm) high.
£500-550 *SWO*

Three heavy bronze groups, camel and rider, arab horse and rider and mounted Indian, c1930, 9in (23cm) high.
£1,500-2,000 *P[WP]*

A reproduction bronze figure, 13in (33cm) high.
£250-300 *SWO*

An Austrian cold painted bronze figure of a magpie.
£500-550 *SWO*

A bronze equestrian study of a stallion, 58in (147cm) high.
£900-1,200 *BWe*

A bronze statuette, after a 19thC original, the base signed Kauba, on a green 'marble' plinth, 11in (28cm) high.
£250-300 *WD*

A pair of bronze equestrian figures, signed J. Willis, 12in (30.5cm) wide on oak stands.
£3,000-3,500 *P[PWC]*

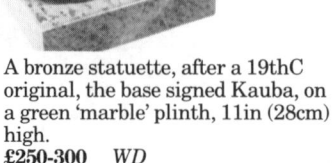

A pair of bronze cranes, 47in (119cm) high.
£600-650 *BWe*

A bronze equestrian group Vainqueuer du Derby, signed P.J. Mêne, cast by F. Barbèdienne, 16in (40.5cm) high.
£1,200-1,500 *P[PWC]*

A pair of bronze statues of Abyssinian cats, 31in (78.5cm) high.
£600-800 *CH*

A pair of Regency bronze candlesticks, 10½in (27cm) high.
£900-1,200 *P*

A pair of Regency bronze candelabra, on tapered columns, cast with laurel at the bases, on flared swagged feet and plinths, 28in (71cm) high.
£2,500-3,000 *P*

A pair of Continental bronze candlesticks, early 18thC, 9in (23cm) high.
£250-300 *KEY*

A pair of Italian bronze baluster shaped vases, with scrolling handles, 17thC, 7in (17cm) high.
£130-180 *CAm*

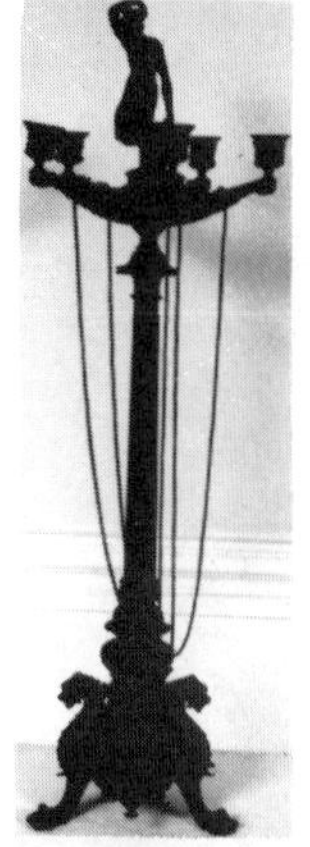

A pair of late Victorian French bronze candelabra, 32in (81cm) high.
£2,200-2,700 *Ba*

Rare because a man and a woman are depicted, whereas usually it is just men.

A bronze twelve-light chandelier in 2 tiers, 18thC, 27½in (70cm) high.
£2,000-2,500 *CAm*

A pair of French gilt bronze and champlevé vases of Japanesque form, on bronze and gilded bases with elephant's head supports, late 19thC, 14in (35cm) high.
£1,500-1,800 *P*

A pair of bronze inkwells, cast as male and female Nubian heads, studded with semi-precious stones, with ceramic eyes, and wearing parcel gilt burnouses, on black marble bases, his 'hair' replaced by a wig, 6in (15cm) high.
£1,500-2,000 *P*

An Empire gilt bronze encrier, on mahogany plinth with gadrooned half-round dishes to either side, and applied dolphin ornament, on ball feet, 10in (25cm) wide.
£1,200-1,500 *P*

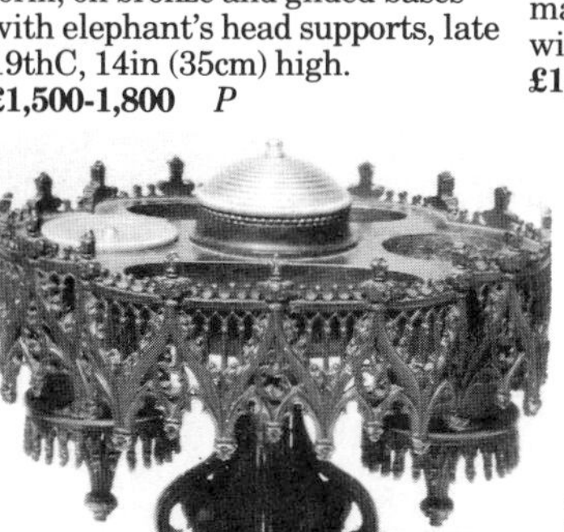

A bronze and ormolu inkwell, with pierced Gothic arcaded frieze, the pierced scrolling shaft flanked by bosses on yellow marble square base, mid-19thC, 6in (15cm) wide.
£400-600 *C*

A James II bronze mortar by Edward Neale of Binford, the waist cast with his initials EN flanking an armorial, with the date 1688 and 2 mermaid reliefs, 5in (13cm) high.
£500-550 *P*

A Stuart bronze mortar, cast on each side with a roundel of the Royal Arms incorporating the initials CR, 17thC, 5in (13cm), and a pestle.
£120-150 *P*

Two Guernsey measures, both marked on the covers by Ns.L.C., Guernsey, between stamped roseheads, with ownership ELG and IRD, 18thC, 11in (28cm) high.
£450-500 *P*

A Guernsey measure, the cover stamped with the Carter arms touch and possibly workmaster's initials CM together with ownership ISM, mid-18thC, 11½in (28.5cm) high.
£250-300 *P*

A Dutch model of a cannon, with a bronze moulded band, dated 1631 and of the period, on a two-wheeled iron mounted wood carriage, barrel 15in (38cm) long.
£1,800-2,200 *CAm*

A large bronze cauldron, with iron swing handle, on tripod with masks, 16thC, 18in (46cm) high.
£1,800-2,200 *CAm*

A bronze reduction of the Vendôme column, on white marble base, mid-19thC, 12in (30.5cm) high.
£2,500-3,000 *C*

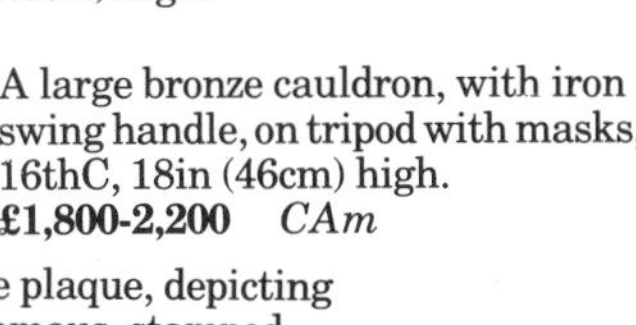

A Flemish bronze plaque, depicting the Supper at Emmaus, stamped indistinctly to the base, late 16thC, 8½in (22cm) high.
£500-800 *P*

Copper

An ebony and oval panelled jelly mould, 6in (15cm).
£50-60 *WW*

A Victorian copper jelly mould, orb and sceptre mark, 5½in (14cm).
£100-120 *WW*

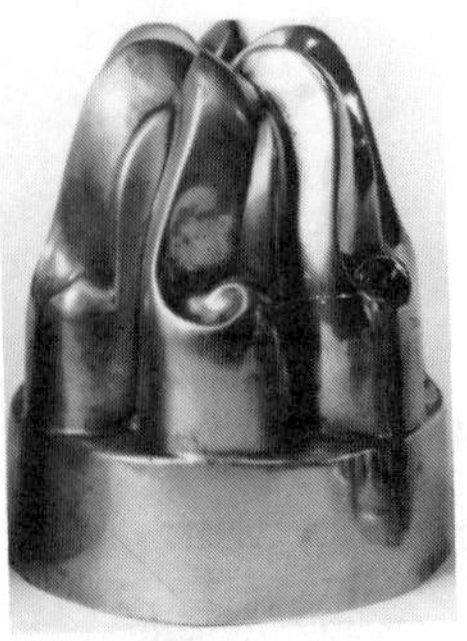

A copper jelly mould, with swirl top, 5½in (14cm).
£100-120 *WW*

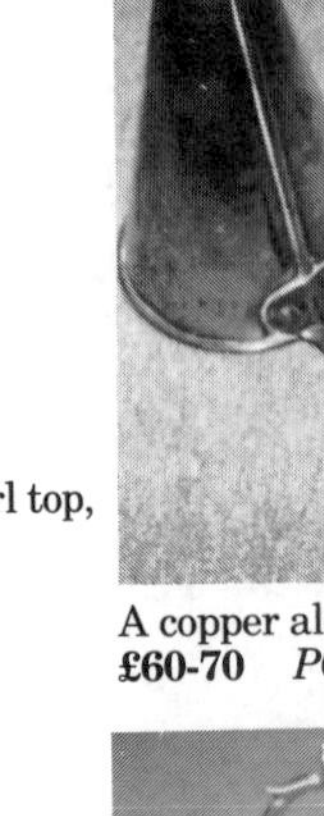

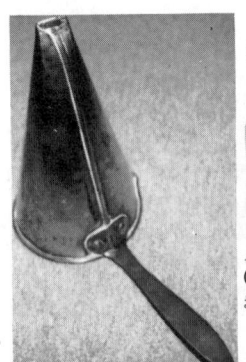

A copper ale muller, 19thC.
£60-70 *PCA*

A copper kettle, 8in (20.5cm) diam.
£60-80 *P[EDH]*

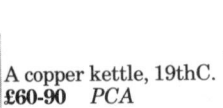

A copper kettle, 19thC.
£60-90 *PCA*

A copper tea kettle, designed by Dr. C. Dresser, with brass and ebony handle, on 3 brass stump feet, with wrought iron stand and copper burner, 31½in (80cm) high.
£400-450 *P[Re]*

A copper kettle, c1800, 12in (30cm) high.
£150-180

A brass and wood trivet, c1880, 8in (20cm) high.
£60-80 *SA*

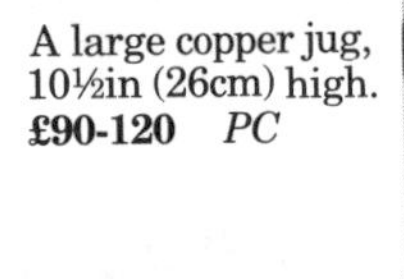

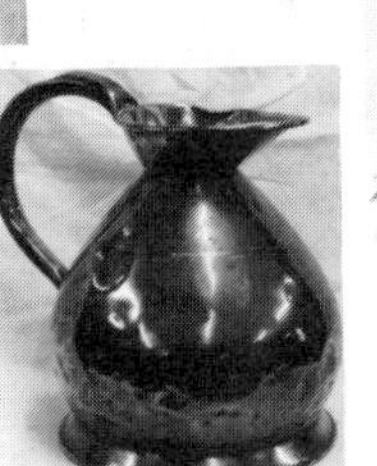

A large copper jug, 10½in (26cm) high.
£90-120 *PC*

A copper kettle, mid-19thC.
£50-70 *PC*

A copper charger, by John Pearson, signed and dated 1895, 24½in (62cm) diam.
£200-300 *ST*

A copper helmet shaped coal scuttle.
£80-100 *P[EDH]*

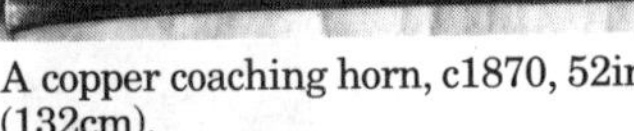

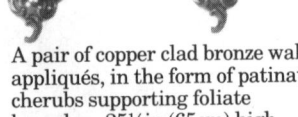

A copper coaching horn, c1870, 52in (132cm).
£120-140 *KEY*

A pair of copper clad bronze wall appliqués, in the form of patinated cherubs supporting foliate branches, 25½in (65cm) high.
£1,600-2,000 *P*

Firemarks

Sun Fire Office Fireman's arm badge, early 19thC, 7cm diam.
£300-400 *P*

Royal Exchange Assurance, lead, raised Royal Exchange Building, policy No. 1072, G.
£1,800-2,200 *P*

FIREMARKS

Glossary
M Mint
E Excellent
G Good
F Fair
P Poor

Condition is stated as a matter of opinion, and takes into account the type of material and rarity of the mark. Policy numbers are impressed unless otherwise stated

The General Insurance Company of Ireland, lead, policy No. 2113, F to G.
£500-600 *P*

Sun Fire Officer, copper, original paint.
£40-50 *KEY*

Worcester firemark, lead, original paint.
£250-300 *KEY*

Dublin Insurance, lead, policy No. 1908, bowknot separated and rejoined, G.
£600-650 *P*

New Bristol Fire Office, lead, policy No. 4423, overpainted, numbers faint, G to E.
£600-650 *P*

Worcester Fire Office, lead, overpainted, G to E.
£300-350 *P*

Norwich Union Fire Insurance, lead, two holes to centre, G to E.
£500-550 *P*

Iron

A tin candlebox, c1790, 12in (30cm) long.
£45-60 *KEY*

A tin hogscraper candlestick, c1830, 8in (20cm).
£35-45 *KEY*

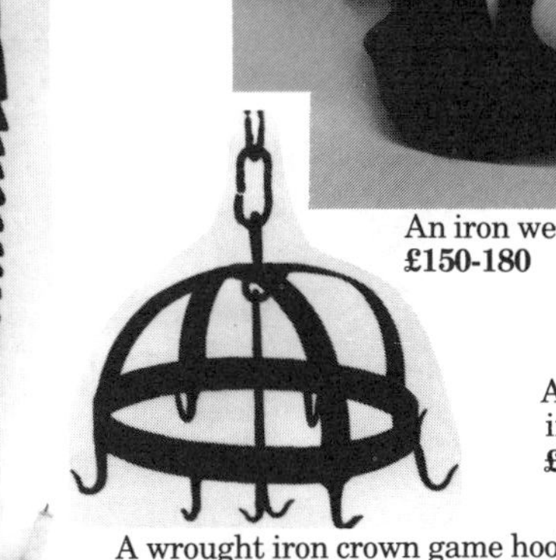

An iron weather vane, 18thC.
£150-180 *KEY*

A wrought iron adjustable candle holder, 18thC.
£200-250 *KEY*

A wrought iron crown game hook, c1770.
£200-230 *KEY*

A Victorian wrought iron cradle.
£400-450 *JeM*

A polychrome and gilt iron heraldic shield, Netherlandish, depicting the quartered Arms of the Royal House of the Netherlands, painted in green, red and cream with gilt highlights, inscribed Pletterij Den Haag, surface colour worn, 19thC, 47in (119cm) high.
£550-650 *CNY*

An iron painted pub sign of a bull, English, c1860.
£600-700 *RYA*

A mid-Victorian black painted cast iron stick stand, the back pierced with scrolling foliage and centred by a mask with semi-circular drip pan and foliate feet, 29in (74cm) high.
£350-400 *C*

A Nuremburg Armada chest, overlaid with strapwork, the interior with an elaborate locking mechanism with 13 locks turned by one key, also 2 padlocks with keys, with 2 heavy loop type carrying handles, 43in (109cm) wide.
£1,800-2,000 *P[WSW]*

A Spanish iron strongbox, the hinged top and sides with strapwork, the sides with carrying handles, with key, 17thC, 20½in (52cm) wide.
£900-1,000 *C*

A Nuremburg iron casket, with an etched decoration of figures in panels divided by bands with foliage, on ball feet, 17thC, 7in (17.5cm) wide.
£850-1,000 *CAm*

Lead

A pair of lead garden figures of seated cherubs, one holding a salver, the other a cup, both with curling locks and swirling diaper, 35½in (90cm) high.
£3,600-4,000 *P*

An English lead plaque, depicting Cupid and Psyche, in a carved giltwood guilloche frame with florets at each corner, 11½in (29cm) high.
£800-900 *P*

Ormolu

A pair of Italian ormolu candlesticks, late 18thC, 10½in (26cm) high.
£450-550 *C*

A set of 4 Louis XV style ormolu wall lights, drilled for electricity, 34½in (87cm) high.
£3,000-3,500 *CNY*

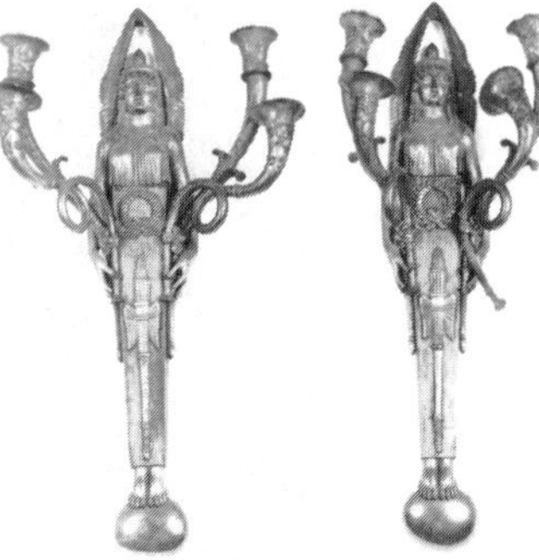

A pair of Regency ormolu wall sconces, 20½in (52cm) high.
£5,000-5,500 *P[Pea]*

A pair of ormolu twin-branched candelabra, on chased cylindrical columns and square plinths, 13½in (34cm) high.
£400-500 *C*

A pair of French ormolu and bronze candelabra, c1870, 32in (81cm) high.
£3,000-3,500 *Ba*

A pair of Empire style ormolu and green patinated twin-branch wall lights, the nozzles and drip pans decorated with lotus and anthemions, 22½in (56cm) high.
£2,000-2,500 *C*

A Directoire ormolu lampe bouillotte, with adjustable green tôle shade, drilled, 26in (66cm) high.
£1,000-1,500 *C*

A pair of ormolu and white marble chenets, each modelled with a putto warming his hands by a tripod brazier while kneeling on a plinth hung with drapery swags, on a white marble base, 11½in (29cm) wide.
£600-800 *C*

A pair of Charles X ormolu vases, 14in (35.5cm) high.
£1,800-2,200 *C*

An ormolu and simulated bronze centrepiece, with fluted oval cut glass bowl, on a foliate circlet supported by 4 scantily clad classical maidens, probably Scandinavian, early 19thC, 11in (28cm) high.
£1,800-2,200 *C*

An ormolu door knocker, the classical mask with vine leaves and grapes, mid-19thC, 7½in (19cm) high.
£400-500 *C*

An ormolu reduction of The Warwick Vase, on moulded square onyx plinth, 17in (43cm) diam.
£1,200-1,600 *C*

A Regency ormolu pen tray, in the form of a classical bath with lion masks and claw feet, on green marble base, 7in (18cm).
£700-900 *C*

Pewter

A pair of pewter hexafoil wine ewers and flat covers, variously incised, late 17th/early 18thC, 6½in (17cm) high.
£600-700 *C*

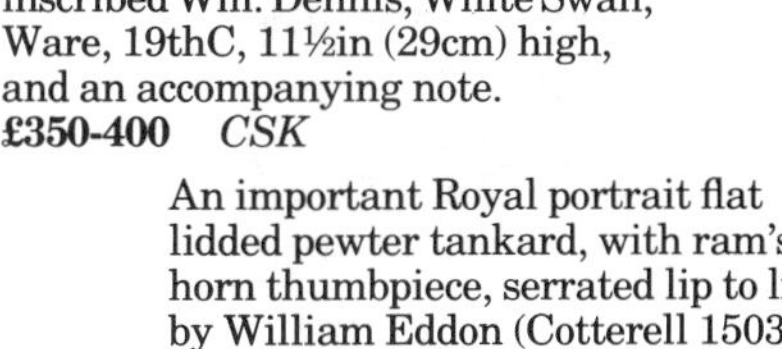

A pewter tankard of gallon capacity, inscribed Wm. Dennis, White Swan, Ware, 19thC, 11½in (29cm) high, and an accompanying note.
£350-400 *CSK*

A French charger, the plain broad border with touchmarks dated 1667, 19in (48.5cm) diam.
£750-850 *CAm*

An important Royal portrait flat lidded pewter tankard, with ram's horn thumbpiece, serrated lip to lid, by William Eddon (Cotterell 1503), c1690, 6in (15cm).
£7,000-8,000 *CSK*

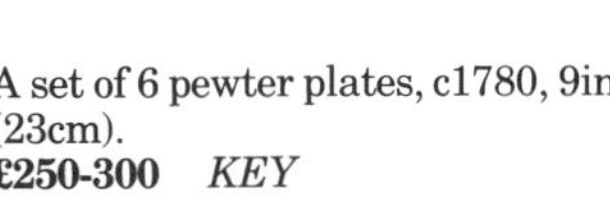

A set of 6 pewter plates, c1780, 9in (23cm).
£250-300 *KEY*

An English 17thC style pewter candlestick, the reeded knopped stem raised on an octagonal base, 8½in (21.5cm) high.
£250-300 *CSK*

A pair of Portuguese 17thC style pewter candlesticks, the knopped stems raised on compressed domed shaped bases, 4in (10cm) high.
£150-200 *CSK*

Miscellaneous

A pair of gilt metal cherub lamps, with hexagonal shades, 14in (35.5cm) high. 19thC
£250-300 *LRG*

A set of 3 polished steel fire tools, each with knopped pommel and ring turned handle and shaft, 19thC, 29in (74cm) long.
£400-450 *CNY*

A spelter bust of Marie Stuart, c1880.
£50-70 *LRG*

A spelter figure of an itinerant fiddler, 19thC, 31in (80cm) high.
£300-350 *PL*

A Britannia metal coffee pot, by Keale, Parkin & Marshall, Sheffield.
£600-650 *TW*

A pair of engraved and gold inlaid steel vases, with a centrepiece holder, Persian, Qajar period, 19thC.
£1,700-2,000 *EMA*

A Nuremburg copper gilt, brass and steel miniature box and key, in the style of Michel Mann, engraved with swags of fruit, 17thC, 6cm wide.
£1,500-1,800 *C*

A pair of gilt metal andirons, with winged lion monopodia and flaming sphere finials, on moulded bases, 19½in (49cm) high.
£800-900 *C*

A South German iron box with gilt copper ajouré mounts, in the style of Michel Mann, internal lock mechanism in need of repair, 17thC, 5cm high.
£1,200-1,500 *C*

A Nuremburg steel casket, each panel engraved with courtly figures within strapwork, the inner lid with lock, shooting 2 bolts, and engraved with scrolls, on bun feet, key replaced, late 16thC, 7½in (19cm) wide.
£800-1,200 *P*

Ivory & Shell

A Flemish carved ivory bust of a girl in a headscarf, inscribed Alph. van Beurden, on the left shoulder, on flared granite socle, late 19thC, 16½in (42cm) high.
£3,500-4,000 *P*

A Dieppe carved ivory bust of Louis XIV, 19thC, 2½in (6.5cm) high, on turned ebonised socle.
£550-650 *P*

An early French carved ivory figure of a young female in classical dress, 13in (33cm) high.
£2,000-2,500 *BWe*

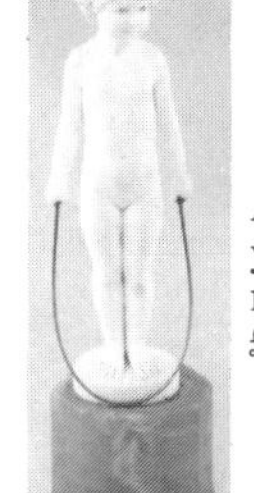

A Preiss carved ivory figure of a young naked girl with skipping rope, 4in (10cm), on onyx plinth.
£500-600 *DN*

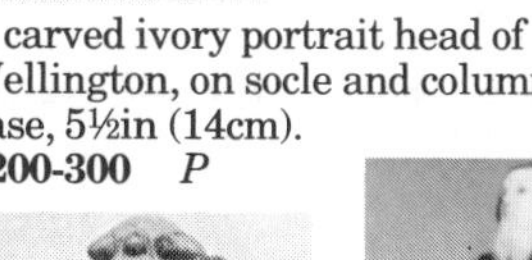

A carved ivory portrait head of Wellington, on socle and column base, 5½in (14cm).
£200-300 *P*

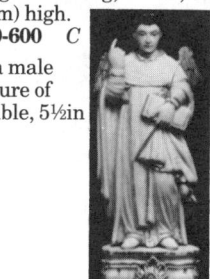

A French carved ivory group of the Madonna and Child, after a 14thC original, 19thC, 11in (28cm) high, in a fitted tooled leather case.
£2,000-3,000 *P*

A Dieppe carved ivory group of a peasant couple, with resigned expressions, in typical costume, early 19thC, 4½in (11cm), on stained socle.
£650-750 *P*

A German wood and ivory figure of a saint, on square sectioned base, 2 fingers missing, 19thC, 8½in (21cm) high.
£400-600 *C*

A pair of carved ivory figures of Joseph and Mary, traces of gilding to the integral plinth base, 18thC, 9½in (24cm) high.
£2,000-3,000 *P*

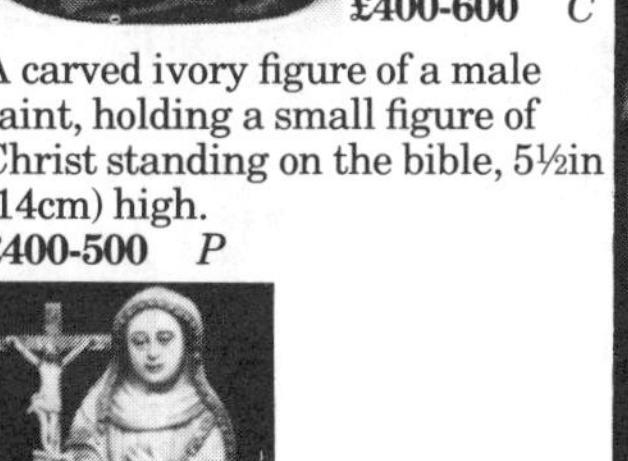

A carved ivory figure of a male saint, holding a small figure of Christ standing on the bible, 5½in (14cm) high.
£400-500 *P*

An ivory statuette of a monastic saint with wings, on a shaped ornamental stand, wings separate, traces of gilding, padded modern Chinese box and shaped stand, 18thC, 8in (20.5cm) high.
£400-500 *C*

A miniature ivory automaton, on square section pedestal, traces of polychrome, one foot missing, his back hollowed, 18thC, 3½in (9cm) high.
£200-300 *C*

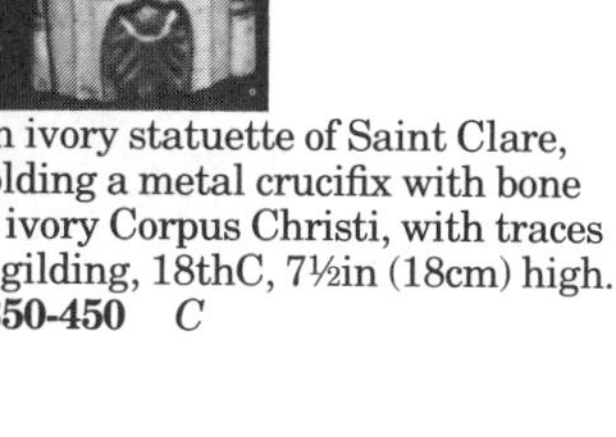

An ivory statuette of Saint Clare, holding a metal crucifix with bone or ivory Corpus Christi, with traces of gilding, 18thC, 7½in (18cm) high.
£350-450 *C*

A carved ivory figure of the kneeling Virgin, with traces of polychrome, 18thC, 7in (17.5cm) high.
£1,500-2,000 *P*

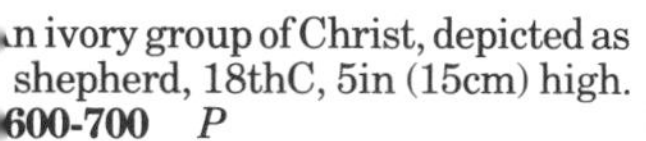

An ivory group of Christ, depicted as a shepherd, 18thC, 5in (15cm) high.
£600-700 *P*

A Flemish ivory group of putti with a goat, in the style of Van Opstal, on an ebony and ivory pedestal, minor breaks and repairs, 18thC, 6½in (17cm) high.
£2,500-3,000 *C*

A carved ivory portrait relief, reputedly of Sir Richard Lovelace, in the manner of Van der Hagen, some repairs to border, 18thC, 3½in (8.5cm).
£350-450 *P*

A part set of 11 of 12 carved ivory portrait reliefs of Caesars, mounted in 2 ripple moulded ebonised frames, 18thC.
£2,000-2,500 *P*

An Indo-Colonial ivory pipe case, with hinged lid extensively applied with relief carved foliage and maskheads, terminating in a cone, 18thC, 21½in (55cm) long.
£3,500-4,500 *P*

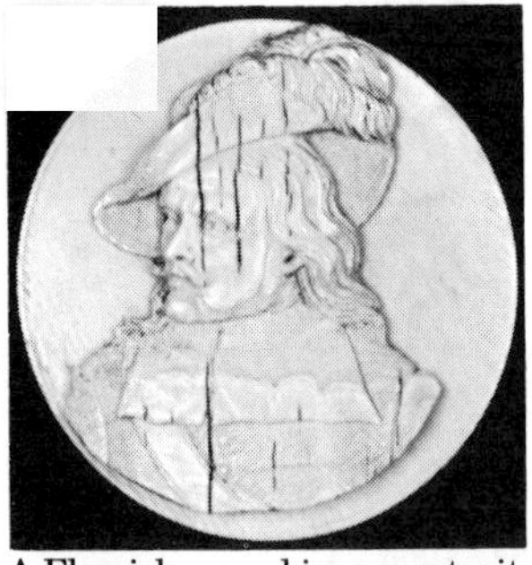

A Flemish carved ivory portrait relief, of a 17thC cavalier, on an ivory mount, 3in (7.5cm) high.
£200-250 *P*

A relief carved bone snuff box lid, depicting a couple in a wood, within a trailing vine surround, late 17thC, mounted on a later ivory box, 3½in (8.5cm).
£200-250 *P*

An ivory casket, on claw supports, probably French, mid-19thC, 15in (38cm) wide.
£4,500-5,000 *P*

A French ivory needle case, carved with shells and other rocaille in shallow relief, 18thC, 4½in (11.5cm).
£400-500 *P*

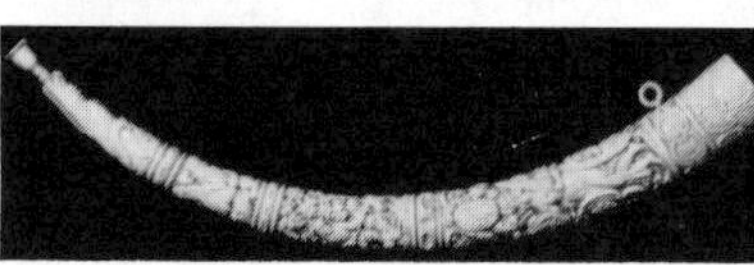

A carved ivory oliphant, probably Dieppe, c1860, 37in (94cm).
£2,000-2,500 *P*

An ivory horn, the upper part carved with a figural finial, the rest covered with leather, dark creamy patina, 21½in (54cm) high, on stand.
£700-800 *CAm*

A pair of curved ivory elephant tusks, on stepped ebonised bases, 72in (182.5cm) high.
£2,000-3,000 *P[Pea]*

A Flemish ebony, tortoiseshell and ivory mirror, with easel support, late 17th/early 18thC, 27½in (70cm) high.
£2,000-2,500 *C*

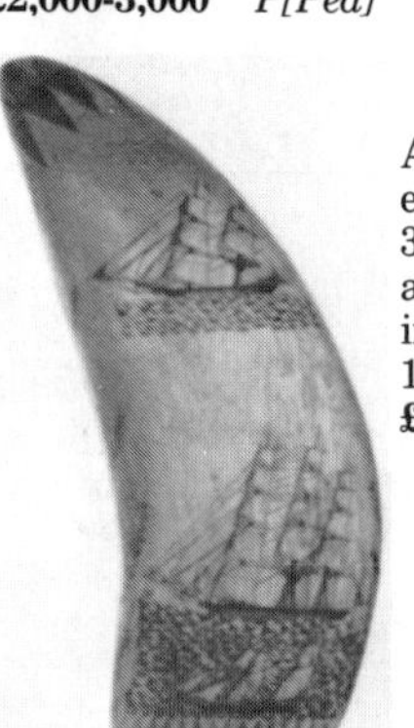

A scrimshawed whale's tooth, engraved on both faces with 3 sailing vessels of graduated size, and on one side a longboat with the inscription 'New Zealand 3rd Oct. 1837 S.D', 6½in (17cm) high.
£800-900 *P*

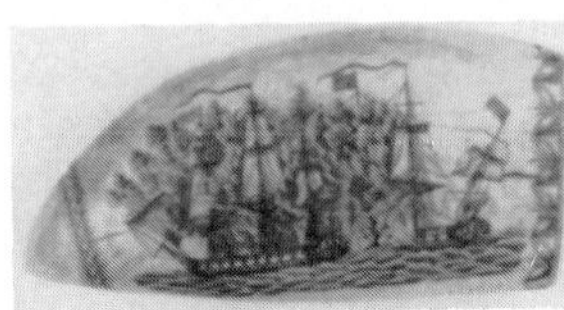

A scrimshaw whale's tooth, engraved on one side with the Battle of the Constitution and the Guerriere, engraved on the reverse with a woman amidst foliage, with foliate border, 6in (15cm) long.
£700-1,000 *C*

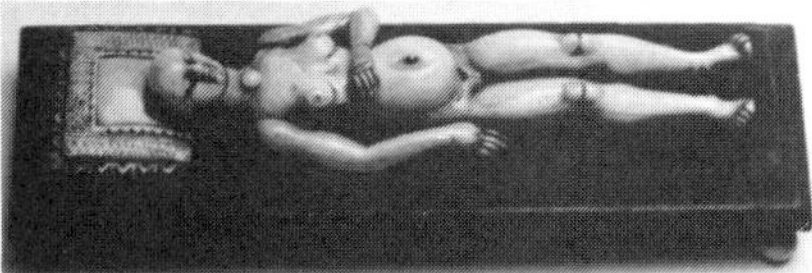

An ivory anatomical female figure, in the style of Stephen Zwick, South German, raised on 4 ivory ball feet, internal organs and one torso pin missing, late 17thC, 9½in (24cm) long.
£1,600-2,000 *CNY*

A Continental ivory ewer, 19thC, 10in (25.5cm) high.
£2,500-3,000 *DN*

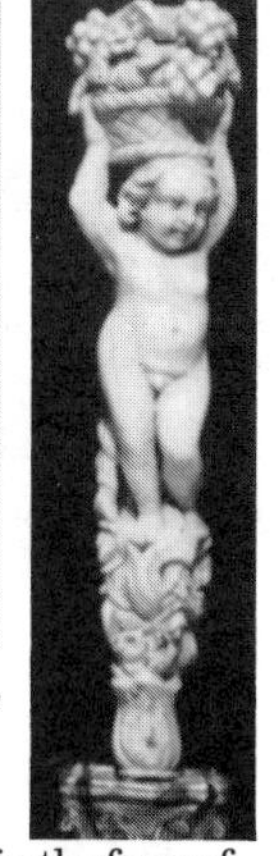

A carved ivory handle, in the form of a cherub, carrying a basket of fruit on his head, supporting a cartouche shaped embossed hand mirror, probably later, 18thC, 13in (33cm) high.
£400-450 *P*

An Indo-Colonial ivory cane handle, in the form of a dragon's head, 5in (13cm) high.
£300-350 *P*

A German lathe-turned ivory cup, some damage, 18thC, 11in (28cm) high.
£4,000-4,500 *C*

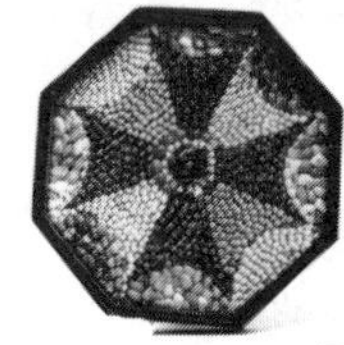

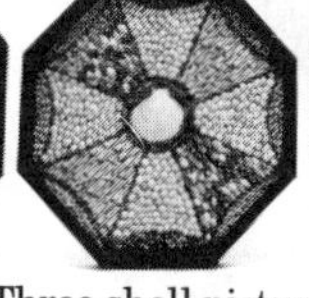

Three shell pictures, in octagonal wooden frames, 19thC, 11in (28cm) wide.
£400-500 *LRG*

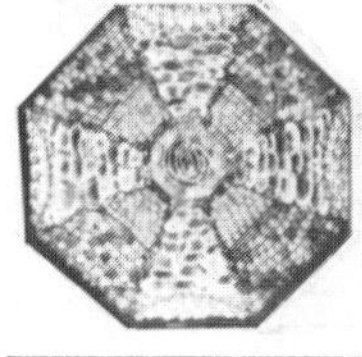

A pair of sailor's shell valentines, one arranged as a cross, the other with the motto 'Be True', in glazed octagonal frames, late 19thC, 21in (53cm) wide.
£400-450 *P*

Tortoiseshell

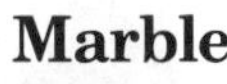

A German tortoiseshell mounted crucifix, with silvered metal appliques, and bulbous Baroque style hexagonal foot, 17thC, 12in (30.5cm) high.
£400-450 *C*

A tortoiseshell box and cover, inset with an ivory panel, carved with 2 reclining lovers, 3in (7.5cm).
£200-250 *DN*

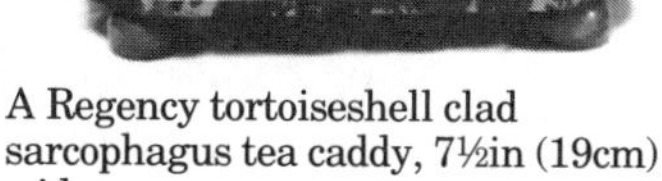

A Regency tortoiseshell clad sarcophagus tea caddy, 7½in (19cm) wide.
£400-600 *P[EDH]*

Marble

A Milanese marble group of The Virgin and Child, by Agostino Busti called Il Bambaia, some damage, early 16thC, 9in (23cm) high.
£4,000-5,000 *C*

A white marble study of a partially nude female, on grey veined marble plinth, 19thC, 33in (84cm) high.
£1,200-1,500 *BWe*

A white marble figure of a barefoot peasant girl, on a grey marble plinth, some damage, 19thC, 22in (56cm) high.
£250-300 *LRG*

A white marble sculpture, probably Diana, in her role as the great mother of Nature goddess, partially clad and holding her breasts, with 2 suckling dogs at her feet, 46in (116.5cm) high.
£4,000-5,000 *P[PWC]*

A marble figure of a nude maiden, seated on a pedestal, signed Pugi, 27in (69cm) high.
£1,500-2,000 *M*

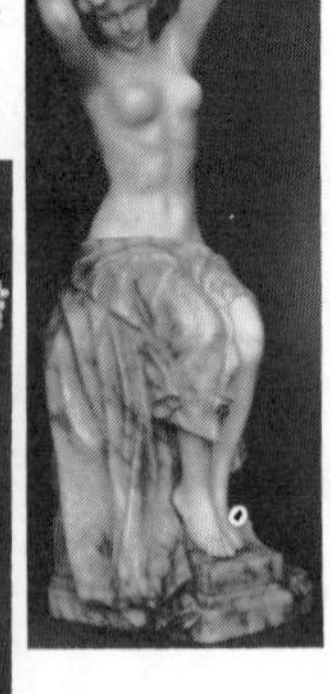

A Victorian carved marble figure of a young girl feeding corn to a dove on her shoulder, 30½in (77cm) high.
£1,500-1,800 *GSP*

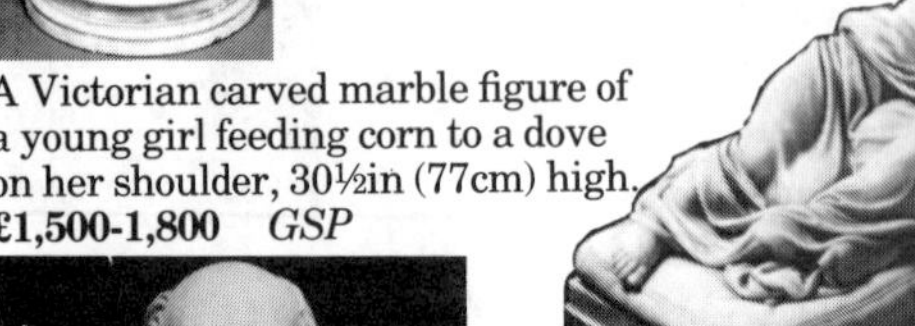

An Italian marble figure of Apollo Belvedere, some restoration, 19thC, 50in (127cm) high.
£7,000-9,000 *C*

An American marble group of 2 children asleep on a mattress, by William Rinehart, on an integral plinth signed W.H. Rinehart Sculpt., lower marble plinth, velvet covered wooden pedestal, 19thC, 35½in (90cm) wide.
£42,000-46,000 *C*

An English marble bust of General George Guy Carlton L'Estrange, inscribed on the reverse 'Lt. General George Carlton L'Estrange' and 'W. Theed 1853', 27½in (70cm) high, on marbleised pedestal.
£1,500-1,700 *C*

A Victorian white marble bust of Sir John Knight by John Durham, 29in (74cm) high.
£600-650 *LRG*

An English marble bust of an elderly gentleman, by Sir Francis Chantrey, wearing a toga, signed Chantry, Sculptor 1816, 24½in (62cm) high.
£4,000-5,000 *C*

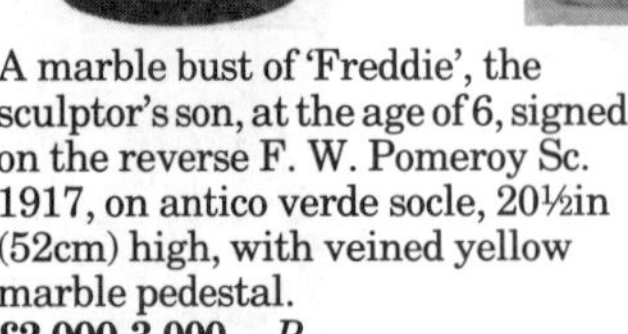

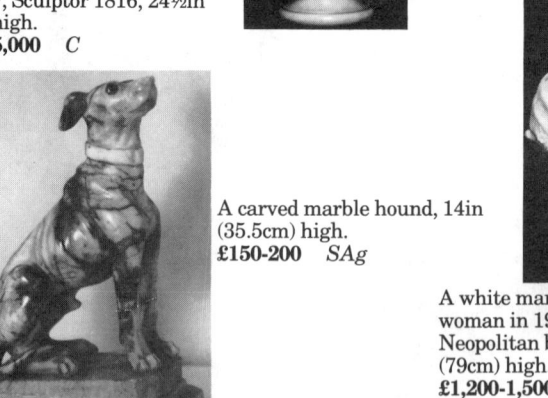

A carved marble hound, 14in (35.5cm) high.
£150-200 *SAg*

A white marble bust of a young woman in 19thC dress and Neopolitan bonnet, on socle, 31in (79cm) high.
£1,200-1,500 *LRG*

A marble bust of 'Freddie', the sculptor's son, at the age of 6, signed on the reverse F. W. Pomeroy Sc. 1917, on antico verde socle, 20½in (52cm) high, with veined yellow marble pedestal.
£2,000-3,000 *P*

An Indian white marble low table, on baluster legs, Jaipur, 28in (71cm) wide.
£500-600 *C*

An Italian Sienna marble miniature sarcophagus, the lid with scrolling ends and inscribed Cornelio. C.N.F. Scipio, with an inscription on black marble base, 8in (20cm) wide.
£1,400-1,700 *C*

An Indian white marble bench, the solid seat on baluster legs, Jaipur, 48in (122cm) wide.
£1,500-2,000 *C*

A pair of Louis XVI style ormolu mounted rouge marble urns, fitted for electricity, early 20thC, 20in (51cm) high.
£1,500-2,000 *N*

◀ A blue marble vase of Louis XVI design, the ovoid body with twin ormolu satyr mask heads, on spreading foot and square plinth, 15½in (40cm) high.
£1,000-1,200 *P*

▶ A gilt metal mounted red marble urn, in the style of Thomas Hope, fitted for electricity, 16½in (42cm) high excluding shade.
£400-500 *C*

A pair of rouge marble Corinthian columns, with ormolu mounts, on square stepped bases, late 19thC, 52in (132cm) high.
£3,000-3,500 *LRG*

Terracotta/Stone

A German/Dutch terracotta bust of the young Bacchus, attributed to Guillaume de Groff, cracked and repaired, on terracotta socle, 17thC, 13½in (34cm) high.
£1,500-2,000 *C*

A terracotta portrait bust of George Washington, after Jean-Antoine Houdon, inscribed Houdon f.1778, French, old staple restoration at the back, early 19thC, 20in (51cm) high, on grey marble socle.
£1,000-1,200 *CNY*

A pair of black and brown mottled marble pedestals, with turned capitals and socles, on square bases, 42½in (108cm) high.
£800-1,200 *C*

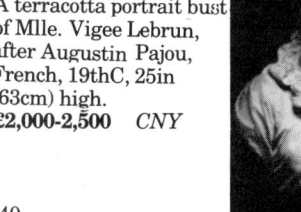

A French terracotta bust of a child, by Gustave Deloye, signed on the rim Gustave Deloye 79, minor abrasions, on marble stand, late 19thC, 12½in (32cm) high.
£1,200-1,500 *C*

A Victorian terracotta bust of Marie Antoinette, 32in (81cm) high.
£1,200-1,500 *Ba*

A painted terracotta bust, c1940, 20in (51cm) high.
£200-250 *BA*

A terracotta portrait bust of Mlle. Vigee Lebrun, after Augustin Pajou, French, 19thC, 25in (63cm) high.
£2,000-2,500 *CNY*

A terracotta ridge tile, straddled by the figure of a winged dragon in the Gothic style, 19thC, 24in (61cm).
£80-120 *LRG*

A French moulded terracotta group, entitled Enfance de Silène, in the manner of Clodion, 19thC, 15in (38cm) high.
£600-700 *P*

A French terracotta group of a satyr and 2 putti, in the manner of Clodion, minor chips and damage to fingers, on octagonal plinth, 19thC, 18½in (47cm) high.
£2,500-3,500 *C*

A terracotta group, sculptured in the manner of George Tinworth, some damage, 18in (46cm).
£100-200 *Bea*

An Italian terracotta relief of The Madonna and Child, after Desiderio da Settignano's 'Sabauda Madonna', 16thC, in a carved walnut frame with sliding glass, 22in (56cm) high.
£1,800-2,200 *C*

An Italian terracotta relief of the raising of Lazurus, some damage, late 17thC, 19in (48cm) high, with a moulded wood frame and backing with old collection of gallery and customs labels.
£2,000-2,500 *CNY*

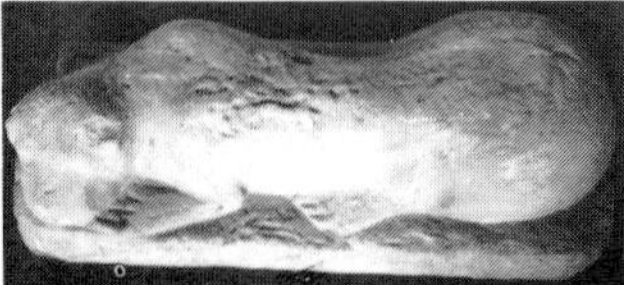
A Limestone otter, English, c1500.
£1,300-1,600 *RP*

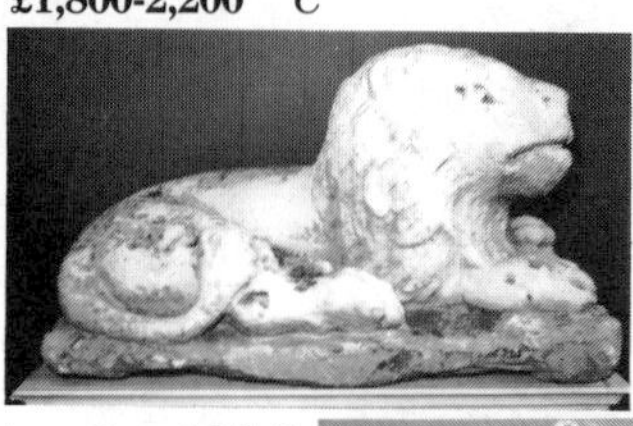
A stone lion, 18thC.
£1,300-1,600 *RP*

Two hardstone planters, the green planter issuing 6 pink and white quartz peonies, the other of 8 flowers and green quartz leaves, 10in (25.5cm) high.
£90-120 *CNY*

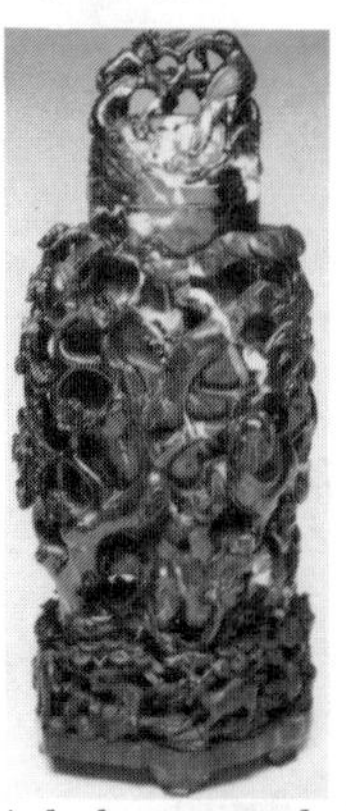
A dark green and white flecked hardstone baluster vase and domed cover, 15in (38cm) high, on elaborate hardwood stand.
£2,400-2,700 *CNY*

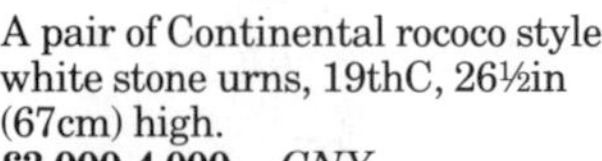
A pair of Continental rococo style white stone urns, 19thC, 26½in (67cm) high.
£3,000-4,000 *CNY*

A set of 4 Italian neo-classical style alabaster urns, fitted for electricity 18in (46cm) high.
£2,000-2,500 *CNY*

A Raeren brown glazed stoneware baluster tankard, with an inscription dated 1600, with contemporary hinged pewter cover, minor chips, 10in (25cm) high.
£900-1,200 *C*

An English Gothic sandstone water stoup, carved with a pair of Green Man faces and twisted foliage behind, with round receptacle in top, 14th/16thC, 11in (28cm) high.
£600-800 *C*

Woodcarvings

An oak panel, 16thC.
£140-180 *KEY*

An oak Renaissance carved panel, 16thC.
£150-200 *KEY*

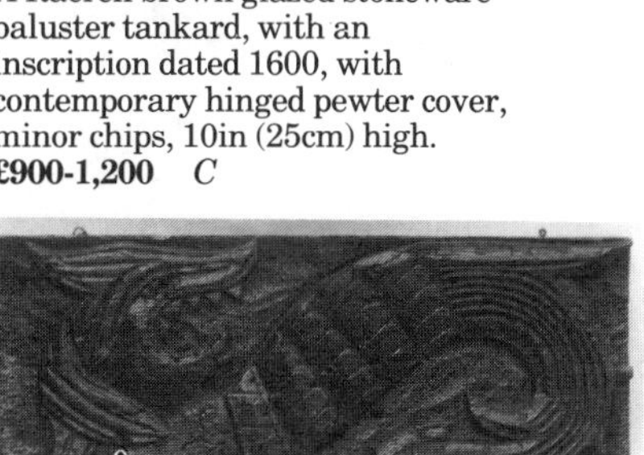

An oak panel of a dragon, 17thC.
£80-90 *KEY*

A pair of walnut carvings, 17thC, 29½in (75cm) high.
£1,000-1,200 *OBA*

A pair of oak carvings, 17thC, 16½in (42cm) high.
£250-300 *PCA*

A carved oak panel depicting Adam and Eve, Flemish, 17thC, 17in (43cm) high.
£500-550 *OBA*

A carved wooden cresting with cupids and flowers, probably Italian, 18thC, 86in (218cm) wide.
£350-450 *LRG*

A French polychromed carving with original decoration, c1710, 27in (68.5cm) high.
£450-550 *RYA*

A Continental carved wooden tankard, with hinged cover and lion finial, on 4 crouching lion supports, 8in (20cm).
£1,500-2,000 *P[WSW]*

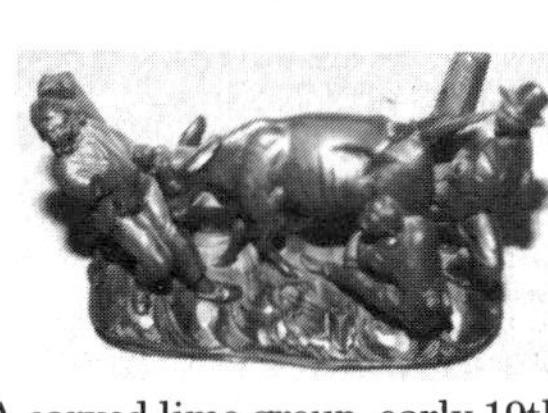

A carved lime group, early 19thC, 10in (25cm).
£250-300 *PCA*

A pair of Régence giltwood wall brackets, early 18thC, 9in (23cm) high.
£5,000-5,500 *CNY*

A pair of English carved oak dogs, 19thC, 9in (23cm).
£700-800 *BHA*

A European carved wood figure of a stag with a tree and glass flower epergne, 11½in (29cm) high.
£80-100 *PC*

A carved lion's head, 19thC.
£250-300 *RIP*

A Swiss carved wood stick stand, 19thC, 35½in (90cm) high.
£1,000-1,500 *DN*

◀ An Edwardian carved wood bear umbrella stand, 35in (89cm).
£400-500 *PC*

A Black Forest carved wood smoker's stand, with musical movement playing 2 airs, the whole supported by a standing bear, 35in (89cm) high. ▶
£700-800 *Bea*

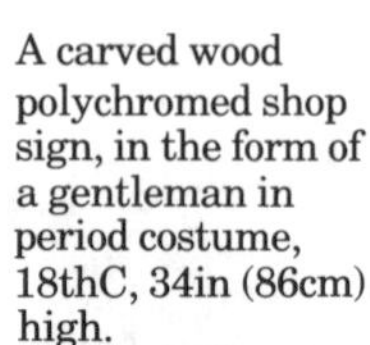

A carved wood polychromed shop sign, in the form of a gentleman in period costume, 18thC, 34in (86cm) high.
£6,000-6,500 *P*

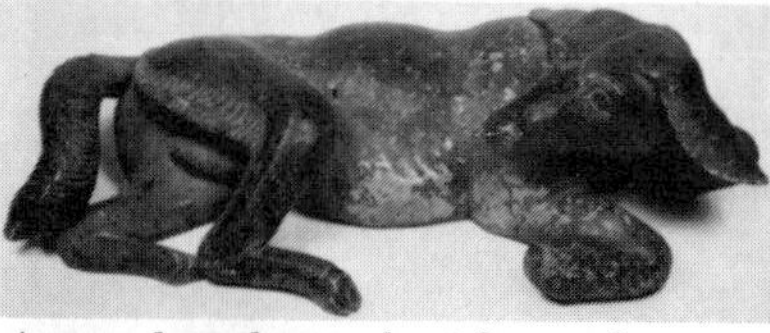

A carved wood recumbent figure of a dog, with large ears and a bushy tail, 34in (86cm) wide.
£3,000-3,500 *C*

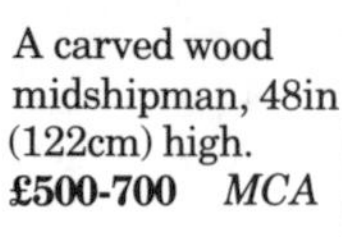

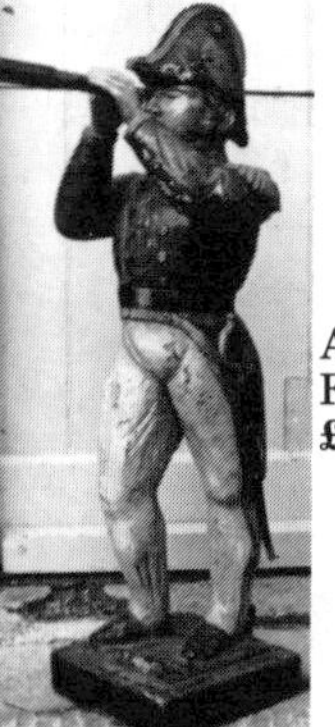

A carved wood midshipman, 48in (122cm) high.
£500-700 *MCA*

A pair of carved oak female figures, Flemish, c1580, 18in (46cm).
£800-850 *OBA*

A dummy board, in the form of Justice, balance missing, early 19thC, 71in (180cm).
£1,000-1,500 *DN*

A Flemish wood figure of St. John, carved in relief, repairs to left thumb and forefinger, 17thC, 13½in (34cm) high.
£6,000-7,000 *C*

A walnut carving of a horse-drover and horse, pulling a section of a tree, from the workshop at Brienz, Switzerland, carved by A. L. B. Huggler, c1900, 34in (86cm) wide.
£1,000-1,200 *P[WSW]*

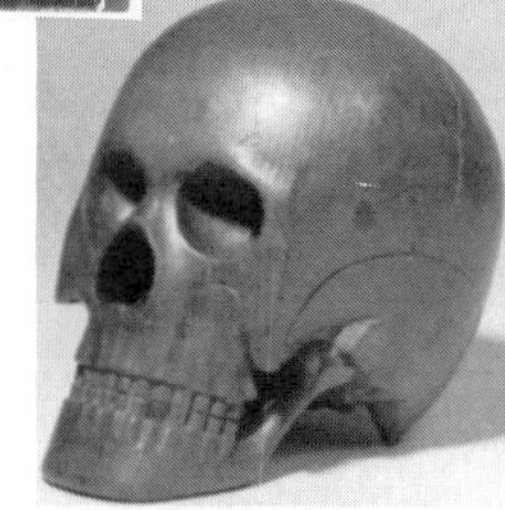

A German pinewood skull, 17thC, 7½in (19cm) high.
£1,600-2,000 *C*

Antiquities

Marble

A Roman marble commemorative tablet, the inscription reading 'Q. Pacuvius Stipius Giulio Isochruso Cognato Suo Locumdonavitob Meritis, 5in (13cm) square.
£300-350 *P*

A Roman marble relief of Eros, the face carved with up-turned reticulated pupils and framed by locks of wavy hair, surrounded by stylised wings, scrolls and foliage, 2nd-3rd Century AD, 8 by 12in (20 by 30cm).
£450-500 *P*

Metalware

A Roman bronze figure of the child, Harpokrates, seated naked on an amphora, c2nd Century AD, 4.7cm long.
£100-120 *P*

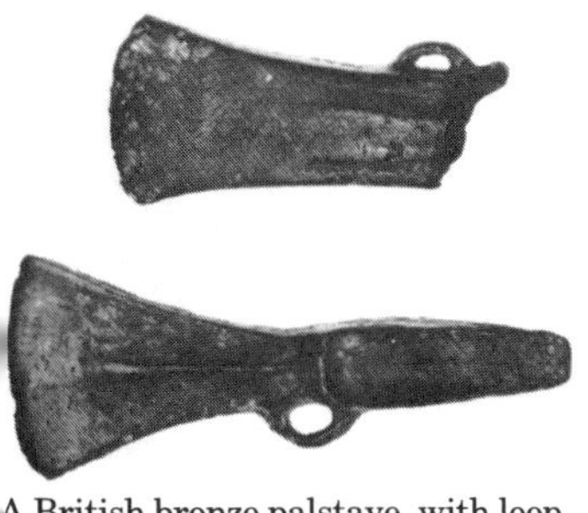

A British bronze palstave, with loop for securing to the haft, 6½in (17cm) long, and a British bronze socket celt with loop, 4½in (12cm) long, both early 1st Millennium.
£350-400 *P*

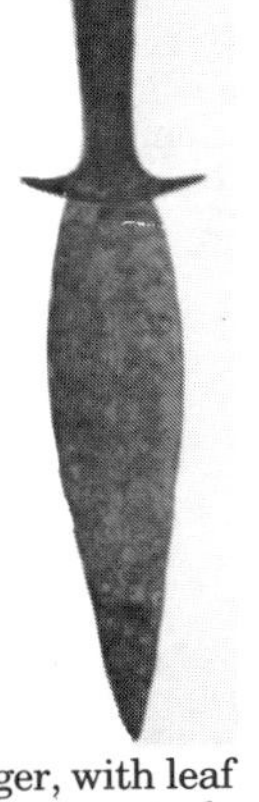

An Amlash bronze dagger, with leaf shaped blade and openwork conical hilt, c2000 BC, 11in (28cm).
£300-350 *P*

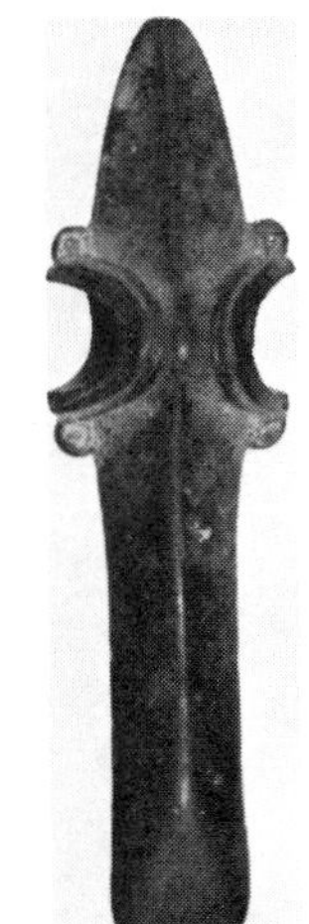

A Syro-Palestinian bronze axe head, with concave ridges around the circular socket, c2000 BC, 6in (15.5cm) long.
£200-250 *P*

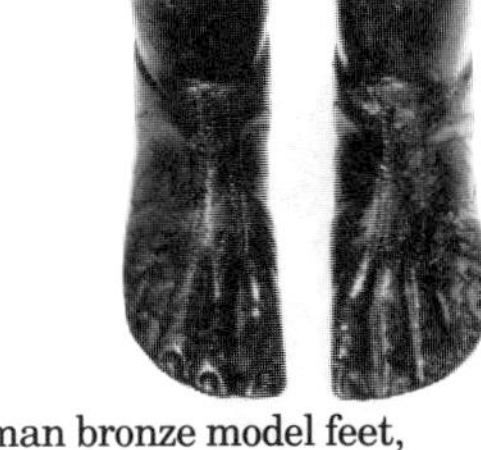

A pair of Roman bronze model feet, socketed, the sandals with dotted ornament, c2nd Century AD, 3in (8cm) long.
£150-200 *P*

A Romano British bronze fibula, with linear decoration and onion shaped terminals, 3rd-4th Century AD, 2½in (6.5cm) long, and a Roman bronze weight in the form of a stylised winged figure, with a loop for suspension, 2½in (6.5cm) high.
£40-80 *P*

A Roman bronze bust of Athena, her hair swept back underneath a plumed helmet, wearing a draped tunic with incised scales, 2nd Century AD, 3½in (8.5cm) high.
£200-250 *P*

Pottery

An Attic red figure miniature krater, decorated with the Anodos of Aphrodite, late 5th-early 4th Century BC, 6½in (16cm) high.
£750-1,000 *CAm*

A Greek geometric pottery pyxis and cover, the rim and cover pierced for attachment, late 8th Century BC, 4½in (11.5cm) diam of rim.
£550-650 *CAm*

A Greek geometric pottery bowl, decorated with concentric banding, zig-zags and a rosette on the base, late 5th Century BC, 8cm diam of rim.
£150-200 *CAm*

A collection of Roman red glaze bowls, with various potter's stamps, Lecoux Potteries, central Gaul, late 2nd Century AD.
£200-250 *P*

The 5 vessels were recovered from Puddingpan Rock, Herne Bay, Kent.

Miscellaneous

A Greek terracotta figure of a cockerel, with painted comb and tail feathers, Boeotia or Rhodes, 1st half 5th Century BC, 8.2cm high.
£300-350 *CAm*

A Boeotian geometric terracotta figure of a horse and rider, tail and rider's head missing, mid-6th Century BC, 4½in (12cm) high.
£250-300 *CAm*

A Boeotian geometric terracotta figure of a horse, with high braided mane, decorated with stripes, rider missing, mid-6th Century BC, 5in (12.5cm) high.
£300-350 *CAm*

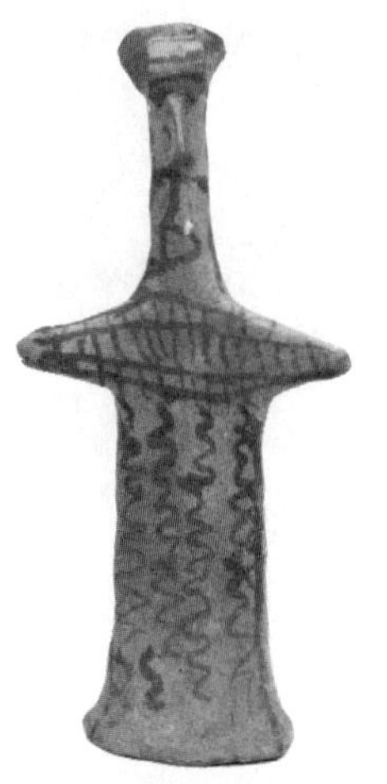

A Khmer stone carving of Buddha, seated in dhyanasana on a stepped snake base, rising to a snake head canopy behind him, some damage, 13th Century, 11½in (29cm) high.
£200-250 *CSK*

An Egyptian Anthropoid wood mask, with traces of red pigment around the large bulbous eyes, Ptolemaic Period, 7in (18cm) high.
£160-220 *P*

A Boeotian terracotta 'Pappades' figure, decorated with stripes and wavy lines, mid-6th Century AD, 7½in (17.5cm) high.
£450-500 *CAm*

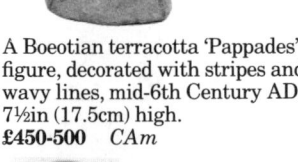

A wood ushabti, the front incised with a line of hieroglyphs, New Kingdom, 7½in (19cm) high.
£600-700 *P*

An Egyptian wood ushabti, painted in yellow, the details applied in black and red with a column of hieroglyphs at the front, New Kingdom, 6½in (16cm) high.
£300-350 *P*

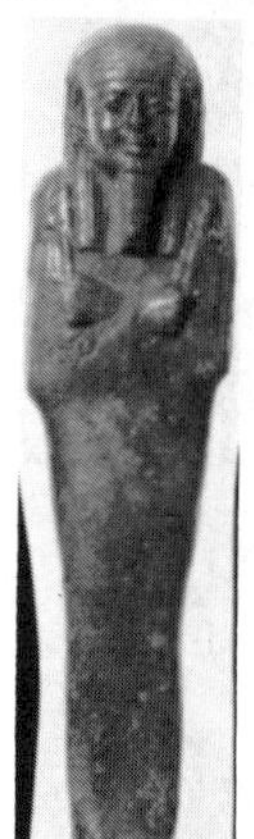

An Egyptian turquoise glaze ushabti carrying a pick, hoe and basket, the back pillar impressed with hieroglyphs, 26th Dynasty, 7½in (19cm) high.
£800-900 *P*

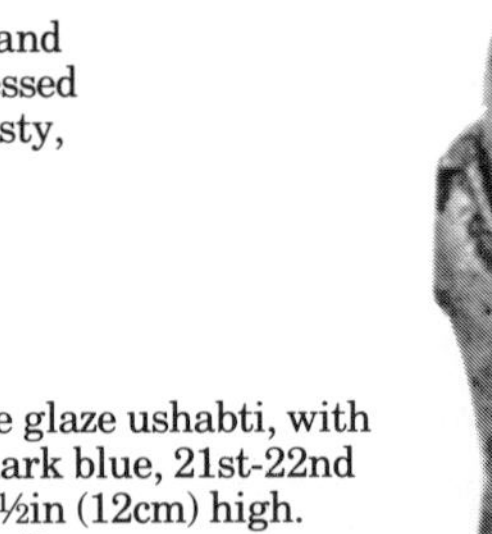

A turquoise glaze ushabti, with details in dark blue, 21st-22nd Dynasty, 4½in (12cm) high.
£200-250 *P*

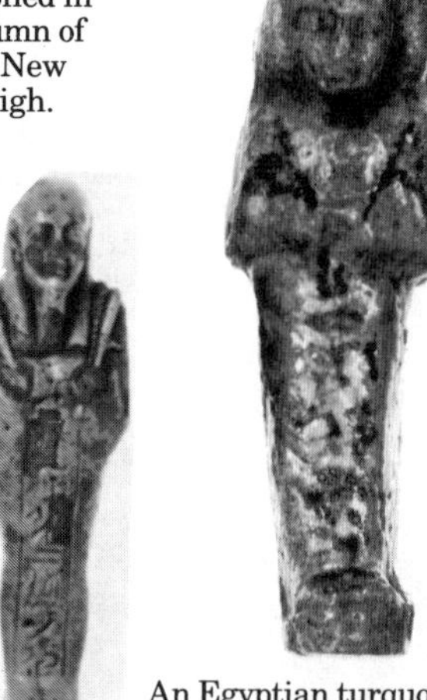

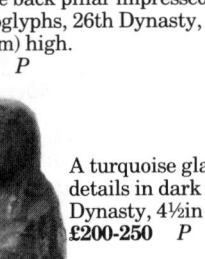

An Egyptian turquoise glaze ushabti, the inscription at the front and the pick and hoe painted in black, late Dynastic Period, 4½in (11.5cm) high.
£200-230 *P*

An Egyptian pale green mottled glaze ushabti, the front impressed with a column of hieroglyphs, 6in (15.5cm), and a pottery ushabti with traces of pale blue glaze with impressed hieroglyphs, 5in (12.5cm) high, both late Dynastic Period.
£300-350 *P*

An Egyptian blue glaze ushabti, the details and 6 lines of hieroglyphs in dark blue glaze, 21st Dynasty, 6½in (16.5cm).
£600-700 *P*

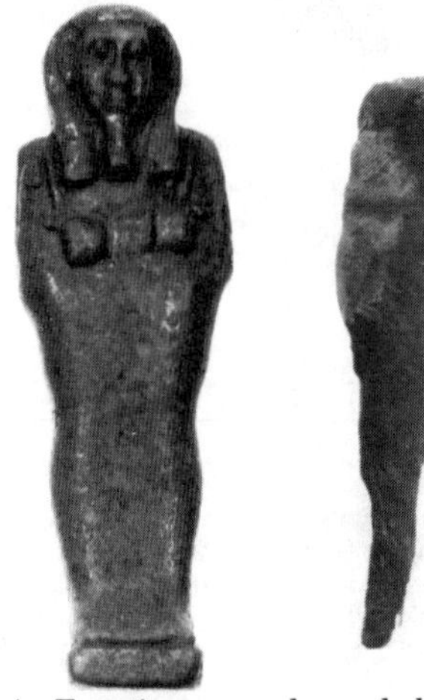

An Egyptian mummified hawk, complete with wrappings, late Dynastic Period, 8¼in (22cm) long.
£300-350 *P*

An Egyptian cartonnage mask with inlaid eyes and gilded face, with scarab, glass paste eyes with blue surrounds and brows, the back of the wig painted with the mummified figure of a deity, Ptolemaic Period, 3rd-1st Century BC, 21in (53cm) high.
£5,000-6,000 *CAm*

An Egyptian green glaze ushabti, the back clearly impressed with a column of hieroglyphs, late Dynastic Period, 4½in (11cm) high.
£160-200 *P*

Rugs & Carpets

An Abadeh rug, the ivory field with traditional vases of flowers, 78 by 56in (198 by 143cm).
£450-550 *P*

An Afshar rug, with short kilim strip at each end, slight damage, 133 by 65in (337 by 165cm).
£1,700-2,000 *C*

An Afshar rug, with double diamond panels on blue ground, 74 by 52in (188 by 132cm).
£800-1,000 *MGM*

An Agra carpet, the ivory field with wine floral spandrels, with turquoise guard stripes, 139 by 116in (353 by 295cm).
£2,500-3,500 *P*

An Afshar rug.
£80-100 *MGM*

pair of Aubusson 'entre fenêtres', ıe ivory fields with neo-classical ɔwer stands, some damage, 19thC, 17in (298cm).
3,000-4,000 *P*

An Aubusson tapestry carpet, in deep rose and ivory within aubergine spandrels, 19thC, 116 by 98in (290 by 249cm).
£6,000-7,000 *P*

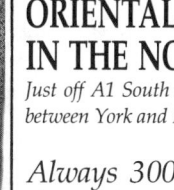

An Aubusson carpet, the central loral spray on a celadon ground, reduced, mid-19thC, 80½ by 76½in 204 by 194cm).
£3,500-4,500 *C*

A Bergama rug, the rust field enclosed by an ivory quartered flowerhead border, 73 by 56½in (185 by 144cm).
£700-900 *P*

An Empire Aubusson carpet, with central flowerhead and a circlet of summer flowers on a khaki ground, 184 by 197in (467 by 500cm).
£4,000-6,000 *C*

GLOSSARY

Abrash	Variations of density in a colour seen in a carpet by irregular horizontal washes, can greatly add to the value
Aniline	Chemical dye, a derivative of coal-tar, first produced in the 1860s, most common in the red-blue-purple range, colours tend to fade (orange-pink, for instance can fade to walnut-brown)
Boteh	Widespread pattern of Persian origin (original meaning 'cluster of leaves'), used in Europe in the Paisley pattern
Ch'ang	Chinese endless knot, the inextricable knot of destiny
Chrome dye	A fast synthetic dye now used in all the major rug weaving areas, colours do not fade
Gol Henai Pattern	Floral pattern associated with Persian rugs, mainly found on Hamadan rugs
Hejira (or Hijra)	The beginning of the Muhammedan calendar, 16 July, AD 622
Herati Pattern	Also called the mahi or fish pattern. This common pattern originated in East Persia
Jufti	'False' knot, either Turkish or Persian, whereby the knots are tied to four, not two, warp threads
Kelim	Also spelled kilim, gilim, gelim. Principally from Anatolia
Madder	Deep red-brown dye
Palas	Caucasian name for kelim
Palmette	A flowerhead of heart-shape with many radiating lobes or petals
Sileh	A corruption of a now lost Caucasian place name. A form of Soumak, sileh pieces tend to be woven with rows of large S-motifs
Soumak	Sumak, Summak, Sumacq, Sumakh, thought to be a corruption of Shemaka, town in south east Caucasus
Spandrels	Architectural term for the space between the curve of an arch and the enclosing mouldings
Swastika	A hooked cross. Chinese symbol for 10,000 (wan) and happiness
Tiraz	Official weaving factory usually set up under Royal patronage

Miller's is a price GUIDE not a price LIST

A Louis Philippe Aubusson rug, the floral sprays on a chocolate ground, 73 by 78in (185 by 198cm).
£2,500-3,500 *C*

A Bergama rug, with plum red field, 77 by 64in (196 by 162cm).
£700-900 *P*

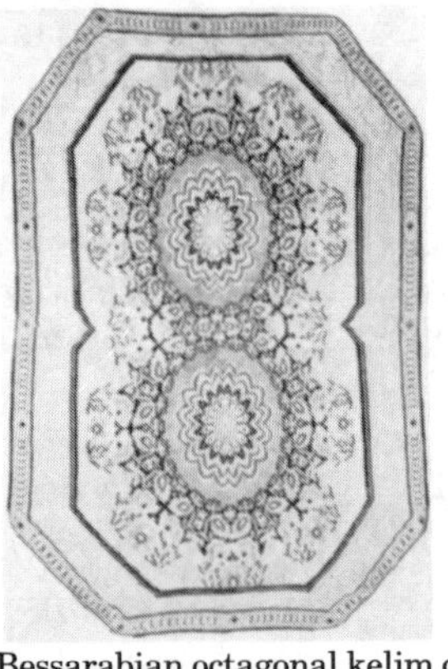

A Bessarabian octagonal kelim of Western influence, with 2 flowerhead medallions, 84 by 57in (212 by 146cm).
£1,000-1,200 *P*

An Aubusson tapestry carpet, the plum field with ivory floral medallion, 19thC, 159 by 118in (404 by 300cm).
£3,000-4,000 *P*

A Beshir prayer rug, the ivory field around a brick red prayer panel, slight wear, repaired, 77 by 40in (196 by 102cm).
£2,000-3,000 *C*

A Bidjov rug, the indigo field covered with stylised birds, animals and human figures in panels of ivory, mauve, tan and light green, 77 by 52in (196 by 132cm).
£1,700-2,000 *C*

A Caucasian carpet, with 3 columns of palmettes, flowerheads, vine and lilies in a tomato red field, slight damage, repairs, late 18thC, 196 by 87in (497 by 222cm).
£6,000-7,000 *C*

A Chodor carpet, the brown field with 4 columns of Tauk Nuska guls divided by secondary guls, very slight wear, 108 by 70in (274 by 178cm).
£900-1,200 *C*

A Ghiordes prayer rug, with plain ivory field, the stepped 'mihrab' with ivory and blue floral stripes, in an ivory and brown floral striped border between pale beige floral stripes, a short kilim strip at each end, slight overall wear, 83 by 58in (210 by 147cm).
£2,000-3,000 *C*

A silk Heriz prayer rug, the dark caramel field with scrolling vine and palmettes flanked by columns supporting a salmon pink 'mihrab', in an ivory palmette and vine border between light blue flowering vine strips, areas of slight wear, replaced selvedges, 72 by 53in (183 by 135cm).
£4,000-4,500 *C*

A Hamadan rug.
£300-400 *MGM*

A Hereke rug, the ivory field with eau-de-nil tracery vine around a turquoise flowerhead lozenge and escutcheon panel within a similar broad red and pale turquoise floral border, signed, 71 by 48in (180 by 122cm).
£1,500-2,000 *C*

A Hereke carpet, the ivory field with scrolling vine in a multiple burgundy and ivory palmette, signature cartouche at one end, 172 by 117in (439 by 296cm).
£2,500-3,000 *C*

A large Hereke carpet, the shaded lilac field with an Ardebil design, in cream, lilac, burgundy and ivory, with signature cartouche, 195 by 162in (495 by 412cm).
£2,500-3,000 *C*

A Heriz carpet, the indigo field with terracotta, powder blue, rose and mustard palmette pendant medallion, 210 by 141in (535 by 360cm).
£4,000-4,500 *P*

An Isfahan rug, with ivory field, 84 by 57in (213 by 144.5cm).
£1,000-1,500 *P[CW]*

An Isfahan Serafian rug, the ivory field with a central red and ice blue medallion, signature cartouche at one end, 94 by 57in (238 by 145cm).
£7,000-7,500 *C*

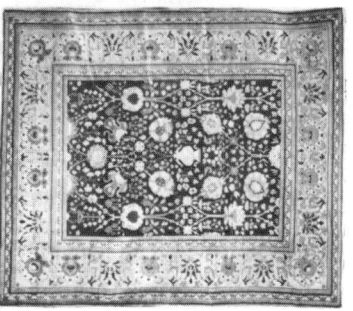

A Hereke rug, the burgundy field with an Isfahan vase carpet design, a signature cartouche at one end, repaired, 101 by 84in (256 by 213cm).
£2,500-3,000 *C*

An Isfahan Tree of Life rug, the ivory field with trees, birds and animals, within a madder cartouche border and 4 guard stripes, 82 by 55in (208 by 139cm).
£1,000-1,500 *Bea*

An Isfahan rug, the crimson field with an ivory cartouche pendant medallion and all over floral and foliate stems, within mustard spandrels and a main indigo floral border, 84 by 56in (213 by 142cm).
£1,000-1,500 *P*

A Daghestan prayer rug, the ivory field with stylised plants and flowerheads, slight wear, 55 by 43in (140 by 109cm).
£1,800-2,200 *C*

A Dhurrie, the ivory field with rows of concentric blue, red and pale blue medallions, alternating with rows of stylised fleur-de-lys, in a shaded lilac border with red key pattern, 116 by 74in (294 by 188cm).
£600-700 *C*

A Davarghin kilim, in dark brown and brick red, 127 by 58in (322 by 147cm).
£800-1,000 *C*

A Derbend corridor rug, on blue ground.
£350-450 *MGM*

A Dhurrie, the shaded pale blue field with central rust brown floral medallion and similar in each corner, areas of repair, one end stained, 192 by 165in (488 by 419cm).
£750-850 *C*

A Derbend runner, the rust field with 5 indigo medallions, octagons and scattered motifs enclosed by an ivory rosette meander border, dated 1890, 196 by 52in (500 by 132cm).
£1,500-2,000 *P*

A Dhurrie, the pale green field with staggered rows of large pale blue flowerhead medallions surrounded by tendrils, in a broad purple flowering vine border, repaired and stained, 162 by 144in (412 by 366cm).
£900-1,000 *C*

A Dhurrie, the light blue field with a stylised angular lattice enclosing large flowering plants, in a shaded buff border of hooked vine, repaired and stained, 157 by 113in (398 by 286cm).
£600-700 *C*

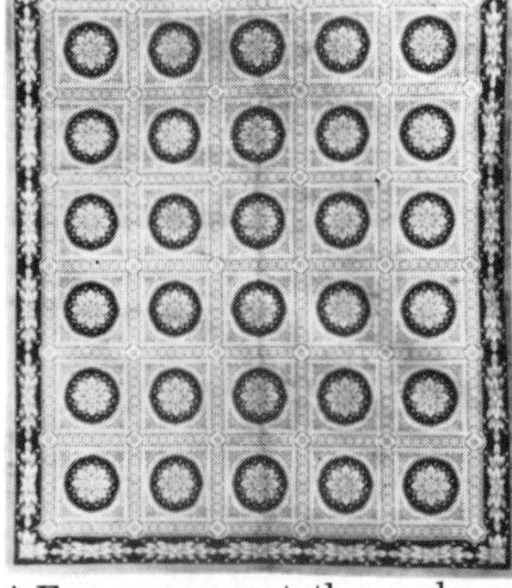

A European carpet, the mushroom brown field with a square floral trellis, enclosing indigo flowerhead roundels with scrolling spandrels in an indigo spray border with outer plain stripe, 142 by 121in (360 by 307cm).
£2,500-3,000 *C*

Make the most of Miller's

Miller's is completely different each year. Each edition contains completely NEW photographs. This is not an updated publication. We never repeat the same photograph.

A Fereghan rug, the indigo herati field with rose herati meander border, 70 by 58in (178 by 147cm).
£550-600 *P*

A needlework carpet, woven in bright colours with a central spray of summer flowers and oval band of foliage, the wide borders with scrolling foliage and fruit on an ivory ground, signed A. Galliard, 1804, repaired, mid-19thC, 109 by 82 in (276 by 208cm).
£5,500-6,000 *C*

RUGS & CARPETS

A Caucasian kilim, the field divided into alternate indigo and brick red bands of stepped and hooked lozenges, slight wear, repaired, 113 by 63in (286 by 160cm).
£900-1,200 *C*

A Caucasian kilim, the field with serrated and stepped medallions in various colours, some damage, repairs, 117 by 68in (297 by 172cm).
£600-800 *C*

A Caucasian kilim, the field divided into broad ivory bands divided by multi-coloured smaller bands of stepped lozenges, 122 by 51in (309 by 130cm).
£700-1,000 *C*

A Chinese carpet, the plain blue field with light blue angular spandrels, 136 by 107in (344 by 272cm).
£4,000-5,000 *C*

A Chinese carpet, the ivory ground woven with a peacock, a crane and 2 swimming ducks, with dark blue outer border, 116 by 84in (290 by 215cm).
£3,500-4,500 *P[PWC]*

A Chichi rug, the indigo field with rows of hooked lozenges divided by rows of octagonal flowerheads, 77 by 49in (196 by 124cm). ▶
£4,000-5,000 *C*

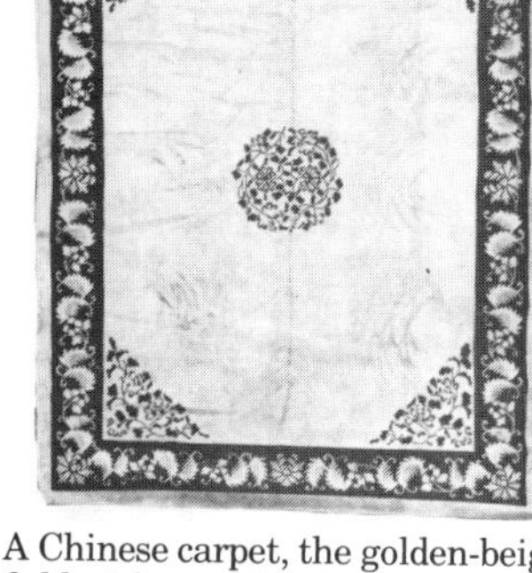

A Chinese carpet, the golden-beige field with open floral roundel and sprays, plain outer stripe, 140 by 108in (355 by 275cm).
£4,500-5,500 *C*

A Caucasian kilim, the blue field with diagonal rows of ivory, red, yellow and brown lozenges, some damage, 116 by 61in (294 by 155cm).
£300-500 *C*

A Chodor rug, the fox brown field with stylised floral lozenges in ivory, burgundy, ice blue and sea green, some wear, repaired, 105 by 61in (266 by 155cm).
£400-600 *C*

A Chelaberd rug, the brick red field filled with stylised flowerheads around sunburst medallions, slight wear, 95 by 58in (241 by 147cm).
£3,000-4,000 *C*

RUGS & CARPETS

A Karabagh kelim, the black ground with 2 bouquets in a floral spray frame, 164 by 74in (416 by 188cm).
£2,500-3,000 *C*

A Karabagh kelim, the black field with 3 bouquets surrounded by sprays with birds and stylised human figures, in an open spray border, repaired, 145 by 62in (368 by 157cm).
£1,000-1,500 *C*

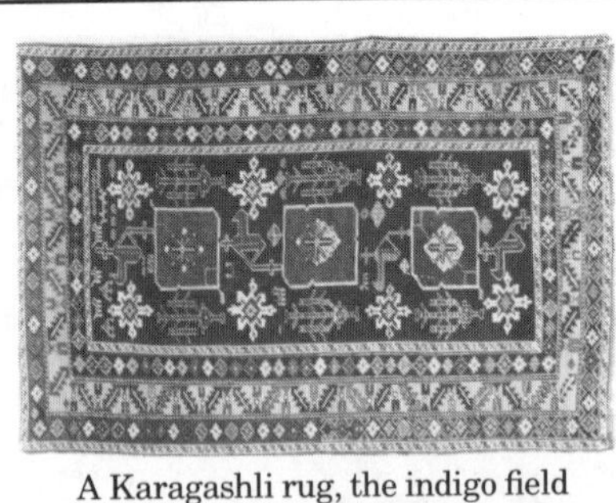

A Karagashli rug, the indigo field with stylised flowerheads, flower vases and animals around 3 red floral medallions, a short kelim strip at each end, very slight overall wear, 54 by 38in (137 by 95.6cm).
£2,500-3,000 *C*

A pair of Kashan rugs of prayer influence, the indigo field with powder blue floral spandrels, enclosed by red floral and indigo palmette panelled borders, 83 by 54in (210 by 138cm).
£3,000-3,500 *P*

A pair of Kashan rugs, each indigo field with a floral design, madder medallion and spandrels, with twin guard stripes, 82 by 53in (208 by 135cm).
£2,000-2,500 *Bea*

A Kashgai rug, the indigo field with all over designs of stylised birds and flowers, with multi-coloured border, 109 by 60in (277 by 151cm).
£1,200-1,500 *P*

A Kashan rug, with central medallion, on a deep pink field, within a deep blue floral border, 72 by 48in (182 by 122cm).
£400-600 *LRG*

A Kashan rug with a Tree of Life, flowers and birds on a pale green field, one main camel ground border and several narrow borders, damaged, 81 by 52in (205 by 132cm).
£1,500-2,000 *DN*

A Kazak rug, 82 by 57in (208 by 145cm).
£5,000-6,000 *DN*

A Kashgai rug, the hooked rust red field with repeated rows of multi-coloured floral botehs, within an ivory serrated leaf and palmette meander border, 50 by 38in (126 by 98cm).
£900-1,000 *P*

A Kazak prayer rug, the red 'mihrab' with green lozenges, blue arch enclosed by an ivory leaf and calyx border, 48 by 40in (122 by 102cm).
£550-650 *P*

A Kazak rug, the red field with 2 columns of light blue and indigo medallions, in an ivory border, a short kelim strip at each end, 81 by 50in (206 by 127cm).
£1,200-1,500 *C*

A Khorrassan prayer rug, the ivory field with flowering tree with palmettes, 2 inscription cartouches between red and blue stripes dated AH 1316 (AD 1898), 90 by 65in (228 by 165cm).
£2,000-3,000 *C*

A pair of Kirman rugs, with ivory fields, central medallions and three line borders, 74 by 45in (188 by 114cm).
£400-500 *Wor*

A Kirman carpet, the ivory field with all over floral and foliate designs in pale blue, rose and ivory, with blue floral border, 110 by 73in (280 by 186cm).
£1,600-2,000 *P*

A Kirman mille fleurs prayer rug, the shaded yellow field with floral sprays issuing from a baluster vase within a light blue floral frame, 109 by 82in (276 by 208cm).
£2,000-2,500 *C*

A Kirman rug, with an inscription cartouche at one end stating 'To the order of (?) Mukhya Kirmani', 84 by 53in (213 by 135cm).
£3,500-4,500 *C*

A Konagkend rug, the indigo field with stylised ivory floral lattice in a broad indigo stylised 'kufic' border between baton, zig-zag and skittle pattern stripes, slight overall wear, repaired, 61 by 49in (155 by 125cm).
£700-1,000 *C*

A Konya carpet, the shaded burgundy field with blue and deep aubergine octagons, with a broad blue border of stylised flowerheads and vine, areas of slight repair and wear, 149 by 67in (379 by 170cm).
£4,000-5,000 *C*

A Kuba rug, the dark brown field with stylised flowerheads, palmettes and animals around 3 ivory and red medallions, in an ivory stepped border, slight damage to one end, 77 by 50in (196 by 127cm).
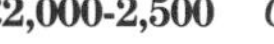
£2,000-2,500 *C*

A Kuba Leshgi rug, the brick red field scattered with stylised flowerheads and blue and ivory octagons around 3 Leshgi medallions, a short kelim strip at each end, very slight overall wear, 55 by 47in (140 by 119cm).
£1,500-2,000 *C*

A Kuba Shirvan rug, the royal blue field scattered with ivory stellar octagons, stylised plants and animals around a string of ivory and royal blue palmette lozenges in a border of red, blue, apricot and green hooked lozenges, braided ends, 66 by 44in (168 by 112cm).
£2,000-2,500 *C*

A Kuba rug, the fox brown field with 3 ivory, red and blue Leshgi medallions, slight wear overall, 68 by 39in (173 by 99cm).
£1,300-1,800 *C*

A Melas prayer rug, the headed brown 'mihrab' with ivory spandrels enclosed by a saffron stella border and meander floral guard stripe, 56 by 47in (142 by 119cm).
£400-800 *P*

A Moghan rug, the ivory field with 2 columns of hooked stepped cruciform medallions, damaged, 92 by 43in (234 by 109cm).
£1,500-2,000 *C*

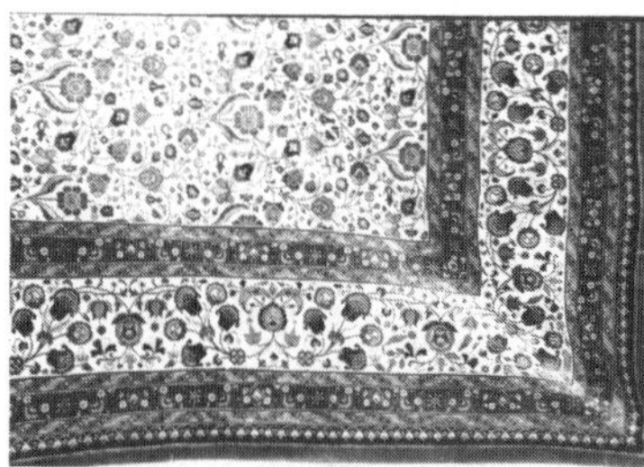

A Persian Qum, with ivory field and 3 inner and 5 outer guard stripes, signed, 163 by 122in (414 by 309cm).
£7,000-8,000 *P[CW]*

A Qashqai kelim, the brick red field with light blue, apricot and brown serrated lozenges, with an ivory border of concentric lozenges, and an outer reciprocal lozenge stripe, 86 by 57in (218 by 145cm).
£500-1,000 *C*

A Kuba rug, the fox brown field with blue, ivory, red and yellow Leshgi medallions, areas of slight wear, small repairs, 104 by 41in (261 by 104cm).
£750-800 *C*

A Moghan rug, the field divided into 2 columns of alternate red and royal blue panels containing octagons, a short kelim strip at each end, 67 by 48in (170 by 122cm).
£4,000-5,000 *C*

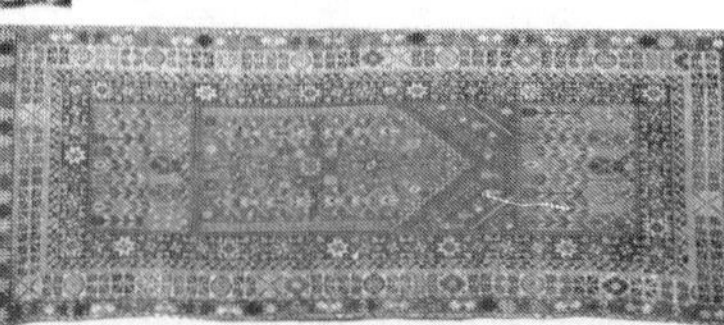

A Moroccan prayer carpet, the brick red field with columns of stylised plants and flower vases, the stepped and hooked green 'mihrab' with similar motifs, with an ivory stylised flowerhead and roundel border, very slight overall wear, Rabat, 216 by 78in (548 by 192cm).
£2,000-3,000 *C*

A Perepedil rug, the blue field with ram's horn and key design, some wear and damage, 70 by 53in (177 by 134cm).
£1,000-1,500 *P[PWC]*

A Mahal rug, the brick red field with a column of flowerheads and flowering vine, between blue and ivory floral stripes, slight wear, 92 by 57in (234 by 145cm).
£750-800 *C*

A Malayir Kelleh, the brick red field with 'herati' pattern, around a string of cusped floral medallions, one end slightly damaged, 159 by 69in (403 by 175cm).
£1,000-1,500 *C*

A Ninghsia rug, the yellow field with a rice grain pattern around a cusped beige, pink and blue floral medallion, areas of corrosion and slight wear, 81 by 55in (206 by 140cm).
£2,000-2,500 *C*

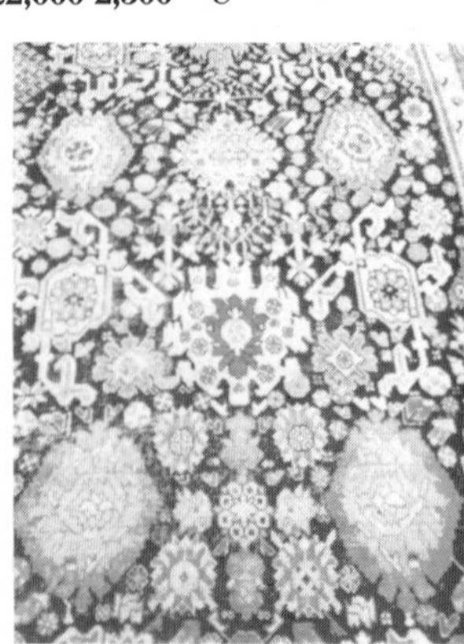

A North West Persian corridor carpet, with indigo field and brick red border between ivory strips, a few areas of slight wear, 238 by 76in (604 by 193cm).
£1,000-1,500 *C*

A Perepedil rug, the indigo field with 'wurma' motifs, stylised peacocks, enclosed by an indigo 'kufic' border, repaired, 61 by 42in (156 by 106cm).
£2,000-2,500 *P*

A Sarouk rug, the indigo field with 'herati' pattern around a yellow hooked medallion, 78 by 52in (198 by 132cm).
£5,000-6,000 *C*

A Shirvan prayer rug, with a broad ivory border of multi-coloured hooked motifs between stripes, 64 by 37in (163 by 94cm).
£2,000-2,500 *C*

A Shirvan prayer rug, the pistachio green field with a lattice of multi-coloured serrated 'boteh', with stylised flowerhead and skittle pattern stripes, slight overall wear and repair, 57 by 43in (145 by 109cm).
£1,000-1,200 *C*

A Qashqai kelim, the brick red field with diagonal rows of multi-coloured hooked lozenges, embroidered skirts at each end, 118 by 62in (299 by 157cm).
£800-1,000 *C*

A Romanian carpet, the burgundy field with a Mughal design, very slight wear, 187 by 141in (474 by 358cm).
£1,000-1,500 *C*

A Senneh rug, the indigo field with 'herati' pattern around ivory and indigo concentric 'boteh' with deer and lions, a kelim strip at each end, 78 by 55in (198 by 142cm).
£4,000-5,000 *C*

A Shirvan rug, the indigo field scattered with stylised flowerheads, birds and human figures, in a brick red stylised glass and serrated leaf border, 59 by 42in (150 by 107cm).
£1,500-2,000 *C*

A Shirvan rug, the indigo field with stepped and serrated medallions, enclosed by a main stylised bird's head border, 64 by 52in (162 by 132cm).
£1,200-1,500 *P*

A Qashqai rug, the indigo field with 'herati' pattern, in a brick red flowering vine border between light blue and ivory flowering vine stripes, associated tassels, 77 by 55in (195 by 140cm).
£4,500-5,000 *C*

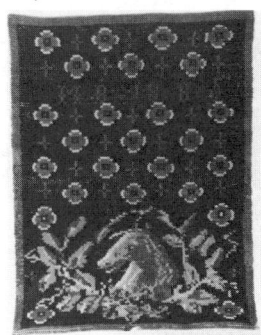

A Rya rug, with chocolate brown field, a horse's head encircled by leafy sprays, in a plain red border inscribed 'MB 1885', 51 by 41in (129 by 104cm).
£600-700 *C*

A Senneh rug, the stepped ivory 'herati' field with an indigo and red medallion, enclosed by a red 'herati' border, 72 by 51in (183 by 130cm).
£700-800 *P*

A Shirvan prayer rug, the saffron 'mihrab' with a trellis design, and an ivory serrated leaf and calyx border, 53 by 37in (135 by 93cm).
£1,200-1,500 *P*

Textiles

Costume

An apron of ivory silk, embroidered in gold and silver thread, and blue, red and green silk, with gold netted insertions, English, c1730, framed and glazed.
£600-650 *CSK*

A pair of Chinese deep horseshoe cuffs of midnight blue silk, embroidered in coloured silks and gold thread, altered, 19thC.
£250-300 *P*

A Chinese midnight blue silk robe, embroidered in coloured silks, the sleeves with ivory silk sleeve bands, lined, 19thC.
£350-400 *P*

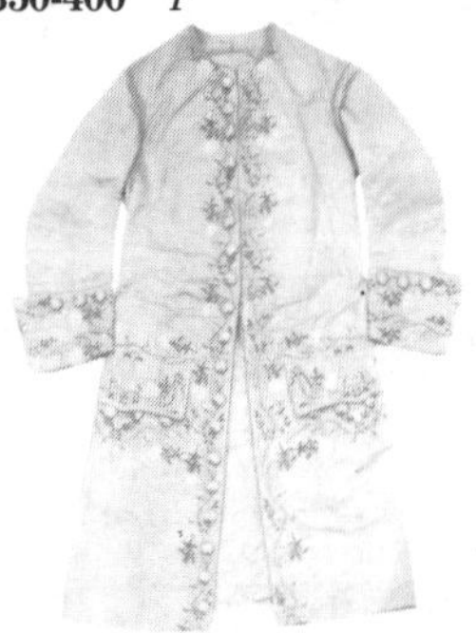

A coat of green linen ribbed silk, embroidered in pink and green with sprays of rosebuds, buttoned full length, with embroidered buttons, European, mid-18thC.
£500-800 *CSK*

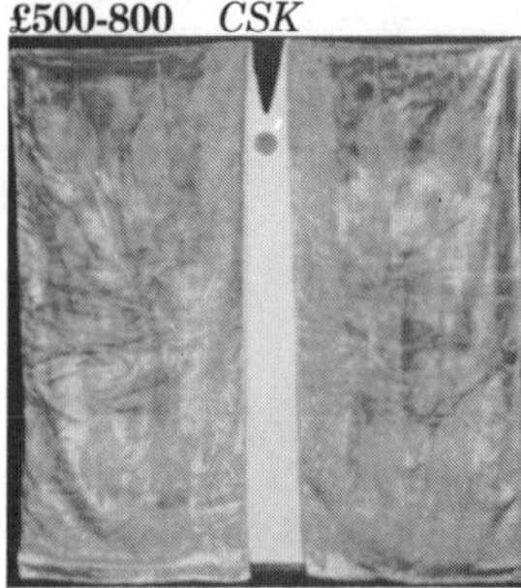

A Chinese robe, of blue kossu silk woven in coloured silks and gilt thread, lined in dark sky blue silk damask, 19thC.
£850-950 *CSK*

A Chinese child's robe, of scarlet silk damask, embroidered in coloured silks, with blue silk lining.
£250-350 *CSK*

A Chinese vest, of midnight blue silk embroidered in coloured silks and metal thread in Pekin knot and satin stitch, lined, 19thC.
£500-600 *P*

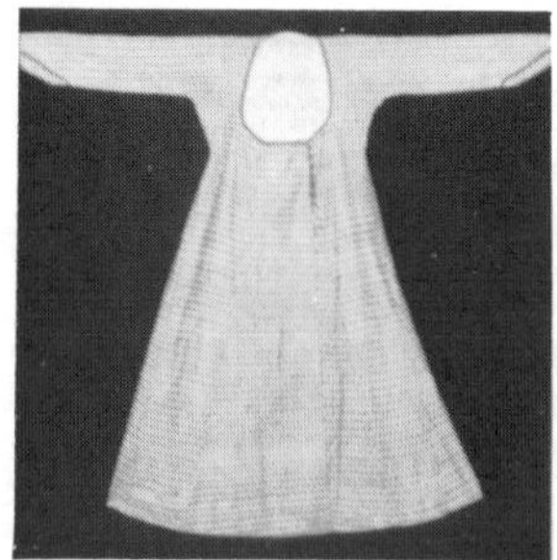

A Turkish coat, woven with rows of florets in red, green and yellow silks on an ivory ground and trimmed with blue braid, lined, early 19thC.
£50-60 *P*

A grey velvet mantle, stencilled in silver and gold with a band of trailing flowers, leaves and cone motifs, with salmon pink lining, and bearing the maker's label as a silk roundel Mariano Fortuny Venise, c1920.
£1,500-2,000 *P*

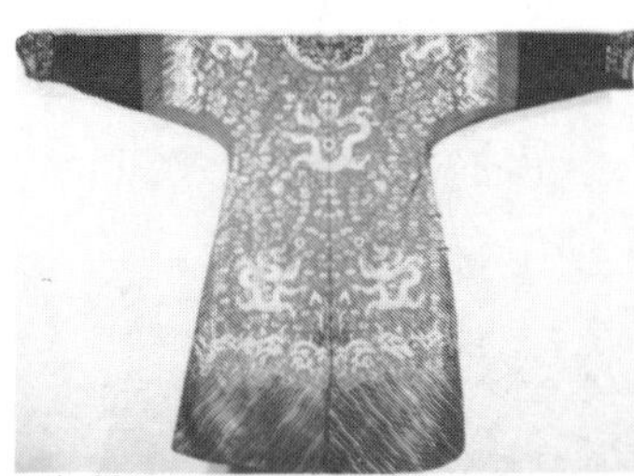

A Chinese dragon robe, of chestnut brown silk embroidered in coloured silks and gilt thread, lined in blue silk damask, 19thC.
£250-350 *CSK*

A Chinese grey silk coat, embroidered in Pekin knot and satin stitch with coloured silks, with embroidered ivory silk sleeve bands, lined, 19thC.
£300-500 *P*

An evening dress, of royal blue loosely woven linen and silk mix gauze, with a deep bias cut frill at the hem and a matching stole edged with a frill, lined in blue silk, by Balenciaga, 10 Avenue George V, Paris, c1965.
£500-600 *CSK*

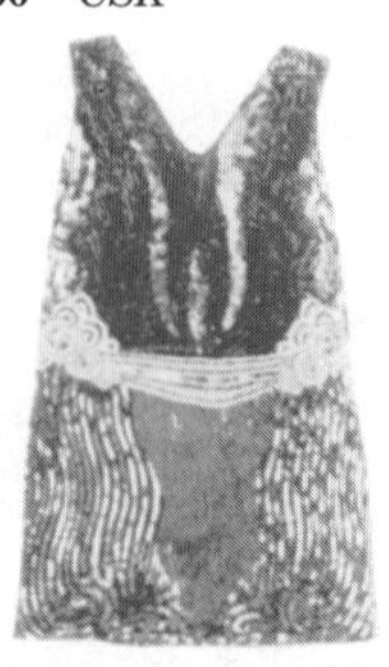

A dress, embroidered with bands of large and small black sequins and bugle beads, with simulated harness belt of clear beads, studded with strass, c1920.
£300-350 *CSK*

A black crêpe dress, the skirt with grey and cream crêpe insertions and ivory silk embroidery, c1920.
£200-250 *P*

An open robe of ivory silk, brocaded in richly coloured silks, mid-18thC.
£300-500 *P*

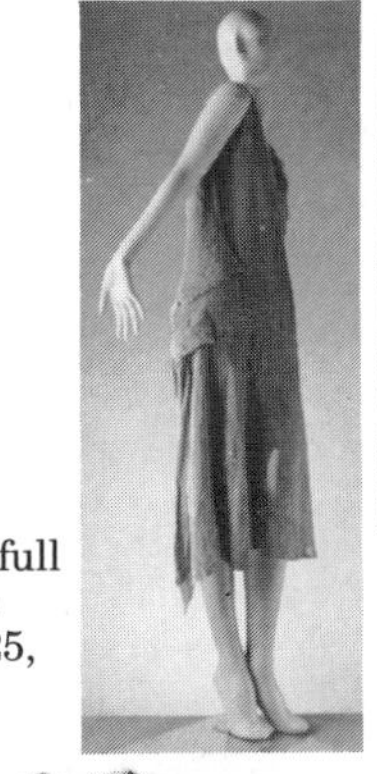

A dusty pink velvet dress with full back bodice and bow trim, with maker's label Chanel, No. 47225, c1920.
£1,200-1,500 *P*

ι red cotton gown, the trained skirt ⁄ith flounced hem and trimmed ⁄ith applied black and white cord, nd a matching looped overskirt, 1870.
350-400 *P*

A burnt orange silk coat, with gold thread brocade, with deep cuffs and collar, c1920.
£120-150 *P*

A young girl's dress of dark green velvet and striped yellow silk, decorated with mother-of-pearl buttons, c1876.
£200-250 *CSK*

A cream crêpe dress, with bias cut skirt and pleated attached scarf, with underdress, the maker's label Molyneux, 48 Grosvenor Street, London, c1930.
£300-400 *P*

A white net dress, with bauble trim, the bodice and upper skirt with cotton cutwork and filet lace overlay, c1910.
£400-450 *P*

A black chiffon and silk dress, with tie to waistline and streamer hemline, bearing maker's label Molyneux, 5 Rue Royale, No. 35767, c1920.
£550-650 *P*

An open robe and petticoat of ivory lustring, with padded decoration down the front, English, c1760.
£3,000-3,500 *CSK*

n ivory silk dress, with ivory iiffon and lace tiered overlay, 1910.
550-600 *P*

An unbleached linen child's frock and pantaloons, trimmed with white braid and buttons, c1810.
£300-500 *CSK*

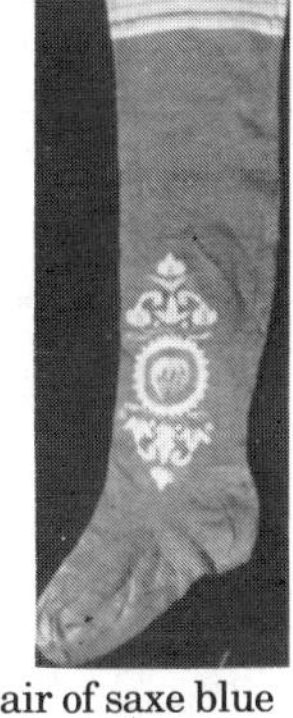

A pink wool suit, with a matching blouse printed with an abstract design, in brown, orange, yellow and turquoise and woven with gilt thread, by Chanel, c1960.
£200-300 *CSK*

A boy's dress, of tartan silk trimmed with a band of sea green velvet and gilt metal buttons chased with a swirling design, lacking one button, c1868.
£300-350 *CSK*

A pair of saxe blue gentleman's silk stockings, embroidered with elaborate clocks in pink, yellow and white, c1740.
£500-800 *CSK*

The Court dress of King Otto of the Hellenes, comprising 'fermeli' and sleeved 'fermeloto ghileki' of blue facecloth, lavishly embroidered with silver braid and silvered metal ball buttons, and with standing collars of scarlet cloth with silver oak leaves and other lace in the Bavarian fashion, and one and a half pairs of leggings, and the court 'terliki' of Queen Amelia of black facecloth embroidered in gold braid and sequins, and a small 'ghileki' of silver lace with insertions of scarlet facecloth and gold lace and silver thread, pseudo buttons decorated with coral, c1835.
£9,000-10,000 *CSK*

A pair of shoes of mustard coloured ribbed silk, the toecaps trimmed with ruched ribbons, sequins and gold braid, the shoe also edged with gold lace, inscribed Miss Alsorne, English, worn, c1770, 3in (7.5cm) heels.
£1,500-1,700 *CSK*

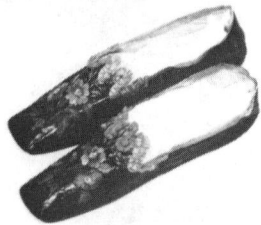

An Edwardian lady's parasol, contained in a brass bound bamboo tube.
£80-120 *SB*

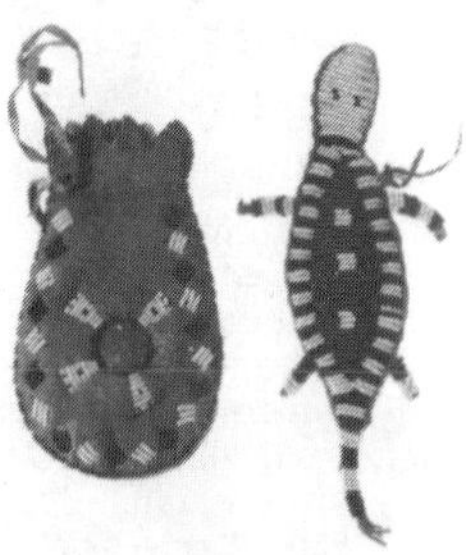

A North American plains Indian leather drawstring purse, with blue and white bead decoration, and an amulet shaped as an alligator worked in blue and white beads on leather, padded.
£100-120 *P*

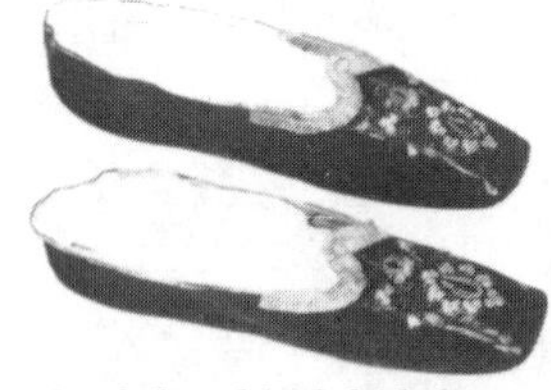

A pair of glacé black kid slippers, the fronts embroidered with bouquets of flowers, trimmed with pale blue silk, c1840.
£550-600 *CSK*

A grey-blue wool frock coat, the collar, borders, cuffs and buttons embroidered in silver thread and sequins with garlands of flowers, lined with scarlet satin, lining torn, c1870.
£500-600 *CSK*

A stomacher of undyed linen, embroidered mainly in green and red silks, c1700.
£500-600 *P*

A pair of glacé black kid slippers, embroidered in coloured silks on the front and heel, lined and trimmed with pink silk, c1840.
£600-650 *CSK*

A wide brimmed Sombrero, of white buckskin with floral decoration in violet silks and sequins on the band, by La Abeja, Talabarteria, Av.5 de Mayo 10 Mex, D.F., c1930.
£50-70 *CSK*

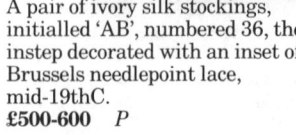

A pair of ivory silk stockings, initialled 'AB', numbered 36, the instep decorated with an inset of Brussels needlepoint lace, mid-19thC.
£500-600 *P*

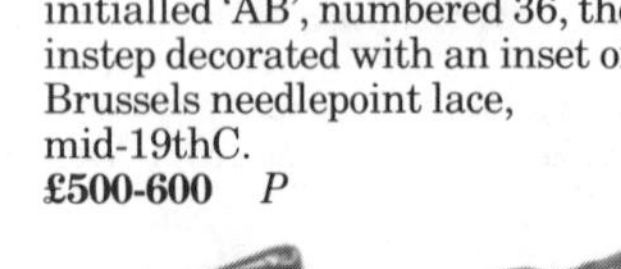

A pair of slippers, of black silk and wool shawl material, woven with a Paisley design, c1840.
£400-500 *CSK*

The Lord Chancellor's bourse, of Lord Eldon, worked in high relief with royal arms in crimson silk, pink and blue silk metal threads, velvet and pearls, early 19thC, 16in (40.5cm) square, in carved wooden case.
£2,000-2,500 *CSK*

John Scot, first Earl of Eldon, 1751-1838, was Chancellor to George III and George IV and, having struggled to return to power under William IV, died in the reign of Queen Victoria. In 1800 a fresh bourse, possibly this one, would have been embroidered with the New Royal Arms, adopted upon the Act of Union. Lord Loughborough would have surrendered the Great Seal in it. At the King's death in 1820 all seals were defaced and became the property of their holders. Presumably this bourse with obsolete device became a perquisite of Eldon at the same time.

Embroidery

An embroidered panel for a stool, worked in coloured wools with a naturalistic spray of roses against a black background, c1875, 25 by 38in (63 by 96cm).
£500-600 *CSK*

A Canton embroidered cover, of peach pink silk satin worked in pastel silks, lined in sky blue silk, late 19th/early 20thC, 92in (233.5cm) square.
£100-150 *CSK*

A large embroidered picture of Nelson's tomb, worked mostly in red, white and blue wools, c1855, 21½ by 29in (54 by 74cm), framed and glazed.
£1,200-1,500 *CSK*

An embroidered picture, worked in coloured wools, mostly browns and greens, with a lion and a tiger, c1860, 11 by 17in (28 by 43cm), framed and glazed.
£200-300 *CSK*

Four panels from an embroidered screen, worked in coloured silks with various scenes, damaged, mid-18thC, each 16in (40.5cm) wide.
£500-600 *CSK*

An embroidered screen, worked in pale coloured silks with 3 panels of the seasons, Spring, Summer and Autumn, damaged, 58 by 18in (147 by 46cm).
£200-300 *CSK*

Lace

A fragment of Mezzo Punto bobbin and needle lace, possibly English, c1690.
£80-120 *AF*

A pair of joined lappets of Brussels needle lace, c1750.
£300-350 *CSK*

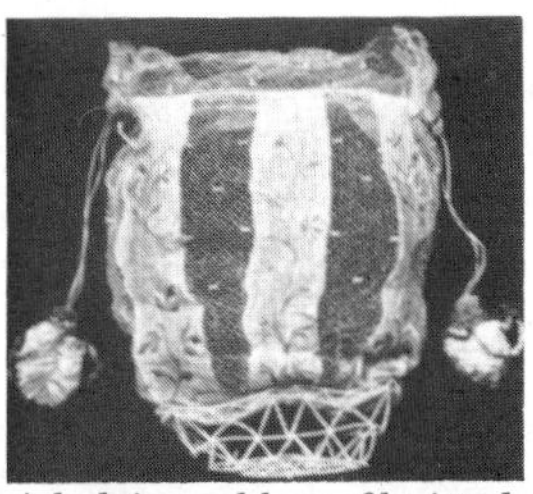

A lady's workbag of knitted and bobbin lace made straw, fastened with bauble trim, the whole worked in pink, brown and cream, mid-18thC.
£500-600 *P*

A deep alb flounce of Flemish bobbin lace, designed with floral motifs, swags, canopies and scrolls, c1760, 104 by 15½in (266 by 39cm).
£120-150 *P*

A flounce of ivory silk blonde lace, joined early 19thC, 157 by 21½in (400 by 55cm).
£150-200 *P*

A bridal veil of tamboured net, designed with flower sprays and sprigs, late 19thC, 79in (200cm) square.
£200-250 *P*

A handkerchief of ivory silk, with scalloped edge trimmed with Valenciennes lace, the border embroidered with houses amidst sprays of leaves and flowers, one corner with initial 'L' surmounted by a coronet, late 19thC.
£200-250 *P*

Possibly bears the initial of Queen Victoria's daughter Louise 1848-1939, who married the Marquess of Lorne, Duke of Argyll.

A cotton voile Christening gown, embroidered and trimmed with lace.
£90-120 *MAN*

A cotton voile Christening gown, pintucked, with lace inserts and trim.
£100-120 *MAN*

Samplers

A needlework sampler, by Ann South, the linen ground embroidered mainly in blue, green and light brown silks, c1650, 28½ by 7½in (73 by 19cm).
£1,200-1,500 *P*

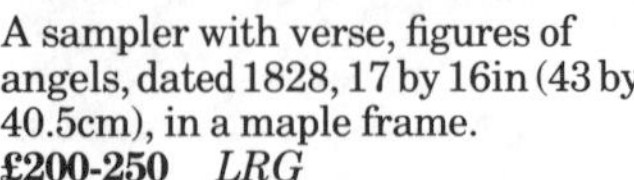

A sampler with verse, figures of angels, dated 1828, 17 by 16in (43 by 40.5cm), in a maple frame.
£200-250 *LRG*

A sampler, by Mary Eades, aged 12 years, embroidered in silks using cross stitch, long stitch and chenille work, c1810, 15 by 12in (38 by 30.5cm), in a maple frame.
£700-900 *MA*

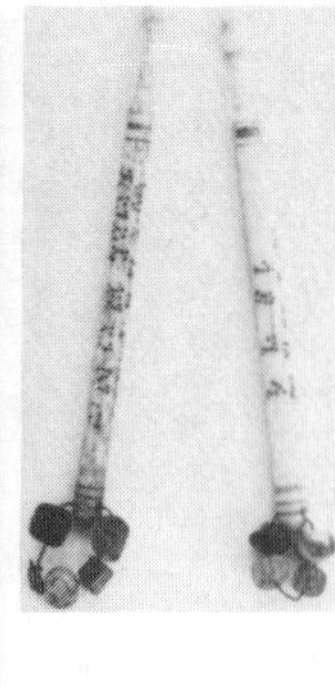

A bone lace bobbin, inscribed 'William Bull Hung 1811', with bead spangles, and another inscribed 'Dear Father 1811', with spangles.
£50-70 *CSK*

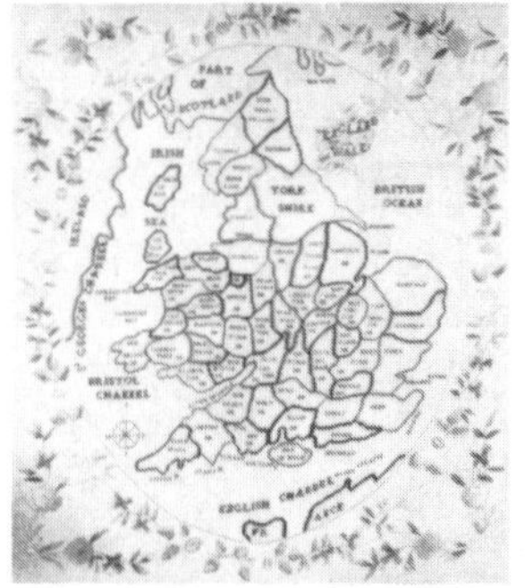

A map sampler of England and Wales, with place names in black silk and the boundaries in coloured silk, 1809, 21 by 19in (53 by 48cm), framed and glazed.
£200-250 *CSK*

A needlework sampler, by Sarah Redfern, 1869, the canvas ground worked in colours, with a poem dedicated to the memory of the King, 41 by 30½in (104 by 77cm), framed and glazed.
£550-650 *P*

The sampler commemorates the arrival of King William III at the Battle of Boyne in 1690, where he was guided across the river by David McKinley after whom the Orange Lodge of Enniskillen is named.

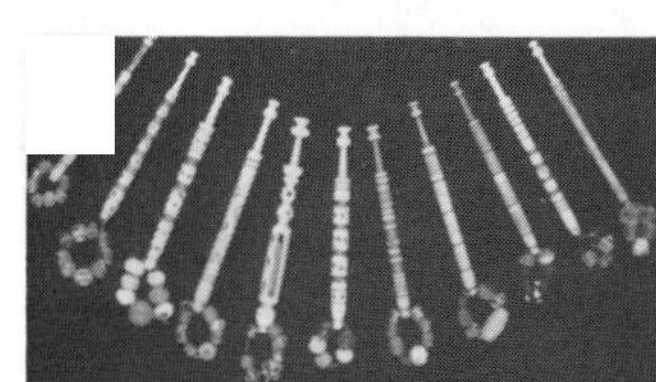

A carved and stained turned bone and brass mother-in-babe bobbin, two others inscribed 'A gift from my mother', and 'My love', and 8 other bone bobbins, some with wire decoration, all with spangles, 19thC.
£250-300 *P*

A Queen Anne strip sampler, by Mary Smith, in the Year of Our Lord 1702, worked in coloured silks with the alphabet and numbers, 18½ by 7in (47 by 18cm), unframed.
£400-450 *DN*

A George II sampler, by Eleanor Ansell, aged 11 years, 1746, worked in coloured silks, some holes, 15 by 12½in (38 by 32cm), unframed.
£800-900 *DN*

A needlework sampler, by Sarah Withington, 1840, the linen ground embroidered mainly in red and green wools, 20½in (52cm) square, in glazed maple frame.
£250-300 *P*

A sampler, with alphabet, verse and figures of plants and birds, dated 1824, 17 by 13in (43 by 33cm).
£350-400 *LRG*

A sampler, by Mary Smith, aged 15 years, c1800, 16 by 12½in (40.5 by 32cm).
£300-500 *MA*

A needlework sampler, by Mary Ann Cash, 1801, the linen ground worked in coloured silks, 14½ by 12in (37 by 30cm), framed and glazed.
£220-250 *P*

A needlework sampler, by Elizabeth Matilda Whitcomb, aged 11, worked at Miss Nicholl's Seminary, March 2, Orchard Street, Kidderminster, 1846, embroidered in coloured silks on a wool ground, 17 by 12½in (43 by 32cm), framed and glazed.
£350-400 *P*

An Armenian needlework sampler, by Souepile Kedeasian, the linen ground embroidered in red and pink threads, mid-19thC, 17½in by 23in (45 by 58cm).
£100-120 *P*

Tapestries

A Coptic fragment of tapestry woven in red and black wool and undyed linen, 5th/7thC, framed and glazed.
£150-250 *P*

Reputed to have originated from a tomb at Thebes.

A Brussels tapestry panel, depicting possibly the Israelites receiving water in the desert, enclosed by a blue acanthus leaf border with fleur-de-lys feathers in panels to the corners above, 17thC, 93 by 55in (237 by 139cm).
£1,700-2,000 *P*

A Peruvian fragment of tapestry, woven in coloured wools, 8th/10thC, mounted, framed and glazed.
£250-350 *P*

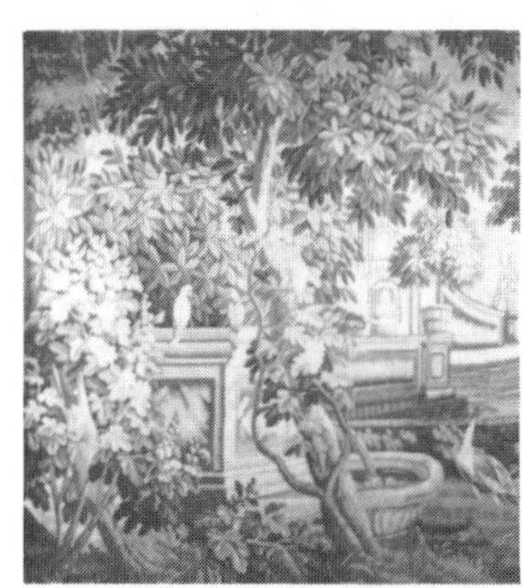

A verdure tapestry, woven in shades of blue, green, brown and red, 17thC, 83 by 78in (210 by 198cm).
£6,000-6,500 *CSK*

A tapestry picture, woven in shades of cream, green, blue and red, mid-18thC, 16½ by 12in (42 by 30.5cm), framed.
£900-1,000 *CSK*

A gros and petit point arched firescreen panel, worked in coloured wools, mid-18thC, 34 by 26in (87.5 by 67cm), in a walnut veneered glazed frame.
£500-550 *P*

A small altar frontal, worked in coloured wools, with Joseph and Christ, flanked by roses in blue and white vases, mounted in ormolu with swags of pink roses against a beaded ground, North European, late 17thC, 26 by 42in (66 by 106cm).
£1,200-1,500 *CSK*

Miscellaneous

A patchwork coverlet, the centre worked in plain and printed cottons, surrounded by mainly pink and blue striped and floral cotton, the reverse worked with alternating panels of patchwork and quilted cotton, 19thC, 110 by 102in (280 by 260cm).
£200-250 *P*

A collection of manufacturer's samples of textiles for chidlren's bedroom curtains, early 20thC, each 11½ by 5in (29 by 12.5cm).
£150-200 *CSK*

A beadwork pin cushion, in the shape of a book, the 'binding' worked in coloured beads, against a green ground, the 'spine' with the intitials MH, the inside lined with pink silk, 5 by 3in (12.5 by 7.5cm).
£120-150 *CSK*

Two pairs of Chinese yellow silk satin curtains, painted in colours, each with later blue border, slightly worn, 72in (182.5cm) high, lined and interlined.
£100-300 *CSK*

An Oriental panel, the fuchsia ground worked in coloured silk threads, with heavy silk thread fringing, lined, with 2 pairs of fringed silk tassels, 102 by 95in (260 by 240cm).
£600-650 *P*

A quilt, depicting a blazing star in pastel shades of crepe, bound in white, some of the patches quilted, American, c1930, 80in (203cm) square.
£200-250 *CSK*

A patchwork coverlet, in brightly printed cottons with a dark border, variously quilted, 105in (266cm) square.
£400-450 *CSK*

A border of French brocade, the ivory silk ground woven in coloured silks, early 19thC, lined.
£250-300 *P*

A damask banquet cloth, depicting the glorification of the Virgin Mary, 17thC, 103 by 81in (262 by 206cm).
£2,500-3,000 *CAm*

A set of 3 Aubusson entre-fenêtres, in deep rose pink and beige, woven in many colours, 19thC, 70in (177.5cm) high, fringed.
£3,500-4,000 *CSK*

A pair of silkwork panels, some staining, 18thC, 12 by 7½in (30.5 by 19cm).
£500-600 *DN*

A Victorian embroidered pelmet, with deep scallops worked in brightly coloured wools, highlighted in silk, c1880, 19 by 62in (48 by 157cm).
£200-250 *CSK*

Fans

An unmounted printed fan leaf, 'St. Batholomew's Fair in 1721', the aquatint engraving tinted, with text, published by J. F. Setchel, the margins overpainted in white, c1780, 22in (56cm) wide, framed and glazed.
£2,000-2,500 *CSK*

A fan, the leaf painted with the family of Darius, the mother-of-pearl sticks carved and pierced, silvered and gilt and backed with mother-of-pearl, guardstick damaged, mid-18thC, 11in (28cm), in glazed fan case.
£800-900 *CSK*

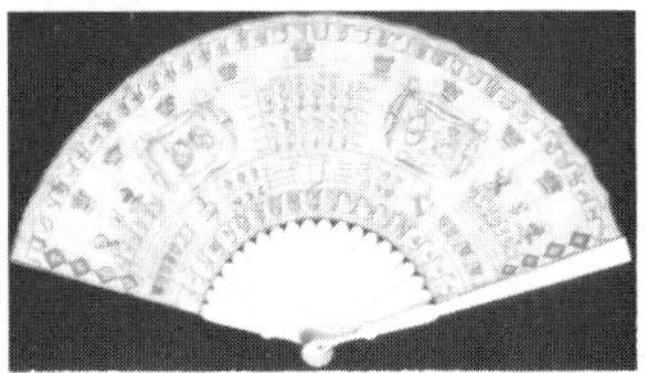

A fan, the leaf an etching in brown of heraldic devices, inscribed 'Pubd. as the Act directs Feb 11 1792, by F. Martin & Co., Enter'd at Stationer's Hall and Sold by Sarah Ashton Fan Maker No. 28 Little Britain', with ivory sticks, 10in (25cm) long.
£350-400 *P*

A fan with ivory sticks, the initial guard carved with the head of a lady, c1890, 14in (35cm) long, in original box inscribed J. Duvelleroy, London 167 Regent Street W.
£400-450 *P*

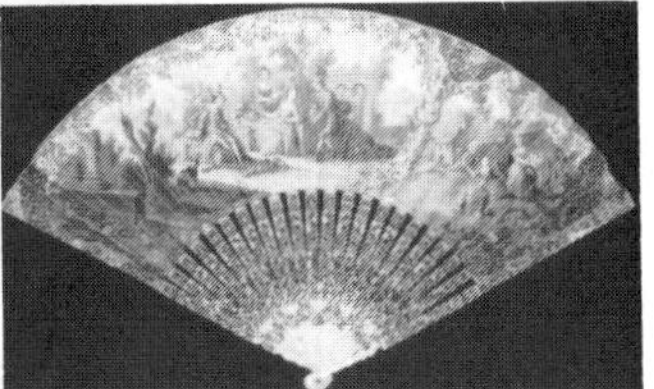

A French fan, with carved, pierced, painted and gilt ivory sticks decorated with mother-of-pearl, c1760, 11in (28cm) long.
£1,700-2,000 *P*

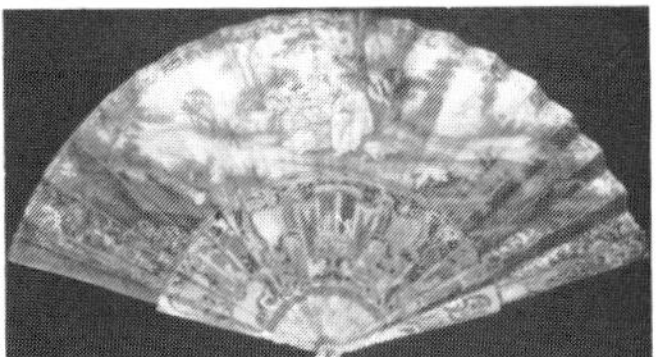

A fan with carved, pierced, silvered and gilt mother-of-pearl sticks, probably German, c1760, 12in (30cm) long.
£500-600 *P*

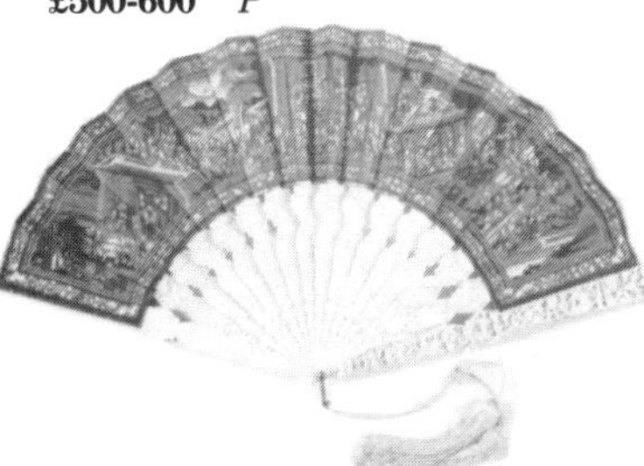

A Canton carved ivory, painted and embellished paper fan, in gouache, fabric and bright coloured ivory, with silver swivel and silk tassels, 19thC, 20in (51cm) wide, in original gilt and black lacquered fitted box.
£500-600 *CNY*

A French fan, the carved, pierced and painted ivory sticks decorated with red and green florets, with gilt highlights, c1750, 10½in (26cm) long, and a shaped case.
£700-800 *P*

A fan, with carved, pierced, silvered and gilt mother-of-pearl sticks, signed Donzel, c1870, 14in (35cm) long, in a shaped, glazed case with gilt gesso frame.
£1,500-2,000 *P*

A gilded horn brisé fan with piqué work, c1810, 6½in (16cm) long.
£250-300 *P*

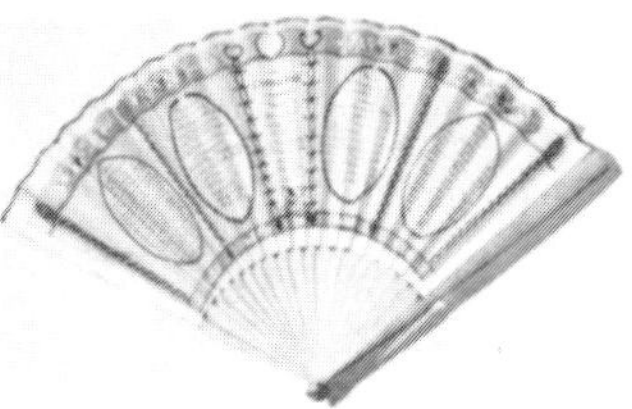

A gauze leaf fan, painted and decorated with sequins, the mother-of-pearl sticks pierced, gilt and hinged for folding, c1890, and another distressed fan.
£50-150 *C*

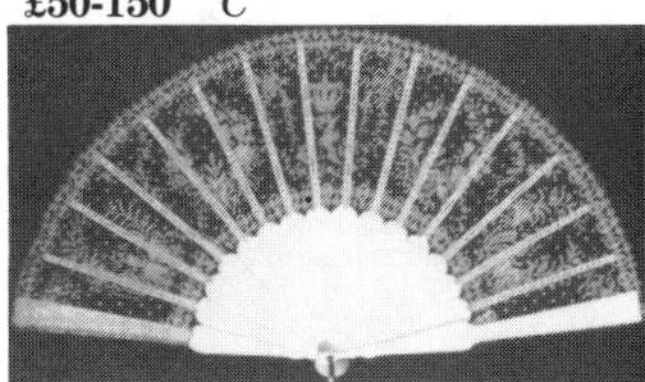

A fan with plain ivory sticks and 18ct gold loop at pivot, c1890, 10½in (27cm) long, in a box.
£500-600 *P*

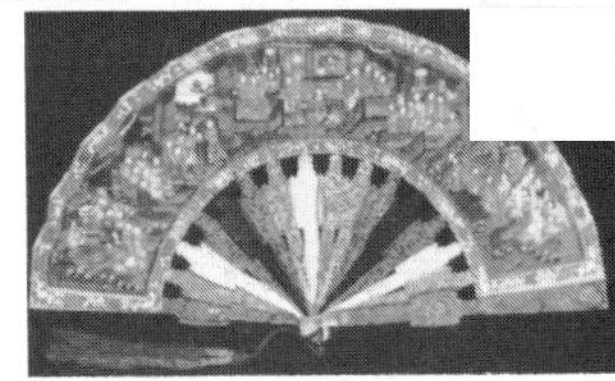

A Chinese fan, with carved and pierced shaped sticks of tortoiseshell, mother-of-pearl, stained and unstained ivory and metal filigree with enamel decoration, c1840, 11in (28cm) long, in a black and gilt lacquer box.
£500-600 *P*

A fan, the leaf painted with the Judgement of Paris, the ivory sticks carved, early 18thC, 10½in (27cm).
£300-500 *CSK*

A fan with plain ivory sticks, the leaf with a hand coloured etching of The Visitation, inscribed M. Gamble 1743, 10in (25.5cm) long.
£150-200 *P*

The Casino fan, the leaf a hand coloured etching, with the rules of the game, published by I. Cook & J. P. Crowder, Wood Street, London, April 1st. 1793, with wooden sticks, leaf damaged, 10in (25.5cm).
£250-300 *CSK*

A French fan, the ivory sticks carved and pierced, c1760, 11in (28cm) long.
£450-550 *P*

A fan, the leaf painted in French with an illustrated encyclopaedia, the ivory sticks pierced, damaged, c1790, 10in (25.5cm).
£500-600 *CSK*

A fan, the leaf painted with pink, red and yellow roses and honeysuckle, signed Mathilde 1889, with tortoiseshell sticks, one guardstick piqué in gold with the initial C.B. or L., with coronet above, 13in (33cm), in box by Vanier Chardin, 82 Boulevard Haussman.
£700-800 *CSK*

An unmounted fan leaf, painted on chicken skin with a Roman marriage after the antique, Italian, c1800, 21in (53cm) wide, in box inscribed from 21 St. James's Place, 23.1.30.
£600-650 *CSK*

A fan, the silk leaf painted, the reserves embroidered with spangles and sequins, the mother-of-pearl sticks carved, pierced and gilt, French, damaged, c1760, 11in (28cm), in contemporary fan box.
£200-300 *CSK*

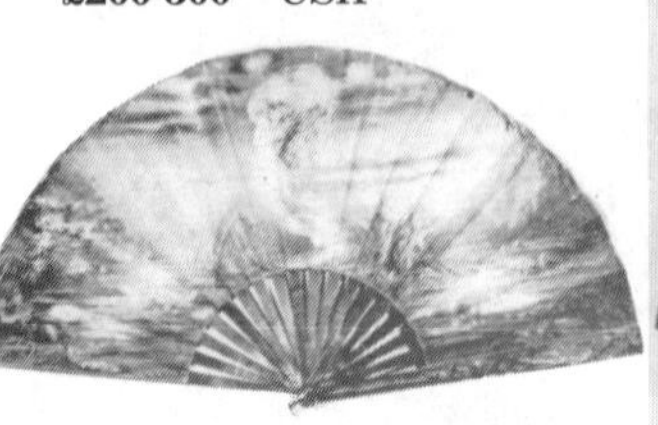

A fan, the leaf painted and signed Michaels, the verso with monogram I.L., with smoked mother-of-pearl sticks, French, repaired, c1895, 14in (35.5cm), in box monogrammed I.L. by A. Howeiler, Paris.
£800-900 *CSK*

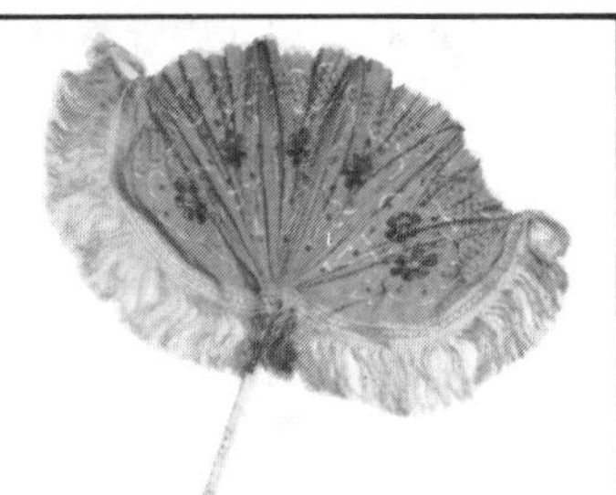

A parasol fan, the mount of strawberry pink silk embroidered in ivory and deeper pink silks, edged with a silk fringe and boned with 5 whalebones, which together with the patent mechanism allow the fan to form a half parasol, the ivory handle carved and pierced, and the metal band inscribed De Givry, rue Romarin 20, Lyon, c1865, 14in (35.5cm) folded.
£2,000-3,000 *CSK*

A French fan with gilded ivory sticks, c1770, 11in (28cm) long.
£300-350 *P*

A French fan with carved, pierced, silvered and gilt mother-of-pearl sticks, c1770, 11in (28cm) long, in a shaped, framed and glazed case.
£300-350 *P*

A Chinese cabriolet fan, with black, pink, silver and gilt lacquer sticks, c1830, 11½in (28.5cm) long, in original box covered in painted silk with label printed in Spanish.
£700-800 *P*

A Chinese telescopic fan, with black and gilt lacquer sticks, the leaf painted and hand coloured both sides, c1840, 11in (26cm) long extended, in original box.
£350-400 *P*

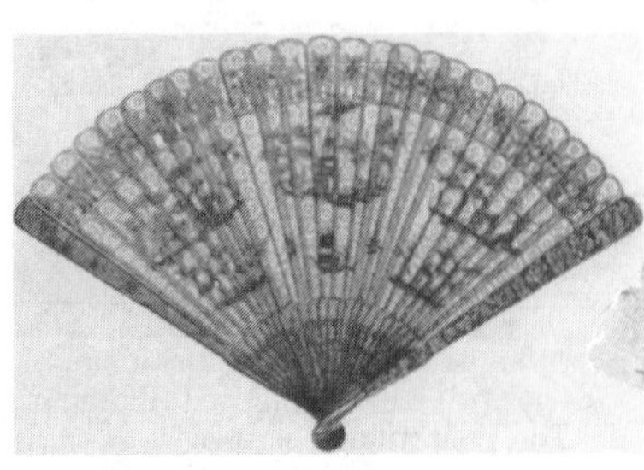

A Chinese silver gilt filigree fan, with mainly blue and green enamel decoration, c1830, 7½in (19.5cm) long.
£600-700 *P*

A Canton ivory brisé fan, carved with birds and flowers, coronet monogrammed C.P.W., c1810, 8in (20cm).
£300-350 *CSK*

Possibly for Charlotte, Princess of Wales.

A Chinese fan of carved and pierced ivory, designed with a central shield, monogrammed DB, c1760, 10in (25.5cm) long.
£450-500 *P*

Dolls

Wax

A poured wax child doll, with swivel head and shoulder plate, fixed blue eyes, pierced ears and blonde mohair wig, the stuffed waisted body dressed in white, body melted, 19in (48cm) high.
£250-300 *CSK*

A poured wax child doll with fixed blue eyes, the long blonde hair inset in groups into head, the stuffed body with wax limbs, wearing underclothes, striped sailor dress and bronze shoes, with Lucy Peck oval stamp on the body, 21in (53cm).
£300-400 *CSK*

A poured wax child doll, with blonde hair inset in slashes, blue eyes, stuffed body and wax limbs, dressed in striped pink silk, with Lucy Peck oval stamp on the body, replaced and damaged foot, 21in (53cm) high.
£250-350 *CSK*

A poured wax child doll, the blonde hair inset in slashes, the stuffed body with wax limbs, dressed in sailor dress with red braid and cap band embroidered 'HMS PET', with Lucy Peck oval stamp on body, 20in (51cm) high.
£300-500 *CSK*

A poured wax child doll, with fixed blue eyes, wearing original purple silk frock with pleated hem and lace decoration, underclothes and petticoat embroidered in purple wool, English underdome, 16in (40.5cm) high.
£500-600 *CSK*

Wooden

A Grödenthal wooden doll, painted in grey, yellow, brown and red, in contemporary tucked cotton dress with pantalettes and petticoat, c1830, 7½in (19cm).
£400-450 *CSK*

A Grödenthal wooden doll, in white printed coat and dress, c1820, 15in (38cm).
£700-800 *CSK*

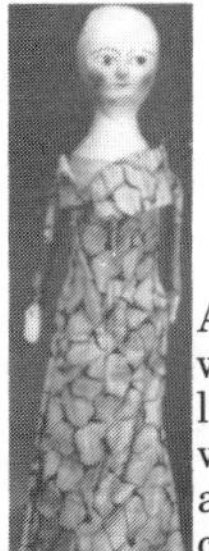

A turned and carved wooden doll, with inset eyes, stitched brows and lashes and bright pink cheeks, the white painted body joined at the hip and shoulder, crack encircling face, c1810, 11½in (29cm).
£500-600 *CSK*

Bisque

A bisque shoulder head doll with swivel neck, with fixed grey/green paperweight eyes, pierced ears, by François Gaultier, minor damage, incised 8 top back of the crown, 25in (64cm).
£4,500-5,000 *P*

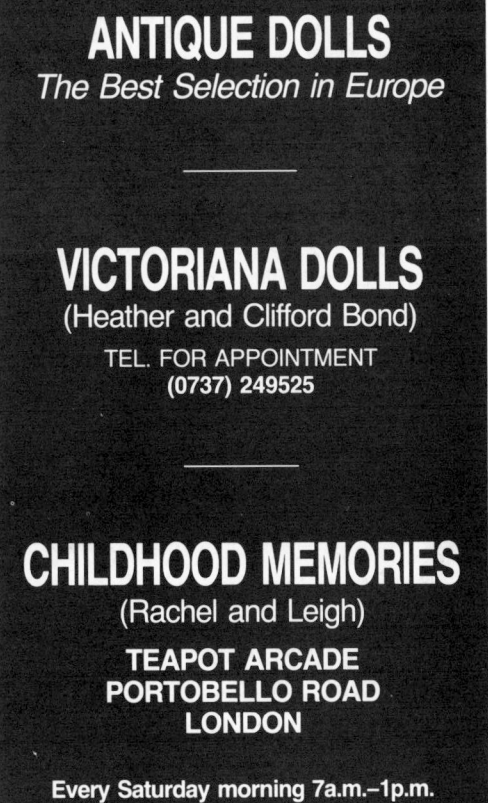

An all bisque Kaiser baby, with painted features and hair, the bent limbed body wearing baby gown, marked 5, 7½in (19cm).
£400-450 *CSK*

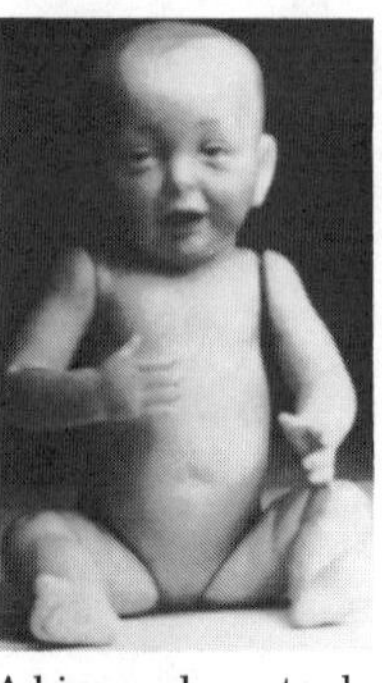

A bisque character baby doll, with blue painted eyes, jointed at shoulder and hip, marked 390214, on the leg 10P 6, 6½in (16.5cm).
£400-450 *CSK*

A Kaiser baby glass-eyed doll, with open/closed mouth, 14½in (37cm).
£1,200-1,500 *HA*

A bisque headed character baby doll, in original clothes, Bahr & Proschild, 14in (35.5cm).
£200-300 *HA*

A bisque headed doll, with fixed blue glass eyes, composition ball jointed body, in blue dress with under-garments and leatherette boots, by Danel et Cie, impressed E5D Depose, 16in (40.5cm).
£500-550 *HCH*

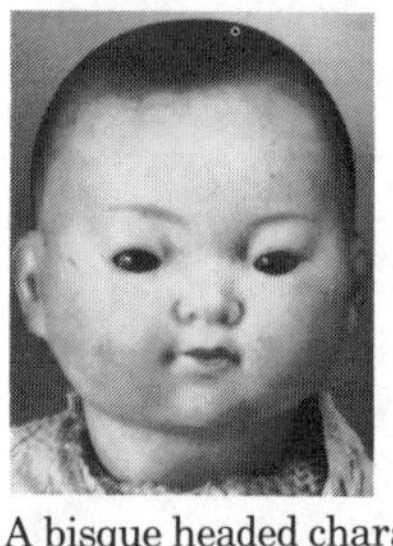

A bisque headed character baby, modelled as an Oriental, with brown sleeping eyes and baby body, marked AM Ellar 4K, 15in (38cm).
£700-800 *CSK*

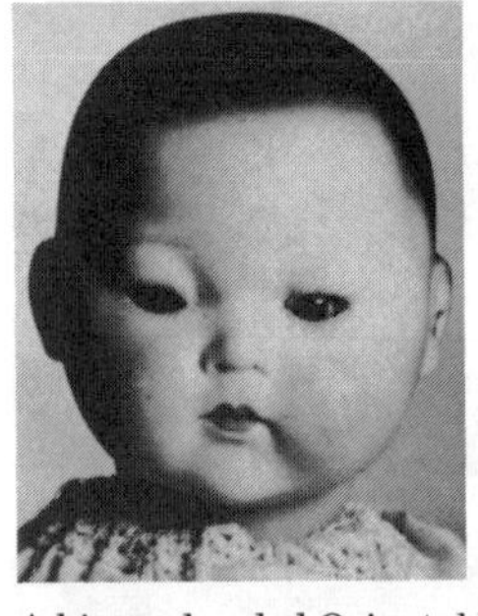

A bisque headed Oriental baby doll, with black sleeping eyes, closed mouth and painted black hair, the bent limbed composition body dressed in cream, marked A.M. 353/3K, 13½in (34cm).
£400-600 *CSK*

A Continental bisque headed sleeping doll, complete with original clothing, late 19thC, 25in (63.5cm).
£300-400 *PC*

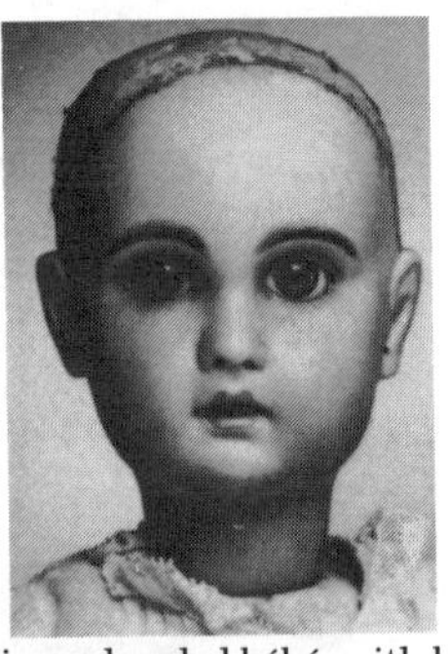

A bisque headed bébé, with blue sleeping eyes, in white tucked dress, marked 1907 10, 23in (58cm).
£1,200-1,500 *CSK*

A bisque headed child doll, with blue sleeping eyes, pierced ears, blonde mohair wig and jointed composition body, marked S, 17½in (44cm).
£500-600 *CSK*

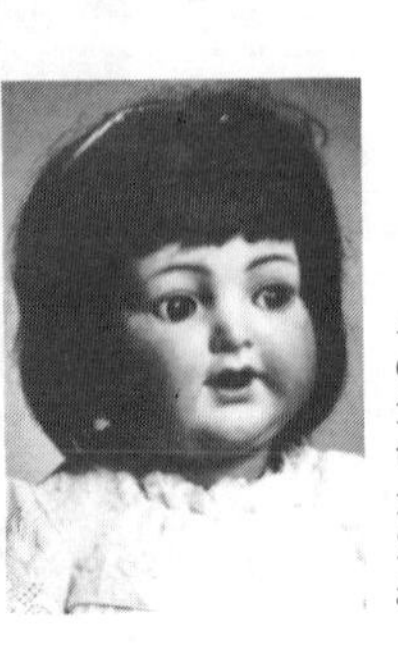

A bisque headed character baby doll, with blue lashed sleeping and flirting eyes, the jointed composition toddler body dressed in white, marked K*R Simon & Halbig 126, 27in (68.5cm).
£600-700 *CSK*

A bisque headed child doll, with blue fixed eyes and blonde mohair wig, the jointed composition body in white dress, marked with a trefoil and 12, Limbach, 19in (48cm).
£900-1,000 *CSK*

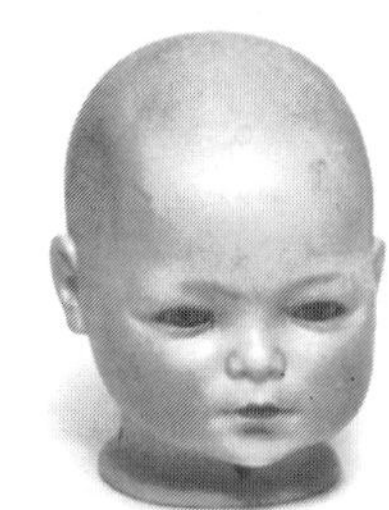

A bisque headed character baby doll, with closed mouth, blue sleeping eyes and flange neck, marked SPB in a star HNPH, head 5in (12.5cm).
£320-370 *CSK*

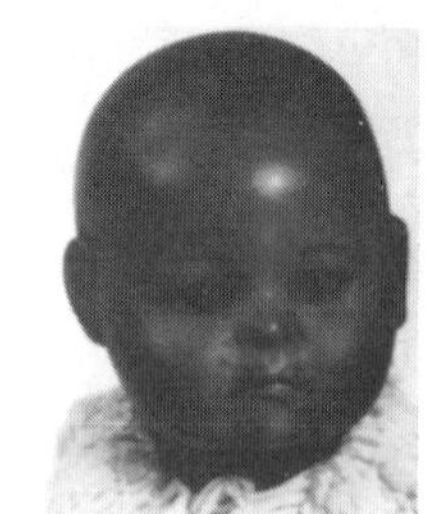

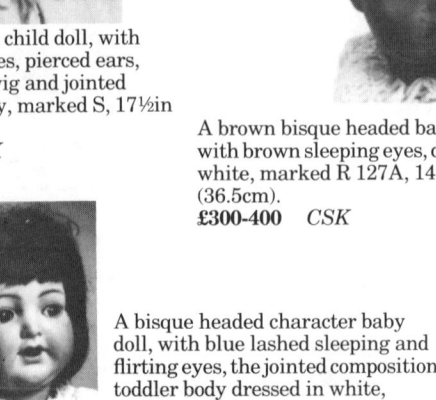

A brown bisque headed baby doll, with brown sleeping eyes, dressed in white, marked R 127A, 14½in (36.5cm).
£300-400 *CSK*

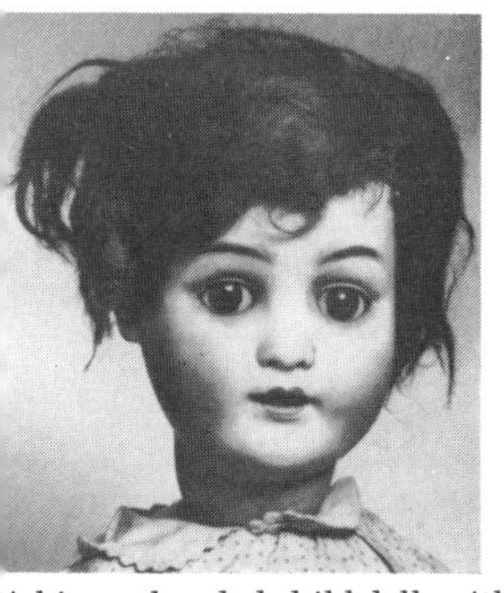

A bisque headed child doll, with blue lashed sleeping eyes, brown mohair wig and pierced ears, the jointed composition body in blue spotted dress, marked ABG 1362.8, 35in (89cm).
£600-700 *CSK*

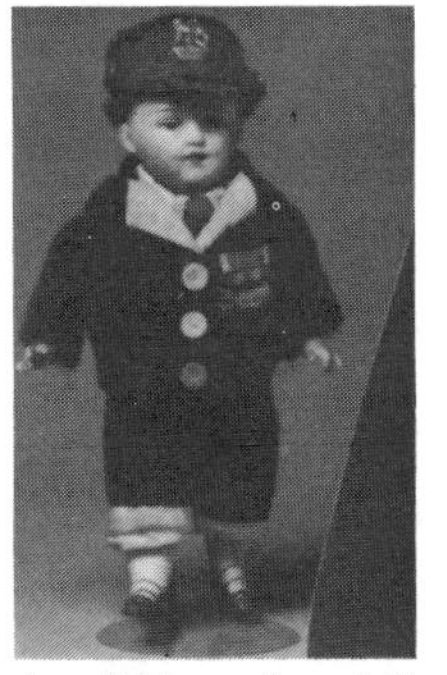

An all bisque boy doll, with blue intaglio eyes, open/closed mouth with 2 teeth, moulded and painted shoes and socks, dressed in a navy wool military costume, marked 150/10, possibly by Hertel, Schwab & Co., 8½in (21.5cm).
£150-200 *CSK*

A bisque headed child doll, with blue sleeping eyes, pierced ears and blonde mohair wig, the jointed composition body in pink smocked dress, white underwear, black shoes and straw hat with feather, marked 192 by Kestner, 12in (30.5cm).
£450-500 *CSK*

A French fashion doll, with glass eyes, pierced ears, with a gusset jointed kid leather body, by Ferdinand Gaultier, 19thC, 13in (33cm).
£1,500-2,000 *HA*

Bru

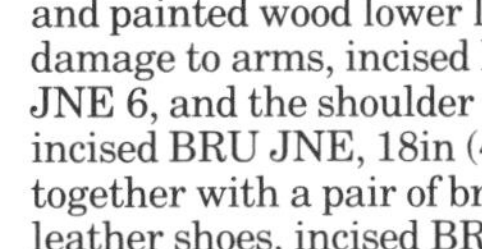

A Bru Jeune bisque headed doll, with fair mohair wig over cork pate, fixed blue paperweight eyes, open/closed mouth, pierced ears and bisque shoulder plate with moulded breasts, the white kid leather body with kid covered wood upper arms and painted wood lower legs, damage to arms, incised BRU JNE 6, and the shoulder plate incised BRU JNE, 18in (46cm), together with a pair of brown leather shoes, incised BRU JNE PARIS, and 4 items of clothing.
£6,500-7,000 *P*

A French bisque headed closed mouth doll, with applied pierced ears and paperweight eyes, dressed in original clothes, Paris bébé, Tête Deposee 16, 35in (89cm).
£5,000-7,000 *HA*

A Bru Jeune R bisque head walking doll, with wig over cork pate, weighted blue eyes, pierced ears, open mouth with upper teeth, and dressed wood and composition body with squeaker, straight limbed legs and jointed arms, marked BRU JNE R 9, 21in (54cm).
£1,800-2,000 *P*

Gebruder Heubach

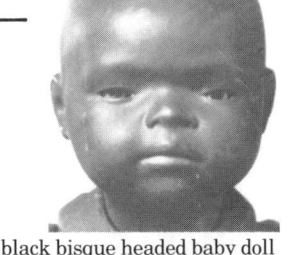

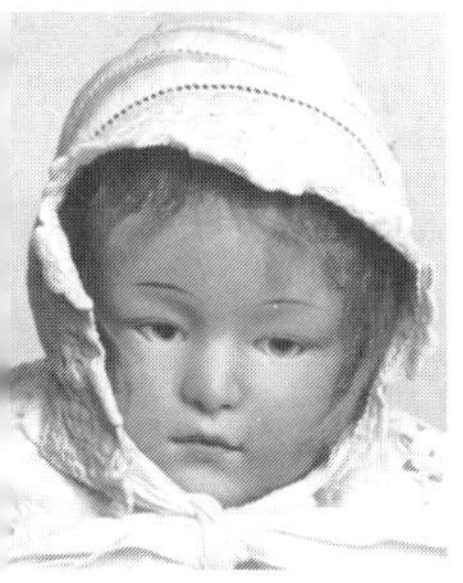

A bisque headed character baby doll, with blue intaglio eyes and blonde mohair wig, the bent limbed composition baby's body dressed in white cotton broderie anglais baby gown and carrying cape and bonnet, marked 6970 4 Germany, with the Gebruder Heubach sunburst, 11½in (29cm).
£250-300 *CSK*

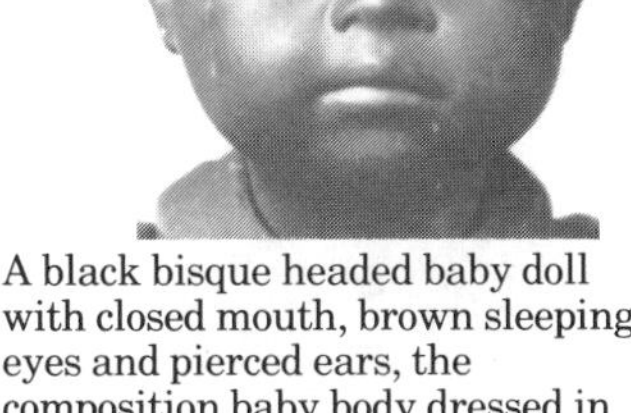

A black bisque headed baby doll with closed mouth, brown sleeping eyes and pierced ears, the composition baby body dressed in original felt petalled skirt, marked Heubach Koppelsdorf 399 2/0, 15in (38cm).
£250-300 *CSK*

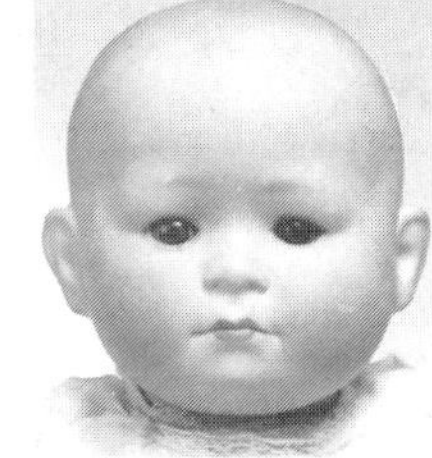

A bisque headed character baby doll, with blue sleeping eyes, closed mouth and painted and moulded hair, the stuffed body dressed in white baby gown, marked Heubach Koppelsdorf 339, 3/0, 14½in (37cm).
£320-360 *CSK*

A bisque headed child doll, with blue lashed sleeping eyes, hair wig and jointed composition body, in contemporary dark blue girl guide uniform with compass and whistle, marked AWW9, 5 Heubach Koppelsdorf by Adolf Wislizerus, 24in (61cm).
£200-250 *CSK*

A bisque figure of a seated fat baby, marked 95 and the Heubach square mark, stamped in green 68, 5in (12.5cm).
£80-100 *CSK*

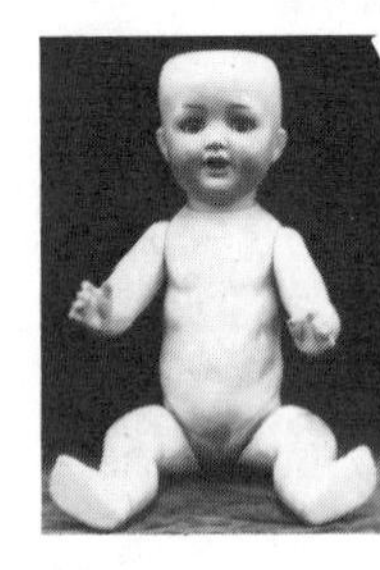

A German bisque headed doll, Heubach Koppelsdorf, No. 3422, early 20thC, 16in (40.5cm).
£250-300 *PC*

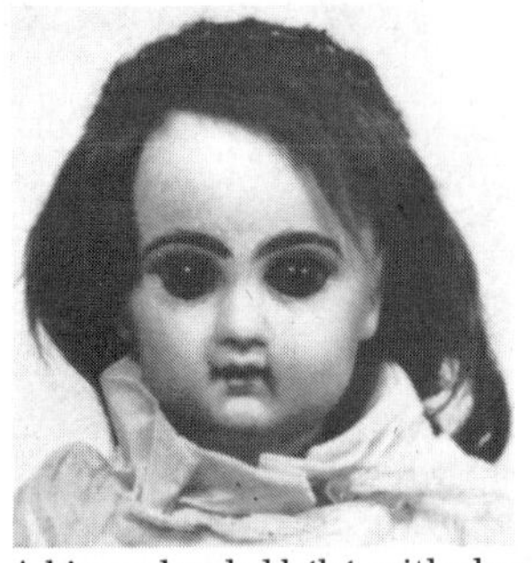

A bisque headed bébé, with closed mouth, fixed brown eyes, pierced ears, long chestnut wig and jointed composition body wearing petticoat tucked frock with lace insertions and bébé Jumeau bronze shoes, stamped in red DEPOSÉ TETE JUMEAU bte S.G.D.G. 2 impressed 2, stamped on body Jumeau Medaille D'or Paris, 11in (28cm).
£1,500-1,700 *CSK*

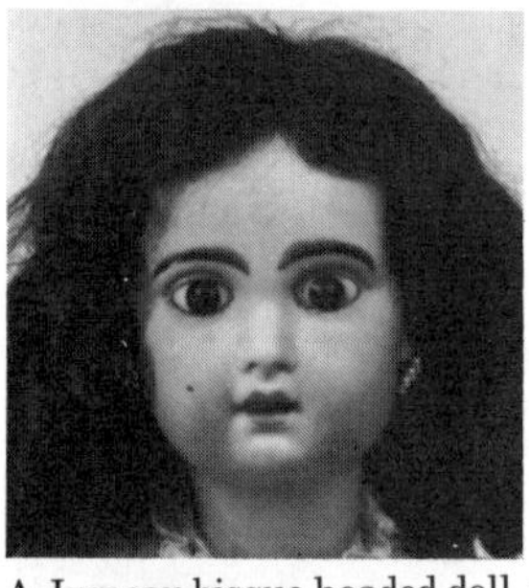

A Jumeau bisque headed doll, with brown wig, fixed brown eyes, pierced ears, jointed composition body dressed in lace trimmed silk, small chip to left eye, paint damage to hands, 25in (63.5cm).
£1,200-1,500 *P*

An Emile Jumeau bisque headed doll, with original clothes, and a trunk of accessories, 12½in (31.5cm).
£4,000-6,000 *HA*

Jumeau

A bisque headed bébé, with blue sleeping eyes, the jointed composition body dressed in blue watered silk with white underclothes, and brown leather shoes, stamped in red Tête Jumeau: Bébé Jumeau diplôme d'honneur sticker on body, 24in (61cm).
£1,000-1,500 *CSK*

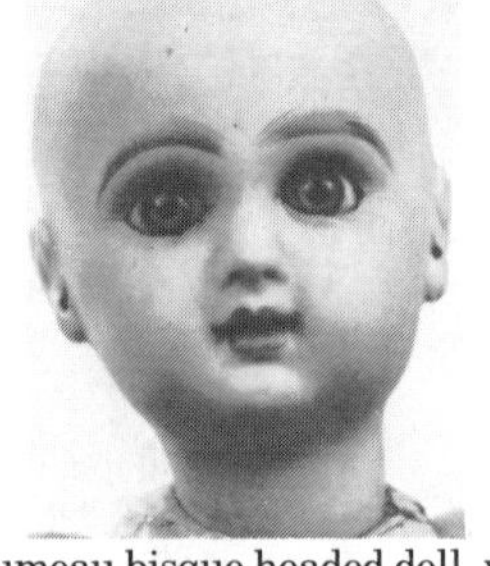

A Jumeau bisque headed doll, with cork pate, fixed blue paperweight eyes, pierced ears, closed mouth and jointed composition body, dressed in lace trimmed green silk, dress distressed, stamped in red Depose Tête Jumeau Bte S.G.D.G.3, the body stamped in blue Jumeau Medaille d'Or Paris, 12in (30cm).
£1,500-1,700 *P*

A Jumeau bisque headed doll, in original clothing with accessories, marked Depose Tête Jumeau Bte SGDG 14, 30½in (76cm).
£5,000-6,000 *HA*

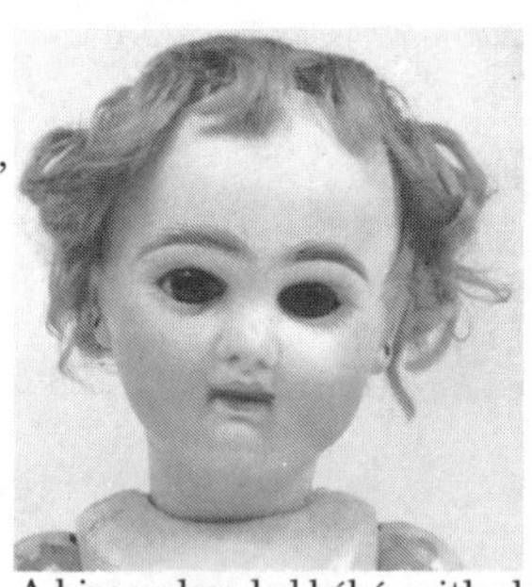

A bisque headed bébé, with closed mouth, fixed brown eyes, pierced ears, blonde wig and fixed wrist, jointed wood and composition body, stamped in red DEPOSE TETE JUMEAU Bte. S.G.D.G. 6, and on the body in blue with the Medaille d'Or mark, 14½in (37cm).
£1,500-2,000 *CSK*

A bisque headed bébé, with fixed blue eyes, brown wig and jointed composition body, dressed in contemporary red and white spotted dress, white underwear and brown leather boots, crack to neck, the head stamped Tête Jumeau in red and body with Bébé Jumeau Diplôme d'Honneur sticker, 25½in (63.5cm).
£1,000-1,200 *CSK*

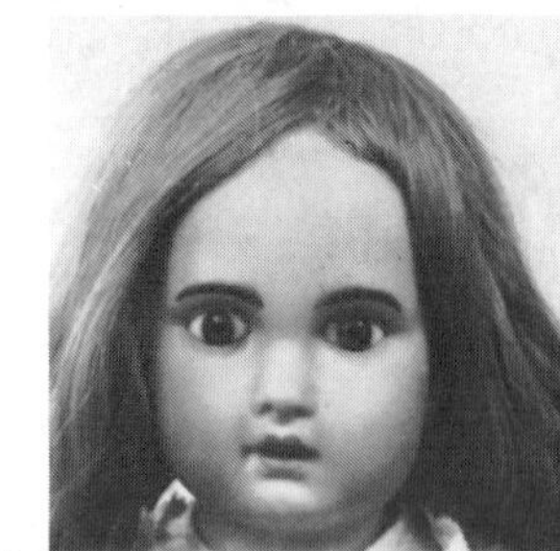

A Jumeau bisque headed doll, with wig, fixed blue paperweight eyes, the jointed composition body dressed in whitework, some repainting to body, marked 1907 12, 26in (66cm).
£1,200-1,500 *P*

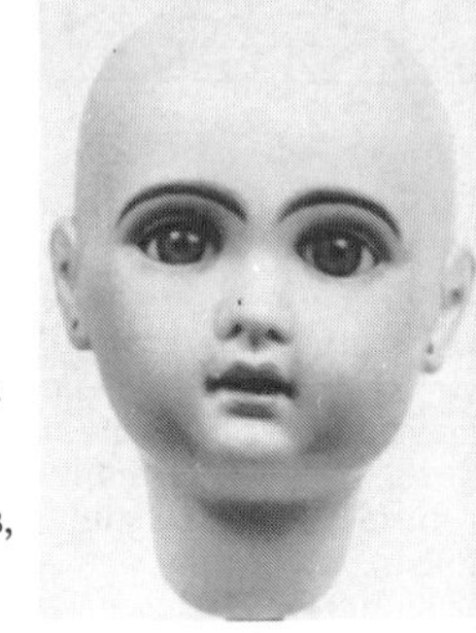

A Jumeau bisque headed doll, with sleeping blue eyes, jointed composition body, dressed in whitework, socks and leather shoes, one hand missing, incised 1907 10.
£1,500-2,000 *P*

J. D. Kestner

A Kestner all-bisque dolls house doll, in original felt outfit, with closed mouth and glass eyes, 3½in (9cm).
£150-250 *HA*

A J. D. Kestner bisque headed googly eyed doll, with dark mohair wig, brown eyes, and straight limbed composition body dressed in red gingham, marked B 6 J.D.K. 221, 10in (25cm).
£1,500-1,800 *P*

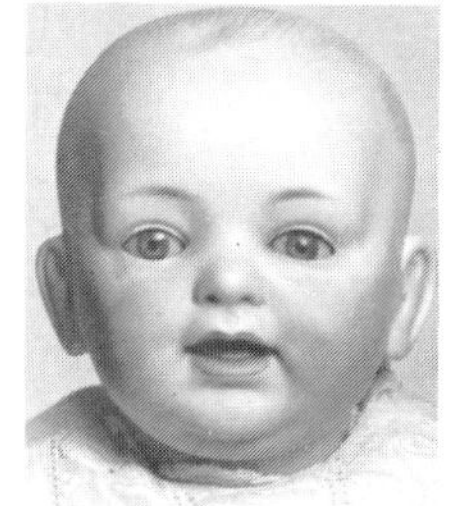

A bisque headed character baby doll, with blue sleeping eyes, open/closed mouth and composition body, in lace edged embroidered frock, marked J.D.K.12, 14½in (37cm).
£600-700 *CSK*

A Kestner bisque headed character doll, with blue sleeping eyes, blonde wig and jointed body, dressed in white with velvet caped coat, marked J13 143, 20in (51cm).
£600-700 *CSK*

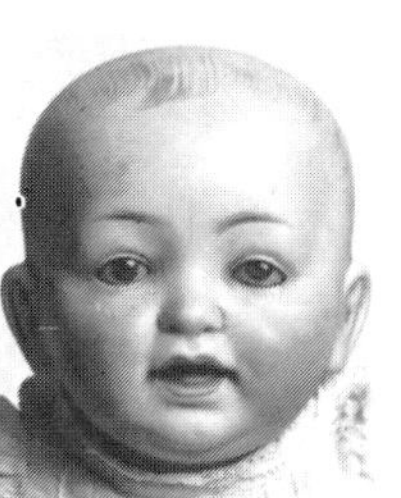

A bisque headed character baby doll, with blue sleeping eyes, open/closed mouth, dressed in cream silk and lace, marked JDK.Y, 10½in (27cm).
£300-400 *CSK*

A J. D. Kestner bisque headed googly eyed doll, with weighted blue eyes, and dressed jointed composition body, body repainted, marked A 5 JDK 221, 12in (30cm).
£3,200-3,600 *P*

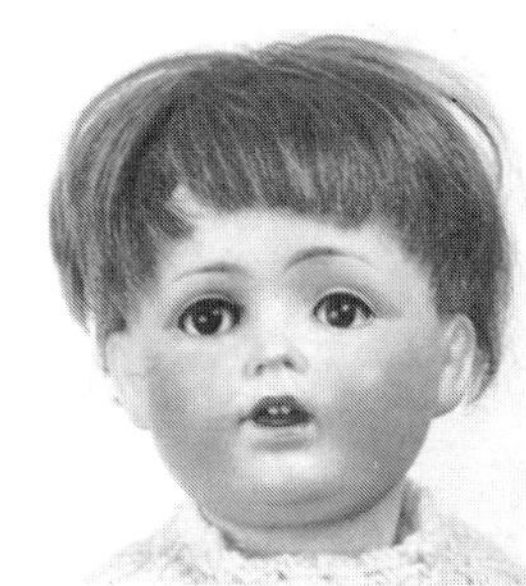

A bisque headed character baby, with brown lashed sleeping eyes and composition body, marked 257 J.D.K.44, 18½in (47cm).
£400-450 *CSK*

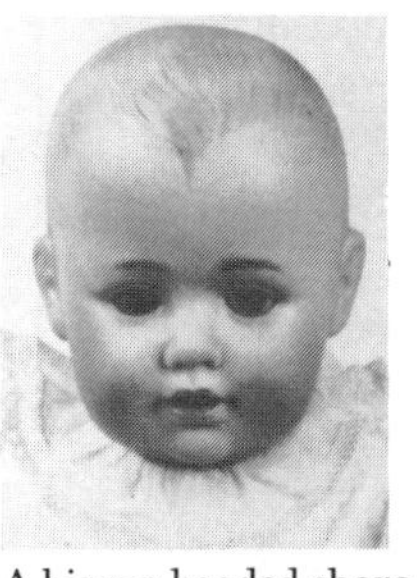

A bisque headed character baby doll, with moulded and painted curl on forehead and above ears, double chin and jointed toddler body, marked JDK 8 and stamped in red on the body Germany, 13½in (34cm).
£600-800 *CSK*

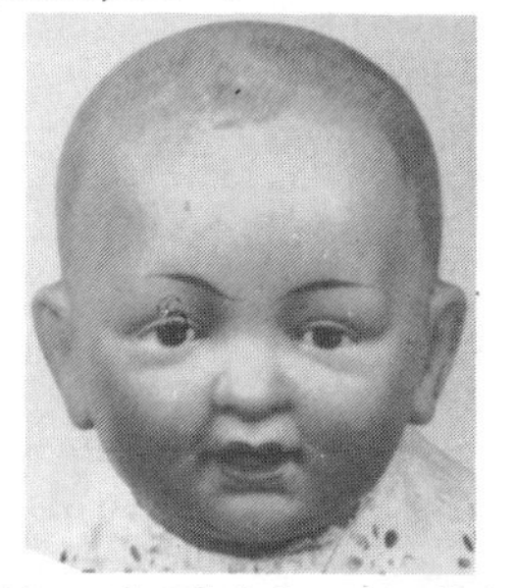

A bisque headed character baby, with brown painted eyes, open/closed mouth and bent limbed baby body, dressed in whitework gown, marked 7, probably Kestner, 11½in (29cm).
£220-260 *CSK*

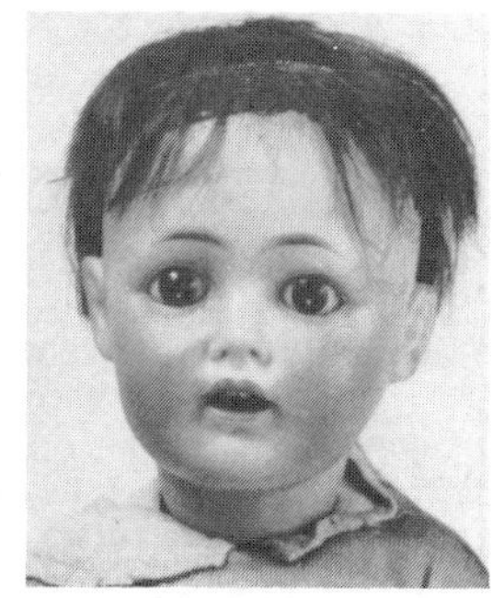

A bisque headed character doll, with brown fixed eyes, the bent limbed body dressed in blue silk suit and white shoes, marked J.D.K. 257, 16in (40.5cm).
£450-500 *CSK*

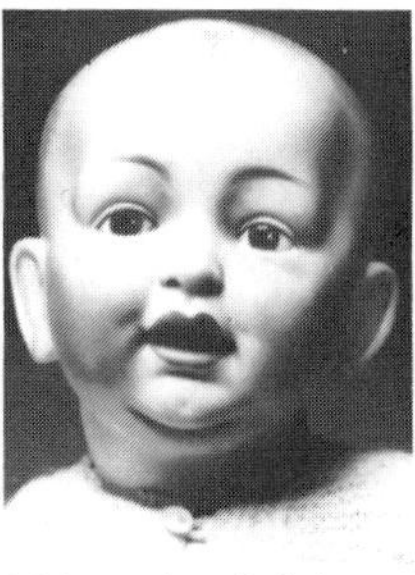

A bisque headed character doll, with painted eyes, open/closed mouth, the bent limbed composition body in knitted outfit, marked J.D.K. 11, 15in (38cm).
£350-400 *CSK*

A Kestner bisque headed child doll, with fixed brown eyes, blonde wig, fixed wrist jointed composition body dressed in fawn, marked 192 3, 12in (30.5cm) high, with a Scotts string and wood dolls swing, with trade label, 25in (63.5cm).
£400-450 *CSK*

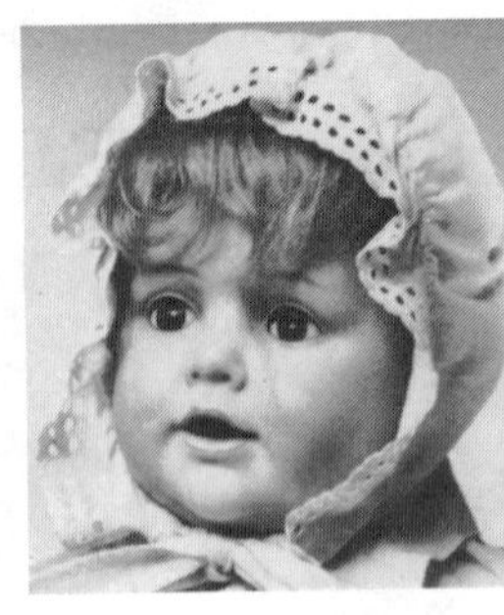

A bisque headed character baby doll, with brown flirting, sleeping eyes, quivering tongue, dimpled cheeks, short blonde wig and composition baby body, wearing nightgown, marked K14 247 J.D.K. 14, 17in (43cm).
£900-1,200 *CSK*

A Lenci painted felt child doll, with blonde wool wig, original hunting pink and black jodhpurs, boots and hat, c1930, 16½in (41cm).
£400-450 *CSK*

A Lenci cloth child doll, with painted face and blonde mohair wig, dressed in original blue and white check felt dress and white apron, c1920, 9in (23cm).
£300-350 *CSK*

Armand Marseille

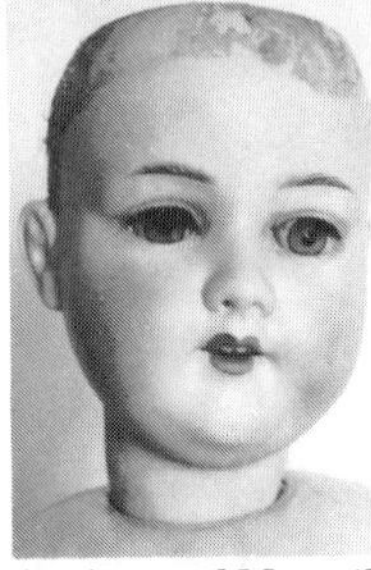

An Armand Marseille bisque headed doll, with open/closed eyes and jointed composition limbs, 390, lacking hair, some damage, 27in (69cm).
£150-200 *P[Re]*

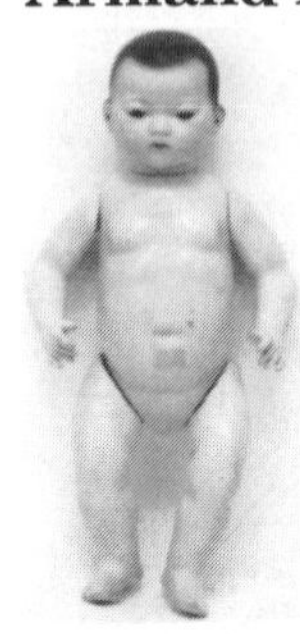

An Armand Marseille Oriental doll, with biscuit Chinese character head, brown glass eyes, slightly yellow coloured composition body, marked A.M. Germany, 353/8k, c1920, 24½in (62cm).
£1,700-2,000 *CAm*

An Armand Marseille 'Just Me' bisque headed doll, with weighted blue eyes, and 5-piece composition body, dressed in lace trimmed cotton, socks and white leather shoes, one hand missing, marked A 310/11/OM, 7in (18cm).
£600-800 *P*

CHARACTER DOLLS

- ★ in 1909 Kammer & Reinhardt introduced a large number of character dolls
- ★ these were modelled from life, showing all the nuances of childish temperament
- ★ a model was made and then a mould taken, which was used about fifty times
- ★ Simon and Halbig cast and painted the heads for many other manufacturers, including Kammer & Reinhardt, such heads are marked K & R, Simon & Halbig, or K & R, S & H and the model number
- ★ early K & R character dolls are of exceptional quality
- ★ the French had remained supreme in the manufacture of dolls, in the 19thC, with Jumeau one of the main exponents
- ★ however, from the 1890s the Germans had perfected equal skills
- ★ after K & R introduced their characters many other makers followed: Heubach, Armand Marseille, Bruno Schmidt, Kestner, and S.F.B.J. (the Societe Francaise de Fabrication de Bebes et Jouets)
- ★ obviously these dolls were expensive and so they were hardly produced in large quantities
- ★ K & R Model 117 is usually considered to be one of the most desirable, in fact any 'pouty' doll is highly collectable
- ★ the most common is model 126
- ★ there are more Heubach characters than any other
- ★ as one gets nearer to the First World War quality tends to decrease and character dolls produced after the war are in many cases, poor quality

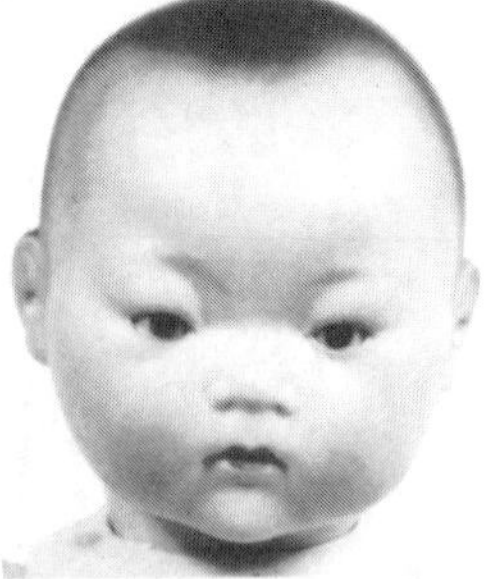

An Armand Marseille bisque headed Oriental doll, with sleeping eyes, and dressed composition toddler body, marked 353/4K, 14in (36cm).
£750-850 *P*

An Armand Marseille bisque headed doll, with open mouth and sleeping eyes, marked A 15M, 34in (86cm).
£700-1,000 *HA*

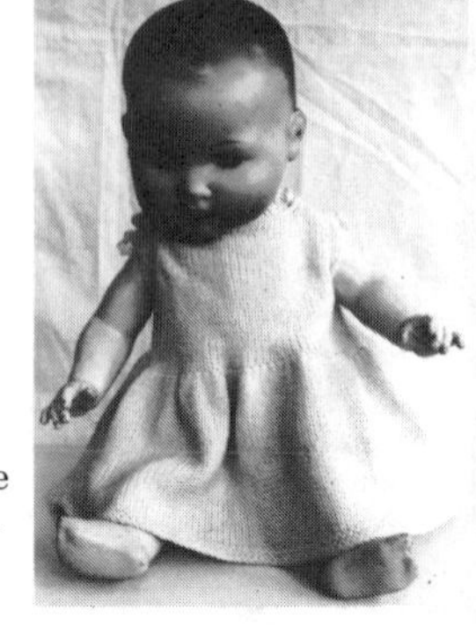

An Armand Marseille bisque headed dream baby, marked AM 351 7/K, 18in (46cm).
£100-200 *HA*

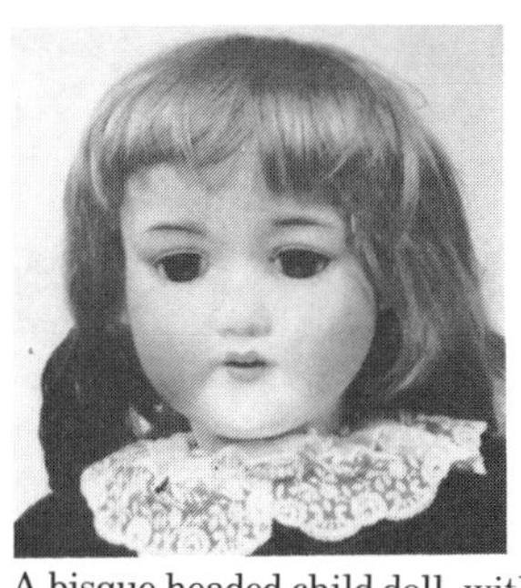

A bisque headed child doll, with jointed wood and composition body, dressed in brown velvet, with white underwear and shoes, marked 390 A.M., 37in (94cm).
£1,000-1,200 *CSK*

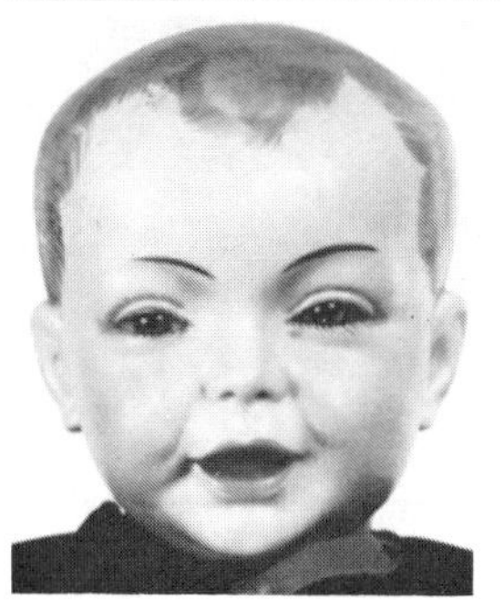

An S.F.B.J. bisque headed character doll, with fixed blue glass eyes, open/closed mouth and dressed straight limbed composition body, marked S.F.B.J. 226 8, 18in (46cm).
£600-800 *P*

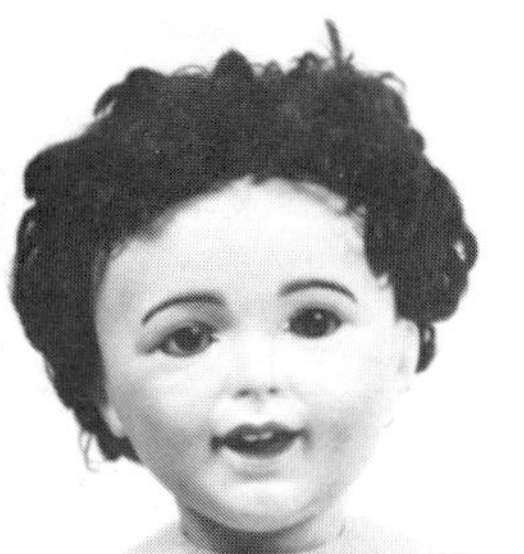

An S.F.B.J. bisque headed character doll, with sleeping brown eyes, open/closed mouth and composition toddler body, hairline crack to forehead, marked 236 12, 24in (61cm).
£250-350 *P*

Schoenau & Hoffmeister

A Schoenau & Hoffmeister 'Princess Elizabeth' bisque headed doll, with blue sleeping eyes, upper moulded teeth, fair hair wig, on composition toddler body, in cream silk embroidered dress, impressed Porzellanfabrik Burggrb, made in Germany, 23in (58cm).
£500-550 *HCH*

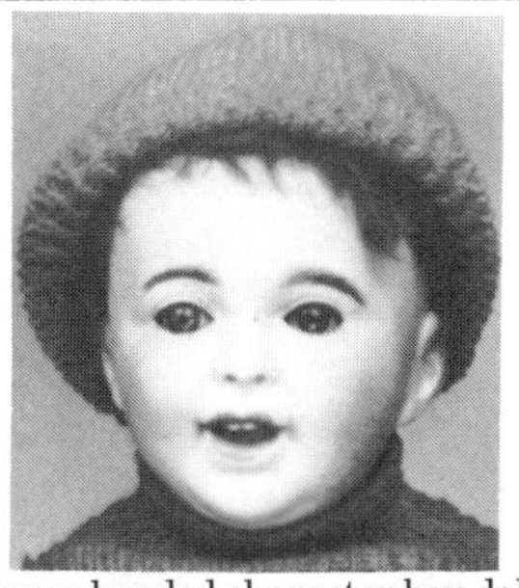

A bisque headed character boy doll, with jointed toddler composition body dressed in red knitted suit, marked S.F.B.J. 236 Paris, 13in (33cm).
£500-600 *CSK*

S.F.B.J.

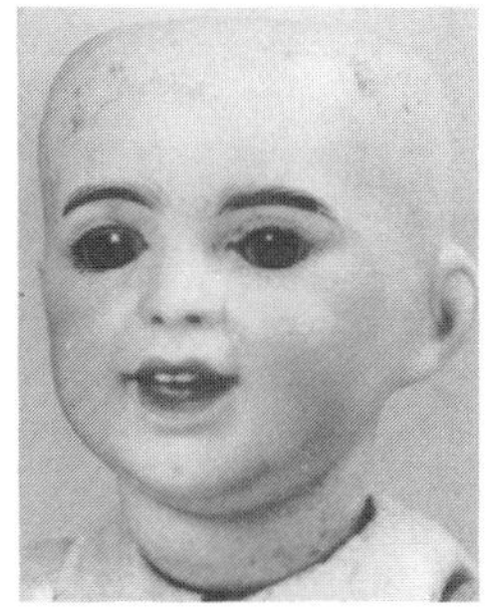

A bisque headed character baby doll, with open/closed mouth, sleeping dark eyes and baby body, marked SFBJ 236 Paris 4, 12½in (32cm).
£400-600 *CSK*

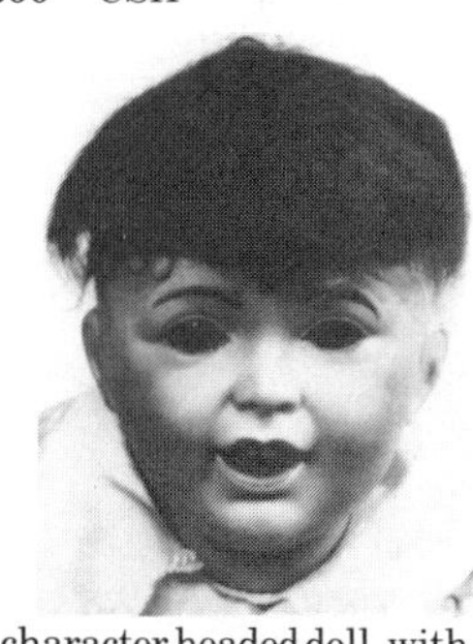

A bisque character headed doll, with open/closed mouth, dark sleeping eyes, composition baby body and silk dress with spare embroidered frock, marked S.F.B.J. 236 Paris 11, 22½in (57cm).
£400-500 *CSK*

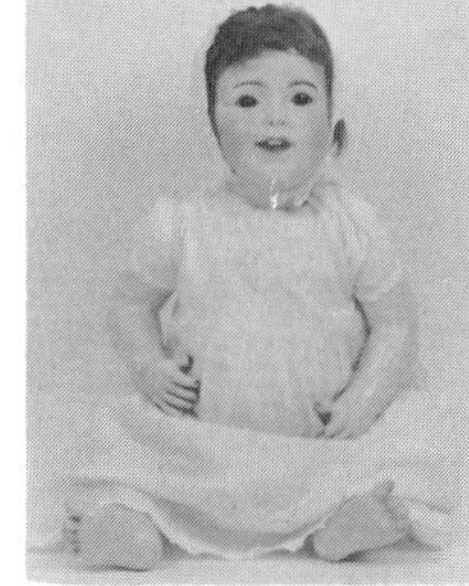

An S.F.B.J. bisque headed doll, with weighted black glass eyes, no pupils, open/closed mouth, and composition toddler body, in white cotton embroidered dress and bonnet, impressed SFBJ 236 Paris 12, c1910, 24in (61cm).
£650-700 *HCH*

Simon & Halbig/ Kammer & Reinhardt

A Kammer & Reinhardt/Simon & Halbig bisque headed character doll, with brown glass eyes, ball jointed composition body, in cream net and lace dress with undergarments and cotton shoes, impressed K*R, Simon & Halbig 117 55, 22in (56cm).
£3,000-3,500 *HCH*

A bisque headed character doll, with painted features and blonde mohair wig, the jointed composition body in whitework dress, white underwear and leather shoes, wig damaged, marked K*R 114 49, 18in (46cm).
£2,000-2,500 *CSK*

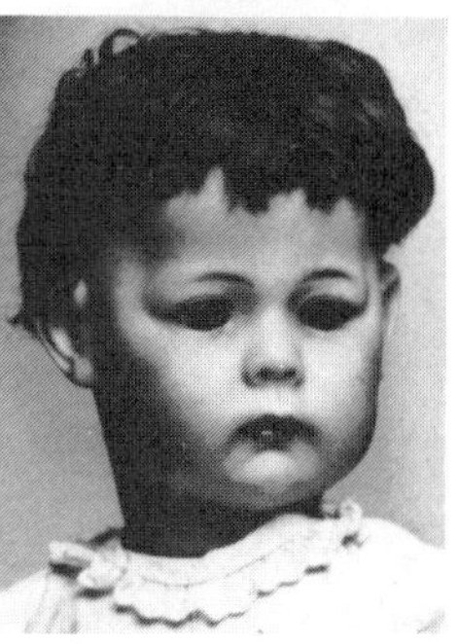

A bisque headed character boy doll, with brown sleeping eyes, golden brown mohair wig, the jointed composition toddler body in cream suit with brown leather shoes, marked K*R Simon & Halbig 115/a 48, 19½in (49cm).
£2,000-2,500 *CSK*

A Simon & Halbig bisque headed doll, with sleeping eyes, 2 moulded upper teeth, fair hair wig, voice box and composition body, in white cotton gown and bonnet, impressed Simon & Halbig Oo Germany 60, 23½in (60cm).
£350-400 *HCH*

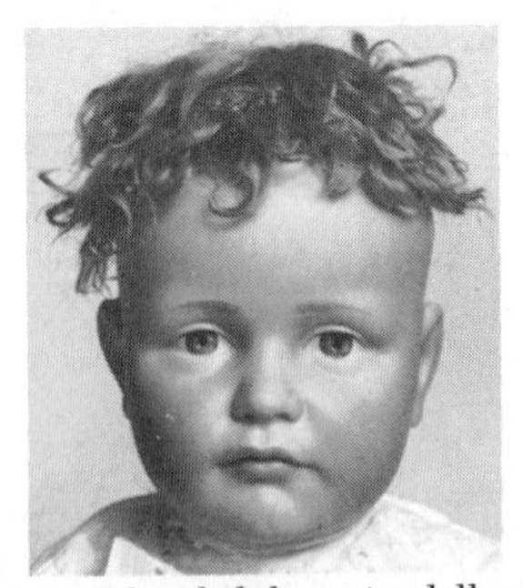

A bisque headed character doll, with grey painted eyes, closed mouth and jointed composition body, marked K*R 114 60, 21in (53cm).
£2,000-3,000 *CSK*

A Simon & Halbig bisque headed doll, with sleeping eyes, pierced ears and composition ball jointed body, clothed, marked S & H Halbig 1079, Germany 14, 30in (76cm).
£650-750 *M*

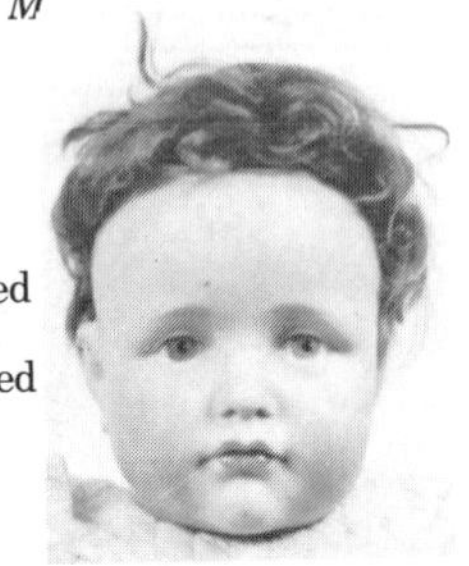

A Kammer & Reinhardt bisque headed character doll, with painted blue eyes, the jointed composition body dressed in whitework, marked K*R 114 46, 18in (46cm).
£2,000-2,500 *P*

Jules Steiner

A bisque headed bébé, with brown eyes, pierced ears, skin wig and composition jointed body, wearing a wool sailor's outfit, with extra clothing, marked Ste.C l and written in red Steiner A.S.G.D.G. Paris Bourgoin Jne, 15in (38cm).
£2,000-2,500 *CSK*

Automata

A Simon & Halbig bisque headed automaton doll, four movement with music, 21in (53cm).
£1,500-2,500 *HA*

An automaton of a young girl, by Simon & Halbig, when the musical mechanism is wound her head, eyes and arms move from side-to-side and the chest shows a positive breathing action, dressed in a sequinned net blouse with matching headdress and blue/grey woven silk costume, trimmed with braid, head marked 1300, 28in (71cm), including musical box base.
£1,200-1,500 *P*

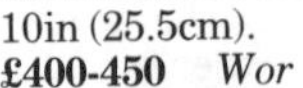

An American clockwork doll, c1862, 10in (25.5cm).
£400-450 *Wor*

A mechanical kid bodied doll, crying 'Mama' and 'Papa', in original clothes, 19thC, 19in (48cm).
£3,000-5,000 *HA*

An automaton, modelled as a Scottish terrier, on small wheels, by Descamps, 11in (28cm).
£200-400 *CSK*

A Bing jumping monkey clockwork automaton, with rust fur covering and felt paws, marked with 2 metal tags, 6in (15cm).
£150-200 *HCH*

A Bing 'cat skier' clockwork automaton, with grey fur body, white shirt and red breeches, leather boots, on metals 'skis' with wheels and holding a wooden stick, the key mechanism concealed in body, marked with metal tag in ear, 8in (20cm).
£450-500 *HCH*

A musical automaton of a lady at her dressing table, by Ferdinand Gaultier, 19thC.
£4,000-5,000 *HA*

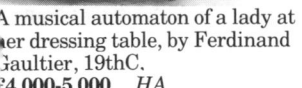

An automaton, of a cow which moos when the head is turned from side-to-side, patented, c1890, 10in (25.5cm) high.
£300-500 *HA*

A tiger automaton, covered in animal skin, pounces, c1880, 14in (35.5cm) long.
£700-1,000 *SH*

Dolls Houses

An eight-piece matching suite, late 19thC.
£250-300 *P*

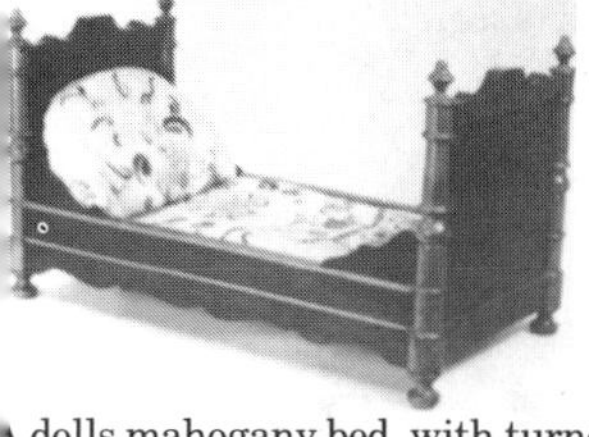

A dolls mahogany bed, with turned ends and Chinese embroidered mattress and pillow, 19½in (49cm) long.
£150-200 *CSK*

An Edwardian dolls house, the front elevation with a portico flanked by bay windows, 33in (84cm) wide.
£1,200-1,500 *Bea*

A mahogany dolls house, with glazed windows, sliding front wall revealing plain interior, c1900, 37in (94cm) wide.
£1,200-1,500 *P[Re]*

Teddy Bears

A silver grey plush covered teddy bear, with boot button eyes, pointed muzzle, hump and elongated limbs, growler inoperative, Steiff button in ear, 28in (71cm).
£2,700-3,000 *CSK*

A Steiff teddy bear, with button in ear.
£800-1,000 *HA*

A golden plush covered teddy bear, in the form of a child's muff, with black boot button eyes, embroidered snout and silk neck cord, 15in (38cm).
£200-250 *CSK*

A Steiff gold plush teddy bear, slightly worn, pads renewed, with metal Steiff disc in left ear, c1907, 25in (63cm).
£2,200-2,500 *HCH*

A golden plush covered teddy bear, with boot button eyes, pointed muzzle, hump and elongated limbs, with growler, Steiff button in ear, 24in (61cm).
£2,500-3,500 *CSK*

A teddy bear, 23in (58cm).
£200-250 *PC*

A pair of twin teddies with button eyes, well loved, c1930, 12in (30.5cm).
£150-250 *HA*

A golden plush covered teddy bear, with pronounced hump, growler inoperative, with Steiff button in ear, 29in (74cm).
£3,000-4,000 *CSK*

A golden plush covered teddy bear, with boot button eyes, cut muzzle, hump and elongated limbs, replaced pads, Steiff button in left ear, 19in (48cm).
£500-700 *CSK*

A cinnamon plush covered teddy bear with glass eyes, large hump and elongated limbs, 12in (30.5cm).
£100-200 *CSK*

A golden plush covered teddy bear with boot button eyes, growler, possibly by Steiff, c1930, 12½in (32cm).
£350-500 *CSK*

A honey plush covered teddy bear, the cut muzzle with central seam, wide set eyes, with elongated pads and small hump, growler inoperative, probably Steiff, c1908, 17in (43cm).
£800-900 *CSK*

Miscellaneous

A pair of advertising dolls with composition shoulder heads, modelled as the 'Bisto Kids', designed by Will Owen, the cloth bodies in original clothes, c1948, 11in (28cm).
£200-300 *CSK*

A painted felt character doll, in original red and white romper suit, with Lenci metal button, probably from the 111 series, c1922, 13in (33cm).
£200-250 *CSK*

A composition headed parasol doll, with fixed blue eyes, blonde wig and pink silk lace bonnet, the skirt forming the parasol covering, the matching cape covering her composition arms, her wooden legs forming the handle, 21in (53cm).
£300-350 *CSK*

A doll's trunk, containing a quantity of clothes, shoes and sandals, including a blue silk velvet and satin dress with watered silk front, 17in (43cm).
£300-350 *CSK*

A collection of dolls clothes, including whitework gowns, shoes and bibs.
£2,500-3,000 *CSK*

A set of painted composition headed Punch & Judy glove puppets, in original clothes, with wooden hands and legs.
£250-300 *CSK*

Two dolls hats.
£75-95 *CSK*

Toys

Lead Soldiers

Heyde set No. 919, Knights in Armour, 1 lance and 6 plumes broken, 50mm scale, c1880, in original box.
£100-150 *CSK*

Britains set No. 2077, King's Troop, Royal Horse Artillery, at the walk, in review order, slightly retouched, 1 plume broken.
£220-250 *CSK*

Britains set No. 9419, Royal Horse Artillery Gun and Team, repainted, in original box, lid with torn sides.
£200-250 *CSK*

Britains set No. 37, Band of the Coldstream Guards, 1 missing.
£160-200 *CSK*

Britains rare set No. 2171, Royal Air Force Colour Party, slightly chipped, in original Regiments of all Nations box.
£2,000-3,000 *CSK*

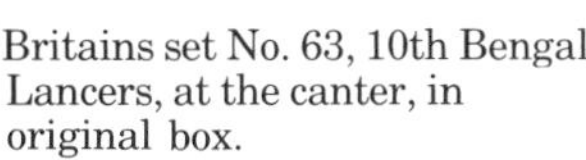

Britains set No. 63, 10th Bengal Lancers, at the canter, in original box.
£900-1,000 *CSK*

Britains very rare set No. 1450, Royal Army Medical Corps, slight damage, c1940, in original box.
£3,000-5,000 *CSK*

Britains display set No. 54, Types of the British Army, including Queen's Bays (2nd Dragoons), 9th Lancers and 1st Life Guards, one sword broken, 3 Life Guards missing.
£300-350 *CSK*

Britains rare special set for Hamleys, Royal Marines Colour Party, rubbed, in original Types of the British Army box.
£2,000-2,500 *CSK*

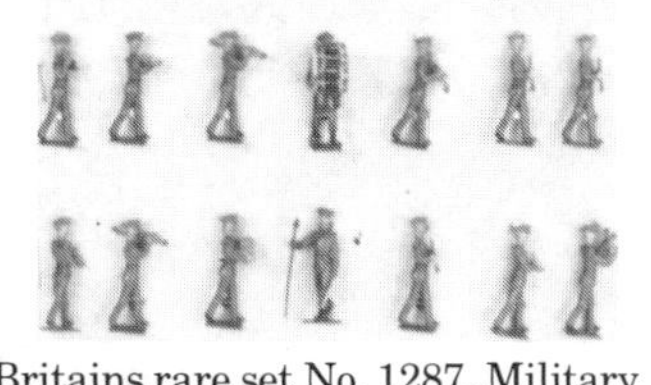

Britains rare set No. 1287, Military Band, some damage, in original box.
£500-700 *CSK*

Britains set No. 460, Colour Party of the Scots Guards, some damage, in original Types of the World's Armies box.
£400-450 *CSK*

Money Banks

A cast iron money box of a golliwog, 6in (15.5cm).
£120-150 *P*

Tinplate

A Bing printed and painted tinplate English houseboat, No. 13662/1, c1904, some damage, 14in (35.5cm) long.
£1,500-2,000 *CSK*

A Bing three-funnel liner, with clockwork mechanism, repainted in red and cream, black lining and tan decks, 2 reproduction flags, mast missing, c1925, 15in (38cm) long.
£400-450 *CSK*

A Bing three-funnel Dreadnought No. 155/115, with clockwork mechanism, finished in battleship grey, lacks masts and flags, worn, c1912, 16in (40.5cm) long.
£350-400 *CSK*

A Bing battleship, with removable deck to reveal clockwork mechanism, finished in dark grey below waterline, grey above, with black painted portholes, tan decks, 2 flags, some retouching, steering wheel broken, c1915, 16in (40.5cm) long.
£400-600 *CSK*

A Carette painted tinplate three-funnel liner, 'Manxman', in original paintwork with white repainted ensign, some chipping, lacks flag on mast, c1910, 11in (28cm).
£350-400 *CSK*

A Metalcraft, No. 820 'Spirit of St. Louis', with instructions, U.S.A., c1928, in original box, worn.
£200-250 *CSK*

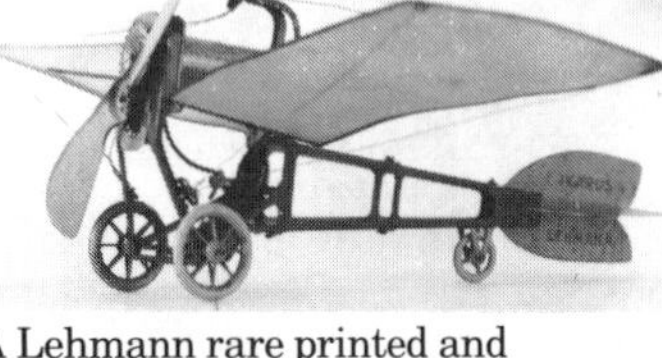

A Lehmann rare printed and painted early monoplane, 'Ikarus', No. 653, the clockwork mechanism firing a two-bladed propeller, with yellow paper wings, all finished in red and yellow, c1920, 10½in (27cm) long.
£1,500-2,000 *RID*

An Ernest Plank riverboat, the painted tinplate steamer with live steam spirit fired mechanism, finished in red below waterline, black above, with white side panels, slight damage, c1920, 16in (40.5cm) long.
£250-300 *CSK*

A Gunda-Werke lithograph tinplate motorcycle and sidecar, with clockwork mechanism, c1920, 6½in (16.5cm).
£850-900 *CSK*

A Lesney Massey Harris 745D tractor.
£150-200 *HCH*

An Arnold printed and painted tinplate motorbike and rider, 'Mac 700', with clockwork mechanism causing the rider to hop on-and-off, in original paintwork, W. German, c1955, 7½in (19cm).
£300-350 *CSK*

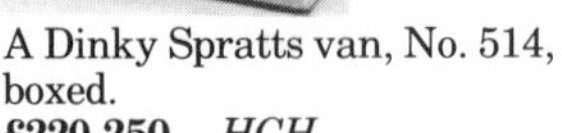

A Dinky Spratts van, No. 514, boxed.
£220-250 *HCH*

An Arcade Toys cast iron 2-piece motorcycle 'COP', in blue, 4in (10cm), with farm tractor in red, 3½in (8cm).
£200-250 *P*

A Tekno Mercedes Tuborg Pilsner delivery lorry, boxed.
£70-100 *P*

Two Spot-On Ford Zodiacs No. 100, with original boxes.
£120-150 *HCH*

A Dinky J. Lyons & Co., van No. 514, boxed.
£250-300 *HCH*

A Spot-On London Transport bus.
£320-350 *HCH*

A Dinky 28/3h Dunlop delivery van, in red and gold, some damage.
£120-150 *CSK*

A Dinky 28/3p Crawford's delivery van, in red and gold, slightly chipped.
£450-500 *CSK*

A Dinky 28/3a Hornby Trains delivery van, in red and gold, very slightly chipped.
£250-300 *CSK*

A Marx free-wheel driven streamlined sports coupé, with red hood, 20in (51cm) long.
£200-300 *P*

A Marx spring action rocket-shaped racer, No. 12, 16in (41cm).
£150-200 *P*

A Marx Drive-ur-self car, clockwork drive, red with blue roof and cream flashes, 14in (36cm) long, boxed.
£200-250 *P*

A Marx battery operated 2-door convertible saloon, 20in (51cm), boxed.
£150-200 *P*

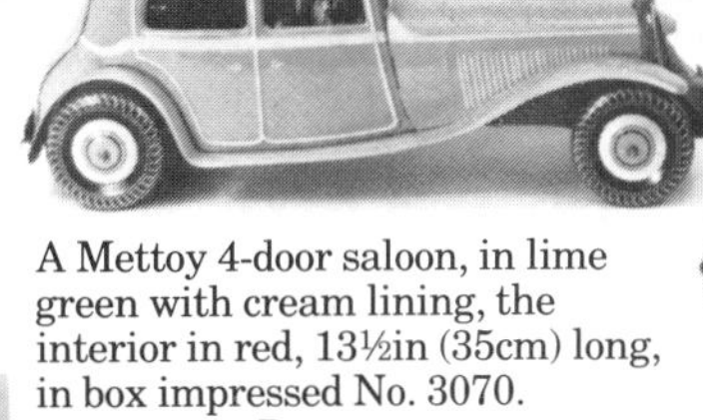
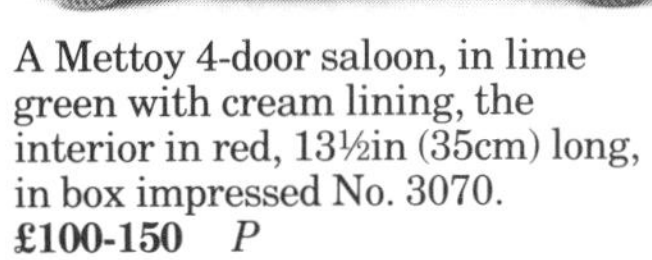

A Mettoy 4-door saloon, in lime green with cream lining, the interior in red, 13½in (35cm) long, in box impressed No. 3070.
£100-150 *P*

A Linemar 200 free-wheeling Chevrolet, in grey and black, c1955, boxed.
£1,500-2,000 *P*

A JEP tinplate Phantom Rolls Royce, finished in white and black, French, many parts missing including clockwork mechanism, replaced parts, repainted, c1930, 19in (48cm) long.
£700-1,000 *CSK*

A battery operated four-door Cadillac State Service car, 19½in (49cm), boxed.
£250-300 *P*

A Mamod tinplate spirit-fired two-seater open tourer, finished in red and off-white, running boards retouched.
£150-200 *P*

A Chad Valley tinplate clockwork saloon car, with number plate CV1 947, 10in (25.5cm) long.
£50-70 *HCH*

Five Corgi Toys Gift Sets No. 5. British Racing cars, including Vanwalls, Lotus Mk.XI's and B.R.M.'s, c1960, in original boxes.
£300-350 *CSK*

A C.I.J. P2 Alfa Romeo painted tinplate 2-seater Grand Prix racing car, with clockwork mechanism powering rear axle, finished in green, French, some damage, c1926, 21in (53cm) long.
£500-700 *CSK*

Walt Disney's Donald Duck Duet, by Marx, boxed.
£260-320 *P*

A painted and lithographed tinplate vis-a-vis, c1910, 5in (12.5cm).
£350-400 *CSK*

Tootsietoy No. 5210 trucks, including a Mack Express semi-trailer 1925, a Mack trailer truck, a Greyhound bus, a fire engine, a wrecker truck and 4 pick-up trucks, one vehicle damaged, c1938, in original box.
£200-250 *CSK*

A Bub lithographed limousine, with clockwork mechanism, battery operated headlamps and rear 'stop' plate, finished in blue and light green, with yellow and blue lining, some damage, c1928, 14½in (37cm) long.
£200-250 *CSK*

A Lehmann early printed and painted tinplate motorcyclist, Echo, EPL 725, with clockwork mechanism, c1910, 9in (23cm).
£2,000-2,400 *CSK*

A Lehmann printed and painted tinplate rickshaw with running coolie, Masuyama, EPL 773, with clockwork mechanism, in original paintwork, some damage, c1925, 7in (18cm) long.
£250-300 *CSK*

A Karl Bub atom rocket ship, boxed.
£120-180 *P*

An Ingap 4-door limousine, with clockwork mechanism, in blue over red, with yellow and black lining, some chipping, right rear wheel damaged, c1930, 11in (28cm) long.
£400-600 *CSK*

An Ichiko printed and painted tinplate Cadillac, with defective friction drive mechansim, finished in red with chrome trimming, c1967, 28in (71cm) long.
£400-500 *CSK*

A Doll & Co., printed and painted carousel, with a hand cranked clockwork mechanism, in red and pink, lacking flag, c1914, 11½in (29cm).
£300-600 *CSK*

An S. Gunthermann clockwork painted and printed tinplate billiards player, the mechanism causing 3 balls to be potted and returned to the player, c1900, 8in (20cm) long, in original box.
£1,000-1,200 *RID*

Make the most of Miller's

In Miller's we do NOT just reprint saleroom estimates. We work from realised prices either from an auction room or a dealer. Our consultants then work out a realistic price range for a similar piece. This is to try to avoid repeating freak results – either low or high.

A German tinplate clockwork army motorcycle and sidecar, with machine gunner, key missing, c1930.
£80-120 *MN*

A German plated tinplate clockwork pool player at table, 11½in (29cm) long.
£400-500 *P*

A Lehmann clockwork zig-zag, No. 640, in good condition, boxed.
£1,000-1,500 *P*

A German clockwork boxing match, post war, boxed, no lid.
£100-120 *P*

Miscellaneous

A quantity of Elastin 70mm scale cowboys and indians, 8 by Lineol, some slight damage, c1938.
£350-400 *CSK*

A group of painted bronze miniature figures of animals, mainly characters from Beatrix Potter's books.
£600-700 *CSK*

A set of Erzegebirge painted carved wood and flock covered composition animals, in original wood box, German, some slight damage, c1860.
£450-500 *CSK*

A toy tin circus, the 14-part ring with 16 various artists and horses, c1830.
£3,000-3,500 *CAm*

An Erzegebirge painted wood Noah's Ark, with opening side panel to reveal 74 carved wood animals and birds and 5 members of the Noah family, in original paintwork, inscribed 'Harry Burney, Keeper of Wild Beasts, Birds, Fishes and Insects', German, some slight damage to animals, c1870, 15½in (38cm) long.
£600-800 *CSK*

An Erzegebirge straw-work Noah's Ark, with opening side panel to reveal 236 animals, birds and insects, Mr & Mrs Noah and 5 members of the family, German, some slight damage, c1870, the ark 19in (48cm) long.
£1,200-1,500 *CSK*

Britains and other makers farm items.
£100-120 *CSK*

Britains Famous Football Teams, Chelsea, in original box.
£300-350 *CSK*

Britains Home Farm items, some damage, all in original boxes.
£300-350 *CSK*

A Noah's Ark, complete with animals, 19thC.
£500-1,000 *HA*

Two wooden rod puppets, with painted faces.
£120-160 *Wor*

An acrobat toy, comprising 4 papier mâché acrobats standing and sliding down on 2 ropes stretched in a stand, in original wood box with sliding top.
£850-950 *CAm*

A wood box with 3 drawers containing Meccano, with 2 instruction booklets, not complete and slightly worn.
£250-300 *CSK*

A pull-along nodding duck, with green velvet head and painted feathers, factory stamp on base, c1880, 6in (15cm) long.
£200-250 *CSK*

A clockwork fur-covered giraffe with clown rider, 12½in (31cm) high.
£60-80 *P*

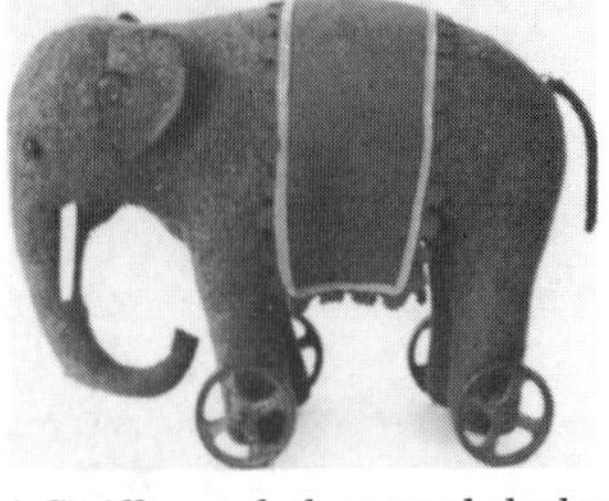

A Steiff grey cloth covered elephant on wheels, with boot button eyes and red blanket, late 19thC, 8in (20cm) high.
£250-300 *CSK*

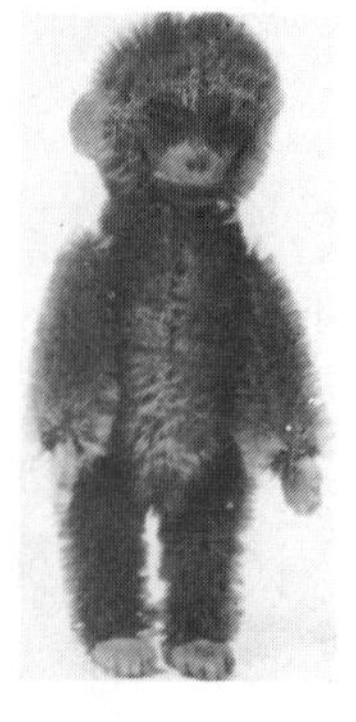

A lavender plush covered monkey, the head removing to reveal a scent bottle with stopper, jointed at shoulders and hips, with felt ears and feet, probably by Schuco, c1920, 3½in (7.5cm) high.
£150-200 *CSK*

A cream plush goose, with felt beak, possibly German, 14in (35.5cm) long.
£50-90 *HCH*

A complete boxed set of Snow White and the 7 Dwarfs, in original clothes, the dwarfs 9½in (24cm) high, in boxes labelled Chad Valley Hygienic Textile Toys, with the name of each toy beneath.
£3,000-4,000 *CSK*

A terracotta headed creche figure, with painted hands and feet, in original cream shirt and tweed breeches, Neapolitan, early 19thC, 16½in (42cm) high.
£350-450 *CSK*

A terracotta headed creche figure, modelled as a Turk, with painted wooden hands and feet, in original blue and gold embroidered jacket and gold Turkish trousers, Neapolitan, early 19thC, 19in (48cm) high.
£350-400 *CSK*

A Chad Valley felt headed character doll, modelled as Snow White, 16½in (41.5cm) high, and 7 dwarfs.
£900-1,000 *CSK*

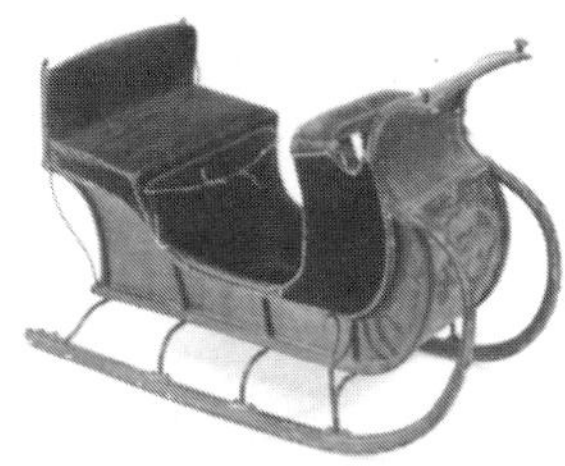

A wood and brass toy sleigh, upholstered in blue velvet, with brass runners, late 19thC, 13in (33cm) long.
£900-1,000 *CSK*

A Victorian child's tricycle, with leather seat, wooden handlebars and horse's head, on metal wheels.
£400-500 *GSP*

A Victorian dolls perambulator.
£200-250 *PC*

A Victorian child's sledge, painted red, on shaped metal runners.
£400-500 *LRG*

A three-wheeled perambulator, with metal rimmed wooden wheels and porcelain handle, the bodywork black with blue and yellow lines, 50in (127cm) long.
£600-700 *CSK*

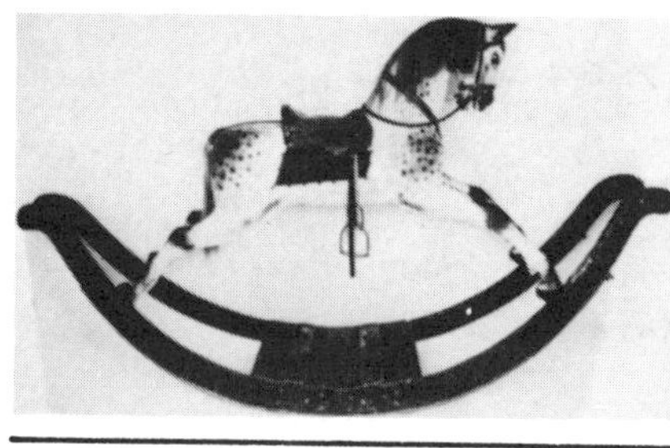

A Victorian wooden rocking horse, with leather saddle, repainted, 86in (218.5cm) long.
£500-600 *PWC*

Models

A Lehmann printed and painted tinplate monorail car, Vineta, EPL No. 656, slightly worn, c1920, 10in (25.5cm) long.
£400-450 *CSK*

A Bing tinplate clockwork tram car.
£200-250 *P*

A Bing gauge 0 clockwork model of an early tramcar, in original claret and cream paintwork, with original lining, slightly chipped, c1906, 7in (18cm) long.
£600-650 *CSK*

A Benefink & Co., model of a horse drawn cart.
£400-450 *LRG*

A scale model Romany caravan, in the style of Dunton, with fully fitted interior, 72in (182.5cm) high.
£1,200-1,500 *Bea*

An early fret-work Type B London bus, British, some very slight damage, c1920, 20½in (51cm) long.
£300-350 *CSK*

A model Guinness brewery wagon, drawn by a pair of horses.
£350-400 *C*

A silver presentation model Chinese coal minehead, with plaque inscribed 'presented to E.J. Nathan, Esq., O.B.E., Joint Chief Manager of the Kailan Mining administration by the members of the senior staff as a token of their esteem and gratitude Autumn 1945', the roof opening to form a cigar box, 21 by 37in (53 by 94cm).
£800-900 *CSK*

A detailed 2in (5cm) scale static display model of a Merryweather twin cylinder horse drawn fire appliance 'Birmingham Fire Brigade', 17 by 26in (43 by 66cm).
£2,500-3,000 *CSK*

A model of the Cotswold Coffee Roasting and Grinding Mill, by R. J. Sare, c1925, 10 by 13in (25.5 by 33cm).
£200-250 *CSK*

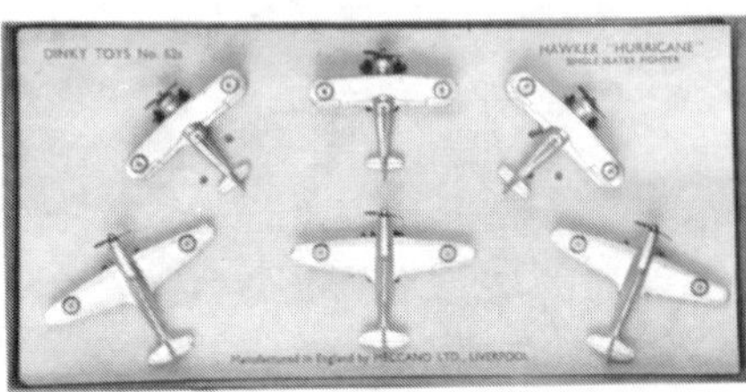

Dinky 60p Gloster Gladiator Bi-planes, with 62s Hawker Hurricane fighters, in 62s set of 6 box.
£550-600 *P*

Aircraft identification models from the 1939-45 war.
£150-200 *PC*

A fully rigged bone and horn model of an 86-gun man-of-war, 23 by 30½in (58 by 77cm).
£1,500-2,000 *CSK*

A fully planked and framed wood pinned rigged model of the ketch Nonsuch of 1650, built by T. E. J. Manning, 29 by 30in (73 by 76cm).
£350-400 *CSK*

A ¼ scale flying model of the Stampe SV4C bi-plane, serial letters G-AYWT, with external details, finished in green with gilded decoration and white letters 'Jaguar', wingspan 83in (210.5cm).
£600-650 *CSK*

MAKE THE MOST OF MILLER'S

Price ranges in this book reflect what one should expect to pay for a similar example. When selling one can obviously expect a figure below. This will fluctuate according to a dealer's stock, saleability at a particular time, etc. It is always advisable to approach a reputable specialist dealer or an auction house which has specialist sales

A model of H.M.S. Bounty, with planked wooden hull, the masts fully rigged with linen sails, 20thC, 26in (66cm) high, in glazed display case.
£220-260 *LBP*

A bone and baleen model of H.M.S. Star, with 46 guns, the stern named and carved in relief, 19thC, 23½in (63cm) long, on wooden stand with glazed case.
£3,500-4,000 *P*

A French bronze group of Roger and Angelica borne by the Hippogriff, cast from a model by Antoine-Louis Barye, by the master founder H, Henri at Hector Brahme foundry, stamped H signed Barye, Roger Ballu, L'oeuvre de Barye, Paris, 1890, 20 by 27½in (51 by 70cm). **£75,000-80,000** *C*

A bronze figure of Mephistopheles, the massive granite base engraved on one side in gold Antocolski, after Markus Antokolski, 19thC, 34in (86cm) high. **£5,000-7,000** *C*

An Austrian bronze model of an owl pouncing on 3 mice, by Caspar Gras, 17thC, 6in (15cm) high, on turned wood socle. **£11,000-15,000** *C*

A French bronze group of an Arab falconer, cast from a model by Pierre Jules Mêne, signed, inscribed Susse Frères Editeurs, Fauconnier a Cheval de P.J. Mene, 19thC, 31 by 30in (78 by 76cm). **£10,000-12,000** *C*

An Italian gilt bronze figure of Hercules supporting a celestial globe, late 16th/early 17thC, 15in (38cm) high. **£105,000-110,000** *C*

An English bronze statuette of Peter Pan, after Sir George Frampton, inscribed on the base, early 20thC, 19in (48cm) high. **£4,000-5,000** *C*

A Venetian gilt bronze statuette of Neptune, in the style of Girolamo Campagna, on a marble pedestal with pietre dura inlaid coat-of-arms of a bishop, with a tower overgown with ivy, 16thC, 16½in high. **£7,000-9,000** *C*

A pair of French gilt and bronze urns, with classical figures in market scenes inscribed EN THI AT OPAI and EK THEAT OPAE, above friezes of sphinx and Athenian decoration, 19thC, 4½in (11cm) high. **£12,000-15,000** *C*

A bronze group of Aeneas carrying his father Anchises followed by Ascanius, after François Girardon and Pierre Lepautre, French, 18thC, 22in (56cm) high. **£5,000-6,000** *CNY*

A Charles X ormolu casket, with English porcelain plaque, carrying handles, 9½in (24cm) wide. **£4,500-5,500**
A pair of ormolu and filigree candlesticks, possibly Italian, c1800, 10in (25cm) high. **£2,000-3,000** *C*

A pair of ormolu and bronze 3-branch wall lights in the Regency style, 19in (48cm) high. **£4,000-5,000** *C*

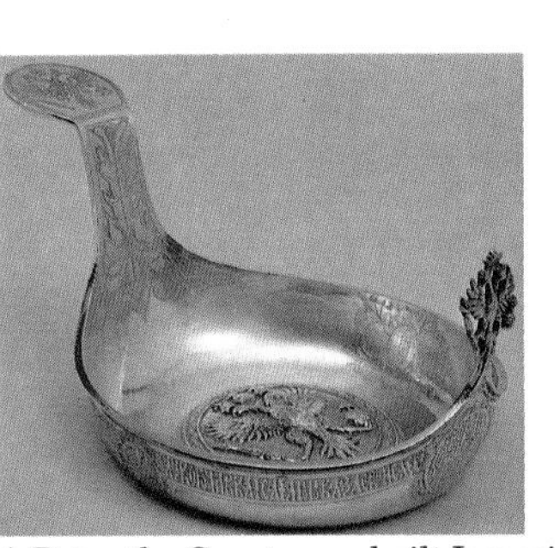

A Peter the Great parcel gilt Imperial presentation kovsh, the silver centre with the Russian double-headed eagle, exterior with Cyrillic engraving, unmarked, c1697, 13½in (34cm) long. **£16,000-20,000** *C*

A pair of Louis XV ormolu and bronze 3-light candelabra, the central shaft entwined by a snake, the white marble plinths on square bases, 19½in (49.5cm) high. **£3,000-4,000** *C*

A French ormolu caryatid herm, a bearded male figure, on a tapering support, early 18thC, 52in (132cm) high. **£42,000-45,000** *C*

A pair of ormolu mounted Chinese red and blue porcelain 8-light candelabra, 19thC, 35in (89cm) high. **£4,000-5,000** *C*

A pair of Empire patinated bronze and ormolu 6-light candelabra, 31½in (80cm) high. **£15,000-20,000** *C*

A pair of Louis XVI ormolu-mounted alabaster pot pourri vases, with bearded satyr's mask handles, 13½in (34.5cm) high. **£6,000-7,000** *C*

A pair of Louis XVI bronze and ormolu chenets, with recumbent lions on lambrequin and fluted shaped pedestals, 23in (58.5cm) wide. **£25,000-30,000** *C*

A pair of George III bronze, ormolu and white marble cassolettes, 10in (25cm) high. **£8,000-9,000** *C*

A pair of ormolu and bronze urn-shaped vases, fitted for electricity as lamps, with pleated silk shades, 34½in (88cm). **£9,000-12,000** *C*

An Empire painted and gilded 8-light chandelier, with stepped circular spreading central support surmounted by a classical maiden, re-decorated, 36in (91.5cm) high. **£5,000-6,000** *C*

An Empire patinated bronze and ormolu 6-light candelabrum, with scrolling foliate candle branches ending in rosettes, 42in (107cm) high. **£9,000-12,000** *C*

A pair of Empire ormolu-mounted bronze ewers, c1815, 22½in (57cm) high. **£10,000-12,000** *CNY*

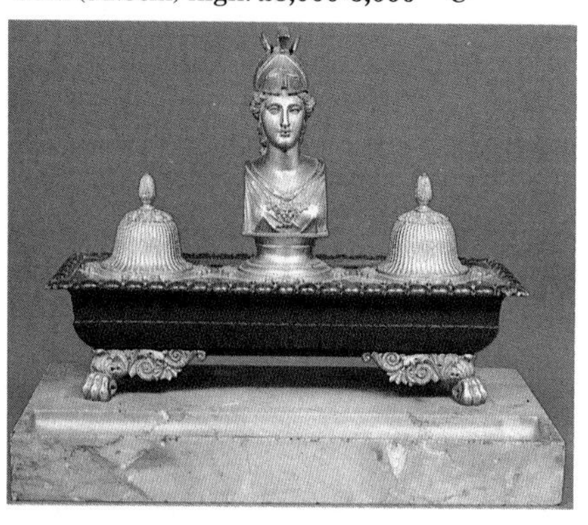

A Charles X ormolu and bronze encrier, surmounted by a bust of Minerva, on a Siena marble base, 14in (35.5cm) wide. **£5,000-6,000** *C*

A pair of Empire ormolu and patinated bronze chenets, formed as recumbent sphinxes, on shaped plinth bases, 15½in (39cm) long. **£18,000-20,000** *C*

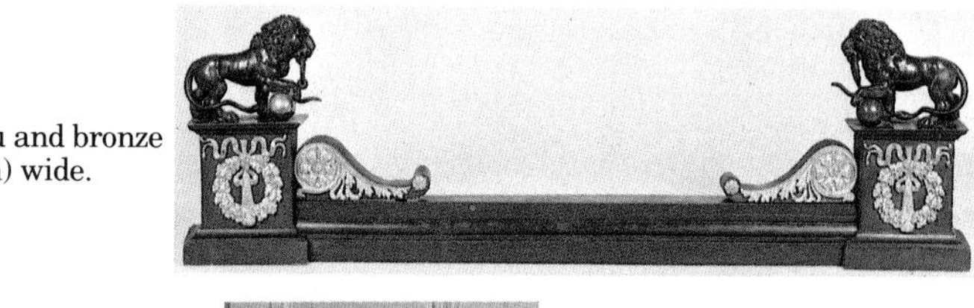

An Empire ormolu and bronze fender, 36in (91cm) wide. **£4,000-5,000** *C*

A pair of Empire patinated steel and ormolu Athéniennes, 17in (43cm) high. **£6,000-7,000** *C*

A pair of ormolu mounted porphyry urns, stamped Ch. Bussierre, 22½in (57cm) high. **£19,000-22,000** *C*

A pair of ormolu wall lights, of Louis XV style, fitted for electricity, 13½in (34cm) high. **£2,500-3,000** *C*

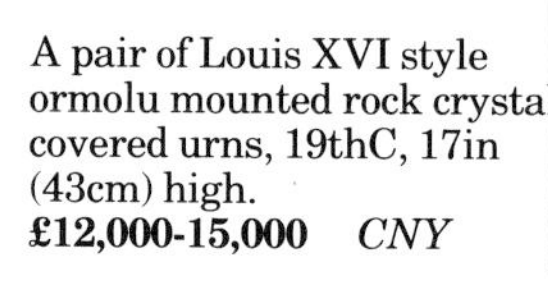

A pair of Louis XVI style ormolu mounted rock crystal covered urns, 19thC, 17in (43cm) high. **£12,000-15,000** *CNY*

A Louis XV ormolu mounted Japanese lacquer and Meissen porcelain encrier, group modelled by J. J. Kändler, damage and repair, blue crossed swords mark, c1749, 17½in (44cm) wide. **£15,000-20,000** *C*

A Flemish ivory statue of St. Sebastian, damage, 17thC, 17in high. **£57,000-60,000** *C*

A pair of Dieppe ivory mirrors, the frames with foliage, lions masks and figures of Pan, initialled FAR, late 19thC, 33in high. **£7,000-9,000** *C*

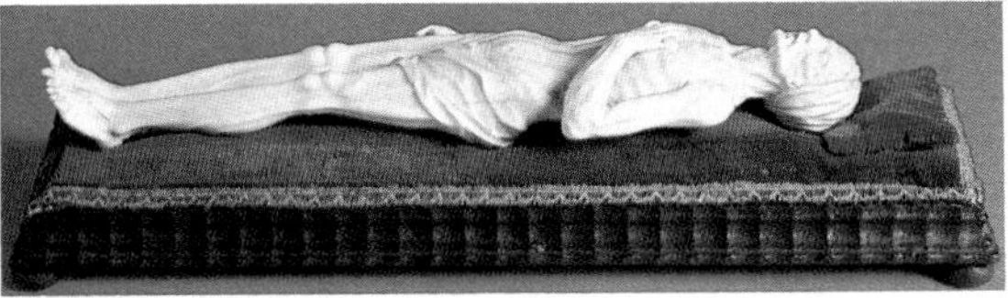

A German ivory cadaver, in the manner of Stephen Zick, slight damage, 17thC, 10in (25cm) long. **£2,000-3,000** *C*

A pair of ormolu mounted Sèvres bleu nouveau pot pourri vases, 16in (41cm) high. **£26,000-30,000** *C*

An English carved marble portrait bust, reputedly Admiral Byng, damage, 18thC, 17in high. **£3,000-4,000** *P*

A white marble bust of Napoleon I, signed by R. Trentanove, Italian, damaged, early 19thC, 21in (54cm) high. **£1,500-2,000** *CNY*

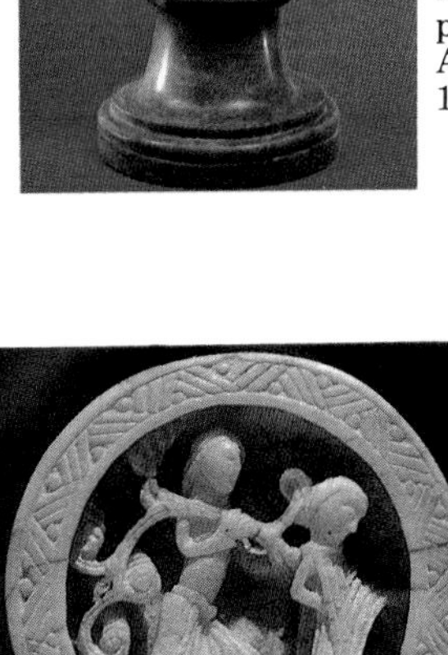

An English walrus ivory games piece, damaged, mid-12thC, 7cm diam. **£25,000-27,000** *P*

A pair of Florentine marble figures of Love Found and Love Abandoned, by Pasquale Romanelli, Firenze 1876/77, minor chips, 63 and 61in. **£46,000-52,000** *C*

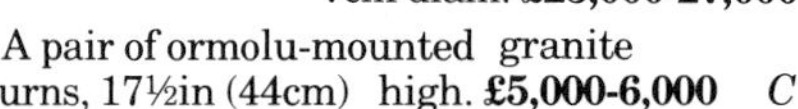

A pair of ormolu-mounted granite urns, 17½in (44cm) high. **£5,000-6,000** *C*

A white marble garden bench, the seat supported by winged sphinxes, 19thC, 70in (178cm) wide.
£9,000-12,000 *C*

An Italian white marble statue of a nude figure by Alfredo Pina, signed in the marble, early 20thC, 32in (81cm) high.
£10,000-15,000 *C*

A matched pair of George III blue-john vases, on stepped square plinths, partly of white marble and slate, 9in (23cm) high. **£6,000-8,000** *C*

Three North German oak statues of Apostles, St. James of Compostela in pilgrim's hat, and 2 others, late 15thC, 2 hands damaged.
£9,000-12,000 *C*

A pair of mottled pink marble urns, with everted lips and tapering bodies, with shaped socles and square bases, 19thC, 30in (76cm) high.
£4,000-5,000 *C*

An English marble figure of Susannah, by Jospeh Gott, 19thC, 48in (120cm), on original pedestal.
£55,000-60,000 *C*

An English marble figure of Ino teaching Bacchus to dance, by Joseph Gott, 57in (145cm) high, on veined marble pedestal.
£215,000-225,000 *C*

An Italian marble group of a boy and a girl, by V. Lusardi, repaired, c1875, 35½in (90cm). **£6,000-8,000** *C*

A terracotta group of a Bacchant and 3 Bacchantes, by Claude-Michel Clodion, French, c1800, 25in (64cm) high, on later base. **£200,000-220,000** *CNY*

A wood sculpture of St. Catherine, with traces of polychrome, late 15thC, 45in (114cm) high.
£20,000-40,000 *H*

An Italian marble figure of a child pulling a thorn from a spaniel's foot, by Giovanni Maria Benzoni, damage, c1846, 43in (110cm).
£10,000-12,000 *C*

An Etruscan bronze figure of a nude ephebe, with beaded decoration around his neck, on marble base, early 5th Century B.C., 4½in (12cm) high. **£42,000-46,000** *C*

A green basalt head of an official wearing a striated wig, Saite Period, mid-7th Century B.C., 4½in (12cm) high. **£30,000-35,000** *C*

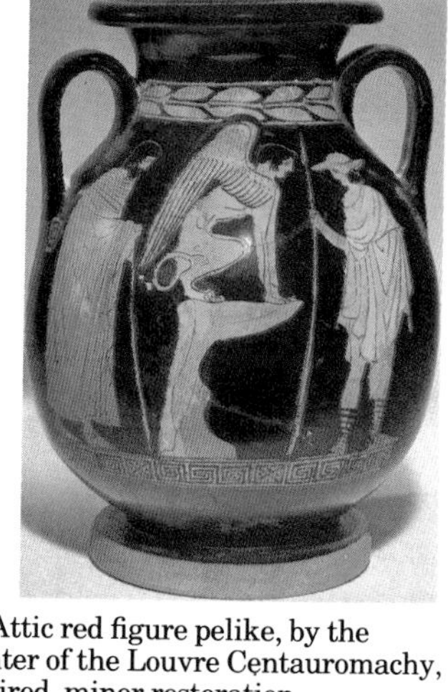

An Attic red figure pelike, by the Painter of the Louvre Centauromachy, repaired, minor restoration, c440 B.C., 14in (35.5cm) high. **£10,000-12,000** *C*

A Bidjar carpet, the ivory field surrounded by indigo arabesque vine, 153 by 84in (390 by 215cm). **£9,000-10,000** *C*

An antique Chinese pillar rug, 127 by 67in (323 by 170cm). **£8,000-9,000** *C*

An Aubusson carpet, the cream ground with a central floral bouquet, surrounded by a gold and rust leaf-tipped border, damage and repairs, c1870, 216 by 127in (574 by 323cm). **£12,000-15,000** *CNY*

An Aubusson tapestry rug, with shaped ivory field and rose surround, 19thC, 71 by 55in (180 by 140cm). **£6,000-7,000** *P*

A George III Adam needlework carpet, with opening for a hearth, 177in (448cm) diam. **£30,000-35,000** *C*

A Bessarabian carpet, repaired, c1890, 101 by 72in (256 by 183cm). **£3,000-4,000** *CNY*

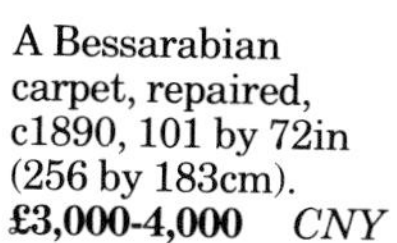

An Aubusson carpet, with an inscription Spe Vivitur, some wear, repaired and backed, mid-19thC, 276 by 232in (701 by 590cm). **£15,000-20,000** *CNY*

An 'Imreli' carpet, the rust brown field with rows of 'spread eagle' guls, reduced, slight wear, early 19thC, 117 by 62in (297 by 157cm).
£12,000-15,000 *C*

An East Persian octagonal carpet, the shaded burgundy field with a lattice enclosing various floral palmettes and sprays, some wear, repairs, backed, 139 by 127in (352 by 322cm).
£9,000-10,000 *C*

A Kashan silk prayer rug, c1920, 56 by 41in (142 by 104cm). **£22,000-26,000** *CNY*

This exceptionally fine rug contains approximately 1,200 knots per square inch and by repute was woven over a period of 8 years.

A Kuba prayer rug, the teal blue ground covered by a pattern of stylised floral and geometric devices, c1890, 59 by 50in (150 by 127cm).
£11,000-14,000 *CNY*

A Melas rug, the rust ground covered by multi-coloured rosettes and leaves, damaged, late 19thC, 71 by 48in (180 by 122cm). **£3,000-4,000** *CNY*

A Herez carpet, the terracotta field with allover angular designs, 148 by 109in (376 by 278cm). **£6,000-7,000** *P*

A Savonnerie carpet, woven in bright colours with summer flowers in picture frame borders, restored, mid-19thC, 262 by 208in (666 by 528cm).
£65,000-75,000 *C*

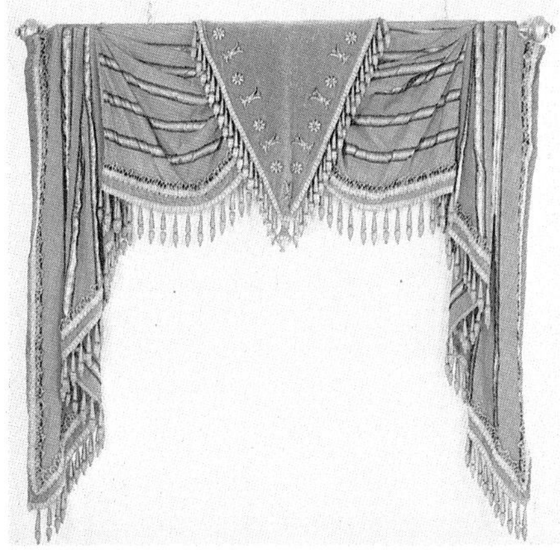

A set of 3 Regency pelmets, attributed to George Bullock, 58in (147cm) high. **£4,000-5,000** *C*

A Buddhist priest's kesi robe, lined in silk, Kangxi, 42 by 108in (106.5 by 274cm). **£4,500-6,000** *CNY*

A sampler, by Ann Tafsell aged 14 in 1830, 18in (46cm), in original frame. **£700-900** *MA*

A lady's informal flowered silk robe, full length, with front overlap closing to the right, 56in (142cm) long. **£2,000-3,000** *CNY*

A needlework purse, English, late 16thC, 5in (12.5cm). **£9,000-10,000** *CSK*

A sampler by Sarah Gaull, aged 14, dated April 27, 1827, 24½in (62cm) high. **£400-600** *MA*

A Scottish sampler, by Isobel Williamson, c1790. **£1,400-1,800** *MA*

A sampler by Mary White, dated August 17, 1835, 4½in (11cm). **£100-150** *MA*

A pair of embroidered gloves, English, c1600, slight wear. **£4,000-5,000** *CSK*

The Penn Family purse, worked in tent stitch, English, mid-17thC, 8 by 6in (20.5 by 15cm). **£55,000-65,000** *CSK*

A needlework casket, the doors concealing 4 drawers and a secret drawer, the lid opening to reveal a mirror and writing compartment, English, mid-17thC, 10 by 12in (25 by 30cm), with key. **£8,000-10,000** *CSK*

A silk cushion cover with 2 figures and an asp, and 4 roundels of flowers in coloured silks, worked with the initials DTM, early 17thC, 14 by 22in (36 by 56cm), framed, glazed. **£7,000-8,000** *CSK*

A box covered in petit point, and 4 boxes, English, early 18thC, 5 by 8in (13 by 20cm), in glazed case. **£15,000-17,000** *CSK*

An Aubusson tapestry entre fenêtre, with neo-classical urn of flowers and sprays, 19thC, 140 by 65in (356 by 165cm). **£4,000-5,000** *P*

A cushion of ivory silk embroidered with the story of Bathsheba, English, mid-17thC, 20 by 22in (51 by 56cm), framed and glazed. **£18,000-20,000** *CSK*

A needlework casket, with mirrored compartment, secret drawers and 2 glass bottles, restored, English, mid-17thC, 11in (28cm) wide. **£18,000-22,000** *CSK*

A needlework casket, containing a mirror, drawers including secret drawers, 2 bottles, English, mid-17thC, 15½in (39cm) wide. **£7,000-8,000** *CSK*

A casket, the lid and sides of ivory satin decorated with scrolled paper work, and 3 other smaller boxes, English, 1687, main box 17in (43cm) wide. **£12,000-15,000** *CSK*

A needlework panel for a cushion cover, worked with the Adoration of the Magi, within a blue border with flowers, fruit and insects, with a unicorn, leopard, lion and stag at each corner, English, c1600, 20 by 22in (51 by 56cm), framed and glazed. **£7,000-8,000** *CSK*

A Brussels tapestry, The Death of Decius Mus, after a cartoon by Peter Paul Rubens, signed in the selvedge Raet with Brussels town mark, 133 by 188in (338 by 477cm). **£10,000-12,000** *C*

A Brussels tapestry woven in silks and wools, with Anthony and Cleopatra and their attendants, with Brussels town mark, late 16thC, 135 by 155in (344 by 394cm). **£18,000-20,000** *C*

A Brussels verdure tapestry, depicting swans on a river with a stone bridge and buildings in the background, repaired, 17thC, 136in (347cm). **£3,500-4,500** *P*

An Italian tapestry woven in silks and wools with a Muse above a figure of Athena flanked by masks and figures, lacking bottom border, Florence or Ferrara, late 16thC, 136 by 160in. **£15,000-20,000** *C*

A valance worked in tent stitch, with Tobias and the very large fish, and the marriage of Tobias and Sara at Ecbatana, c1600, 21 by 66in (53 by 168cm), framed and glazed. **£6,000-7,000** *CSK*

A Brussels tapestry woven in silks and wools, lacking top and bottom border, signed V.Leyniers D.L, c1725, 126 by 158in (320 by 401cm). **£10,000-12,000** *C*

A Brussels tapestry, woven in wools and silks with King Numitor and his attendants, with Romulus and Remus to the left, outside the city of Albalonga, late 16thC, 120 by 152in. **£18,000-20,000** *C*

A Brussels tapestry woven in silks and wools with Bacchus seated in a chariot, lacking borders, 17thC, with later slip, 109 by 148in (277 by 376cm). **£18,000-20,000** *C*

A Britains Royal Horse Artillery at the gallop in steel helmets, No. 1339, some damage and repairs, c1940. **£8,000-10,000** *P*

A Britains The Sovereign's Escort, No. 2081, comprising 222 pieces, in good condition, 1953. **£4,000-5,000** *P*

A Britains Royal Horse Artillery at the halt, No. 318, service dress, some damage and wear, 1933. **£7,000-8,000** *P*

Left. A Steiff dark plush teddy bear, worn, Steiff button to l. ear, 26in (66cm). **£2,200-2,600**

Right. A Danel & Cie French bisque head Paris-Bebe, marked, 16in (40cm). **£2,500-3,000** *P*

Britains Vertunni, Louis XV of France, his wife, mistress, mother, 2 Royal Guards and a gentleman, original paint. **£200-250** *P*

A Britains scale figure of the Colonel-in-Chief, the Welsh Guards, excellent, 1947, 70mm. **£1,500-2,000** *P*

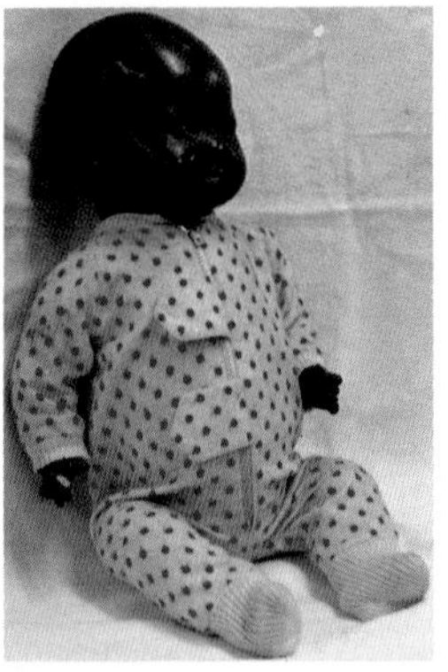

An Armand Marseille bisque head negro baby doll. **£100-150** *PC*

Above. A French bisque doll, in original dress, marked 14, 9½in (24cm). **£1,500-2,000** *P*

Left. An Emile Jumeau bisque head doll, incised 6 EJ and stamped, damaged, 17in (43cm). **£1,000-1,200** *P*

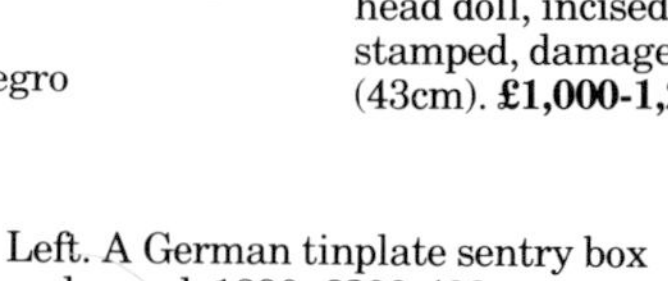

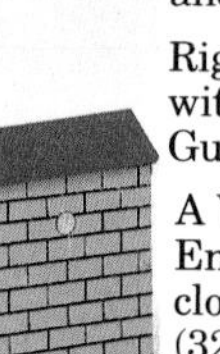

Left. A German tinplate sentry box and guard, 1890. **£300-400**

Right. A German tinplate sentry box with mounted sentry of the Royal Horse Guards, 1890. **£400-500** *P*

A William and Mary wooden doll, English, with painted face, damage, clothing distressed, c1690, 12½in (32cm). **£25,000-30,000** *P*

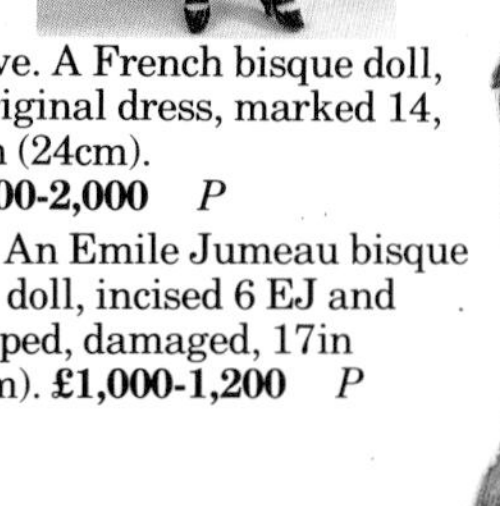

A double manual harpsicord, by Jacob Kirkman, 1761, 37in (94cm) wide.
£80,000-83,000 *C*

A painted metal submarine, 'Unterseeboot', by Bing, c1902, lacks periscope, 18in (46cm), with damaged box. **£2,000-2,500** *CSK*

A Marklin PLM 2nd class bogie coach, in original livery, c1921, 12½in (32cm), in original wood box.
£1,200-1,500 *CSK*

A mounted figure by Roger Berdou, entitled 'Garde Impériale TARTES LITHUANIENS Trompette 1812', signed, 5.4cm. **£200-250** *P*

A Marklin gauge 1 live steam, spirit fired model of GWR 4–6–2 Pacific locomotive and tender No. 111, The Great Bear, c1909, 27in S.266 *CSK*

A grand pianoforte, 7 octaves, No. 82771, by Erard, Paris, with amboyna case with ebonised lines, 55½in (140cm) wide. **£5,000-6,000** *C*

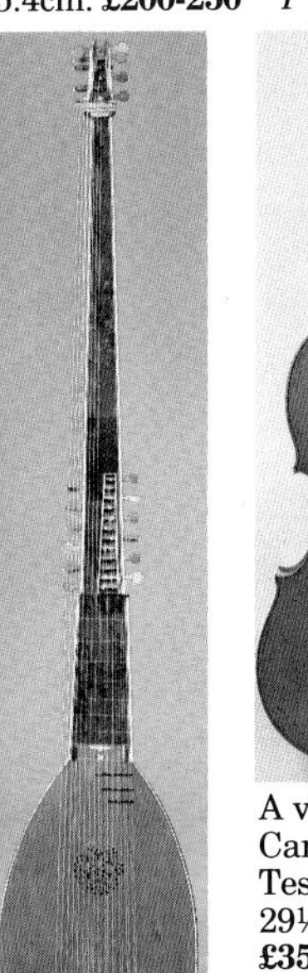

A chitarrone, by David Tecchler, 1725, 71in (180cm) long.
£20,000-25,000 *C*

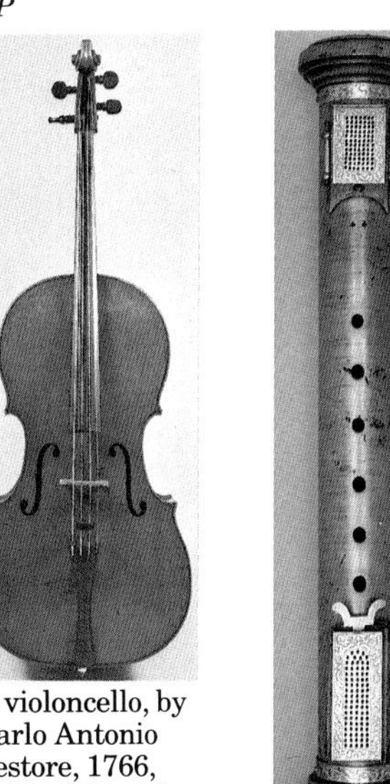

A violoncello, by Carlo Antonio Testore, 1766, 29½in (75cm) long.
£35,000-45,000 *C*

A columnar alto recorder, by Hans Rauch von Schratt, mid-16thC, 20in.
£45,000-48,000 *C*

A Louis XVI style ormolu mounted purplewood and marquetry grand piano, the works by Erard, the case by P. Sormani, 75in (190.5cm) wide.
£10,000-12,000 *CNY*

A 1956 Bentley S1 Continental 2-door drophead coupé, coachwork by Park Ward, Registration No. PLG 123, Chassis No. BC 77 BG, Engine No. BA 76128 UE 3764. **£60,000-65,000** *CSK*

A 1931 Rolls Royce 20/25 doctor's coupé, coachwork by Windover, Registration No. GP5803, Chassis No. G0510, Engine No. D9E. **£40,000-45,000** *CSK*

A 1962 Mercedes-Benz 300SL roadster, Chassis No. 1980421000298, Engine No. 19898010003022, left hand drive. **£65,000-70,000** *CSK*

A leather travelling writing cabinet, with fitted interior, gilt tooled SG monogram, French, early 18thC, 10½in (26cm) high. **£1,200-1,500** *C*

A French walnut and ebony casket, early 17thC, 18in (46cm) wide. **£9,000-10,000** *C*

A leather travelling canteen, tooled with the cypher of Catherine II, the box late 18thC, 13in (33cm) high. **£12,000-15,000** *C*

A Bing tinplate clockwork omnibus, the sides litho- graphed with Auto-Omnibus Gesellschaft, in near mint condition, c1911, 12in (30cm), with box base. **£9,000-10,000** *P*

A gilt brass mounted kingwood coffre fort, with inlaid oyster veneered top, late 17thC, 25in (64cm) wide. **£2,500-3,500** *C*

A Chinese export brass bound painted leather coffer, early 19thC, 47in (119cm) wide. **£3,500-4,000** *CNY*

An Empire morocco leather dispatch box, 27in (69cm) wide. **£5,000-6,000** *C*

A Victorian mother-of-pearl inlaid and painted papier mâché tea caddy, impressed on base Clay, King Street, Covent Garden, 7½in. **£100-150** *HCH*

A stoneware bottle vase, by Hans Coper, impressed HC seal, c1955, 19½in (49cm) high.
£9,000-14,000 *C*

A Venini vase, acid stamped Venini Murano Italia, engraved Fulvio Bianconi 60, 11in (28cm) high.
£20,000-30,000 *C*

A monumental stoneware vase, by Hans Coper, 15½in (40cm) high. **£20,000-25,000** *C*

A Seguso 'valva' vase, designed by Flavio Poli, c1958, 6in (15cm) high.
£4,000-6,000 *C*

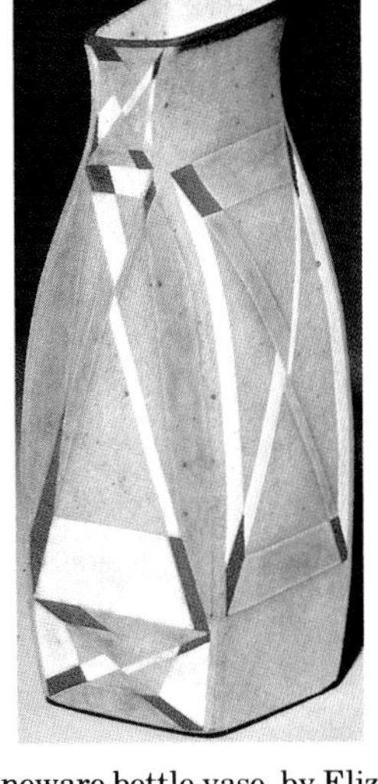

A stoneware bottle vase, by Elizabeth Fritsch, with painted design, 11in (28cm) high.
£6,000-7,000 *C*

A stoneware bottle, by Lucie Rie, impressed LR seal, 16½in (41.5cm) high.
£4,500-5,500 *C*

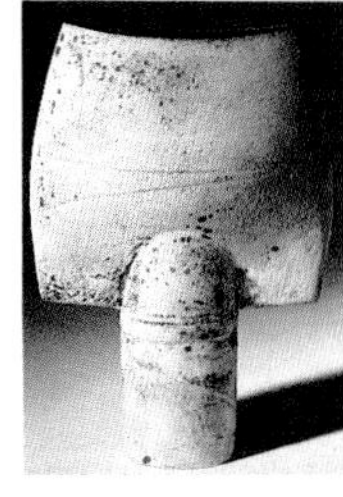

A stoneware 'spade form', by Hans Coper, impressed HC seal, 7in (18cm) high.
£5,000-5,500 *C*

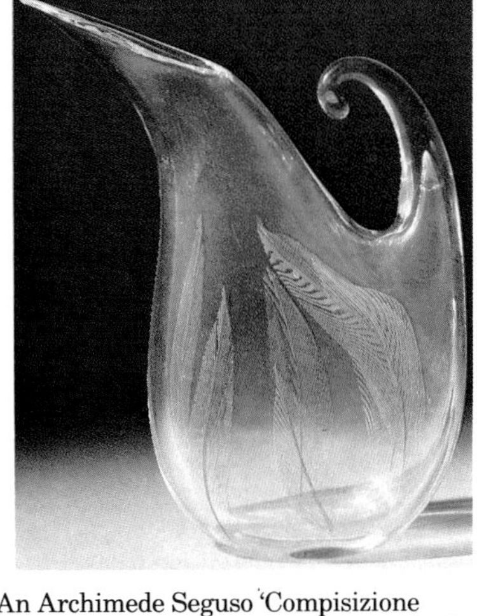

An Archimede Seguso 'Compisizione Piume' carafe, c1960, 11½in (29cm) high.
£5,000-7,000 *C*

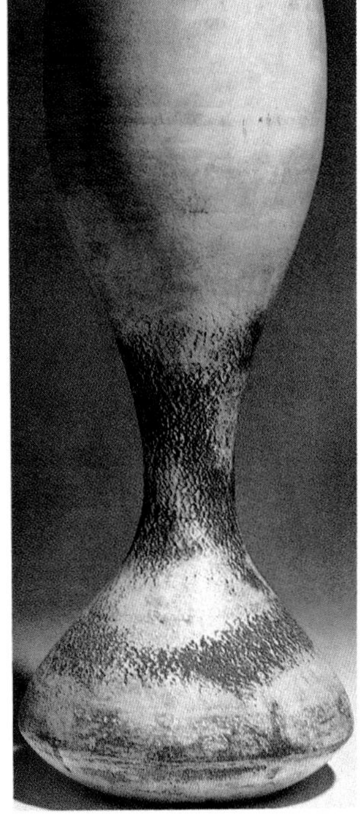

A tall 'hour glass' vase, by Hans Coper, the matt manganese body covered in a buff slip heavily burnished on waist, and ochre blistering, impressed HC seal, 18in (45.5cm) high. **£19,000-22,000** *C*

A stoneware bowl, by Lucie Rie, covered in a thick pitted glaze run pooling to reveal turquoise glaze beneath with iron brown and cobalt blue flecks, impressed LR seal, 13in (33cm) diam. **£5,000-6,000** *C*

A Paul Ysart pre-World War II paperweight, black glass with PY cane and Monart label, c1935, 3in (7.5cm). **£700-850** *FA*

A Vasart paperweight, with concentric millefiori rings and multi-coloured filigree spokes, c1955, 2½in (6cm). **£30-50** *FA*

A Paul Ysart paperweight, with PY cane, a rose with millefiori border, on a black ground, c1975, 3in (7.5cm). **£350-400** *FA*

A Paul Ysart paperweight, with red aventurine dragonfly on a blue ground, unsigned, c1960, 3in (7.5cm). **£230-270** *FA*

A Paul Ysart paperweight, a blue flower on a dark blue ground with millefiori border, unsigned, c1960, 3in (7.5cm). **£120-170** *FA*

A Paul Ysart paperweight, with PY cane, millefiori on a black ground, c1975, 3in (7.5cm). **£270-320** *FA*

A lady's lacquered wood chair, with kidney-shaped seat, some damage and restoration, Kangxi, 32½in (82.5cm) high. **£3,000-4,000** *CNY*

A scarlet and gold lacquer low table, with foliate ormolu frame, 44in (111cm).
£5,000-6,000 *C*

A pair of painted lacquer chairs, Mieguishi, Jiaqing.
£5,000-6,000 *CNY*

A pair of Huanghuali armchairs, minor repair, 17thC.
£6,000-8,000 *CNY*

A Huanghuali altar table, 17th/18thC, 57in (145cm). **£5,500-7,000** *CNY*

A Ming Huanghuali and Huangyangmu Kang table, the underside with traces of lacquer, 21in (53cm) square.
£5,000-7,000 *CNY*

A pair of Huanghuali armchairs, with caned seats, 17th/18thC, 47in (119cm) high. **£6,000-8,000** *CNY*

A lithograph in colours, by Jules Chéret, 1893, 48½in high. **£1,000-1,500** *CSK*

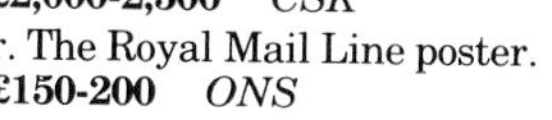

l. Anchor Line poster. **£350-450** *ONS*
c. Lithograph in colours, Leopoldo Metlicovitz, 1904, 56in (142cm) high.
£2,000-2,500 *CSK*
r. The Royal Mail Line poster.
£150-200 *ONS*

A massive cloisonné enamel and gilt bronze tripod censer and cover, late Qing Dynasty, 33in diam. **£6,000-8,000** *C*

A gilt splashed bronze sectional beaker vase, Qing Dynasty, 25in (63cm) high. **£5,000-6,000** *CHK*

A tilemaker's incense burner and cover, restored, Wanli mark, 41in (104cm). **£2,500-3,500** *CNY*

A pair of Chinese paintings on glass, 18thC, in later giltwood frames, 5½ by 3½in (14 by 8.5cm). **£6,000-7,000** *C*

A Peking enamel and gilt copper box and cover, slight damage, Yongzheng/early Qianlong. **£1,000-1,500** *CNY*

A cloisonné enamel panel, minor pitting, 18thC, 46in (117cm) high. **£4,000-6,000** *C*

A pair of Chinese export reverse painted glass pictures, after a European print, with carved wooden frames, one cracked, c1795, 16in (41cm). **£4,000-5,000** *Bon*

A pair of cloisonné and champlevé enamel vases, minor pitting, mid/late Qing Dynasty, 25in. **£5,000-6,000** *C*

A pair of cloisonné enamel vases, minor damage, c1800, 27in (68cm). **£3,000-4,000** *C*

A pair of cloisonné enamel vases, restored, some pitting, Qianlong 6-character seal marks and of the period, 10½in (26.5cm) high. **£4,000-6,000** *C*

A pair of cloisonné enamel and gilt bronze censers and covers, late 18th/19thC, 15½in (39cm) wide. **£5,000-7,000** *C*

A pair of cloisonné enamel horses, minor damage, late Qing Dynasty, 28in (71cm) wide. **£5,000-6,000** *C*

A pale celadon and jade two-handled cup, Qianlong 4-character seal mark and of the period, 5½in (14cm) wide. **£5,000-6,000** *C*

A celadon jade vase and cover, deeply carved with archaistic dragons, with lion mask ring handles, 18th/19thC, 16in (41cm). **£7,500-8,500** *C*

A spinach jade two-handled bowl, small chips, 18thC, 10½in (26cm) wide, in fitted box. **£3,500-5,000** *C*

A wooden model of a reclining falcon, realistically modelled, on socle base, Dynasty XVIII, 5in (13cm) high. **£5,000-6,000** *C*

A Korean inlaid black lacquer box and cover, inset in shell with a fruiting vine, fitted with bronze hinges, side handles and front lock, minor damage, 17th/18thC, 8½in (21.5cm) wide. **£10,000-12,000** *CHK*

A jade group of 3 Immortals, 18thC, 6in (15cm) wide. **£7,500-8,500** *CHK*

A pair of Chinese painted carved wooden figures, with nodding heads and plaited hair, late 18th/early 19thC, the gentleman 46in (117cm) high, on later painted plinths 21in (53cm) high. **£12,000-14,000** *C*

A jade fish bowl, 18thC, 5½in (14.5cm) diam, with wood stand. **£20,000-25,000** *CHK*

A six-tiered lacquer box and cover, Ming Dynasty, 11in (28cm) high. **£10,000-12,000** *CHK*

A four-tiered inlaid black lacquer box and cover, inset with shell, 16thC, 10½in (27cm). **£5,000-6,000** *CHK*

A pale celadon jade double gourd shaped vase and domed cover, Qianlong, 12in (30cm) high. **£10,000-12,000** *CNY*

A gilt lacquered figure of the Buddha, Ming Dynasty, 41in (104cm) high. **£8,000-10,000** *CNY*

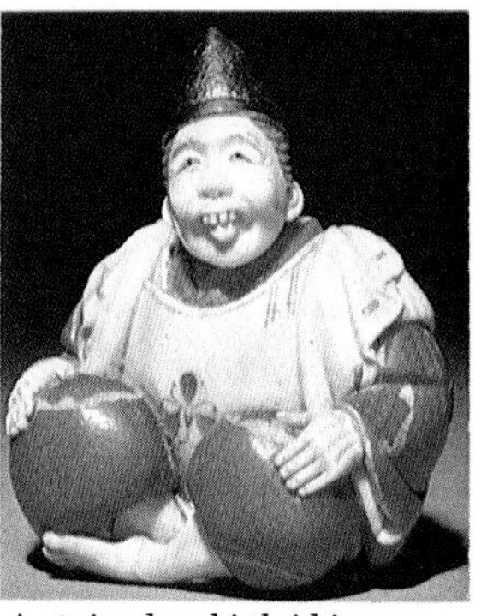

A stained and inlaid ivory netsuke, Temple Servant, signed Yasumasa, late 19thC, 4.9cm. **£2,500-3,500** *C*

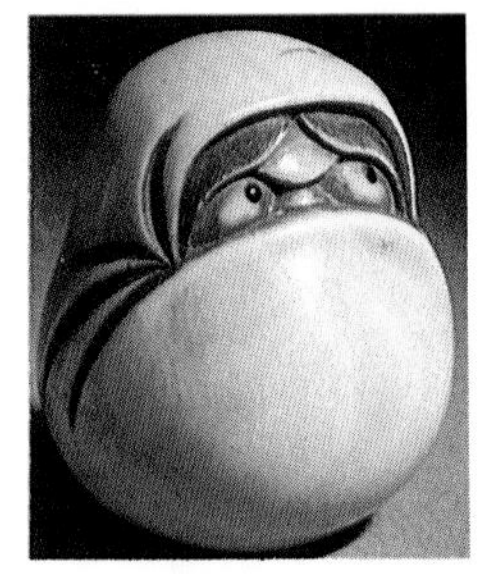

An ivory netsuke, Daruma Doll, signed Mitsuhiro and kao, 1810-75, small age cracks, 4cm high. **£2,500-3,500** *C*

A stained and painted ivory netsuke Fly on an Octopus Tentacle, signed Mitsuhiro and kao, 1810-75, 5.6cm long. **£8,000-9,000** *C*

An ivory netsuke, Ox and Calf, signed Mitsuharu, 18thC, 5.7cm long. **£7,000-8,000** *C*

An ivory netsuke, Crane, signed Masatoshi, 20thC, 4.5cm long. **£7,000-8,000** *C*

An ivory netsuke, Dog and Awabe Shell, signed Tomotada, 18thC, 3.5cm high. **£7,000-9,000** *C*

An ivory netsuke, Songoku the Magical Monkey, Mitsuhiro, Ohara, 1810-75, 5cm. **£8,000-9,000** *C*

An ivory netsuke, Ryujin, signed Masatoshi, 20thC, 9.2cm high. **£4,000-6,000** *C*

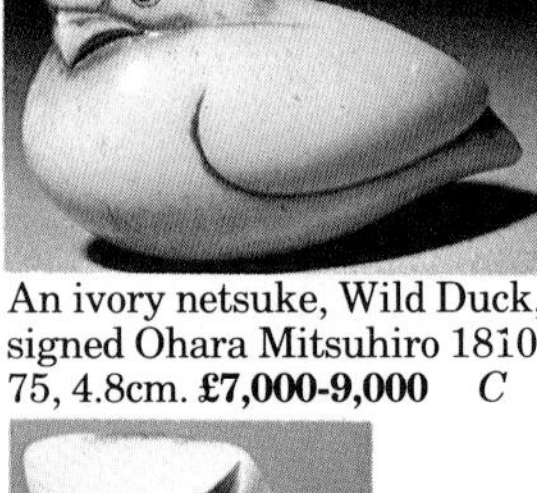

An ivory netsuke, Wild Duck, signed Ohara Mitsuhiro 1810-75, 4.8cm. **£7,000-9,000** *C*

A netsuke carved from stag antler, Owl, signed Masatoshi, 20thC, 4.5cm high. **£3,500-4,500** *C*

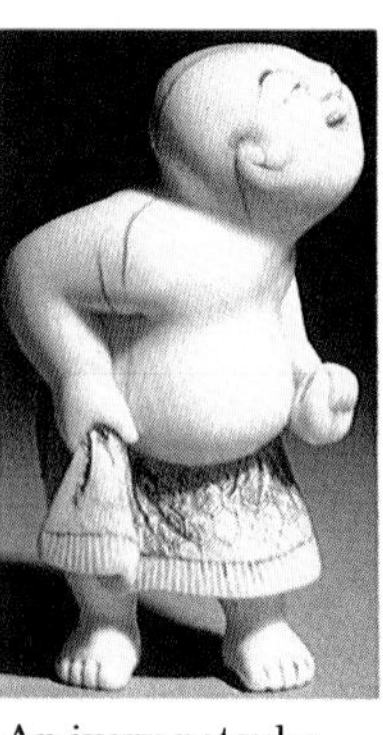

An ivory netsuke, Young Wrestler, signed Masanao, of Kyoto, age crack, 18thC, 4.9cm high. **£5,000-7,000** *C*

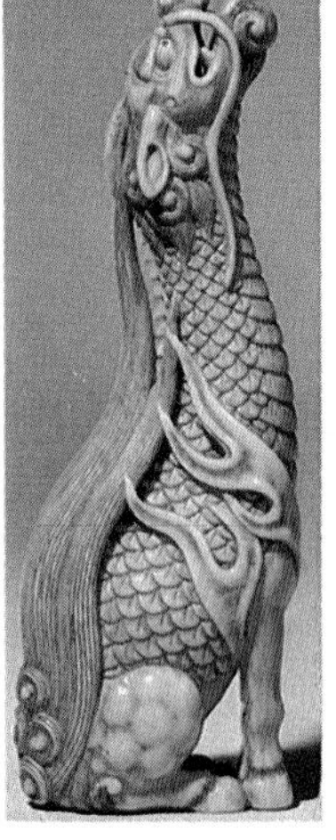

An ivory netsuke, Seated Kirin, signed Yoshimasa, c1800, 10.5cm high. **£27,000-30,000** *C*

An ivory netsuke, Karashishi and Young with a tama, signed Eijusai Masayoshi, 19thC, 4cm. **£9,000-10,000** *C*

An ivory netsuke, Tiger and Monkey, signed Kaigyokusai, with seal Masatsugu, 1813-92, 3.9cm long. **£15,000-20,000** *C*

An ivory netsuke, Omori Hikoshichi and the Witch, signed Shoko, 20thC, 5cm. **£8-9,000** *C*

A neo-classical ormolu and cut glass chandelier, fitted for electricity, early 19thC, 36in (91cm) high. **£8,000-10,000** *C*

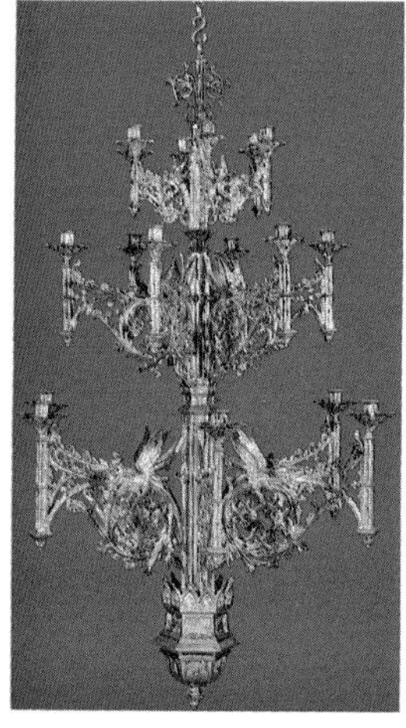

An early Victorian brass 18-light chandelier, restorations, 56in (142cm) high. **£5,000-6,000** *C*

An ormolu and rock crystal 8-light chandelier, fitted for electricity, 34in (86cm) high. **£2,000-2,500** *C*

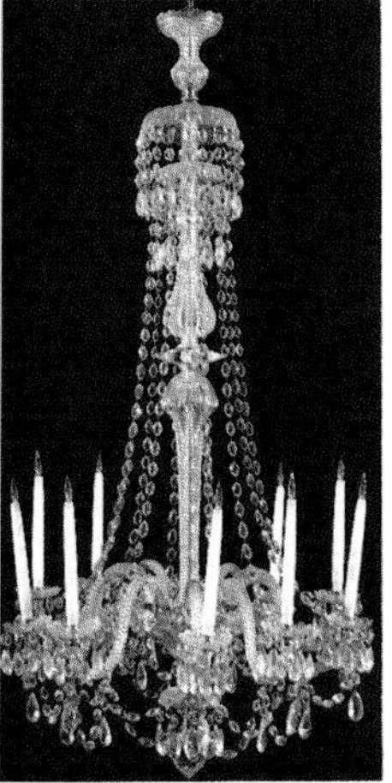

A cut glass 10-light chandelier, mid-19thC, 65in (165cm) high. **£5,000-7,000** *C*

An Empire ormolu chandelier in the manner of Thomire, 28½in (72cm). **£8,500-10,000** *C*

A pair of Regency ormolu and cut glass twin light candelabra, 16in (40.5cm) high. **£2,000-3,000** *C*

A Russian ormolu and tôle 10-branch chandelier, lacking one wreath, early 19thC, 25in (63.5cm) wide. **£3,500-4,500** *C*

A cut glass chandelier, 72in (182cm). **£27,000-30,000** *C*

A pair of Louis XVI ormolu and bronze 3-light candelabra, 29in (74cm) high. **£7,000-8,000** *C*

A pair of Regency bronzed and ormolu lamps, fitted for electricity, 31in (79cm). **£18,000-20,000** *C*

A pair of Louis XV ormolu candelabra, formed as river Gods, possibly Italian, 8½in (22cm) wide. **£10,000-12,000** *C*

A two-tiered brass chandelier, in the Flemish Gothic style, wired for electricity, with later fittings, 48½in (123cm) high. **£7,000-8,000** *CNY*

A pair of Charles X ormolu and bronze oil lamps, 32in (81cm) high. **£5,000-6,000** *C*

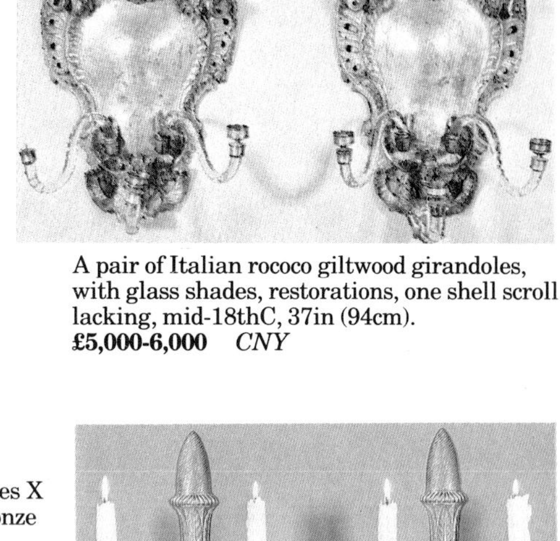

A pair of Italian rococo giltwood girandoles, with glass shades, restorations, one shell scroll lacking, mid-18thC, 37in (94cm).
£5,000-6,000 *CNY*

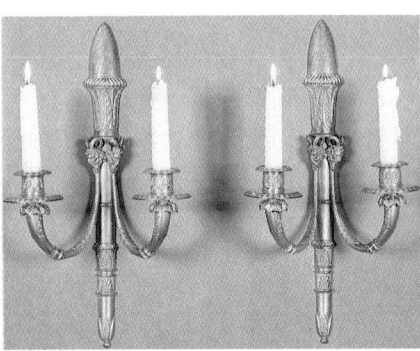

A set of 4 Empire ormolu wall lights, 19thC, 16in (40.5cm) high.
£3,500-4,500 *CNY*

Walter Tyler, mahogany and brass bi-unial magic lantern.
£750-850 *CSK*

A pair of Empire style ormolu and rock crystal candelabra, 28in.
£13,000-15,000 *CNY*

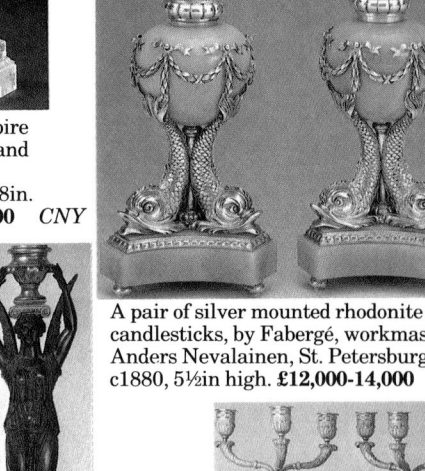

A pair of silver mounted rhodonite candlesticks, by Fabergé, workmaster Anders Nevalainen, St. Petersburg, c1880, 5½in high. **£12,000-14,000** *CG*

A pair of ormolu and bronze candlesticks, 30in, c1825. **£5,000-6,000** *C*

A Russian ormolu cut glass chandelier, late 18thC, 17in (43cm). **£13,000-15,000** *C*

A pair of Charles X ormolu and bronze three-light candelabra, 21in (53cm) high. **£2,000-3,000** *C*

A pine pedestal desk, c1880, 48in (122cm) wide. **£550-650** *SSD*

A pine 6 drawer chest, c1870, 24in (61cm) wide. **£350-400** *SSD*

A pine 4 drawer chest, c1890, with later plate rack, 39in (99cm). **£450-550** *SSD*

A pine cupboard, c1890, 39in (99cm). **£350-400** *SSD*

A pine kneehole desk, c1880, 51in (130cm). **£450-550** *SSD*

A pine display cabinet, c1890, 45in (114cm). **£300-350** *SSD*

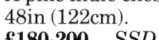

A pine mule chest, c1800, 48in (122cm). **£180-200** *SSD*

A pine washstand, c1840, 30in (76cm). **£120-140** *SSD*

A pine 4 drawer chest, c1880, 39in (99cm). **£220-250** *SSD*

A pine maid servant's hiring chest, with fitted interior, c1860, 30in (76cm). **£150-200** *SSD*

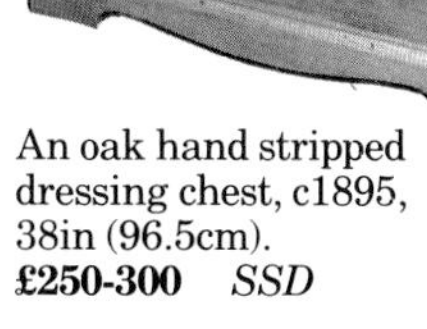

An oak hand stripped dressing chest, c1895, 38in (96.5cm). **£250-300** *SSD*

A composite 'Maximilian' half-armour, some damage and repairs, partly German and partly Italian, 16thC.
£13,000-15,000 *CSK*

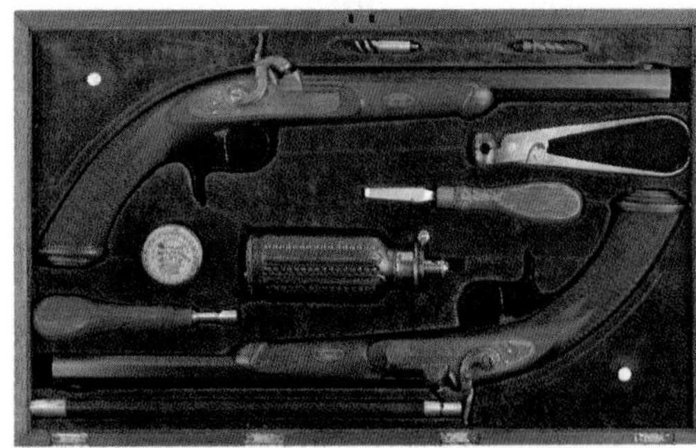

A cased pair of percussion duelling pistols, by Joseph Jakob, signed, mid-19thC, 16in (41cm), with velvet lined case and accessories. **£2,000-3,000** *CNY*

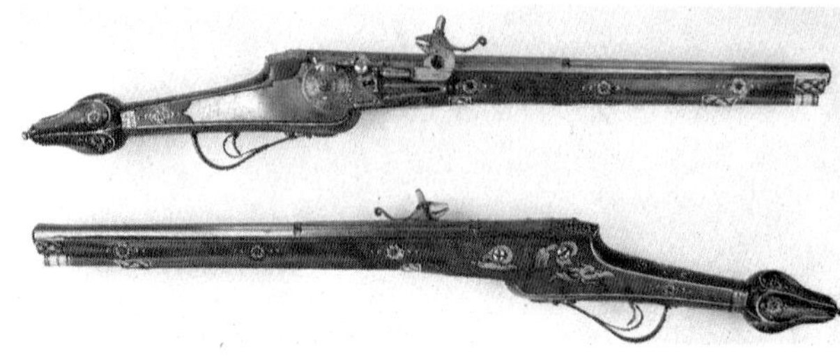

A pair of German wheel-lock holster pistols, by Hans Fleischer, dated 1610, maker's mark CT, Christopher Dressler, minor damage, restorations, 29½in (75cm).
£28,000-30,000 *CNY*

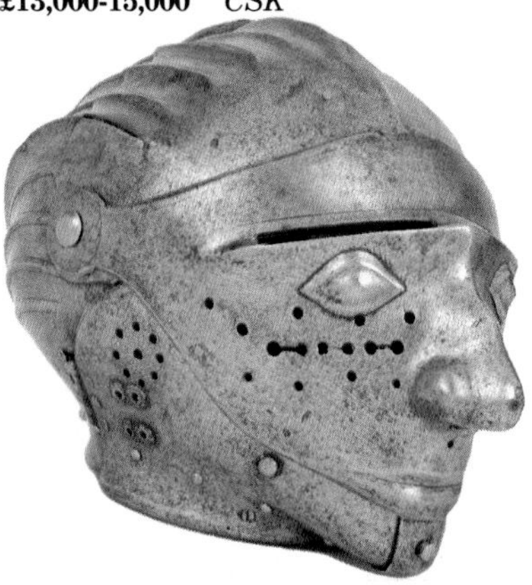

An armet in the manner of Hans Seusenhofer of Innsbruck, damaged, repaired, c1520, 9in (23cm).
£35,000-40,000 *CSK*

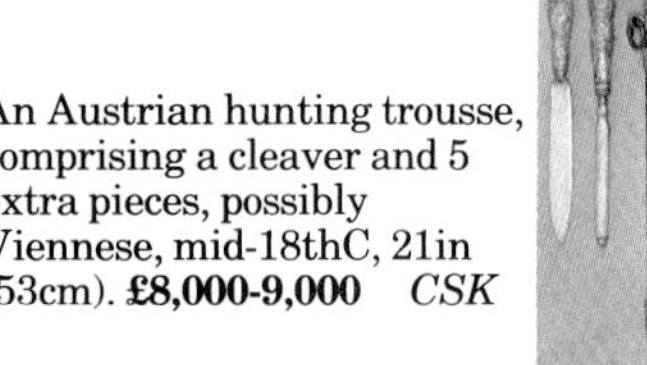

An Austrian hunting trousse, comprising a cleaver and 5 extra pieces, possibly Viennese, mid-18thC, 21in (53cm). **£8,000-9,000** *CSK*

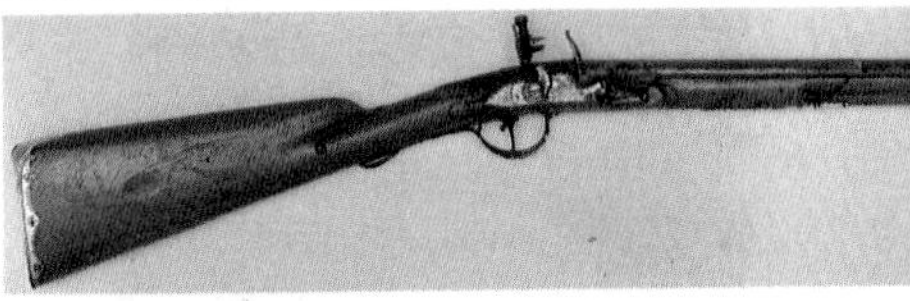

A Russian flintlock gun by G. Permjakov, c1770, restored, 32in. **£9-10,000** *CSK*

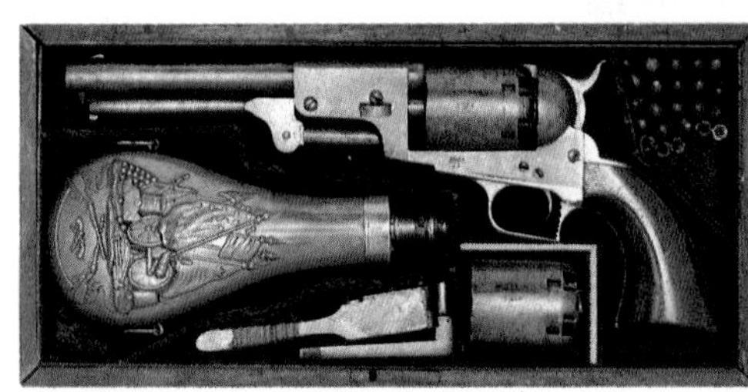

Above. A Colt Hartford-English dragoon percussion revolver, mid-19thC 14½in (37cm).
£8,000-9,000 *CSK*

A 12-gauge D.B. hammerless sidelock gun by J. Woodward, No. 7004, 14½in. **£12-15,000** *CNY*

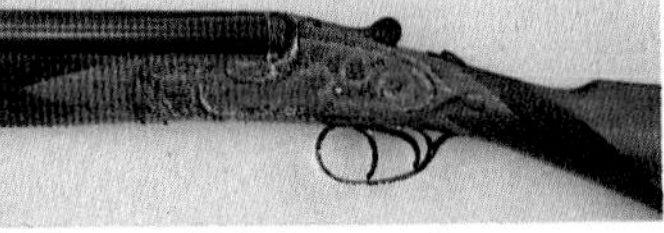

A pair of percussion pistols, by John Dickson & Son, Edinburgh, London proof marks, 1894, 12in. **£6-8,000** *CSK*

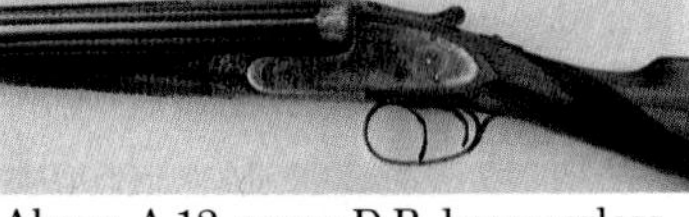

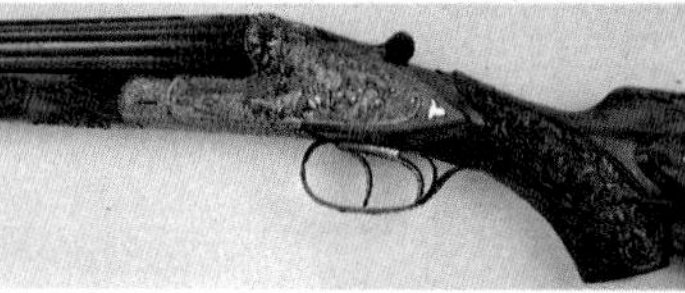

Above. A 12-gauge D.B. hammerless self-opening sidelock ejector gun by J. Purdey. **£9,000-12,000** *CNY*

Right. A German 12-gauge D.B. hammerless sidelock ejector gun. **£5,000-7,000** *CNY*

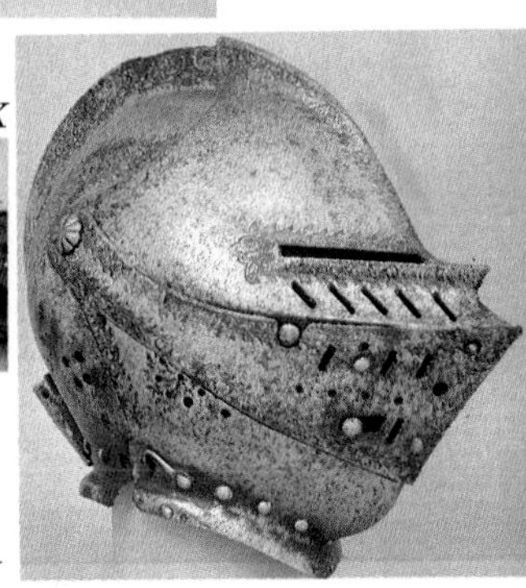

An etched close helmet in Wolfgang and Franz Grosschedel of Landshut style, repaired, c1560, 11in. **£14,000-16,000** *CSK*

A model of the sailing yacht Shamrock III, with gaff rig and paper sails, early 20thC, 75in (190.5cm).
£500-550 *PC*

A wooden model of H.M.S. Victory, 19½in (50cm) long, in glazed mahogany case.
£4,200-4,500 *P*

A Swedish model of the sailing boat, Wardo, c1895, 33½in (85cm) long.
£100-150 *Mer*

A Bing 3RE 4–4–2 LNWR tank locomotive No. 44, wheels and motor replaced, pre World War I.
£350-400 *P*

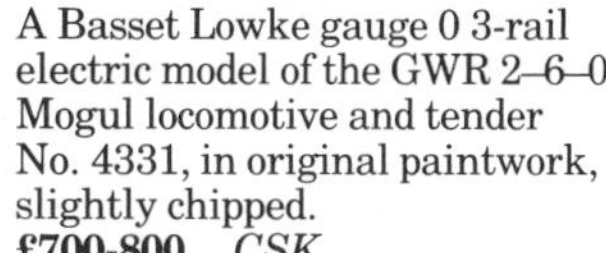

A Basset Lowke gauge 0 3-rail electric model of the GWR 2–6–0 Mogul locomotive and tender No. 4331, in original paintwork, slightly chipped.
£700-800 *CSK*

A Bing for Basset Lowke 3RE 4–4–0 George The Fifth and tender No. 2663, pre World War I.
£150-200 *P*

A Bing gauge 1 3-rail electric model of the G.C.R. 4–6–0 locomotive and 6-wheeled tender No. 423, Sir Sam Fay, in original paintwork, converted from clockwork, very slightly chipped, 2 lanterns missing, c1914.
£1,500-2,000 *CSK*

A Bing tinplate clockwork King Edward VII 0 Gauge locomotive, No. 1902 in black livery, with red and gold lines, marked G.B.N. Dep.
£70-100 *HCH*

A Hornby gauge 0 3-rail electric 20V model of the SR 4–4–2 No. E36 locomotive and tender No. 1759, in green livery, with smoke deflector plates, repainted, lacks bulb.
£160-200 *CSK*

A Hornby gauge 0 3-rail electric 20V model of the LMS No. E220 Special Compound locomotive and tender No. 1185, in original paintwork, with boxes, worn.
£300-350 *CSK*

A Hornby gauge 0 clockwork model of the LNER No. 2 4–4–4 tank locomotive, in original paintwork and box.
£130-180 *CSK*

Two Hornby gauge 0 No. 2 LMS saloon coaches and a No. 2 Pullman coach, all in original paintwork, slightly worn, all lacking connectors, with boxes.
£160-200 *CSK*

A finely engineered 3½in (9cm) gauge model of the 2–8–2 locomotive and tender, Kratos, built by H. G. Horn, 10 by 55in (25.5 by 139.5cm).
£2,000-2,500 *CSK*

A 2in (5cm) scale model of the Burrel Gold Medal double crank compound, 2 speed, 3 shaft tractor, Reg. No. AD 7782 'Pouss-Nouk-Nouk', built by G. S. Lane, 20 by 29in (50 by 73.5cm).
£3,000-4,000 *CSK*

A well engineered 5in (12.5cm) gauge model of the B.R. 0–4–0 side tank locomotive built to the designs of Ajax, 14 by 28in (35.5 by 71cm).
£1,000-1,300 *CSK*

Games

Chess Sets

A Jaques Staunton ivory chess set, stained red and natural, both kings stamped Jaques London under the base, some variation in red staining, late 19thC, king 3in (7.5cm), in original leather casket, gilt stamped The 'Staunton' Chessmen, with green label to the base.
£1,200-1,500 *P*

A Jaques Staunton 'Club' weighted set, in boxwood and ebony, 20thC, king 4in (10cm), in mahogany box with green label, and a mahogany framed holly and coromandel veneered board with Jaques & Son label, 22in (56cm).
£1,200-1,600 *P*

An early Jaques Staunton ivory set, stained red and natural, white king stamped Jaques London under base, king 3in (7.5cm), contained in a carton pierre casket, with red label bearing registration No.
£800-1,200 *P*

An Anglo-Indian stained green and plain ivory chess set, one replacement piece, with a Cantonese ivory and tortoiseshell chess board, c1800, 18in (46cm).
£1,400-1,800 *CSK*

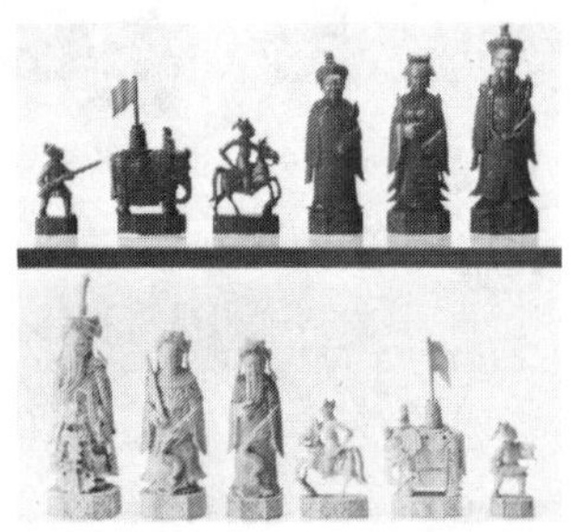

A Chinese carved ivory chess set, in blonde and magenta, elaborately carved upon canted bases, 19thC, red king 5in (13cm).
£700-1,000 *Bon*

A British Chess Company 'Staunton Chessman' ivory set, stained red and natural, king 4½in (11cm), in original rosewood box with label, torn, 11in (28cm) wide.
£1,000-1,200 *P*

The British Chess Company of Stroud, Glos., were in production c1900, and the smaller 'Royal' set in boxwood and ebony was produced in large numbers.

A Lund ivory playing set, the white king stamped Willm. Lund, Maker, 24 Fleet Street, red queen lacking knop, one red pawn base only, early 19thC, king 3in (8cm).
£500-600 *P*

A Vizagapatam horn and ivory set, the knopped stems and spreading bases with egg-and-tongue carving, black king lacking finial, 19thC, king 4in (10cm).
£600-700 *P*

An Indian 'Muslim' ivory set, the 2 sides stained with brown and red rings, the pawns, king and queen of domed form, king 2in (5.5cm).
£1,500-2,000 *P*

A bone 'pulpit' set, dark stained and natural, one black pawn missing, upper section of black king lacking, some restoration required, probably 19thC, king 5in (13cm).
£2,500-3,000 *P*

A Lund pattern ivory set, the pieces stained red and natural, 19thC, king 3½in (9cm), in mahogany box.
£400-500 *P*

A Wedgwood jasper part chess set, to the design of John Flaxman, each pawn to a different design, some damage, king 3½in (8.5cm).
£2,000-2,500 *P*

Two letters and a photograph from Josiah Wedgwood & Sons, dated 1923, indicate that this is an early example of its type.

Musical Instruments

A violin by Sebastian Kloz in Mittenwald, bearing the label AN 1780, length of back 14in (35.5cm), with a bow, in case.
£3,000-3,500 *P*

A violin by Benjamin Banks, bearing the label Benj. Banks, Catherine Street, Salisbury, 1773, length of back, 14in (35.5cm).
£4,000-4,500 *P*

A violin by Charles J. B. Collin-Mezin, bearing the maker's label Rue de Faub Poissonniere No. 29, dated 1899, and signed on the inner lower back, length of back 14in (35.5cm), in case.
£2,000-3,000 *P*

A violin by George Pyne, bearing the maker's label G. Pyne, Maker, London, dated 1887, with maker's script brand above, length of back 14in (35.5cm), in case.
£2,500-3,000 *P*

A violin by William H. Luff, bearing the maker's label in London, dated 1976, length of back 14in (35.5cm).
£3,500-4,000 *P*

A violin by Joan Carol Kloz, bearing the maker's label In Mittenwald An 1741, length of back 14in (35.5cm), with a silver mounted bow by G. Winterling, in a shaped leather case.
£1,700-2,000 *P*

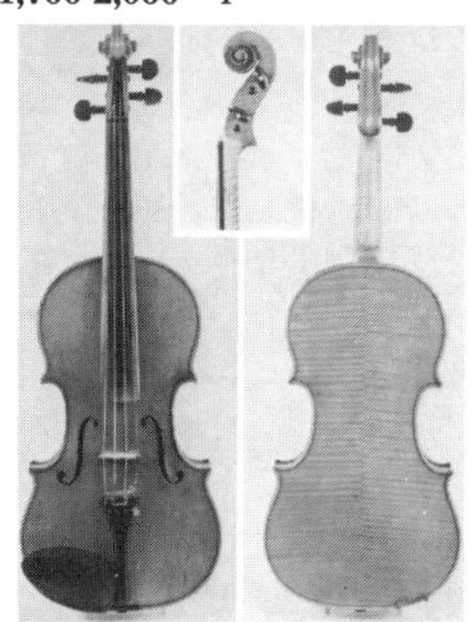

A violin by Giuseppe Pedrazzini, bearing the maker's label in Cremonese fece in Milano L'Anno 1937, with maker's signature and brand, a second label of Boosey & Hawkes, sale agents London above, length of back 14in (35.5cm), with a bow, in case with cover.
£7,000-8,000 *P*

A violin by Paul François Blanchard, after Guarneri, bearing the maker's label Fait par Paul Blanchard a Lyon en 1896, No. 385, length of back 14in (35.5cm), in case.
£5,500-6,000 *P*

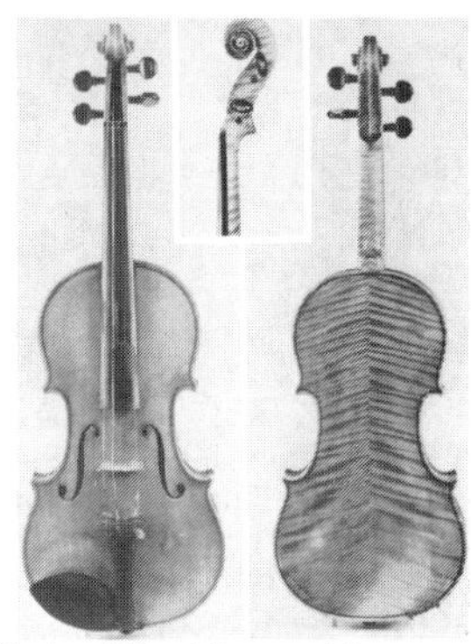

A violin by Albert Laurent in Brussels, bearing the maker's label dated 1913, length of back 14in (35.5cm), with 2 silver mounted bows, one with nickel adjuster, and leather case with cover.
£3,500-4,000 *P*

A violin by Johannes Barnardus Cuypers fecit L'Hage, bearing a manuscript label dated 1810, length of back 14in (35.5cm), in case.
£5,000-6,000 *P*

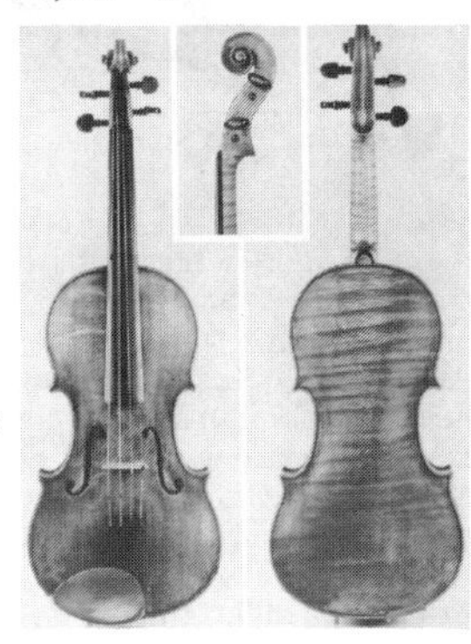

A violin by Antonio Bagatella, bearing the maker's label Antonius Bagatella delectans fecit Pata VII anno 1749, length of back 14in (35.5cm), with nickel mounted bow in a velvet lined shaped case.
£12,000-15,000 *P*

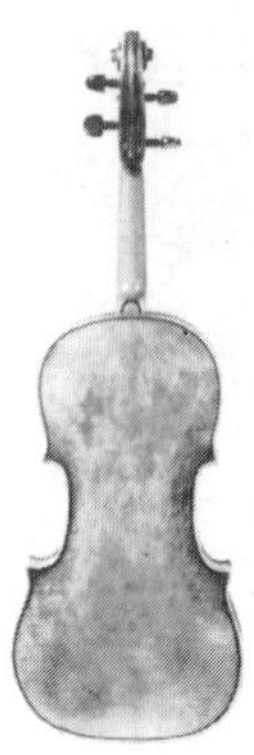

An English viola, probably by John Wilkinson, unlabelled, the one-piece back of plain wood, the scroll of faint figure, the table of medium grain, the varnish of a deep golden colour, length of back 16½in (42cm).
£1,500-2,000 *C*

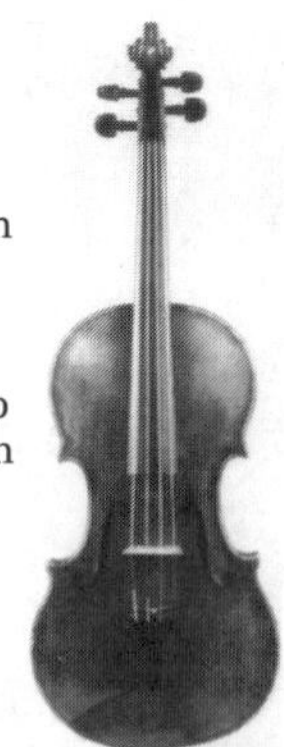

An English viola by Charles Craske, labelled George Craske... Sold by / William E. Hill & Sons, London, the varnish of a red brown colour over a golden ground, length of back 16in (40.5cm), in case.
£3,500-4,500 *C*

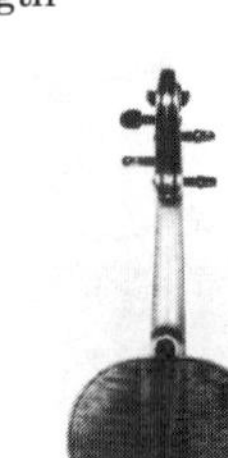

A French viola, labelled Mansuy à Paris, the varnish of a red brown colour, c1890, length of back 16in (40.5cm), in case.
£800-1,200 *C*

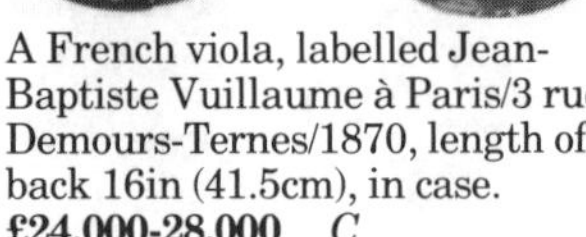

A French viola, labelled Jean-Baptiste Vuillaume à Paris/3 rue Demours-Ternes/1870, length of back 16in (41.5cm), in case.
£24,000-28,000 *C*

An Italian viola, labelled Ferdinandus Gagliano Filius/ Nicolai fecit Neap 1775, the front and back double-purfled and decorated with fleur-de-lys design, the varnish of a dark golden colour, length of back 14in (35.5cm), in case.
£17,000-20,000 *C*

An Italian viola, attributed to Stefano Scarampella in Mantua, c1870, length of back 16in (41.5cm), in case.
£5,000-7,000 *P*

An English violoncello by Henry Jay, unlabelled, length of back 29in (73.5cm).
£5,000-6,000 *C*

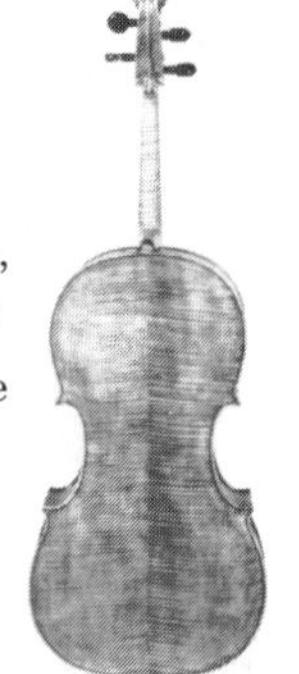

A violoncello, probably Neapolitan, the two-piece back of medium curl, the ribs and scroll similar, c1790, length of back 29in (73.5cm), in case with bow.
£10,000-15,000 *C*

A French double bass, unlabelled, c1900, length of back 44in (111.5cm).
£3,500-4,500 *C*

An English double bass, labelled Thomas Kennedy / London 1831, the table of medium grain, length of back 44½in (112cm).
£20,000-23,000 *C*

A single manual harpsichord, by Jacob & Abraham Kirkman, the nameboard inscribed Jacobus et Abraham Kirckman Londini Fecerunt 1774, in a crossbanded mahogany case with brass strap hinges, with walnut interior, 37½in (95cm) wide, on modern trestle stand.
£15,000-20,000 *C*

A George IV mahogany and rosewood banded pianoforte, by Astor and Co. of Bishopsgate, with ivory keyboard, a lightwood maker's label, 2 drawers outlined with ebony stringing, on turned lobed legs, with flowerhead pressed and lobed gilt metal collars, 68in (172.5cm) wide.
£2,000-2,500 *Bon*

An English spinet, in crossbanded mahogany case, c1740, 74in (188cm) wide, on later stand.
£3,000-4,000 *C*

A gold flute, by Rittershausen, engraved 5000/E. Rittershausen/ Berlin, Boehm system, open G#, the barrel section encrusted with diamonds, rubies and sapphires, sounding length 24in (61cm), in case.
£6,000-7,000 *C*

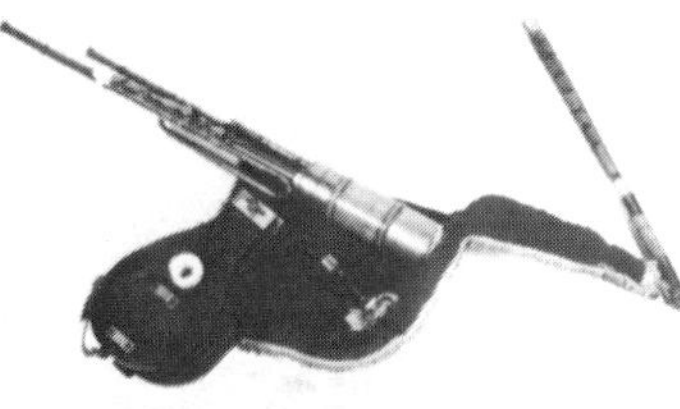

A set of boxwood uillean pipes, by Coyne, stamped on the drones Coyne/Dublin, ivory and brass mounts, the regulator with 4 brass keys, the pastoral style chanter with double note holes, with bag and bellows, early 19thC.
£1,000-1,500 *C*

A 'Margot' 44-note piano orchestrion, by H. Peters & Co., Leipzig, 28-note piano section, 10-note mandolin, 10-note xylophone, cymbal, triangle and 2 drums, in oak case, 97in (246cm) high, with 2 barrels and weight.
£4,500-5,500 *CSK*

A Steinway boudoir grand piano, No. 35559, the foliate carved rosewood case on scroll carved cabriole legs, 84in (213cm).
£2,000-3,000 *Bea*

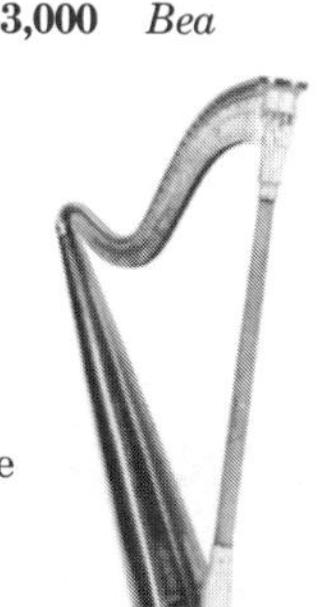

A mid-Victorian harp by I. A. Stumpff, ebonised and gilt decorated and transfer printed, the brass harmonica curve inscribed Patent Harp, Invented by I.A. Stumpff, No. 44 Great Portland Street, Portland Place, London, 67in (170cm) high.
£550-600 *LBP*

A rosewood concertina, by Thomas Dawkins & Co., London No. 24506, in original case.
£150-200 *P[EDH]*

Musical Boxes

A mandolin musical box, No. 15838, playing 6 airs, in carved wood case, extreme brass tooth and many dampers missing, 33in (84cm) wide, the cylinder 19½in (49cm).
£3,000-3,500 *CSK*

A 15¾in (40cm) polyphon disc musical box playing on a single comb, in walnut case with marquetry inlay to lid, 19½in (49.5cm) wide, complete with winding handle and 41 discs.
£900-1,000 *HCH*

A Swiss chalet cylinder musical box, playing 8 airs, c1860, on wall bracket.
£4,000-4,500 *SH*

An 18-key chamber barrel organ, by Longhurst (?), London, in mahogany case with simulated pipes to the Gothic front, on square reeded legs with barrel compartment, pipes dismantled and in poor condition, 71in (180cm) high.
£1,000-1,500 *CSK*

A cylinder musical box by George Bondon, with 3 mandarins striking 6 bells, 8 airs, c1880, 19 by 10in (48 by 25.5cm), with original tune sheet.
£3,000-3,500 *SH*

A polyphon 15⅝in (39.5cm) periphery-drive disc musical box, the case with quartered veneer and inlaid lid, lid interior restored, with winding handle and 12 discs.
£1,000-1,500 *P*

A 12 air musical box, in inlaid rosewood case.
£1,500-2,000 *MGM*

A 2-air manivel, c1880, 3in (7.5cm) diam.
£100-150 *SH*

A Swiss musical box, by Nicole Freres, Geneva, No. 45006, with si[x] 13in (33cm) cylinders, each playing 6 tunes, contained in a rosewood and marquetry cabinet mounted on a writing table, with tulipwood and walnut crossbanding, a drawer fitted with a writing slide, and pen and ink compartments, on hexagonal legs, late 19thC, 38½in (96.5cm) wide.
£3,500-4,000 *DN*

A Lépee mandolin pinned cylinder musical box, playing 4 airs, contained in rosewood case, with brass and pewter inlay, c1870, 24in (61cm) wide.
£3,000-4,000 *SH*

Phonographs

A Pandora phonograph model, manufactured by Excelsior, plays 2 minute cylinders, complete with play back head and recording head, German, c1905.
£300-500 *SH*

An Edison Diamond Disc phonograph, Chippendale Laboratory Model (C19) No. SM106640, with gilt fittings, mahogany case and Edison record pan, 51½in (130cm) high, with 19 discs.
£500-700 *CSK*

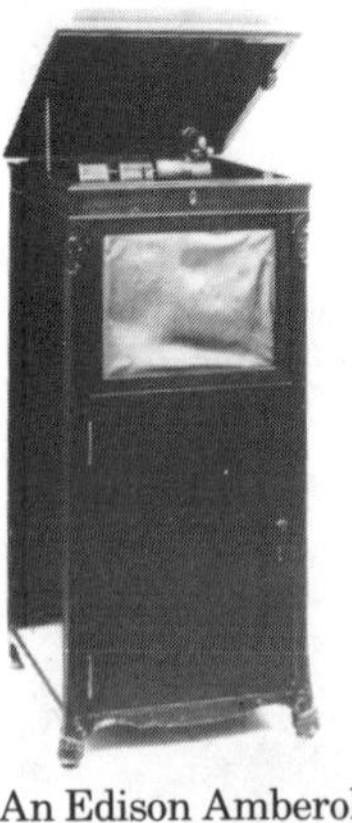

An Edison Amberola 1A phonograph, No. SM950, in mahogany case, with maroon enamelled 2-minute and 4-minute traversing mandrel mechanism, Diamond A and Model M combination reproducers, grille fret removed, 49in (124.5cm) high.
£1,200-1,500 *CSK*

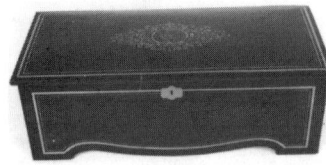

A coin-in-slot phonograph, Type BS, in oak case with curved glass front and transfer, now with adapted Zonophone horn.
£1,200-1,500 *CSK*

Gramophones

An oak cased horn gramophone, with soundbox and brown embossed fluted tinplate horn.
£250-300 *P*

Miscellaneous

An oak Berliner 7in (18cm) record cabinet with folding lid, carved plinth moulding and spaces for 32 records, containing 7 American issue Berliners by Cal. Stewart and others.
£500-600 *CSK*

The Emor 'globe', by Emor Radio Ltd., made for the domestic market, the stem and globe chromium plated, tuned by rotating globe, other controls in stem, 1947, 54in (137cm).
£450-500 *MET*

The price new was £14.14s.0d.

An Edison Bell discophone, with trumpet speaker.
£300-350 *P[EDH]*

An Amourette organette in the form of a chalet, with 2 mirrored compartments with dancing dolls, one doll missing, the 16-note mechanism mounted behind, with 17 discs, various case parts loose or missing, 14in (35.5cm) wide.
£500-600 *CSK*

A Melodia table top paper-roll organette, by the American Mercantile Co., in mahogany case with gilt transfer decoration, with 9 rolls, 12½in (32cm) wide.
£300-350 *P*

An AMI juke box with 200 selection, model JEJ200, Serial No. 491033, with records, c1960.
£600-700 *OT*

A musical picture clock, with 2-train French movement, striking on wire gong and 3-air snuff box musical movement, in giltwood frame, 29½ by 34½in (75 by 87cm).
£1,500-2,000 *CSK*

A miniature barrel organ, with 7 tunes, signed Josef Celis.
£2,500-3,000 *Clo*

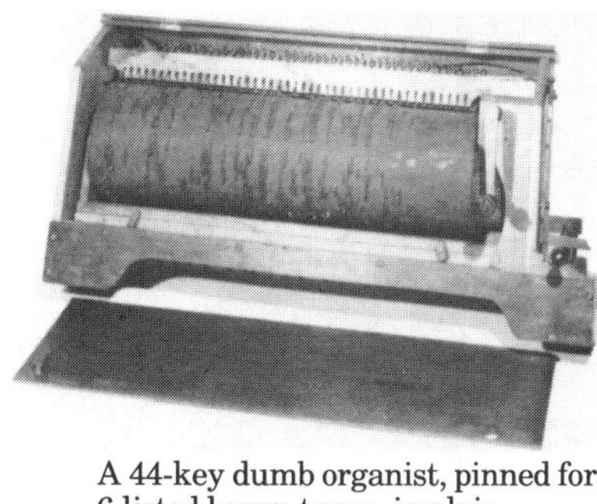

A 44-key dumb organist, pinned for 6 listed hymn tunes, in plain mahogany case with crank, 31in (79cm) wide.
£700-800 *CSK*

A wireless and horn speaker with eliminator for running off mains electricity, c1920.
£70-100 *MY*

A French singing bird, c1860, 11in (28cm) high.
£1,000-1,500 *SH*

'His Master's Voice' model dog, 15in (38cm) high.
£90-120 *WRe*

Boxes

A satinwood and a rosewood tea caddy, 19thC.
£150-200 *LRG*

A George III mahogany tea caddy, decorated with marquetry panels and boxwood stringing, 6½in (16.5cm).
£400-450 *DN*

A tortoiseshell 2 compartment caddy, inlaid with mother-of-pearl floral decoration, late Georgian.
£800-1,000 *TW*

A Sheraton style satinwood tea caddy, with marquetry decoration on harewood to lid, 6½in (16.5cm).
£700-750 *JD*

A William and Mary style oyster veneered lace box, the lid with boxwood stringing, 21in (53cm).
£800-900 *P*

A Dutch parquetry tea caddy, 18thC.
£120-150 *LRG*

A mahogany tea caddy, 18thC, 8½in (21cm).
£70-100 *PCA*

A Georgian mahogany Sheraton pattern knife box, with boxwood inlay, 9in (23cm) wide.
£500-600 *PC*

A William and Mary walnut crossbanded marquetry lace box, 19½in (50cm).
£1,200-1,500 *P*

A pair of George III mahogany knife boxes, with ebony line borders, one with fitted interior, the other with interior fittings removed.
£1,500-2,000 *DN*

A mahogany and curled paper tea caddy, stained and inset with urns, flowers and lambrequin ornament, the top with chequer stringing, late 18thC, 6in (15cm).
£600-700 *CSK*

A Georgian fruitwood tea caddy, in the form of an apple, 4½in (11cm).
£500-700 *P*

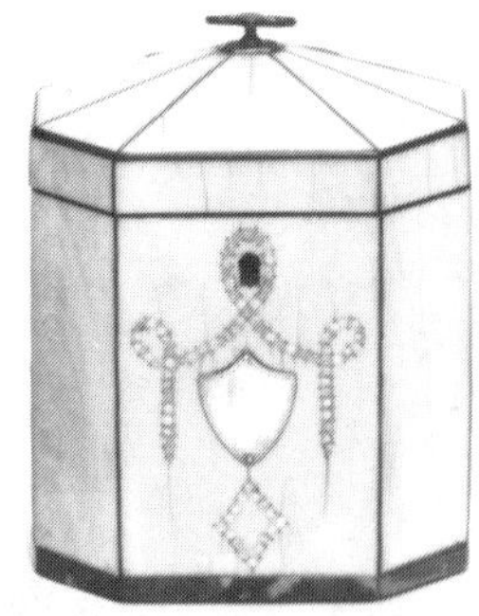

An Adam ivory caddy, with tortoiseshell angles and shell pique decoration, 5in (15cm).
£1,200-1,500 *GSP*

A Regency tortoiseshell veneered tea caddy, with ribbed front, enclosing a pair of lidded compartments, with turned ivory knop and ball feet, c1820, 5½in (14cm) wide.
£700-800 *N*

A French straw-work workbox, worked in a 3-coloured diapered pattern, pink, gold and green, opening to reveal 2 hand coloured German etchings with French manuscript titles, the body opening to reveal a fully fitted interior, the base and some box lids with pink stencilled paper, c1750, 7½in (19cm) wide.
£900-1,000 *CSK*

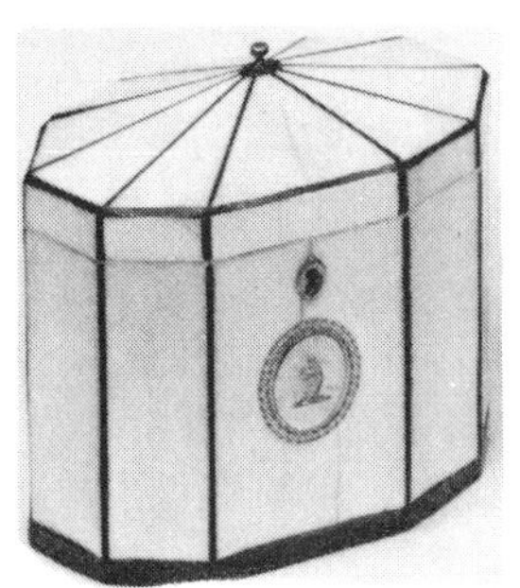

A George III ivory veneered and horn strung tea caddy, with an oval crest, replaced hinges, 5½in (13.5cm) wide.
£1,000-1,200 *P*

A brass inlaid coromandel writing case, the interior with blue velvet and 2 cut glass ink bottles, 19thC, 14in (35.5cm) wide.
£350-400 *HCH*

A Regency tea caddy.
£350-400 *HP*

A coromandel veneered writing box, inlaid with brass stringing, the domed lid opening to reveal a fitted interior, mid-19thC, 16in (40.5cm) wide.
£200-250 *WIL*

A Victorian burr walnut stationery box, in the form of a miniature piano, the raised back with lift-up top to reveal compartment, the lower section with lift-up top to reveal a pair of cut glass ink bottles, 10in (25.5cm) wide.
£200-300 *HCH*

A satinwood tea caddy, with inlaid decoration, early 19thC.
£500-600 *DN*

An Italian pokerwork cedarwood writing box, the slope lined with silk, enclosing a fitted interior, 17thC, 24½in (61cm) wide.
£600-800 *C*

A rosewood tea caddy, with mother-of-pearl inlay, 19thC. 12½in (31cm).
£250-300 *PCA*

A North Italian oak fall-front casket, inlaid in foliate carved marine ivory, with fitted interior, 17thC, 9in (23cm) wide.
£450-500 *CSK*

A George III mahogany serpentine front knife box, the kingwood crossbanded front enclosing an interior now fitted for stationery, with a crested silver escutcheon, 15in (38cm) high.
£300-400 *Bea*

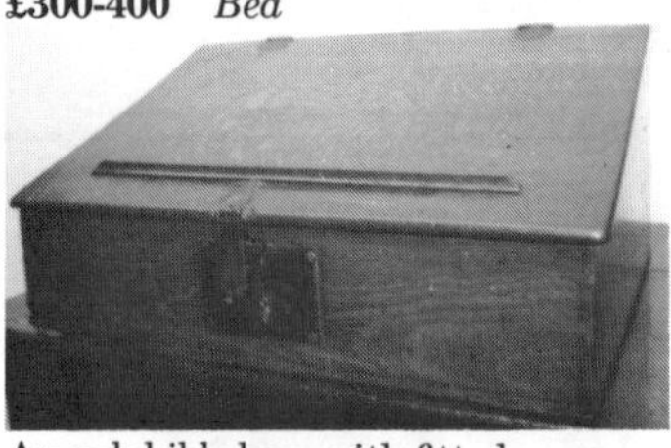

An oak bible box, with fitted interior, 18thC, 24½in (62cm).
£300-350 *PCA*

A giltmetal mounted mother-of-pearl casket, the domed lid applied with straps and carrying handle, 19thC, 10in (25.5cm).
£130-170 *C*

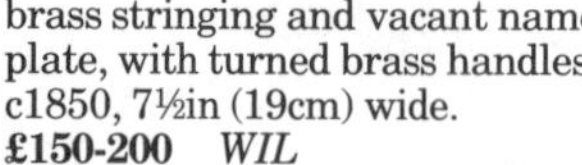

A mahogany collectors box, with brass stringing and vacant name plate, with turned brass handles, c1850, 7½in (19cm) wide.
£150-200 *WIL*

A Dutch marquetry set of 6 gilded spirit flasks, stoppers and matching wine glass.
£750-950 *CB*

A brass bound rosewood box, containing a set of 2 gilded ruby glass tea caddies, a spirit flask and stopper, a sugar bowl and cover, the box 10in (25.5cm) wide.
£750-950 *CB*

A Georgian Stilton box.
£2,000-2,500 *HP*

An oak box, 18thC, 9in (23cm).
£50-70 *PCA*

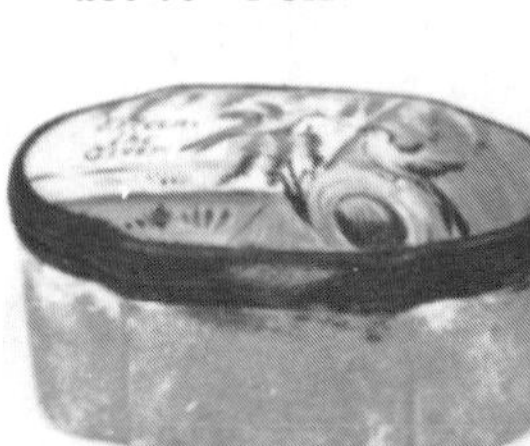

A box, painted with doves, with green base, 2in (5cm) wide.
£120-150 *P[PWC]*

A Continental agate box, the cover overlaid with gold mounts, 19thC, 3in (7cm).
£550-600 *DN*

A box, the top with gilt floral spray within a cartouche, the base with painted floral sprays on a lilac ground, 2in (5cm) wide.
£80-100 *P[PWC]*

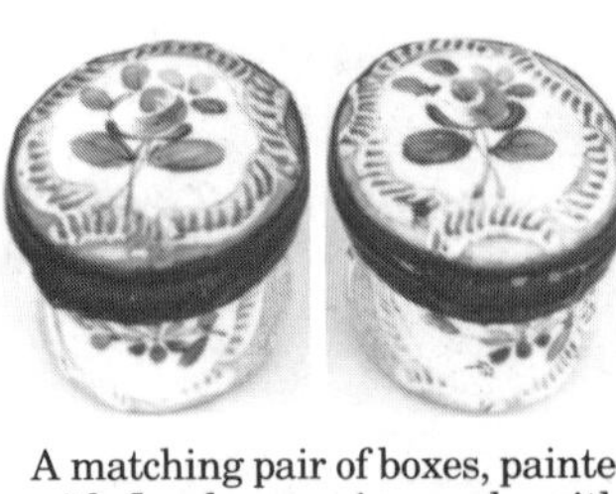

A matching pair of boxes, painted with floral sprays in panels, with blue and pink grounds, 2cm.
£300-350 *P[PWC]*

A patch box, the lid printed with black on white named view of Salisbury Cathedral, turquoise base, 1½in (4cm) wide.
£250-300 *P[PWC]*

A Batavian silver mounted burr walnut casket, with foliate angle mounts and coat-of-arms, with escutcheon and carrying handles, mid-18thC, 13in (33cm) high.
£750-800 *C*

An Oriental floral and foliate carved ivory box, with finely decorated gilt hinged cover, 3in (7.5cm) wide.
£550-600 *GC*

An Italian gilt metal box, one side with micro-mosaic allegorical panel, the other with ROTIA in raised letters, 19thC.
£4,500-5,000 *DN*

A French black lacquered and buhl perfume box, the interior covered with silk, with 3 bottles and matching stoppers decorated in gold leaf.
£350-400 *FHF*

Electrical

A brass electric fire, c1900, 34 by 23in (86 by 58cm).
£60-75 *COB*

A William and Mary lace box, veneered in walnut with oyster top and front, 21 by 16½in (53 by 42cm).
£900-1,200 *DN*

A mahogany Tunbridgeware box, 19thC, 9in (23cm).
£50-70 *PCA*

Enamel

A George III South Staffordshire enamel tea caddy, painted with designs after J. Pillement and C. Fenn, damage, c1765, 6in (15cm) high.
£1,500-2,000 *N*

A Limoges enamel plaque of a Turkish bath, signed R-Blanchet, Limoges, 9½ by 8in (24 by 20cm).
£2,000-2,500 *C*

A Staffordshire enamel box, damaged, 18thC, 5½in (14cm) diam.
£300-350 *P[CW]*

An inlaid wall salt box, mid-19thC.
£300-350 *WW*

Typewriters

A red Mignon No. 2 typewriter, with English type and spare German keyplate, serial No. 1907, in a bentwood case, lacks folding paper table, case recovered, handle detached.
£1,200-1,500 *P*

A Merrit typewriter, with rubber type, in wooden case, some damage.
£300-350 *P*

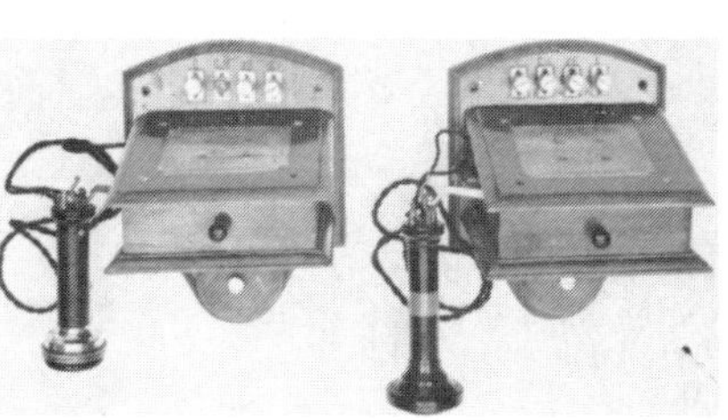
A pair of mahogany cased wall telephones, of Prof. D. E. Hughes/Crossley loose carbon electrode microphone type, with bells beneath and 2 similar ebonite earpieces, late 19thC, 9½in (24cm) high.
£250-300 *P*

Transport

A single Victoria, finished and upholstered in green, 95in (241cm) long.
£2,000-4,000 *P*

A 1901 International charette side entrance tonneau, Engine No. 42.
£15,000-18,000 *P*

A 1919 A.B.C. Scootamota, designed by Granville Bradshaw, Engine No. IB239.
£1,200-1,500 *C*

A 1924 Buick Regent 1½ ton van, converted from a hearse, Engine No. 1216436.
£7,000-8,000 *P*

A 1927 Austin Seven (Chummy) 2-door tourer, Engine No. M12427.
£5,000-6,000 *P*

A 1950 B.S.A. A10 Golden Flash 650cc solo motorcycle, plunger model, Engine No. ZA10-2043, with maker's handbook and tool kit.
£1,500-2,000 *C*

A 1942 Harley Davidson 1,200cc side valve motorcycle combination.
£5,000-6,000 *C*

An Ordinary bicycle, Humber Meteor, with iron frame, wood handles and solid rubber tyres, renewed, c1878, 40in (101.5cm) diam.
£650-750 *WHB*

An Edwardian baby's pram, with black paintwork and upholstery.
£200-250 *LRG*

l. A brass Lucas Kings Own No. F144 oil sidelight, 8½in (21.5cm) high.
£90-100

r. A black painted and nickel plated Lucas Kings Own No. F141 oil sidelight, 8½in (20.5cm) high.
£70-90 *ONS*

A collection of 6 motoring and cycling colour posters, advertising the Triumph Fifteen, Bean Cars, Wolseley and Morris.
£90-100 *CSK*

A gradient meter, by Tapley & Co., Southampton, with a silvered rise-and-fall dial, nickel plated brass case and dashboard brackets.
£60-80 *P*

Three Riley Alpine instruction books.
£50-60 *CSK*

A catalogue for Bugatti Competition and Racing Models, for the year 1932, missing card, containing a print of the Type 51 Grand Prix Standard 2-seater.
£180-250 *CSK*

A North British Railway copper lamp with bull's-eye lens, mounted with brass plate inscribed Hawick Up Home, internals missing, 24in (61cm) high.
£200-250 *ONS*

A pair of brass Bleriot oil sidelights, 14in (35.5cm) high.
£600-700 *ONS*

Aero Club, a Brooklands badge, numbered 188, good enamel, post 1930.
£650-700 *P*

An R.A.C. associated member's badge, in nickelled brass with enamel crest and disc for 1914, 6in (15cm) high.
£250-300 *CSK*

A brass R.A.C. full member's badge, stamped No. DF384, c1910, chipped, 5in (12.5cm) high.
£70-90 *CSK*

A Watford dashboard clock, with silvered dial, heavy brass case with bevelled glass, 8-day movement and button activated hand setting, c1910, 3½in (9cm) diam.
£80-100 *CSK*

A pair of Lucas new 'Alto-de-Luxe grill fronted horns, with restored chrome cases, 5in (12.5cm) diam.
£200-300 *CSK*

The cast brass nameplate from Lifeboat No. 12, S.S. Titanic, 12½in (32cm).
£6,000-6,500 *ONS*

An MG radiator, restored, c1950, 24in (61cm) high.
£200-250 *CSK*

A Bentley winged 'B', stamped J. Fray Ltd., c1920, on early original Bentley radiator cap, 8in (20cm) wide.
£400-450 *CSK*

An Austin winged steering wheel mascot, mounted on radiator cap, inscribed Austin Motor Co., stamped Rd 286069, c1910, 4 by 5in (10 by 12.5cm).
£900-1,200 *CSK*

A chrome plated mascot, victory, a female standing on one leg with arms outstretched, holding a ribbon.
£180-220 *P*

A Jaguar mascot, the shaped base stamped Gordon Crosby, c1930, 8in (20cm) long, on original SS 100 Jaguar radiator cap.
£300-400 *CSK*

A glass car mascot of a butterfly girl, the base inscribed Red-Ashay-Reg. 611338, 1935, 9½in (24cm) high.
£650-750 *P*

Leather & Luggage

A travelling dressing set, with silver mounts, 1901, Birmingham, in an alligator skin case.
£450-500 *LRG*

A Louis Vuitton trunk, fitted with 2 trays, covered with a brown chequer board design, labelled Louis Vuitton, 454 Strand, Paris, 1 Rue Scribe, No. 35832, c1890, 30in (76cm) wide.
£700-800 *CSK*

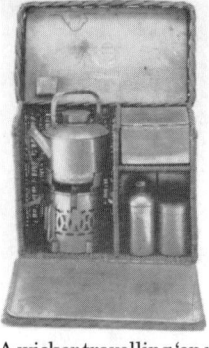

A wicker travelling 'en route' set, by Drew & Sons, Piccadilly, 12in (30.5cm) wide.
£250-300 *CSK*

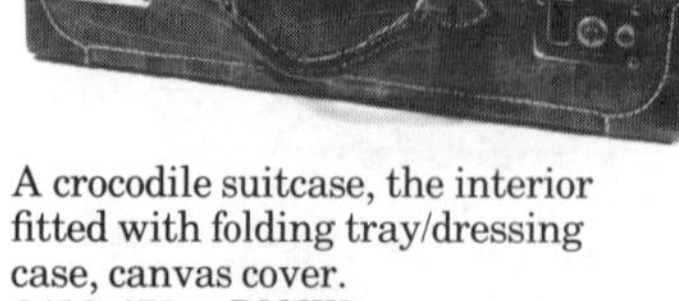

A crocodile suitcase, the interior fitted with folding tray/dressing case, canvas cover.
£400-450 *P[CW]*

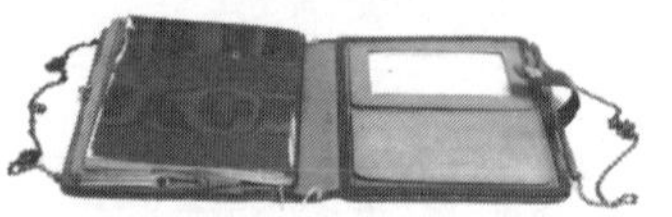

An Edwardian lady's crocodile carry-all.
£200-250 *SB*

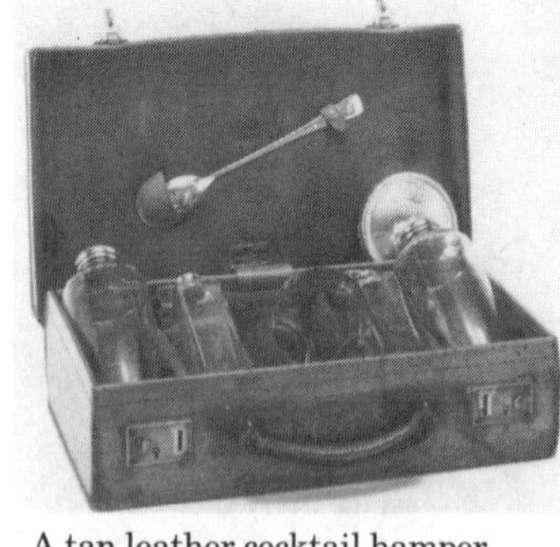

A tan leather cocktail hamper, made for Brooks Brothers, New York, 15in (38cm) wide.
£350-400 *CSK*

A British officer's valise, formerly the property of Col. H. Harford, 1852-1937, Adj. of the 99 Foot, the Duke of Edinburgh's Regiment.
£750-850 *SB*

This valise was actually used by the Colonel during the Zulu Wars.

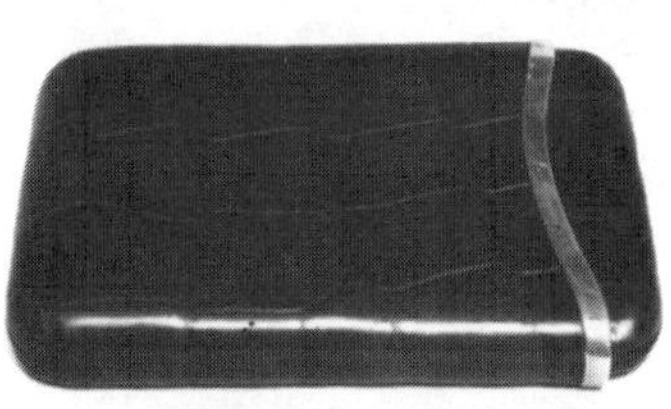

A crocodile cigar holder, c1930.
£200-250 *SB*

A crocodile and silver wallet.
£200-250 *SB*

A snakeskin suitcase, c1940.
£500-550 *SB*

A Hermes python bag, with box, c1950.
£2,300-2,500 *SB*

A crocodile cased clock, c1920.
£150-200 *SB*

A hunting decanter set in leather box, with brass decoration, early 19thC.
£700-800 *SB*

An Asprey crocodile travelling case, with integral folding toilet case, containing extensive silver gilt fittings, including lidded bottles, brushes, and a mirror, marked London 1914, the reverse of the lid stamped Asprey, London, with initialled waterproof canvas cover.
£1,200-1,500 *P*

 LEATHER & LUGGAGE

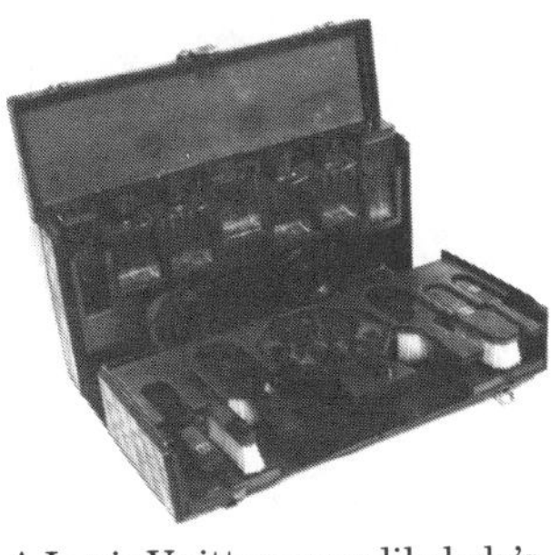

A Louis Vuitton crocodile lady's necessaire, fittings in crystal and tortoiseshell, c1920.
£5,000-6,000 *SB*

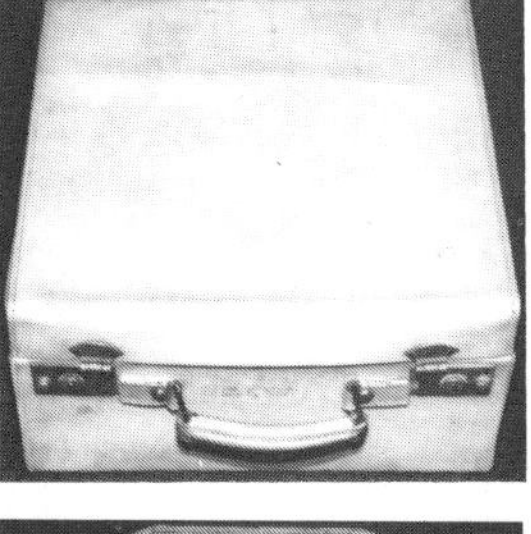

Two pieces of vellum luggage, and one other.
£70-100 each *GAL*

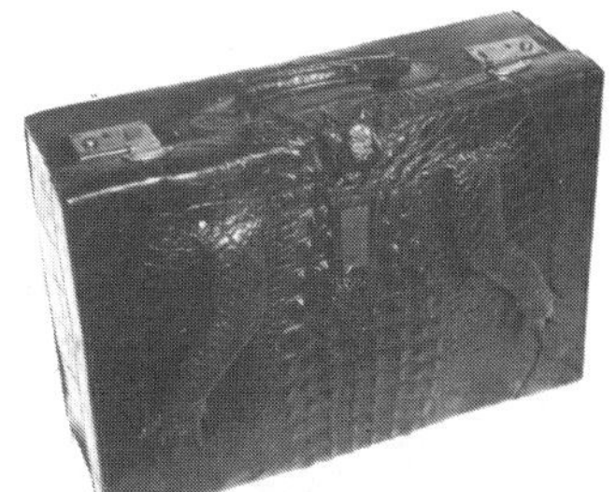

An Australian crocodile case, c1940.
£600-700 *SB*

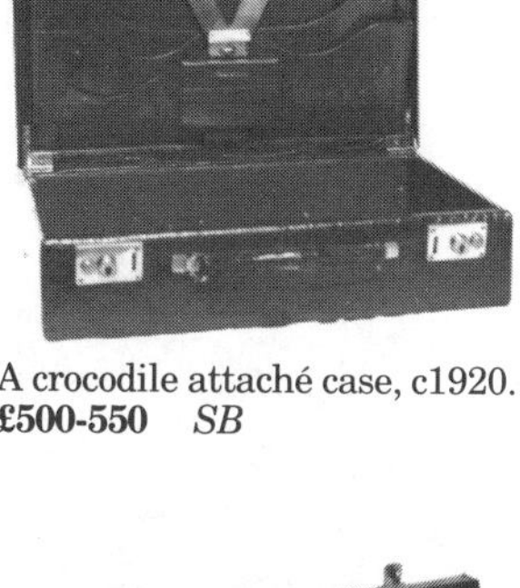

A crocodile attaché case, c1920.
£500-550 *SB*

An Edwardian Gladstone bag.
£400-500 *SB*

An American crocodile hat box, c1940.
£900-1,000 *SB*

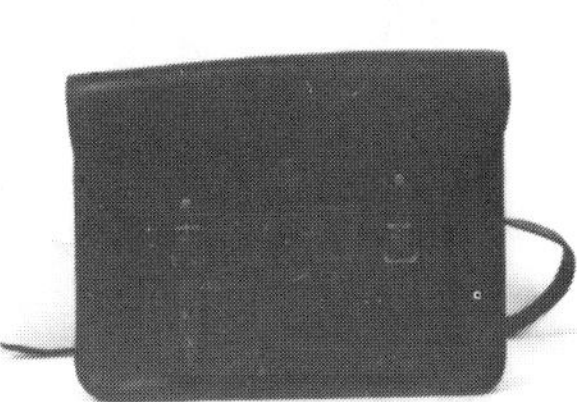

A school satchel, 13in (33cm).
£20-25 *AL*

An Asprey fitted travelling case, the fittings in silver and crystal, c1920.
£5,500-6,000 *SB*

A Victorian coaching trunk.
£250-300 *SB*

A leather folding stool.
£22-25 *AL*

A Louis Vuitton hide gentleman's suitcase, with crystal and silver fittings.
£4,000-5,000 *SB*

A pair of ladies crocodile sling-back shoes, c1950.
£150-200 *SB*

A Victorian crocodile jewellery box, c1890.
£900-1,200 *SB*

A Drew & Sons fitted crocodile case, with tortoiseshell fittings, c1930.
£5,000-5,500 *SB*

Two crocodile wallets, with gold corners, c1950.
£250-300 *SB*

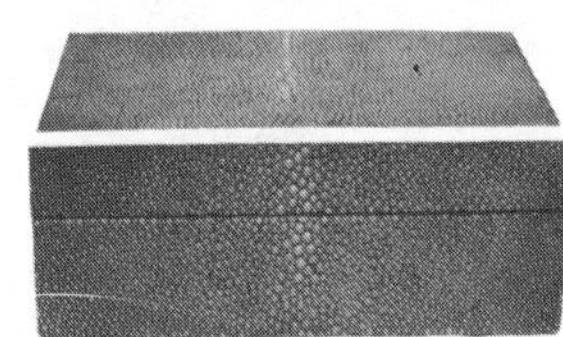

A shagreen cigarette box, c1920.
£150-200 *SB*

A pair of gentleman's crocodile shoes, c1940.
£140-180 *SB*

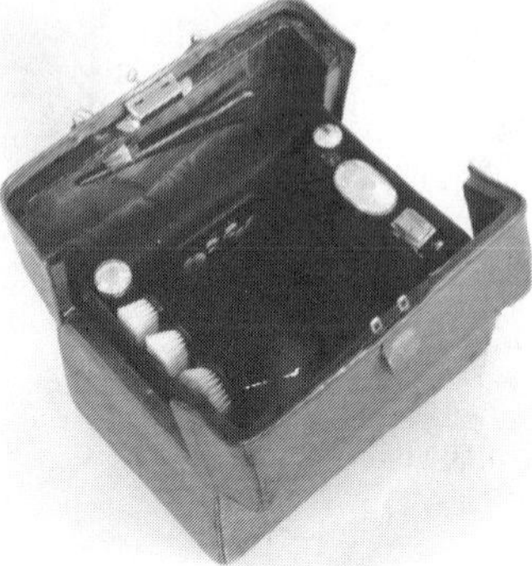

A lady's leather carrying toilet case, the fittings with silver mounts, and an ebony brush set.
£120-180 *MGM*

A shagreen clutch bag, c1920.
£400-450 *SB*

A crocodile leather case, lined with suede, with key, 16in (40.5cm) long.
£300-350 *CSK*

A Louis Vuitton shoe carrier, c1950.
£900-1,200 *SB*

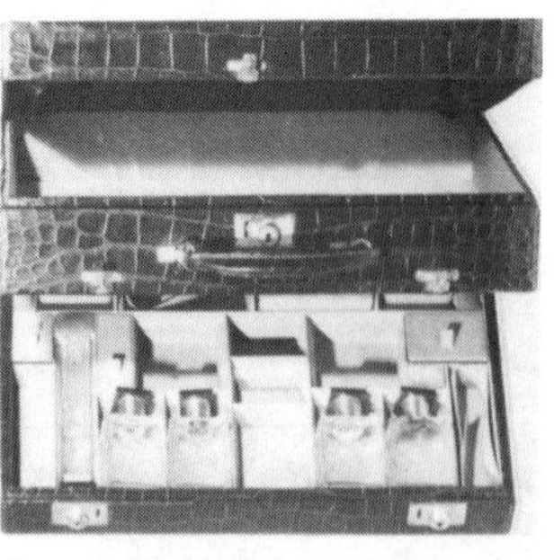

A pair of field boots, with wooden trees, c1914.
£150-200 *SB*

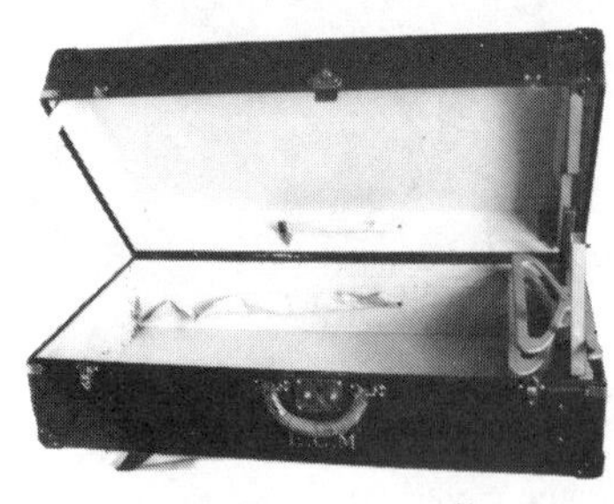

A Louis Vuitton travelling case, c1950.
£1,000-1,200 *SB*

A Louis Vuitton suitcase, c1950.
£500-550 *SB*

A crocodile suit/dressing case, opening into 3 sections, one lined with ivory watered silk, the other with compartments and 5 glass bottles with silver and tortoiseshell tops, monogrammed L.S., the suitcase lid similarly initialled, lacking some fittings, 18in (46cm) long, in foul weather case.
£200-300 *CSK*

Make the most of Miller's

Miller's is completely different each year. Each edition contains completely NEW photographs. This is not an updated publication. We never repeat the same photograph.

A Hermes crocodile bag, with jewellery box under, c1950.
£4,000-4,500 *SB*

Sport

Fishing

A Hardy Perfect, with ivorine handle, a false aluminium lineguard added, 1896, 3in (8cm).
£50-65 *JMG*

A Victorian salmon reel, in ebonite and nickel plated brass, with turned ebony knob, c1890, 4½in (11.5cm).
£40-60 *JMG*

A Hardy Uniqua fly reel with ivorine handle, horseshoe drum latch, check patented 1910, 3in (8cm).
£25-40 *JMG*

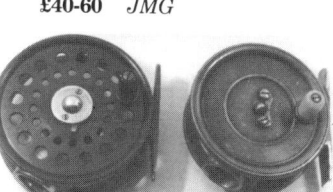

A brass and laburnum Perth style salmon fly reel, owner's name engraved on face, c1880, 4¼in (11cm).
£40-70 *JMG*

l. An Ogden Smith fly reel, with perforated drum face and bronze line guard, c1950, 3in (7.5cm).
£15-25

r. A Westley Richards fly reel, with ivorine handle, bronze line guard, brass telephone latch, calliper check, c1915, 2¾in (7cm).
£20-35 *JMG*

A Hardy Silex No. 2, extra wide for mahseer fishing, c1915, 4½in (11.5cm).
£20-30 *JMG*

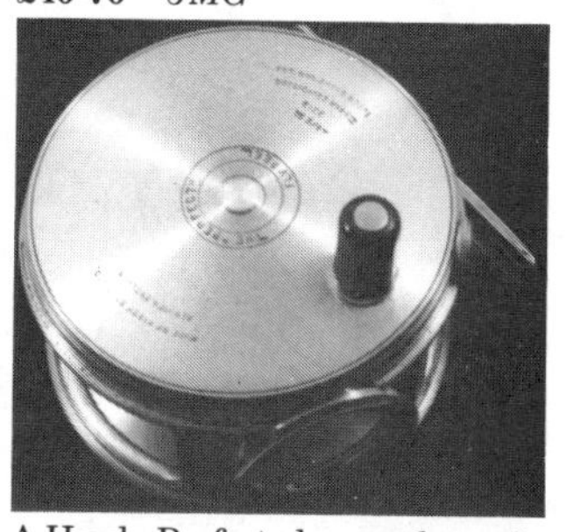

A Hardy Perfect, drum salmon fly reel, 3¾in (9.5cm).
£60-80 *JMG*

An Allcock aerial casting reel, with vulcanite drum, c1898, 3in (7.5cm).
£50-80 *JMG*

A Hardy Sunbeam, lacquered bright finish, c1940, 2¾in (7cm).
£30-45 *JMG*

A Hardy Fortuna big game sea reel, post war, restored to mint condition, 7in (18cm).
£120-180 *JMG*

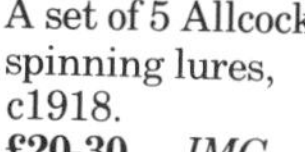

A set of 5 Allcock spinning lures, c1918.
£20-30 *JMG*

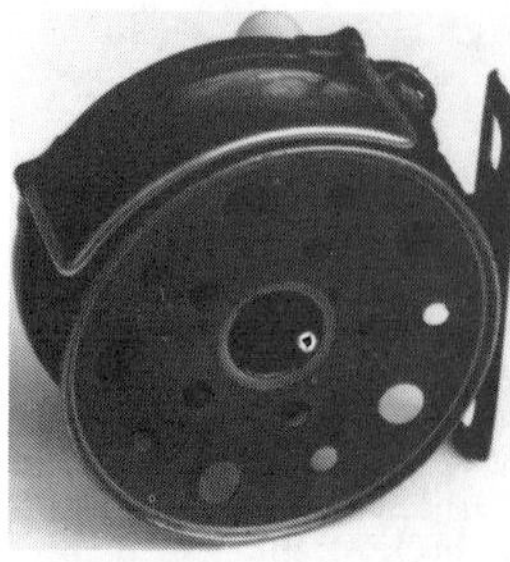

A Hardy brass Perfect, with ivory handle and Bickerdyke nickel silver lineguard, c1891, 3½in (9cm).
£1,500-2,000 *JES*

A nickel plated brass Hardy crankwind trout fly reel, with offset pillars and horn handle, c1890, 2¼in (6cm).
£500-550 *JES*

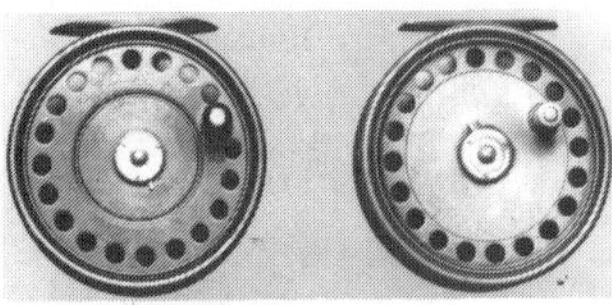

l. A Hardy St. John fly reel, c1925, 4in (10cm).
£45-60

r. A Hardy L.R.H. lightweight trout fly reel, c1935, 3in (7.5cm).
£40-70 *JES*

A Hardy salmon Perfect with duplicated Mk II check, c1925, 3¾in (9.5cm).
£200-250 *JES*

A Hardy Bougle trout dry fly reel with offset pillars, c1915, 3in (7.5cm).
£650-700 *JES*

A brass collar fitting wynch by Hayward of Birmingham, with turned bone handle, drum locking mechanism and horsehair line, c1860, 3½in (9cm) overall.
£200-250 *JES*

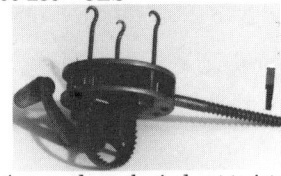

A geared crankwind gut twister, c1880, 4 by 5½in (10 by 14cm).
£100-120 *JES*

Top. A wooden pike lure, by DAM of Berlin, c1950, 5in (12.5cm).
£5-10

Bottom. An Edward Vom Hofe of New York spoon bait, the SAMS, nickel silver, patented 1908, 4½in (11.5cm).
£5-10 *JMG*

l. A Hardy Sunbeam trout fly reel, c1938, 3¼in (8cm).
£40-60

r. A Hardy Sunbeam trout fly reel, c1930, 3in (7.5cm).
£40-60 *JES*

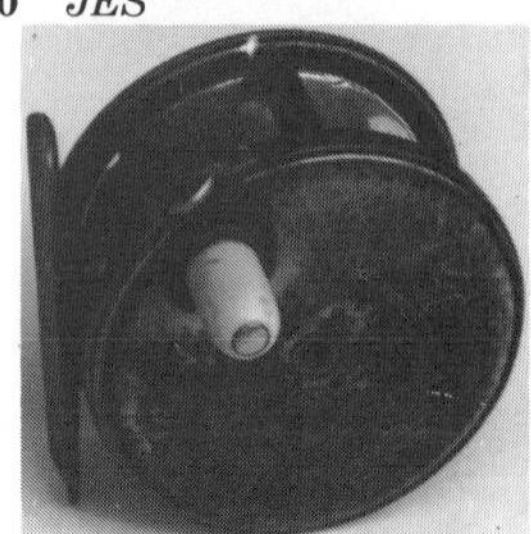

A drum alloy Hardy trout dry fly Perfect, c1901, 2½in (6.5cm).
£400-450 *JES*

A Hardy Zane Grey game fishing reel, in Monel metal with leather thumb brake guard, c1930, 4¼in (11cm).
£500-600 *JES*

A Greasaline gun, a device for permanently greasing a fly line, to be fixed to the rod butt with line running through 2 holes, c1935.
£3-5 *JMG*

Three early style fly-tying vices and holders, c1900.
£10-20 *JMG*

A keep net.
£15-20 *AL*

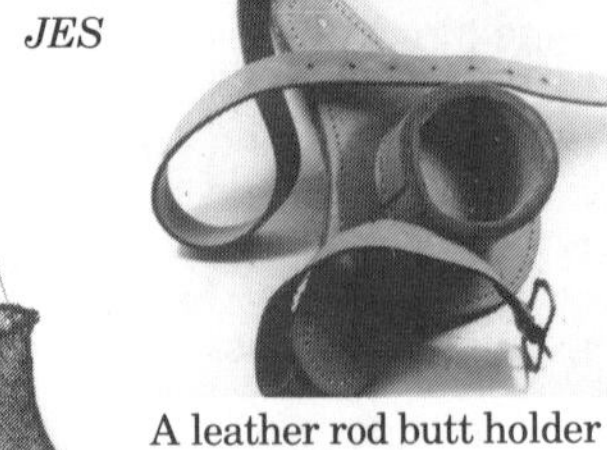

A leather rod butt holder for big game fishing.
£5-10 *JMG*

An electroplated fishing prize cup, dated 1844, 10½in (27cm) high.
£40-60 *JMG*

A Hardy case showing examples of different sizes of spinning lines, 2 missing, c1930.
£2-3 *JMG*

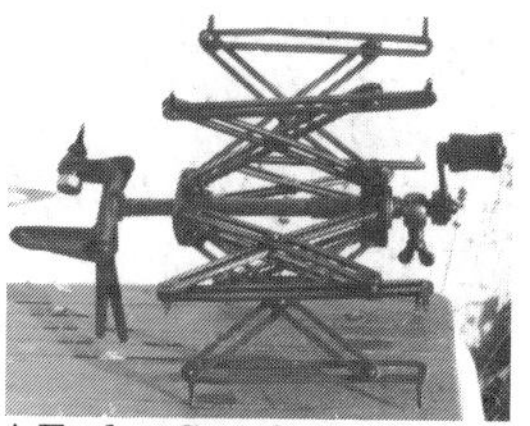

A Farlow Sextile brass linedrier, 1st model, c1910.
£30-40 *JMG*

A carved wood angling trophy, c1903, 50in (127cm) wide.
£800-850 *N*

A bait tin, 10in (25.5cm) wide.
£20-25 *AL*

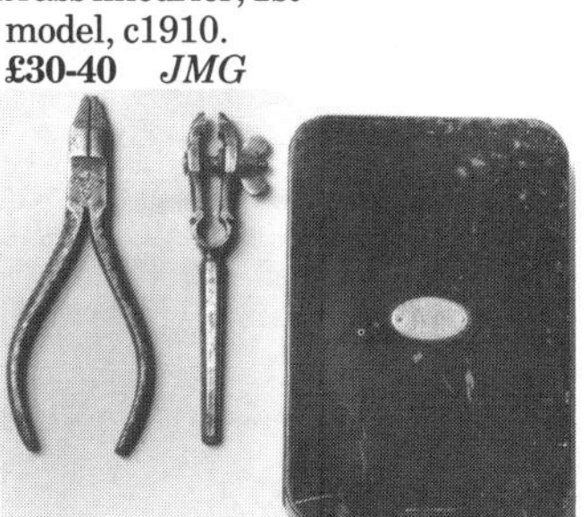

A Hardy trace making box, with tools, c1931, 5 by 3in (12.5 by 7.5cm).
£60-90 *JES*

A Hardy wicker creel with leather shoulder strap, c1938, 14in (35.5cm) wide.
£50-70 *JES*

A pastel salmon trophy painting in oak frame, c1920, 65 by 30in (165 by 76cm).
£200-250 *JES*

A box of flies, probably suitable for American bass, size 2/0 double hooks, in original box, by Murdoch of Redditch, c1938.
£8-12 *JMG*

A Hardy Club dry fly box, in mahogany, c1917, 6in (15cm) wide.
£130-150 *JES*

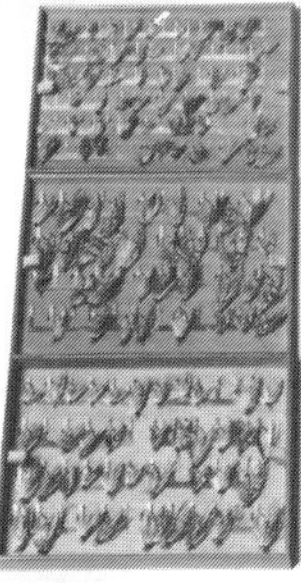

A Hardy Roxburgh polished teak fly cabinet, c1924, 10in (25.5cm) wide.
£420-460 *JES*

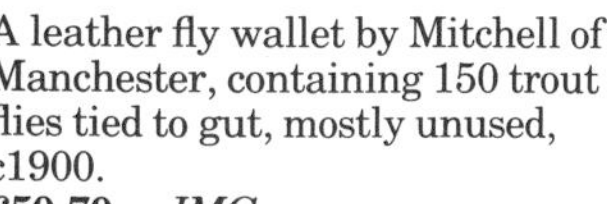

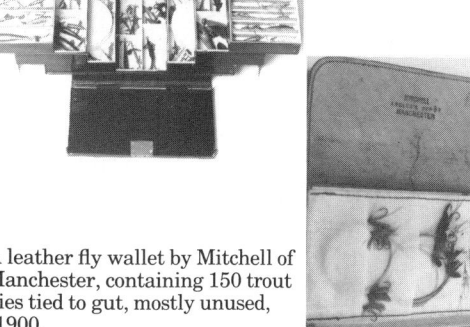

A cantilever black japanned bait cabinet, c1875, 12in (30.5cm) wide.
£120-150 *JES*

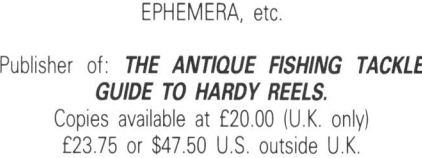

A leather fly wallet by Mitchell of Manchester, containing 150 trout flies tied to gut, mostly unused, c1900.
£50-70 *JMG*

A Farlow Multum in Parvo black japanned salmon fly box, with 5 lift-out trays, each with 24 fly clips, designed by G. Ashley Dodd, Esq., as catalogued in 1909.
£20-30 *JMG*

A Mascot-type dry fly black japanned box, 1920.
£15-25 *JMG*

A Hardy Halford dry fly box, with Halford fly names printed on the lids, one replaced, c1930.
£20-30 *JMG*

Golfing

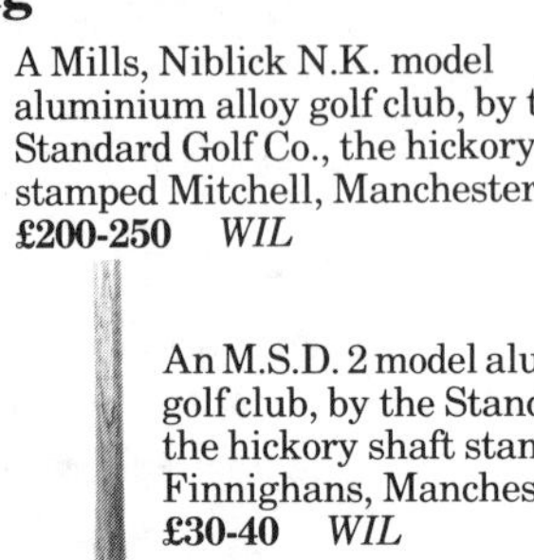

A Mills, Niblick N.K. model aluminium alloy golf club, by the Standard Golf Co., the hickory shaft stamped Mitchell, Manchester.
£200-250 *WIL*

An M.S.D. 2 model aluminium alloy golf club, by the Standard Golf Co., the hickory shaft stamped Finnighans, Manchester.
£30-40 *WIL*

A Copeland jug, decorated with a golfing scene, on a green ground with biscuit ground borders, 6in (15cm) high.
£150-200 *GC*

A bronze metal statue of a golfer, 10½in (26.5cm) high.
£150-200 *P*

A silver ashtray, by James Dixon & Sons, Sheffield, 1928, mounted with a figure of a devil smoking a pipe, standing next to a silver golf bag containing 5 clubs, 8in (20cm) diam, 20 grammes gross.
£600-700 *P*

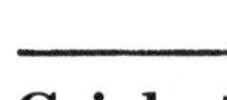

Cricket

The Hambledon Cricket Stone, printed legend and printed marks, 3in (7.5cm) high.
£600-700 *CSK*

A Staffordshire pottery mug, the body decorated with 3 cricket figures in white relief and silver lustre, 4in (10cm).
£120-150 *P*

A Robinson & Leadbetter full length parian statue of W. G. Grace, bat missing, 12½in (31.5cm) high.
£1,000-1,500 *P*

A Mintons pottery mug, M.C.C. 1787-1937, the rim decorated in club colours and cypher printed in black, 1937, 4½in (10.5cm).
£150-200 *P*

A pair of Continental porcelain figures of Young England and his Sister, decorated in colours, on oval bases, 12½in (32cm).
£500-600 *P*

A Coalport porcelain plate commemorating W. G. Grace's century of centuries, printed in red with portrait and dates, within semi-gadrooned rim, chipped and stained, 9in (23cm).
£150-200 *P*

Seven colour plates, Wanostracht (N), Felix on the Bat, 1st edition, 1845.
£550-600 *P*

A Mintons pottery ashtray, M.C.C. 1787-1937, the rim decorated in club colours and cypher printed in black, 1937, 5½in (13.5cm).
£70-100 *P*

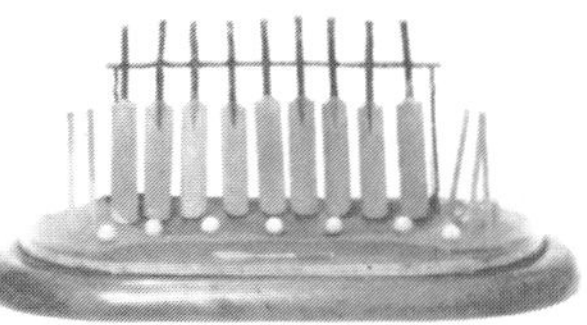

A cricketer's compendium, with wooden base and glass dome, containing a rack of 9 cricket bats, 2 wickets, 7 balls and other sporting equipment on green baize, 12½ by 9½in (32 by 24cm).
£400-450 *P*

W. Lambert, Cricketer's Guide, 5th edition, pull-out copper engraving opposite frontispiece.
£200-250 *P*

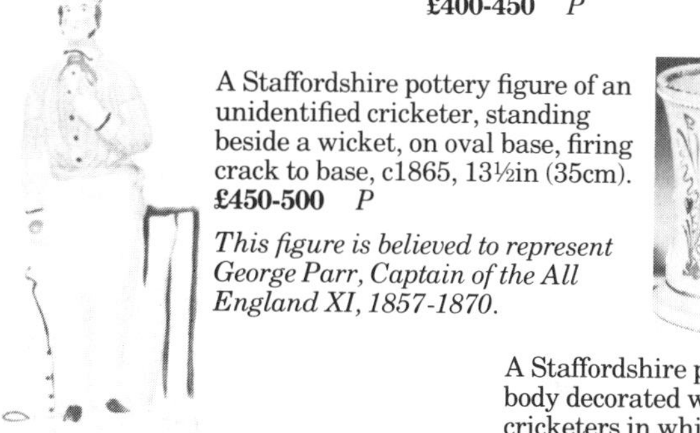

A Staffordshire pottery figure of an unidentified cricketer, standing beside a wicket, on oval base, firing crack to base, c1865, 13½in (35cm).
£450-500 *P*

This figure is believed to represent George Parr, Captain of the All England XI, 1857-1870.

A Staffordshire pottery mug, the body decorated with figures of cricketers in white relief and silver lustre, handle restored, 19thC, 3in (8cm).
£40-60 *P*

A Robinson & Leadbetter parian bust of W. G. Grace, 6½in (17cm).
£750-900 *P*

Miscellaneous

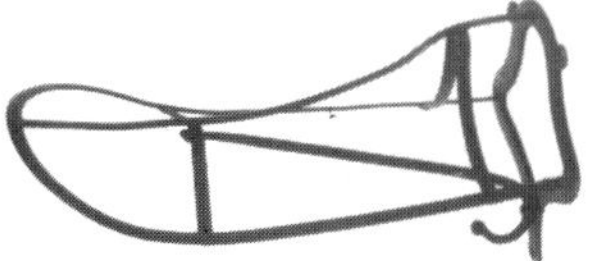

An iron saddle rack.
£20-30 *AL*

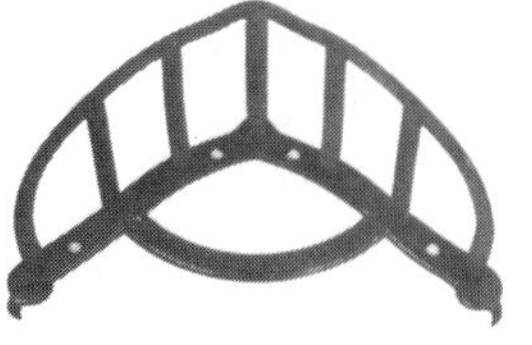

A cast iron painted bridle rack.
£30-50 *AL*

A pair of leather boxing gloves, pre-war.
£40-60 *SB*

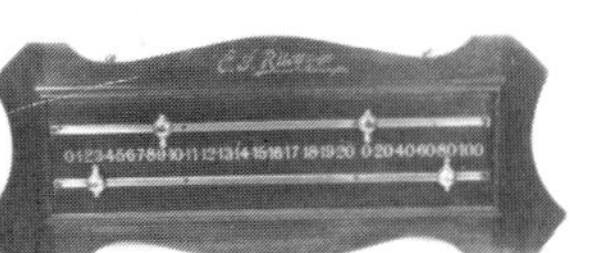

A Riley billiard marker, 25in (63.5cm) long.
£30-50 *AL*

A Victorian mahogany quarter-size snooker/dining table, with 3 leaves to top, with cues, set of balls and scoreboard, 89 by 48in (226 by 122cm).
£800-900 *HCH*

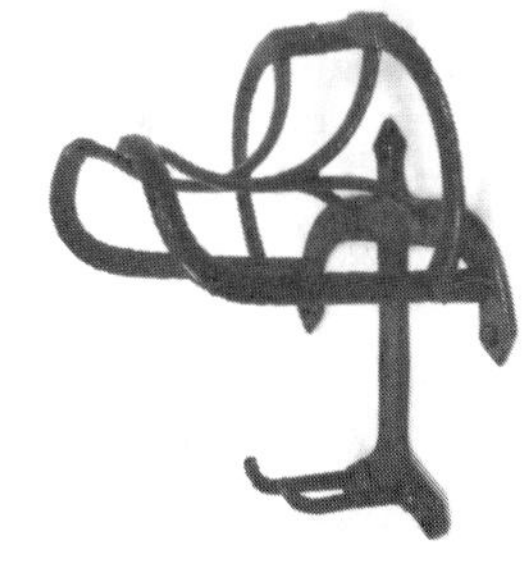

A riding tack rack.
£30-50 *AL*

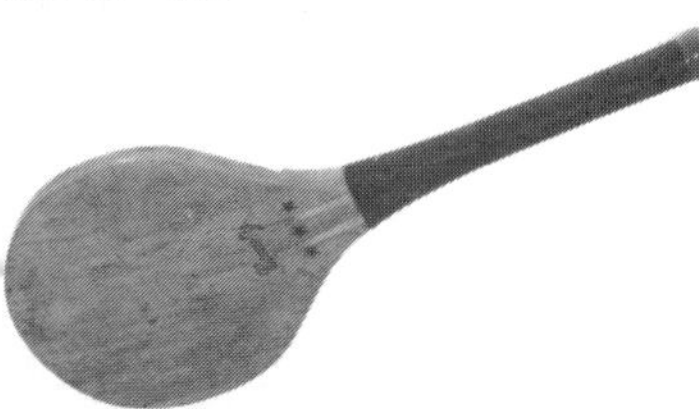

A Sussex stove ball bat, 11in (28cm).
£20-30 *AL*

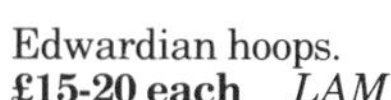

Hockey sticks –
Old Tyme. **£20-25**
Modern Indian head. **£15-20** *AL*

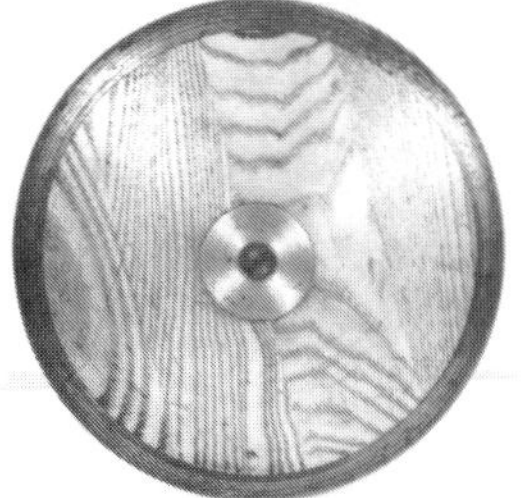

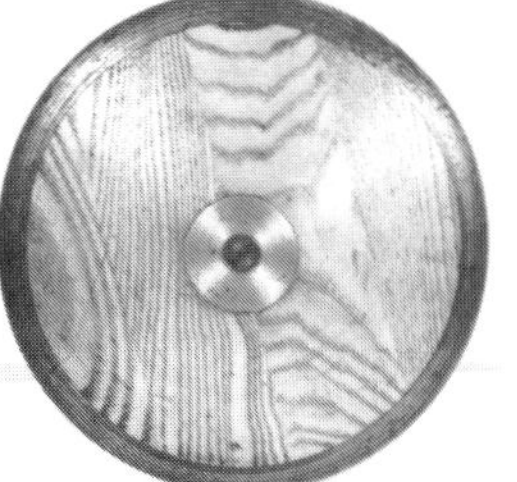

A discus, 8in (20.5cm) diam.
£20-25 *AL*

A Continental silver chalice-shaped trophy, Montreux Lawn Tennis Club, 24th April 1905, 9½in (24cm).
£600-700 *P*

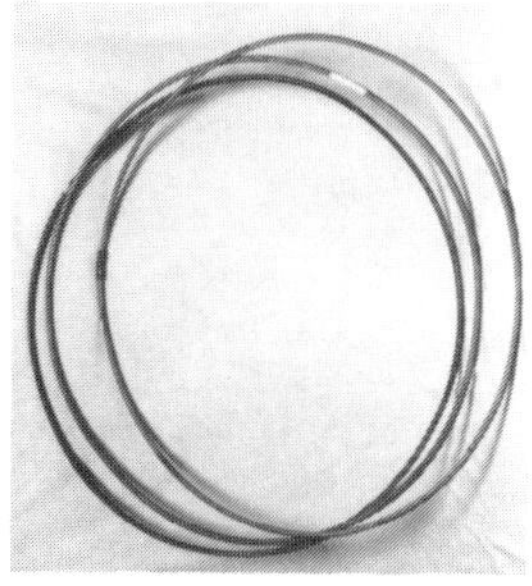

Edwardian hoops.
£15-20 each *LAM*

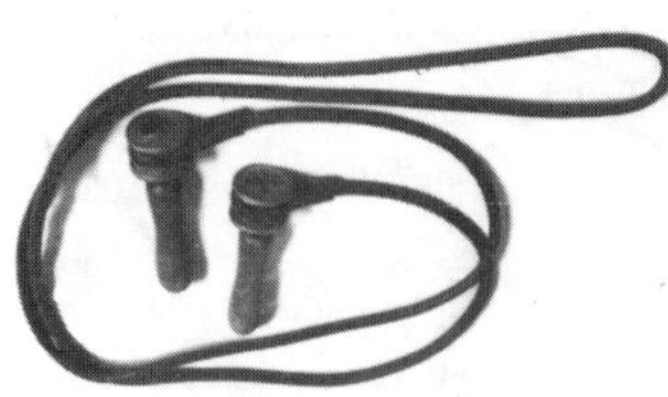

An Edwardian leather skipping rope.
£10-15 *LAM*

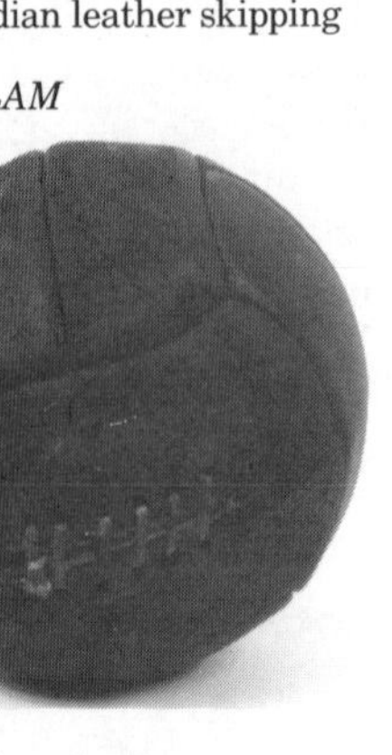

A football.
£20-25 *AL*

A bronzed metal figure of a tennis player, 11½in (29cm) high.
£300-350 *P*

A B.A.N. Co. automatic 'penny arcade' football machine, c1915.
£1,200-2,000 *P*

A 15ct. gold Football League Championship medal, for the season 1911-12, the medal having been presented to Mr. R. B. Middleton, the secretary of Blackburn Rovers Football Club.
£250-300 *P*

A programme for the F.A. Cup Final of 1923, the first occasion that the game was staged at Wembley Stadium.
£200-250 *P*

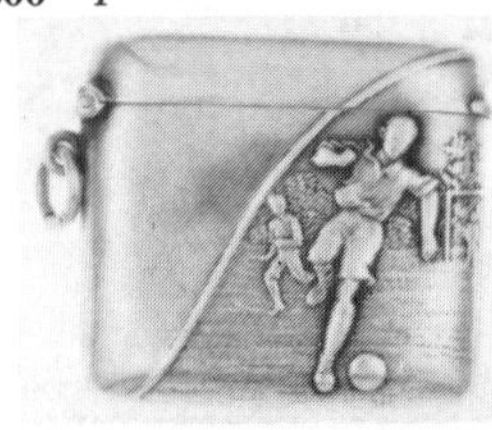

A silver footballing vesta case, Birmingham 1907, the front of the case embossed with 3 footballers in action.
£200-250 *P*

A pottery jug, inscribed on the front 'Sheffield Wednesday, English Cup Winners, April 18th, 1896', the reverse giving details of each match won during the competition, 4½in (11.5cm) high.
£550-650 *P*

A modern plaster portrait bust of Sayers, overcoloured in bronze, on inscribed plinth, 12in (30.5cm).
£100-150 *P*

A china figure of a boxer, 10½in (27cm).
£150-200 *P*

A creamware mug, with an image of Johnson and Perrins at Banbur on the side, some wear, 4½in (12cm) high.
£200-250 *P*

A mid-Victorian wine goblet, finely engraved with an image of 2 unidentified boxers in combat in the ring, 6½in (17cm) high.
£300-400 *P*

A white jug with red markings, 5½in (14cm).
£200-250 *P*

Crafts

A stoneware shallow bowl, by Lucie Rie, covered in a thick white pitted glaze with iron brown flecks, the centre with unglazed band, impressed LR seal, c1955, 13in (33cm).
£1,500-1,800 *C*

A stoneware vase, by Lucie Rie, impressed LR seal, 10½in (27cm) high.
£900-1,000 *C*

A stoneware bottle vase, by Lucie Rie, covered with a mottled turquoise, bluish-green and pale lavender spiral with matt bronze and fluxed rim, impressed LR seal, c1975, 11in (28cm) high.
£1,500-2,000 *C*

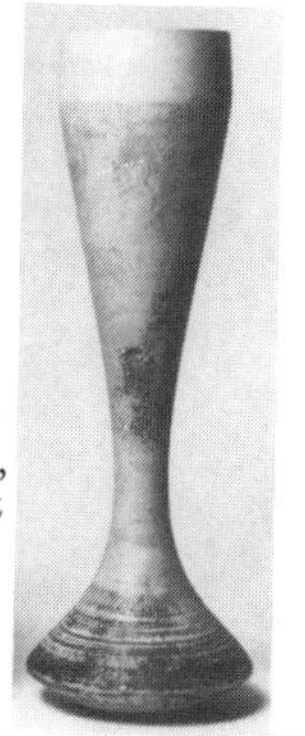

A stoneware vase, by Hans Coper, the manganese brown body covered in a buff slip with burnished areas to body and foot revealing brown body, the foot with ochre blistering, slight rim restoration, impressed HC seal, c1970, 16in (41cm).
£7,500-8,500 *C*

A stoneware beaker, by Lucie Rie and Hans Coper, the exterior covered in a pitted matt manganese glaze, the interior in a shiny white glaze, impressed LR and HC seals, c1958, 4in (10cm) high.
£300-350 *C*

A stoneware black bottle form, by Hans Coper, covered in a matt manganese glaze, impressed HC seal, c1970, 6in (15cm).
£5,500-6,500 *C*

A stoneware teapot, by Michael Cardew, with strap handle and grip, covered in a mushroom coloured glaze with iron brown and blue brushwork, impressed MC and Wenford Bridge Pottery seals, c1970, 9½in (23.5cm) high.
£650-750 *C*

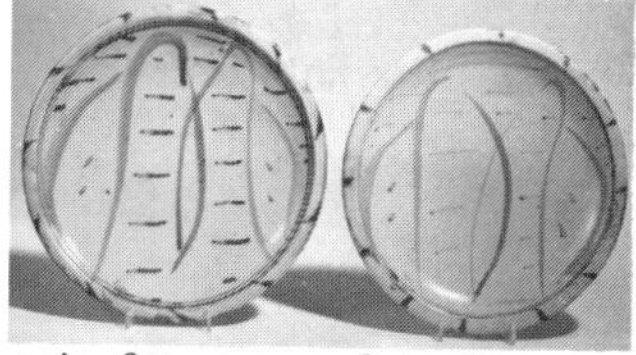

A pair of stoneware plates, by Michael Cardew, covered in a light mushroom coloured glaze with olive brown, and blue brushwork, impressed MC and Wenford Bridge seals, c1978, 10in (26cm) high.
£200-300 *C*

A stoneware sculpture of a cat, by Rosemary Wren, covered in a matt white, pale green and iron brown glaze, impressed Wren seal, 9½in (24.5cm) wide.
£100-120 *C*

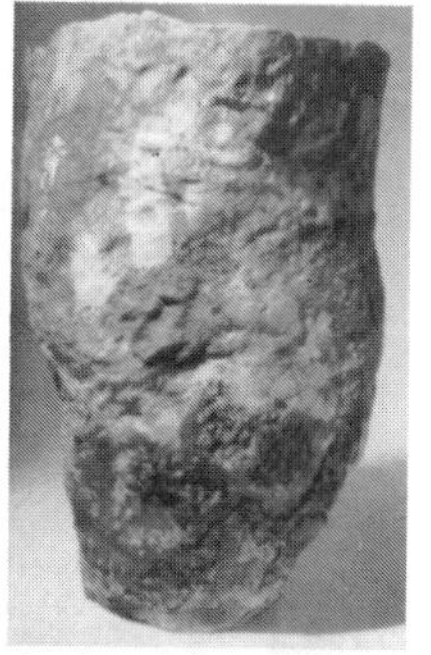

A stoneware asymmetrical vase, by Ewen Henderson, the hand built form laminated with pale lavender and brown clays covered in pitted and textured turquoise, white, amber and buff glazes, 22in (56cm) high.
£1,200-1,500 *C*

A stoneware baluster shaped vase by Janet Leach, covered in a mottled iron brown and mirrored black glaze over which run a pale lavender glaze stopping short of the foot, impressed JL and St. Ives seals, c1960, 12½in (31cm) high.
£200-250 *C*

An early slip decorated raku bowl, by Bernard Leach, covered in a translucent pitted and flecked pale beige glaze with cobalt blue band to outer rim, trailed with amber slip grape clusters, kiln damage, impressed BL and St. Ives seals, c1928, 9½in (24cm) wide.
£500-600 *C*

A stoneware jar, by John Leach, decorated in wax resist, with speckled greenish white dolomite glaze, impressed JL seal and Muchelney, 12in (30.5cm).
£250-350 *C*

A thickly potted stoneware vase, by William Staite Murray, covered in a finely crackled semi-translucent mushroom coloured glaze with iron brown and grey brushwork of stylised foliage, impressed M seal, 8in (20.5cm) high.
£500-600 *C*

A large slab-built porcelain vase, by Ljerka Njers, textured and decorated with muslin lace and leaves glazed in shades of green, amber, blue and white, with stylised flowers and foliage, painted monogram LN, 11½in (29cm) high.
£250-350 *C*

A stoneware pebble, by Eileen Lowenstein, covered in a run pale olive green glaze decorated with finely crackled translucent lime green flowerhead, impressed EL, 8in (20cm) high.
£100-150 *C*

A grey earthenware bowl, by Birch, the interior covered in a finely crackled translucent pale blue glaze, 10½in (26.5cm) wide.
£120-200 *C*

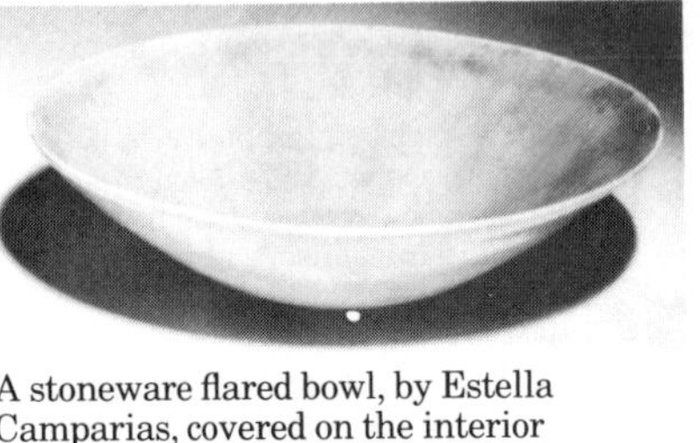

A stoneware flared bowl, by Estella Camparias, covered on the interior with a streaked lavender, purple, and turquoise glaze, the exterior with a run turquoise glaze, impressed E seal, 10in (25.5cm) diam.
£200-250 *C*

A brown stoneware torso, by Roger Perkins, the sculpted figure on triangular section stone base, 29½in (74cm) high.
£200-250 *C*

A porcelain bowl, by Henry Hammond, painted with bands of fishes, covered in a finely crackled translucent celadon glaze, impressed seal, 2½in (6cm) high.
£200-250 *C*

A stoneware plate, by Seth Cardew, decorated in iron brown and blue brushwork against a pale mushroom ground, impressed SC and Wenford Bridge seals, 14in (35.5cm) diam.
£150-200 *C*

An early St. Ives slip decorated eathenware jug, with strap handle, covered in a lustrous pale brown glaze and decorated with mustard yellow, slip flaking, impressed St. Ives and obscured square seals, 9in (23cm).
£50-100 *C*

A stoneware pouring vessel by Walter Keeler, covered in a mottled blue grey salt glaze, 5½in (13.5cm) high.
£220-260 *C*

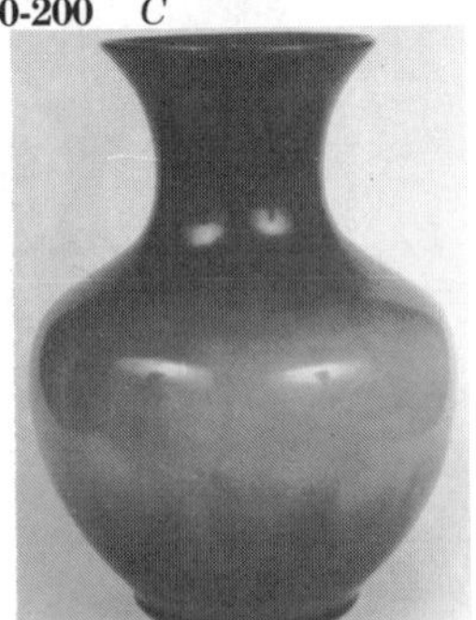

A pair of Studio pottery vases, slight damage to one, c1900, 9in (23cm) high.
£70-80 *TVA*

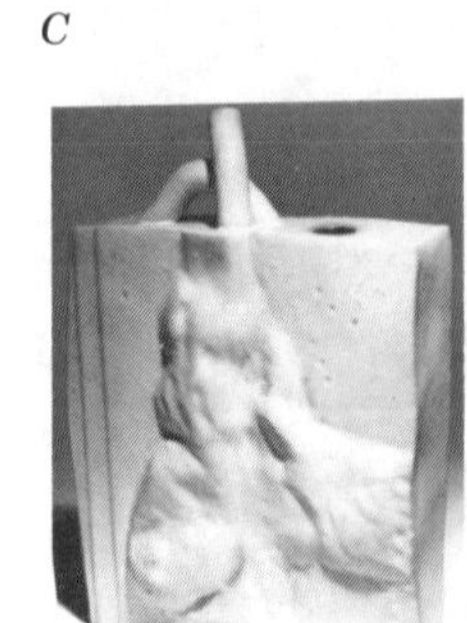

A stoneware sculpture, by Gordon Baldwin, covered in a white slip with pink tinges, impressed GB seal and painted title 'For Nic Barbow Box for a friend GB 74', 14in (35.5cm) high.
£250-300 *C*

A stoneware vase, by John Ward, covered in a matt white glaze over a speckled pale greenish brown glaze, slight restoration, impressed J W seal, 7½in (19cm) high.
£100-150 *C*

Tribal Art

A Baga head for an altar, Elek etc. with glossy dark patina, old damage, 17½in (44cm).
£400-600 *CSK*

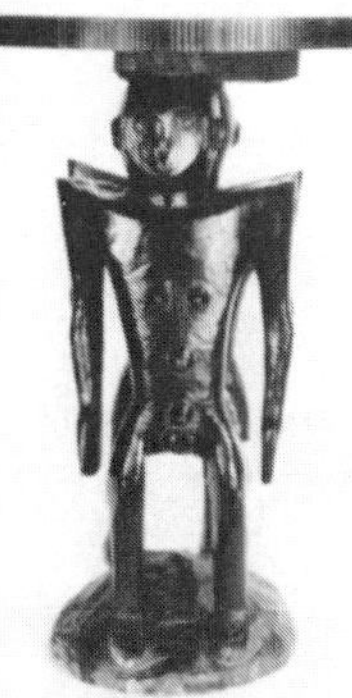

A Tiv wood table, the figures with scarification on their heart-shaped faces, dark glossy patina, replacement circular top, 27in (68cm) high.
£400-600 *CSK*

An Awka (Ibo) stool on curved supports, with dark glossy patina, 13½in (34cm) high.
£500-600 *CSK*

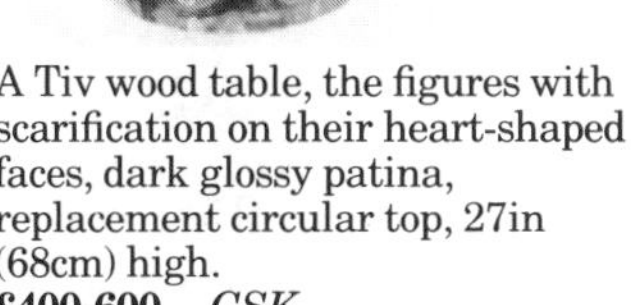

A Hawaiian wood spear, ihe laumake, of kauila wood, minor chips, 102in (260cm) long.
£2,000-3,000 *CSK*

A Trobriand Islands wood washboard, with a seated figure at the top, 29in (73cm) high.
£500-600 *CSK*

A Pokot wood headrest, on 3 legs flaring from central support, 6½in (16cm) high.
£100-200 *CSK*

A New Guinea wood pigment dish, with dark glossy patina with extensive remains of lime and pale mud, middle Sepik, 16in (40cm).
£7,000-10,000 *CSK*

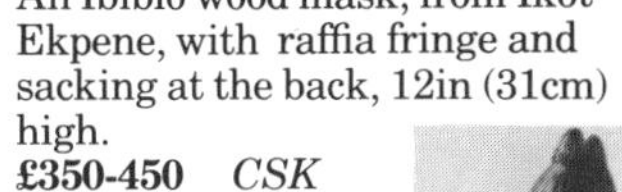

An Ibibio wood mask, from Ikot Ekpene, with raffia fringe and sacking at the back, 12in (31cm) high.
£350-450 *CSK*

A Mbete wood dance crest, minor damage, 23½in (60cm) high.
£1,500-2,000 *CSK*

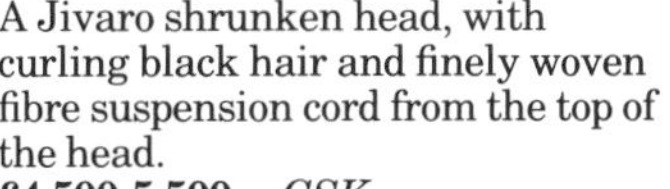

A Jivaro shrunken head, with curling black hair and finely woven fibre suspension cord from the top of the head.
£4,500-5,500 *CSK*

A female Ibeji, from Oro, near Ila-Orangun, 10½in (27cm) high.
£1,000-1,200 *CSK*

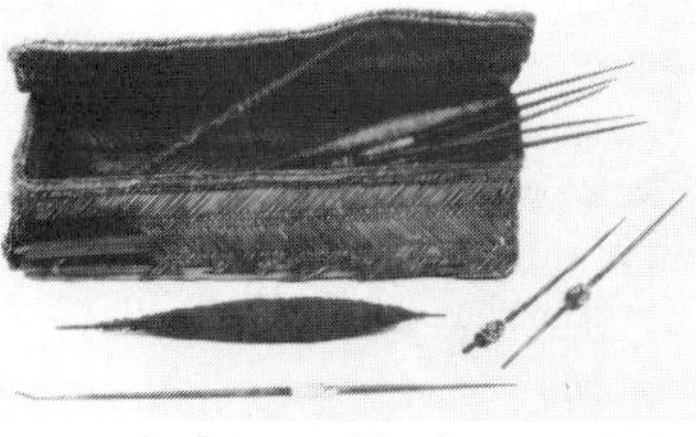

An Inca workbasket containing spinning instruments, 12in (30.5cm) wide.
£400-600 *P*

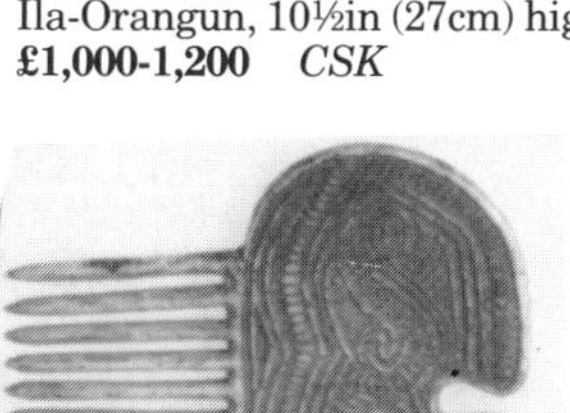

A Maori bone comb, 5in (12.5cm) high.
£150-200 *P*

A Congo ivory staff with rounded resin finial, 14in (35cm) high.
£100-150 *P*

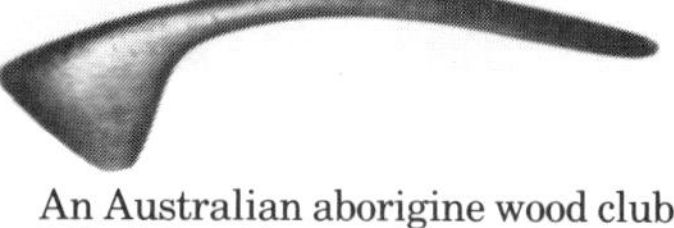

An Australian aborigine wood club, 21in (53cm) long, with another aborigine club from New South Wales and a Fiji ula with incised grip.
£400-600 *P*

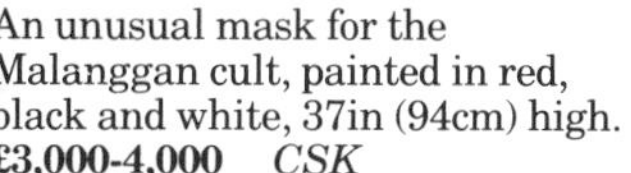

An unusual mask for the Malanggan cult, painted in red, black and white, 37in (94cm) high.
£3,000-4,000 *CSK*

A Zuni pottery jar, decorated in brown and red on a white ground, 10½in (27cm) high.
£1,500-2,000 *P*

A Fiji wood paddle club, incised with circles, triangles and diamonds, 46½in (118cm) long, together with a Sudanese hide shield.
£100-150 *P*

A Senufo bird, porpianong, with square wings, painted with black and red dots on a white ground, 53in (135cm) high.
£1,200-1,500 *CSK*

A Bambara iron horseman, the right leg deficient, 8in (20cm) high.
£500-600 *CSK*

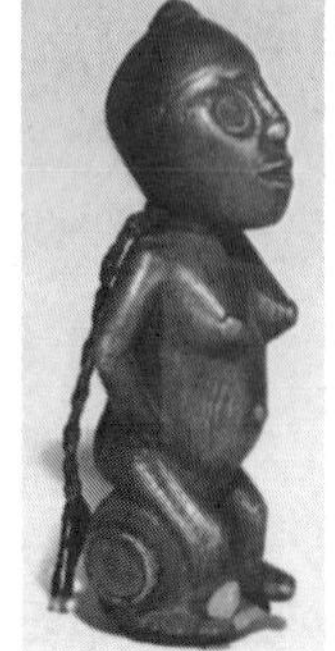

A Kongo female figure, one glass eye missing, one foot chipped, 3in (8cm) high.
£2,000-2,500 *CSK*

A Baule mask, with black patina, damaged, 15½in (39cm) high.
£1,200-1,500 *CSK*

A Baule mask, with finely carved face, reddish-brown patina, 11in (28cm) high.
£9,000-10,000 *CSK*

A small square box and cover, 3in (8cm), with another box and 2 covers, damaged.
£150-200 *DN*

l. A covered flask woven with multi-coloured bands with figures, 10½in (26cm).
£150-200

r. A covered flask, damaged, 5½in (14cm), and another flask woven with geometrical bands, 7in (18cm).
£50-100 *DN*

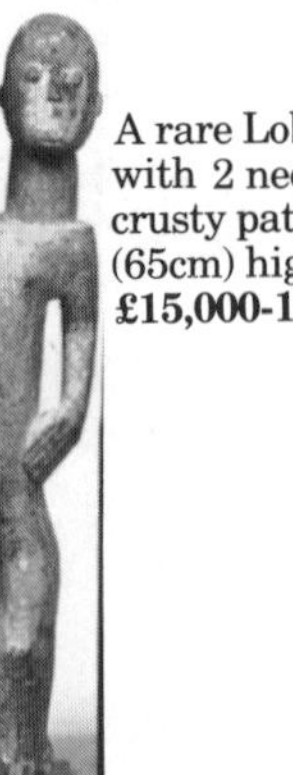

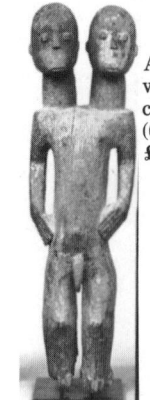

A rare Lobi figure carved with 2 necks side by side, crusty patina, 26in (65cm) high.
£15,000-17,000 *CSK*

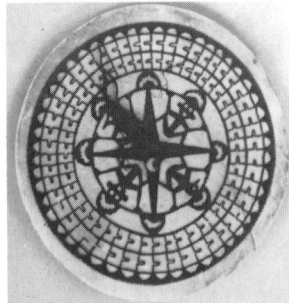

A Solomon Islands shell ornament, with 4 figures within bands of geometric motifs, 4½in (11cm) wide.
£600-700 *CSK*

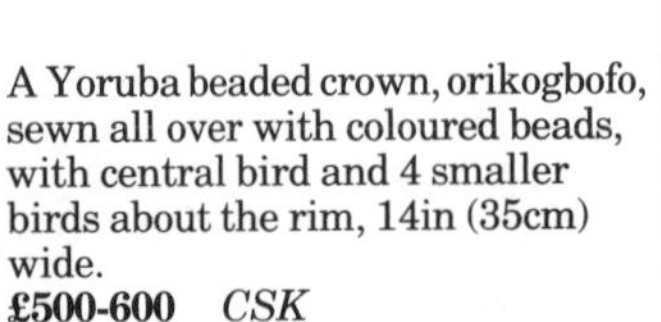

A Yoruba beaded crown, orikogbofo, sewn all over with coloured beads, with central bird and 4 smaller birds about the rim, 14in (35cm) wide.
£500-600 *CSK*

Make the most of Miller's

Miller's is completely different each year. Each edition contains completely NEW photographs. This is not an updated publication. We never repeat the same photograph.

Ephemera

Cigarette Cards

B.A.T, Indian Chiefs, a set of 50.
£60-80 *P*

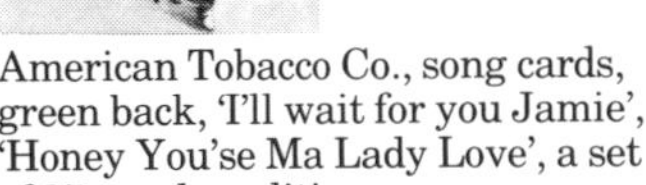

American Tobacco Co., song cards, green back, 'I'll wait for you Jamie', 'Honey You'se Ma Lady Love', a set of 25, good condition.
£60-80 *P*

Wills, Builders of the Empire, a set of 50.
£90-120 *P*

F & J Smith, Cricketers, a set of 50, one slightly rubbed.
£550-650 *P*

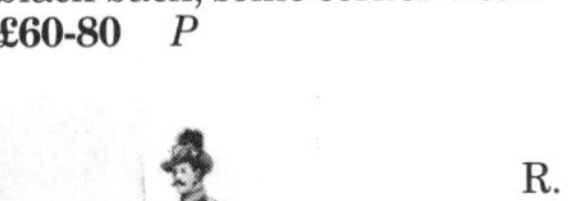

T. P. & R. Goodbody, 2 cards with black back, some corner wear.
£60-80 *P*

R. J. Lea, Modern Miniatures, a set of 50, including the rare numbers 1, 8, 12, 32, No. 1 creased.
£200-250 *P**

J. Clot & Cie, trade cards, a slot-in album containing 150 cards, captions in German.
£50-100 *P*

T. Brankston & Co., Colonial Troops, 10 cards, slight corner marks.
£150-200 *P*

Godfrey Phillips, Types of British Soldiers, 12 cards.
£75-100 *P*

Hill, Battleships and Crests, a set of 25.
£200-250 *P*

A. I. Jones, Nautical Terms, a set of 12.
£250-300 *P*

Edwards, Ringer & Bigg, Calendar for 1905, Exmoor Hunt back.
£80-100 *P*

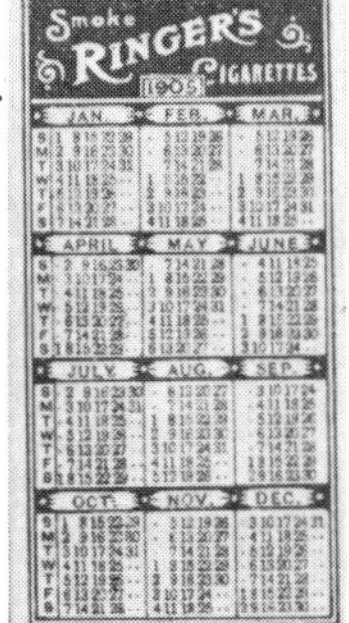

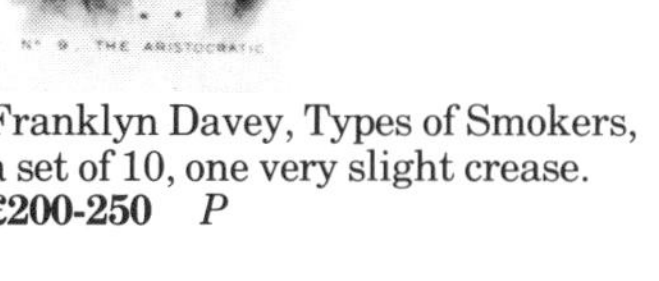

Franklyn Davey, Types of Smokers, a set of 10, one very slight crease.
£200-250 *P*

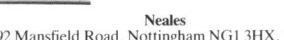

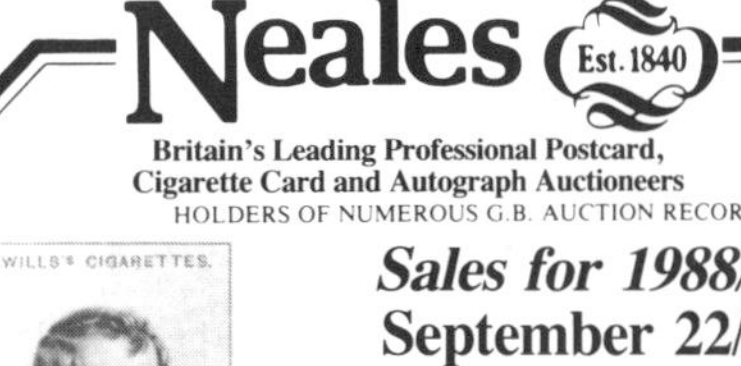

John Sinclair, World's Coinage, a set of 50.
£250-300 *P*

National Cigarette and Tobacco Company, National Types, sailor girls, a set of 25.
£180-200 *P*

American Tobacco Co., Beauties, 'Star Girls', black typeset back, a set of 24 plus one other.
£70-100 *P*

Wills, unissued series, The Life of H.M. King Edward VIII, a set of 50, minor edge staining.
£250-300 *P*

Postcards

A woven silk postcard, R.M.S. Titanic, unused.
£220-250 *ONS*

A photographic postcard of Colonel W. F. Cody mounted on his horse, inscribed by subject 'Buffalo Bill'.
£350-400 *CSK*

A head and shoulders portrait postcard of Montgomery Clift, inscribed.
£80-100 *CSK*

A Valentine mobile, addressed to 'Miss Josephine J. Morrison, 201 West 55 St., New York City, repaired, c1903, 21in (53.5cm) high.
£350-400 *CSK*

A collection of 180 Valentines and greetings cards, contained in 2 albums, c1900.
£350-400 *CSK*

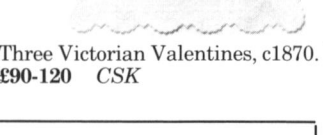

Three Victorian Valentines, c1870.
£90-120 *CSK*

A collection of German Victorian and Edwardian Valentines.
£25-30 *CSK*

Victorian Valentines, embossed, in pierced and gilded paper lace, now pasted on loose sheets.
£30-50 *CSK*

Miller's is a price Guide not a price List

The price ranges given reflect the average price a purchaser should pay for similar items. Condition, rarity of design or pattern, size, colour, pedigree, restoration and many other factors must be taken into account when assessing values.

Posters

John Hassall-Little Tich in Lord Tom Noddy at the Garrick Theatre, lithograph in colours, printed by David Allen & Sons, 30 by 20in (76 by 51cm), and 3 others.
£300-350 *CSK*

H.M. Queen Alexandra, a cabinet card portrait study, 1899, with another.
£260-300 *CSK*

G. C. R. England's Greatest Poet, Shortest and Quickest Route to Stratford on Avon, double royal, on linen.
£180-220 *ONS*

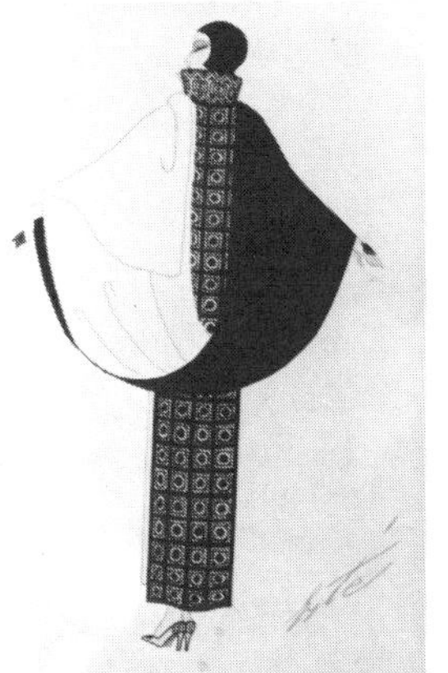

Erte, a watercolour and gouache costume drawing, signed, framed and glazed, 14 by 10½in (35.5 by 27cm).
£550-650 *CH*

Austin Cooper, Take Your Car by L.N.E.R. and Save Road Fatigue.
£120-150 *ONS*

Nestle's Milk advert, 2 cats on wall.
£16-20 *N*

Sainsbury's Cocoa, Negro Boy advert, slight scruffing.
£12-15 *N*

Frank H. Mason, Havens and Harbours on the L.N.E.R., Lowestoft.
£60-75 *ONS*

E. Hamilton, Ellerman's City Line To and From India.
£180-220 *ONS*

John Hassall, Skegness Is So Bracing, by L.N.E.R.
£550-650 *ONS*

Fred Taylor, Why Not Visit London For A Few Days, by L.N.E.R.
£650-700 *ONS*

Tom Purvis, East Coast by L.N.E.R.
£1,500-2,000 *ONS*

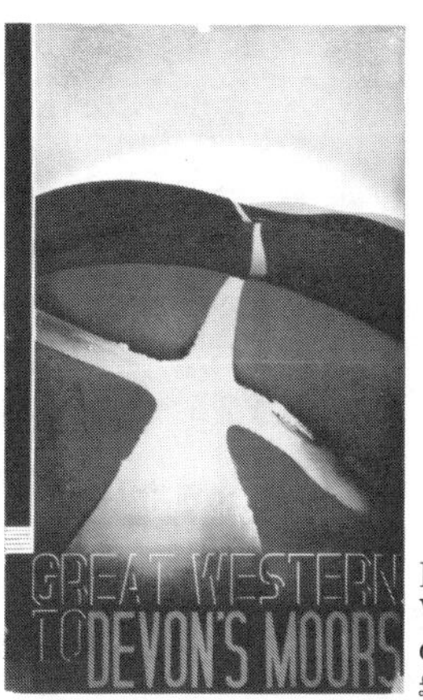

E. McKnight Kauffer, Great Western To Devon's Moors, No. 12, dated 1932.
£650-700 *ONS*

Septimus E. Scott, To Edinburgh By Pullman, by L.N.E.R.
£500-550 *ONS*

G. H. Davis, Holland America Line, Southampton to New York, and United States Lines, damage.
£350-400 *ONS*

Peek Frean & Co., a coloured lithograph, 40½ by 24½in (102 by 62cm), in wooden frame.
£250-300 *CSK*

A. R. Thomson, Take Me By The Flying Scotsman, by L.N.E.R.
£600-700 *ONS*

Weber, Winter Sports Expresses, by Southern Railway, double royal, 1934.
£120-150 *ONS*

Tom Purvis, Yorkshire Moors, L.N.E.R., quad. royal.
£400-500 *ONS*

T. D. Kerr, Golfing In Southern England And On The Continent, Southern Railway, double royal, 1932.
£250-300 *ONS*

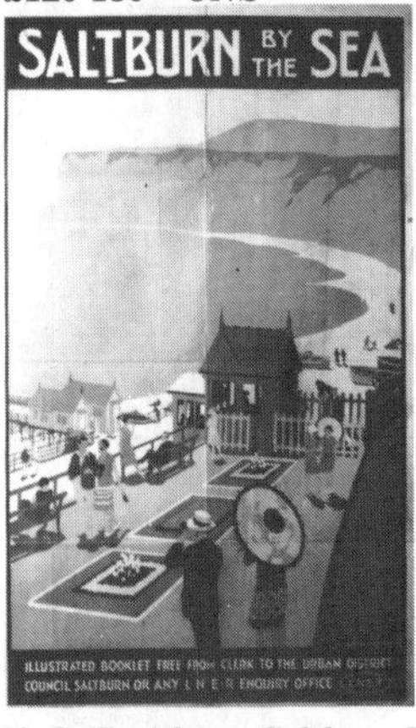

H. G. Gawthorn, Saltburn By The Sea, L.N.E.R., double royal.
£350-450 *ONS*

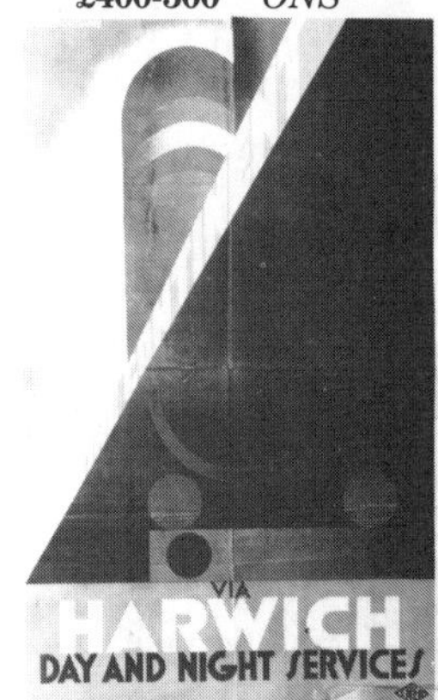

Adolphe Mouron Cassandre, The Continent via Harwich, double royal.
£800-1,000 *ONS*

Severin, The Devon Belle, by Southern Railway, 1947.
£360-400 *ONS*

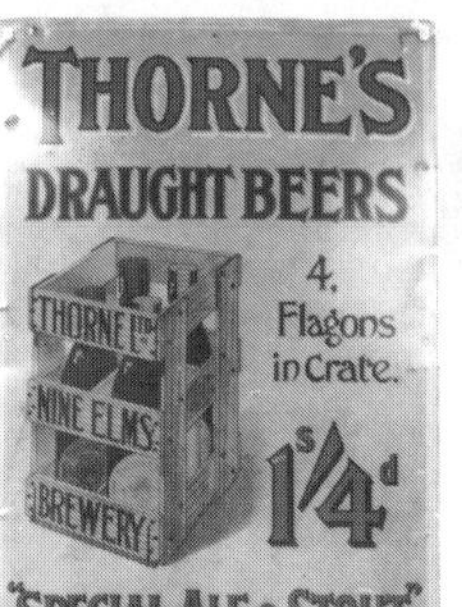

Thorne's Draught Beers, 19in (48cm) high.
£60-70 *AL*

A Bovril mirror, 8in (20.5cm) diam.
£25-30 *AL*

An enamel sign, c1950, 22 by 16in (56 by 40.5cm).
£75-100 *COB*

Suffragette banner, in cream cotton edged with purple satin, and press cuttings.
£180-220 *CSK*

An advertising poster, 1860, 23 by 18in (58 by 45.5cm).
£40-50 *COB*

Norman Hartnell, a design for H.M. Queen Elizabeth II Coronation dress, signed, dated December 18, 1952.
£250-300 *CSK*

W. & D. Downey, an official portrait study of the future King Edward VIII's Christening group, inscribed by subjects on image, 'Victoria R. I. & little Edward Albert, July 6, 1894' 'Albert Edward' and 'George', 11½ by 7in (29 by 18cm).
£2,000-2,500 *CSK*

Dorothy Wilding, a pair of portrait photographs of George VI and Queen Elizabeth, in silver Cartier frames, with silver gilt crowns, signed on mounts 'Elizabeth R' and 'George R 1947', in original fitted cases, 10½ by 14in (26 by 35cm).
£3,500-4,000 *P*

A full length portrait photograph, H.M. Queen Elizabeth and H.R.H. Prince Philip, mounted on card, inscribed 'Elizabeth R' and 'Philip, 1957', 9½ by 7in (24 by 18cm), framed and glazed.
£450-500 *CSK*

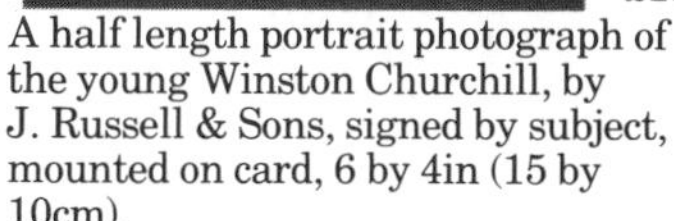

A half length portrait photograph of the young Winston Churchill, by J. Russell & Sons, signed by subject, mounted on card, 6 by 4in (15 by 10cm).
£800-1,000 *CSK*

Photographs

Sir Winston Churchill, a half-length portrait study, mounted on card, 5 by 4½in (12.5 by 11cm), with a typescript note, A Souvenir of 10 Downing Street, 1940-45.
£500-600 *CSK*

W. & D. Downey, a half-length portrait photograph of H.R.H. Edward, Prince of Wales, inscribed 'Edward Christmas 1910', 5½ by 4in (14 by 10cm), framed and glazed.
£80-100 *CSK*

Disneyalia

Walt Disney Productions, 'Nana', from Peter Pan, initialled.
£110-150 *CSK*

Walt Disney Productions, 'Captain Hook' from Peter Pan, watercolour, pen and ink, heightened in white, initialled, c1953.
£150-200 *CSK*

Walt Disney Productions, 'Peter Pan', watercolour, pen and ink, heightened in white, initialled, c1953.
£150-200 *CSK*

Walt Disney Productions, 'Tinkerbell', from Peter Pan, c1953.
£110-130 *CSK*

A wooden Mickey Mouse from a fairground, c1930, 30 by 27in (76 by 68.5cm).
£75-100 *COB*

A battery operated plastic clock, c1960, 12in (30.5cm) square.
£30-45 *COB*

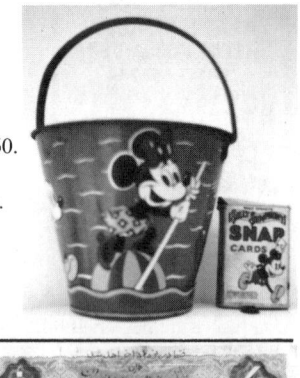

A tin bucket, c1950.
£25-35

Snap cards, c1930.
£10-15 *COB*

Scripophily

Banque de Syrie et du Liban, Lebanon, 100 Livres, Specimen, 1945, uncirculated.
£450-500 *C*

Trinidad and Tobago, Royal Bank of Canada, 5 Dollars, Jan 2, 1909.
£30-50 *C*

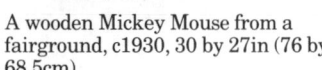

Banque de Syrie et du Grand-Liban, 1 Livre, unadopted, slight staining left side, 1925.
£250-300 *C*

South Africa, Zuid Afrikaansche Republiek, £1, arms at centre, green, pin hole, 25.1.1872.
£20-50 *C*

Imperial Bank of Persia, 100 Tomans, outline seal, payable at Yezd only, handwritten signatures, 18 Jun 1913.
£2,000-2,500 *C*

Russian State Credit Note, 100 Roubles, portrait of Catherine II on reverse, right corner torn, 1892.
£70-100 *C*

Film & Theatre

Laurence Olivier and Vivien Leigh, a signed head and shoulders portrait of Vivien Leigh and a film still signed by Laurence Olivier.
£100-150 *CSK*

Stan Laurel and Oliver Hardy, a half length publicity photograph, and an autographed postcard.
£300-350 *CSK*

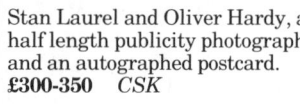

Charlie Chaplin, a head and shoulders profile publicity photograph, inscribed, 10 by 8in (25.5 by 20.5cm), re-issue of a c1920 photograph, and a half length photograph of Chaplin, c1920, 7 by 5in (18 by 12.5cm).
£180-220 *CSK*

Charlie Chaplin, a plaster advertising figure, 12in (30.5cm).
£450-500 *CSK*

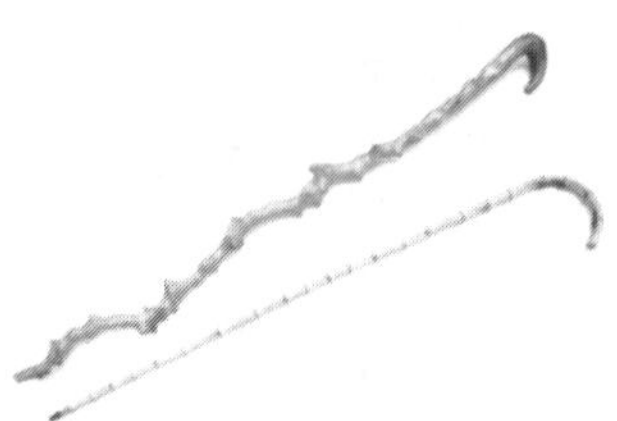

A bamboo cane with metal tip, allegedly used by Charlie Chaplin in City Lights, 1931, 36½in (92.5cm) long, with a crooked walking stick used by Harry Lauder.
£5,500-6,000 *CSK*

Charlie Chaplin, a china portrait bust with manufacturer's printed stamp on base, Flesh Pots, Stoke-on-Trent, England, 1978, 12in (30.5cm) high.
£60-80 *CSK*

Charlie Chaplin, a glazed china salt cellar, c1925, 4in (10cm), and a cruet, c1920, 5½in (14cm) high.
£75-100 *CSK*

Charlie Chaplin, a collection of 5 photographs, one by Witzel.
£60-100 *CSK*

I. Claudius, a theatrical copy of a Roman Soldier's brigandine, 1937.
£100-150 *CSK*

Marilyn Monroe, a skin-tight 'shimmy' black satin dress, worn in the film Some Like It Hot, 1959.
£18,000-20,000 *CSK*

Louis Armstrong, signed programme, 1959.
£100-120 *N*

Charlie Chaplin, two pressed tin confectionery moulds, 8in (20cm), and 2 complementary cast figures, c1920.
£100-120 *CSK*

Charlie Chaplin, a typescript letter, signed, dated April 11 1916, framed and glazed.
£220-250 *CSK*

Two hundred and fifty postcards and publicity stills, mostly signed by subjects, contained in one album and loose.
£300-350 *CSK*

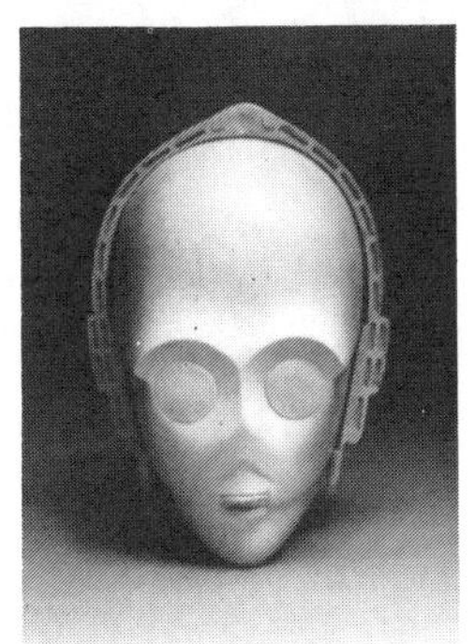

Star Wars, the original fibreglass mould used to make the robotic head of C.3.P.O., 1977.
£220-250 *CSK*

Charlie Chaplin, Motion Picture Employee Identification Card No. 42655, issued 6.11.42.
£4,000-4,500 *CSK*

Mary Pickford and Douglas Fairbanks, a full length seated portrait photograph by Abbe, signed, dated July 14th 1924, 14 by 10½in (35.5 by 26cm), framed and glazed.
£200-250 *CSK*

Douglas Fairbanks, Snr., a pair of imitation steins, and one other, in hand painted moulded plaster, 1954.
£75-100 *CSK*

Bing Crosby, an imitation printed silk dressing gown, worn by Bing Crosby whilst making the film We're Not Dressing, 1934.
£250-300 *CSK*

A programme for the opening of Going My Way, signed, creased.
£80-100 *N*

Katharine Hepburn, signed photograph, 8 by 10in (20.5 by 25.5cm).
£170-200 *N*

Bette Davis, signed, 8 by 10in (20.5 by 25.5cm).
£50-75 *N*

Rudolph Valentino as the Sheik, scuffed, 14 by 16in (35.5 by 41cm).
£550-650 *N*

Miscellaneous

A white Bakelite plaque, c1945, 30 by 12in (76 by 30.5cm).
£50-75 *COB*

Four gold and silver watch chain fobs, one inscribed Lieut. H. G. Lowe, R.N.R. Titanic.
£2,000-2,500 *ONS*

A cast brass plate, inscribed Edinburgh Castle, 1948-1976, 8 by 14in (20 by 36cm), mounted on wood plaque.
£300-350 *ONS*

An iron ship rivet, inscribed R.M.S. Titanic 1912, 4.5cm diam.
£500-600 *ONS*

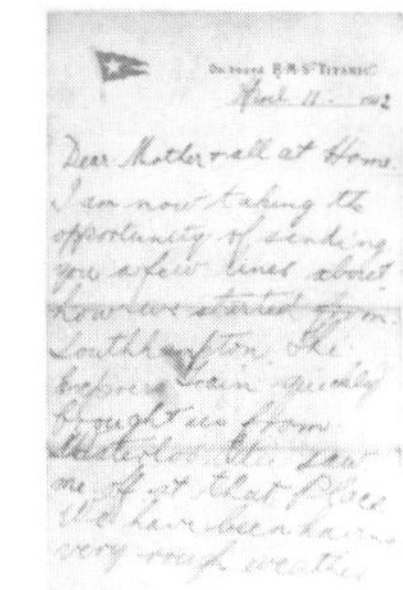

An autographed letter, 'On board R.M.S. Titanic', on official writing paper, signed by Thomas Mudd, April 11th, 1912.
£600-700 *ONS*

A bronze Carpathia medal, the reverse inscribed 'Presented to the Captain, Officers and crew of R.M.S. Carpathia, in recognition of gallant and heroic services from the survivors of the SS Titanic, April 15th, 1912', 1½in (4cm).
£800-900 *ONS*

A leather bound visitors book, used at Windsor Castle and St. James' Palace, 1909-1922.
£300-350 *P[Pea]*

A saddler's carved wood painted sign, in the form of a caricature of the jockey Fred Archer, 51in (130cm).
£850-1,000 *B*

ORIENTAL

Bamboo

A bamboo stick stand, c1870, 34in (86cm) high.
£100-120 *AL*

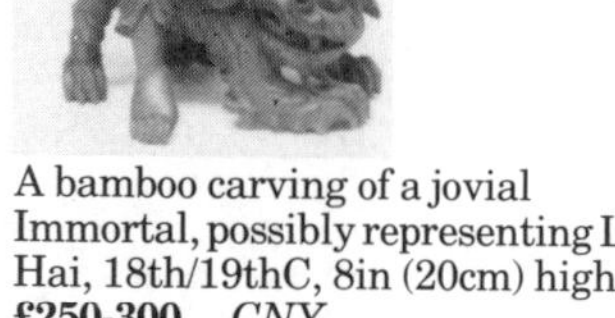

A bamboo carving of a jovial Immortal, possibly representing Liu Hai, 18th/19thC, 8in (20cm) high.
£250-300 *CNY*

A bamboo carving of a group of Buddhistic lions, damage, 18thC, 12½in (32cm) high.
£450-500 *CNY*

A bamboo magazine rack, c1870, 18½in (47cm) high.
£70-100 *AL*

A polychrome cloisonné enamel tripod censer and domed cover, slight damage, c1800, 20½in (52cm) high.
£3,500-4,000 *CNY*

Cloisonné & Enamel

An enamelled earthenware figure of a nio, restored foot, 19thC, 21½in (54cm) high.
£600-650 *CNY*

A cloisonné enamel incense burner, in the form of a caparisoned elephant, 6in (15cm) high, and a blue ground cloisonné enamel jar and cover, some damage, Qianlong, 10½in (27cm) high.
£400-600 *CNY*

A cloisonné enamel figure of a quail, feet damaged and repaired, Qianlong/Jiaqing, 5in (12.5cm) high.
£300-350 *CNY*

Furniture

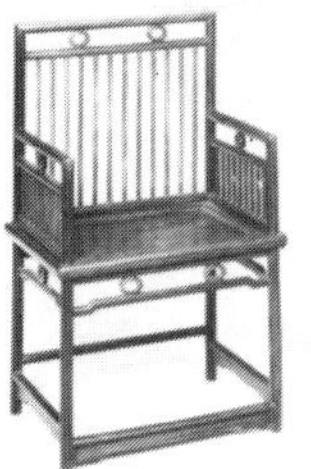

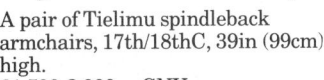

A pair of Tielimu spindleback armchairs, 17th/18thC, 39in (99cm) high.
£1,500-2,000 *CNY*

A pair of Hongmu spindleback armchairs, 18thC, 33in (84cm) high.
£2,500-3,000 *CNY*

A pair of Hongmu armchairs, the backs and sides carved with 'linghzi' clusters growing on contorted branches, some repair, 19thC, 39in (99cm) high.
£2,500-3,000 *CNY*

A pair of carved and gilt red lacquer armchairs, slight damage, 40in (101cm) high.
£400-450 *CNY*

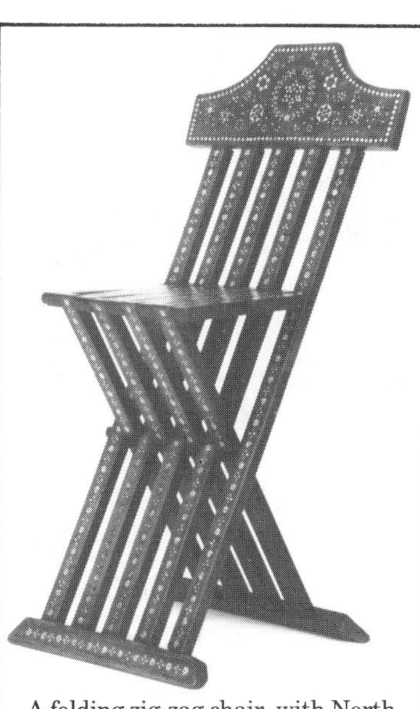

A folding zig-zag chair, with North Italian penwork, 19thC.
£400-450 *DLL*

A Chinese export hardwood pedestal table, inlaid with marquetry and bone, late 19thC, 54in (137cm).
£900-1,200 *CSK*

A Hongmu deck armchair, 19thC.
£500-550 *CNY*

A mother-of-pearl inlaid stepped low table, the superstructure fitted with a single drawer, with pierced apron below, some damage, late Ming, 40in (102cm) wide.
£2,000-2,500 *CNY*

A gilt and black lacquer miniature cabinet, chips, sealmark under lid, Meiji period, 14in (35.5cm) high.
£800-1,000 *CNY*

A Turkish table in ebony, sandalwood and mother-of-pearl, 19thC, 20in (51cm) high.
£450-550 *DLL*

Miller's is a price Guide not a price List

The price ranges given reflect the average price a purchaser should pay for similar items. Condition, rarity of design or pattern, size, colour, pedigree, restoration and many other factors must be taken into account when assessing values.

A Japanese hardwood shodana, decorated with shibayama panels depicting birds, flowers and parcel gilt, 53in (134.5cm).
£3,000-3,500 *CSK*

A Canton gilt and black lacquer sewing table, the hinged cover opening to reveal a fitted interior with pierced ivory accessories, including bobbins and pin boxes, slight wear, mid-19thC, 28in (71cm high.
£1,500-2,000 *CNY*

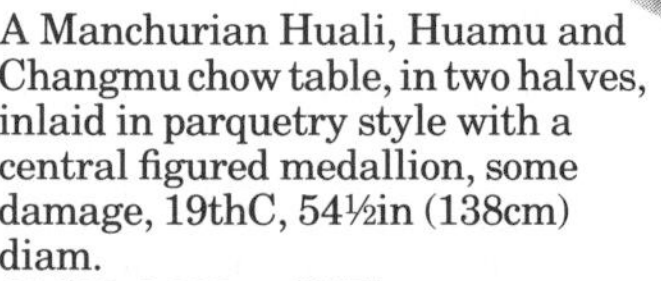

A Manchurian Huali, Huamu and Changmu chow table, in two halves, inlaid in parquetry style with a central figured medallion, some damage, 19thC, 54½in (138cm) diam.
£1,500-2,000 *CNY*

An Islamic Syrian table, inlaid with silver, mother-of-pearl and ivory, with Mashrabiya panels and geometric top, 19thC, 28in (71cm) high.
£850-1,000 *DLL*

A Chinese black and gold lacquer coffer, the sides with brass carrying handles, basically mid-18thC, 54in (137cm) wide.
£3,500-4,000 *CNY*

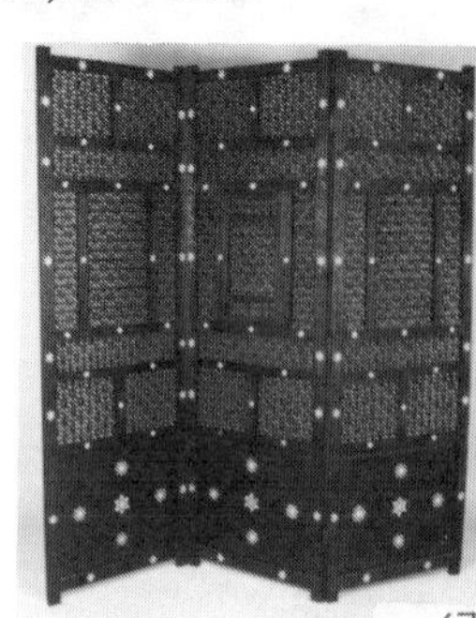

A Victorian Damascan folding screen, with Mashrabiya turnings, 80in (203cm) high.
£500-700 *DLL*

A pair of Japanese lacquer cabinets on stands, each with an arrangement of drawers, hinged compartment and doors, decorated with birds and poultry in landscapes, metal mounts, 19in (48.5cm) wide.
£850-1,000 *P[PWC]*

A Chinese padouk altar table, 48in (122cm) wide.
£1,000-1,500 *N*

Glass

Chinese rock crystal koro and over, early 19thC.
450-500 *SW*

Horn

A pair of horn vases, with plated mounts and stands.
£300-400 *PC*

A rhinoceros horn libation cup, some damage, 18thC, 7in (17.5cm) wide, on fitted wood stand.
£2,500-3,000 *C*

A rhinoceros horn libation cup, carved on one side at the foot with 4 figures on a small punt, 17thC, 6½in (16cm) wide, with wood stand carved as a lotus cluster.
£4,000-4,500 *C*

Ivory

A Chinese carved ivory figure of a sage with red, blue and gilt decoration, on shaped base, 19thC, 9½in (24cm) high.
£360-400 *BWe*

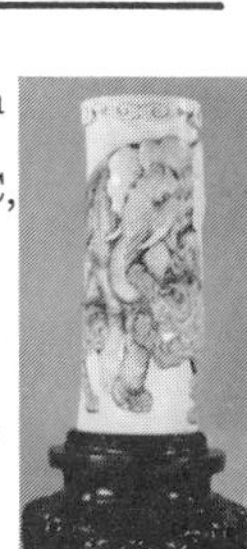

A Japanese carved ivory tusk vase, finely detailed and shaded with elephant attacked by tigers, on carved hardwood stand, Meiji period, 28½in (72cm) high.
£1,000-1,500 *N*

n ivory okimono of a girl standing, ressed in a kimono, holding a unch of millet in one hand, signed Iideyuki on a red tablet, 8½in 21.5cm) high.
600-700 *AAn*

Jade

A mother-of-pearl inlaid and jade set hardwood sceptre, of 3 variously sized celadon jade plaques, carved with Immortals, repaired, 22in (56cm) long.
£500-600 *CNY*

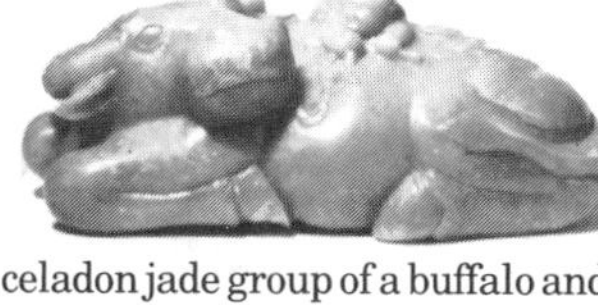

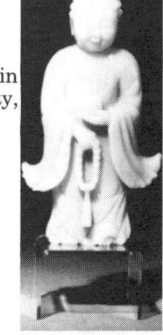

A celadon jade group of a buffalo and boy, 14in (35.5cm) wide.
£2,000-2,500 *C*

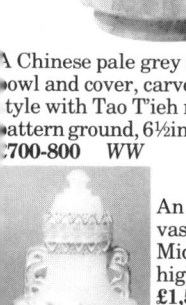

Chinese pale grey speckled jade owl and cover, carved in archaic tyle with Tao T'ieh masks on a key attern ground, 6½in (16.5cm) wide.
700-800 *WW*

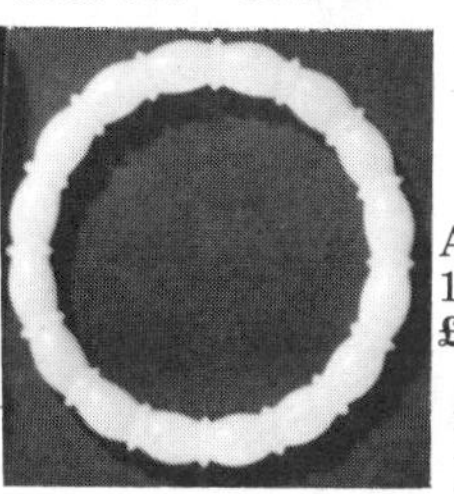

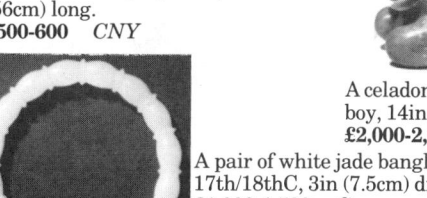

A pair of white jade bangles, 17th/18thC, 3in (7.5cm) diam.
£1,000-1,500 *C*

A creamy celadon jade standing Buddhist figure, carved from a thin section of stone, late Qing Dynasty, 8in (20cm) high, wood stand.
£1,200-1,500 *C*

An embellished pale celadon jade vase and cover, some hardstone loss, Mid Qing Dynasty, 5in (12.5cm) high.
£1,500-2,000 *C*

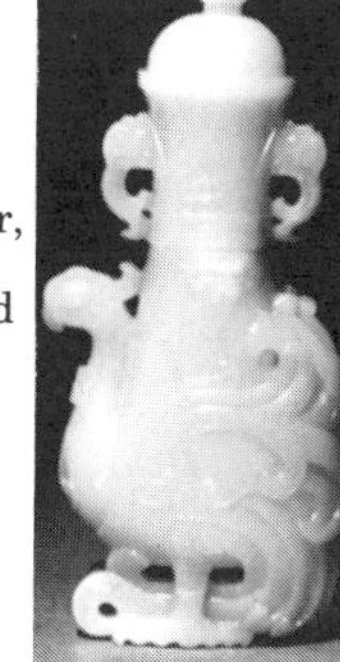

A pale celadon jade vase and cover, with animal mask loose ring handles, 7½in (19.5cm) high, wood stand.
£4,500-5,000 *C*

A Mughal celadon jade box and cover in the form of a leaf, the finial with a gilt and red glass inset agate top, interior chips, early 19thC, 4in (9.5cm) high.
£1,500-2,000 *C*

A green and russet jade carving of a phoenix, seated with its head on its back and holding a lotus spray in its beak, 19thC, 9in (23cm) wide.
£1,400-1,800 *C*

Lacquer

A black and gilt lacquered tea chest and hinged cover, cover repaired, 19thC, 13in (33cm) wide.
£1,300-1,600 *CNY*

Two Ming style gilt lacquer figures of seated dignitaries, each enthroned on red lacquered horseshoe-backed chairs, the top rails terminating in gold dragons' heads, their detachable heads with official hats, one figure holding a gold ingot in his right hand, also detachable, minor damage, 36in (91.5cm) high.
£5,000-6,000 *CNY*

A gilt and dry lacquer figure of a martial official, his crimson lined robes in dark red, some gilt, some flaking, Ming Dynasty, 39½in (101cm) high.
£4,000-4,500 *CNY*

A pair of Indian silver anklets, Kutch Valley dowry pieces.
£800-1,000 *TA*

Metal

A gold and silver inlaid bronze wheel fitting, Warring States, 4½in (11cm) long.
£2,000-2,500 *C*

A Ming bronze arrow vase, some damage, possibly 16thC, 20½in (52.5cm) high.
£2,000-2,500 *C*

A bronze figure of Buddha on a tortoise base, in 3 sections, mandorla missing, late Ming, 18½in (47cm) high.
£1,500-2,000 *CNY*

A Sino-Tibetan gilt bronze figure of a monk, 17th/18thC, 6½in (16.5cm) high.
£500-600 *CNY*

A Japanese bronze ornamental incense burner, cast as a caparisoned trumpeting elephant, minor damage, incised 2-character mark on an applied plaque inscribed 'Shomin', late 19thC, 24½in (62cm) high.
£1,200-1,500 *CNY*

A bronze model of a trumpeting elephant, 32in (81cm) long.
£600-800 *CNY*

A bronze TLV mirror, cast with a central pierced boss within a square panel with small knops, Han Dynasty, 5½in (14cm) diam, fitted box.
£1,300-1,500 *C*

A bronze mount, probably a sword chape, Zhou Dynasty/Warring States, 3½in (8.5cm) long, fitted box.
£1,000-1,200 *C*

A group of gilt bronze ornaments, Tang Dynasty, 1 to 2in (2.5 to 5cm) wide.
£1,000-1,500 *C*

A bronze tripod cauldron, ding, cast with a band of 3 panels of zoomorphic motifs amongst leiwen, some encrustation, late Shang/early Western Zhou Dynasty, 6in (15cm) high.
£800-1,000 *C*

A gilt bronze figure of a recumbent unicorn, areas of gilt rubbed, 17thC, 10½in (27cm) long.
£2,000-2,500 *C*

A carved ivory netsuke, rat, signed.
£120-150 *PC*

Tsuba

A bronze alloy Tsuba, Japanese sword guard, adorned with crane standing under a pine tree.
£75-100 *RW*

Miscellaneous

A coral carving of 2 female Immortals, on the back of a phoenix, some repair, 6in (15cm) high, fixed wood stand.
£300-400 *CNY*

Netsuke

A carved ivory netsuke, man with kiln, 4.5cm.
£50-80 *PC*

A carved ivory netsuke, figure of a monkey, signed.
£80-100 *PC*

Wood

A rustic style two-handled censer, minor repairs, 9in (23cm) wide.
£450-550 *CNY*

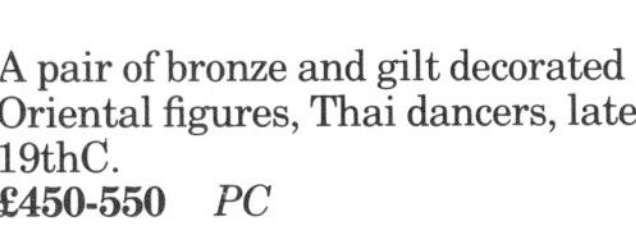

An Islamic tortoiseshell, mother-of-pearl and ivory box, 19thC, 16½in (42cm) wide.
£350-450 *DLL*

A carved ivory netsuke, figures on raft.
£20-30 *PC*

A lacquered wood netsuke, of a seated karashishi on a pierced brocade ball, 18th/19thC, 1½in (4cm).
£180-220 *CSK*

A hardwood carving of Liu Hai, the jovial Immortal standing with his left leg resting on the back of his three-legged toad, base cracks, 19thC, 15in (38cm).
£300-400 *CNY*

A pair of Chinese Lotus shoes, for bound feet, 19thC.
£60-180

Two Mandarin hat buttons, worn on the top of hats to represent rank by their colour, 19thC.
£30-80 *LW*

A pair of bronze and gilt decorated Oriental figures, Thai dancers, late 19thC.
£450-550 *PC*

A Japanese ebonised Aesthetic clock set, 18 to 10in (45.5 to 25.5cm) high.
£550-650 *AO*

RUSSIAN

Icons and Works of Art

An icon of the Resurrection surrounded by feasts, with brass basma, 19thC, 12½ by 10½in (31 by 27cm).
£600-650 *P*

The Annunciation, painted in subdued colours with architectural background, 18thC in 16thC style, 12 by 10in (30.5 by 25.5cm).
£1,200-1,600 *C*

Saint John the Baptist, with silver chased and repoussé halo and engraved basma on the borders, c1700, 12½ by 10½in (31.5 by 26.5cm).
£1,200-1,500 *C*

Mother of God of Vladimir, painted in sepia in the traditional manner, some restoration, 17thC, 11½ by 9in (29 by 23cm).
£1,000-1,500 *C*

An icon, the Image of the Saviour 'not made with hands', tooled gilt background in blue, white, purple, red and green to resemble enamel, 10½ by 8½in (26.5 by 21.5cm), ebonised frame.
£300-350 *P[PWC]*

The Pokrov, 19thC, 18 by 15in (46 by 38cm).
£1,200-1,500 *C*

Archangel Gabriel of the Deisis, painted in vivid colours on gold ground, Palekh School, c1800, 21 by 11in (53 by 28cm).
£2,000-2,400 *C*

Vladimirskaya Mother of God, realistically painted, with a silver gilt repoussé and engraved oklad, marked with unrecorded Cyrillic marks CG, 12 by 10½in (30.5 by 26.5cm).
£1,000-1,500 *C*

Four panels from a portable iconastas, each painted in 3 rows, with the Prophets, Festivals and Saints, 19thC, each panel 33 by 4in (84 by 10cm).
£1,300-1,600 *C*

Tolga Mother of God, painted on gold ground in shades of brown in a traditional manner, c1800, 25½ by 19in (64.5 by 48cm).
£1,500-2,000 *C*

Iverskaya Mother of God, realistically painted with silver gilt repoussé and chased oklad and applied shaded enamel haloes, marked with initials of Ivan Alexseev Alexeevich, Moscow, 1899-1908, 9 by 7in (23 by 18cm).
£1,000-1,500 *C*

The Resurrection and Descent into Hell, painted in the traditional manner, 19thC, 14 by 12½in (35.5 by 31.5cm).
£800-1,000 *C*

A wing of a Greek triptych with the Nativity painted on shaped panel, in vivid colours, restoration, c1600, 8½ by 5in (22 by 12.5cm).
£2,200-2,500 *C*

A Greek triptych, painted in vivid colours on gold ground, with silver repoussé haloes, probably Macedonian, c1700, 13 by 21in (33 by 54cm).
£2,600-3,000 *C*

Miscellaneous

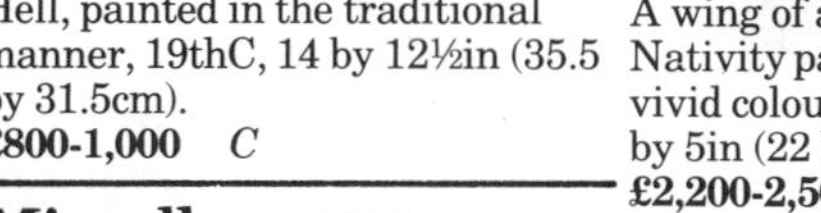

A set of 12 shaded enamel teaspoons, white metal, marked with initials of Constantin Skvortsov, Moscow, c1910.
£1,500-2,000 *C*

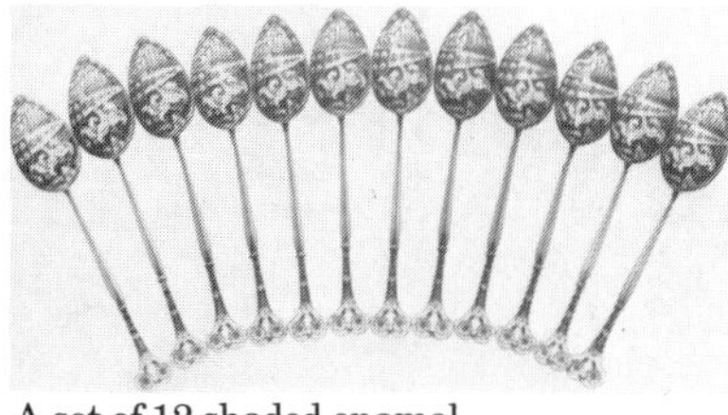

A parcel gilt silver kovsh, engraved in Cyrillic, the base with inscription 'given by Mamamie Countess of Pembroke to her daughter Countess of Clanwilliam' marked with unrecorded initials CC, Moscow, 1856, 7in (18cm), with matching sugar sifter, 337 grammes.
£1,400-1,700 *C*

A silver cake basket, engraved with initials AMS and dated 23 August 1896, with swing handle, marked Klebnikov, St. Petersburg, 1880, 10in (25.5cm), 111.5 grammes.
£750-850 *C*

An openwork enamel gold locket, opening to reveal 4 rotating photograph frames, with blue ground plaque with gold figure 'XXV', with initials FW, St. Petersburg, c1870, 1½in (3.5cm).
£600-800 *C*

A five-piece tea service, with knop finials, minor dents, white metal, marked A. Hempel and unknown maker's marks PJS, St. Petersburg, c1900, tray 22in (56cm) long, 4,950 grammes.
£2,000-2,500 *C*

A porcelain Easter egg, the white ground with gold panels enclosing blue blossoms, 19thC, 3½in (9cm) high.
£800-900 *C*

A Russian parcel gilt sugar basket and cream jug, in raised coloured enamels, stamped 88, 11 MA, late 19thC.
£1,500-2,000 *P[Pea]*

An enamel military cigarette case, the cover with opaque white enamel order of Saint George suspended from an enamelled black and orange ribbon, with cabochon sapphire, marked with unrecorded Cyrillic initials AF, St. Petersburg, c1912, in a red leather case stamped 'Annerl, 3 December, 1898 Weihnachten 1915', 4in (10cm), 140 grammes gross.
£2,000-2,500 *C*

A large silver mounted cut glass kovsh, applied with 4 cabochon semi-precious stones, some damage, marked Khlebnikov with Imperial Warrant, Moscow, c1890, 18in (45.5cm) long, 619 grammes gross.
£3,000-3,500 *C*

A porcelain kovsh, with gilt and green border, by Kornilov Factory, St. Petersburg, 19thC, 8½in (21cm) wide.
£500-600 *C*

A crystal vase, with white metal rim and base, by the 15th Artel, Moscow, c1910, 15in (38cm).
£1,000-1,300 *C*

A porcelain sauce boat and stand, from the service of the Grand Duke Alexander Alexandrovitch, with the Imperial cypher of the Grand Duke, within large gold ring, by the Imperial Porcelain Factory, period of Alexander II and Alexander III.
£500-600 *C*

A porcelain Easter egg, painted on blue ground, late 19thC, 4in (10cm) high.
£650-750 *C*

A Russian pastille burner, probably Gardner, some restoration, c1820.
£500-600 *BHA*

A porcelain figure of a young girl, by the Popov Factory, with underglaze blue impressed mark and impressed Cyrillic K, c1845, 5in (12.5cm) high.
£900-1,000 *C*

A bronze group of a father and son seated on a sleigh, both dressed in fur-trimmed overcoats and hats, mounted on a malachite base, 19thC, 7½in (19cm).
£1,000-1,200 *C*

A malachite and ormolu clock, with enamel chaptered cast ormolu dial, c1850, 4½in (11.5cm) wide.
£1,200-1,500 *C*

A quartz desk seal, designed as a seated brown bear holding a clear bottle, realistically carved, 19thC, 3½in (9cm) high.
£700-900 *C*

A carved oak chair, each arm rest formed as an axe, the front legs and back formed as a yoke duga with carved Russian adage, a pair of gloves resting on the back of the seat, the third foot formed as a branch, the back leg bifurcated, attributed to V. P. Shutov.
£1,200-1,800 *C*

A papier mâché lacquer photograph album, with velvet spine and plain black lacquered back cover, enclosing 19 pages, with clasp, stamped Lukutine Factory, with gilt Imperial Eagle, mid-19thC, 9in (23cm) long.
£350-450 *C*

Lighting

A giltmetal hall lantern, with glazed panels and 3 candle branches, fitted for electricity, 32in (81cm) high.
£1,700-2,000 *C*

A mid-Victorian giltmetal and blue glass column oil lamp, with Corinthian capital and stepped square plinth, fitted for electricity, 38in (95.5cm) high.
£1,500-2,000 *C*

A pair of giltmetal sconces of 17thC design, the shaped embossed backplates with portrait busts and baldacchinos with single scrolling branches, 15in (38cm) high.
£400-600 *C*

A pair of French Barbedienne candlesticks, signed, late 19thC, 14in (35.5cm).
£850-900 *BHA*

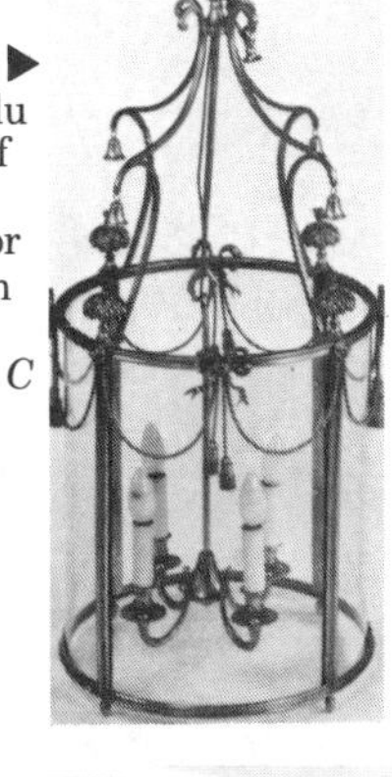

A pair of ormolu hall lanterns of Louis XVI design, fitted for electricity, 17in (43cm) diam.
£4,000-5,000 *C*

A Continental bronze gasolier, c1880, converted for electricity, 42in (122cm) high.
£2,000-2,500 *FF*

A pair of Austrian bronzed and gilded 3-light wall lights, late 18thC, 14in (35.5cm) high.
£1,500-2,000 *C*

An Edwardian cast brass chandelier, with cut glass pineapple shades, fitted for electricity, c1905, 36in (91.5cm) high.
£1,400-1,700 *FF*

A pair of rock crystal and giltmetal pricket candlesticks, with hexagonal drip-pans and faceted multi-baluster stems on stepped hexagonal bases, 11in (28cm) high.
£2,200-2,500 *C*

A giltmetal hall lantern, with Gothic pattern glazed body, 19thC, fitted for electricity, 37in (94cm) high.
£4,500-5,000 *C*

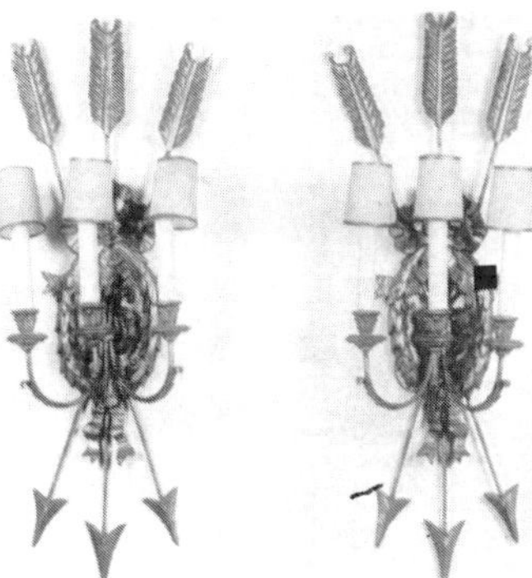

A pair of giltwood 3-branch wall lights, with ribbon tied arrow-and-wreath backplates and scrolling branches, fitted for electricity, 36in (91.5cm) high.
£1,200-1,500 *C*

A Dutch style chandelier, 19thC, 24in (61cm) diam.
£350-400 *ARC*

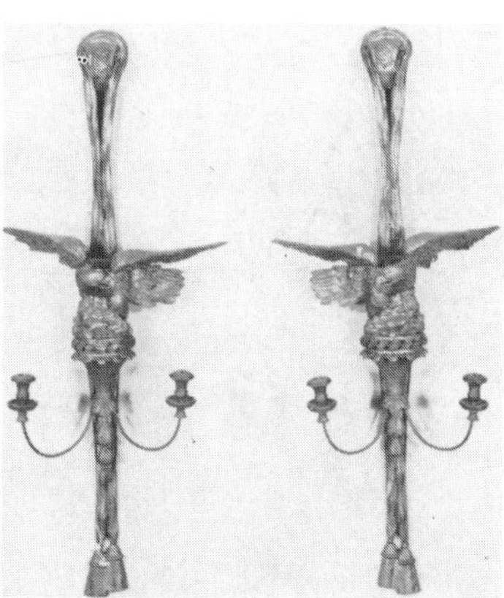

A pair of George III style giltwood wall lights, 47½in (120cm) high.
£1,500-2,000 *CNY*

Papier Mâché

A Victorian papier mâché and inlaid nursing chair.
£250-300 *LRG*

An early Victorian black lacquered papier mâché tray, decorated with gilt, slight damage, 32in (81cm) wide.
£500-600 *Bea*

Two Regency black lacquered papier mâché trays, decorated in colours and gilt, some damage, the larger 30in (76cm) wide.
£1,300-1,500 *Bea*

A graduated set of 3 Victorian papier mâché trays, with gilt foliate decoration.
£750-800 *JD*

A papier mâché snap-top occasional table, with black lacquer and mother-of-pearl, 19thC, 26in (66cm) diam.
£350-450 *LRG*

An early Victorian papier mâché tray, painted in colours and gilt, registration tablet for 1846, 32in (81cm) wide.
£550-600 *PWC*

A papier mâché and mother-of-pearl inlaid inkstand and pair of glass inkwells, 19thC, 11in (28cm) wide.
£80-100 *PC*

A papier mâché tray, with serpentine raised borders, decorated with gilt foliage and insects, old repair, early 19thC, 29½in (75cm).
£500-550 *WW*

A Stockmann painted papier mâché snuff box, the lid painted with 'Loth avec les filles', after Raphael, the interior of the lid inscribed with title, the interior of base inscribed with '1475 St.St', early 19thC, 4in (10cm) diam, cased.
£450-500 *HCH*

A Victorian ebonised and gilt papier mâché table, 24½in (62cm).
£850-1,000 *DN*

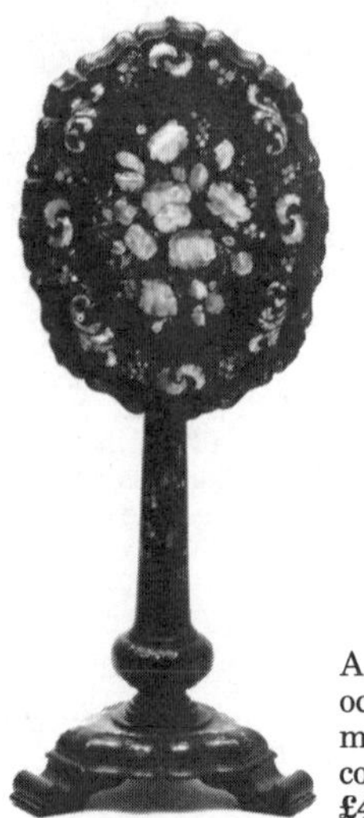

A Victorian papier mâché occasional table, inlaid with mother-of-pearl, with adjustable column.
£400-500 *LRG*

A pair of papier mâché pole screens, 19thC.
£650-750 *DN*

Sewing

A Wheeler & Wilson-type S. Davis & Co., walnut 'Davenport' treadle sewing machine, serial No. 21535, some damage, c1870, 38in (96cm) high.
£1,500-2,000 *P*

A tailor's dummy, 59in (150cm) high.
£70-90 *AL*

A Grover & Baker hand sewing machine, serial No. 441414, with transfer, brass disc and gilt lining, on mahogany base, c1873.
£1,200-1,500 *P*

A mahogany sewing box, the central handle flanked by 2 hinged lids, with sectioned interior, early 19thC, 7½in (19cm) square.
£100-130 *WIL*

A French satinwood workbox, decorated with painted panels, the fitted interior lined in blue silk, containing needlework tools, early 19thC, 14in (35cm) wide.
£1,500-2,000 *P*

Miniatures

A miniature of a gentleman, wearing a red uniform with dark blue and gold facings, c1810, 3in (7.5cm).
£300-350 *Bon*

A miniature of a gentleman, wearing a blue uniform, his powdered hair en queue, c1875, 4cm, later chased gold and silver frame.
£200-250 *Bon*

A miniature of an officer, in a red uniform with cream coloured collar, silver epaulettes and black sash, and black feathered beret, in bright cut gold frame, c1770, 4.5cm.
£200-250 *Bon*

A miniature portrait of the Duchess of Montagu, daughter of the Great Duke of Marlborough, documented, by Bernard Lens, signed monogram on ivory, c1720, 5 by 4½in (12.5 by 11cm).
£270-300 *TVA*

A miniature of a gentleman, in a dark blue coat and white cravat, his powdered hair tied back, gilded metal frame with plaited hair reverse, c1790, 6cm.
£200-250 *Bon*

Pine Furniture
Beds

A pine bed, c1860, 36in (91.5cm) wide.
£200-250 *AL*

A cane and pine carved bed head and foot, 66in (167.5cm) wide.
£500-550 *LAM*

A beech bed, c1870, 43in (109cm) wide.
£200-250 *AL*

Bookcases

A George III style pine breakfront bookcase, 74in (188cm).
£2,500-3,000 *Bon*

A William IV bookcase, with false drawers, 50in (127cm).
£500-550 *UP*

A pine glazed bookcase, 49in (124.5cm).
£600-650 *LAM*

A pine bookcase, the glazed doors enclosing a green watered silk interior between entrelacs, on a plinth base, 57in (145cm).
£3,000-5,000 *C*

A Continental bookcase, c1860, 43in (109cm) wide.
£450-500 *UP*

A pine bookcase, 71in (180cm).
£600-650 *LAM*

Chairs

A pine chair, c1840.
£75-100 *AL*

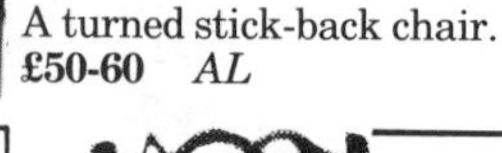

A turned stick-back chair.
£50-60 *AL*

A miniature elm rocking chair, c1900, 11in (28cm) high.
£100-125 *SA*

An Irish chair, c1860.
£120-150 *UP*

A scroll back Windsor chair.
£40-60 *AL*

A child's chair, 26in (66cm) high.
£25-50 *LAM*

A lathe back chair.
£50-70 *AL*

A wheel back chair.
£150-200 *AL*

Chests

A pine, walnut and fruitwood chest, applied with split bobbin mouldings, on bun feet, 17thC, 31in (79cm).
£1,000-1,500 *P*

A bowfront chest of drawers, painted in blue, c1820, 41½in (105cm).
£300-350 *RP*

A pine mule chest with 2 drawers, unused, c1830, 42in (107cm).
£400-450 *AL*

A painted pine linen chest, c1830, 43in (109cm).
£900-1,000 *RP*

An original painted pine chest of drawers, c1850, 41in (104cm).
£450-500 *AP*

A painted pine chest of drawers, c1840, 42in (106.5cm).
£300-350 *RP*

A painted pine chest of drawers, c1830, 36½in (92cm).
£300-350 *RP*

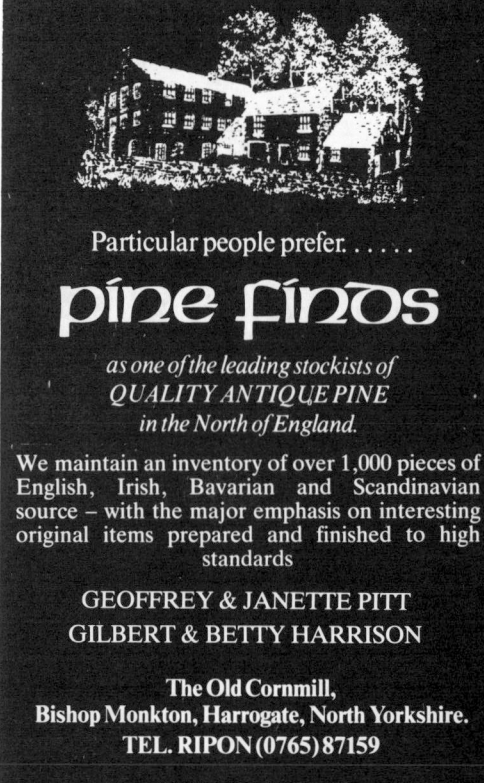

A chest of drawers, with scroll decoration, c1850, 36in (91.5cm).
£300-350 *AL*

A miniature chest of drawers, c1870, 15½in (38cm).
£100-120 *AL*

A pine combination chest of drawers, c1860, 40in (101.5cm).
£300-350 *AL*

A pine dressing chest, c1850, 42in (106.5cm).
£350-400 *AL*

A chest of drawers, c1880, 33in (84cm).
£75-100 *PAC*

A Continental four drawer chest, c1860, 42in (106.5cm).
£230-270 *UP*

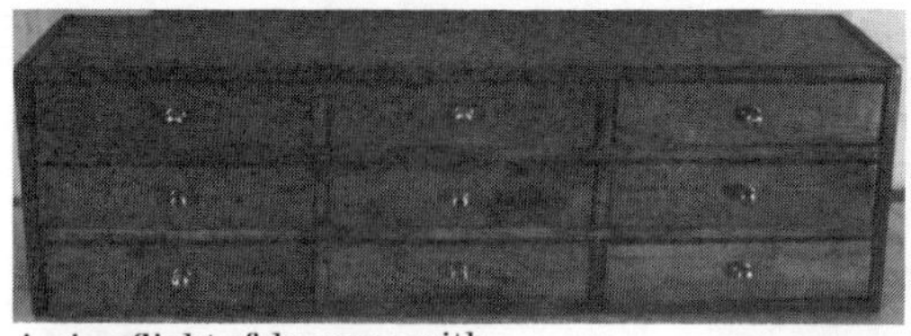

A pine flight of drawers, with original brass handles, c1860, 37in (94cm).
£160-200 *AL*

A chest of drawers.
£500-600 *Clo*

A Victorian mule chest.
£300-350 *Clo*

A pine nest of drawers, 19in (48cm) wide.
£300-350 *PH*

A bowfront chest of drawers, unusually sound, 34in (86cm).
£400-450 *PH*

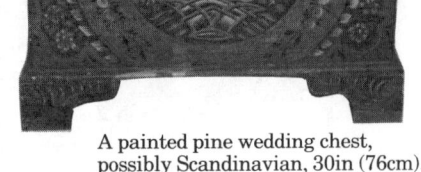

A painted pine wedding chest, possibly Scandinavian, 30in (76cm).
£350-400 *PH*

A specimen chest, 29in (74cm).
£500-550 *PH*

A pine specimen chest, with fitted drawers, 23in (58cm).
£300-350 *LAM*

A dressing chest, with mirror front, the lifting lid revealing a secret drawer, 35in (89cm).
£400-500 *LAM*

A small pine chest of drawers, with new brass handles, 30in (76cm) high.
£200-225 *LAM*

A painted pine chest of drawers, 42in (106.5cm).
£500-600 *RP*

A painted pine chest of drawers, 40in (101.5cm).
£250-300 *AL*

Commodes

A pine commode, c1850, 25in (63.5cm).
£230-270 *AL*

Cupboards

A pine corner cupboard, with painted dome, c1760, 50in (127cm).
£4,000-5,000 *PH*

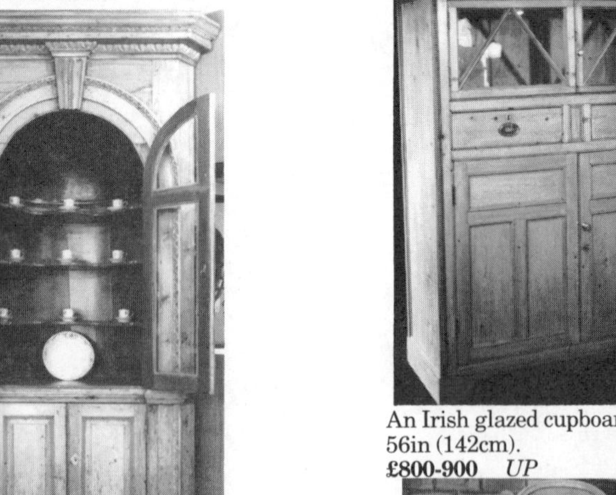

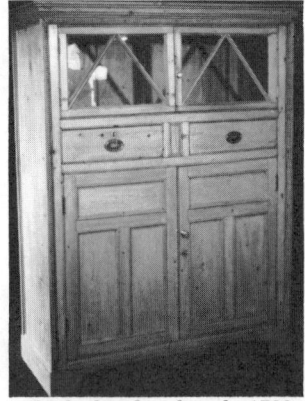

An Irish glazed cupboard, c1780, 56in (142cm).
£800-900 *UP*

A French armoire, c1780.
£2,000-2,500 *Clo*

An Irish food cupboard, c1780, 57in (144cm).
£1,400-1,700 *UP*

A two-piece corner cupboard, c1780, 44in (112cm).
£600-700 *UP*

A Normandy buffet, c1780, 58in (147cm).
£2,300-2,600 *MCA*

An Irish panelled food cupboard, c1780, 50in (127cm).
£750-800 *UP*

An Irish food cupboard, with fitted interior, c1800, 51in (129.5cm).
£900-1,000 *UP*

An Irish astragal glazed cabinet, c1800, 49in (124.5cm).
£750-800 *UP*

A food cupboard, c1850, 58in (147cm).
£700-800 *UP*

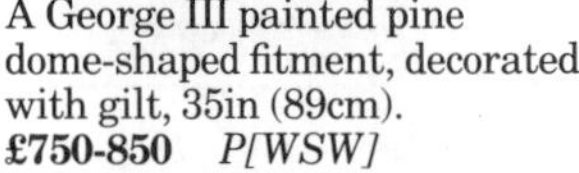
A George III painted pine dome-shaped fitment, decorated with gilt, 35in (89cm).
£750-850 *P[WSW]*

A Normandy buffet, c1840, 56in (142cm).
£3,500-4,000 *PH*

A pine linen press, c1840, 47½in (120cm).
£700-750 *AL*

A two-door panelled cupboard, c1840, 75½in (191cm) high.
£550-600 *AL*

A pine huffer, c1840, 39in (99cm).
£250-300 *AL*

A French buffet, c1860, 50in (127cm).
£350-400 *UP*

A spice cupboard, c1860, 19in (48cm).
£120-160 *AL*

A mid-European drapers cabinet, 71in (180cm).
£1,200-1,500 *MCA*

A pine cupboard, 84in (213cm) high.
£300-350 *SAn*

An Irish glazed cabinet, c1840, 51in (130cm).
£550-650 *UP*

A two-door pine cupboard, c1850, 83½in (212cm) high.
£400-500 *AL*

A French buffet, 84in (213cm) high.
£2,800-3,300 *JeB*

A two-door cupboard with 9 drawers, c1860, 78in (198cm) high.
£700-800 *AL*

A pot cupboard, 17in (43cm).
£30-50 *PAC*

An astragal glazed cupboard, mid-19thC.
£300-350 *PH*

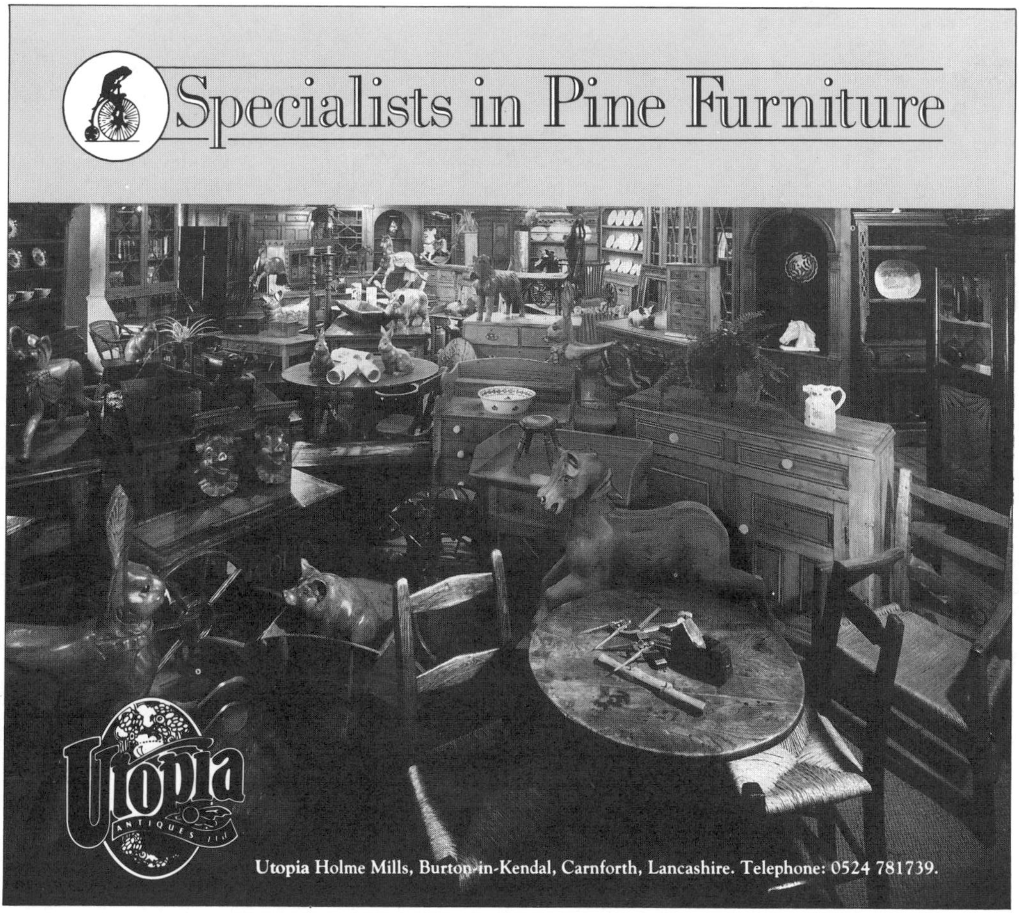

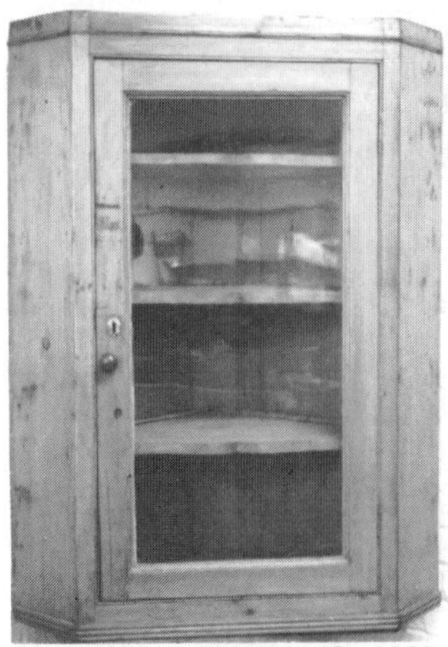

A glazed corner cupboard, c1860, 35in (89cm).
£350-400 *AL*

A butler's cupboard, c1870, 106in (269cm).
£1,500-1,800 *UP*

A bedside cabinet, c1910.
£100-120 *Clo*

A pine cupboard, 52in (132cm).
£650-750 *SAn*

A pine linen press, 50in (127cm).
£600-650 *SAn*

A hand painted pine cupboard, c1900, 25½in (65cm).
£140-180
Two Scandinavian boxes, c1820.
£50-70 each
A bargeware watering can.
£40-60 *Mer*

A Normandy marriage armoire, 51in (129.5cm).
£3,500-4,000 *PH*

A painted pine corner cupboard, with original glazing, 46in (116.5cm).
£1,500-2,000 *PH*

A corner cupboard, 43in (109cm).
£650-700 *LAM*

A pine cupboard, 20in (51cm).
£80-100 *LAM*

Desks

A pedestal desk, 61in (155cm).
£650-700 *PH*

A carved pine desk, with cabriole legs, c1880, 72in (182.5cm).
£2,000-2,500 *PH*

A Queen Anne bureau, with fitted interior, 35in (89cm).
£750-850 *GC*

A pine desk, with later leathered slope, c1860, 53in (134.5cm).
£500-550 *AL*

An Irish plate rail dresser, c1800, 61in (155cm).
£500-600 *UP*

Dressers

A Devonshire dresser, with glazed top, 51in (129.5cm).
£900-1,000 *PH*

A dresser base, c1700, 90in (228.5cm).
£3,500-4,000 *PH*

A dresser base, c1840, 73in (185cm).
£550-600 *AL*

A pine dresser, c1840, 42in (106.5cm).
£500-600 *AL*

An Irish dresser, c1840, 55in (139.5cm).
£850-900 *UP*

An early pine dresser, 48in (122cm).
£550-600 *LAM*

Dressing Tables

A painted pine dressing table, 18thC, 42in (106.5cm).
£1,000-1,200 *AP*

A dressing table, with mirror, 42in (106.5cm).
£250-300 *PH*

Settles

An Irish high back settle, c1820, 74in (188cm).
£400-450 *UP*

Mirrors

A pine frame, c1860, 30 by 26½in (76 by 67cm).
£80-100 *AL*

A carved pine mirror, 68in (172.5cm) high.
£900-1,000 *PH*

A carved pine bench, 72in (182.5cm).
£450-500 *SAn*

A Dutch carved pine bench in the baroque taste, on trestle end supports, with blue squab, 18thC, 74in (188cm).
£2,000-2,500 *P*

Sideboards

A pine sideboard, 72in (182.5cm).
£400-450 *SAn*

A Victorian sideboard, 72in (182.5cm).
£400-450 *SAn*

A pine sideboard, 47in (119cm).
£250-350 *SAn*

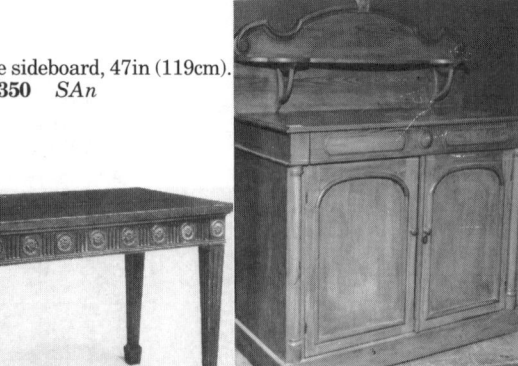

Two George III grained pine serving tables, one inscribed underneath 'This next to Servants Hall', the other '. . . East table', the larger 59in (149.5cm).
£8,000-10,000 *CSK*

Stools

A pine piano seat, c1900.
£180-220 *Clo*

Tables

A pine console table, heavily carved, c1850, 46in (116.5cm).
£2,000-2,500 *AO*

A large pine table, c1850, 120in (304.5cm).
£550-600 *AL*

A painted pine table, c1830, 36in (91.5cm).
£350-400 *AP*

A Regency painted pine side table, fitted with frieze drawer, 30in (76cm).
£1,200-1,500 *P[Re]*

A cricket table, c1850, 29in (73cm) diam.
£250-300 *AL*

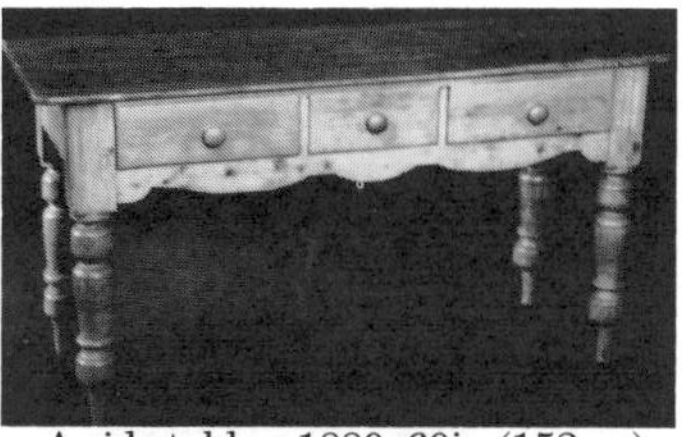
A side table, c1880, 60in (152cm).
£250-300 *UP*

A bedside adjustable table, c1850, 32in (81cm) high.
£150-200 *AL*

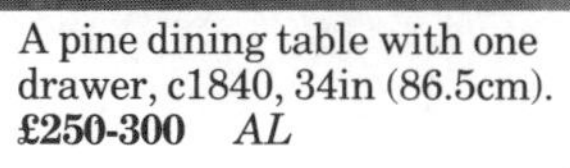
A pine dining table with one drawer, c1840, 34in (86.5cm).
£250-300 *AL*

A pine table with slotted shelf, c1850, 59in (149.5cm).
£300-350 *AL*

A painted pine table, 31in (78.5cm).
£200-250 *RP*

Wardrobes

A painted pine armoire, with domed top, 48in (122cm).
£400-450 *LAM*

A combination pine wardrobe, c1870, 79in (200.5cm) high.
£850-950 *AL*

A Scottish pine two-door wardrobe, with carved decoration, 45in (114cm).
£450-500 *LAM*

A double wardrobe, 96in (243.5cm).
£1,500-2,000 *SAn*

A French pine armoire, c1780, 50in (127cm).
£1,500-2,000 *MCA*

Washstands

A painted pine washstand, 19thC, 36in (91.5cm).
£160-200 *RP*

A pine washstand, with shelf and one drawer, c1830, 25in (63cm).
£180-220 *AL*

A pair of pine sculpted greyhounds, 42in (106.5cm).
£500-700 *MCA*

Miscellaneous

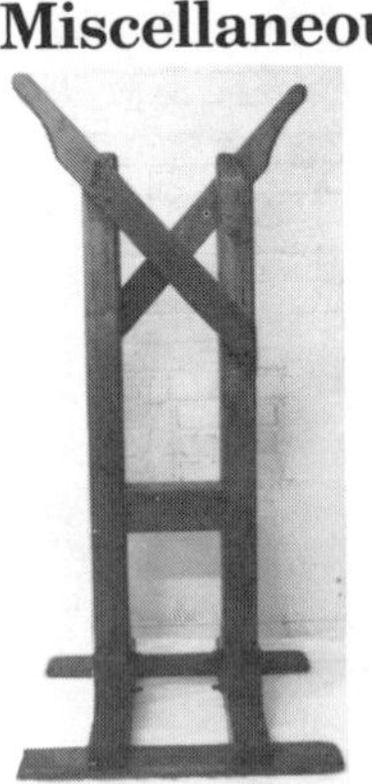
A pine stand, c1860, 55in (139.5cm).
£100-120 *AL*

A pitch pine box, 44in (111.5cm).
£90-100 *LAM*

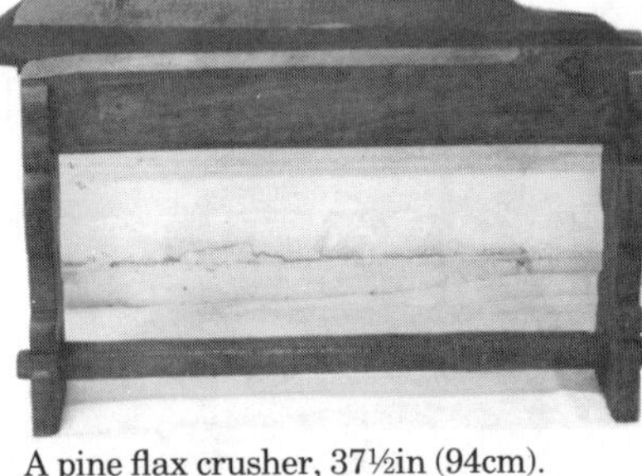
A pine flax crusher, 37½in (94cm).
£90-100 *AL*

Pine bookshelves, 48in (122cm) high.
£100-120 *LAM*

A set of steps, 23in (58.5cm) high.
£30-50 *LAM*

A pine corn bin, 37in (94cm).
£80-100 *PAC*

A pine box, 36in (91.5cm).
£50-75 *PAC*

A small pine box, 29in (74cm).
£30-40 *PAC*

A small pine box, 15in (38cm).
£50-70 *LAM*

A small pine box, c1850, 20in (53cm).
£70-90 *AL*

A pine lead lined double trough, 46in (116.5cm).
£300-350 *PH*

From the Dairy Department of Reading University.

A pine hall stand, carved in the form of a bear, 85in (216cm) high.
£1,200-1,500 *Wor*

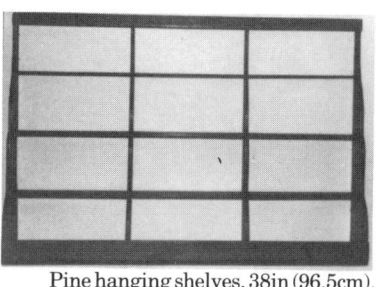

Pine hanging shelves, 38in (96.5cm).
£80-90 *AL*

A pair of French carved fireplace surrounds, 19thC, 59 by 79in (150 by 200cm).
£6,000-6,500 *PH*

Pine shelves, with bobbin supports, c1850, 50in (127cm) high.
£125-150 *AL*

A cattle trough, c1860, 120in (304cm).
£200-250 *AL*

A pine reeded fire surround, 51 by 59in (130 by 150cm).
£200-250 *LAM*

A pine croquet box, 35½in (90cm).
£30-50 *PAC*

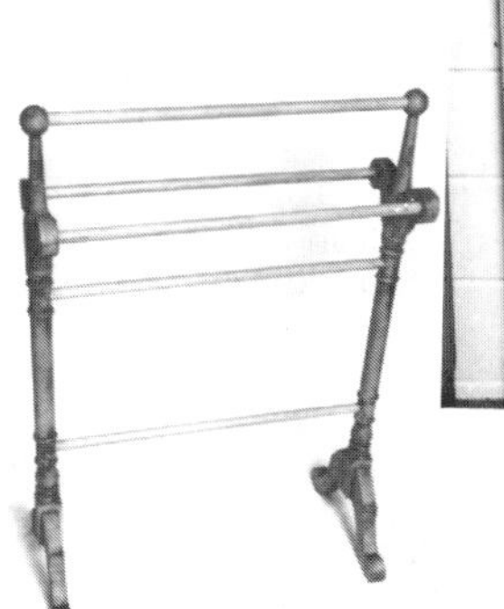

A pine towel rail, 25in (63.5cm).
£30-50 *LAM*

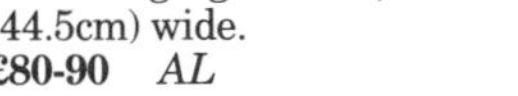

Pine hanging shelves, 17½in (44.5cm) wide.
£80-90 *AL*

A hatters block, 8in (20cm) high.
£30-40 *LAM*

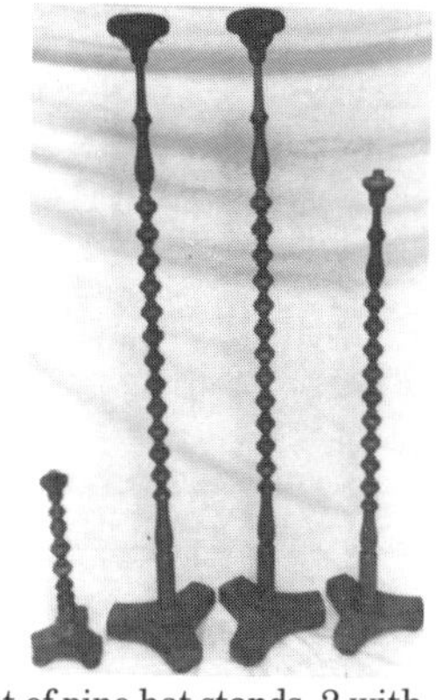

A set of pine hat stands, 2 with original pads, 13 to 38in (33 to 96.5cm) high.
£20-30 *PAC*

Shipping Goods

A grandmother miniature oak longcase clock, 65in (165cm) high.
£250-300 *MY*

A mahogany wall clock, damaged, 24in (61cm) high.
£70-90 *MY*

A Victorian mahogany waisted clock.
£125-175 *PAC*

A bronze model of a pointer dog, on marble base.
£100-130 *MY*

A pair of Satsuma vases, 13½in (34cm) high.
£75-100 *PAC*

A short handled copper warming pan, 32in (81cm).
£60-80 *PAC*

An oil lamp, in Continental glass, converted, 28in (71cm).
£50-75 *PAC*

A box commode, 19in (48cm) high.
£50-70 *MY*

A mahogany toilet mirror.
£70-100 *MY*

A mahogany toilet mirror, with drawers, 26in (66cm) high.
£100-150 *MY*

A spinners oak chair, 37in (94cm).
£50-80 *MY*

A set of 4 Queen Anne style mahogany chairs, 41in (104cm).
£100-150 *PAC*

A captain's chair in elm, 28in (71cm).
£75-100 *PAC*

An Arts and Crafts plant holder, 37in (94cm).
£40-60 *PAC*

An oak lowboy, a late Victorian copy, 30½in (78cm).
£300-400 *PAC*

A Victorian mahogany pot cupboard, 32in (81cm) high.
£75-100 *PAC*

A mahogany chest of drawers, with brass handles, 42in (106.5cm).
£250-300 *PAC*

A walnut desk conversion, with featherbanded top, free standing, 42in (106.5cm).
£200-300 *PAC*

A mahogany dressing table, converted to a desk, 48in (122cm).
£200-300 *PAC*

A Georgian mahogany bureau, 42in (106.5cm).
£700-750 *MY*

A Victorian walnut specimen chest, 15in (38cm).
£175-225 *PAC*

A mahogany chest of drawers, with bracket feet, 40in (101.5cm) high.
£200-250 *PAC*

A mahogany linen press, with brass handles, 42in (106.5cm).
£450-550 *PAC*

A mahogany nest of tables, 24in (61cm) high.
£100-125 *PAC*

An Edwardian walnut games table, 24½in (62cm) high.
£75-100 *PAC*

A Victorian mahogany bidet, used as a coffee table, 23in (58cm).
£50-75 *PAC*

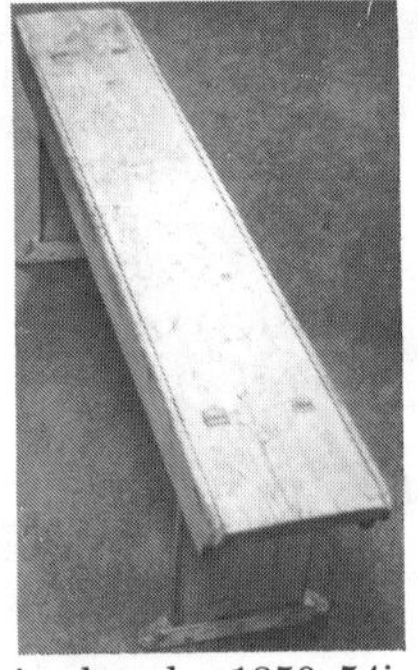

A pine bench, c1850, 54in (137cm).
£65-75 *AL*

A washstand, c1820, 41in (104cm).
£150-200 *UP*

A pine and elm box, 39in (99cm).
£150-170 *LAM*

A pitch pine serving table, 29in (73cm) high.
£120-150 *LAM*

A drop-leaf table, 65in (165cm) extended.
£250-300 *LAM*

Kitchenalia

A milk bucket and measure, late 19thC.
£50-70 *MY*

A lignum vitae coffee grinder, c1770.
£450-500 *RYA*

A Norwegian finely carved pudding box, with original polychrome decoration, dated 1839.
£800-850 *RYA*

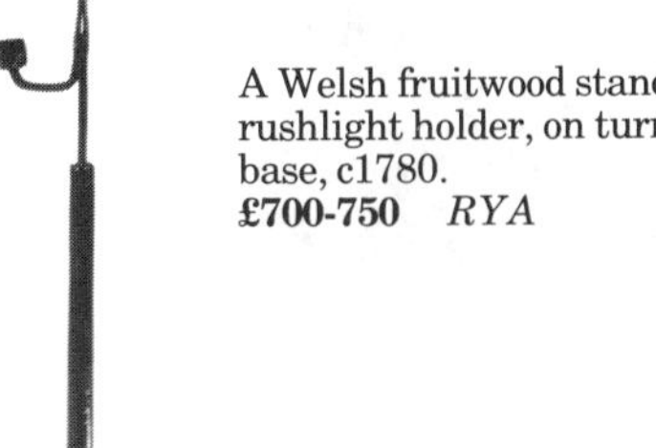

A Welsh fruitwood standing rushlight holder, on turned conical base, c1780.
£700-750 *RYA*

A Norwegian kasa, with original painted decoration, c1780.
£1,200-1,500 *RYA*

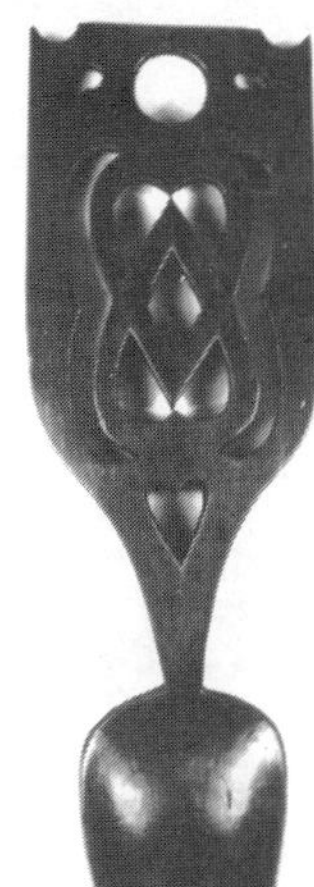

A Welsh walnut spoon, early 19thC.
£300-320 *RYA*

A pair of figure carved nutcrackers, English, c1650.
£400-430 *RYA*

A pair of George III turned yew candlesticks.
£450-550 *RYA*

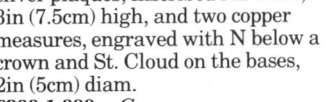

A pair of turned oak egg cups, with silver plaques, inscribed NB 1798, 3in (7.5cm) high, and two copper measures, engraved with N below a crown and St. Cloud on the bases, 2in (5cm) diam.
£900-1,000 *C*

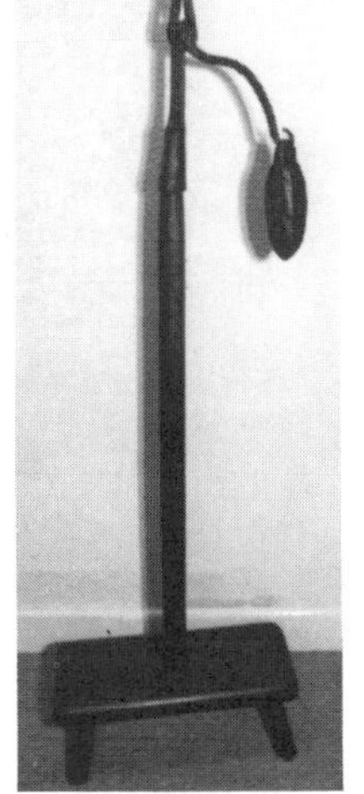

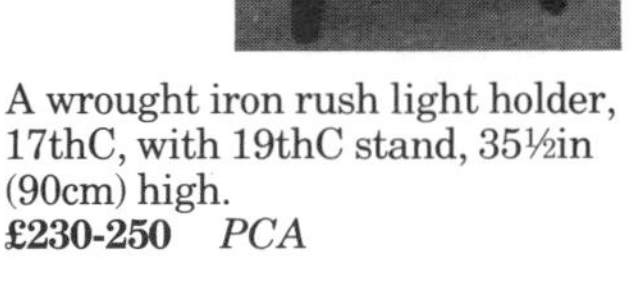

A wrought iron rush light holder, 17thC, with 19thC stand, 35½in (90cm) high.
£230-250 *PCA*

A creamware jelly mould, c1775, 6in (15cm) long.
£35-50 *CA*

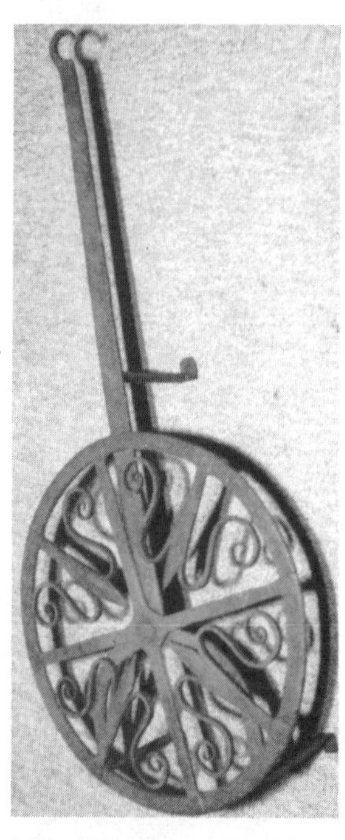
A wrought iron revolving grill, early 19thC.
£150-200 *PCA*

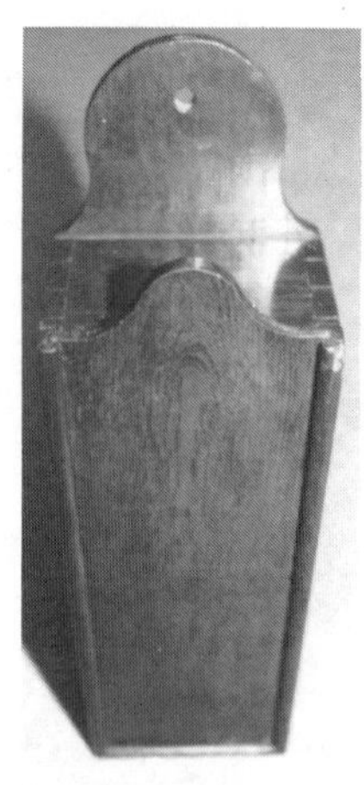
An oak candle box, 18thC, 17½ by 5in (44 by 13cm).
£80-90 *PCA*

A rhubarb forcer, 28in (71cm) high.
£70-100 *WRe*

A set of ceramic feet, for standing a dresser on stone floors.
£40-60 *AL*

A tin bell-shaped chocolate mould, 5½in (14cm) high.
£25-30 *AL*

A selection of Mauchline ware napkin rings, with transfer picture of Isle of Wight and Beachy Head.
£6-20 each *DEL*

A Macintosh's tin, 16in (40.5cm) high.
£20-25 *AL*

A copper saucepan, stamped H.E. Cars.
£30-40 *ONS*

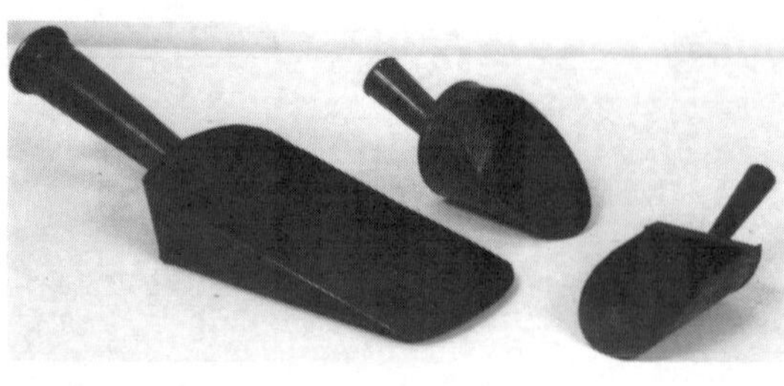
A selection of tin scoops, 5½ to 12in (14 to 30.5cm).
£6-12 each *AL*

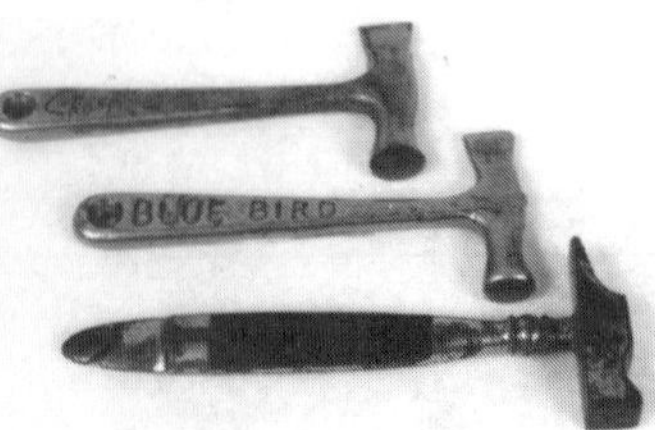

Three toffee hammers:
Sharps, 4in (10cm).
£3-5

Blue Bird, 4in (10cm).
£5-7

Bone handle, 5in (12.5cm).
£7-9 *AL*

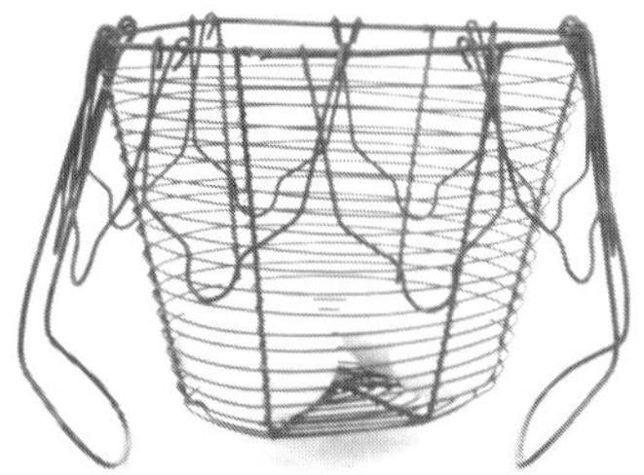

A Victorian egg basket, 6½in (16.5cm) high.
£30-40 *AL*

A stone hot water bottle, now filled with sand for use as a door stop, 12in (30.5cm) long.
£20-30 *AL*

A T. G. Green spot pattern jug, 4in (10cm) high.
£8-10 *AL*

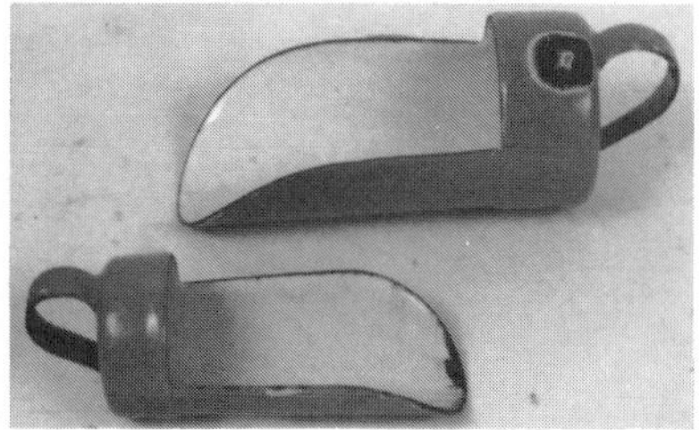

Enamel scoops:
Top. 4½in (11.5cm).
£7-9

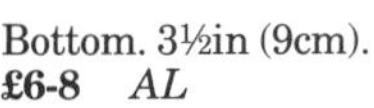

Bottom. 3½in (9cm).
£6-8 *AL*

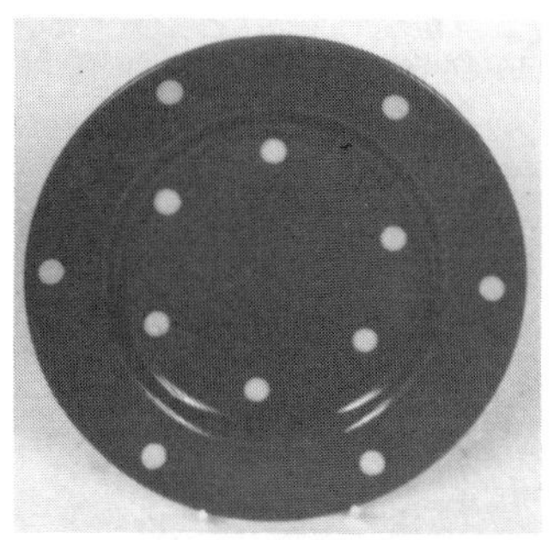

A T. G. Green spot pattern plate, 7in (18cm).
£5-7 *AL*

A clothes dryer, 32in (81cm) high.
£35-40 *AL*

Two T. G. Green & Co. Cornish kitchenware oval cups and saucers.
£9-12 each *AL*

Easimix bowl, with platform for easy mixing.
£14-17 *AL*

T. G. Green & Co. Cornish kitchenware,
Sultanas and Flour 5in (12.5cm),
Sugar 4in (10cm).
£12-16 each *AL*

A bee collection box and comb, 18in (46cm).
£50-70 *AL*

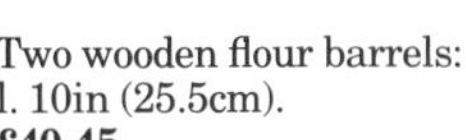

Two wooden flour barrels:
l. 10in (25.5cm).
£40-45

r. 6½in (16.5cm).
£35-40 *AL*

Three milk cans, tin with brass rim, 3 to 8in (7.5 to 20.5cm).
£25-40 each *AL*

A wall egg rack for one dozen eggs, 15in (38cm) high.
£30-35

China eggs.
£2-4 each *AL*

A bread slicer.
£60-80 *LAM*

An Edwardian marmalade slicer.
£25-45 *LAM*

An egg rack.
£18-20 *LAM*

A Spong miniature knife sharpener and cleaner.
£20-40 *LAM*

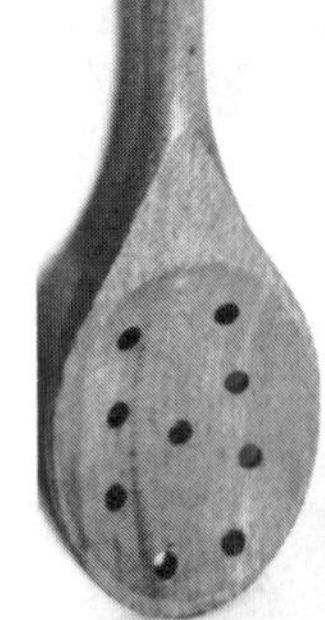

A wooden draining spoon.
£7-10 *LAM*

A grater/slicer.
£25-30 *LAM*

A pine sleeve board.
£12-15 *LAM*

A pine plate rack.
£70-80 *LAM*

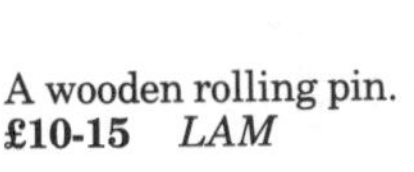

A wooden rolling pin.
£10-15 *LAM*

A wooden trough, 18 by 12in (46 by 30.5cm).
£15-20

Cleaver.
£10-15

Butter pat.
£5-10 *LAM*

A rub-a-tub, 16½in (42cm) diam.
£30-35 *AL*

A meat tenderiser.
£10-15 *LAM*

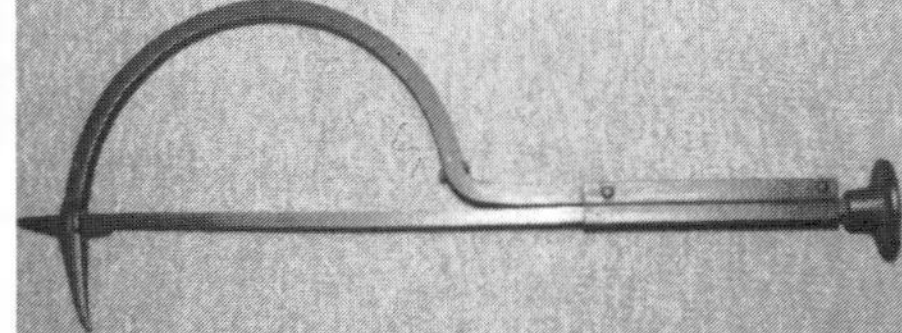

A pair of baby scales, 15in (38cm) high.
£40-50 *AL*

An enamel candlestick.
£10-12 *AL*

Sundry Trades

A wrought iron thatcher's needle, 19thC.
£30-35 *PCA*

A chemist's ball, 21in (53cm) high.
£600-630 *JeB*

A metal bound oak tub, 19thC, 14in (36cm).
£80-100 *PCA*

An oak costrel, with glass ends, 19thC, 10½in (26cm) high.
£80-100 *PCA*

A lacemaker's lamp with hollow baluster stem and plain moulded foot, c1880, 10½in (27cm).
£100-150 *P*

An oak silk thrower, 18thC, 25½in (64cm) long.
£80-100 *PCA*

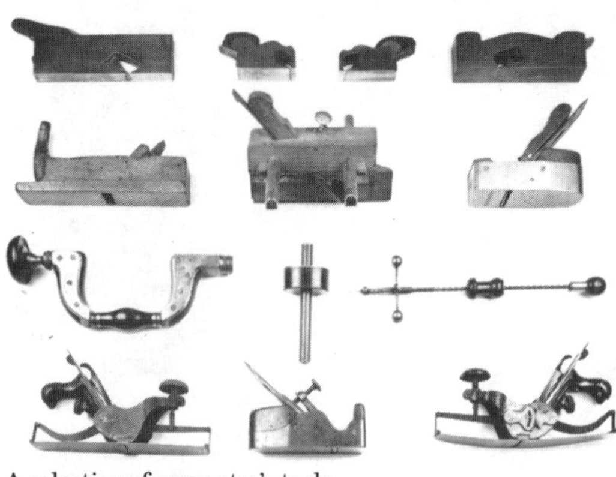

A selection of carpenter's tools.
£500-600 *P[PWC]*

A collection of farm and country trade tools, gag 19in (48cm), thatcher's comb 10in (26cm), castrating iron 10in (26cm) and balance 9in (23cm).
£25-50 each *BA*

The Dining Room

A mahogany cigar box, 19thC, 8in (22cm).
£150-200 *PCA*

A pair of twig armchairs and a table, chair 34in (86cm) high.
£600-650 *JeB*

Games & Pastimes

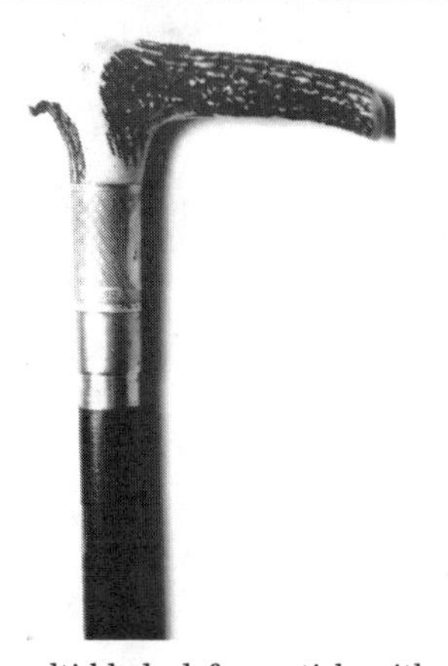

A multi-blade defence stick, with 6 spring-out blades operated from the handle, c1900.
£380-420 *MG*

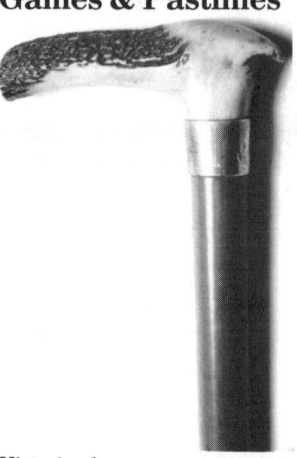

A Victorian horse measuring stick, with boxwood rule and brass pull-out level, c1890.
£140-180 *MG*

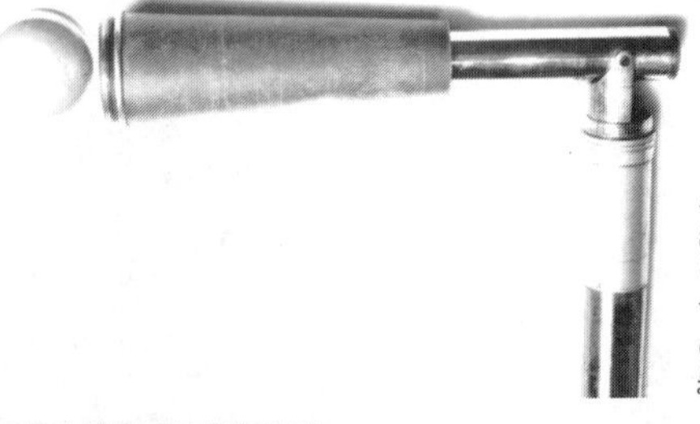

A telescopic bird spotter cane, Continental, with malacca shaft, c1890.
£200-280 *MG*

Miscellaneous

A French walnut spinning wheel, 19thC, 28in (71cm) high.
£250-350 *BA*

A naval rum barrel, with Royal coat-of-arms, late 19thC, 25in (63cm) high.
£150-200 *PC*

A wooden framed wire bird cage.
£170-200 *Wor*

Jewellery

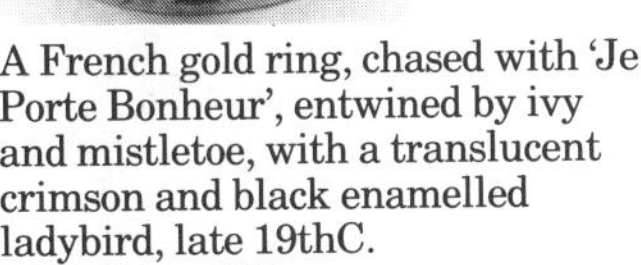

A French gold ring, chased with 'Je Porte Bonheur', entwined by ivy and mistletoe, with a translucent crimson and black enamelled ladybird, late 19thC.
£200-250 *DN*

An old cut diamond and pearl three-stone ring, centre stone approx 1.65ct.
£2,000-2,500 *DN*

A large sapphire cluster ring, 19thC.
£700-800 *DN*

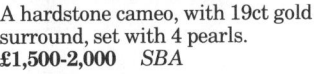

A Victorian gold, diamond and turquoise ring.
£300-400 *HCH*

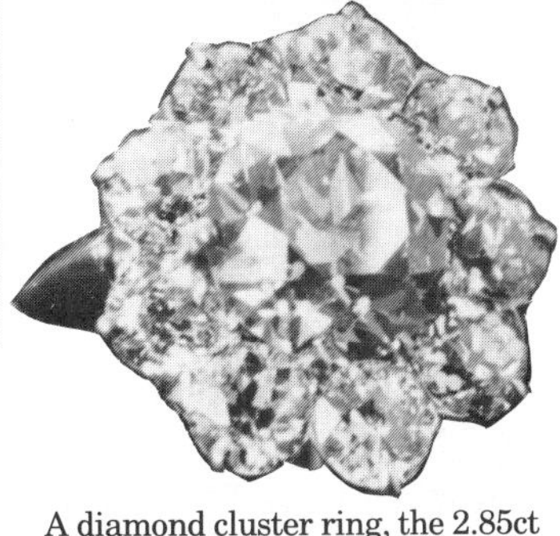

A diamond cluster ring, the 2.85ct centre stone surrounded by 9 white diamonds, set in silver with gold band and under bezel.
£7,000-8,000 *PVH*

A hardstone cameo, with 19ct gold surround, set with 4 pearls.
£1,500-2,000 *SBA*

A deep carved coral brooch, in 18ct gold filigree surround, c1850, 1½in (4cm).
£600-700 *SBA*

A shell cameo, of a Grecian lady's head, with 9ct gold leaf effect surround, c1880.
£300-400 *SBA*

A shell cameo, with 18ct gold surround set with turquoise stones, c1870.
£1,300-1,500 *SBA*

An Italian shell cameo brooch, set in Victorian gilded pinchbeck mount.
£300-350 *PVH*

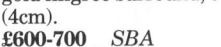

▶ A diamond mounted bracelet, the leaf shaped links with rows of graduated brilliant and baguette cut stones.
£2,500-3,000 *Bea*

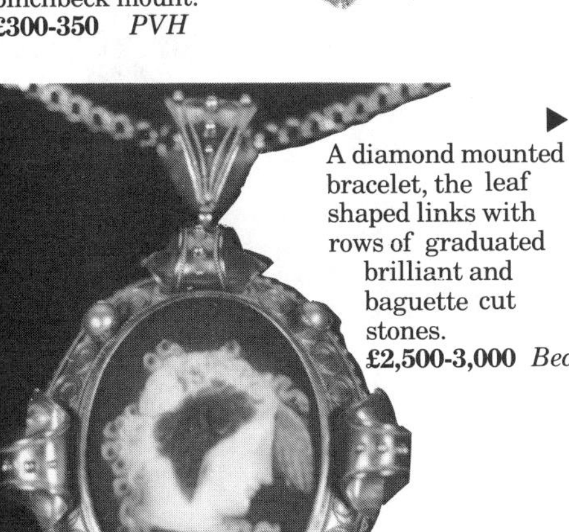

A Victorian sardonyx cameo brooch/pendant, c1865.
£2,500-3,000 *LG*

An Edwardian Italian shell cameo, in low content Continental gold, possibly 7ct.
£120-160 *PVH*

British hallmarking laws require that this brooch should be described a 'metal' set. The lowest acceptable standard for gold in this country is 9ct. Other standards are 14ct, 18ct and 22ct. Pure gold is 24ct, therefore lower carats constitute a proportion of 24 parts: i.e. 9ct = 9 parts in 24. 18ct = 18 parts in 24.

A shell cameo of a cherub, with 18ct gold surround, c1870.
£700-800 *SBA*

A shell cameo with 9ct gold surround, c1880, 2½in (6cm) wide.
£500-600 *SBA*

A Georgian shell cameo of a gentleman's head, with 18ct gold surround, c1860, 3in (7.5cm).
£800-900 *SBA*

A large cameo on stand, surrounded by mosaic floral pattern, c1880.
£800-900 *SBA*

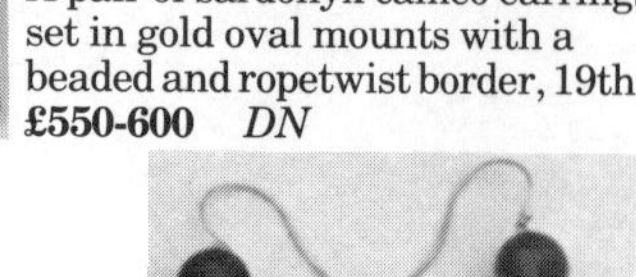

A pair of sardonyx cameo earrings, set in gold oval mounts with a beaded and ropetwist border, 19thC.
£550-600 *DN*

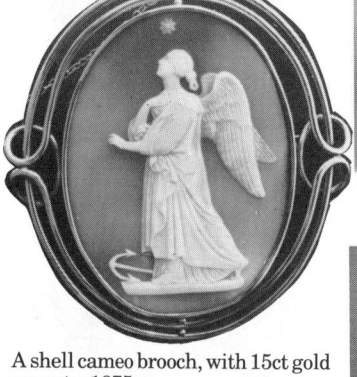

A shell cameo brooch, with 15ct gold mount, c1875.
£650-750 *PVH*

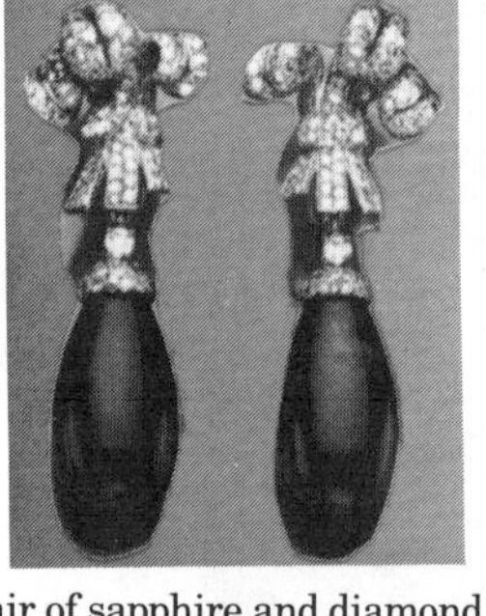

A pair of sapphire and diamond pendant earrings, from The Duchess of Windsor's collection, with 2 Burmese blue sapphires 75.33ct.
£250,000-300,000 *PVH*

A pair of Victorian deep green enamelled pendant earrings, mounted in 9ct gold, with matching pendant, a few seed pearls missing.
£350-400 *DN*

A Victorian 9ct gold bangle, with 3 sapphires and 2 diamonds.
£400-450 *PC*

A pair of Victorian tortoiseshell drop earrings, with carved monogram centres and mounted by family crest, c1875.
£600-700 *PVH*

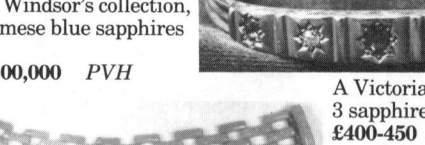

A carved coral bracelet, c1870.
£600-650 *LG*

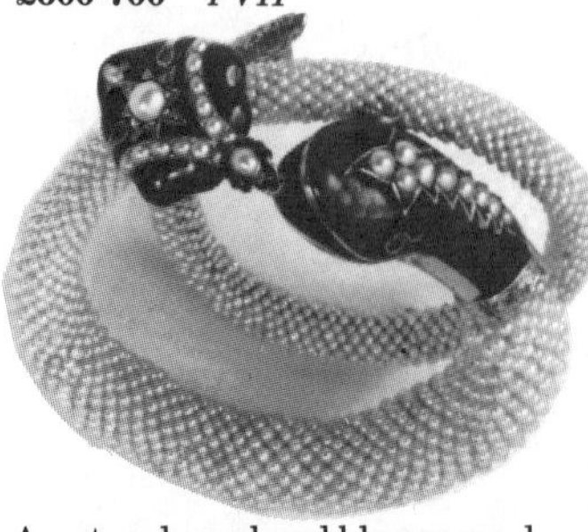

A natural pearl and blue enamel snake bracelet, c1840.
£4,500-5,000 *GL*

An 18ct gold bracelet, with 8 sapphires alternating with 7 diamonds.
£350-450 *Wor*

A sapphire and diamond flexible bracelet, from The Duchess of Windsor's collection, by Van Cleef and Arpels of Paris, for 'The Marriage Contract 18.5.37'.
£650,000+ *PVH*

An Art Deco 18ct white gold bracelet, set with diamonds.
£6,000-7,000 *PVH*

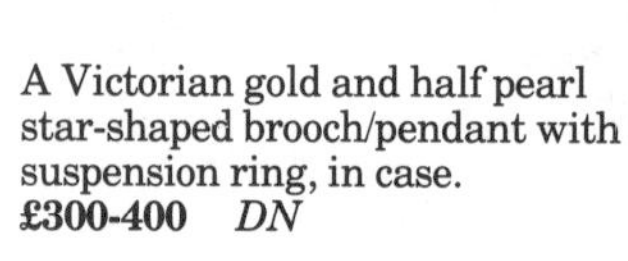

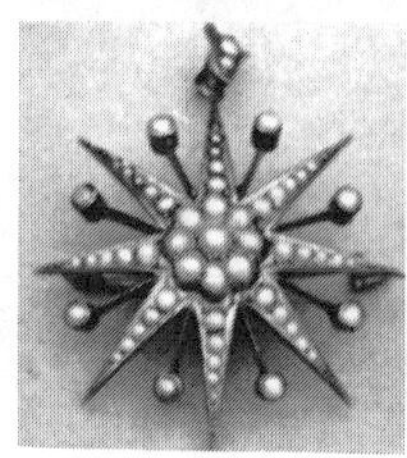

A Victorian gold and half pearl star-shaped brooch/pendant with suspension ring, in case.
£300-400 *DN*

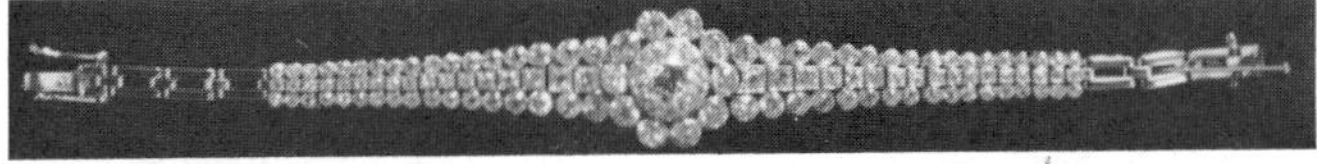
A white gold and platinum bracelet set with brilliant cut diamonds, c1935.
£5,000-6,000 *PVH*

A gold, ruby and diamond insect brooch, in the form of a bee.
£600-700 *Bea*

A gold, sapphire, diamond, ruby and seed pearl butterfly brooch, late 19thC.
£800-1,000 *Bea*

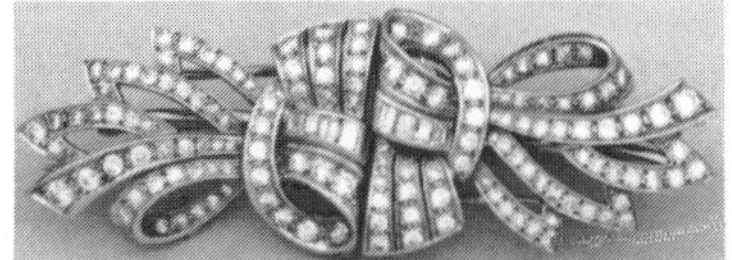
A diamond set scroll double dress clip, set in white gold.
£1,300-1,500 *DN*

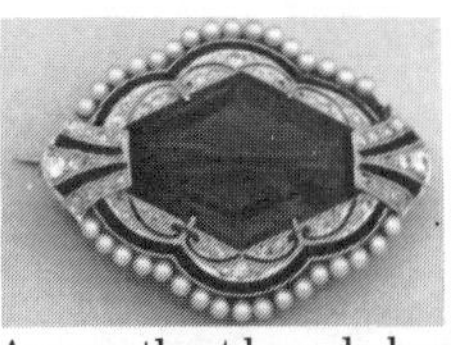
An amethyst brooch, bordered by small rose cut diamonds, calibre jet and seed pearls with open scroll platinum setting, one pearl missing.
£500-650 *DN*

A gold, ruby and diamond brooch, mid-19thC.
£3,000-3,500 *Bea*

A layered agate cameo brooch, mid-19thC.
£700-800 *Bea*

A 15ct gold and enamelled ceremonial coat-of-arms pendant, with motto 'Salus Populi', by Spencer of London.
£180-240 *DN*

A gold and diamond ribbon bow brooch, late 19thC.
£1,400-1,600 *Bea*

A gold and diamond crescent brooch, late 19thC.
£1,000-1,200 *Bea*

A sapphire and diamond frog brooch, with collet set sapphire eyes, set in silver and gold, 19thC.
£4,000-5,000 *DN*

An old cut diamond crescent brooch, with 15 stones set in gold and silver, late 19thC.
£450-550 *DN*

A pietra dura floral brooch, in gold scalloped mount, mid-19thC.
£50-100 *PC*

A French agate cameo, with 18ct gold surround, blue enamel and diamonds set in 4 stars and 4 arrows, c1840.
£650-700 *SBA*

A Victorian reverse carved intaglio brooch, c1870, 1in (2.5cm) diam.
£900-1,000 *LG*

A diamond set brooch, with flower shaped suspension, 53 variously sized stones set in gold.
£2,000-2,500 *GC*

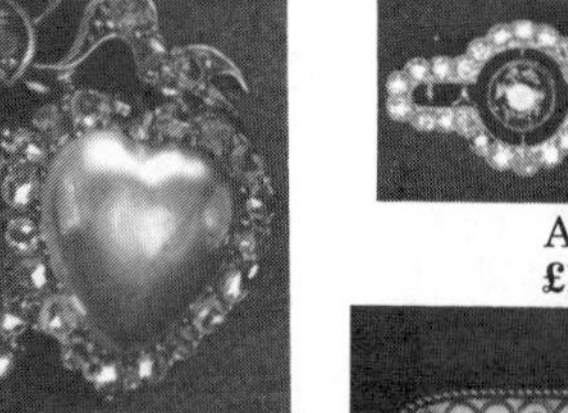

An Art Deco brooch, set with 5cts of diamonds mounted in platinum, c1925, 4cm.
£4,000-4,500 *LM*

A Kutchinsky 18ct gold, diamond and ruby brooch.
£1,200-1,500 *DN*

A diamond brooch/clasp, 19thC.
£2,200-2,500 *DN*

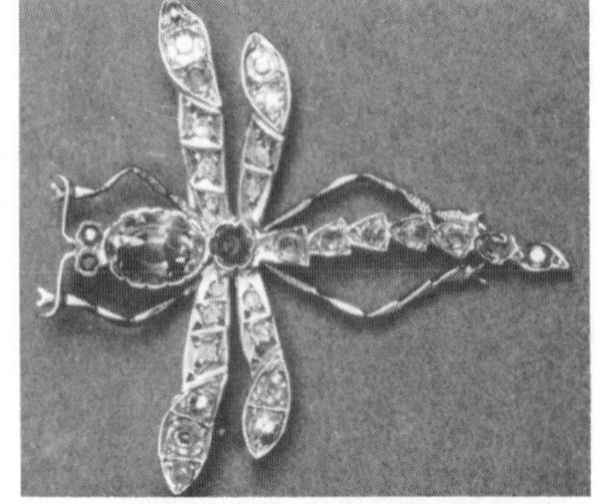

An amethyst pale sapphire, ruby and rose diamond dragonfly.
£400-500 *DN*

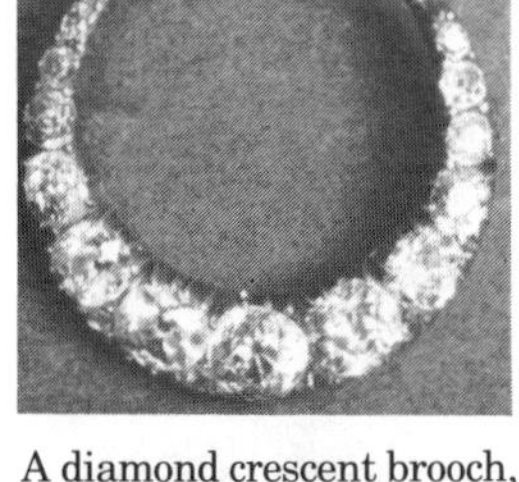

A diamond crescent brooch, 19thC.
£1,500-2,000 *DN*

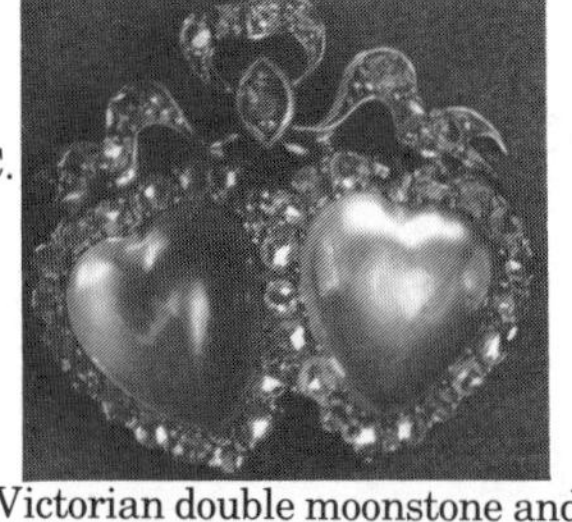

A Victorian double moonstone and rose diamond heart brooch.
£700-800 *DN*

A sapphire and diamond bar brooch.
£1,700-2,000 *DN*

A Victorian gold, pearl and sapphire bar brooch.
£300-350 *DN*

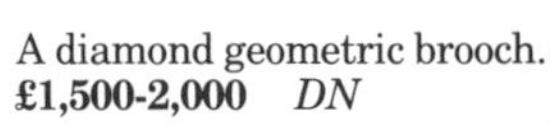

A diamond geometric brooch.
£1,500-2,000 *DN*

A diamond and pearl pendant, 19thC.
£3,500-4,000 *DN*

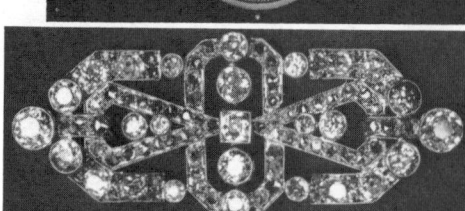

A late Victorian silver and gold brooch, set with sapphires, diamonds, natural pearls, garnets and rubies, with detachable pin to make into a pendant, 4.5cm.
£1,700-2,000 *PVH*

A brilliant and baguette cut diamond brooch, set in platinum and white gold, c1930.
£2,500-3,000 *PVH*

An 18ct gold, diamond and baroque pearl floral spray brooch.
£1,700-2,000 *HCH*

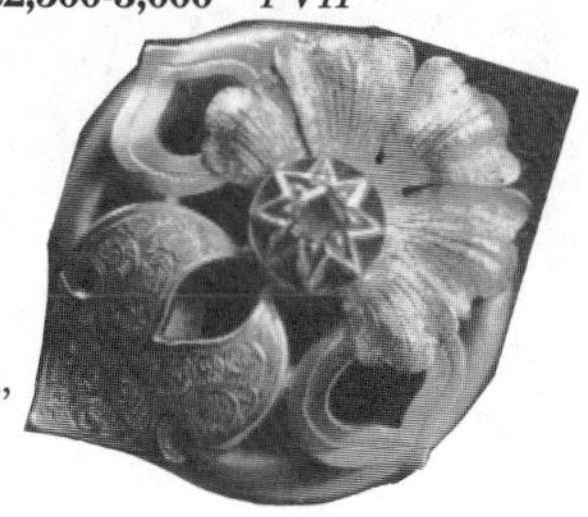

A mid-Victorian 15ct gold brooch, set with an emerald.
£350-450 *PVH*

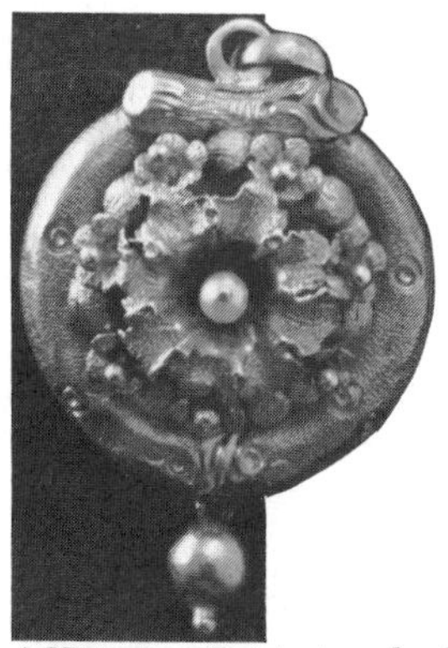

A Victorian 15ct textured gold brooch, set with natural pearls, with locket back for photograph, c1860.
£250-300 *PVH*

An 18ct gold brooch, with miniature on glass, late 19thC.
£850-1,000 *PVH*

CAUTIONARY NOTE

- ★ caution is recommended in the purchase of pieces which appear to be from the Victorian to the Art Deco period
- ★ during the past few years some excellent unhallmarked reproductions have found their way on to the market; they are made with such skill and precision that it is almost impossible to distinguish them from the originals
- ★ the importance of buying from reputable and knowledgeable sources cannot be stressed strongly enough

A platinum, diamond and seed pearl pendant, suspending a diamond drop within a cagework frame millegrain set with brilliant and rose cut diamonds from a bow tied ribbon and with single pearl drop, on chain.
£1,500-1,800 *Bea*

A William IV gold brooch, set with natural pearls around carnelian centre, with rock crystal aperture for hair or miniature.
£350-450 *PVH*

A gold and diamond mounted portrait miniature pendant, the miniature painted on ivory, within a diamond set frame.
£500-600 *Bea*

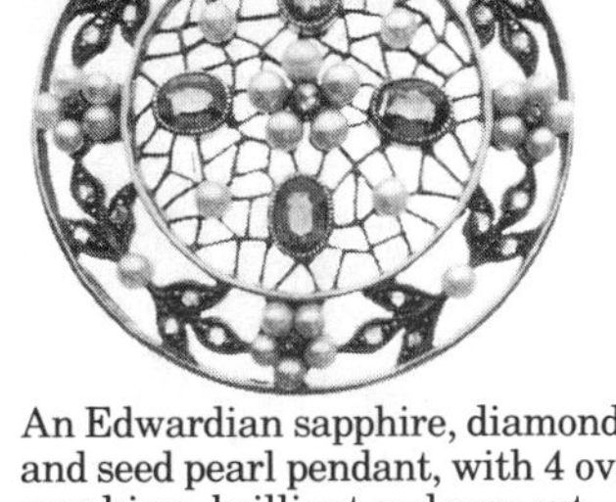

An Edwardian sapphire, diamond and seed pearl pendant, with 4 oval sapphires, brilliant and rose cut diamonds.
£850-950 *Bea*

A gold and rose diamond photograph pendant, the frame of rose diamonds, suspended from a ribbon tied bow, late 19thC.
£500-600 *Bea*

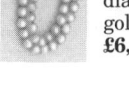

A French gold, ruby and diamond oval pendant, pavé set with rose diamonds and calibre cut rubies with oval ruby centre stone on a quatrefoil glass frame, glass damaged, suspended from a ribbon bow motif.
£650-750 *Bea*

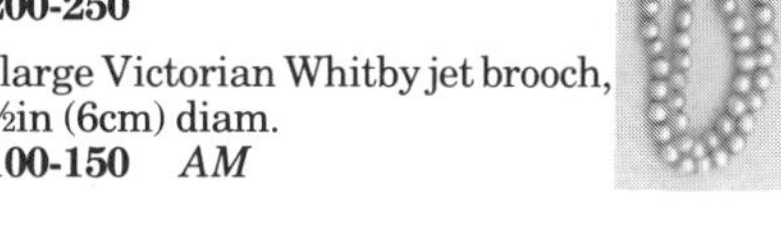

A Victorian Whitby jet necklace, with ribbon fastening, 16in (40.5cm) long.
£200-250

A large Victorian Whitby jet brooch, 2½in (6cm) diam.
£100-150 *AM*

A double row of graduated pearls, with a 19thC navette shaped diamond set clasp of 21 stones, set in gold.
£6,500-7,500 *DN*

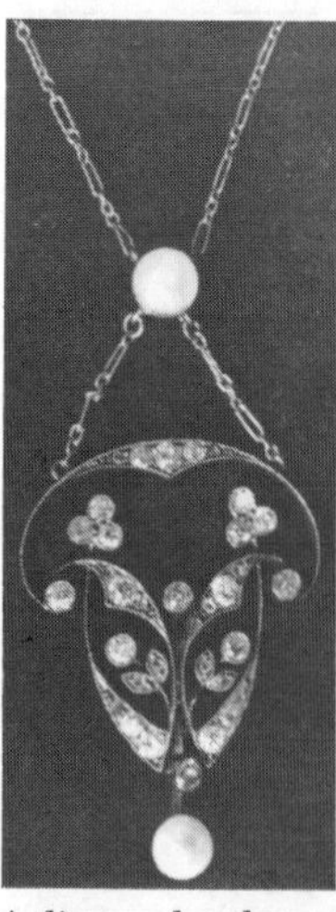
A diamond and pearl pendant.
£400-500 *PC*

A 15ct gold floral and scroll design articulated pendant, set with pearls.
£250-300 *PC*

A Victorian opal and diamond pendant.
£1,300-1,500 *LG*

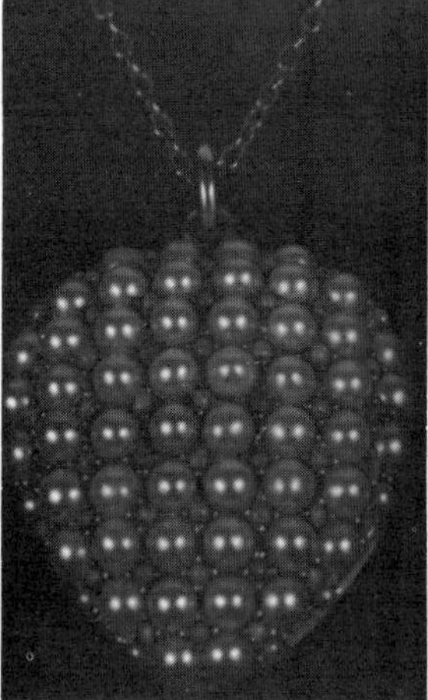
A Victorian gold, pearl and turquoise heart locket and chain, c1880, 3cm long.
£1,800-2,000 *LG*

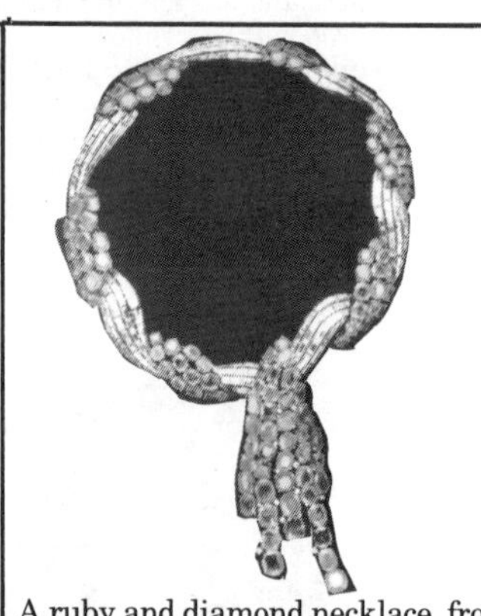
A ruby and diamond necklace, from the Duchess of Windsor's collection, a birthday present from the Duke of Windsor to the Duchess on the occasion of her 40th birthday, on 19th June 1936, re-made by Van Cleef and Arpels in 1939.
£1,700,000+ *PVH*

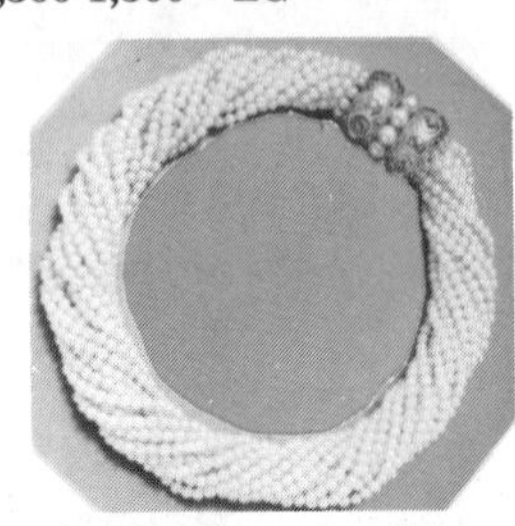
A 15 row simulated pearl necklace, from the Duchess of Windsor's collection, the clasp of 2 tubular rings of gold set with diamonds and a row of cultured pearls, by Darde et Fils, c1960.
£32,000-40,000 *PVH*

A red coral bead necklace.
£100-150 *PC*

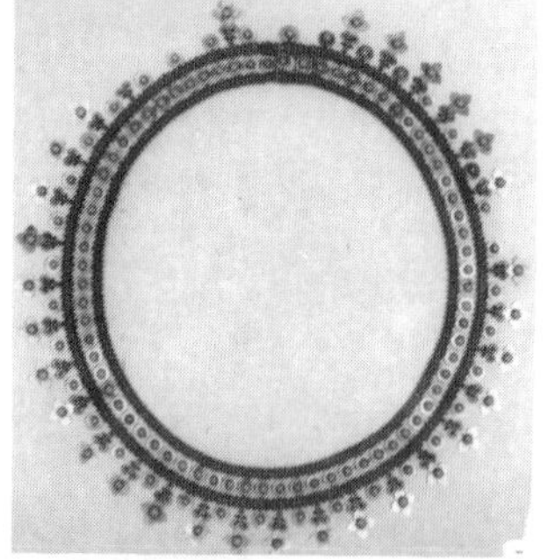
A Victorian 18ct gold, turquoise and pearl necklace.
£2,500-3,000 *DN*

A cushion shaped blue 206.82ct sapphire, from the Duchess of Windsor's collection, surrounded by 11.31ct baguette and brilliant cut diamonds, by Cartier, Paris, 1951.
£212,000+ *PVH*

A tiara, formed as 3 flowerhead and leaf sprays pavé set with brilliant cut diamonds, centre stone .75ct, dividing to form 3 spray brooches, c1880, the fitted velvet lined case stamped E. White, 20 Cockspur St., Pall Mall.
£4,000-4,500 *P[Pea]*

An Art Nouveau pendant, the carved ivory face set in silver and enamel with baroque natural pearls and cut tourmalines, c1890, 12cm overall.
£1,200-1,500 *PVH*

Arms & Armour

Armour

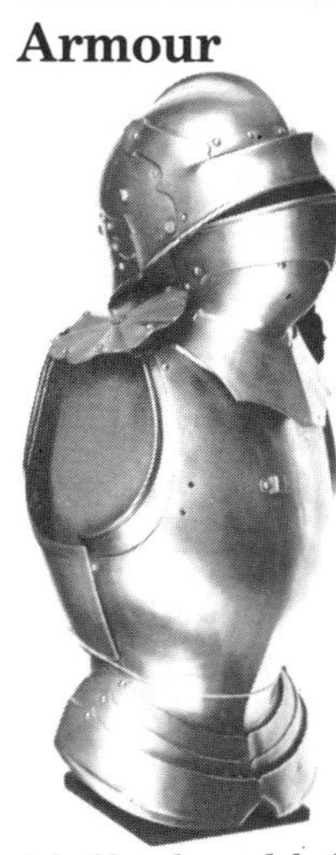

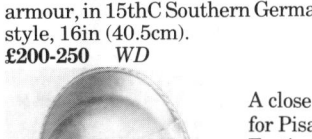

A half-scale model of a Gothic armour, in 15thC Southern German style, 16in (40.5cm).
£200-250 *WD*

A composite half-armour, European, slightly damaged, mid-16thC.
£1,400-1,600 *CSK*

A composite Innsbruck half armour, some damage, c1555.
£6,000-6,500 *CSK*

A Japanese suit of armour.
£700-900 *WAL*

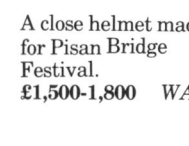

A close helmet made for Pisan Bridge Festival.
£1,500-1,800 *WAL*

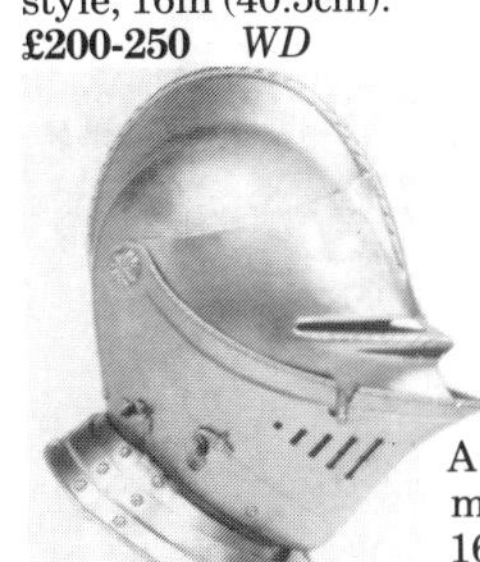

A close helmet, a modern copy of a 16thC helmet, 13in (33cm) high.
£250-300 *CSK*

A Cuirassier helmet, probably Italian, old riveted and brazed internal patches, c1600, 11½in (29cm) high.
£1,000-1,200 *CSK*

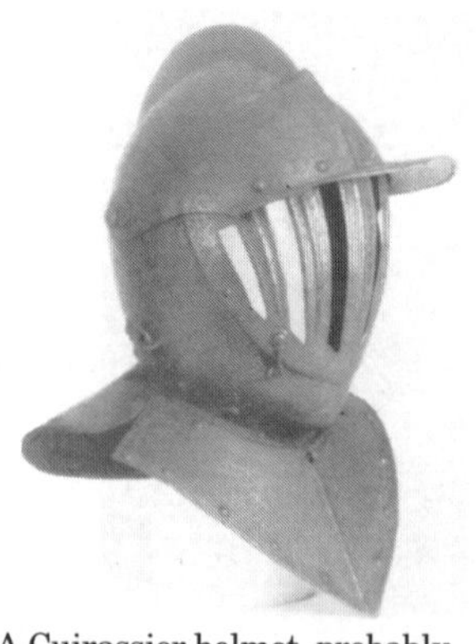

A Cuirassier helmet, probably German, early 17thC, 13in (33cm).
£1,600-1,800 *CSK*

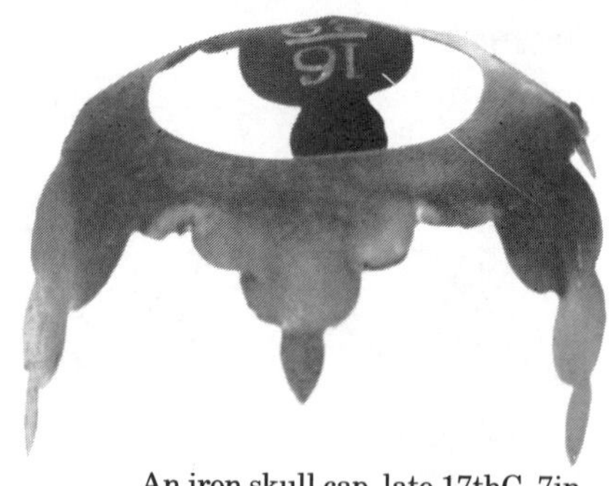

An iron skull cap, late 17thC, 7in (18cm) diam.
£200-250 *WD*

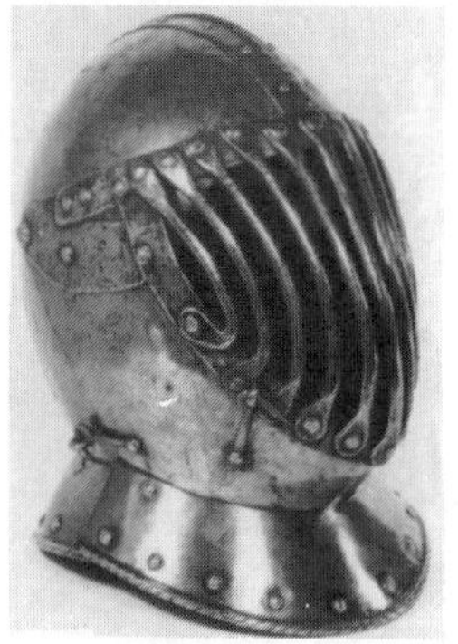

A close helmet, mainly 17thC.
£850-950 *P*

A German peaked burgonet.
£1,000-1,500 *WAL*

A Dutch Zwolletown guard spontoon.
£400-450

A German mace, mid-16thC.
£3,000-3,500 *WAL*

Cannon

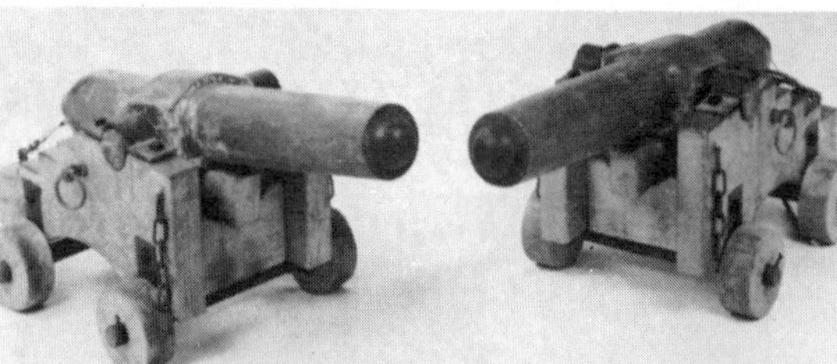

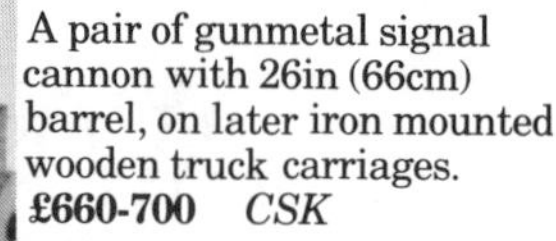

A pair of gunmetal signal cannon with 26in (66cm) barrel, on later iron mounted wooden truck carriages.
£660-700 *CSK*

An Indo-Persian devil's head helmet, Kulah Khud.
£450-500 *WAL*

Edged Weapons – Bayonets

Crossbows

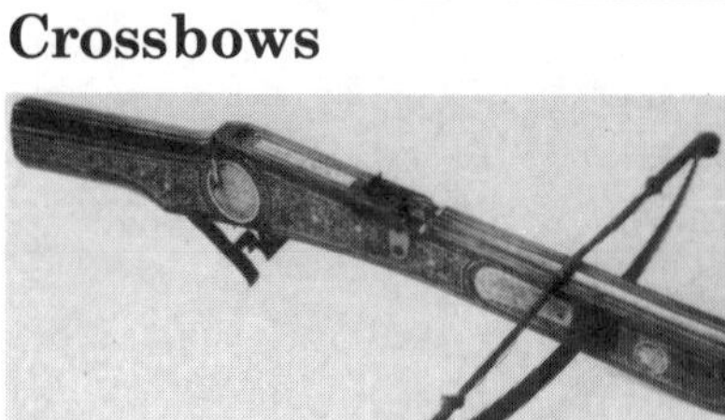

A German sporting crossbow, engraved Conradus Wirtz, rear sight lacking, dated 1620, with a crossbow bolt with iron socket head and wood shaft, flights lacking.
£2,000-3,000 *P*

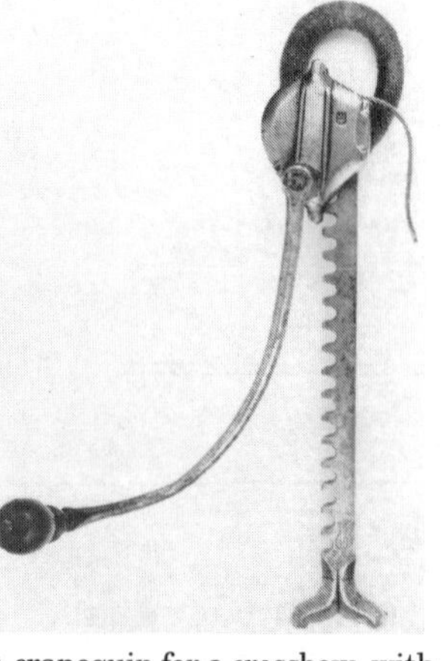

A cranequin for a crossbow, with plain wheel case struck with maker's mark in a brass inlaid shield, ratchet bar engraved with a bud, later wooden crank handle, flat belt hook, and later cord loop, late 15th/early 16thC, 13in (33cm).
£800-900 *CSK*

A bayonet, British pattern 1859, minor damage to scabbard leather.
£200-250 *WD*

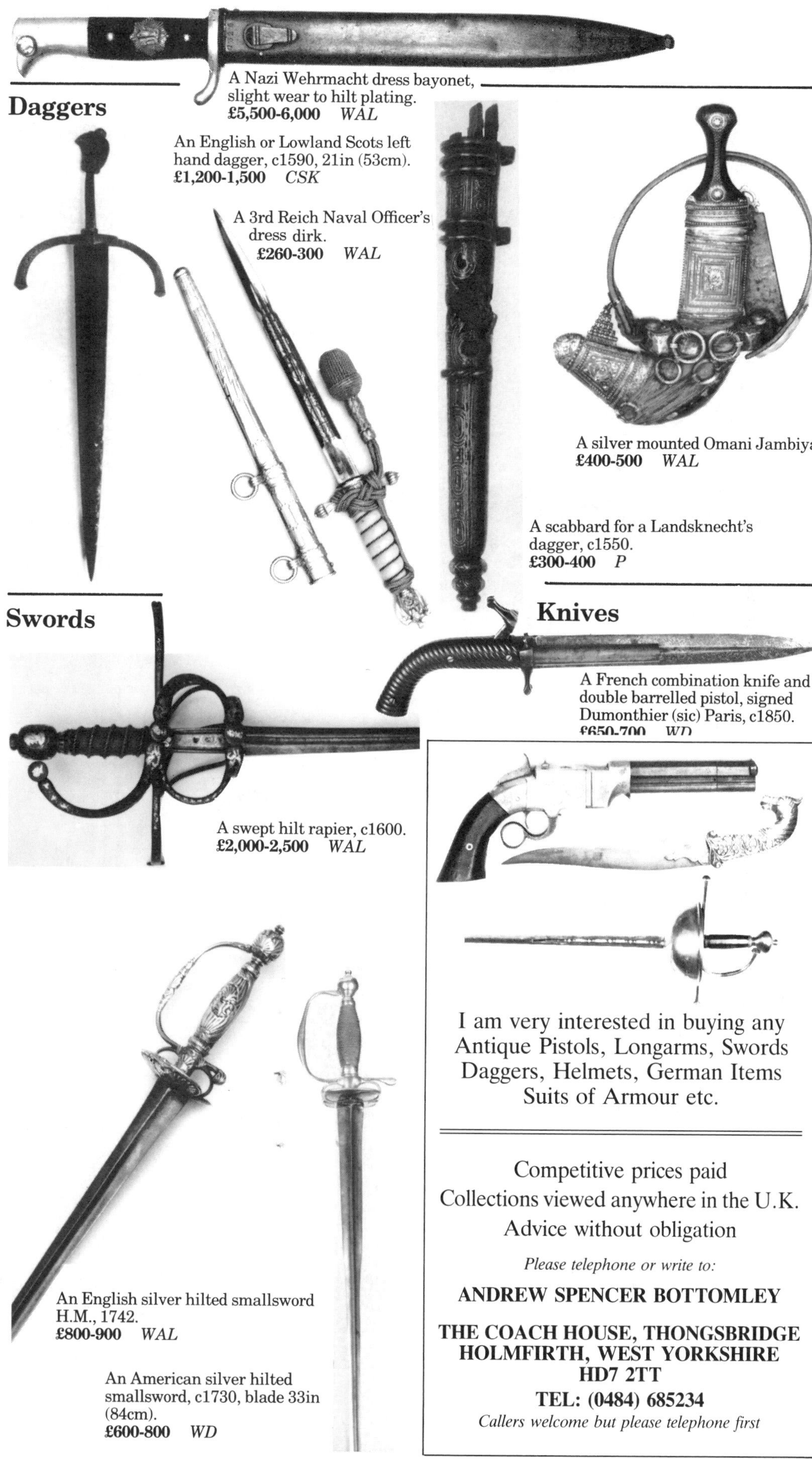

A Nazi Wehrmacht dress bayonet, slight wear to hilt plating.
£5,500-6,000 *WAL*

Daggers

An English or Lowland Scots left hand dagger, c1590, 21in (53cm).
£1,200-1,500 *CSK*

A 3rd Reich Naval Officer's dress dirk.
£260-300 *WAL*

A silver mounted Omani Jambiya.
£400-500 *WAL*

A scabbard for a Landsknecht's dagger, c1550.
£300-400 *P*

Swords

A swept hilt rapier, c1600.
£2,000-2,500 *WAL*

An English silver hilted smallsword H.M., 1742.
£800-900 *WAL*

An American silver hilted smallsword, c1730, blade 33in (84cm).
£600-800 *WD*

Knives

A French combination knife and double barrelled pistol, signed Dumonthier (sic) Paris, c1850.
£650-700 *WD*

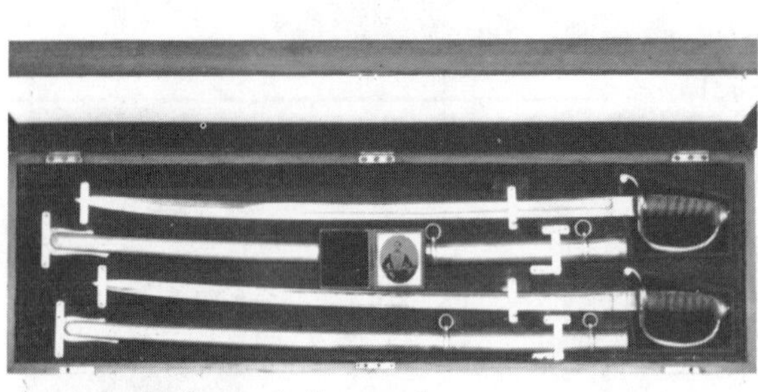

A cased pair of presentation swords to Cpl. Poles, 1st West Yorkshire Yeomanry.
£1,600-1,800 *WAL*

A German sabre, by Stroblberger in München, some damage, 19thC, blade 33in (81cm).
£1,300-1,500 *CSK*

A Rifle Officer's sword, with Indian Mutiny interest.
£550-650 *WAL*

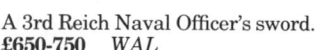

A German 3rd Reich presentation Forestry cutlass given to high officials for dedicated service, by Karl Eickhorn, Solingen, c1935.
£1,500-2,000 *GW*

A 3rd Reich Naval Officer's sword.
£650-750 *WAL*

A Prussian Garde Officer's sword, 1889 pattern.
£1,300-1,500 *WAL*

Swords – Eastern

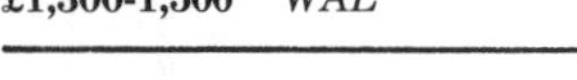

An Indian sabre with European curved fullered blade, minor repairs, 18th/19thC, blade 30in (76cm).
£1,200-1,500 *CSK*

An Indian Shamshir, early 19thC.
£650-750 *WAL*

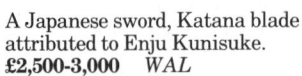

A Japanese sword, Katana blade attributed to Enju Kunisuke.
£2,500-3,000 *WAL*

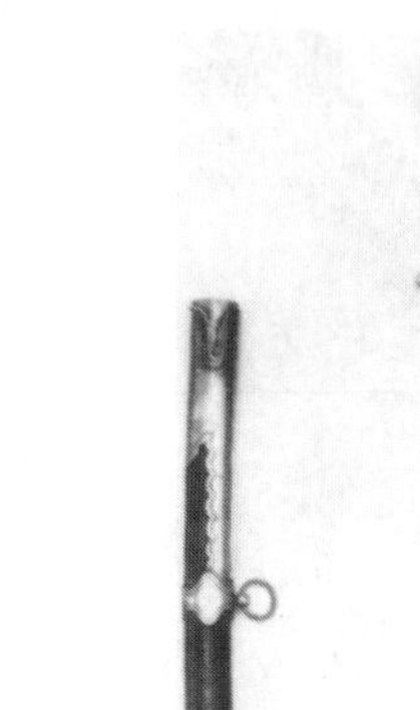

A Turkish Shamshir, stamped with Turkish hallmarks, blade 33½in (85cm).
£600-650 *P*

Blunderbusses

A brass barrelled flintlock blunderbuss, fore-end restored, barrel 15½in (39.5cm).
£500-600 *P*

A brass barrelled flintlock blunderbuss, the engraved lock signed Waters & Gill, 12in (30cm).
£950-1,000 *P*

A brass barrelled flintlock blunderbuss, engraved London, signed Joyner, and stamped with an ordnance mark, 14in (36cm).
£950-1,000 *P*

A flintlock blunderbuss with bayonet, by REA.
£650-750

A flintlock blunderbuss by Wilson.
£700-750 *WAL*

Muskets & Sporting

A matchlock musket, the two-stage sighted barrel struck with maker's mark C.R. at the breech, North European, c1630, 41in (104cm).
£700-800 *P*

An Austrian rifled flintlock sporting carbine, c1770.
£500-800 *WAL*

An Elliott flintlock Cavalry carbine.
£1,200-1,500 *WAL*

An Italian matchlock musket, 16thC.
£1,200-1,500 *WAL*

A British Naval flintlock musketoon.
£2,000-2,500
A seven shot volley gun.
£2,200-2,500 *WAL*

Two Japanese matchlocks,
gun. **£500-550**
rifle. **£900-1,000** *WAL*

A double barrelled 12-bore sidelock ejector shotgun, by George Gibbs, Serial No. C581, nitro proof, re-barrelled by makers in 1979, barrels 28in (71cm), in plush lined leather case with maker's trade label.
£1,300-1,500 *P*

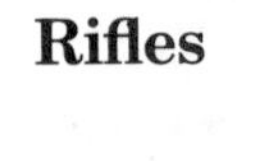

Rifles

An American Hall's Patent military flintlock rifle.
£1,200-1,500 *WAL*

A Belgian percussion target rifle.
£1,600-2,000 *WAL*

A .360 express NP double barrelled sporting rifle, by William Evans, cased.
£2,000-2,500 *WAL*

A German double barrelled percussion sporting gun/rifle.
£1,500-2,000 *WAL*

An American 9-shot Porter's Patent turret percussion rifle.
£1,600-1,800 *WAL*

Pistols

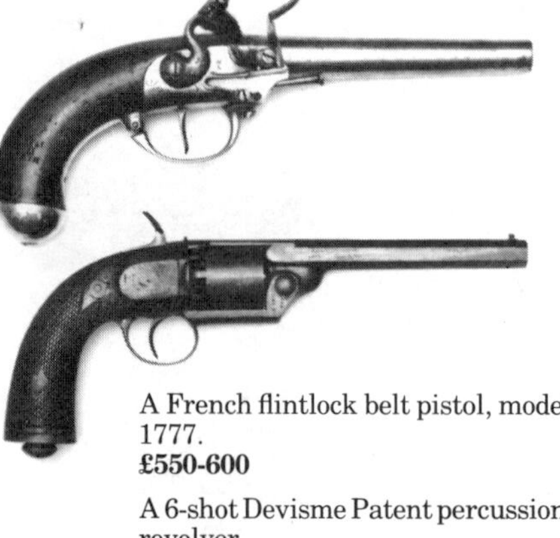

A French flintlock belt pistol, model 1777.
£550-600

A 6-shot Devisme Patent percussion revolver.
£750-800 *WAL*

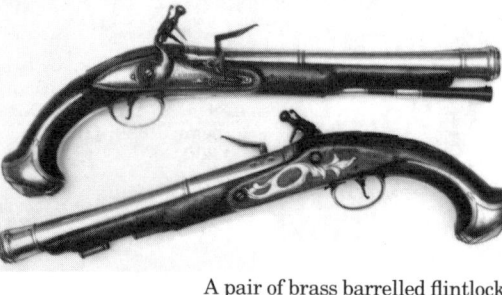

A pair of brass barrelled flintlock blunderbuss pistols, by Clemmes.
£2,200-2,500 *WAL*

A Scottish percussion belt pistol.
£1,200-1,500 *WAL*

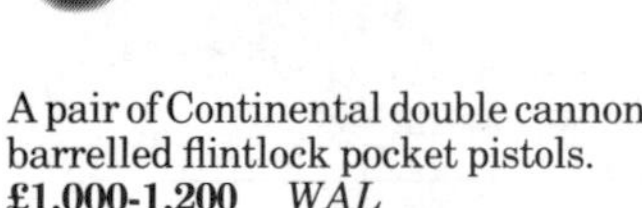

A pair of Continental double cannon barrelled flintlock pocket pistols.
£1,000-1,200 *WAL*

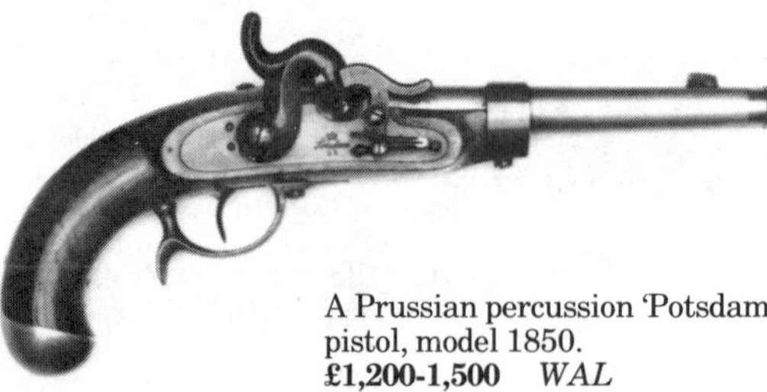

A Prussian percussion 'Potsdam' pistol, model 1850.
£1,200-1,500 *WAL*

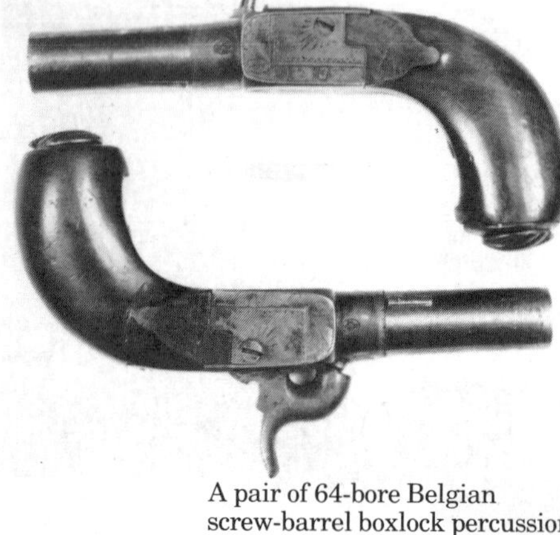

A pair of 64-bore Belgian screw-barrel boxlock percussion muff pistols, c1855, barrel 4cm.
£200-250 *WD*

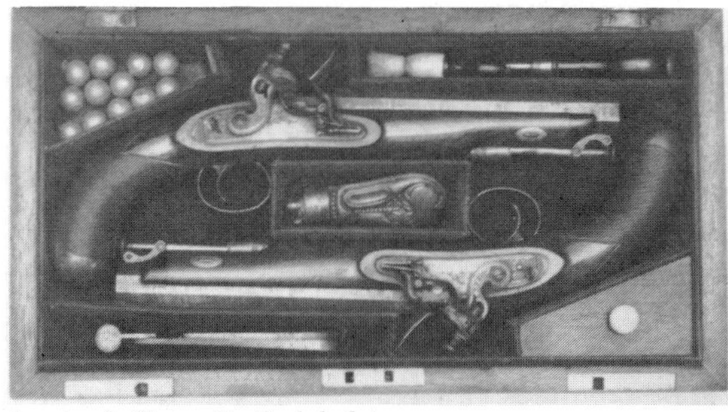

A pair of officers flintlock holster pistols by Hamburger & Co., cased.
£1,400-1,600 *WAL*

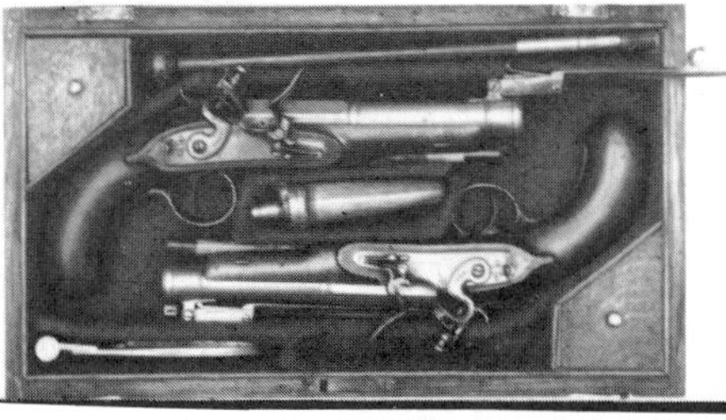

A pair of brass barrelled flintlock pistols by Wilson, cased.
£2,300-2,600 *WAL*

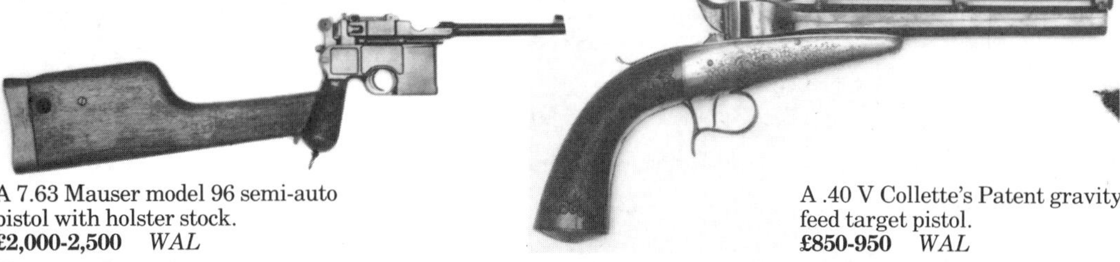

A 7.63 Mauser model 96 semi-auto pistol with holster stock.
£2,000-2,500 *WAL*

A .40 V Collette's Patent gravity feed target pistol.
£850-950 *WAL*

Revolvers

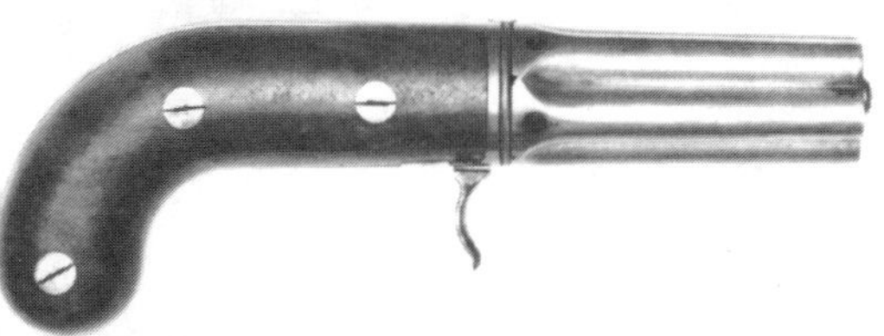

A 5 shot 2nd model pepperbox by Budding.
£1,000-1,500 *WAL*

An 8-shot Austrian pepperbox revolver.
£1,000-1,200 *WAL*

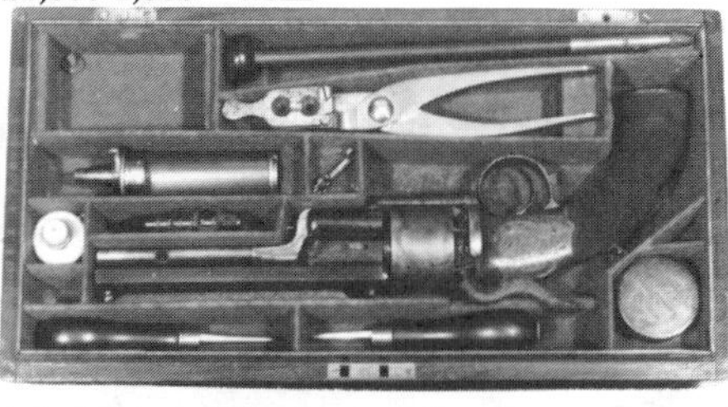

A 6-shot transitional percussion revolver by T. K. Baker, cased.
£1,000-1,200 *WAL*

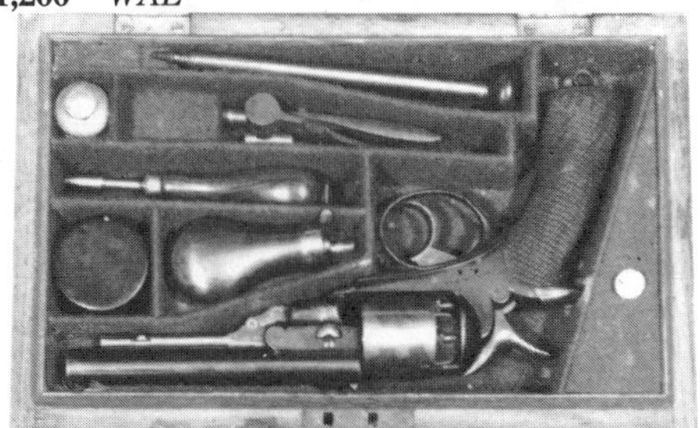

A 5-shot double action percussion revolver, by Daw, cased.
£900-1,000 *WAL*

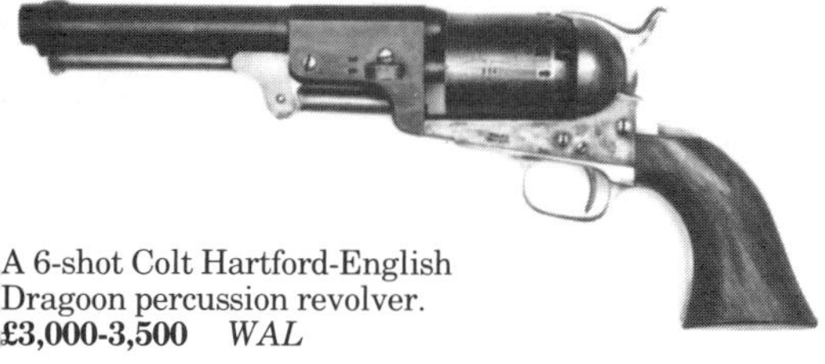

A 6-shot Colt Hartford-English Dragoon percussion revolver.
£3,000-3,500 *WAL*

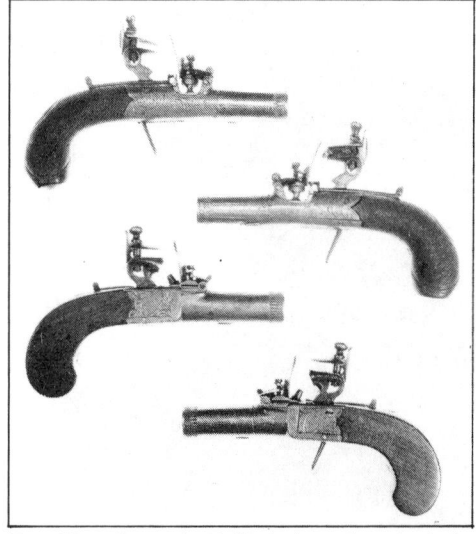

A 120 bore Beaumont-Adams 5-shot double action percussion pocket revolver, serial No. 461, retailed by Deane & Son, 30 King William Street, London Bridge, on an 1851 model frame, barrel 4in (10cm).
£850-1,000 *WD*

Medals & Orders

Louisbourg silver medal, 1758.
£950-1,000 *WAL*

Military General Service 2 bar medal, 1793.
£2,500-2,800 *WAL*

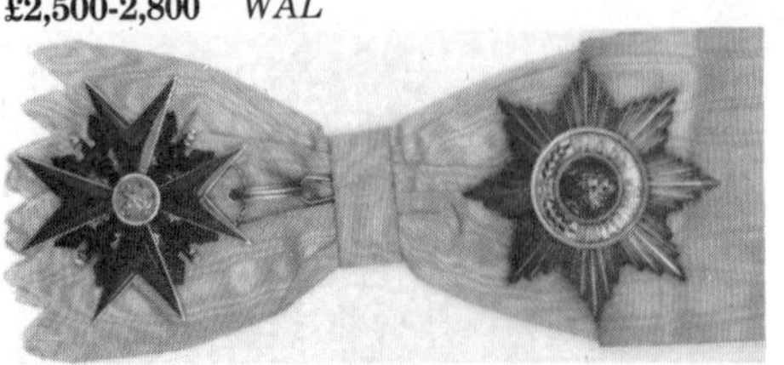

Prussian Order of the Black Eagle, Grand Cross.
£3,200-3,500 *WAL*

Naval General Service Medal, Trafalgar bar.
£800-1,000 *WAL*

Order of the Bath, Civil, Knight Grand Cross, breast star.
£650-750 *WAL*

Prussian Order of Hohenzollern Grand Cross, star with swords, breast star.
£1,800-2,000 *WAL*

Officer's Pugaree badge Coldstream Guards.
£350-400 *WAL*

Militaria, Badges & Plates

Other ranks, Shako Badge, Tower Hamlets Rifles.
£210-250 *WAL*

Officer's plain brooch, Highland Lt. Infantry.
£400-450 *WAL*

Third Reich Auxiliary Cruiser badge, with diamonds.
£4,500-5,000 *WAL*

Shoulder belt plate Royal Monmouth Regt.
£250-300 *WAL*

Helmets

Imperial Austrian Pilots badge.
£350-400 *WAL*

A Victorian Troopers helmet, Lothian & Berwickshire Yeomanry.
£1,000-1,500 *WAL*

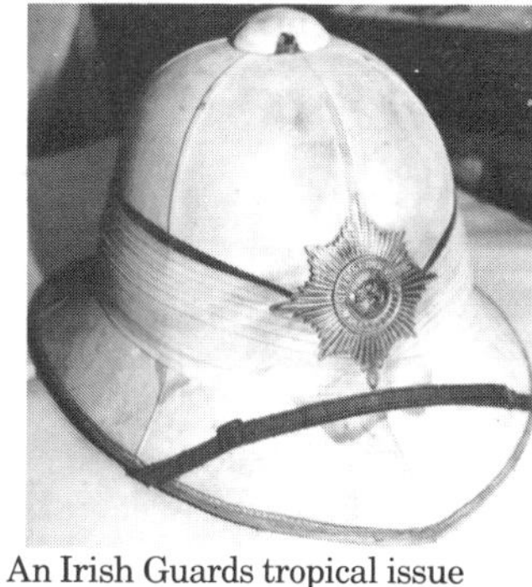

An Irish Guards tropical issue topee, white linen covered with Pugri with regimental Pugri badge in white metal, probably special band/musicians issue, c1900.
£75-100 *GW*

Powder Flasks

A Sykes Patent revolver flask, the brass collar and top with 3 position charger, bag shaped copper body, minor damage, 6in (15cm).
£80-100 *WD*

A presentation signed photograph of Kaiser Wilhelm II.
£1,200-1,500 *WAL*

Thirteen toy soldiers, Nazi period.
£450-500 *WAL*

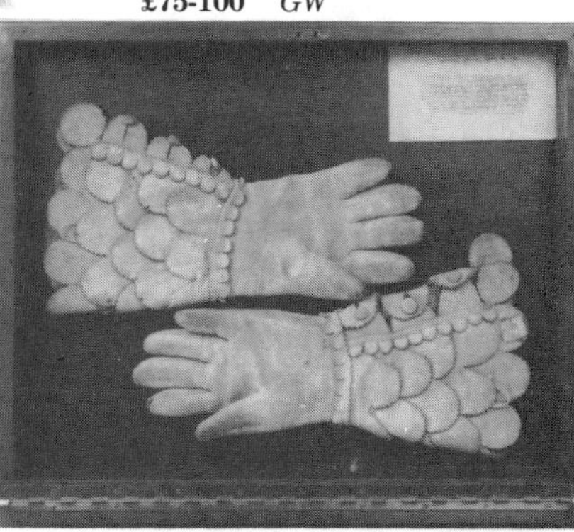

A pair of buff leather gauntlets, contained in a framed and glazed case, 17thC.
£3,500-4,000 *P*

Miscellaneous

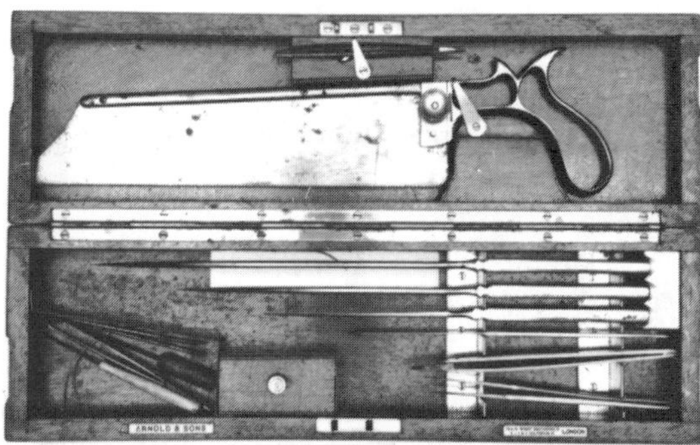

A Victorian set of surgeon's instruments, cased.
£450-500 *WAL*

Coins

A George V specimen set of 12 gold and silver coins, £5 to Maundy penny, 1911, in a lined case.
£2,000-2,500 *GC*

AUCTIONEERS

Auctioneers
in the South of England

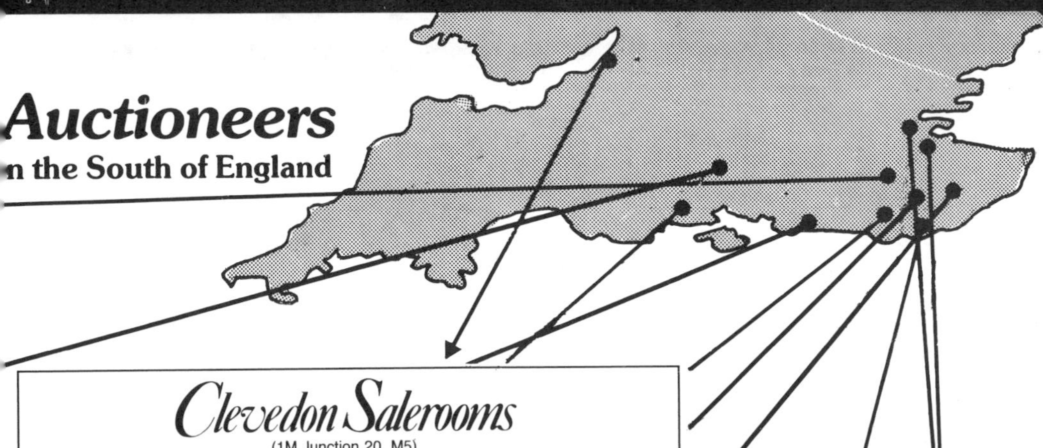

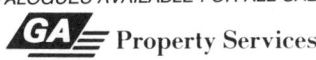

D.M.NESBIT
& Company

HOBBS &
CHAMBERS
INCORPORATING D·N·PERRY & COMPANY

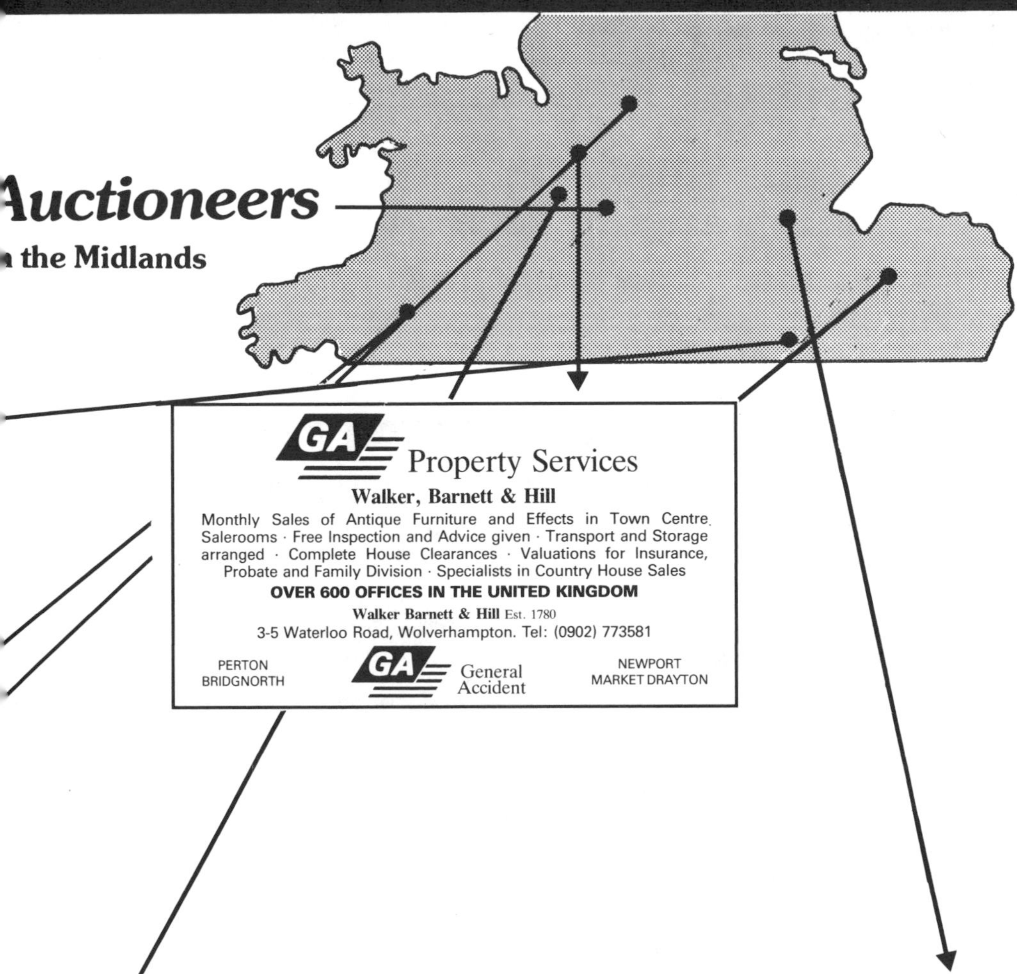

William H. Brown

FINE ART

– Fine Art Auctioneers and Valuers –

What we do . . .

SALES

- *Regular auction sales of antiques and fine art at our main salerooms*
- *Regular auction sales of general furniture and effects at all salerooms*
- *Contents sales on vendors' premises*
- *Total House clearance for executors*

VALUATIONS

Valuations and Inventories for Insurance, Probate, Capital Transfer, Capital Gains Tax and Family Division

ADVICE

Free Advisory Service at the salerooms

Where we do it . . .

Wilbys William H. Brown
11 Regent Street South
Barnsley
South Yorkshire S70 2HT
(0226) 299221

William H. Brown
The Auction Rooms
11-14 East Hill
Colchester
Essex CO1 2QX
(0206) 868070

William H. Brown
Stanilands Auction Room
28 Netherhall Road
Doncaster DN1 2PW
(0302) 67766

William H. Brown
Westgate Hall
Westgate
Grantham
Lincolnshire NG31 6LT
(0476) 68861

Aldreds William H. Brown
Aldreds Auction Room
Kitchener Road
Great Yarmouth
Norfolk NR30 4HU
(0493) 844891

Morphets
4 & 6 Albert Street
Harrogate
North Yorkshire HG1 1JL
(0423) 530030

William H. Brown
The Warner Auction Rooms
16-18 Halford Street
Leicester LE1 1JB
(0533) 519777

William H. Brown
Northgate House
Sleaford
Lincolnshire NG34 7BZ
(0529) 306868

White & Kingston
18-19 Sheep Market
Spalding
Lincolnshire PE11 1PG
(0775) 66991

Olivers
Olivers Rooms
Burkitts Lane
Sudbury
Suffolk
(0787) 880305

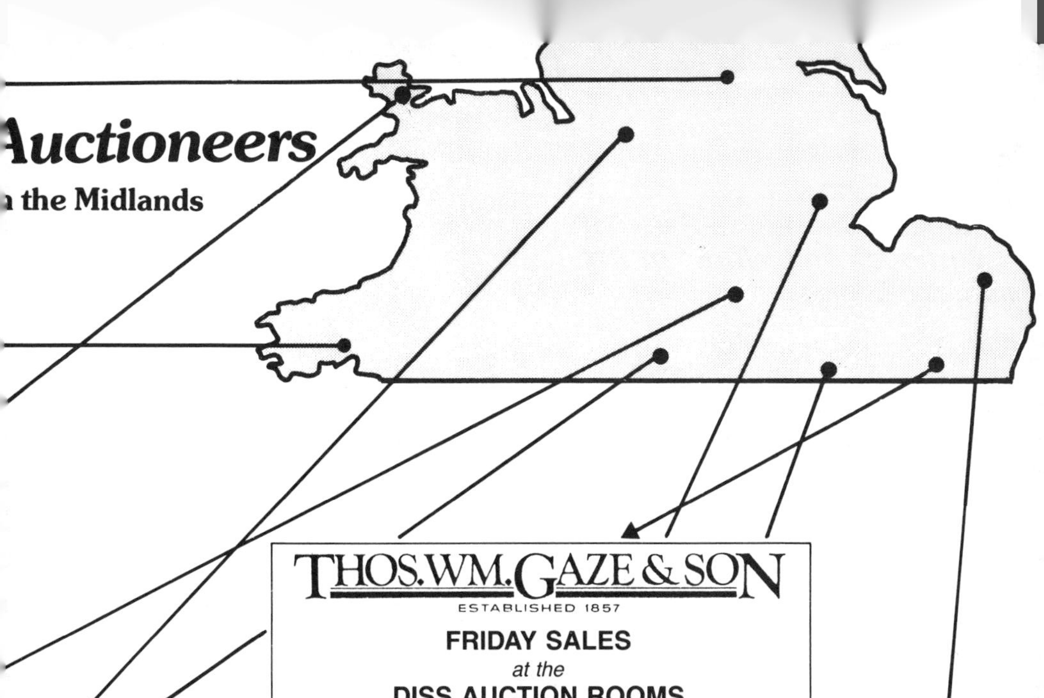

Auctioneers
the Midlands

Auctioneers

Scotland and the North of England

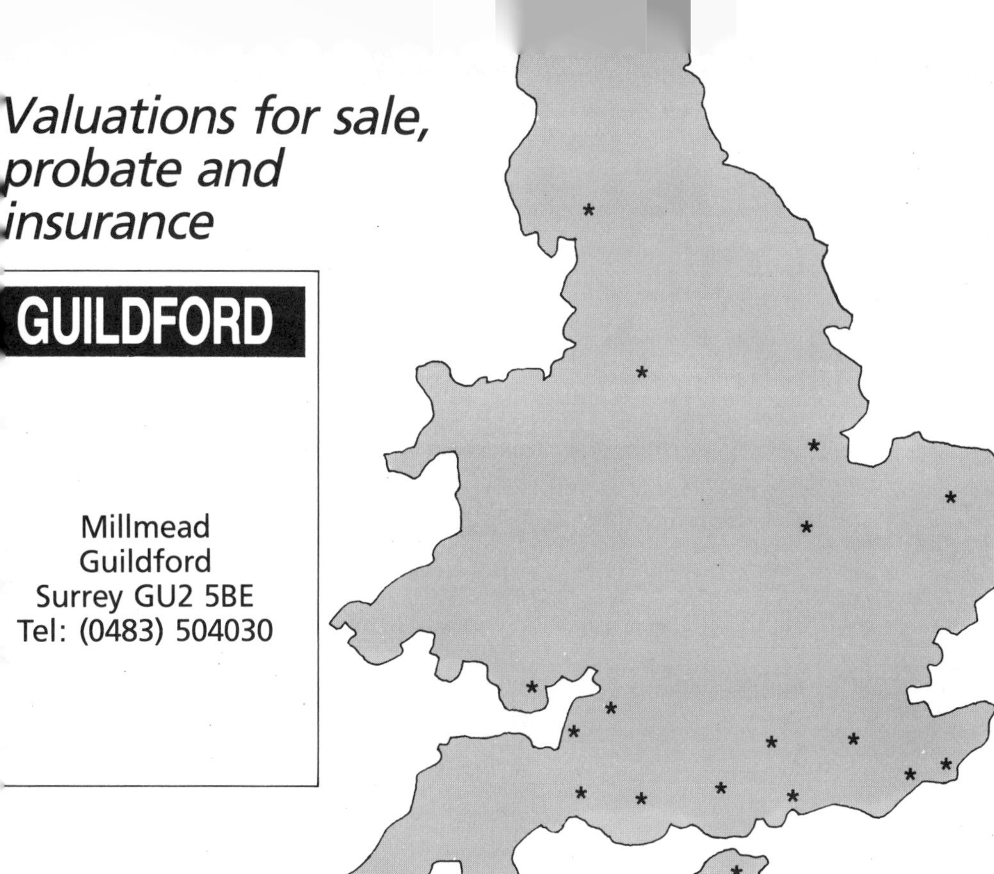

Seventeen salerooms throughout the U.K.

ENGLISH LAKE DISTRICT

Regular Antique
Auctions
Tel: (0229) 55205

SEVENOAKS

49 London Road
Sevenoaks
Kent TN13 1UU
Tel: (0732) 740310

CHICHESTER

Baffins Hall
Baffins Lane
Chichester
West Sussex PO19 1UA
Tel: (0243) 787548

SLEAFORD

67 Northgate
Sleaford
Lincs. NG34 7BB
Tel: (0529) 302946

DIRECTORY OF AUCTIONEERS

This directory is by no means complete. Any auctioneer who holds frequent sales should contact us for inclusion in the 1990 Edition. Entries must be received by April 1989. There is, of course, no charge for this listing. Entries will be repeated in subsequent editions unless we are requested otherwise.

London

Academy Auctioneers & Valuers,
Windsor Hall, Windsor Road,
Ealing, W5
Tel: 01-992 2518/01-868 2812

Allen of Lee Ltd,
165 Lee High Road, SE13
Tel: 01-852 3145

Bethnal Green Auctions,
4-6 Ellsworth Street, E2
Tel: 01-739 7348

Bonhams, Montpelier Galleries,
Montpelier Street, Knightsbridge,
SW7
Tel: 01-584 9161

Camden Auctions,
The Saleroom, Hoppers Road,
Winchmore Hill, N21
Tel: 01-886 1550

Christie Manson & Woods Ltd,
8 King Street, St James's, SW1
Tel: 01-839 9060

Christie's Robson Lowe,
47 Duke Street, London, SW1
Tel: 01-839 4034/5

Christie's South Kensington Ltd,
85 Old Brompton Road, SW7
Tel: 01-581 7611

Colney Hatch Auctions,
54/56 High Street, Hornsey, N8
Tel: 01-340 5334

Forrest & Co,
79-85 Cobbold Road, Leytonstone,
E11
Tel: 01-534 2931

Stanley Gibbons Auctions Ltd,
399 Strand, WC2
Tel: 01-836 8444

Glendining & Co,
Blenstock House, 7 Blenheim
Street, New Bond Street, W1
Tel: 01-493 2445

Harmers of London Stamp
Auctioneers Ltd,
91 New Bond Street, W1
Tel: 01-629 0218

Jackson-Stops & Staff,
14 Curzon Street, W1
Tel: 01-499 6291

Lefrevre & Partners (Auctioneers)
Ltd,
The Persian Carpet Galleries,
152 Brompton Road, SW3
Tel: 01-584 5516

London Bridge Auction,
6/8 Park Street, London Bridge,
SE1
Tel: 01-407 9577

Lots Road Chelsea Auction
Galleries,
71 Lots Road, Worlds End,
Chelsea, SW10
Tel: 01-351 7771/01-352 2349

Thomas Moore,
217-219 Greenwich High Road,
SE10
Tel: 01-858 7848

Newington Green Auctions,
55 Green Lanes, N16
Tel: 01-226 4442 & 0368

North West London Auctions,
Lodge House, 9-17 Lodge Lane,
North Finchley, N12
Tel: 01-445 9000

Onslow Auctioneers,
14-16 Carroun Road, London, SW8.
Tel: 01-793 0240

Phillips,
Blenstock House, 7 Blenheim
Street, New Bond Street, W1
Tel: 01-629 6602

Rippon Boswell & Co,
The Arcade, Sth Kensington
Station, SW7
Tel: 01-589 4242

Sotheby's,
34-35 New Bond Street, W1
Tel: 01-493 8080

Southgate Antique Auction
Rooms,
Rear of Southgate Town Hall,
Green Lanes, Palmers Green, N13
Tel: 01-886 7888

Waltham Forest Auctions,
101 Hoe Street, E17
Tel: 01-520 2998

Greater London

Hogg Robinson,
Bonsor Penningtons, 82A Eden
Street, Kingston, Surrey
Tel: 01-541 4139

Croydon Auctions Rooms (Rosan
& Co)
144-150 London Road, Croydon
Tel: 01-688 1123/4/5

Parkins,
18 Malden Road, Cheam, Surrey
Tel: 01-644 6633 & 6127

Avon

Alder King, Black Horse Agencies,
The Old Malthouse, Comfortable
Place, Upper Bristol Road, Bath
Tel: (0225) 447933

Aldridges, Bath,
The Auction Galleries, 130-132
Walcot Street, Bath
Tel: (0225) 62830 & 62839

Blessley Davis,
42 High Street, Chipping Sodbury,
Bristol
Tel: (0454) 312848/313033

G.A. Property Services,
Clevedon Salerooms, Sixways,
Clevedon
Tel: (0272) 876699

Osmond Tricks,
Regent Street Auction Rooms,
Clifton, Bristol
Tel: (0272) 737201

Phillips Auction Rooms of Bath,
1 Old King Street, Bath
Tel: (0225) 310609 & 319709

Prudential Fine Art Auctioneers,
71 Oakfield Road, Clifton, Bristol
Tel: (0272) 734052
also at:
Station Road, Weston-super-Mare
Tel: (0934) 33174

Taviner's Auction Rooms,
Prewett Street, Redcliffe, Bristol
Tel: (0272) 25996

Woodspring Auction Rooms,
Churchill Road, Weston-super-
Mare
Tel: (0934) 28419

Bedfordshire

Peacock,
The Auction Centre, 26 Newnham
Street, Bedford
Tel: (0234) 66366

Berkshire

Chancellors Hollingsworths,
31 High Street, Ascot
Tel: (0990) 27101

Dreweatt, Neate,
Donnington Priory, Donnington,
Newbury
Tel: (0635) 31234

Holloway's
12 High Street, Streatley, Reading
Tel: (0491) 872318

Humble & Hollis,
Old Street, Beaconsfield
Tel: (0895) 832875

Martin & Pole,
5a & 7 Broad Street, Wokingham
Tel: (0734) 780777

Thimbleby & Shorland,
31 Great Knollys Street, Reading
Tel: (0734) 508611

Vanderpump & Wellbelove,
40 Prospect Street, Caversham,
Reading
Tel: (0734) 482002

Duncan Vincent Fine Art &
Chattel Auctioneers,
105 London Street, Reading
Tel: (0734) 594748

Buckinghamshire

Hetheringtons Nationwide,
The Amersham Auction Rooms,
125 Station Road, Amersham
Tel: (0494) 729292

Geo Wigley & Sons,
Winslow Sale Room, Market
Square, Winslow
Tel: (029 671) 2717

Cambridgeshire

Cheffins Grain & Comins,
2 Clifton Road, Cambridge
Tel: (0223) 358721/213343

Prudential Fine Art Auctioneers,
The Saleroom, Market Square, St
Ives, Huntingdon
Tel: (0480) 68144

Grounds & Co
2 Nene Quay, Wisbech
Tel: (0945) 585041

Hammond & Co,
Cambridge Place, off Hills Road,
Cambridge
Tel: (0223) 356067

Maxey & Son,
1-3 South Brink, Wisbech
Tel: (0945) 583123/4

Cheshire

Andrew, Hilditch & Son,
19 The Square, Sandbach
Tel: (0270) 762048/767246

Bridgfords Ltd,
The Alderley Saleroom, 1 Heyes
Lane, Alderley Edge
Tel: (0625) 585347

Brocklehurst,
King Edward Street, Macclesfield
Tel: (0625) 29236

Burlings,
St Mary's Saleroom, Buxton Old
Road, Disley
Tel: (06632) 4854

Robert I Heyes,
Hatton Buildings, Lightfoot
Street, Hoole, Chester
Tel: (0244) 28941

Highams Auctions,
Waterloo House, Waterloo Road,
Stalybridge
Tel: 061-303 2924/061-303 1091

Jackson-Stops & Staff,
25 Nicholas Street, Chester
Tel: (0244) 28361

Frank R Marshall & Co,
Marshall House, Church Hill,
Knutsford
Tel: (0565) 53284/53461

Phillips in Chester,
New House, 150 Christleton Road,
Chester
Tel: (0244) 313936

Prudential Fine Art Auctioneers,
Trinity House, 114 Northenden
Road, Sale, Manchester
Tel: 061-962 9237

Rothwell & Co Auctioneers,
Waterloo House, Waterloo Road,
Stalybridge
Tel: 061-338 8698

Sotheby's
Booth Mansion, 28-30 Watergate
Street, Chester
Tel: (0244) 315531

Peter Wilson,
Victoria Gallery, Market Street,
Nantwich
Tel: (0270) 623878

Wright Manley,
Beeston Sales Centre, 63 High
Street, Tarporley
Tel: (0829) 260318

Cleveland

Norman Hope & Partners,
2 South Road, Hartlepool
Tel: (0429) 267828

Lithgow Sons & Partners,
The Auction Houses, Station Road,
Stokesley, Middlesbrough
Tel: (0642) 710158 & 710326

Thomas Watson & Son,
North Ormesby Road,
Middlesbrough
Tel: (0642) 242979

Cornwall

W H Cornish,
Central Auction Rooms, Castle
Street, Truro
Tel: (0872) 72968

Eric Distin & Dolton,
58 Fore Street, Saltash
Tel: (07555) 2355
also at:
7 New Road, Callington
Tel: (0579) 83322
also at:
18 Dean Street, Liskeard
Tel: (0579) 44366

Lambrays, incorporating
R J Hamm ASVA,
Polmorla Walk, The Platt,
Wadebridge
Tel: (020 881) 3593

W H Lane & Son,
St Mary's Auction Rooms,
64 Morrab Road, Penzance
Tel: (0736) 61447

David Lay,
Penzance Auction House,
Alverton, Penzance
Tel: (0736) 61414

Miller & Co,
Lemon Quay Auction Rooms,
Lemon Quay, Truro
Tel: (0872) 74211

Phillips Cornwall,
Cornubia Hall, Par
Tel: (072 681) 4047

Pooley and Rogers,
9 Alverton Street, Penzance and
Regent Auction Rooms, Penzance
Tel: (0736) 63816/7 and (0736)
68814

also at:
5 Street-an-Pol, St Ives
Tel: (0736) 795451

Rowse Jeffery & Watkins,
5 Fore Street, Lostwithiel
Tel: (0208) 872245

Western Galleries t/as Old Town Hall Auctions,
High Street, Falmouth
Tel: (0326) 319437

Cumbria

Mitchells,
Fairfield House, Cockermouth
Tel: (0900) 822016

Alfred Mossops & Co,
Loughrigg Villa, Kelsick Road, Ambleside
Tel: (09663) 3015

Prudential Fine Art Auctioneers,
2 Market Street, Ulverston
Tel: (0229) 55205

James Thompson,
64 Main Street, Kirkby Lonsdale
Tel: (0468) 71555

Thomson, Roddick & Laurie,
24 Lowther Street, Carlisle
Tel: (0228) 28939 & 39636

Tiffen, King & Nicholson,
12 Lowther Street, Carlisle
Tel: (0228) 25259

Derbyshire

Noel Wheatcroft & Son,
The Matlock Auction Gallery,
39 Dale Road, Matlock
Tel: (0629) 4591

Devon

Bearnes,
Avenue Road, Torquay
Tel: (0803) 296277

Michael J Bowman,
6 Haccombe House, Nr Netherton, Newton Abbot
Tel: (0626) 872890

Eric Distin & Dolton,
2 Bretonside, Plymouth
Tel: (0752) 663046

Peter J Eley,
Western House, 98-100 High Street, Sidmouth
Tel: (03955) 2552

Robin A Fenner & Co
51 Bannawell Street, Tavistock
Tel: (0822) 4974

Gribble, Booth & Taylor,
West Street, Axminster
Tel: (0297) 32323

Charles Head & Son,
113 Fore Street, Kingsbridge
Tel: (0548) 2352

Michael G Matthews,
Devon Fine Art Auction House,
Dowell Street, Honiton
Tel: (0404) 41872/3137

Michael Newman,
The Central Auction Rooms,
Kinterbury House, St Andrew's Cross, Plymouth
Tel: (0752) 669298

Phillips,
Alphin Brook Road, Alphington, Exeter
Tel: (0392) 39025/6

Potburys of Sidmouth,
High Street, Sidmouth
Tel: (039 55) 2414

Rendells,
Stone Park, Ashburton
Tel: (0364) 53017

G S Shobrook & Co,
20 Western Approach, Plymouth
Tel: (0752) 663341

John Smale & Co,
19 Cross Street, Barnstaple
Tel: (0271) 42000/42916

Spencer Thomas & Woolland,
Church Street Auction Rooms, Exmouth
Tel: (0395) 267403

David Symonds, FSVA,
The Estate Office, High Street, Crediton
Tel: (03632) 2700/4100

Taylors,
Honiton Galleries, 205 High Street, Honiton
Tel: (0404) 2404

Taylor, Lane & Creber,
The Western Auction Rooms,
38 North Hill, Plymouth
Tel: (0752) 670700

Ward & Chowen,
1 Church Lane, Tavistock
Tel: (0822) 2458

Whitton & Laing,
32 Okehampton Street, Exeter
Tel: (0392) 52621

Dorset

S W Cottee & Son,
The Market, East Street, Wareham
Tel: (09295) 2826

Hy Duke & Son,
Fine Art Salerooms, Weymouth Ave, Dorchester
Tel: (0305) 65080
also at:
The Weymouth Saleroom,
St Nicholas Street, Weymouth
Tel: (0305) 783488

Garnet Langton Auctions,
Burlington Arcade, Bournemouth
Tel: (0202) 22352

House & Son,
Lansdowne House, Christchurch Road, Bournemouth
Tel: (0202) 26232

John Jeffery & Son,
Minster House, The Commons, Shaftesbury
Tel: (0747) 3331

William Morey & Sons,
The Saleroom, St Michaels Lane, Bridport
Tel: (0308) 22078

Prudential Fine Art Auctioneers,
Sturminster Newton
Tel: (0258) 72244

Riddetts of Bournemouth,
Richmond Hill, Bournemouth Square, Bournemouth
Tel: (0202) 25686

County Durham

Denis Edkins,
Auckland Auction Room,
58 Kingsway, Bishop Auckland
Tel: (0388) 603095

Thomas Watson & Son,
Northumberland Street, Darlington
Tel: (0325) 462559

Wingate Auction Co,
Station Lane, Station Town, Wingate
Tel: (0429) 837245

Essex

Abridge Auction Rooms,
Market Place, Abridge
Tel: (037881) 2107/3113

Ambrose,
149 High Road, Loughton
Tel: 01-508 2121

Cooper Hirst,
The Granary Saleroom, Victoria Road, Chelmsford
Tel: (0245) 258141/260535

Grays Auction Rooms,
Ye Old Bake House, Alfred Street, Grays
Tel: (0375) 381181

Paskell & Cann,
The Auction Rooms, 11-14 East Hill, Colchester
Tel: (0206) 868070

Spurgeon & Gilchrist,
1st Floor, Tokenhouse Chambers, Rosemary Road, Clacton-on-Sea
Tel: (0255) 422472

John Stacey & Sons,
Leigh Auction Rooms, 86-90 Pall Mall, Leigh-on-Sea
Tel: (0702) 77051

Vosts' Fine Art Auctioneers,
Layer Marney, Colchester
Tel: (0206) 331005

Edwin Watson & Son,
1 Market Street, Saffron Walden
Tel: (0799) 22058

J M Welch & Son,
Old Town Hall, Great Dunmow
Tel: (0371) 2117/8

Gloucestershire

Bruton, Knowles & Co,
111 Eastgate Street, Gloucester
Tel: (0452) 21267

Fraser Glennie & Partners,
The Old Rectory, Siddington, Nr Cirencester
Tel: (0285) 3938

Hobbs & Chambers,
Market Place, Cirencester
Tel: (0285) 4736
also at:
15 Royal Crescent, Cheltenham
Tel: (0242) 513722

Jackson-Stops & Staff,
Dollar Street House, Cirencester
Tel: (0285) 3334

Ken Lawson t/as Specialised Postcard Auctions,
25 Gloucester Street, Cirencester
Tel: (0285) 69057

Mallams,
26 Grosvenor Street, Cheltenham
Tel: (0242) 35712

Moore, Allen & Innocent,
33 Castle Street, Cirencester
Tel: (0285) 61831

Sandoe Luce Panes,
The Wotton Auction Rooms,
Tabernacle Road, Wotton-under-Edge
Tel: (0453) 844733

Hampshire

Andover Saleroom,
41A London Street, Andover
Tel: (0264) 64820

Austin & Wyatt,
79 High Street, Fareham
Tel: (0329) 234211/4

Michael G Baker, FSVA,
Beales Furniture & Fine Art Dept,
13a The Hundred, Romsey
Tel: (0794) 513331

Elliott & Green, Nationwide Anglia,
The Salerooms, Emsworth Road, Lymington
Tel: (0590) 77225

Fox & Sons,
5 & 7 Salisbury Street, Fordingbridge
Tel: (0425) 52121

GA Property Services,
The Romsey Auction Rooms,
86 The Hundred, Romsey
Tel: (0794) 513331

Stanley Gibbons Auctions Ltd,
5 Parkside, Christchurch Road, Ringwood
Tel: (04254) 77107

Hampshire Auction Room,
135 St Mary Street, Southampton
Tel: (0703) 333593

Hants & Berks Auctions,
40 George Street, Kingsclere
Tel: (0635) 298181
also at:
Heckfield Village Hall, Heckfield, Berks

Jacobs & Hunt,
Lavant Street, Petersfield
Tel: (0730) 62744/5

Martin & Stratford,
The Auction Mart, Market Square, Alton
Tel: (0420) 84402

May & Son,
18 Bridge Street, Andover
Tel: (0264) 23417

D M Nesbit & Co,
7 Clarendon Road, Southsea
Tel: (0705) 864321

Prudential Fine Art Auctioneers,
54 Southampton Road, Ringwood
Tel: (04254) 3333
also at:
The Red House, Hyde Street, Winchester
Tel: (0962) 62515

Hereford & Worcester

Banks & Silvers,
66 Foregate Street, Worcester
Tel: (0905) 23456

Blinkhorn & Co,
41-43 High Street, Broadway
Tel: (0386) 852456

Coles, Knapp & Kennedy,
Georgian Rooms & Tudor House, Ross-on-Wye
Tel: (0989) 62227/63553/4

Maurice Fellows,
6 The Tything, Worcester
Tel: (0905) 27755

Andrew Grant,
St Mark's House, St Mark's Close, Worcester
Tel: (0905) 357547

Arthur G Griffiths & Son,
57 Foregate Street, Worcester
Tel: (0905) 26464

Philip Laney & Jolly,
12a Worcester Road, Gt Malvern
Tel: (06845) 63121/2

Lear & Lear,
71 Church Street, Malvern
Tel: (06845) 61767/8
also at:
46 Foregate Street, Worcester
Tel: (0905) 25184/25194/25494

Phipps & Pritchard,
Bank Buildings, Kidderminster
Tel: (0562) 2244/6 & 2187

Russell, Baldwin & Bright,
Fine Art Saleroom, Ryelands Road, Leominster
Tel: (0568) 3897

Village Auctions,
Sycthampton Community Centre, Ombersley
Tel: (0905) 421007

Hertfordshire

Brown & Merry,
41 High Street, Tring
Tel: (044 282) 6446

George Jackson & Son,
Paynes Park House, Paynes Park, Hitchin
Tel: (0462) 55212

M & B Nesbitt,
The Antique Centre, 23 Hydeway, Welwyn Garden City
Tel: (07073) 34901

Norris & Duvall,
106 The Fore Street, Hertford
Tel: (0992) 582249

Pamela & Barry Auctions,
The Village Hall, High Street, Sandridge, St Albans
Tel: (0727) 61180

G E Sworder & Sons,
Chequers, 19 North Street,
Bishops Stortford
Tel: (0279) 52441

Watsons,
Water Lane, Bishops Stortford
Tel: (0279) 52361/4

Humberside North

Gilbert Baitson, FSVA,
The Edwardian Auction Galleries,
194 Anlaby Road, Hull
Tel: (0482) 223355/645241/865831

Broader & Spencer,
18 Quay Road, Bridlington
Tel: (0262) 70355/6

H Evans & Sons,
1 Parliament Street, Hull
Tel: (0482) 23033

F A Larard & Sons,
18 Wednesday Market, Beverley
Tel: (0482) 868555

Humberside South

Dickinson, Davy & Markham,
10 Wrawby Street, Brigg
Tel: (0652) 53666

Isle of Man

Chrystals Auctions,
St James Chambers, Athol Street,
Douglas
Tel: (0624) 73986

Isle of Wight

Prudential Fine Art Auctioneers,
Cross Street Salerooms, Newport
Tel: (0983) 523812

Watson Bull & Porter,
Auction Rooms, 79-81 Regent
Street, Shanklin
Tel: (0983) 863 441

Way, Riddett & Co,
Town Hall Chambers, Lind Street,
Ryde
Tel: (0983) 62255

Kent

Albert Andrews Auctions & Sales,
Maiden Lane, Crayford, Dartford
Tel: (0322) 528868

Bracketts,
27-29 High Street, Tunbridge
Wells
Tel: (0892) 33733

County Group,
Butler & Hatch Waterman,
102 High Street, Tenterden
Tel: (05806) 2083/3233

GA Auction Galleries,
39-41 Bank Street, Ashford
Tel: (0233) 24321

GA Auction Galleries,
40 Station Road West, Canterbury
Tel: (0227) 763337

Geering & Colyer,
22-24 High Street, Tunbridge
Wells
Tel: (0892) 515300

Stewart Gore,
100-102 Northdown Road,
Margate
Tel: (0843) 221528/9

Hobbs Parker,
Romney House, Ashford Market,
Elwick Road, Ashford
Tel: (0233) 22222

Ibbett Mosely,
125 High Street, Sevenoaks
Tel: (0732) 452246

Kent Sales,
'Giffords', Holmesdale Road, South
Darenth
Tel: (0322) 864919

Lawrence Butler & Co, (inc. F W
Butler & Co),
Fine Art Salerooms, Butler House,
86 High Street, Hythe
Tel: (0303) 66022/3

B J Norris,
'The Quest', West Street,
Harrietsham, Nr Maidstone
Tel: (0622) 859515

One One Five Auctioneers,
R B Lloyd, 115 Main Road,
Sutton-at-Hone, Dartford
Tel: (0322) 862112

Phillips,
11 Bayle Parade, Folkestone
Tel: (0303) 45555

Prudential Fine Art Auctioneers,
16 High Street, Hythe
Tel: (0303) 67473

Prudential Fine Art Auctioneers,
49 London Road, Sevenoaks
Tel: (0732) 740310

James B Terson & Son,
27-29 Castle Street, Dover
Tel: (0304) 202173

St John Vaughan,
53 High Street, Tenterden
Tel: (05806) 3200
also at:
The Sandwich Sale Room,
The Drill Hall, The Quay,
Sandwich
Tel: (0304) 611044

Walter & Randall,
7-13 New Road, Chatham
Tel: (0634) 41233

Peter S Williams, FSVA,
Orchard End, Sutton Valence,
Maidstone
Tel: (0622) 842350

Lancashire

Artingstall & Hind,
378-380 Deansgate, Knott Mill,
Manchester
Tel: 061-834 4559

Capes Dunn & Co,
The Auction Galleries, 38 Charles
Street, Manchester
Tel: 061-273 6060/1911

Cromford Auction Room,
Heron Street, Oldham
Tel: 061-627 0407

Entwistle Green,
The Galleries, Kingsway, Ansdell,
Lytham St Annes
Tel: (0253) 735442

Highams Auctions,
Southgate House, Southgate
Street, Rhodes Bank, Oldham
Tel: 061-626 1021/061-665 1881/
061-624 8580

Johnson Kelly,
33 Bradshawgate, Bolton
Tel: (0204) 384384

Robert Maybin & Co (Auctions),
The Sale Rooms, 88 Stansfield
Street, Blackburn
Tel: (0254) 676976

**McKennas, formerly Hothersall,
Forrest, McKenna & Sons,
Bank Salerooms, Harris Court,
Clitheroe
Tel: (0200) 25446/22695**

Mills & Radcliffe,
101 Union Street, Oldham
Tel: 061-624 1072

J R Parkinson Son & Hamer
Auctions, The Auction Rooms,
Rochdale Road, Bury
Tel: (061 761) 1612/7372

John E Pinder & Son,
Stone Bridge, Longridge, Preston
Tel: (077478) 2282

Smythe, Son & Walker,
174 Victoria Road West, Cleveleys
Tel: (0253) 852184 & 854084

Warner & Wignall Ltd,
The Mill, Earnshaw Bridge,
Leyland Lane, Leyland
Tel: (0772) 453252/451430

Leicestershire

Gildings,
64 Roman Way, Market
Harborough
Tel: (0858) 410 414

Oadby Auctions,
The Churchgate Saleroom,
25 Churchgate, Leicester
Tel: (0533) 21416

Snushall Auctions,
The Saleroom, Wordsworth Road,
Leicester
Tel: (0533) 702801

David Stanley Auctions,
Stordon Grange, Osgathorpe,
Loughborough
Tel: (0530) 222320

Walker Walton Hanson,
4 Market Place, Oakham
Tel: (0572) 3377

William H Brown,
The Warner Auction Rooms,
16/18 Halford Street, Leicester
Tel: (0533) 519777

Lincolnshire

Brogden & Co,
38/39 Silver Street, Lincoln
Tel: (0522) 31321

William H Brown,
Fine Art Dept, Westgate Hall,
Westgate, Grantham
Tel: (0476) 68861

William H Brown,
Northgate House, Sleaford
Tel: (0529) 306868

James Eley & Son,
1 Main Ridge West, Boston
Tel: (0205) 61687

Henry Spencer & Sons,
38 St Mary's Street, Stamford
Tel: (0780) 52136

**Lyall & Co,
Auction Salerooms, Spalding
Road, Bourne
Tel: (0778) 422686**

Thomas Mawer & Son,
63 Monks Road, Lincoln
Tel: (0522) 24984

Prudential Fine Art Auctioneers,
67 Northgate, Sleaford
Tel: (0529) 302946

John H Walter,
1 Mint Lane, Lincoln
Tel: (0522) 25454

White & Kingston,
18-19 Sheep Street, Spalding
Tel: (0775) 66991

Wright & Hodgkinson,
Abbey Road, Bourne
Tel: (07782) 2567

Merseyside

Ball & Percival,
132 Lord Street and 21 Hoghton
Street, Southport
Tel: (0704) 36900

Hartley & Co,
12 & 14 Moss Street, Liverpool
Tel: 051-263 6472/1865

Robert I Heyes & Associates,
9 Hamilton Street, Birkenhead
Tel: 051-647 9104

Kingsley Galleries,
3-4 The Quadrant, Hoylake,
Wirral
Tel: 051-632 5821

Lavelle and Lavelle,
St Helens Auction Rooms,
The Galleries, 3 George Street,
St Helens
Tel: (0744) 59258

Outhwaite & Litherland,
Kingsway Galleries, Fontenoy
Street, Liverpool
Tel: 051-236 6561/3

Talbot Wilson & Co Ltd,
Tynwald Road, W Kirby, Wirral
Tel: 051-625 6491

Eldon E Worrall,
15 Seel Street, Liverpool
Tel: 051-709 2950

Norfolk

Noel D Abel,
32 Norwich Road, Watton
Tel: (0953) 881204

Aldreds William H Brown,
Aldreds Auction Room, Kitchener
Road, Great Yarmouth
Tel: (0493) 844891

Ewings,
Market Place, Reepham, Norwich
Tel: (0603) 870473

Thos Wm Gaze & Son,
10 Market Hill, Diss
Tel: (0379) 51931

Charles Hawkins & Sons,
Lynn Road, Downham Market
Tel: (0366) 382112

Nigel F Hedge,
28B Market Place, North
Walsham
Tel: (0692) 402881

Hilhams,
Baker Street, Gorleston, Great
Yarmouth
Tel: (0493) 662152 & 600700

James Norwich Auctions Ltd,
33 Timberhill, Norwich
Tel: (0603) 624817/625369

G A Key,
8 Market Place, Aylsham
Tel: (0263) 733195

Prudential Fine Art Auctioneers,
Station Road, Wymondham
Tel: (0953) 603031

Northamptonshire

M B Carney, FSVA,
Brackley Auction Rooms, Hill
Street, Brackley
Tel: (0280) 701124

T W Arnold Corby & Co,
30-32 Brook Street, Raunds
Tel: (0933) 623722

Goldsmith & Bass,
15 Market Place, Oundle
Tel: (0832) 72349

Heathcote Ball & Co,
Albion Auction Rooms, Old Albion
Brewery, Commercial Street,
Northampton
Tel: (0604) 22735

R L Lowery & Partners,
24 Bridge Street, Northampton
Tel: (0604) 21561

Southam & Sons,
Corn Exchange, Thrapston,
Kettering
Tel: (08012) 4486

H Wilford Ltd,
Midland Road, Wellingborough
Tel: (0933) 222760 & 222762

Northumberland

Louis Johnson & Co Ltd,
Morpeth
Tel: (0670) 513025/55210

Nottinghamshire

Arthur Johnson & Sons Ltd,
The Nottingham Auction Rooms,
The Cattle Market, Meadow Lane,
Nottingham
Tel: (0602) 869128

Neales of Nottingham,
192 Mansfield Road, Nottingham
Tel: (0602) 624141

John Pye & Sons,
Corn Exchange, Cattle Market, London Road, Nottingham
Tel: (0602) 866261

C B Sheppard & Son,
The Auction Galleries, Chatsworth Street, Sutton-in-Ashfield
Tel: (0773) 872419

Henry Spencer & Sons Ltd,
20 The Square, Retford
Tel: (0777) 706767

Walker Walton Hanson (Auctions),
The Nottingham Auction Mart, Byard Lane, Bridlesmith Gate, Nottingham
Tel: (0602) 54272

Oxfordshire

Green & Co,
33 Market Place, Wantage
Tel: (02357) 3561/2

Holloways,
49 Parsons Street, Banbury
Tel: (0295) 53197/8

Mallams,
24 St Michael's Street, Oxford
Tel: (0865) 241358

Messengers,
27 Sheep Street, Bicester
Tel: (08692) 52901

Phillips Inc Brooks,
39 Park End Street, Oxford
Tel: (0865) 723524

Simmons & Sons,
32 Bell Street, Henley-on-Thames
Tel: (0491) 571111

Shropshire

Bowen Son & Watson,
The Oswestry Auction Rooms, 35 Bailey Street, Oswestry
Tel: (0691) 652367
also at:
Ellesmere
Tel: (0691) 712534

Cooper & Green,
3 Barker Street, Shrewsbury
Tel: (0743) 50081

John German,
43 High Street, Shrewsbury
Tel: (0743) 69661/4

Hall, Wateridge & Owen,
Welsh Bridge Salerooms, Shrewsbury
Tel: (0743) 60212

McCartneys,
25 Corve Street, Ludlow
Tel: (0584) 2636

Nock, Deighton & Son,
10 Broad Street, Ludlow
Tel: (0584) 2364/3760

Perry & Phillips,
Newmarket Salerooms, Newmarket Buildings, Listley Street, Bridgnorth
Tel: (07462) 2248

Somerset

Cooper & Tanner, Nationwide Anglia,
44a Commercial Road, Shepton Mallet
Tel: (0749) 2607 & 2624

Dores, The Auction Mart,
Vicarage Street, Frome
Tel: (0373) 62257

W R J Greenslade Co,
13 Hamet Street, Taunton
Tel: (0823) 77121
also at:
Priory Saleroom, Winchester Street, Taunton

King Miles,
25 Market Place, Wells
Tel: (0749) 73002

The London Cigarette Card Co Ltd,
Sutton Road, Somerton
Tel: (0458) 73452

Nuttall Richards & Co,
The Square, Axbridge
Tel: (0934) 723969

Phillips, Sanders & Stubbs,
32 The Avenue, Minehead
Tel: (0643) 2281/3

Wellington Salerooms, Mantle Street, Wellington
Tel: (082347) 4815

Staffordshire

Bagshaws,
17 High Street, Uttoxeter
Tel: (08893) 2811

Hall & Lloyd,
South Street Auction Rooms, Stafford
Tel: (0785) 58176

Louis Taylor,
Percy Street, Hanley, Stoke-on-Trent
Tel: (0782) 260222

Wintertons,
St Mary's Chambers, Lichfield
Tel: (0543) 263256

Suffolk

Abbotts (East Anglia) Ltd,
The Hill, Wickham Market, Woodbridge
Tel: (0728) 746321

Boardman Fine Art,
Station Road Corner, Haverhill
Tel: (0440) 703784

Diamond, Mills & Co,
117 Hamilton Road, Felixstowe
Tel: (0394) 282281

Durrant's,
10 New Market, Beccles
Tel: (0502) 712122

Flick & Son,
Ashford House, Saxmundham
Tel: (0728) 3232/4

Charles Hawkins,
Royal Thoroughfare, Lowestoft
Tel: (0502) 2024

James-in Suffolk,
31 St John's Street, Bury St Edmunds
Tel: (0284) 702415

January,
Rothsay Sale Rooms, 124 High Street, Newmarket
Tel: (0638) 668679

Lacy Scott,
Fine Art Department, The Auction Centre, 10 Risbygate Street, Bury St Edmunds
Tel: (0284) 63531

Neal Sons & Fletcher,
26 Church Street, Woodbridge
Tel: (03943) 2263/4

Olivers, William H Brown,
Olivers Rooms, Burkitts Lane, Sudbury
Tel: (0787) 880305

Oxborrows, Arnott & Calver,
14 Church Street, Woodbridge
Tel: (03943) 2244/5

Phillips,
Dover House, Wilsey Street, Ipswich
Tel: (0473) 55137

Tuohy & Son,
Denmark House, 18 High Street, Aldeburgh
Tel: (072885) 2066

H C Wolton & Son,
6 Whiting Street, Bury St Edmunds
Tel: (0284) 61336

Surrey

Clark Gammon,
The Guildford Auction Rooms, Bedford Road, Guildford
Tel: (0483) 66458

Lawrences,
Norfolk House, 80 High Street, Bletchingley
Tel: (0883) 843323

Messengers,
93 High Street, Godalming
Tel: (04868) 23567

Prudential Fine Art Auctioneers,
Millmead, Guildford
Tel: (0483) 504030

Stephen R Thomas,
15 Milton Road, Egham
Tel: (0784) 31122

Wentworth Auction Galleries,
21 Station Approach, Virginia Water
Tel: (09904) 3711

White & Sons, Vernon Smith,
104 High Street, Dorking
Tel: (0306) 887654

Harold Williams Bennett & Partners, 2-3 South Parade, Merstham, Redhill
Tel: (07374) 2234/5

P F Windibank,
18-20 Reigate Road, Dorking
Tel: (0306) 884556

Sussex – East

Ascent Auction Galleries,
11-12 East Ascent, St Leonards-on-Sea, E Sussex
Tel: (0424) 420275

Burstow & Hewett,
Abbey Auction Galleries and Granary Sale Rooms, Battle
Tel: (04246) 2374

Clifford Dann Auction Galleries,
20-21 High Street, Lewes
Tel: (0273) 480111

Eastbourne Auctioneers,
10 Cornfield Lane, Eastbourne
Tel: (0323) 411315

Fryers Auction Galleries,
Terminus Road, Bexhill-on-Sea
Tel: (0424) 212994

Gorringes Auction Galleries,
15 North Street, Lewes
Tel: (0273) 472503

Graves, Son & Pilcher,
Fine Arts, 71 Church Road, Hove
Tel: (0273) 735266

Hove Auction Galleries,
115 Church Road, Hove
Tel: (0273) 736207

Raymond P Inman,
Auction Galleries, 35 & 40 Temple Street, Brighton
Tel: (0273) 774777

Lewes Auction Rooms (Julian Dawson),
56 High Street, Lewes
Tel: (0273) 478221

Meads of Brighton,
St Nicholas Road, Brighton
Tel: (0273) 202997

Phillips, Bexhill,
120 Marina, St Leonards-on-Sea
Tel: (0424) 434854

Prudential Fine Art Auctioneers,
Rye Auction Galleries, Cinque Ports Street, Rye
Tel: (0797) 222124

Wallis & Wallis,
West Street Auction Galleries, Lewes
Tel: (0273) 480208

E Watson & Sons,
Heathfield Furniture Salerooms, The Market, Burwash Road, Heathfield
Tel: (04352) 2132

Sussex – West

T Bannister & Co,
Market Place, Haywards Heath
Tel: (0444) 412402

Peter Cheney,
Western Road Auction Rooms, Western Road, Littlehampton
Tel: (0903) 722264 & 713418

Garth Denham,
Horsham Auction Galleries, Warnham, Horsham
Tel: (0403) 53837/53699

R H Ellis & Sons,
44-46 High Street, Worthing
Tel: (0903) 38999

Fox & Sons,
31 Chatsworth Road, Worthing
Tel: (0903) 205565

G Knight & Son,
West Street, Midhurst
Tel: (073081) 2456

Prudential Fine Art Auctioneers,
Baffins Hall, Baffins Lane, Chichester
Tel: (0243) 787548

Sotheby's in Sussex,
Summers Place, Billingshurst
Tel: (040381) 3933

Stride & Son,
Southdown House, St John's Street, Chichester
Tel: (0243) 780207

Sussex Auction Galleries,
59 Perrymouth Road, Haywards Heath
Tel: (0444) 414935

Turner, Rudge & Turner,
29 High Street, East Grinstead
Tel: (0342) 313022

Tyne & Wear

Anderson & Garland,
Fine Art Salerooms, Anderson House, Market Street, Newcastle-upon-Tyne
Tel: 091-232 6278

Anderson & Garland,
The Fine Art Sale Rooms, Marlborough House, Marlborough Crescent, Newcastle-upon-Tyne
Tel: 091-232 6278

Boldon Auction Galleries,
24a Front Street, East Boldon
Tel: (0783) 372630

Thomas N Miller,
18-22 Gallowgate, Newcastle-upon-Tyne
Tel: 091-232 5617

Warwickshire

Bigwood Auctioneers Ltd,
The Old School, Tiddington, Stratford-upon-Avon
Tel: (0789) 69415

John Briggs & Calder,
133 Long Street, Atherstone
Tel: (08277) 68911

Locke & England,
18 Guy Street, Leamington Spa
Tel: (0926) 27988

Seaman of Rugby,
Auction House, 132 Railway Terrace, Rugby
Tel: (0788) 2367

West Midlands

Allsop Sellers,
8 Hagley Road, Stourbridge
Tel: (0384) 392122

Biddle & Webb,
Icknield Square, Ladywood Middleway, Birmingham
Tel: 021-455 8042

Cariss Residential,
20-22 High Street, Kings Heath, Birmingham 14
Tel: 021-444 5311

Ronald E Clare,
Clare's Auction Rooms, 70 Park Street, Birmingham
Tel: 021-643 0226

Peter Clark Antiques,
36 St Mary's Row, Moseley, Birmingham
Tel: 021-449 8245

Codsall Antiques Auctions,
Codsall Village Hall, Codsall, Wolverhampton
Tel: (0902) 66728

Collins, Son & Harvey North,
42/44 High Street, Erdington, Birmingham
Tel: 021-382 8870

Frank H Fellows & Sons,
Bedford House, 88 Hagley Road, Edgbaston, Birmingham
Tel: 021-454 1261 & 1219

Giles Haywood,
The Auction House, St Johns Road, Stourbridge
Tel: (0384) 370891

Henley-in-Arden Auction Sales Ltd,
The Estate Office, Warwick Road, Henley-in-Arden, Solihull
Tel: (05642) 3211

James & Lister Lea,
11 Newhall Street, Birmingham
Tel: 021-236 1751

Adrian Keefe & Partners,
The Auction Room, Trinity Road, Dudley
Tel: (0384) 73181

Midland Auctions,
14 Lowwood Road, Erdington, Birmingham
Tel: 021-373 0212

Phillips,
The Old House, Station Road, Knowle, Solihull
Tel: (05645) 6151

K Stuart Swash, FSVA,
Stamford House, 2 Waterloo Road, Wolverhampton
Tel: (0902) 710626

Walker Barnett & Hill,
3 Waterloo Road, Wolverhampton
Tel: (0902) 773531

Weller & Dufty Ltd,
141 Bromsgrove Street, Birmingham
Tel: 021-692 1414

Wiltshire

Allen & Harris,
Saleroom & Auctioneers Dept, The Planks (off The Square), Old Town, Swindon
Tel: (0793) 615915

Berry, Powell & Shackell,
46 Market Place, Chippenham
Tel: (0249) 653361

Dennis Pocock & Drewett,
20 High Street, Marlborough
Tel: (0672) 53471

Dreweatt, Neate, Farrant & Wightman,
Blagrove House, 2/3 Newport Street, Old Town, Swindon
Tel: (0793) 33301

Geoffrey Taylor & Co,
13 Market Place, Devizes
Tel: (0380) 2321

Woolley & Wallis,
The Castle Auction Mart, Castle Street, Salisbury
Tel: (0722) 21711

Yorkshire – East

Dee & Atkinson,
The Exchange, Driffield
Tel: (0377) 43151

Yorkshire – North

Boulton & Cooper Ltd,
Forsyth House, Market Place, Malton
Tel: (0653) 692151

H C Chapman & Son,
The Auction Mart, North Street, Scarborough
Tel: (0723) 372424

Lawson, Larg,
St Trinity House, King's Square, York
Tel: (0904) 21532

Morphets of Harrogate,
4-6 Albert Street, Harrogate
Tel: (0423) 530030

M Philip H Scott,
Church Wynd, Burneston, Bedale
Tel: (0677) 23325

Renton & Renton,
16 Albert Street, Harrogate
Tel: (0423) 61531

Stephenson & Son,
43 Gowthorpe, Selby
Tel: (0757) 706707

G A Suffield & Co,
27 Flowergate, Whitby
Tel: (0947) 603433

Geoffrey Summersgill, ASVA,
8 Front Street, Acomb, York
Tel: (0904) 791131

Tennants,
26-27 Market Place, Leyburn
Tel: (0969) 23451

Ward Price & Co,
Royal Auction Rooms, Queen Street, Scarborough
Tel: (0723) 365455

Wells Cundall,
15 Market Place, Malton
Tel: (0653) 695581

D Wombell & Son,
Bell Hall, Escrick, York
Tel: (090 487) 531

Yorkshire – South

Eadon Lockwood & Riddle,
2 St James' Street, Sheffield
Tel: (0742) 71277

Wilbys, William H Brown,
Regent Street South, Barnsley
Tel: (0226) 299221

Wilkinson & Beighton,
Woodhouse Green, Thorncroft, Nr Rotherham
Tel: (0709) 700005

William H Brown,
Stanilands Auction Room,
28 Nether Hall Road, Doncaster
Tel: (0302) 67766

Yorkshire – West

Bond Street Auctions,
23 Bond Street, Dewsbury, Wakefield
Tel: (0924) 469381

Butterfield's,
The Auction Galleries, Riddings Road, Ilkley
Tel: (0943) 603313

Dacre Son & Hartley,
Victoria Hall Salerooms, Little Lane, Ilkley
Tel: (0943) 816363

Ernest R de Rome,
12 New John Street, Bradford
Tel: (0274) 734116

Eddisons,
Auction Rooms, 4-6 High Street, Huddersfield
Tel: (0484) 533151

Laidlaws,
Crown Court Salerooms (off Wood Street), Wakefield
Tel: (0924) 375301

W Mackay Audsley, FRVA,
11 Morris Lane, Kirkstall, Leeds 5
Tel: (0532) 758787

Phillips,
17a East Parade, Leeds
Tel: (0532) 448011

John H Raby & Son,
Salem Auction Rooms, 21 St Mary's Road, Bradford
Tel: (0274) 491121

Windle & Co,
The Four Ashes, 535 Great Horton Road, Bradford
Tel: (0274) 572998

Chas E H Yates & Son,
The Salerooms, Otley Road, Guiseley
Tel: (0943) 74165

Channel Islands

Langlois Ltd,
Don Street, St Helier, Jersey
Tel: (0534) 22441
also at:
St Peter Port, Guernsey
Tel: (0481) 23421

Le Gallais Auctions Ltd,
36 Hillgrove Street, St Helier, Jersey
Tel: (0534) 58789

Martel, Maides & Le Pelley,
The Property Centre, 50 High Street, St Peter Port, Guernsey
Tel: (0481) 713463

Ireland

James Adam & Sons,
26 St Stephens Green, Dublin 2
Tel: 0001 760261

Frank Murphy Auctions,
Main Street, Abbeyleix, Co Laois
Tel: (0502) 01035 3502

Northern Ireland

Temple Auctions Limited,
133 Carryduff Road, Temple
Tel: (084 663) 777

Scotland

John Anderson,
33 Cross Street, Fraserburgh, Aberdeenshire
Tel: (0346) 28878

Christie's Scotland,
164-166 Bath Street, Glasgow
Tel: (041 332) 8134

B L Fenton & Sons,
Forebank Auction Halls,
84 Victoria Road, Dundee
Tel: (0382) 26227

Frasers (Auctioneers),
28-30 Church Street, Inverness
Tel: (0463) 232395

J & J Howe,
24 Commercial Street, Alyth, Perthshire
Tel: (08283) 2594

Thomas Love & Sons Ltd,
The Auction Galleries, 52 Canal Street, Perth
Tel: (0738) 24111

McTears (Robert McTear & Co),
Royal Exchange Showrooms, Glasgow
Tel: 041-221 4456

John Milne,
9 North Silver Street, Aberdeen
Tel: (0224) 639336

Robert Paterson & Son,
8 Orchard Street, Paisley, Renfrewshire
Tel: (041 889) 2435

Phillips in Scotland,
207 Bath Street, Glasgow
Tel: 041-332 3386
also at:
65 George Street, Edinburgh
Tel: 031-225 2266

L S Smellie & Sons Ltd,
Within the Furniture Market, Lower Auchingramont Road, Hamilton
Tel: (0698) 282007

West Perthshire Auctions,
Dundas Street, Cowie, Perthshire

Wales

T Brackstone & Co,
19 Princes Drive, Colwyn Bay, Clwyd
Tel: (0492) 30481

Dodds Property World,
K Hugh Dodd & Partners,
Victoria Auction Galleries,
Chester Street, Mold, Clwyd
Tel: (0352) 2552

Graham H Evans, FRICS, FRVA,
Auction Sales Centre, The Market Place, Kilgetty, Dyfed
Tel: (0834) 812793 & 811151

John Francis,
Curiosity Salerooms, King Street, Carmarthen
Tel: (0267) 233456

King Thomas,
Lloyd Jones & Company,
Bangor House, High Street, Lampeter, Dyfed
Tel: (0570) 422550

Morgan Evans & Co Ltd,
28-30 Church Street, Llangefni, Anglesey, Gwynedd
Tel: (0248) 723303

Prudential Fine Art Auctioneers,
56 Machen Place, Cardiff
Tel: (0222) 374320

Rennies,
1 Agincourt Street, Monmouth
Tel: (0600) 2916

Wingett's Auction Gallery,
29 Holt Street, Wrexham, Clywd
Tel: (0978) 353553

DIRECTORY OF SPECIALISTS

This directory is in no way complete. If you wish to be included in next year's directory or if you have a change of address or telephone number, please could you inform us by April 1st 1989. Entries will be repeated in subsequent editions unless we are requested otherwise. Finally we would advise readers to make contact by telephone before a visit, therefore avoiding a wasted journey, which nowadays is both time consuming and expensive.
Any entry followed by (R) denotes a specialist who undertakes restoration work.

ANTIQUITIES

London

Astarte Gallery,
Britannia Hotel, Grosvenor Square, W1
Tel: 01-409 1875

City Forum Auctions,
108 Belsize Avenue, NW3
Tel: 01-433 1305

Charles Ede,
37 Brook Street, W1
Tel: 01-493 4944

Faustus Fine Art,
Upper Gallery, 90 Jermyn Street, SW1
Tel: 01-930 1864

Diana Foley,
L 18-21 Grays in the Mews, Davies Mews, W1

Hadji Baba,
36 Davies Street, W1
Tel: 01-499 9363/9384

Thomas Howard Sneyd,
35 Furscroft, George Street, W1
Tel: 01-723 1976

Khalili Gallery,
15c Clifford Street, Bond Street, W1
Tel: 01-734 4202

Jonathan Mankowitz,
C 29 Grays in the Mews, Davies Street, W1

C J Martin,
85 The Vale, Southgate, N14
Tel: 01-882 1509

Nigel Mills,
51 Crescent Road, South Woodford, E18
Tel: 01-504 2569

Pars Antique,
H 16/17 Grays in the Mews, Davies Street, W1
Tel: 01-629 3788/01-399 8801

Simmons & Simmons,
K 37/38 Grays in the Mews, Davies Street, W1
Tel: 01-629 9321

Annie Trotter and Ian Parsons,
A 10 Davies Mews, W1
Tel: 01-629 2813

Nicholas Wright,
42A Christchurch Avenue, NW6
Tel: 01-459 7123

Dorset

Centurion Coins,
Stour House, 11 Stour Road, Christchurch
Tel: (0202) 478592/474462

Glos

Brian L Carter,
25 Park Street, Cirencester
Tel: (045 36) 6719

Hants

Phil Goodwin,
3 Apollo Drive, Crookhorn, Portsmouth
Tel: (0705) 266866/452001

Michael Harrison,
Truelocke Antiques,
109 High Street, Odiham
Tel: (025671) 2387

Herts

David Miller,
51 Carlisle Avenue, St Albans
Tel: (0727) 52412

Kent

C J Denton,
PO Box 25, Orpington
Tel: (0689) 73690

Lancs

H & M J Burke,
Old Packet House Building, South Worsley

Middx

M & H Kashden,
19 The Lawns, Pinner
Tel: 01-421 3568

Somerset

Fox & Co,
30 Princes Street, Yeovil
Tel: (0935) 72323

Sussex

Agora,
18 Regent Arcade, East Street, Brighton
Tel: (0273) 26663

Yorks

Wilton House Gallery,
95 Market Street, Pocklington
Tel: (07592) 4858

ARCHITECTURAL ANTIQUES

London

Antique Fireplace Warehouse,
194-196 Battersea Park Road, SW11
Tel: 01-627 1410

Nigel Bartlett,
67 St Thomas Street, SE1
Tel: 01-378 7895

H Crowther Ltd,
Garden Leadwork (R),
5 Chiswick High Road, W4
Tel: 01-994 2326

Fortress,
23 Canonbury Lane, Islington, N1
Tel: 01-359 5875

Lassco,
Market Street, EC2
Tel: 01-739 0448

Lamont Antiques,
151 Tower Bridge Road, SE1
Tel: 01-403 0126

Miles D'Agar Antiques,
533 Kings Road, SW10
Tel: 01-352 6143

H W Poulter & Son,
279 Fulham Road, SW10
Tel: 01-352 7268

Westland Pilkington Antiques,
The Clergy House, Mark Street, EC2
Tel: 01-739 8094

Avon

David J Bridgwater,
14 Fountain Buildings, Lansdown Road, Bath
Tel: (0225) 69288/63652

Nigel Busek,
56 Stokes Croft, Bristol
Tel: (0272) 424257

Robert Mills,
Unit 3, Satelite Business Park, Blackswarth Road, Redfield, Bristol
Tel: (0272) 556542

Walcot Reclamation,
108 Walcot Street, Bath
Tel: (0225) 444404

Berks

The Fire Place (Hungerford) Ltd,
Old Fire Station, Charnham Street, Hungerford
Tel: (0488) 834420

Cheshire

Nostalgia,
61 Shaw Heath, Stockport
Tel: 061-477 7706

Cumbria

The Holme Firth Company,
Holme Mill, Holme, Nr. Carnforth
Tel: (0524) 781423

Derbyshire

Havenplan's Architectural Emporium,
The Old Station, Station Road, Killamarsh, Nr. Sheffield
Tel: (0742) 489972

Devon

Architectural Antiques,
Savoy Showroom, New Road, South Molton
Tel: (076 95) 3342

Ashburton Marbles,
Englands Antique Fireplaces,
6 West Street, Ashburton
Tel: (0364) 53189

Cantabrian Antiques,
16 Park Street, Lynton
Tel: (0598) 53282

Dorset

Talisman Antiques,
The Old Brewery, Wyke, Gillingham
Tel: (074 76) 4423

Glos

Architectural Heritage,
Taddington Manor, Taddington, Nr. Cutsdean, Cheltenham
Tel: (0386) 73414

Hayes & Newby,
The Pit, 70 Hare Lane, Gloucester
Tel: (0452) 31145

Gt Manchester

Antique Fireplaces,
1090 Stockport Road, Levenshulme
Tel: 061-431 8075

Hants

Glover & Stacey Ltd,
Malthouse Premises, Kingsley, Nr Bordon
Tel: (042 03) 5754 or evenings (0420) 89067

Hereford & Worcester

Bailey's Architectural Antiques,
The Engine Shed, Ashburton Industrial Estate, Ross-on-Wye
Tel: (0989) 63015

Lancs

James Cook,
Barn House, Wigan Road, Cuerden, Preston
Tel: (0772) 321390

W J Cowell & Sons,
Church Hill House, Durdon Lane, Broughton, Preston
Tel: (0772) 862034

Middx

Crowther of Syon Lodge,
London Road, Isleworth
Tel: 01-560 7978/7985

Oxon

Oxford Architectural Antiques
The Old Depot, Nelson Street, Jericho, Oxford
Tel: (0865) 53310

Shropshire

Architectural Antiques,
140 Corve Street, Ludlow
Tel: (0584) 6207

Sussex

Brighton Architectural Salvage,
33 Gloucester Road, Brighton
Tel: (0273) 681656

Yorks

Andy Thornton Architectural Antiques Ltd,
Ainleys Industrial Estate, Elland
Tel: (0422) 75595

Cupid Architectural,
West Royd Cottage, West Royd Avenue, King Cross, Halifax
Tel: (0422) 63585

Robert Aagaard Ltd,
Frogmire House, Stockwell Road, Knaresborough
Tel: (0423) 864805

Wilts

Relic Antiques,
Brillscote Farm, Lea, Nr Malmesbury
Tel: (0666) 822332

Wales

M & A Main Architectural Antiques (R),
The Old Smithy, Cerrig-y-Drudion, Corwen
Tel: (049 082) 491

Victorian Fireplaces (Simon Priestley),
Saturdays only: Ground Floor, Cardiff Antique Centre, 69-71 St Mary Street, Cardiff
Tel: (0222) 30970
Any other time: Tel: (0222) 26049

ARMS & MILITARIA

London

The Armoury of St James's,
17 Piccadilly Arcade, SW1
Tel: 01-493 5082

Michael C German,
38b Kensington Church Street, W8
Tel: 01-937 2771

Tradition,
5a Shepherd Street, W1
Tel: 01-493 7452

Avon
Chris Grimes Militaria,
13 Lower Park Row, Bristol
Tel: (0272) 298205

Glos
HQ 84,
82-84 Southgate Street, Gloucester
Tel: (0452) 27716

Hants
Romsey Medal Centre,
112 The Hundred, Romsey
Tel: (0794) 512069

Surrey
Casque & Gauntlet Antiques,
55/59 Badshot Lea Road, Badshot Lea, Farnham
Tel: (0252) 20745

West Street Antiques,
63 West Street, Dorking
Tel: (0306) 883487

Sussex
Military Antiques (by appointment only),
42 Janes Lane, Burgess Hill
Tel: (044 46) 3516 & 43088

Wallis & Wallis,
West Street Galleries, Lewes
Tel: (0273) 480208

George Weiner,
2 Market Street, The Lanes, Brighton
Tel: (0273) 729948

Yorks
The Antique Shop,
226 Harrogate Road, Leeds
Tel: (0532) 681785

Andrew Spencer Bottomley (by appointment only),
The Coach House, Thongs Bridge, Holmfirth
Tel: (0484) 685234

Wales
Hermitage Antiques,
10 West Street, Fishguard
Tel: (0348) 873037

ART DECO & ART NOUVEAU

London
Baptista Arts,
Stand D2/3, Chenil Galleries,
183 King's Road, SW3
Tel: 01-352 5799

Bizarre,
24 Church Street, NW8
Tel: 01-724 1305

Butler & Wilson,
189 Fulham Road, SW3
Tel: 01-352 3045

Chilton,
Stand A11/12, Chenil Galleries,
181-183 King's Road, SW3
Tel: 01-352 2163

Church Street Antiques,
8 Church Street, NW8
Tel: 01-723 7415

T Coakley,
Stand D13, Chenil Galleries,
181-183 King's Road, SW3
Tel: 01-351 2914

Cobra & Bellamy,
149 Sloane Street, SW1
Tel: 01-730 2823

Editions Graphiques Gallery,
3 Clifford Street, W1
Tel: 01-734 3944

The Facade,
196 Westbourne Grove, W11
Tel: 01-727 2159

Galerie 1900,
267 Camden High Street, NW1
Tel: 01-485 1001

Gallery '25,
4 Halkin Arcade, Motcomb Street, SW1
Tel: 01-235 5178

Patrick & Susan Gould,
L17, Grays Mews, Davies Mews, W1
Tel: 01-408 0129

Jazzy Art Deco,
67 Camden Road, Camden Town, NW1
Tel: 01-267 3342/01-960 8988

John Jesse and Irina Laski Ltd,
160 Kensington Church Street, W8
Tel: 01-229 0312

Helen Lane,
212 Camden High Street, NW1
Tel: 01-267 6588

Lewis M Kaplan Associates Ltd,
50 Fulham Road, SW3
Tel: 01-589 3108

The Lamp Gallery,
355 New Kings Road, SW6
Tel: 01-736 6188

John & Diana Lyons Gallery,
47-49 Mill Lane, West Hampstead, NW6
Tel: 01-794 3537

P & J,
K13-J28 Grays Mews, Davies Mews, W1
Tel: 01-499 2719

Plaza Decorative Arts,
187 Kingston Road, Wimbledon, SW19
Tel: 01-540 0239

Pruskin Gallery,
73 Kensington Church Street, W8
Tel: 01-937 1994

Paul Reeves,
32B Kensington Church Street, W8
Tel: 01-937 1594

Simon Tracy,
18 Church Street, NW8
Tel: 01-724 5890

West Hampstead Trade Centre,
Blackburn Road, NW6
Tel: 01-328 2221

Ziggurat,
J 22 Grays Mews, Davies Mews, W1
Tel: 01-629 3788

Berks
Lupin Antiques,
134 Peascod Street, Windsor
Tel: (0753) 856244

Dorset
Michael Howell,
912-914 Christchurch Road, Boscombe, Bournemouth
Tel: (0202) 425435

Gt Manchester
AS Antiques,
26 Broad Street, Salford
Tel: 061-737 5938

Bizarre,
Unit 19, The Corn Exchange Hall, Corn Exchange Buildings, Hanging Ditch, Manchester
Tel: 061-835 2255/061-998 6106

Herts
Ziggurat,
2 Morley Cottages, Chells Manor, Stevenage
Tel: (0438) 727084

Lancs
Decoroy,
105 New Hall Lane, Preston
Tel: (0772) 705371

Leics
Birches Antique Shop,
15 Francis Street, Stoneygate, Leicester
Tel: (0533) 703235

Merseyside
Osiris Antiques (Paul & Carol Wood),
24 Princes Street, Southport
Tel: (0704) 60418
(Closed Tues & Thurs)

Surrey
Decodence, Sheena Taylor,
59 Brighton Road, Surbiton
Tel: 01-390 1778

Galerie 39,
39 Kew Road, Richmond
Tel: 01-948 1633 & 3337

Peter & Debbie Gooday,
20 Richmond Hill, Richmond
Tel: 01-940 8652

Sussex
Armstrong-Davis Gallery,
The Square, Arundel
Tel: (0903) 882752

20th Century Arts,
64 Middle Street, Brighton
Tel: (0273) 206091

Warwickshire
Alaister Hendy,
59A Smith Street, Warwick
Tel: (0926) 316680

Castle Antiques,
1 Mill Street, Warwick
Tel: (0926) 498068

Yorks
Carlton Gallery,
60A Middle Street, Driffield
Tel: (0482) 443954

Dragon Antiques,
10 Dragon Road, Harrogate
Tel: (0423) 62037

Mr Muir Hewitt,
Halifax Antiques Centre, Queens Road/Gibbet Street, Halifax
Tel: (0422) 66657

Scotland
The Rendezvous Gallery,
100 Forest Avenue, Aberdeen
Tel: (0224) 323247

Wales
Paul Gibbs Antiques,
25 Castle Street, Conway
Tel: (0492) 593429

BOOKS

Staffs
The Old House,
47 High Street, Kinver
Tel: (0384) 872940

BOXES, TREEN & WOODEN OBJECTS

London
Simon Castle,
38B Kensington Church Street, W8
Tel: 01-937 2268

Halcyon Days,
14 Brook Street, W1
Tel: 01-629 8811

Alistair Sampson Antiques,
156 Brompton Road, SW3
Tel: 01-589 5272

Berks
Mostly Boxes,
92-52b High Street, Eton
Tel: (0753) 858470

Charles Toller,
Hall House, 20 High Street, Datchet
Tel: (0753) 42903

Bucks
A & E Foster (by appointment only),
Little Heysham, Forge Road, Naphill
Tel: (024 024) 2024

Hants
Gerald Austin Antiques,
2A Andover Road, Winchester
Tel: (0962) 69824 Ext 2

House of Antiques,
4 College Street, Petersfield
Tel: (0730) 62172

Millers of Chelsea,
Netherbrook House, 86 Christchurch Road, Ringwood
Tel: (04254) 2062

Leics
Stable Antiques,
35 Main Street, Osgathorpe
Tel: (0530) 222463

Oxon
Key Antiques,
11 Horse Fair, Chipping Norton
Tel: (0608) 3777

Sussex
Michael Wakelin & Helen Linfield,
10 New Street, Petworth
Tel: (0798) 42417

CAMERAS

London
Vintage Cameras Ltd,
254/256 Kirkdale, Sydenham
Tel: 01-778 5416 & 5841

Herts
P Coombs,
87 Gills Hill Lane, Radlett
Tel: (09276) 6949

CARPETS

London
David Black Oriental Carpets,
96 Portland Road, Holland Park, W11
Tel: 01-727 2566

Hindustan Carpets Ltd,
B Block, 53/79 Highgate Road, NW5
Tel: 01-485 7766

Mayfair Carpet Gallery,
6-8 Old Bond Street, W1
Tel: 01-493 0126/7

Swillet Rug Restorations (R),
(Warehouse), 8 Albert Wharf,
17 New Wharf Road, N1
Tel: 01-833 3529

Vigo Carpet Gallery,
6a Vigo Street, W1
Tel: 01-439 6971

Vigo Sternberg Galleries,
37 South Audley Street, W1
Tel: 01-629 8307

Bucks
Swillet Rug Restorations (R),
22 Lodge Lane, Chalfont-St-Giles
Tel: (024 04) 4776

Devon
Sheelagh Lewis,
5A High Street, Totnes
Tel: (0803) 863024

Dorset
J L Arditti (Old Oriental Rugs),
88 Bargates, Christchurch
Tel: (0202) 485414

Essex
Robert Bailey (by appointment only),
1 Roll Gardens, Gants Hill
Tel: 01-550 5435

Glos
Thornborough Galleries,
28 Gloucester Street, Cirencester
Tel: (0285) 2055

Kent
Persian Rugs, R & G King,
Ulnes Farm, Mathews Lane,
W Peckham, Hadlow
Tel: (0732) 850228

Somerset
M & A Lewis,
Oriental Carpets & Rugs, 8 North Street, Wellington
Tel: (082 347) 7430

Sussex
Lindfield Galleries,
59 High Street, Lindfield
Tel: (04447) 3817

Yorks
Gordon Reece Gallery,
Finkle Street, Knaresborough
Tel: (0423) 866219/866502

London House Oriental Rugs & Carpets,
London House, High Street,
Boston Spa By Wetherby
Tel: (0937) 845123

Omar (Harrogate) Ltd,
8 Crescent Road, Harrogate
Tel: (0423) 503675

Scotland
Whytock & Reid,
Sunbury House, Belford Mews,
Edinburgh
Tel: 031-226 4911

CLOCKS WATCHES & BAROMETERS

London
Asprey PLC,
165-169 New Bond Street, W1
Tel: 01-493 6767

Bobinet Ltd,
102 Mount Street, W1
Tel: 01-408 0333/4

Aubrey Brocklehurst,
124 Cromwell Road, SW7
Tel: 01-373 0319

Camerer Cuss & Co,
17 Ryder Street, St James's, SW1
Tel: 01-930 1941

Chelsea Clocks,
479 Fulham Road
Tel: 01-731 5704
Also at:
69 Portobello Road
Tel: 01-727 5417

City Clocks,
Lambs Passage, Chiswell Street, EC1
Tel: 01-628 6749

The Clock Clinic Ltd,
85 Lower Richmond Road, SW15
Tel: 01-788 1407

Philip & Bernard Dombey,
174 Kensington Church Street, W8
Tel: 01-229 7100

Gerald Mathias (R),
R5/8 Antiquarius, 136 King's Road, SW3
Tel: 01-351 0484

North London Clock Shop Ltd (R),
72 Highbury Park, N5
Tel: 01-226 1609

Pieces of Time,
1-7 Davies Mews, W1
Tel: 01-629 2422

R E Rose, FBHI,
731 Sidcup Road, Eltham, SE9
Tel: 01-859 4754

Strike One (Islington) Ltd,
51 Camden Passage
Tel: 01-226 9709

Temple Brooks,
12 Mill Lane, NW6
Tel: 01-452 9696

Avon
Smith & Bottrill,
The Clock House, 17 George Street, Bath
Tel: (0225) 22809

Berks
Richard Barder Antiques,
Crossways House, Near Newbury
Tel: (0635) 200295

Medalcrest Ltd,
Charnham House, Charnham Street, Hungerford
Tel: (0488) 84157

Times Past Antiques Ltd,
59 High Street, Eton
Tel: (0753) 857018

Bucks
The Guild Room,
The Lee, Great Missenden
Tel: (024 020) 463

The Old Town Clock Shop,
1-3 Aylesbury End, Beaconsfield
Tel: (049 46) 6783

Cambs
Rodney T Firmin,
16 Magdalene Street, Cambridge
Tel: (0223) 67372

Cheshire
Peter Bosson Antiques,
10B Swan Street, Wilmslow
Tel: (0625) 525250 & 527857

Coppelia Antiques
Holford Lodge, Plumley Moor Road, Plumley
Tel: (056 581) 2197

Derek Rayment Antiques (R),
Orchard House, Barton Road,
Barton, Nr Farndon
Tel: (0829) 270429

Cornwall
Ian Tuck (R),
The Friary, Trethurgy, St Austell
Tel: (0726) 850039

Cumbria
Don Burns,
The Square, Ireby, Carlisle
Tel: (096 57) 477

Derbyshire
Derby Clocks,
974 London Road, Derby
Tel: (0332) 74996

Derbyshire Clocks,
104 High Street West, Glossop
Tel: (045 74) 62677

D J Mitchell,
Temple Antiques, Glenwood Lodge, Temple Walk, Matlock Bath
Tel: (0629) 4253

Devon
Musgrave Bickford Antiques,
6 The Village, Wembworthy,
Chulmleigh
Tel: (083 78) 3473

Dorset
Good Hope Antiques,
2 Hogshill Street, Beaminster
Tel: (0308) 862119

Tom Tribe & Son,
Bridge Street, Sturminster Newton
Tel: (0258) 72311

Essex
It's About Time (R),
863 London Road, Westcliff-on-Sea
Tel: (0702) 72574 & 205204

Littlebury Antiques,
58/60 Fairycroft Road, Saffron Walden
Tel: (0799) 27961

Mark Marchant,
Market Square, Coggeshall
Tel: (0376) 61188

Tempus Fugit (appointment only),
c/o Trinity House, Trinity Street,
Halstead
Tel: (0787) 475409

Trinity Clocks,
26 Trinity Street, Colchester
Tel: (0206) 46458

Glos
J & M Bristow Antiques,
28 Long Street, Tetbury
Tel: (0666) 52222

Gerard Campbell,
Maple House, Market Place,
Lechlade
Tel: (0367) 52267

Montpellier Clocks Ltd,
13 Rotunda Terrace, Montpellier Street, Cheltenham
Tel: (0242) 242178

Colin Elliott,
4 Great Norwood Street,
Cheltenham
Tel: (0242) 528590

Saxton House Gallery,
High Street, Chipping Camden
Tel: (0386) 840278

South Bar Antiques,
Digbeth Street, Stow-on-the-Wold
Tel: (0451) 30236

Hants
Charles Antiques,
101 The Hundred, Romsey
Tel: (0794) 512885

Evans & Evans,
40 West Street, Alresford
Tel: (096 273) 2170

Gerald E Marsh,
32A The Square, Winchester
Tel: (0962) 54505

Hereford & Worcester
G & V Taylor Antiques,
Winforton Court, Winforton
Tel: (054 46) 226

Herts
Country Clocks (R),
3 Pendley Bridge Cottages, Tring Station, Tring
Tel: (044 282) 5090

John de Haan,
12A Seaforth Drive, Waltham Cross
Tel: (0992) 763111 & (0920) 2534

Isle of Wight
Museum of Clocks,
Alum Bay
Tel: (0983) 754193

Kent
John Chawner Antiques,
44 Chatham Hill, Chatham
Tel: (0634) 811147 & (0843) 43309

Hadlow Antiques,
No. 1 The Pantiles, Tunbridge Wells
Tel: (0892) 29858

Henry Hall Antique Clocks,
19 Market Square, Westerham
Tel: (0959) 62200

The Old Clock Shop,
63 High Street, West Malling
Tel: (0732) 843246

Derek Roberts Antiques,
24/25 Shipbourne Road, Tonbridge
Tel: (0732) 358986

Malcolm G Styles (R),
Tunbridge Wells
Tel: (0892) 30699

Anthony Woodburn,
Orchard House, Leigh,
Nr Tonbridge
Tel: (0732) 832258

Lancs
Kenneth Weigh, Signwriting & Numbering,
9 Links Road, Blackpool
Tel: (0253) 52097

Leics
Bonington Clocks,
12 Market Place, Kegworth
Tel: (05097) 2900

Clock Replacements (R),
239 Welford Road, Leicester
Tel: (0533) 706190

G K Hadfield (R),
Blackbrook Hill House, Tickow Lane, Shepshed
Tel: (0509) 503014

C Lowe & Sons Ltd (R),
37-40 Churchgate, Loughborough
Tel: (0509) 217876

Lincs
Pinfold Antiques, 3 Pinfold Lane,
Ruskington
Tel: (0526) 832200

Merseyside
T Brown Horological Restorers (R),
12 London Road, Liverpool 3
Tel: 051-709 4048

Middx
Onslow Clocks,
48 King Street, Twickenham
Tel: 01-892 7632

Norfolk
Delawood Antiques & Clock Restoration (R),
10 Westgate, Hunstanton
Tel: (048 53) 2903

Oxon
Laurie Leigh Antiques,
36 High Street, Oxford
Tel: (0865) 244197

Telling Time,
57 North Street, Thame
Tel: (084 421) 3007

Witney Antiques,
96-98 Corn Street, Witney
Tel: (0993) 3902

Somerset
Michael & Judith Avis (R),
The Barton, Simonsbath,
Minehead
Tel: (064383) 428

Shelagh Berryman,
15 The Market Place, Wells
Tel: (0749) 76203

Bernard G House,
Mitre Antiques, 13 Market Place,
Wells
Tel: (0749) 72607

Edward A Nowell,
21-23 Market Place, Wells
Tel: (0749) 72415

Matthew Willis,
Antique Clocks, 3 Wells Road,
Glastonbury
Tel: (0458) 32103

Suffolk

AN Antiques,
Home Farm, South Green, Eye
Tel: (0379) 870367

Bullivant Antiques (R),
White Gates, Elmswell Road, Great Ashfield
Tel: (0359) 40040

Surrey

BS Antiques,
39 Bridge Road, East Molesey
Tel: 01-941 1812

The Clock Shop,
64 Church Street, Weybridge
Tel: (0932) 4047 & 55503

Roger A Davis, Antiquarian Horologist,
19 Dorking Road, Great Bookham
Tel: (0372) 57655 & 53167

Douglas Dawes (by appointment only),
Antique Clocks, Linfield
Tel: (0342) 834965

Hampton Court Antiques,
75 Bridge Road, East Molesey
Tel: 01-941 6398

E Hollander Ltd,
The Dutch House, Horsham Road, South Holmwood, Dorking
Tel: (0306) 888921

Horological Workshops,
204 Worplesdon Road, Guildford
Tel: (0483) 576496

R Saunders Antiques,
71 Queens Road, Weybridge
Tel: (0932) 42601

Geoffrey Stevens,
26-28 Church Road, Guildford
Tel: (0483) 504075

Surrey Clock Centre,
3 Lower Street, Haslemere
Tel: (0428) 4547

Sussex

Adrian Alan Ltd,
4 Frederick Place, Brighton
Tel: (0273) 25277

Michael J O'Neill,
Swan House, Market Square, Petworth
Tel: (0798) 42616

Sam Orr and Magnus Broe,
36 High Street, Hurstpierpoint
Tel: (0273) 832081

David & Sarah Pullen,
29/31 Sea Road, Bexhill-on-Sea
Tel: (0424) 222035

Tyne & Wear

Hazel Cottage Clocks,
Eachwick, Dalton, Newcastle on Tyne
Tel: (06614) 2415

T P Rooney, Grad BHI (R),
191 Sunderland Road, Harton Village, South Shields
Tel: 091-456 2950

Warwickshire

J Mason Antique Clocks,
Glympton House, 3 New Road, Water Orton
Tel: (021 747) 5751

West Midlands

Ashleigh House Antiques,
5 Westbourne Road, Birmingham
Tel: 021-454 6283

Osborne's (R),
91 Chester Road, New Oscott, Sutton Coldfield
Tel: 021-355 6667

Wiltshire

Avon Antiques,
26-27 Market Street, Bradford-on-Avon
Tel: (022 16) 2052

P A Oxley,
The Old Rectory, Cherhill, Nr Calne
Tel: (0249) 816227

The Salisbury Clock Shop,
107 Exeter Street, Salisbury
Tel: (0722) 337076

Yorks

Brian Loomes,
Calf Haugh Farm, Pateley Bridge
Tel: (0423) 711163

The Clock Shop,
Hilltop House, Bellerby, Nr Leyburn
Tel: (0969) 22596

Haworth Antiques (R),
Harrogate Road, Huby, Nr Leeds
Tel: (0423) 74293
Also at:
26 Cold Bath Road, Harrogate
Tel: (0423) 521401

Keith Stones Grandfather Clocks,
5 Ellers Drive, Bessacarr, Doncaster
Tel: (0302) 535258

Scotland

Browns Clocks Ltd,
203 Bath Street, Glasgow
Tel: 041-248 6760

Christopher Wood (appointment only),
Harlaw House, Kelso
Tel: (057 37) 321

DOLLS, TOYS & GAMES

London

Dr Colin Baddiel,
Stand B24/B25, Grays Mews, 1-7 Davies Mews, W1
Tel: 01-408 1239

Jilliana Ranicar-Breese,
Martin Breese Ltd, 7A Jones Arcade, Westbourne Grove (Sats only). Tel: 01-727 9378

Stuart Cropper,
Gray's Mews, 1-7 Davies Mews, W1
Tel: 01-499 6600

Donay Antiques,
12 Pierrepont Row, N1
Tel: 01-359 1880

Engine 'n' Tender,
19 Spring Lane, Woodside, SE25
Tel: 01-654 0386

Pete McAskie,
Stand D10-12 Basement, Grays Mews Antiques, 1-7 Davies Mews, W1
Tel: 01-629 2813

The Dolls House Toys Ltd,
29 The Market, Covent Garden, WC2
Tel: 01-379 7243

The Singing Tree,
69 New King's Road, SW6
Tel: 01-736 4527

Cornwall

Mrs Margaret Chesterton,
33 Pentewan Road, St Austell
Tel: (0726) 72926

Dorset

Hobby Horse Antiques,
29 West Allington, Bridport
Tel: (0308) 22801

Glos

Lilian Middleton's Antique Dolls' Shop & Dolls' Hospital,
Days Stable, Sheep Street, Stow-on-the-Wold
Tel: (0451) 30381

China Doll,
31 Suffolk Parade, Cheltenham
Tel: (0242) 33164

Kent

Hadlow Antiques,
1 The Pantiles, Tunbridge Wells
Tel: (0892) 29858

Staffs

Multro Ltd,
10 Madeley Street, Tunstall, Stoke-on-Trent
Tel: (0782) 813621

Surrey

Heather & Clifford Bond,
Victoriana Dolls
Tel: (073 72) 49525

Curiosity Shop,
72 Stafford Road, Wallington
Tel: 01-647 5267

Doll Shop (appointment only),
18 Richmond Hill, Richmond
Tel: 01-940 6774

Elizabeth Gant,
52 High Street, Thames Ditton
Tel: 01-398 0962

Sussex

Doll & Teddy Bear Restorer (R)
Wendy Foster, Minto, Codmore Hill, Pulborough
Tel: (079 82) 2707

Rathbone Law,
7-9 The Arcade, Worthing
Tel: (0903) 200274

West Midlands

Woodsetton Antiques,
65 Sedgley Road, Woodsetton, Dudley
Tel: (0384) 277918

Yorks

Andrew Clark,
12 Ingfield, Oakenshaw, Bradford
Tel: (0274) 675342

John & Simon Haley,
2 Lanehead Road, Soyland, Sowery Bridge
Tel: (0422) 822148/60434

Wales

Museum of Childhood Toys & Gift Shop,
1 Castle Street, Beaumaris, Anglesey, Gwynedd
Tel: (0248) 712498

EPHEMERA

London

Jilliana Ranicar-Breese, Martin Breese Ltd,
164 Kensington Park Road, Notting Hill Gate, W11
Tel: 01-727 9378 (by appointment only)
Also at:
7A Jones Arcade, Westbourne Grove (Sats only)
Also at:
Roger's Arcade, 65 Portobello Road (Sats only)

Gilda Conrich Antiques,
Tel: 01-226 5319
(by appointment only)

Dodo,
3 Denbigh Road, London, W11
Tel: 01-229 3132

Donay,
35 Camden Passage, N1
Tel: 01-359 1880

M & R Glendale,
Antiquarian Booksellers, 9A New Cavendish Street, W1
Tel: 01-487 5348

David Godfrey's Old Newspaper Shop,
37 Kinnerton Street, SW1
Tel: 01-235 7788

Jubilee,
1 Pierrepont Row, Camden Passage, N1
Tel: 01-607 5462

Pleasures of Past Times,
11 Cecil Court, Charing Cross Road, WC2
Tel: 01-836 1142

Danny Posner,
The Vintage Magazine Shop,
39/41 Brewer Street, W1
Tel: 01-439 8525

Peter Stockham at Images,
16 Cecil Court, Charing Cross Road, WC2
Tel: 01-836 8661

Avon

Michael & Jo Saffell,
3 Walcot Buildings, London Road, Bath
Tel: (0225) 315857

Bucks

Omniphil Ltd,
Germains Lodge, Fullers Hill, Chesham
Tel: (0494) 771851
Also at:
Stand 110, Gray's Antique Market, 58 Davies Street, W1
Tel: 01-629 3223

Essex

G K R Bonds Ltd,
PO Box 1, Kelvedon
Tel: (0376) 71138

Hants

Cobwebs,
78 Northam Road, Southampton
Tel: (0703) 227458

Kent

Mike Sturge,
17 Market Buildings Arcade, Maidstone
Tel: (0622) 54702

Notts

Neales of Nottingham,
192 Mansfield Road, Nottingham
Tel: (0602) 624141

Surrey

Richmond Antiquary,
28 Hill Rise, Richmond
Tel: 01-938 0583

FISHING TACKLE

Dorset

Yesterday Tackle & Books,
67 Jumpers Road, Christchurch
Tel: (0202) 476586

Kent

Alan Clout,
36 Nunnery Fields, Canterbury
Tel: (0227) 455162

Sussex

N Marchant-Lane
Willow Court, Middle Street, Petworth
Tel: (0798) 43443

Scotland

Jamie Maxtone Graham,
Lyne Haugh, Lyne Station, Peebles
Tel: (07214) 304

Jess Miller,
PO Box 1, Birnam, Dunkeld, Perthshire
Tel: (03502) 522

FURNITURE

London

Asprey PLC,
165-169 New Bond Street, W1
Tel: 01-493 6767

F E A Briggs Ltd,
73 Ledbury Road, W1
Tel: 01-727 0909 & 01-221 4950

C W Buckingham,
301-303 Munster Road, SW6
Tel: 01-385 2657

Butchoff Antiques,
233 Westbourne Grove, W11
Tel: 01-221 8174

Rupert Cavendish Antiques (Biedermeir),
6-10 King Road, London, SW6
Tel: 01-731 7041/01-736 6024

John Creed Antiques Ltd,
3 & 5A Camden Passage, N1
Tel: 01-226 8867

Eldridge,
99-101 Farringdon Road, EC1
Tel: 01-837 0379 & 0370

Etna Antiques,
81 Kensington Church Street, W8
Tel: 01-937 3754

John Keil Ltd,
154 Brompton Road, SW3
Tel: 01-589 6454

C H Major (Antiques) Ltd,
154 Kensington Church Street, W8
Tel: 01-229 1162

Mallett & Son (Antiques) Ltd,
40 New Bond Street, W1
Tel: 01-499 7411

M & D Seligmann,
37 Kensington Church Street, W8
Tel: 01-937 0400

Michael Marriott Ltd,
588 Fulham Road, SW6
Tel: 01-736 3110

Murray Thomson Ltd,
141 Kensington Church Street, W8
Tel: 01-727 1727

Oola Boola Antiques,
166 Tower Bridge Road, SE1
Tel: 01-403 0794

Phelps Ltd,
133-135 St Margaret's Road,
E Twickenham
Tel: 01-892 1778 & 7129

Alistair Sampson Antiques,
156 Brompton Road, SW3
Tel: 01-589 5272

Arthur Seager Ltd,
25a Holland Street, Kensington, W8
Tel: 01-937 3262

Stair & Co,
120 Mount Street, W1
Tel: 01-499 1784/5

Terry Antiques,
175 Junction Road, N19
Tel: 01-263 1219

William Tillman,
30 St James's Street, SW1
Tel: 01-839 2500

O F Wilson Ltd,
Queen's Elm Parade, Old Church Street, SW3
Tel: 01-352 9554

Robert Young Antiques,
68 Battersea Bridge Road, SW11
Tel: 01-228 7847

Zal Davar Antiques,
26a Munster Road, SW6
Tel: 01-736 1405 & 2559

Avon

Cottage Antiques,
The Old Post Office, Langford Place, Langford, Nr Bristol
Tel: (0934) 862597

Trevor Micklem Antiques Ltd,
Frog Pool Farm, Moorwood, Oakhill, Bath
Tel: (0749) 840 754

Berks

Mary Bellis Antiques,
Charnham Close, Hungerford
Tel: (0488) 82620

Biggs of Maidenhead,
Hare Hatch Grange, Twyford
Tel: (073 522) 3281

The Old Malthouse,
Hungerford
Tel: (0488) 82209

Medalcrest Ltd,
Charnham House, Charnham Street, Hungerford
Tel: (0488) 84157

Charles Toller,
Hall House, 20 High Street, Datchet
Tel: (0753) 42903

Bucks

Jeanne Temple Antiques,
Stockwell House, 1 Stockwell Lane, Wavendon, Milton Keynes
Tel: (0908) 583597

A & E Foster (by appointment only),
Little Heysham, Forge Road, Naphill
Tel: (024 024) 2024

Cambs

Clover Antiques,
5-6 Soham Road, Fordham
Tel: (0638) 720250

Old School Antiques,
Chittering
Tel: (0223) 861831

Cheshire

Coppelia Antiques,
Holford Lodge, Plumley Moor Road, Plumley
Tel: (056 581) 2197

Derbyshire Antiques Ltd,
157-159 London Road South, Poynton
Tel: (0625) 873110

Townwell House Antiques,
52 Welsh Row, Nantwich
Tel: (0270) 625953

Cumbria

Haughey Antiques,
Market Street, Kirkby Stephen
Tel: (0930) 71302

Fenwick Pattison,
Bowmanstead, Coniston
Tel: (0966) 41235

Shire Antiques,
The Post House, High Newton, Newton in Cartmel, Nr Grange-over-Sands
Tel: (0448) 31431

Townhead Antiques,
Newby Bridge
Tel: (0448) 31321

Jonathan Wood Antiques,
Broughton Hall, Cartmel, Grange-over-Sands
Tel: (044 854) 234

Derbyshire

The Antique Home Ltd,
7 The Old Court House, George Street, Buxton
Tel: (0298) 77042

Maurice Goldstone & Son,
Avenel Court, Bakewell
Tel: (062 981) 2487

Spurrier-Smith Antiques,
28B & 41 Church Street, Ashbourne
Tel: (0335) 43669 and (home) (077 389) 368

Yesterday Antiques,
6 Commercial Road, Tideswell, Nr Buxton
Tel: (0298) 871932

Devon

Ian McBain & Sons,
Exeter Airport, Clyst Honiton, Exeter
Tel: (0392) 66261

Dorset

Dodge & Son,
28-33 Cheap Street, Sherborne
Tel: (0935) 815151

Johnsons of Sherborne Ltd,
South Street, Sherborne
Tel: (0935) 812585

Talisman Antiques,
The Old Brewery, Wyke, Gillingham
Tel: (074 76) 4423

Essex

F G Bruschweiler,
41-67 Lower Lambricks, Rayleigh
Tel: (0268) 773761

Stonehall Antiques,
Trade Warehouse, Down Hall Road, Matching Green, Nr Harlow
Tel: (0279) 731440

Glos

Baggott Church Street Ltd,
Church Street, Stow-on-the-Wold
Tel: (0451) 30370

Paul Cater,
High Street, Moreton-in-Marsh
Tel: (0608) 51888

Country Life Antiques,
Sheep Street, Stow-on-the-Wold
Tel: (0451) 30776
Also at:
Grey House, The Square, Stow-on-the-Wold
Tel: (0451) 31564

Gloucester House Antiques,
Market Place, Fairford
Tel: (0285) 712790

Huntington Antiques Ltd,
The Old Forge, Church Street, Stow-on-the-Wold
Tel: (0451) 30842

Painswick Antiques & Interiors,
Beacon House, Painswick
Tel: (0452) 812578

Antony Preston Antiques Ltd,
The Square, Stow-on-the-Wold
Tel: (0451) 31586

Stone House Antiques,
St Mary's Street, Painswick
Tel: (0452) 813540

Studio Antiques Ltd,
Bourton-on-the-Water
Tel: (0451) 20352

Hants

C W Buckingham,
Twin Firs, Southampton Road, Cadnam
Tel: (0703) 812122

Cedar Antiques,
High Street, Hartley Wintney
Tel: (025 126) 3252

Mark Collier Antiques,
24 The High Street, Fordingbridge
Tel: (0425) 52555

R C Dodson,
85 Fawcett Road, Southsea
Tel: (0705) 829481

House of Antiques,
4 College Street, Petersfield
Tel: (0730) 62172

Lita Kay of Lyndhurst,
13 High Street, Lyndhurst
Tel: (042 128) 2337

Millers of Chelsea Antiques Ltd,
Netherbrook House, 86 Christchurch Road, Ringwood
Tel: (04254) 2062

Truelocke Antiques,
109 High Street, Odiham
Tel: (0256) 702387

Hereford & Worcester

Gavina Ewart,
60-62 High Street, Broadway
Tel: (0386) 853371

Great Brampton House Antiques Ltd,
Madley
Tel: (0981) 250244

Jean Hodge Antiques,
Peachley Manor, Lower Broadheath, Worcester
Tel: (0905) 640255

Jennings of Leominster,
30 Bridge Street, Leominster
Tel: (0568) 2946

Herts

C Bellinger Antiques
91 Wood Street, Barnet
Tel: 01-449 3467

John Bly,
50 High Street, Tring
Tel: (044 282) 3030

Collins Antiques,
Corner House, Wheathampstead
Tel: (058) 283 3111

Phillips of Hitchin (Antiques) Ltd,
The Manor House, Hitchin
Tel: (0462) 32067

Humberside

Geoffrey Mole,
400 Wincolmlee, Hull
Tel: (0482) 27858

Kent

Chislehurst Antiques,
7 Royal Parade, Chislehurst
Tel: 01-467 1530

Nigel Coleman Antiques,
High Street, Brasted
Tel: (0959) 64042

Conquest House Antiques,
Conquest House, 17 Palace Street, Canterbury
Tel: (0227) 464587

Furnace Mill,
Lamberhurst
Tel: (0892) 890285

John McMaster,
5 Sayers Square, Sayers Lane, Tenterden
Tel: (058 06) 2941

The Old Bakery Antiques (Mr & Mrs D Bryan),
St Davids Bridge, Cranbrook
Tel: (0580) 713103

Steppes Hill Farm Antiques,
Stockbury, Sittingbourne
Tel: (0795) 842205

Sutton Valence Antiques,
Sutton Valence, Maidstone
Tel: (0622) 843333 & 843499

Lancs

De Molen Ltd,
Moss Hey Garages, Chapel Road, Marton Moss, Blackpool
Tel: (0253) 696324

West Lancs Exports,
Black Horse Farm, 123 Liverpool Road, South Burscough, Nr Ormskirk
Tel: (0704) 894634

Leics

Leicester Antiques Complex,
9 St Nicholas Place, Leicester
Tel: (0533) 533343

Lowe of Loughborough,
37-40 Church Gate, Loughborough
Tel: (0509) 217876

Lincs
Kirkby Antiques Ltd,
Kirkby-on-Bain, Woodhall Spa
Tel: (0526) 52119 & 53461

Geoff Parker Antiques Ltd,
Haltoft End, Freiston, Nr Boston
Tel: (0205) 760444

Laurence Shaw Antiques,
Spilsby Road, Horncastle
Tel: (06582) 7638 & (065888) 600

Middx
Binstead Antiques,
21 Middle Lane, Teddington
Tel: 01-943 0626

J W Crisp Antiques,
166 High Street, Teddington
Tel: 01-977 4309

Phelps Ltd,
133-135 St Margaret's Road,
E Twickenham
Tel: 01-892 1778

Norfolk
Arthur Brett & Sons Ltd,
40-44 St Giles Street, Norwich
Tel: (0603) 628171

Peter Howkins Antiques,
39, 40 & 135 King Street, Great Yarmouth
Tel: (0493) 851180

Pearse Lukies,
Bayfield House, White Hart Street, Aylsham
Tel: (0263) 734137

Rossendale Antiques (Ian Shaw),
Rossendale, The Street,
Rickinghall, Diss
Tel: (0379) 898485

Northants
Paul Hopwell Antiques,
30 High Street, West Haddon
Tel: (078 887) 636

Notts
Matsell Antiques Ltd,
2 & 4 Derby Street, off Derby Road,
Nottingham
Tel: (0602) 472691 & 288267

Oxon
David John Ceramics,
11 Acre End Street, Eynsham
Tel: (0865) 880786

Elizabethan House Antiques,
28 & 55 High Street, Dorchester-on-Thames
Tel: (0865) 340079

Key Antiques,
11 Horse Fair, Chipping Norton
Tel: (0608) 3777

Peter Norden Antiques,
High Street, Burford
Tel: (099 382) 2121

Manfred Schotten Antiques,
The Crypt, High Street, Burford
Tel: (099 382) 2302

Telling Time,
57 North Street, Thame
Tel: (084 421) 3007

Zene Walker,
The Bull House, High Street,
Burford
Tel: (099 382) 3284

Witney Antiques,
96-98 Corn Street, Witney
Tel: (0993) 3902

Shropshire
Castle Lodge,
Ludlow
Tel: (0584) 2838

Castle Gate Antiques,
15 Castle Gate, Shrewsbury
Tel: (0743) 61011 (evenings)

R G Cave & Sons Ltd,
17 Broad Street, Ludlow
Tel: (0584) 3568

Dodington Antiques,
15 Dodington, Whitchurch
Tel: (0948) 3399

Doveridge House of Neachley,
Long Lane, Nr Shifnal
Tel: (090 722) 3131/2

F C Manser & Son Ltd,
53/54 Wyle Cop, Shrewsbury
Tel: (0743) 51120

Paul Smith,
The Old Chapel, Old Street,
Ludlow
Tel: (0584) 2666

M & R Taylor (Antiques),
53 Broad Street, Ludlow
Tel: (0584) 4169

White Cottage Antiques,
Tern Hill, Nr Market Drayton
Tel: (063 083) 222

Somerset
Grange Court Antiques,
Corfe, Nr Taunton
Tel: (082 342) 498

Peter Murray Antique Exports,
Station Road, Bruton
Tel: (0749) 812364

Edward A Nowell,
21-23 Market Place, Wells
Tel: (0749) 72415

Suffolk
David Gibbins Antiques,
21 Market Hill, Woodbridge
Tel: (039 43) 3531

Hubbard Antiques,
16 St Margaret's Green, Ipswich
Tel: (0473) 226033

Michael Moore Antiques,
The Old Court, Nethergate Street,
Clare
Tel: (0787) 277510

Peppers Period Pieces (R),
22-24 Churchgate Street, Bury St Edmunds
Tel: (0284) 68786

Randolph,
97 & 99 High Street, Hadleigh
Tel: (0473) 823789

Surrey
Churchill Antiques Gallery Ltd,
65 Quarry Street, Guildford
Tel: (0483) 506662

Dorking Desk Shop,
41 West Street, Dorking
Tel: (0306) 883327 & 880535

Hampshires of Dorking,
48-52 West Street, Dorking
Tel: (0306) 887076

J Hartley Antiques,
186 High Street, Ripley
Tel: (0483) 224318

Heath-Bullock,
8 Meadrow, Godalming
Tel: (048 68) 22562

Ripley Antiques,
67 High Street, Ripley
Tel: (0483) 224981

Swan Antiques,
62a West Street, Dorking
Tel: (0306) 881217

Anthony Welling Antiques,
Broadway Barn, High Street,
Ripley
Tel: (0483) 225384

Wych House Antiques,
Wych Hill, Woking
Tel: (048 62) 64636

Sussex
A27 Antiques Warehouses,
Chaucer Industrial Estate, Dittons Road, Polegate
Tel: (032 12) 7167 & 5301

Bursig of Arundel,
The Old Candle Factory, Tarrant Street, Arundel
Tel: (0903) 883456

Humphry Antiques,
East Street, Petworth
Tel: (0798) 43053

Richard Davidson,
Lombard Street, Petworth
Tel: (0798) 42508

The Grange Antiques,
High Street, Robertsbridge
Tel: (0580) 880577

Lakeside Antiques,
The Old Cement Works, South Heighton, Newhaven
Tel: (0273) 513326

John G Morris Ltd,
Market Square, Petworth
Tel: (0798) 42305

The Old Mint House,
High Street, Pevensey, Eastbourne
Tel: (0323) 761251

David and Sarah Pullen,
29/31 Sea Road, Bexhill-on-Sea
Tel: (0424) 222035

Southey Gilbert Ward Ltd,
Units 5 & 6, Cliffe Industrial Estate, Lewes
Tel: (0273) 474222

Village Antiques,
2 & 4 Cooden Sea Road, Little Common, Bexhill-on-Sea
Tel: (042 43) 5214

Tyne & Wear
Harold J Carr Antiques,
Field House, Rickleton,
Washington
Tel: (091) 388 6442

West Midlands
John Hubbard Antiques,
224-226 Court Oak Road,
Harborne, Birmingham
Tel: 021-426 1694

Rock House Antiques & Collectors Centre,
Rock House, The Rock, Tettenhall, Wolverhampton
Tel: (0902) 754995

Wilts
Avon Antiques,
26-27 Market Street, Bradford-upon-Avon
Tel: (022 16) 2052

Robert Bradley,
71 Brown Street, Salisbury
Tel: (0722) 333677

Combe Cottage Antiques,
Castle Combe, Nr Chippenham
Tel: (0249) 782250

Ian G Hastie, BADA,
46 St Ann Street, Salisbury
Tel: (0722) 22957

Robert Kime Antiques,
Dene House, Lockeridge
Tel: (067 286) 250

Monkton Galleries,
Hindon
Tel: (074 789) 235

Paul Wansbrough,
Seend Lodge, Seend,
Nr Melksham
Tel: (038 082) 213

K & A Welch,
1a Church Street, Warminster
Tel: (0985) 214687 & 213433 (evenings)

Yorks
Robert Aagaard Ltd,
Frogmire House, Stockwell Road,
Knaresborough
Tel: (0423) 864805
(Specialises in fireplaces)

Barmouth Court Antiques,
Abbeydale House, Barmouth Road, Sheffield
Tel: (0742) 582160 & 582672

Derbyshire Antiques Ltd,
27 Montpellier Parade, Harrogate
Tel: (0423) 503115/64242

Bernard Dickinson,
88 High Street, Gargrave
Tel: (075 678) 285

Jeremy A Fearn,
The Old Rectory, Winksley, Ripon
Tel: (076 583) 625

W F Greenwood & Sons Ltd,
2 & 3 Crown Place, Harrogate
Tel: (0423) 504467

Old Rectory Antiques,
The Old Rectory, West Heslerton,
Malton
Tel: (094 45) 364

Robert Morrison & Son,
Trentholme House, 131 The Mount, York
Tel: (0904) 55394

R M S Precious,
King William House, High Street,
Settle
Tel: (072 92) 3946

Scotland
John Bell of Aberdeen Ltd,
Balbrogie, By Blackburn,
Kinellar, Aberdeenshire
Tel: (0224) 79209

Paul Couts Ltd,
101-107 West Bow, Edinburgh
Tel: 031-225 3238

Letham Antiques,
20 Dundas Street, Edinburgh
Tel: 031-556 6565

Roy Sim Antiques,
21 Allan Street, Blairgowrie,
Perthshire
Tel: (0250) 3860 & 3700

Unicorn Antiques,
54 Dundas Street, Edinburgh
Tel: 031-556 7176

FURNITURE – PINE

London
Adams Antiques,
47 Chalk Farm Road, NW1
Tel: 01-267 9241

The Barewood Company,
58 Mill Lane, West Hampstead,
NW6
Tel: 01-435 7244

Chest of Drawers,
281 Upper Street, Islington, N1
Tel: 01-359 5909

Islington Artefacts,
12-14 Essex Road, Islington, N1
Tel: 01-226 6867

Olwen Carthew,
109 Kirkdale, SW26
Tel: 01-699 1363

Princedale Antiques,
70 Princedale Road, W11
Tel: 01-727 0868

Remember When,
683-685 Finchley Road, NW2
Tel: 01-433 1333

Scallywag,
187-191 Clapham Road,
Stockwell, London, SW9
Tel: 01-274 0300

This & That (Furniture),
50 & 51 Chalk Farm Road, NW1
Tel: 01-267 5433

Avon

Abbas Combe Pine,
4 Upper Maudlin Street, Bristol
Tel: (0272) 299023

Pennard House Antiques,
3/4 Piccadilly, London Road, Bath
Tel: (0225) 313791

Robert Pugh,
13 Walcot Buildings, London Road, Bath
Tel: (0225) 317516

Bucks

The Pine Merchants,
52 High Street, Gt Missenden
Tel: (024 06) 2002

Cornwall

Tim & Claire Belton,
Maidenland, St Kew, Nr Bodmin
Tel: (0208) 84242

Co Durham

Horsemarket Antiques,
27 Horsemarket, Barnard Castle
Tel: (0833) 37881

Devon

The Ark Antiques,
76 Fore Street, Topsham
Tel: (039287) 6251

Chancery Antiques,
8-10 Barrington Street, Tiverton
Tel: (0884) 252416/253190

Country Cottage Furniture,
The Old Smithy, Back Street, Modbury
Tel: (0548) 830888

Fine Pine,
Woodland Road, Harbertonford
Tel: (080 423) 465

Glos

Bed of Roses Antiques,
12 Prestbury Road, Cheltenham
Tel: (0242) 231918

Country Homes,
61 Long Street, Tetbury
Tel: (0666) 52342

Denzil Verey Antiques,
The Close, Barnsley House, Barnsley, Nr Cirencester
Tel: (028 574) 402

Gloucester House Antiques,
Market Place, Fairford
Tel: (0285) 712790

Hants

C W Buckingham,
Twin Firs, Southampton Road, Cadnam
Tel: (0703) 812122

Craftsman Furniture (Steve Hudson),
Castle Trading Estate, Portchester, Portsmouth
Tel: (0705) 219911

Millers of Chelsea Antiques Ltd,
Netherbrook House,
86 Christchurch Road, Ringwood
Tel: (04254) 2062

The Pine Cellars,
38 Jewry Street, Winchester
Tel: (0962) 67014

The Pine Co,
104 Christchurch Road, Ringwood
Tel: (042 54) 3932

Hereford & Worcester

The Hay Galleries Ltd,
4 High Town, Hay-on-Wye
Tel: (0497) 820356

Jennings of Leominster,
30 Bridge Street, Leominster
Tel: (0568) 2946

La Barre Ltd,
The Place, 116 South Street, Leominster
Tel: (0568) 4315

Marshall Bennett Restorations,
Eagle Lane, High Street, Cleobury Mortimer,
Nr Kidderminster, Worcester
Tel: (0299) 270553

Paul Somers Interiors incorporating Woodstock Interiors,
Unicorn Yard, Belle Vue Terrace, Malvern, Worcester
Tel: (068 45) 60297

Herts

Out of Town,
21 Ware Road, Hertford
Tel: (0992) 582848

Humberside

Bell Antiques,
68 Harold Street, Grimsby
Tel: (0472) 695110

The Hull Pine Co,
Bean Street, 253 Anlaby Road, Hull
Tel: (0482) 227169

Paul Wilson Pine Furniture,
Perth Street West, Hull
Tel: (0482) 447923 & 448607

Kent

Barnside Antiques,
Meopham Green, Meopham
Tel: (0474) 814682

Empire Antiques,
The Old Council Yard, Gazen Salts, Strand Street, Sandwich
Tel: (0304) 614474

Penny Lampard,
28 High Street, Headcorn
Tel: (0622) 890682

Andrée L Martin,
100 Sandgate High Street, Folkestone
Tel: (0303) 48560

The Old Bakery Antiques (Mr & Mrs D Bryan),
St Davids Bridge, Cranbrook
Tel: (0580) 713103

The Plough Pine Shop,
High Street, Eastry, Dover
Tel: (0304) 617418

Sissinghurst Antiques,
Hazelhurst Cottage, The Street, Sissinghurst, Nr Cranbrook
Tel: (0580) 713893

Traditional Furniture,
248 Seabrook Road, Seabrook, Hythe
Tel: (0303) 39931

Lancs

Robert Sheriff,
Moss Hey Garages, Chapel Road, Marton Moss, Blackpool
Tel: (0253) 696324

Cottage Furniture,
Farnworth Park Industrial Estate, Queen Street, Farnworth, Bolton
Tel: (0204) 700853

Enloc Antiques,
Old Corporation Yard, Knotts Lane, Colne
Tel: (0282) 861417

Utopia Pine,
Holme Mills, Carnforth
Tel: (0524) 781739

Leics

Richard Kimbell Antiques,
Riverside, Market Harborough
Tel: (0858) 33444

Riverside Trading,
Riverside Industrial Estate, Market Harborough
Tel: (0858) 64110/64825

Lincs

Allens Antiques,
Moor Farm, Stapleford
Tel: (052 285) 392

J & J Palmer Ltd,
42/44 Swinegate, Grantham
Tel: (0476) 70093

Stowaway (UK) Ltd,
2 Langton Hill, Horncastle
Tel: (065 82) 7445

Norfolk

Rossendale Antiques (Ian Shaw),
Rossendale, The Street, Rickinghall, Diss
Tel: (0379) 898485

Northants

Acorn Antiques,
The Old Mill, Moat Lane, Towcester
Tel: (0327) 52788

The Country Pine Shop,
Northampton Road, West Haddon
Tel: (078887) 430

Oxon

Market Place Antiques,
35 Market Place, Henley-on-Thames
Tel: (0491) 57287

Julie Strachey,
Southfield Farm, Weston-on-the-Green
Tel: (0869) 50833/2

Somerset

Chalon,
Hambridge Mill, Hambridge, Ilminster
Tel: (0458) 252374

Crewkerne Antiques Centre,
42 East Street, Crewkerne
Tel: (0460) 76755

Grange Court Antiques,
Corfe, Taunton
Tel: (0823) 42498

Peter Murray Antique Exports,
Station Road, Bruton
Tel: (0749) 812364

Pennard House Antiques,
East Pennard, Shepton Mallet
Tel: (074 986) 266

Staffs

Anvil Antiques Ltd,
Cross Mills, Cross Street, Leek
Tel: (0538) 371657

Aspleys Antiques,
Compton Mill, Compton, Leek
Tel: (0538) 373396 & 373346

Directmoor Ltd,
The Coppice Farm, Nr Moorcourt, Oakamoor
Tel: (0588) 702419/387474

Gemini Trading,
Limes Mill, Abbotts Road, Leek
Tel: (0538) 387834

Johnsons,
Park Works, Park Road, Leek
Tel: (0538) 386745

Stone-wares,
The Stripped Pine Shop,
24 Radford Street, Stone
Tel: (0785) 815000

Suffolk

Michael Moore Antiques,
The Old Court, Nethergate Street, Clare
Tel: (0787) 277510

Surrey

Manor Antiques,
High Street, Old Woking
Tel: (048 62) 24666

Odiham Antiques,
High Street, Compton, Guildford
Tel: (0483) 810215

F & L Warren,
The Sawmills, Firgrove Hill, Farnham
Tel: (0252) 726713

Wych House Antiques,
Wych Hill, Woking
Tel: (048 62) 64636

Pine Warehouse at:–
34 London Road, Staines (off The Crooked Billet roundabout A30)
Tel: (0784) 65331

Sussex

Drummer Pine,
Hailsham Road, Herstmonceux
Tel: (0323) 833542/833661

Hillside Antiques,
Units 12-13, Lindfield Enterprise Park, Lewes Road, Lindfield
Tel: (044 47) 3042

Ann Lingard,
Ropewalk Antiques, Ropewalk, Rye
Tel: (0797) 223486

Peppers Antique Pine,
Crouch Lane, Seaford
Tel: (0323) 891400

Polegate Antique Centre,
Station Road, Polegate
Tel: (032 12) 5277

Graham Price Antiques Ltd,
A27 Antiques Complex, Unit 4,
Chaucer Industrial Estate, Dittons Road, Polegate
Tel: (032 12) 7167 & 7681

Touchwood (Mervyn & Sue),
The Square, Herstmonceux
Tel: (0323) 832020

Michael Wakelin & Helen Lindfield,
10 New Street, Petworth
Tel: (0798) 42417

Wilts

Ray Coggins Antiques,
The Old Brewery, Newtown, Bradford-on-Avon
Tel: (02216) 3431

James Henry Antiques,
29 The Parade, Marlborough
Tel: (0672) 53652

Yorks

Daleside Antiques,
St Peter's Square, Cold Bath Road, Harrogate
Tel: (0423) 60286

Early Days,
7 Kings Court, Pateley Bridge, Harrogate
Tel: (0423) 711661

Michael Green,
Library House, Regent Parade, Harrogate
Tel: (0423) 60452

Manor Barn Pine,
Burnside Mill, Main Street, Addinsham, Ilkley
Tel: (0943) 830176

Pine Finds,
The Old Corn Mill, Bishop Monkton, Harrogate
Tel: (0765) 87159

Smith & Smith Designs,
58A Middle Street North, Driffield
Tel: (0377) 46321

Ireland

Alain Chawner,
The Square, Collon, Co Louth
Tel: (010 353 41) 26270

Albert Forsythe,
Mill Hall, 66 Carsontown Road, Saintfield, Co Down, Northern Ireland
Tel: (0238) 510398

Delvin Farm Galleries,
Gormaston, Co Meath
Tel: (0001) 412285

Luckpenny Antiques,
Kilmurray House, Shinrone, Birr, Co Offaly, Southern Ireland
Tel: (010 353 505) 47134

W J Somerville,
Shamrock Antiques Ltd,
Killanley, Ballina, Co Mayo
Tel: (096) 36275

Scotland

A & P Steadman,
Unit 1, Hatston Industrial Estate, Kirkwall, Orkney
Tel: (0856) 5040

Wales

Heritage Restorations,
Maes y Glydfa, Llanfair, Caereinion, Welshpool, Powys
Tel: (0938) 810384

Maclean,
Dudley & Marie Thorpe, Tiradda, Llansadwrn, Dyfed
Tel: (0550) 777-509

GLASS

London

Asprey PLC,
165-169 New Bond Street, W1
Tel: 01-493 6767

Phyllis Bedford Antiques,
3 The Galleries, Camden Passage, N1
Tel: 01-354 1332;
home 01-882 3189

Christine Bridge,
78 Castelnau, SW13
Tel: 01-741 5501

W G T Burne (Antique Glass) Ltd,
11 Elystan Street, SW3
Tel: 01-589 6074

Delomosne & Son Ltd,
4 Campden Hill Road, W8
Tel: 01-937 1804

Eila Grahame,
97C Kensington Church Street, W8
Tel: 01-727 4132

Lloyds of Westminster,
5A Motcomb Street, SW1
Tel: 01-235 1010

S W Parry (Old Glass),
Stand A4-A5 Westbourne Antique Arcade, 113 Portobello Road, W11 (Sat only)
Tel: 01-740 0248 (Sun to Fri)

J F Poore,
5 Wellington Terrace, W2
Tel: 01-229 4166

Pryce & Brise Antiques,
79 Moore Park Road, Fulham, SW6
Tel: 01-736 1864

Gerald Sattin Ltd,
25 Burlington Arcade, Piccadilly, W1
Tel: 01-493 6557

Mark J West,
Cobb Antiques Ltd,
39B High Street, Wimbledon Village, SW19
Tel: 01-946 2811

R Wilkinson & Son (R),
43-45 Wastdale Road, Forest Hill, SE23
Tel: 01-699 4420

Avon

Somervale Antiques,
6 Radstock Road, Midsomer Norton, Bath
Tel: (0761) 412686

Dorset

A & D Antiques,
21 East Street, Blandford Forum
Tel: (0258) 55643

Quarter Jack Antiques,
The Quarter Jack, Bridge Street, Sturminster Newton
Tel: (0258) 72558

Hants

Stockbridge Antiques,
High Street, Stockbridge
Tel: (0264) 810829

Todd & Austin Antiques & Fine Art
2 Andover Road, Winchester
Tel: (0962) 69824

Somerset

Abbey Antiques,
51 High Street, Glastonbury
Tel: (0458) 31694

Suffolk

Maureen Thompson,
Sun House, Long Melford
Tel: (0787) 78252

Surrey

Shirley Warren (by appointment only),
42 Kingswood Avenue, Sanderstead
Tel: 01-657 1751

Shirley Warren (shop),
333B Limpsfield Road, Sanderstead
Tel: 01-651 5180

Sussex

Rusthall Antiques,
Chateaubriand Antique Centre, High Street, Burwash
Tel: (0435) 882535 & (0892) 20668 (evenings)

Warwickshire

Sharon Ball (Antique glass & collectables),
Unit 41, Stratford-on-Avon Antique Centre, Ely Street, Stratford-on-Avon
Tel: (0789) 204180

Scotland

Janet Lumsden,
51A George Street, Edinburgh
Tel: 031-225 2911

William MacAdam (appointment only),
86 Pilrig Street, Edinburgh
Tel: 031-553 1364

GRAMOPHONES, PHONOGRAPHS & RADIOS

Avon

The Vintage Wireless Co,
Tudor House, Cossham Street, Mangotsfield, Bristol
Tel: (0272) 565474

Devon

Brian Taylor Antiques,
24 Molesworth Road, Stoke, Plymouth
Tel: (0752) 569061

Somerset

Philip Knighton (R),
The Wellington Workshop,
14 South Street, Wellington
Tel: (082 347) 7332

West Midlands

Woodsetton Antiques,
65 Sedgley Road, Woodsetton, Dudley
Tel: (0384) 277918

ICONS

London

Maria Andipa,
Icon Gallery, 162 Walton Street, SW3
Tel: 01-589 2371

Mark Gallery,
9 Porchester Place, Marble Arch, W2
Tel: 01-262 4906

JEWELLERY

London

Hirsh Fine Jewels,
Diamond House, Hatton Garden, EC1
Tel: 01-405 6080/01-404 4392

Glos

South Bar Antiques (Cameos),
Digbeth Street, Stow-on-the-Wold
Tel: (0451) 30236

Hereford & Worcester

Old Curiosity Antiques,
11 Tower Buildings, Blackwell Street, Kidderminster
Tel: (0562) 742859

Norfolk

Peter & Valerie Howkins,
39, 40 & 135 King Street, Great Yarmouth
Tel: (0493) 844639

Somerset

Edward A Nowell,
21-23 Market Place, Wells
Tel: (0749) 72415

Sussex

Rusthall Antiques,
Chateaubriand Antique Centre, High Street, Burwash
Tel: (0435) 882535 (0892) 20668 (evenings)

KITCHENALIA

Lancs

Kitchenalia,
89 Berry Lane, Longridge, Nr Preston
Tel: (077478) 5411

LIGHTING

London

Judy Jones,
194 Westbourne Grove, W11
Tel: 01-229 6866

The Lamp Gallery,
355 New Kings Road, SW6
Tel: 01-736 6188

Hereford & Worcester

Fritz Fryer,
27 Gloucester Road, Ross-on-Wye, Hereford
Tel: (0989) 64738 & 84512

MARINE ANTIQUES

Devon

Temeraire,
63 Brownston Street, Modbury
Tel: (0548) 830317

Essex

Littlebury Antiques,
58/60 Fairycroft Road, Saffron Walden
Tel: (0799) 27961

METALWARE

London

Christopher Bangs (by appointment only),
Tel: 01-352 3384

Jack Casimir Ltd,
The Brass Shop, 23 Pembridge Road, W11
Tel: 01-727 8643

Arthur Davidson Ltd,
78-79 Jermyn Street, SW1
Tel: 01-930 6687

Robert Preston,
1 Campden Street, W8
Tel: 01-727 4872

Alistair Sampson Antiques,
156 Brompton Road, SW3
Tel: 01-589 5272

Avon

Cottage Antiques,
The Old Post Office, Langford Place, Langford, Nr Bristol
Tel: (0934) 862597

Beds

Christopher Sykes Antiques,
The Old Parsonage, Woburn, Milton Keynes
Tel: (052 525) 259/467

Berks

Rye Galleries,
60-61 High Street, Eton
Tel: (0753) 862637

Bucks

Albert Bartram,
177 Hivings Hill, Chesham
Tel: (0494) 783271

Cumbria

Stable Antiques,
Oakdene Country Hotel, Garsdale Road, Sedbergh
Tel: (0587) 20280

Glos

Country Life Antiques,
Sheep Street, Stow-on-the-Wold
Tel: (0451) 30776
Also at:
Grey House, The Square, Stow-on-the-Wold
Tel: (0451) 31564

Oxon

Robin Bellamy Ltd,
97 Corn Street, Witney
Tel: (0993) 4793

Elizabethan House Antiques,
28 & 55 High Street, Dorchester-on-Thames
Tel: (0865) 340079

Key Antiques,
11 Horse Fair, Chipping Norton
Tel: (0608) 3777

Lloyd & Greenwood Antiques,
Chapel House, High Street, Burford
Tel: (099 382) 2359

Suffolk

Brookes Forge (R),
Flempton, Bury St Edmunds, Suffolk
Tel: (028 484) 473 business
(0449) 781376 home

Sussex

Michael Wakelin & Helen Linfield,
10 New Street, Petworth
Tel: (0798) 42417

Wilts

Avon Antiques,
26-27 Market Street, Bradford-on-Avon
Tel: (022 16) 2052

Combe Cottage Antiques,
Castle Combe, Chippenham
Tel: (0249) 782250

Rupert Gentle Antiques,
The Manor House, Milton Lilbourne, Nr Pewsey
Tel: (0672) 63344

Yorks

Windsor House Antiques (Leeds) Ltd,
18-20 Benson Street, Leeds
Tel: (0532) 444666

MUSICAL INSTRUMENTS

London

Mayflower Antiques,
117 Portobello Road, W11
Tel: 01-727 0381
(Sats only 7am-3pm)

Essex

Mayflower Antiques,
2 Una Road, Parkeston, Harwich
Tel: (0255) 504079

Kent

David Bailey Pianos Warehouse,
Ramsgate Road, Sandwich
Tel: (0304) 613948

Glos

Vanbrugh House Antiques,
Park Street, Stow-on-the-Wold
Tel: (0451) 30797

Oxon

Laurie Leigh Antiques,
36 High Street, Oxford
Tel: (0865) 244197

Somerset

Shelagh Berryman,
Musical Boxes,
15 The Market Place, Wells
Tel: (0749) 76203

Suffolk

The Suffolk Piano Workshop,
The Snape, Maltings
Tel: (072 888) 677

Sussex

Sound Instruments,
Lower Barn Farm, Horsted Green, Nr Uckfield
Tel: (0825) 61594

ORIENTAL

Somerset

Ron & F Fairbrass,
48 West Street, Crewkerne
Tel: (0460) 76941

Sussex

Linda Loveland Fine Arts,
18-20 Prospect Place, Hastings
Tel: (0424) 441608

PORCELAIN

London

Albert Amor Ltd,
37 Bury Street, St James's, SW1
Tel: 01-930 2444

Antique Porcelain Co Ltd,
149 New Bond Street, W1
Tel: 01-629 1254

Susan Becker,
18 Lower Richmond Road, SW15
Tel: 01-788 9082

David Brower Antiques,
113 Kensington Church Street, W8
Tel: 01-221 4155

Cale Antiques,
24 Cale Street, Chelsea Green, SW3
Tel: 01-589 6146

Cathay Antiques,
12 Thackeray Street, W8
Tel: 01-937 6066

Belinda Coote Antiques,
29 Holland Street, W8
Tel: 01-937 3924

Craven Antiques,
17 Garson House, Gloucester Terrace, W2
Tel: 01-262 4176

Marilyn Delion,
Stand 7 (Basement), Portobello Road, W11
Tel: 01-937 3377

Delomosne & Son Ltd,
4 Campden Hill Road, W8
Tel: 01-937 1804

H & W Deutsch Antiques,
111 Kensington Church Street, W8
Tel: 01-727 5984

Miss Fowler,
1A Duke Street, Manchester Square, W1
Tel: 01-935 5187

Graham & Oxley (Antiques) Ltd,
101 Kensington Church Street, W8
Tel: 01-229 1850

Grosvenor Antiques Ltd,
27 Holland Street, Kensington, W8
Tel: 01-937 8649

Harcourt Antiques,
5 Harcourt Street, W1
Tel: 01-723 5919

Heirloom & Howard Ltd,
1 Hay Hill, Berkeley Square, W1
Tel: 01-493 5868

Hoff Antiques Ltd,
66A Kensington Church Street, W8
Tel: 01-229 5516

Klaber & Klaber,
2A Bedford Gardens, Kensington Church Street, W8
Tel: 01-727 4573

D M & P Manheim Ltd,
69 Upper Berkeley Street, Portman Square, W1
Tel: 01-723 6595

Mayfair Gallery,
97 Mount Street, W1
Tel: 01-499 5315

Mercury Antiques,
1 Ladbroke Road, W11
Tel: 01-727 5106

St Jude's Antiques,
107 Kensington Church Street, W8
Tel: 01-727 8737

Edward Salti,
43 Davies Street, W1
Tel: 01-629 2141

Gerald Sattin Ltd,
25 Burlington Arcade, Piccadilly, W1
Tel: 01-493 6557

Jean Sewell (Antiques) Ltd,
3 Campden Street, Kensington Church Street, W8
Tel: 01-727 3122

Simon Spero,
109 Kensington Church Street, W8
Tel: 01-727 7413

Aubrey Spiers Antiques,
Shop C5, Chenil Galleries, 183 King's Road, SW3
Tel: 01-352 7384

Constance Stobo,
31 Holland Street, W8
Tel: 01-937 6282

Earle D Vandekar of Knightsbridge Ltd,
138 Brompton Road, SW3
Tel: 01-589 8481/3398

Venner's Antiques,
7 New Cavendish Street, W1
Tel: 01-935 0184

Winifred Williams,
3 Bury Street, St James's, SW1
Tel: 01-930 4732

Avon

Andrew Dando,
4 Wood Street, Queen Square, Bath
Tel: (0225) 22702

Berks

Len's Crested China,
Twyford Antiques Centre, Nr Reading
Tel: (0753) 35162

The Old School Antiques,
Dorney, Windsor
Tel: (062 86) 3247

Cornwall

Mrs Margaret Chesterton,
33 Pentewan Road, St Austell
Tel: (0726) 72926

London Apprentice Antiques,
Pentewan Road, St Austell
Tel: (0726) 63780

Derbys

C B Sheppard Antiques
(appointment only),
Hurst Lodge, Chesterfield Road, Tibshelf
Tel: (0773) 872419

Devon

David J Thorn,
2 High Street, Budleigh Salterton
Tel: (039 54) 2448

Glos

Gloucester House Antiques,
Market Place, Fairford
Tel: (0285) 712790

L Greenwold,
Digbeth, Digbeth Street, Stow-on-the-Wold
Tel: (0451) 30398

Hamand Antiques,
Friday Street, Painswick
Tel: (0452) 812310

Pamela Rowan,
High Street, Blockley, Nr Moreton-in-Marsh
Tel: (0386) 700280

Studio Antiques Ltd,
Bourton-on-the-Water
Tel: (0451) 20352

Wain Antiques,
45 Long Street, Tetbury
Tel: (0666) 52440

Hants

Gerald Austin Antiques,
2A Andover Road, Winchester
Tel: (0962) 69824 Ext 2

Goss & Crested China Ltd,
62 Murray Road, Horndean
Tel: (0705) 597440

Rogers of Alresford,
16 West Street, Alresford
Tel: (096 273) 2862

Hereford & Worcester

Gavina Ewart,
60-62 High Street, Broadway
Tel: (0386) 853371

Sabina Jennings,
Newcourt Park, Lugwardine
Tel: (0432) 850752

M Lees & Sons,
Tower House, Severn Street, Worcester
Tel: (0905) 26620

Kent

Beaubush Antiques,
95 Sandgate High Street, Folkestone
Tel: (0303) 49099

Dunsdale Lodge Antiques,
Brasted Road, Westerham
Tel: (0959) 62160

The History in Porcelain Collector,
High Street, Shoreham Village, Nr Sevenoaks
Tel: (095 92) 3416

Steppes Hill Farm Antiques,
Stockbury, Sittingbourne
Tel: (0795) 842205

Wakefield Ceramic Fairs (Fred Hynds),
1 Fountain Road, Strood, Rochester
Tel: (0634) 723461

W W Warner (Antiques) Ltd,
The Green, Brasted
Tel: (0959) 63698

Lancs

Burnley Antiques & Fine Arts Ltd,
336A Colne Road, Burnley
Tel: (0282) 20143/65172

Leics

Charnwood Antiques,
54 Sparrow Hill, Loughborough
Tel: (0509) 231750

Norfolk

T C S Brooke,
The Grange, Wroxham
Tel: (060 53) 2644

Margaret Corson,
Irstead Manor, Neatishead
Tel: (0692) 630274

Oxon

Castle Antiques,
Lamb Arcade, Wallingford, Oxon
Tel: (0491) 35166

David John Ceramics,
11 Acre End Street, Eynsham, Oxford
Tel: (0865) 880786

Shropshire

Castle Gate Antiques,
15 Castle Gate, Shrewsbury
Tel: (0743) 61011 evenings

F C Manser & Son Ltd,
53-54 Wyle Cop, Shrewsbury
Tel: (0743) 51120

Teme Valley Antiques,
1 The Bull Ring, Ludlow
Tel: (0584) 4686

Tudor House Antiques,
33 High Street, Ironbridge
Tel: (095 245) 3237

Somerset

Ray Antonies Antiques,
86 Holyrood Street, Chard
Tel: (0460) 67163

Suffolk

Crafers Antiques,
The Hill, Wickham Market, Woodbridge
Tel: (0728) 747347

Surrey

Elias Clark Antiques Ltd,
1 The Cobbles, Bletchingley
Tel: (0883) 843714

J P Raison (by appointment only),
Heathcroft, Walton Heath, Tadworth
Tel: (073 781) 3557

Whittington Galleries,
22 Woodend, Sutton
Tel: 01-644 9327

Sussex

Barclay Antiques,
7 Village Mews, Little Common, Bexhill-on-Sea
Tel: (0797) 222734 home

Geoffrey Godden,
Chinaman, 17-19 Crescent Road, Worthing
Tel: (0903) 35958

William Hockley Antiques,
East Street, Petworth
Tel: (0798) 43172

Leonard Russell,
21 King's Avenue, Newhaven
Tel: (0273) 515153

Wilts

The China Hen,
9 Woolley Street, Bradford-on-Avon
Tel: (022 16) 3369

Mark Collier Antiques,
High Street, Downton
Tel: (0725) 21068

Yorks

Brian Bowden,
199 Carr House Road, Doncaster
Tel: (0302) 65353

Angela Charlesworth,
99 Dodworth Road, Barnsley
Tel: (0226) 282097/203688

David Love,
10 Royal Parade, Harrogate
Tel: (0423) 65797

Nanbooks,
Undercliffe Cottage, Duke Street, Settle
Tel: (072 92) 3324

Wales

Brenin Porcelain & Pottery,
Old Wool Barn, Verity's Court, Cowbridge, South Glamorgan
Tel: (044 63) 3893

Gwalia Antiques,
Main Street, Goodwick, Fishguard, Dyfed
Tel: (0348) 872634

POTTERY

London

Britannia,
Stand 101, Gray's Market, 58 Davies Street, W1
Tel: 01-629 6772

Cale Antiques,
24 Cale Street, Chelsea Green, SW3
Tel: 01-589 6146

Gerald Clark Antiques,
1 High Street, Mill Hill Village, NW7
Tel: 01-906 0342

Belinda Coote Antiques,
29 Holland Street, W8
Tel: 01-937 3924

Marilyn Delion,
Stand 7 (Basement), Portobello Road, W11
Tel: 01-937 3377

Richard Dennis,
144 Kensington Church Street, W8
Tel: 01-727 2061

Graham & Oxley (Antiques) Ltd,
101 Kensington Church Street, W8
Tel: 01-229 1850

Jonathan Horne,
66C Kensington Church Street, W8
Tel: 01-221 5658

D M & P Manheim Ltd,
69 Upper Berkeley Street, Portman Square, W1
Tel: 01-723 6595

J & J May,
40 Kensington Church Street, W8
Tel: 01-937 3575

Mercury Antiques,
1 Ladbroke Road, W11
Tel: 01-727 5106

Oliver Sutton Antiques,
34C Kensington Church Street, W8
Tel: 01-937 0633

Rogers de Rin,
76 Royal Hospital Road, SW3
Tel: 01-352 9007

St Jude's Antiques,
107 Kensington Church Street, W8
Tel: 01-727 8737

Alistair Sampson Antiques,
156 Brompton Road, SW3
Tel: 01-589 5272

Constance Stobo,
31 Holland Street, W8
Tel: 01-937 6282

Earle D Vandekar of Knightsbridge Ltd,
138 Brompton Road, SW3
Tel: 01-589 8481 & 3398

Cornwall

Mrs Margaret Chesterton,
33 Pentewan Road, St Austell
Tel: (0826) 72926

Cumbria

Kendal Studio Pottery,
2-3 Wildman Street, Kendal
Tel: (0539) 23291

Devon

David J Thorn,
2 High Street, Budleigh Salterton
Tel: (039 54) 2448

Glos

Wain Antiques,
45 Long Street, Tetbury
Tel: (0666) 52440

Hants

Goss & Crested China Ltd,
62 Murray Road, Horndean
Tel: (0705) 597440

Millers of Chelsea,
Netherbrook House, Christchurch Road, Ringwood
Tel: (0425) 472062

Rogers of Alresford,
16 West Street, Alresford
Tel: (096 273) 2862

Kent

A C Scott,
Dunsdale Lodge Antiques, Brasted Road, Westerham
Tel: (0959) 62160

W W Warner (Antiques) Ltd,
The Green, Brasted
Tel: (0959) 63698

Lancs

Burnley Antiques & Fine Arts Ltd (appointment only),
336A Colne Road, Burnley
Tel: (0282) 65172

Norfolk

Margaret Corson,
Irstead Manor, Neatishead
Tel: (0692) 630274

Suffolk

Crafers Antiques,
The Hill, Wickham Market, Woodbridge
Tel: (0728) 747347

Surrey

Elias Clark Antiques Ltd,
1 The Cobbles, Bletchingley
Tel: (0883) 843714

Whittington Galleries,
22 Woodend, Sutton
Tel: 01-644 9327

Sussex

Ron Beech,
150 Portland Road, Hove
Tel: (0273) 724477

Leonard Russell,
21 King's Avenue, Newhaven
Tel: (0273) 515153

Warwickshire

Beehive Antiques,
9 Smith Street, Eastgate, Warwick
Tel: (0926) 497194

Wilts

Bratton Antiques,
Market Place, Westbury
Tel: (0373) 823021

Yorks

Angela Charlesworth,
99 Dodworth Road, Barnsley
Tel: (0226) 282097/203688

The Crested China Company,
The Station House, Driffield
Tel: (0377) 47042

Nanbooks,
Undercliffe Cottage, Duke Street, Settle
Tel: (072 92) 3324

Wales

Brenin Porcelain & Pottery,
Old Wool Barn, Verity's Court, Cowbridge, South Glamorgan
Tel: (044 63) 3893

Isle of Man

Rushton Ceramics,
Tynwald Mills, St Johns
Tel: (0624) 71618

SCIENTIFIC INSTRUMENTS

London

Jilliana Ranicar-Breese, Martin Breese Ltd,
164 Kensington Park Road, Notting Hill Gate, W11
Tel: 01-727 9378
(Optical Toys/Illusion)

Arthur Davidson Ltd,
78-79 Jermyn Street, SW1
Tel: 01-930 6687

Mariner Antiques Ltd,
55 Curzon Street, W1
Tel: 01-499 0171

Mayfair Microscopes Ltd,
64 Burlington Arcade, W1
Tel: 01-629 2616

Mayflower Antiques,
117 Portobello Road, W11
Tel: 01-727 0381
(Sats only 7am-3pm)

Arthur Middleton Ltd,
12 New Row, Covent Garden, WC2
Tel: 01-836 7042/7062

Trevor Philip & Sons Ltd,
75A Jermyn Street, St James's, SW1
Tel: 01-930 2954/5

David Weston Ltd,
44 Duke Street, St James, SW1
Tel: 01-839 1051-2-3

Harriet Wynter Ltd (by appointment only),
50 Redcliffe Road, SW10
Tel: 01-352 6494

Beds

Christopher Sykes Antiques,
The Old Parsonage, Woburn, Milton Keynes
Tel: (052 525) 259/467

Devon

Galaxy Arts,
38 New Street, Barbican, Plymouth
Tel: (0752) 667842

Essex

Mayflower Antiques,
2 Una Road, Parkeston, Harwich
Tel: (0255) 504079

Glos

Country Life Antiques,
Sheep Street, Stow-on-the-Wold
Tel: (0451) 30776
Also at:
Grey House, The Square, Stow-on-the-Wold
Tel: (0451) 31564

Wain Antiques,
45 Long Street, Tetbury
Tel: (0666) 52440

Kent

Hadlow Antiques,
No. 1 The Pantiles, Tunbridge Wells
Tel: (0892) 29858

Norfolk

Margaret Corson,
Irstead Manor, Neatishead
Tel: (0692) 630274

Humbleyard Fine Art,
Waterfall Cottage, Mill Street, Swanton Morley
Tel: (036 283) 793
Also at:
Coltishall Antiques Centre, Coltishall, Norfolk

Turret House (Dr D H Morgan),
27 Middleton Street, Wymondham
Tel: (0953) 603462

Surrey

Whittington Galleries,
22 Woodend, Sutton
Tel: 01-644 9327

SILVER

London

Asprey PLC,
165-169 New Bond Street, W1
Tel: 01-493 6767

N Bloom & Son (Antiques) Ltd,
40-41 Conduit Street, W1
Tel: 01-629 5060

Bond Street Galleries,
111-112 New Bond Street, W1
Tel: 01-493 6180

J H Bourdon-Smith,
24 Mason's Yard, Duke Street, St James's, SW1
Tel: 01-839 4714

H & W Deutsch Antiques,
111 Kensington Church Street, W8
Tel: 01-727 5984

Howard Jones,
43 Kensington Church Street, W8
Tel: 01-937 4359

London International Silver Co,
82 Portobello Road, W11
Tel: 01-979 6523

S J Phillips Ltd,
139 New Bond Street, W1
Tel: 01-629 6261/2

Gerald Sattin Ltd,
25 Burlington Arcade, Piccadilly, W1
Tel: 01-493 6557

S J Shrubsole Ltd,
43 Museum Street, WC1
Tel: 01-405 2712

Cheshire

Watergate Antiques,
56 Watergate Street, Chester
Tel: (0244) 44516

Kent

Ralph Antiques,
40A Sandwich Industrial Estate, Sandwich
Tel: (0304) 611949/612882

Steppes Hill Farm Antiques,
Stockbury, Sittingbourne
Tel: (0795) 842205

Oxon

Thames Gallery,
Thameside, Henley-on-Thames
Tel: (0491) 572449

Shropshire
F C Manser & Son Ltd,
53-54 Wyle Cop, Shrewsbury
Tel: (0743) 51120

Somerset
Edward A Nowell,
21-23 Market Place, Wells
Tel: (0749) 72415

Yorks
Georgian House,
88 Main Street, Bingley
Tel: (0274) 568883

TEXTILES

London
Matthew Adams,
A1 Rogers Antique Galleries,
65 Portobello Road, W11
Tel: 01-579 5560

Gallery of Antique Costume & Textiles,
2 Church Street, Marylebone, NW8
Tel: 01-723 9981

Linda Wrigglesworth,
Grays Inn, The Mews, 1-7 Davies Mews, W1
Tel: 01-408 0177

Kent
The Lace Basket,
1A East Cross, Tenterden
Tel: (05806) 3923

Norfolk
Mrs Woolston,
Design House, 29 St Georges Street, Norwich
Tel: (0603) 623181
Also at:
Long Melford Antique Centre

Sussex
Celia Charlotte's Antiques,
7 Malling Street, Lewes
Tel: (0273) 473303

WINE ANTIQUES

London
Brian Beat,
36 Burlington Gardens, W1
Tel: 01-437 4975

Graham Bell,
177/8 Grays Antique Market,
58 Davies Street, W1
Tel: 01-493 1148

Eximious Ltd,
10 West Halkin Street, W1
Tel: 01-627 2888

Richard Kihl,
164 Regent's Park Road, NW1
Tel: 01-586 3838

Avon
Robin Butler,
9 St Stephen's Street, Bristol
Tel: (0272) 276586

Beds
Christopher Sykes Antiques,
The Old Parsonage, Woburn, Milton Keynes
Tel: (052 525) 259 & 467

Cumbria
Bacchus Antiques,
Longlands at Cartmel
Tel: (044 854) 475

Warwickshire
Colliers, Bigwood & Bewlay
The Old School, Tiddington, Stratford-upon-Avon
Tel: (0789) 69415

FAIR ORGANISERS

London
KM Fairs,
58 Mill Lane, NW6
Tel: 01-794 3551

Philbeach Events Ltd,
Earl's Court Exhibition Centre,
Warwick Road, SW5
Tel: 01-385 1200

Berks
Bridget Fraser,
Granny's Attic Antique Fairs,
Dean House, Cookham Dean
Tel: (062 84) 3658

Silhouette Fairs (inc Newbury Antique & Collectors' Fairs),
25 Donnington Square, Newbury
Tel: (0635) 44338

Cheshire
Susan Brownson,
Antique Fairs North West,
Brownslow House, Gt Budworth, Northwich
Tel: (0606) 891267 &
(061962) 5629

Pamela Robertson,
8 St George's Crescent, Queen's Park, Chester
Tel: (0244) 678106

Cornwall
West Country Antiques & Collectors' Fairs (Gerry Mosdell),
Hillside, St Issey, Wadebridge
Tel: (084 14) 666

Essex
Robert Bailey Antiques Fairs,
1 Roll Gardens, Gants Hill
Tel: 01-550 5435

Stephen Charles Fairs,
3 Leigh Hill, Leigh-on-Sea
Tel: (0702) 714649/556745 &
(0268) 774977

Heirloom Markets,
11 Wellfields, Writtle, Chelmsford
Tel: (0245) 422208

Herts
Bartholomew Fayres,
Executive House, The Maltings,
Station Road, Sawbridgeworth
Tel: (0279) 725809

Humberside
Seaclef Fairs,
78 Humberston Avenue,
Humberston, Grimsby
Tel: (0472) 813858

Kent
Darent Fairs,
Whitestacks Cottage, Crockenhill Lane, Eynsford
Tel: (0474) 63992

Tudor Fairs,
59 Rafford Way, Bromley
Tel: 01-460 2670

Wakefield Ceramic Fairs (Fred Hynds),
1 Fountain Road, Strood, Rochester
Tel: (0634) 723461

Notts
Top Hat Exhibitions Ltd,
66-72 Derby Road, Nottingham
Tel: (0602) 419143

Oxon
Portcullis Fairs,
6 St Peter's Street, Wallingford
Tel: (0491) 39345

Staffs
Waverley Fairs,
at Kinver, Womburn, Bromsgrove, Bridgnorth
Tel: (021 550) 0309

Suffolk
Camfair (Ros Coltman),
Longlands, Kedington, Haverhill
Tel: (0440) 704632

Emporium Fairs,
Longlands, Kedington, Haverhill
Tel: (0440) 704632

Surrey
Antiques & Collectors' Club,
No. 1 Warehouse, Horley Row, Horley
Tel: (0293) 772206

Joan Braganza,
76 Holmesdale Road, Reigate
Tel: (073 72) 45587

Cultural Exhibitions Ltd,
8 Meadrow, Godalming
Tel: (048 68) 22562

Historic and Heritage Fayres
Tel: 01-398 5324

Sussex
Ron Beech,
150 Portland Road, Hove
Tel: (0273) 724477

Brenda Lay,
Dyke Farm, West Chiltington Road, Pulborough
Tel: (079 82) 2447

Penman Antique Fairs,
Cockhaise Mill, Lindfield,
Haywards Heath
Tel: (044 47) 2514

Yorks
Bowman Antique Fairs,
PO Box 37, Otley
Tel: (0532) 843333
Also in:
Cheshire, Cleveland, Lincs, Staffs

SHIPPERS

London
Featherston Shipping Ltd,
24 Hampton House, 15-17 Ingate Place, SW8
Tel: 01-720 0422

Lockson Services Ltd,
29 Broomfield Street, E14
Tel: 01-515 8600

Stephen Morris Shipping,
89 Upper Street, N1
Tel: 01-359 3159

Phelps Ltd,
133-135 St Margaret's Road,
E Twickenham
Tel: 01-892 1778/7129

Pitt & Scott Ltd,
20/24 Eden Grove, N7
Tel: 01-607 7321

Avon
A J Williams,
Griffen Court, 19 Lower Park Row, Bristol
Tel: (0272) 297754

Dorset
Alan Franklin Transport,
Unit 8, 27 Black Moor Road,
Ebblake Industrial Estate,
Verwood
Tel: (0202) 826539 & 826394 &
827092

Essex
Victor Hall Antique Exporters,
The Old Dairy, Cranes Farm Road, Basildon
Tel: (0268) 289545/6

Hants
Colin Macleod's Antiques Warehouse,
139 Goldsmith Avenue,
Tel: (0705) 816278

Humberside
Geoffrey Mole,
400 Wincolmlee, Hull
Tel: (0482) 27858

Lancs
GG Antique Wholesalers,
25 Middleton Road, Middleton,
Morecambe
Tel: (0524) 51565

West Lancs Antique Exports,
Black Horse Farm, 123 Liverpool Road, South Burscough, Nr Ormskirk
Tel: (0704) 894634/35720

Lincs
Laurence Shaw Antiques,
Spilsby Road, Horncastle
Tel: (06582) 7638

Middx
Burlington Northern Air Freight,
Unit 8, Ascot Road, Clockhouse Lane, Feltham
Tel: (0784) 244152

Staffs
Aspleys Antiques,
Compton Mill, Compton, Leek
Tel: (0538) 373396

Sussex
British Antiques Exporters Ltd,
Queen Elizabeth Avenue, Burgess Hill
Tel: (044 46) 45577

Lou Lewis,
Avis Way, Newhaven
Tel: (0273) 513091

Graham Price Antiques Ltd,
A27 Antiques Complex, Unit 4,
Chaucer Industrial Estate, Dittons Road, Polegate
Tel: (032 12) 7167 & 7681

Peter Semus Antiques,
The Warehouse, Gladstone Road, Portslade
Tel: (0273) 420154/202989

SJB Shipping,
Chewton High Street, Angmering
Tel: (0903) 770198/785560

Scotland
Mini-Move Maxi-Move (Euro) Ltd,
27 Jock's Lodge, London Road,
Edinburgh
Tel: 031-652 1255

TRADE SUPPLIERS

London
Air Improvement Centre Ltd,
23 Denbigh Street, London, SW1
Tel: 01-834 2834

Green & Stone of Chelsea – Art Supplies, Framing Service,
259 King's Road, London, SW3
Tel: 01-352 6521/0837

Kent
C & A J Barmby,
Fine Art Accessories, 68 Judd Road, Tonbridge, Kent
Tel: (0732) 356479

Lancs
GG Antique Wholesalers,
25 Middleton Road, Middleton,
Morecambe
Tel: (0524) 51565

Sussex
Loveland Antiques,
18-20 Prospect Place, Hastings
Tel: (0424) 441608

Westham Desk Leathers,
High Street, Westham, Pevensey
Tel: (0323) 766483

West Midlands

Retro Products,
174 Norton Road, Stourbridge
Tel: (0384) 373332

Yorks

Stanley Tools Ltd,
Woodside, Sheffield, S Yorkshire
Tel: (0742) 78678

ANTIQUE CENTRES & MARKETS

London

Atlantic Antique Centres,
15 Flood Street, SW3
Tel: 01-351 5353

Alfies Antique Market,
13-25 Church Street, NW8
Tel: 01-723 6066

Antiquarius Antique Market,
135/141 King's Road, Chelsea, SW3
Tel: 01-351 5353

Bermondsey Antique Market & Warehouse,
173 Bermondsey Street, SE1
Tel: 01-407 2040

Bond Street Antique Centre,
124 New Bond Street, W1

Camden Passage Antique Centre,
357 Upper Street, Islington, N1
Tel: 01-359 0190

Chenil Galleries,
181-183 King's Road, SW3
Tel: 01-351 5353

Georgian Village,
Camden Passage, Islington, N1
Tel: 01-226 1571

Grays,
1-7 Davies Mews, 58 Davies Street, W1
Tel: 01-629 7034

Hampstead Antique Emporium,
12 Heath Street, NW3
Tel: 01-794 3297

London Silver Vaults,
Chancery House, 53-65 Chancery Lane, WC2
Tel: 01-242 3844

The Mall Antiques Arcade,
359 Upper Street, Islington, N1
Tel: 01-359 0825/3111

Avon

Bath Antique Market,
Guinea Lane, Paragon, Bath
Tel: (0225) 22510

Clifton Antiques Market,
26/28 The Mall, Clifton
Tel: (0272) 741627

Great Western Antique Centre,
Bartlett Street, Bath
Tel: (0225) 24243

Beds

Woburn Abbey Antiques Centre,
Woburn Abbey
Tel: (052 525) 350

Berks

Twyford Antiques Centre,
1 High Street, Twyford
Tel: (0734) 342161

Bucks

Great Missenden Antique Arcade,
76 High Street, Gt Missenden
Tel: (024 06) 2819 & 2330

Cambs

Collectors' Market,
Dales Brewery, Gwydir Street (off Mill Road), Cambridge

Cheshire

Antique & Collectors Fair,
The Guildhall, Watergate Street, Chester
(no telephone number)

Chester Antique Centre
(Antique Forum Ltd),
41 Lower Bridge Street, Chester
Tel: (0244) 314991

Cleveland

Mother Hubbard's Antiques Arcade,
140 Norton Road, Stockton-on-Tees
Tel: (0642) 615603

Cumbria

Cockermouth Antiques Market,
Main Street, Cockermouth
Tel: (0900) 824346

J W Thornton Antiques,
Supermarket, North Terrace,
Bowness-on-Windermere
Tel: (0229) 88745 (0966) 22930 & 25183

Devon

Barbican Antiques Market,
82-84 Vauxhall Street, Barbican, Plymouth
Tel: (0752) 266927

New Street Antique Centre,
27 New Street, The Barbican, Plymouth
Tel: (0752) 661165

Sidmouth Antiques Market,
132 High Street (next to Fords), Sidmouth
Tel: (03955) 77981

Torquay Antique Centre,
177 Union Street, Torquay
Tel: (0803) 26621

Dorset

Antique Market,
Town Hall/Corn Exchange, Dorchester
Tel: (0963) 62478

Antique Market,
Digby Hall, Sherborne
Tel: (0963) 62478

Antiques Trade Warehouse,
28 Lome Park Road, Bournemouth
Tel: (0202) 292944

Barnes House Antiques Centre,
West Row, Wimborne Minster
Tel: (0202) 886275

Essex

Antique Centre,
Doubleday Corner, Coggeshall
Tel: (0376) 62646

Baddow Antiques & Craft Centre,
The Bringy, Church Street, Great Baddow
Tel: (0245) 71137 & 76159

Boston Hall Antiques Fair,
Boston Hall Hotel, The Leas, Westcliff-on-Sea
Tel: (0702) 714649

Maldon Antiques & Collectors' Market,
United Reformed Church Hall, Market Hill, Maldon
Tel: (078 75) 2826

Orsett Antiques Fair,
Orsett Hall, Prince Charles Avenue, Orsett
Tel: (0702) 714649

Trinity Antiques Centre,
7 Trinity Street, Colchester
Tel: (0206) 577775

Glos

Antique Centre,
London House, High Street, Moreton-in-Marsh
Tel: (0608) 51084

Cheltenham Antique Market,
54 Suffolk Road, Cheltenham
Tel: (0242) 29812/32615/20139

Cirencester Antique Market,
Market Place (Antique Forum Ltd), Cirencester
Tel: 01-262 1168 & 01-263 4045

Gloucester Antique Centre,
1 Severn Road, Gloucester
Tel: (0452) 29716

Tewkesbury Antique Centre,
78 Church Street, Tewkesbury
Tel: (0684) 294091

Hants

Winchester Craft & Antique Market,
King's Walk, Winchester
Tel: (0962) 62277

Hereford & Worcester

Leominster Antiques Market,
14 Broad Street, Leominster
Tel: (0568) 2189/2155

Herts

The Herts & Essex Antiques Centre,
The Maltings, Station Road, Sawbridgeworth
Tel: (0279) 722044

St Albans Antique Market,
Town Hall, Chequer Street, St Albans
Tel: (0727) 66100 & 50427

Kent

The Antiques Centre,
120 London Road, Sevenoaks
Tel: (0732) 452104

Canterbury Antique Centre,
Latimers, Ivy Lane (Nr Coach Park), Canterbury
Tel: (0227) 60378

Canterbury Weekly Antique Market,
Sidney Cooper Centre, Canterbury
(No telephone number)

Hoodeners Antiques & Collectors' Market,
Red Cross Centre, Lower Chantry Lane, Canterbury
Tel: (022 770) 437

Hythe Antique Centre,
The Old Post Office, 5 High Street, Hythe
Tel: (0303) 69643

Noah's Ark Antique Centre,
King Street, Sandwich
Tel: (0304) 611144

The Old Rose Gallery (Antique Market),
152 High Street, Sandgate
Tel: (0303) 39173

Rochester Antiques & Flea Market, Rochester Market,
Corporation Street, Rochester
Tel: 01-262 1168 & 01-263 4045

Sandgate Antiques Centre,
61-63 Sandgate High Street, Sandgate (Nr Folkestone)
Tel: (0303) 38987

Westerham Antique Centre,
18 Market Square, Westerham
Tel: (0959) 62080

Lancs

Castle Antiques,
Moore Lane, Clitheroe
Tel: (0254) 35820

Eccles Used Furniture & Antique Centre,
325/7 Liverpool Road, Patricroft Bridge, Eccles
Tel: 061-789 4467

Manchester Antique Hypermarket,
Levenshulme Town Hall,
965 Stockport Road, Levenshulme
Tel: 061-224 2410

North Western Antique Centre,
New Preston Mill (Horrockses Yard), New Hall Lane, Preston
Tel: (0772) 798159

Leics

The Kibworth Antique Centre,
5 Weir Road, Kibworth
Tel: (053 753) 2761

Leicester Antique Centre Ltd,
16-26 Oxford Street, Leicester
Tel: (0533) 553006

Lincs

The Antique Centre,
1 Spilsby Road, Wainfleet
Tel: (0754) 880489

Lincolnshire Antiques Centre,
Bridge Street, Horncastle
Tel: (06582) 7794

Norfolk

Coltishall Antiques Centre,
High Street, Coltishall
Tel: (0603) 738306

Holt Antiques Centre,
Albert Hall, Albert Street, Holt
Tel: (0362) 5509 & (0263) 733301

Norwich Antique & Collectors' Centre,
Quayside, Fye Bridge, Norwich
Tel: (0603) 612582

The Old Granary Antique & Collectors' Centre,
King Staithe Lane, off Queen's Street, King's Lynn
Tel: (0553) 5509

Northants

Finedon Antiques Centre,
3 Church Street, Finedon
Tel: (0933) 680316

The Village Antique Market,
62 High Street, Weedon
Tel: (0327) 42015

Northumberland

Colmans of Hexham (Saleroom & Antique Fair),
15 St Mary's Chare, Hexham
Tel: (0434) 603812/605522

Notts

East Bridgford Antiques Centre,
Main Street, East Bridgford
Tel: (0949) 20540 & 20741

Newark Art & Antiques Centre,
The Market Place, Chain Lane, Newark
Tel: (0636) 703959

Nottingham Antique Centre,
British Rail Goods Yard, London Road, Nottingham
Tel: (0602) 54504/55548

Top Hat Antiques Centre,
66-72 Derby Road, Nottingham
Tel: (0602) 419143

Oxon

The Antique Centre,
Laurel House, Bull Ring, Market Place, Deddington
Tel: (0869) 38968

Shropshire

Ironbridge Antique Centre,
Dale End, Ironbridge
Tel: (095 245) 3784

Ludlow Antiques Centre,
29 Corve Street, Ludlow
Tel: (0584) 5157

Shrewsbury Antique Market,
Frankwell Quay Warehouse (Vintagevale Ltd), Shrewsbury
Tel: (0734) 50916

Stretton Antiques Market,
Sandford Avenue, Church Stretton
Tel: (06945) 402
also: (05884) 374

Somerset

Crewkerne Antiques Centre,
42 East Street, Crewkerne
Tel: (0460) 76755

Taunton Antiques Centre,
27/29 Silver Street, Taunton
Tel: (0823) 89327

Staffs

The Antique Centre,
Royal Hotel, Walsall
Tel: (0922) 24555

Barclay House,
Howard Place, Shelton,
Stoke-on-Trent
Tel: (0782) 657674/274747

Bridge House Antiques &
Collectors' Centre,
56 Newcastle Road, Stone
Tel: (0785) 818218

Rugeley Antique Centre,
161/3 Main Road, Rugeley
Tel: (088 94) 77166

Suffolk

Old Town Hall Antique Centre,
High Street, Needham Market
Tel: (0449) 720773

St John's Antique Centre,
31-32 St John's Street, Bury St
Edmunds
Tel: (0284) 3024

Waveney Antique Centre,
The Old School, Peddars Lane,
Beccles
Tel: (0502) 716147

Surrey

Antique Centre,
22 Haydon Place, Corner of Martyr
Road, Guildford
Tel: (0483) 67817

Andrew Cottrell Galleries,
7/9 Church Street, Godalming
Tel: (048 68) 7570

Farnham Antique Centre,
27 South Street, Farnham
Tel: (0252) 724475

Maltings Market,
Bridge Square, Farnham
Tel: (0252) 726234

The Old Forge Antiques Centre,
The Green, Godstone
Tel: (0883) 843230

The Old Smithy Antique Centre,
7 High Street, Merstham
Tel: (073 74) 2306

Victoria & Edward Antiques,
61 West Street, Dorking
Tel: (0306) 889645

Sussex – East

Antique Market,
Leaf Hall, Seaside, Eastbourne
Tel: (0323) 27530

Bexhill Antiques Centre,
Old Town, Bexhill
Tel: (0424) 210182

Chateaubriand Antique
Centre
High Street, Burwash
Tel: (0435) 882535

Heathfield Antiques Centre,
Heathfield Market, Heathfield
Tel: (042 482) 387

Lewes Antiques Centre,
20 Cliffe High Street, Lewes
Tel: (0273) 476148

Newhaven Flea Market,
28 South Way, Newhaven
Tel: (0273) 517207

St Leonards Antique Dealers,
Norman Road, St Leonards-on-Sea
Tel: (0424) 444592

Polegate Antique Centre,
97 Station Road, Polegate
Tel: (032 12) 5277

Seaford's 'Barn Collectors' Market',
The Barn, Church Lane, Seaford
Tel: (0323) 890010

Strand Antiques,
Strand House, Rye
Tel: (0797) 222653

Sussex – West

Antiques Market,
Parish Hall, South Street, Lancing
Tel: (0903) 32414

Arundel Antiques Market,
5 River Road, Arundel
Tel: (0903) 882012

Midhurst Antiques Market,
Knockhundred Row, Midhurst
Tel: (073 081) 4231

Mostyns Antiques Centre,
64 Brighton Road, Lancing
Tel: (0903) 752961

Petworth Antiques Market,
East Street, Petworth
Tel: (0798) 42073

Robert Warner & Son Ltd,
South Farm Road, Worthing
Tel: (0903) 32710

Treasure House Antiques Market,
Rear of High Street, in Crown
Yard, Arundel
Tel: (0903) 883101

Tyne & Wear

Newcastle Antiques Centre,
64-80 Newgate Street, Newcastle-
upon-Tyne
Tel: (0632) 614577

Warwickshire

Antiques Etc,
22 Railway Terrace, Rugby
Tel: (0788) 62837

Bidford-on-Avon Antiques Centre,
High Street, Bidford-on-Avon
Tel: (0789) 773680

Kenilworth Monthly Antique
Market,
Greville Suite,
De Montfort Hotel,
Kenilworth
Tel: (0926) 55253

Vintage Antique Market,
36 Market Place, Warwick
Tel: (0926) 491527

Warwick Antique Centre,
16-18 High Street, Warwick
Tel: (0962) 492482

West Midlands

Birmingham Thursday Antique
Centre,
141 Bromsgrove Street,
Birmingham
Tel: 021-692 1414

The City of Birmingham Antique
Market,
St Martins Market, Edgbaston
Street, Birmingham
Tel: 021-267 4636

Rock House Antiques & Collectors
Centre,
Rock House, The Rock,
Tettenhall,
Wolverhampton
Tel: (0902) 754995

Yorks – North

Grove Collectors' Centre,
Grove Road, Harrogate
Tel: (0423) 61680

Harrogate Antique Centre,
The Ginnel, Corn Exchange
Building, Harrogate
Tel: (0423) 508857

West Park Antiques Pavilion,
20 West Park, Harrogate
Tel: (0423) 61758

York Antique Centre,
2 Lendal, York
Tel: (0904) 641445

Yorks – South

Treasure House Antiques and
Antique Centre,
8-10 Swan Street, Bawtry
Tel: (0302) 710621

Yorks – West

Halifax Antique Centre,
Queen's Road/Gibbet Street,
Halifax
Tel: (042. . 366657

Scotland

Bath Street Antique Centre,
203 Bath Street, Glasgow
Tel: 041-248 4220

Corner House Antiques,
217 St Vincent Street, Glasgow
Tel: 041-221 1000

The Victorian Village,
57 West Regent Street, Glasgow
Tel: 041-332 0808

Wales

Cardiff Antique Centre,
69-71 St Mary Street, Cardiff
Tel: (0222) 30970
(Open Thurs & Sat)

Graham H Evans, FRICS,
Auction Sales Centre,
Kilgetty, Nr Saundersfoot, Dyfed
Tel: (0834) 812793

INDEX

D

E

F

O

P

Q

R

S

T

U

V

W

Y

Z

TRADE AND RETAIL ANTIQUES

16,000 sq. ft. of Refurbished Shops, Showrooms and Trade Warehouses

Whatever your interest –
Furniture, Clocks,
China, Porcelain, Glass, Jewellery,
Paintings and Objet d'Art,
Georgian, Victorian and Edwardian.

The widest choice for the collector of individual items.

A comprehensive and professional service to the trade.

Experienced in packing and export to Europe, The Far East, America and Australia.

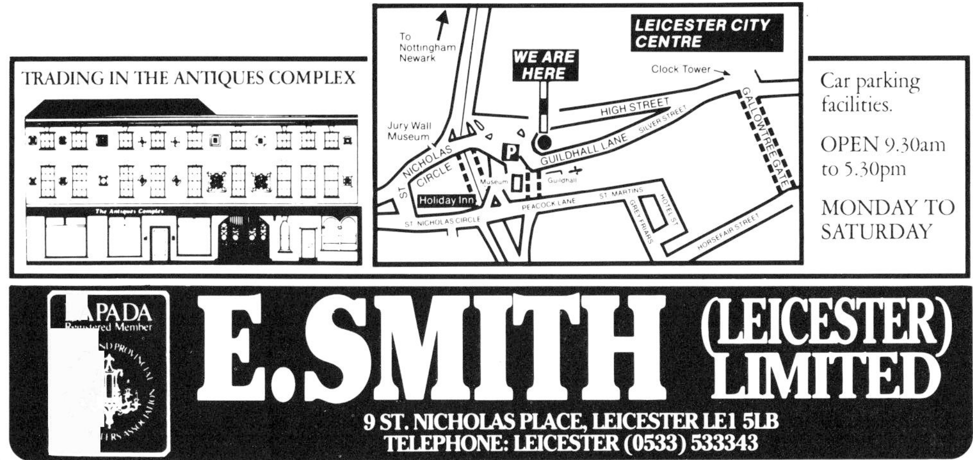